Prentice Hall

Algebra 1

Randall I. Charles

Basia Hall

Dan Kennedy

Allan E. Bellman

Sadie Chavis Bragg

William G. Handlin

Stuart J. Murphy

Grant Wiggins

PEARSON

Boston, Massachusetts • Chandler, Arizona • Glenview, Illinois • Upper Saddle River, New Jersey

Acknowledgments appear on page T859, which constitutes an extension of this copyright page.

Copyright © 2011 Pearson Education, Inc., or its affiliates. All Rights Reserved. Printed in the United States of America. This publication is protected by copyright, and permission should be obtained from the publisher prior to any prohibited reproduction, storage in a retrieval system, or transmission in any form or by any means, electronic, mechanical, photocopying, recording, or likewise. For information regarding permissions, write to Pearson Curriculum Group Rights & Permissions, One Lake Street, Upper Saddle River, New Jersey 07458.

Pearson, Prentice Hall, Pearson Prentice Hall, and MathXL are trademarks, in the U.S. and/or other countries, of Pearson Education, Inc., or its affiliates.

SAT® is a trademark of the College Entrance Examination Board.
ACT® is a trademark owned by ACT, Inc.
ExamView® is a registered trademark of eInstruction Corporation.
TI-Nspire™ is a trademark of Texas Instruments Incorporated.
Use of the trademarks implies no relationship, sponsorship, endorsement, sale, or promotion on the part of Pearson Education, Inc., or its affiliates.

PEARSON

ISBN-13: 978-0-13-369704-9
ISBN-10: 0-13-369704-5
7 8 9 10 V056 17 16 15

Algebra 1 *Teacher's Edition Contents*

ADP END-OF-COURSE EXAM CONTENT STANDARDS
for Algebra 1

The following chart shows the alignment of the ADP Algebra 1 End-of-Course Exam Content Standards to the lessons and features in Pearson's *Prentice Hall Algebra 1* text.

Content Standards		Where to Find
Number Sense		
O1.a	Use properties of number systems within the set of real numbers to verify or refute conjectures or justify reasoning and to classify, order, and compare real numbers.	Lessons: 1-3, 1-4, 1-5, 1-6, 1-7
O1.b	Use rates, ratios and proportions to solve problems, including measurement problems.	Lessons: 2-6, 2-7, 2-8
O1.c	Apply the laws of exponents to numerical expressions with integral exponents to rewrite them in different but equivalent forms or to solve problems.	Lessons: 7-2, 7-3, 7-4
O1.d	Use the properties of radicals to rewrite numerical expressions containing square roots in different but equivalent forms or to solve problems.	Lessons: 1-3, 10-3 Concept Byte: p. 605
Algebraic Expressions		
O2.a	Apply the laws of exponents to algebraic expressions with integral exponents to rewrite them in different but equivalent forms to solve problems.	Lessons: 7-1, 7-3, 7-5
O2.b	Add, subtract, and multiply polynomial expressions.	Lessons: 8-1, 8-2, 8-3, 8-4
O2.c	Factor simple polynomial expressions.	Lessons: 8-5, 8-6, 8-7
O2.d	Use the properties of radicals to convert algebraic expressions containing square roots in different but equivalent forms or to solve problems.	Lessons: 10-2, 10-3
Linear Functions		
L1.a	Recognize, describe and represent linear relationships using words, tables, numerical patterns, graphs and equations. Translate among these representations.	Lessons: 4-2, 4-4, 4-5, 4-6, 4-7
L1.b	Describe, analyze and use key characteristics of linear functions and their graphs.	Lessons: 4-2, 5-1, 5-2, 5-3, 5-4, 5-5, 5-6, 6-1 Concept Byte: p. 305
L1.c	Graph the absolute value of a linear function and determine and analyze its key characteristics.	Lesson: 5-8 Concept Byte: p. 347
L1.d	Recognize, express and solve problems that can be modeled using linear functions. Interpret their solutions in terms of the context of the problem.	Lessons: 4-1, 5-1, 5-3, 5-4, 5-5, 5-6
Linear Equations and Inequalities		
L2.a	Solve single-variable linear equations and inequalities with rational coefficients.	Lessons: 2-3, 2-4, 3-1, 3-2, 3-3, 3-4, 3-6, 3-7
L2.b	Solve equations involving the absolute value of a linear expression.	Lesson: 3-7
L2.c	Graph and analyze the graph of the solution set of a two-variable linear inequality.	Lesson: 6-5 Concept Byte: p. 402
L2.d	Solve systems of linear equations in two variables using algebraic and graphic procedures.	Lessons: 6-1, 6-2, 6-3, 6-4
L2.e	Recognize, express and solve problems that can be modeled using single-variable linear equations, one- or two-variable inequalities, or two-variable systems of linear equations. Interpret their solutions in terms of the context of the problem.	Lessons: 1-8, 1-9, 2-1, 2-2, 2-3, 2-4, 3-2, 3-3, 3-4, 3-6, 3-7, 6-1, 6-2, 6-3, 6-4, 6-5

Content Standards		Where to Find
Non-linear Functions		
N1.a	Recognize, describe, represent and analyze a quadratic function using words, tables, graphs or equations.	Lessons: 9-1, 9-2, 9-3, 9-4
N1.b	Analyze a table, numerical pattern, graph, equation or context to determine whether a linear, quadratic or exponential relationship could be represented.	Lessons: 4-3, 5-7, 7-6, 7-7, 9-7
N1.c	Recognize and solve problems that can be modeled using a quadratic function. Interpret the solution in terms of the context of the original problem.	Lessons: 9-1, 9-2, 9-3, 9-4, 9-8
Non-linear Equations		
N2.a	Solve equations involving several variables for one variable in terms of the others.	Lesson: 2-5
N2.b	Solve single-variable quadratic equations.	Lessons: 9-3, 9-4, 9-5, 9-6
Data and Statistics		
D1.a	Interpret and compare linear models for data that exhibit a linear trend in the context of a problem.	Lesson: 5-7 Concept Byte: p. 341
D1.b	Use measures of center and spread to compare and analyze data sets.	Lessons: 12-3, 12-4
D1.c	Evaluate the reliability of reports based on data published in the media.	Lesson: 12-5 Concept Byte: p. 748
Probability		
D2.a	Use counting principles to determine the number of ways an event can occur. Interpret and justify solutions.	Lesson: 12-6
D2.b	Apply probability concepts to determine the likelihood an event will occur in practical situations.	Lessons: 12-7, 12-8 Concept Bytes: pp. 763, 771

Algebra 1 Pacing

This Leveled Pacing Chart is provided as a guide to help you customize your course and to provide for differentiated instruction.

The suggested number of days for each chapter is based on a traditional 45-minute class period and on a 90-minute block period. The total of 160 days of instruction leaves time for assessments, projects, assemblies, or other special days that vary from school to school.

KEY
✓ = Algebra 1 Content
○ = Reviews the previous year
✗ = Content for Enrichment

	Basic	Average	Advanced
Chapter 1 Foundations for Algebra		**Traditional 12**	**Block 6**
1-1 Variables and Expressions	○	○	○
1-2 Order of Operations and Evaluating Expressions	✓	○	○
1-3 Real Numbers and the Number Line	✓	○	○
1-4 Properties of Real Numbers	✓	✓	✓
1-5 Adding and Subtracting Real Numbers	✓	○	○
Concept Byte: Always, Sometimes, or Never	✓	✓	✓
1-6 Multiplying and Dividing Real Numbers	✓	✓	✓
Concept Byte: Closure	✓	✓	✓
1-7 The Distributive Property	✓	✓	✓
1-8 An Introduction to Functions	✓	✓	✓
Concept Byte: Using Tables to Solve Equations	✓	✓	✓
Review: Graphing in the Coordinate Plane	○	○	○
1-9 Patterns, Equations and Graphs	✓	✓	✓
Chapter 2 Solving Equations		**Traditional 12**	**Block 6**
Concept Byte: Modeling One-Step Equations	✓	✓	✓
2-1 Solving One-Step Equations	○	○	○
2-2 Solving Two-Step Equations	✓	✓	✓
2-3 Solving Multi-Step Equations	✓	✓	✓
Concept Byte: Modeling Equations With Variables on Both Sides	✓	✓	✓
2-4 Solving Equations With Variables on Both Sides	✓	✓	✓
2-5 Literal Equations and Formulas	✓	✓	✓
Concept Byte: Finding Perimeter, Area, and Volume	○	○	○
2-6 Ratios, Rates, and Conversions	✓	✓	✓
2-7 Solving Proportions	✓	✓	✓
2-8 Proportions and Similar Figures	✓	✓	✓
2-9 Percents	✓	○	○
2-10 Change Expressed as a Percent	✓	○	○
Chapter 3 Solving Inequalities		**Traditional 20**	**Block 10**
3-1 Inequalities and Their Graphs	✓	✓	✓
3-2 Solving Inequalities Using Addition or Subtraction	✓	✓	✓
3-3 Solving Inequalities Using Multiplication or Division	✓	✓	✓
Concept Byte: More Algebraic Properties	✓	✓	✓
Concept Byte: Modeling Multi-Step Inequalities	✓	✓	✓
3-4 Solving Multi-Step Inequalities	✓	✓	✓
3-5 Working With Sets	✓	✓	✓

	Basic	Average	Advanced
Chapter 3 Solving Inequalities Cont.		**Traditional 20**	**Block 10**
3-6 Compound Inequalities	✓	✓	✓
3-7 Absolute Value Equations and Inequalities	✓	✓	✓
3-8 Unions and Intersections of Sets	✓	✓	✓
Chapter 4 An Introduction to Functions		**Traditional 12**	**Block 6**
4-1 Using Graphs to Relate Two Quantities	✓	✓	✓
4-2 Patterns and Linear Functions	✓	✓	✓
4-3 Patterns and Nonlinear Functions	✓	✓	✓
4-4 Graphing a Function Rule	✓	✓	✓
Concept Byte: Graphing Functions and Solving Equations	✓	✓	✓
4-5 Writing a Function Rule	✓	✓	✓
4-6 Formalizing Relations and Functions	✓	✓	✓
4-7 Sequences and Functions	✓	✓	✓
Chapter 5 Linear Functions		**Traditional 18**	**Block 9**
5-1 Rate of Change and Slope	✓	✓	✓
5-2 Direct Variation	✓	✓	✓
Concept Byte: Investigating $y = mx + b$	✓	✓	✓
5-3 Slope-Intercept Form	✓	✓	✓
5-4 Point-Slope Form	✓	✓	✓
5-5 Standard Form	✓	✓	✓
5-6 Parallel and Perpendicular Lines	✓	✓	✓
5-7 Scatter Plots and Trend Lines	✓	✓	✓
Concept Byte: Collecting Linear Data	✓	✓	✓
5-8 Graphing Absolute Value Functions	✓	✓	✓
Concept Byte: Characteristics of Absolute Value Graphs	✗	✗	✗
Chapter 6 Systems of Equations and Inequalities		**Traditional 12**	**Block 6**
6-1 Solving Systems by Graphing	✓	✓	✓
Concept Byte: Solving Systems Using Tables and Graphs	✓	✓	✓
Concept Byte: Solving Systems Using Algebra Tiles	✓	✓	✓
6-2 Solving Systems Using Substitution	✓	✓	✓
6-3 Solving Systems Using Elimination	✓	✓	✓
Concept Byte: Matrices and Solving Systems	✗	✗	✗
6-4 Applications of Linear Systems	✓	✓	✓
6-5 Linear Inequalities	✓	✓	✓
6-6 Systems of Linear Inequalities	✓	✓	✓
Concept Byte: Graphing Linear Inequalities	✓	✓	✓
Chapter 7 Exponents and Exponential Functions		**Traditional 12**	**Block 6**
7-1 Zero and Negative Exponents	✓	✓	✓
7-2 Scientific Notation	✓	✓	✓
7-3 Multiplication Powers With the Same Base	✓	✓	✓
Concept Byte: Powers of Powers and Powers of Products		✗	✗
7-4 More Multiplication Properties of Exponents	✓	✓	✓
7-5 Division Properties of Exponents	✓	✓	✓

	Basic	Average	Advanced
Chapter 7 Exponents and Exponential Functions		**Traditional 12**	**Block 6**
7-6 Exponential Functions	✓	✓	✓
Concept Byte: Geometric Sequence	✓	✓	✓
7-7 Exponential Growth and Decay	✓	✓	✓
Chapter 8 Polynomials and Factoring		**Traditional 12**	**Block 6**
8-1 Adding and Subtracting Polynomials	✓	✓	✓
8-2 Multiplying and Factoring	✓	✓	✓
Concept Byte: Using Models to Multiply	✓	✓	✓
8-3 Multiplying Binomials	✓	✓	✓
8-4 Multiplying Special Cases	✓	✓	✓
Concept Byte: Using Models to Factor	✓	✓	✓
8-5 Factoring $x^2 + bx + c$	✓	✓	✓
8-6 Factoring $ax^2 + bx + c$	✓	✓	✓
8-7 Factoring Special Cases	✓	✓	✓
8-8 Factoring by Grouping	✓	✓	✓
Chapter 9 Quadratic Functions and Equations		**Traditional 20**	**Block 10**
9-1 Quadratic Graphs and Their Properties	✓	✓	✓
9-2 Quadratic Functions	✓	✓	✓
Concept Byte: Collecting Quadratic Data	✗	✗	✗
9-3 Solving Quadratic Equations	✓	✓	✓
Concept Byte: Finding Roots	✓	✓	✓
9-4 Factoring to Solve Quadratic Equations	✓	✓	✓
9-5 Completing the Square	✓	✓	✓
9-6 The Quadratic Formula and the Discriminant	✓	✓	✓
9-7 Linear, Quadratic, and Exponential Models	✓	✓	✓
Concept Byte: Performing Regressions	✗	✗	✗
9-8 Systems of Linear and Quadratic Equations	✓	✓	✓
Chapter 10 Radical Expressions and Equations		**Traditional 10**	**Block 5**
10-1 The Pythagorean Theorem	✓	✓	✓
Concept Byte: Distance and Midpoint Formulas	✓	✓	✓
10-2 Simplifying Radicals	✓	✓	✓
10-3 Operations with Radical Expressions	✓	✓	✓
10-4 Solving Radical Equations	✓	✓	✓
10-5 Graphing Square Root Functions	✓	✓	✓
Concept Byte: Right Triangle Ratios	✗	✗	✗
10-6 Trigonometric Ratios	✗	✗	✗
Chapter 11 Rational Expressions and Functions		**Traditional 10**	**Block 5**
11-1 Simplifying Rational Expressions	✓	✓	✓
11-2 Multiplying and Dividing Rational Expressions	✓	✓	✓
Concept Byte: Dividing Polynomials Using Algebra Tiles	✓	✓	✓
11-3 Dividing Polynomials	✓	✓	✓
11-4 Adding and Subtracting Rational Expressions	✓	✓	✓
11-5 Solving Rational Expressions	✓	✓	✓

	Basic	Average	Advanced
Chapter 11 Rational Expressions and Functions Cont.		**Traditional 10**	**Block 5**
11-6 Inverse Variation	✓	✓	✓
11-7 Graphing Rational Functions	✓	✓	✓
Concept Byte: Graphing Rational Functions	✓	✓	✓
Chapter 12 Rational Expressions and Functions		**Traditional 10**	**Block 5**
12-1 Organizing Data Using Matrices	✓	✓	✓
12-2 Frequency and Histograms	✓	✓	✓
12-3 Measures of Central Tendency and Dispersion	✓	✓	✓
Concept Byte: Standard Deviation	✓	✓	✓
12-4 Box-and-Whisker Plots	✓	✓	✓
Concept Byte: Designing Your Own Survey	✓	✓	✓
12-5 Samples and Surveys	✓	✓	✓
Concept Byte: Misleading Graphs and Statistics	✓	✓	✓
12-6 Permutations and Combinations	✓	✓	✓
12-7 Theoretical and Experimental Probability	✓	✓	✓
Concept Byte: Conducting Simulations	✓	✓	✓
12-8 Probability of Compound Events	✓	✓	✓
Concept Byte: Conditional Probability	✓	✓	✓

BIGideas

These Big Ideas are the organizing ideas for the study of important areas of mathematics: algebra, geometry, and statistics.

Algebra

Properties

- In the transition from arithmetic to algebra, attention shifts from arithmetic operations (addition, subtraction, multiplication, and division) to use of the *properties* of these operations.
- All of the facts of arithmetic and algebra follow from certain properties.

Variable

- Quantities are used to form expressions, equations, and inequalities.
- An expression refers to a quantity but does not make a statement about it. An equation (or an inequality) is a statement about the quantities it mentions.
- Using variables in place of numbers in equations (or inequalities) allows the statement of relationships among numbers that are unknown or unspecified.

Equivalence

- A single quantity may be represented by many different expressions.
- The facts about a quantity may be expressed by many different equations (or inequalities).

Solving Equations & Inequalities

- Solving an equation is the process of rewriting the equation to make what it says about its variable(s) as simple as possible.
- Properties of numbers and equality can be used to transform an equation (or inequality) into equivalent, simpler equations (or inequalities) in order to find solutions.
- Useful information about equations and inequalities (including solutions) can be found by analyzing graphs or tables.
- The numbers and types of solutions vary predictably, based on the type of equation.

Proportionality

- Two quantities are *proportional* if they have the same ratio in each instance where they are measured together.
- Two quantities are *inversely proportional* if they have the same product in each instance where they are measured together.

Function

- A function is a relationship between variables in which each value of the input variable is associated with a unique value of the output variable.
- Functions can be represented in a variety of ways, such as graphs, tables, equations, or words. Each representation is particularly useful in certain situations.
- Some important families of functions are developed through transformations of the simplest form of the function.
- New functions can be made from other functions by applying arithmetic operations or by applying one function to the output of another.

Modeling

- Many real-world mathematical problems can be represented algebraically. These representations can lead to algebraic solutions.
- A function that models a real-world situation can be used to make estimates or predictions about future occurrences.

xx

Statistics and Probability

Data Collection and Analysis

- Sampling techniques are used to gather data from real-world situations. If the data are representative of the larger population, inferences can be made about that population.
- Biased sampling techniques yield data unlikely to be representative of the larger population.
- Sets of numerical data are described using measures of central tendency and dispersion.

Data Representation

- The most appropriate data representations depend on the type of data—quantitative or qualitative, and univariate or bivariate.
- Line plots, box plots, and histograms are different ways to show distribution of data over a possible range of values.

Probability

- Probability expresses the likelihood that a particular event will occur.
- Data can be used to calculate an experimental probability, and mathematical properties can be used to determine a theoretical probability.
- Either experimental or theoretical probability can be used to make predictions or decisions about future events.
- Various counting methods can be used to develop theoretical probabilities.

Geometry

Visualization

- Visualization can help you see the relationships between two figures and connect properties of real objects with two-dimensional drawings of these objects.

Transformations

- Transformations are mathematical functions that model relationships with figures.
- Transformations may be described geometrically or by coordinates.
- Symmetries of figures may be defined and classified by transformations.

Measurement

- Some attributes of geometric figures, such as length, area, volume, and angle measure, are measurable. Units are used to describe these attributes.

Reasoning & Proof

- Definitions establish meanings and remove possible misunderstanding.
- Other truths are more complex and difficult to see. It is often possible to verify complex truths by reasoning from simpler ones using deductive reasoning.

Similarity

- Two geometric figures are similar when corresponding lengths are proportional and corresponding angles are congruent.
- Areas of similar figures are proportional to the squares of their corresponding lengths.
- Volumes of similar figures are proportional to the cubes of their corresponding lengths.

Coordinate Geometry

- A coordinate system on a line is a number line on which points are labeled, corresponding to the real numbers.
- A coordinate system in a plane is formed by two perpendicular number lines, called the x- and y-axes, and the quadrants they form. The coordinate plane can be used to graph many functions.
- It is possible to verify some complex truths using deductive reasoning in combination with the distance, midpoint, and slope formulas.

Using Your Book for Success

Foundations for Algebra

2 Solving Equations

Visual See It!

Reasoning Try It!

Practice Do It!

3

Solving Inequalities

An Introduction to Functions

Visual See It!

Reasoning Try It!

Practice Do It!

5

Linear Functions

6

Systems of Equations and Inequalities

Visual **See It!**

Reasoning **Try It!**

Practice **Do It!**

7

Exponents and Exponential Functions

8

Polynomials and Factoring

Visual See It!

Reasoning Try It!

Practice Do It!

9

Quadratic Functions and Equations

10 Radical Expressions and Equations

Visual See It!

Reasoning Try It!

Practice Do It!

11

Rational Expressions and Functions

12 Data Analysis and Probability

Visual See It!

Reasoning Try It!

Practice Do It!

Are you ready for your training?

Visit **myPearsonTraining.com** and learn how you can attend an instructor-led Webinar or view a step-by-step tutorial whenever you want! We offer a comprehensive Web site of self-paced Adobe® Flash® tutorials that show teachers step by step how to get started using their Pearson textbooks and technology products.

As a teacher, your time is valuable. So we've developed just-in-time training that's available on your schedule, when you need it.

At **myPearsonTraining.com**, you can watch step-by-step tutorials or connect with one of our online trainers for a virtual seminar (Webinar) about your textbook and technology. We're ready when you are!

Get Ready!

 Converting Fractions to Decimals

Write as a decimal.

1. $\frac{7}{10}$ 2. $6\frac{2}{5}$ 3. $\frac{8}{1000}$ 4. $\frac{7}{2}$ 5. $\frac{3}{11}$

Lesson 1-2

 Using Order of Operations

Simplify each expression.

6. $(9 \div 3 + 4)^2$ 7. $5 + (0.3)^2$ 8. $3 - (1.5)^2$ 9. $64 \div 2^4$

10. $4 \div (0.5)^2$ 11. $(0.25)4^2$ 12. $2(3 + 7)^3$ 13. $-3(4 + 6 \div 2)^2$

Lesson 1-2

 Evaluating Expressions

Evaluate each expression for $a = -2$ and $b = 5$.

14. $(ab)^2$ 15. $(a - b)^2$ 16. $a^3 + b^3$ 17. $b - (3a)^2$

Lesson 2-10

 Finding Percent Change

Tell whether each percent change is an increase or decrease. Then find the percent change. Round to the nearest percent.

18. $15 to $20

19. $20 to $15

20. $600 to $500

21. $2000 to $2100

Lesson 4-6

 Understanding Domain and Range

Find the range of each function with domain $\{-2, 0, 3.5\}$.

22. $f(x) = -2x^2$ 23. $g(x) = 10 - x^3$ 24. $y = 5x - 1$

 **Looking Ahead Vocabulary**

25. If you say that a plant has new growth, has the size of the plant changed? What do you think the *growth factor* of the plant describes?

26. In a mathematical expression, an exponent indicates repeated multiplication by the same number. How would you expect a quantity to change when it experiences *exponential growth*?

27. Tooth decay occurs when tooth enamel wears away over time. If *exponential decay* models the change in the number of dentists in the United States over time, do you think the number of dentists in the United States is increasing or decreasing?

Answers

Get Ready!

1. 0.7
2. 6.4
3. 0.008
4. 3.5
5. $0.\overline{27}$
6. 49
7. 5.09
8. 0.75
9. 4
10. 16
11. 4
12. 2000
13. -147
14. 100
15. 49
16. 117
17. -31
18. 33% increase
19. 25% decrease
20. 17% decrease
21. 5% increase
22. $\{-8, 0, -24.5\}$
23. $\{18, 10, -32.875\}$
24. $\{-11, -1, 16.5\}$
25. yes; how quickly the plant grows
26. The quantity would increase rapidly.
27. decreasing

Get Ready!

Assign this diagnostic assessment to determine if students have the prerequisite skills for Chapter 7.

Lesson	Skill
Skills Handbook, page T790	Converting Fractions to Decimals
1-2	Using Order of Operations
1-2	Evaluating Expressions
2-10	Finding Percent Change
4-6	Understanding Domain and Range

To remediate students, select from these resources (available for every lesson).
- Online Problems (PowerAlgebra.com)
- Reteaching (All-in-One Teaching Resources)
- Practice (All-in-One Teaching Resources)

Why Students Need These Skills

CONVERTING FRACTIONS TO DECIMALS
Equivalence of real numbers will be extended to include scientific notation.

USING ORDER OF OPERATIONS
The order of operations is necessary when simplifying expressions with exponents.

EVALUATING EXPRESSIONS
Evaluating an expression for a specific variable is a means to check that the simplification of the expression was done correctly.

FINDING PERCENT CHANGE
Finding percent of change will prepare students to use percent of change to write exponential functions.

UNDERSTANDING DOMAIN AND RANGE
The concept of domain and range will be extended to exponential functions.

Looking Ahead Vocabulary

GROWTH FACTOR Ask students how the term growth factor may relate to the concept of growing patterns.

EXPONENTIAL GROWTH Show students an example of a pattern that has exponential growth, such as 2, 4, 8, 16, 32, 64, ….

EXPONENTIAL DECAY Ask students to name examples of other items that decay over time, such as fossils, or bacteria cells.

Chapter 7 Overview

UbD Understanding by Design

Chapter 7 expands on students' understandings and skills related to exponential expressions. In this chapter, students will develop the answers to the Essential Questions posed on the opposite page as they learn the concepts and skills bulleted below.

BIG idea **Equivalence**

ESSENTIAL QUESTION How can you represent very large and very small numbers?

• Students will learn to write numbers in scientific notation.

BIG idea **Properties**

ESSENTIAL QUESTION How can you simplify expressions involving exponents?

• Students will define and use zero and negative exponents.
• Students will learn the rules for multiplying powers.
• Students will learn the rules for dividing powers.

BIG idea **Functions**

ESSENTIAL QUESTION What are the characteristics of exponential functions?

• Exponential functions may show growth or decay

CHAPTER 7

Exponents and Exponential Functions

PowerAlgebra.com

Your place to get all things digital

VIDEO Download videos connecting math to your world.

VOCABULARY Math definitions in English and Spanish

SOLVE IT! The online Solve It will get you in gear for each lesson.

DYNAMIC ACTIVITIES Interactive! Vary numbers, graphs, and figures to explore math concepts.

ONLINE PROBLEMS Download Step-by-Step Problems with Instant Replay.

ONLINE HOMEWORK Get and view your assignments online.

MathXL FOR SCHOOL Extra practice and review online

Check out this photo! The bacteria population in the Grand Prismatic Spring in Yellowstone National Park causes the different colors you see around the spring.

Did you know you can use exponents to describe the growth of a population? You'll learn how in this chapter.

Vocabulary

English/Spanish Vocabulary Audio Online:

English	Spanish
compound interest, p. 456	interés compuesto
decay factor, p. 457	factor de decremento
exponential decay, p. 457	decremento exponencial
exponential function, p. 447	función exponencial
exponential growth, p. 455	incremento exponencial
growth factor, p. 455	factor incremental
scientific notation, p. 420	notación científica

PowerAlgebra.com

Chapter 7 Overview

Use these online assets to engage your students. There is support for the Solve It and step-by step solutions for Problems.

VIDEO Show the student-produced video demonstrating relevant and engaging applications of the new concepts in the chapter.

VOCABULARY Find online definitions for new terms in English and Spanish.

SOLVE IT! Start each lesson with an attention-getting Problem. View the Problem online with helpful hints.

My Math Video

00:04:04

My Math Video

FACILITATE Use this photo to discuss the concept of exponential growth. Exponential growth provides a real-world application for many topics in this chapter, including exponents and exponential functions.

Q Bacteria in the Grand Prismatic Pool in Yellowstone account for its unique color pattern. What factors might affect the size of the bacteria population? **[Answers may vary. Samples: availability of food and the size of the pool]**

Q How might the growth rate of the population relate to the population size? **[Answers may vary. Sample: The growth rate increases with size.]**

Q Can the population continue to grow indefinitely? Explain. **[No. The pool can only support a finite population of bacteria.]**

Q Under certain conditions, bacteria demonstrate exponential growth, where the rate of growth is proportional to the size of the population. What are other examples of exponential growth? **[Answers may vary. Samples: compound interest, Moore's Law for computer processing speed, the spread of viruses]**

ERROR PREVENTION

If you use an exponential function to explain exponential growth, emphasize that the variable in an exponential function is in the exponent, not the base. Students may confuse exponential functions with monomials, where the variable is in the base.

EXTENSION

Have students investigate other examples of exponential growth. Students might look up the speed of computer processors over a ten-year period, the population of Earth since 1900, or Internet usage since 1990. Then, have students graph their results and share them with the class.

BIG ideas

1 Equivalence

Essential Question: How can you represent very large and very small numbers?

2 Properties

Essential Question: How can you simplify expressions involving exponents?

3 Function

Essential Question: What are the characteristics of exponential functions?

Chapter Preview

PowerAlgebra.com | Chapter 7 Exponents and Exponential Functions | 413

 Increase students' depth of knowledge with interactive online activities.

 Show Problems from each lesson solved step by step. Instant replay allows students to go at their own pace when studying online.

 Assign homework to individual students or to an entire class.

 Prepare students for the Mid-Chapter Quiz and Chapter Test with online practice and review.

Math Background

Equivalence

BIG idea A single quantity may be represented by many different expressions. The facts about a quantity may be expressed by many different equations (or inequalities).

ESSENTIAL UNDERSTANDINGS

7-1 The idea of exponents can be extended to include zero and negative exponents.

7-2 Powers of 10 are an easy way to write and compare very large or very small numbers. Scientific notation is a shorthand way to write numbers using powers of 10.

Properties

BIG idea All of the facts of arithmetic and algebra follow from certain properties.

ESSENTIAL UNDERSTANDINGS

7-3 to 7-5 Properties of exponents make it easier to simplify products or quotients of powers with the same base or powers raised to a power or products raised to a power.

Function

BIG idea A function is a relationship between variables in which each value of the input variable is associated with a unique value of the output variable. Functions can be represented in a variety of ways, such as graphs, tables, equations, or words. Each representation is particularly useful in certain situations. Some important families of functions are developed through transformations of the simplest form of the function.

ESSENTIAL UNDERSTANDINGS

7-6 to 7-7 The parent of the family of exponential functions is $y = ab^x$. The independent variable is an exponent. This family of functions can model growth or decay of an initial amount.

Properties of Exponents

You can use properties of exponents to multiply and divide powers with the same base. Consider the following three cases:

1) $4^5 \cdot 4^2$

The bases of the powers are the same. To *multiply* powers with the same base, *add* the exponents.

$$4^5 \cdot 4^2 = 4^{5+2} = 4^7$$

2) $\dfrac{4^5}{4^2}$

The bases of the powers (4) are the same. To *divide* powers with the same base, *subtract* the exponents.

$$\frac{4^5}{4^2} = 4^{5-2} = 4^3$$

3) $3^4 \cdot 2^5$

The bases of the powers are not the same. The exponential properties of multiplication and division illustrated above do not apply.

Common Errors With Properties of Exponents

When multiplying powers with the same base, students often make the mistake of multiplying the powers rather than adding them.

Consider the first case from above. The correct answer is found by adding the exponents to get $4^5 \cdot 4^2 = 4^{5+2} = 4^7$. However, because this problem involves multiplication, students will often multiply the exponents and get $4^5 \cdot 4^2 = 4^{5 \cdot 2} = 4^{10}$.

The situation is further complicated by another property of exponents. When a power is raised to a power, the exponents are multiplied: $(4^5)^2 = 4^{5 \cdot 2} = 4^{10}$.

In this case, students will often raise the exponent to the power rather than multiplying the exponents, and get $(4^5)^2 = 4^{5^2} = 4^{25}$.

Remind students that another way to write $(4^5)^2$ is $(4^5)(4^5)$. They can add the powers to get 4^{10}.

Scientific Notation

The Earth's mass is
5,973,600,000,000,000,000,000,000 kg. You can see
how it is difficult to read or write this amount correctly.

This illustrates why scientists, engineers, and
mathematicians prefer to write very large or very small
numbers using scientific notation.

A number in scientific notation is written as the product
of two factors in the form $a \times 10^n$, where n is an integer
and $1 \leq |a| < 10$.

To write the Earth's mass in scientific notation, find the
two numbers of the product.

To find the first number a, start to the right of the last
zero. Move to the left until you get to the right of the first
number, counting the number of times you move.

5,973,600,000,000,000,000,000,000

The first number of the product is 5.9736.

You moved 24 times, so 24 is the power of ten. The
Earth's mass in scientific notation is 5.9736×10^{24}.

Common Errors With Scientific Notation

Students are often confused when working with numbers
in scientific notation in which the power of ten involves a
negative exponent.

Consider 0.0056

Students may correctly move the decimal three places
to the right. But they might associate this rightward
movement with a positive exponent and write 5.6×10^3.
Because the decimal was moved right, the exponent
should be negative, so write 5.6×10^{-3}.

Exponential Functions

The basic shape of the graph of an exponential function
can be determined by the values of a and b in the
exponential function $y = ab^x$.

If $a > 0$ and $b > 1$,
the graph will look like:

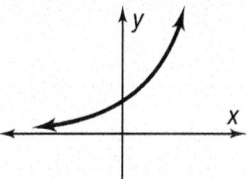

If $a > 0$ and $b < 1$,
the graph will look like:

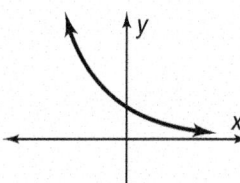

If $a < 0$ and $b > 1$,
the graph will look like:

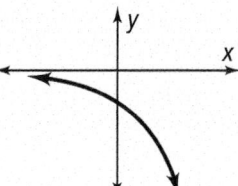

If $a < 0$ and $b < 1$,
the graph will look like:

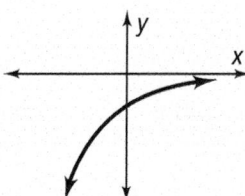

Common Errors With Exponential Functions

Students may struggle to understand how the value of an
exponential function can decrease while the value of the
exponent itself is increasing.

For example in the equation $y = 2^x$, as x gets larger so
does y.

But in the equation $y = \left(\frac{1}{2}\right)^x$, as x gets larger y gets
smaller.

Stress the importance of the value of b in the exponential
function $y = a \cdot b^x$. If $b < 0$, the behavior of the
function can be counterintuitive to students.

EXPONENTS AND EXPONENTIAL FUNCTIONS
Pacing and Assignment Guide

		TRADITIONAL			BLOCK
Lesson	Teaching Day(s)	Basic	Average	Advanced	Block
7-1	1	Problems 1-4 Exs. 9–46 all, 48–58 even, 60, 62, 64, 73–91	Problems 1-4 Exs. 9–45 odd, 47–65, 73–91	Problems 1-4 Exs. 9–45 odd, 47–91	**Day 1** Problems 1-4 Exs. 9–45 odd, 47–65, 73–91
7-2	1	Problems 1-3 Exs. 11–34 all, 52–70	Problems 1-3 Exs. 11–33 odd, 52–70	Problems 1-3 Exs. 11–33 odd, 52–70	Problems 1-3 Exs. 11–33 odd, 52–70
	2	Problems 4-5 Exs. 35-39 all, 40–44 even, 46, 48–49	Problems 4-5 Exs. 35–39 odd, 40–49	Problems 4-5 Exs. 35–39 odd, 40–51	**Day 2** Problems 4-5 Exs. 35–39 odd, 40–49
7-3	1	Problems 1-2 Exs. 8–28 all, 72–87	Problems 1-2 Exs. 9–27 odd, 72–87	Problems 1-4 Exs. 9–35 odd, 37–87	Problems 1-2 Exs. 9–27 odd, 72–87
	2	Problems 3-4 Exs. 29–36 all, 38–56 even, 57, 58–64 even	Problems 3-4 Exs. 29–35 odd, 37–64		**Day 3** Problems 3-4 Exs. 29–35 odd, 37–64
7-4	1	Problems 1-3 Exs. 10–29 all, 78–93	Problems 1-3 Exs. 11–29 odd, 78–93	Problems 1-3 Exs. 11–29 odd, 78–93	Problems 1-3 Exs. 11–29 odd, 78–93
	2	Problems 4-5 Exs. 30–46 all, 48–66 even, 70	Problems 4-5 Exs. 31–45 odd, 47–70	Problems 4-5 Exs. 31–45 odd, 47–77	**Day 4** Problems 4-5 Exs. 31–45 odd, 47–70
7-5	1	Problems 1-2 Exs. 8–32 all, 54, 94–110	Problems 1-4 Exs. 9–47 odd, 49–87, 94–110	Problems 1-4 Exs. 9–47 odd, 49–110	Problems 1-4 Exs. 9–47 odd, 49–87, 94–110
	2	Problems 3-4 Exs. 33–48 all, 50–52 even, 60–72 even, 78–80 all, 84, 86			
7-6	1	Problems 1-4 Exs. 8–29 all, 30–46 even, 52–65	Problems 1-4 Exs. 9–29 odd, 30–46, 52–65	Problems 1-4 Exs. 9–29 odd, 30–65	**Day 5**
7-7	1	Problems 1-3 Exs. 9–27 all, 28–42 even, 46–61	Problems 1-3 Exs. 9–27 odd, 28–43, 46–61	Problems 1-3 Exs. 9–27 odd, 28–61	
Review	1	Chapter 7 Review	Chapter 7 Review	Chapter 7 Review	**Day 6** Chapter 7 Review
Assess	1	Chapter 7 Test	Chapter 7 Test	Chapter 7 Test	Chapter 7 Test
Total		**13 Days**	**12 Days**	**11 Days**	**6 Days**

Note: Pacing does not include Concept Bytes and other feature pages.

Resources

	For the Chapter	7-1	7-2	7-3	7-4	7-5	7-6	7-7
Planning								
Teacher Center Online Planner & Grade Book	I	I	I	I	I	I	I	I
Interactive Learning & Guided Instruction								
My Math Video	I							
Solve It!		I TM	I TM	I TM	I TM	I TM	I TM	I TM
Student Companion (SP)*		P M	P M	P M	P M	P M	P M	
Vocabulary Support		I P M	I P M	I P M	I P M	I P M	I P M	I P M
Got It? Support		I P	I P	I P	I P	I P	I P	I P
Dynamic Activity					I	I	I	I
Online Problems		I	I	I	I	I	I	I
Additional Problems		M	M	M	M	M	M	M
English Language Learner Support (TR)		E P M	E P M	E P M	E P M	E P M	E P M	E P M
Activities, Games, and Puzzles		E M	E M	E M	E M	E M	E M	E M
Teaching With TI Technology With CD-ROM							✓ P	✓ P
TI-Nspire™ Support CD-ROM		✓	✓	✓	✓	✓	✓	✓
Lesson Check & Practice								
Student Companion (SP)*		P M	P M	P M	P M	P M	P M	P M
Lesson Check Support		I P	I P	I P	I P	I P	I P	I P
Practice and Problem Solving Workbook (SP)		P	P	P	P	P	P	P
Think About a Plan (TR)*		E P M	E P M	E P M	E P M	E P M	E P M	E P M
Practice Form G (TR)*		E P M	E P M	E P M	E P M	E P M	E P M	E P M
Standardized Test Prep (TR)*		P M	P M	P M	P M	P M	P M	P M
Practice _Form K_ (TR)*		E P M	E P M	E P M	E P M	E P M	E P M	E P M
Extra Practice	E M							
Find the Errors!	M							
Enrichment (TR)		E P M	E P M	E P M	E P M	E P M	E P M	E P M
Answers and Solutions CD-ROM	✓	✓	✓	✓	✓	✓	✓	✓
Assess & Remediate								
ExamView CD-ROM	✓	✓	✓	✓	✓	✓	✓	✓
Lesson Quiz		I TM	I TM	I TM	I TM	I TM	I TM	I TM
Quizzes and Tests _Form G_ (TR)*	E P M				E P M			E P M
Quizzes and Tests _Form K_ (TR)*	E P M				E P M			E P M
Reteaching (TR)*		E P M	E P M	E P M	E P M	E P M	E P M	E P M
Performance Tasks (TR)*	P M							
Cumulative Review (TR)*	P M							
Progress Monitoring Assessments	I P M							

(TR) Available in All-In-One Teaching Resources   *Spanish available

1 Interactive Learning

Solve It!

PURPOSE To use patterns to derive the properties of zero and negative exponents.

PROCESS Students may determine a pattern to complete the final three rows of the table. Students may construct a table for an expression such as 5^x to test their conjectures.

FACILITATE

Q What pattern do you see as you complete the 2^x column? **[As the exponent decreases by 1, each term is $\frac{1}{2}$ of the previous term.]**

Q What pattern do you see as you complete the 10^x column? **[As the exponent decreases by 1, each term is $\frac{1}{10}$ of the previous term.]**

Q What do you notice in the row where zero is the exponent? **[An exponent of zero results in a value of 1 in both tables.]**

Q How are the terms x^2 and x^{-2} related? **[x^2 and x^{-2} are reciprocals.]**

ANSWER See Solve It in Answers on next page.

CONNECT THE MATH Positive exponents are a notation for repeated multiplication. Students should understand that negative exponents are a notation for repeated division.

2 Guided Instruction

Take Note

Emphasize to students that 7^3 indicates to multiply by 7 three times, while 7^{-3} means to divide by 7 three times.

7-1 Zero and Negative Exponents

Objective To simplify expressions involving zero and negative exponents

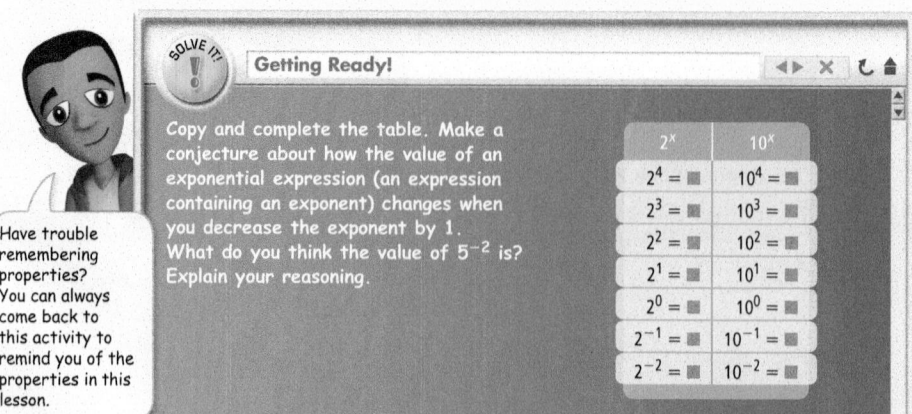

> Getting Ready!
>
> Copy and complete the table. Make a conjecture about how the value of an exponential expression (an expression containing an exponent) changes when you decrease the exponent by 1.
> What do you think the value of 5^{-2} is? Explain your reasoning.

2^x	10^x
$2^4 = \blacksquare$	$10^4 = \blacksquare$
$2^3 = \blacksquare$	$10^3 = \blacksquare$
$2^2 = \blacksquare$	$10^2 = \blacksquare$
$2^1 = \blacksquare$	$10^1 = \blacksquare$
$2^0 = \blacksquare$	$10^0 = \blacksquare$
$2^{-1} = \blacksquare$	$10^{-1} = \blacksquare$
$2^{-2} = \blacksquare$	$10^{-2} = \blacksquare$

Have trouble remembering properties? You can always come back to this activity to remind you of the properties in this lesson.

The patterns you found in the Solve It illustrate the definitions of zero and negative exponents.

Essential Understanding You can extend the idea of exponents to include zero and negative exponents.

Consider 3^3, 3^2, and 3^1. Decreasing the exponents by 1 is the same as dividing by 3. If you continue the pattern, 3^0 equals 1 and 3^{-1} equals $\frac{1}{3}$.

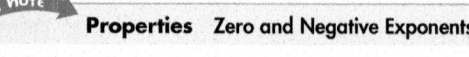

Properties   Zero and Negative Exponents

Zero as an Exponent For every nonzero number a, $a^0 = 1$.

Examples $4^0 = 1$ $(-3)^0 = 1$ $(5.14)^0 = 1$

Negative Exponent For every nonzero number a and integer n, $a^{-n} = \frac{1}{a^n}$.

Examples $7^{-3} = \frac{1}{7^3}$ $(-5)^{-2} = \frac{1}{(-5)^2}$

7-1 Preparing to Teach

UbD

BIG idea   **Properties**

ESSENTIAL UNDERSTANDING

- Extend the use of exponents to include zero and negative exponents.

Math Background

Students should already be familiar with various meanings of the $-$ (negative) symbol. The symbol is used to represent the opposite of a positive number and is also used to indicate the difference of two numbers, as in subtraction. A third meaning of the symbol is introduced in this lesson. Students learn that a negative symbol in an exponent is used to indicate the reciprocal of a power. For example, 10^{-5} means the same as $\frac{1}{10^5}$.

Support Student Learning

Use the **Algebra 1 Companion** to engage and support students during instructions. See Lesson Resources at the end of this lesson for details.

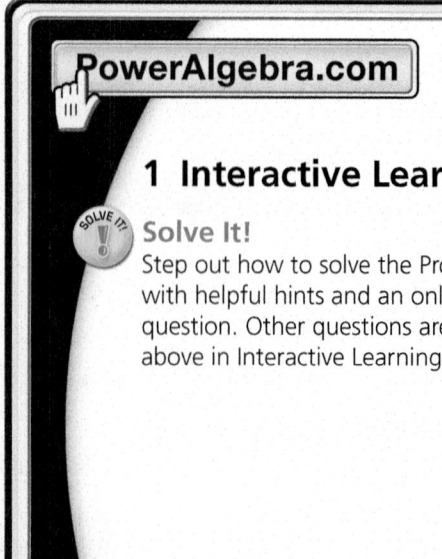

> PowerAlgebra.com
>
> # 1 Interactive Learning
>
> ## Solve It!
> Step out how to solve the Problem with helpful hints and an online question. Other questions are listed above in Interactive Learning.

Why can't you use 0 as a base with zero exponents? The first property on the previous page implies the following pattern.

$$3^0 = 1 \qquad 2^0 = 1 \qquad 1^0 = 1 \qquad 0^0 = 1$$

However, consider the following pattern.

$$0^3 = 0 \qquad 0^2 = 0 \qquad 0^1 = 0 \qquad 0^0 = 0$$

It is not possible for 0^0 to equal both 1 and 0. Therefore 0^0 is undefined.

Why can't you use 0 as a base with a negative exponent? Using 0 as a base with a negative exponent will result in division by zero, which is undefined.

 Problem 1 Simplifying Powers

What is the simplified form of each expression?

Ⓐ 9^{-2}

$9^{-2} = \dfrac{1}{9^2}$ Use the definition of negative exponent.

     $= \dfrac{1}{81}$ Simplify.

Ⓑ $(-3.6)^0 = 1$ Use the definition of zero as an exponent.

✓ **Got It? 1.** What is the simplified form of each expression?
   a. 4^{-3} **b.** $(-5)^0$ **c.** 3^{-2} **d.** 6^{-1} **e.** $(-4)^{-2}$

An algebraic expression is in simplest form when powers with a variable base are written with only positive exponents.

  Problem 2 Simplifying Exponential Expressions

What is the simplified form of each expression?

Ⓐ $5a^3b^{-2}$

$5a^3b^{-2} = 5a^3\left(\dfrac{1}{b^2}\right)$ Use the definition of negative exponent.

     $= \dfrac{5a^3}{b^2}$ Simplify.

Ⓑ $\dfrac{1}{x^{-5}}$

$\dfrac{1}{x^{-5}} = 1 \div x^{-5}$ Rewrite using a division symbol.

     $= 1 \div \dfrac{1}{x^5}$ Use the definition of negative exponent.

     $= 1 \cdot x^5$ Multiply by the reciprocal of $\frac{1}{x^5}$, which is x^5.

     $= x^5$ Identity Property of Multiplication

✓ **Got It? 2.** What is the simplified form of each expression?
   a. x^{-9} **b.** $\dfrac{1}{n^{-3}}$ **c.** $4c^{-3}b$ **d.** $\dfrac{2}{a^{-3}}$ **e.** $\dfrac{n^{-5}}{m^2}$

PowerAlgebra.com   **Lesson 7-1** Zero and Negative Exponents   **415**

Think

Can you use the definition of zero as an exponent when the base is a negative number?
Yes, the definition of zero as an exponent is true for all nonzero bases.

Think

Which part of the expression do you need to rewrite?
The base b has a negative exponent, so you need to rewrite it with a positive exponent.

Problem 1

Q Why is 9^{-2} not considered to be in simplified form? **[A numerical expression is not considered in simplified form if a further operation can be done.]**

Q Will any number raised to a zero exponent equal 1? Explain. **[Yes; as long as the number raised to the zero exponent is not 0.]**

Got It?   ERROR PREVENTION

If students give an answer of -64 for 1a, or -9 for 1c, or 16 for 1e, they are likely confusing the property of a negative exponent with the rules for multiplying integers.

Problem 2

Q What does the fraction bar represent in 2B? **[division]**

Q How do you divide by a fraction? **[Multiply by the reciprocal of the fraction.]**

Got It?   ERROR PREVENTION

For 2c, if students give an answer of $\frac{b}{4c^3}$, point out that 4 has an exponent of positive 1 and is not part of the base raised to a negative exponent. It should stay in the numerator of the simplified form of the expression. It may help to simplify $(4c)^{-3}b$ so that students understand the difference.

2 Guided Instruction

 Each Problem is worked out and supported online.

Problem 1
Simplifying Powers

Problem 2
Simplifying Exponential Expressions
       Animated

Problem 3
Evaluating an Exponential Expression
       Animated

Problem 4
Using an Exponential Expression
       Animated

Support in Algebra 1 Companion
• Vocabulary
• Key Concepts
• Got It?

Answers

Solve It!

2^x	10^x
$2^4 = 16$	$10^4 = 10{,}000$
$2^3 = 8$	$10^3 = 1000$
$2^2 = 4$	$10^2 = 100$
$2^1 = 2$	$10^1 = 10$
$2^0 = 1$	$10^0 = 1$
$2^{-1} = \frac{1}{2}$	$10^{-1} = \frac{1}{10}$
$2^{-2} = \frac{1}{4}$	$10^{-2} = \frac{1}{100}$

$n^{x-1} = \dfrac{n^x}{n}$

$5^{-2} = \dfrac{1}{25}$ because of the pattern

$2^{-2} = \dfrac{1}{2^2}$ and $10^{-2} = \dfrac{1}{10^2}$

Got It?

1. a. $\frac{1}{64}$ **b.** 1   **c.** $\frac{1}{9}$ **d.** $\frac{1}{6}$ **e.** $\frac{1}{16}$

2. a. $\frac{1}{x^9}$ **b.** n^3 **c.** $\frac{4b}{c^3}$ **d.** $2a^3$ **e.** $\frac{1}{m^2n^5}$

Problem 3

> **Q** What does it mean to evaluate an algebraic expression? **[Substitute values for all variables, and simplify the resulting numerical expression.]**
>
> **Q** When you evaluate the expression $3(2)^3$, which operation is performed first? Explain. **[The order of operations says to evaluate the power first.]**

Got It?

Have students simplify each expression using both methods shown in the Problem. This should verify that whichever method is used, if steps are done correctly, the simplest forms for each part will be equal.

Problem 4

> **Q** What does the expression $1000 \cdot 3^h$ indicate about the growth of the bacteria each hour? **[The population triples each hour.]**
>
> **Q** Is there a value of h for which the number of bacteria is a negative number? Explain. **[No; 2^h is positive for every value of h. When multiplying 1000 by a positive number, the product will always be a positive number.]**

When you evaluate an exponential expression, you can simplify the expression before substituting values for the variables.

 **Problem 3** Evaluating an Exponential Expression

What is the value of $3s^3t^{-2}$ for $s = 2$ and $t = -3$?

Method 1 Simplify first.

$$3s^3t^{-2} = \frac{3(s)^3}{t^2}$$
$$= \frac{3(2)^3}{(-3)^2}$$
$$= \frac{24}{9} = 2\frac{2}{3}$$

Method 2 Substitute first.

$$3s^3t^{-2} = 3(2)^3(-3)^{-2}$$
$$= \frac{3(2)^3}{(-3)^2}$$
$$= \frac{24}{9} = 2\frac{2}{3}$$

Plan

How do you simplify the expression?
Use the definition of negative exponent to rewrite the expression with only positive exponents.

Got It? 3. What is the value of each expression in parts (a)–(d) for $n = -2$ and $w = 5$?

   a. $n^{-4}w^0$ **b.** $\frac{n^{-1}}{w^2}$ **c.** $\frac{n^0}{w^6}$ **d.** $\frac{1}{nw^{-1}}$

   e. Reasoning Is it easier to evaluate n^0w^0 for $n = -2$ and $w = 3$ by simplifying first or by substituting first? Explain.

 **Problem 4** Using an Exponential Expression

Population Growth A population of marine bacteria doubles every hour under controlled laboratory conditions. The number of bacteria is modeled by the expression $1000 \cdot 2^h$, where h is the number of hours after a scientist measures the population size. Evaluate the expression for $h = 0$ and $h = -3$. What does each value of the expression represent in the situation?

Know	Need	Plan
$1000 \cdot 2^h$ models the population.	Values of the expression for $h = 0$ and $h = -3$	Substitute each value of h into the expression and simplify.

$$1000 \cdot 2^h = 1000 \cdot 2^0 \qquad \text{Substitute 0 for } h.$$
$$= 1000 \cdot 1 = 1000 \qquad \text{Simplify.}$$

The value of the expression for $h = 0$ is 1000. There were 1000 bacteria at the time the scientist measured the population.

$$1000 \cdot 2^h = 1000 \cdot 2^{-3} \qquad \text{Substitute } -3 \text{ for } h.$$
$$= 1000 \cdot \frac{1}{8} = 125 \qquad \text{Simplify.}$$

The value of the expression for $h = -3$ is 125. There were 125 bacteria 3 h before the scientist measured the population.

Additional Problems

1. What is the simplified form of each expression?

   a. 6^{-2} **b.** $(-9.3)^0$

   ANSWER a. $\frac{1}{36}$ **b.** 1

2. What is the simplified form of each expression?

   a. $3a^{-2}b^3$ **b.** $\frac{1}{x^{-6}}$

   ANSWER a. $\frac{3b^3}{a^2}$ **b.** x^6

3. What is the value of $2a^{-2}b^4$ for $a = -2$ and $b = 1$?

   ANSWER $\frac{1}{2}$

4. A population of birds doubles every 8 years. The expression $6400 \cdot 2^t$ models a population of 6400 birds after t periods of 8 years. Evaluate the expression for $t = 0$ and $t = -2$. Describe what each value of the expression represents in the situation.

   ANSWER 6400, 1600; The current population is 6400 birds. The population 16 years ago was 1600 birds.

Answers

Got It? (continued)

3. a. $\frac{1}{16}$ **b.** $-\frac{1}{50}$

   c. $\frac{1}{15,625}$ **d.** $-\frac{5}{2}$

   e. It is easier to simplify first: that gives you $1 \times 1 = 1$.

Got It? **4.** A population of insects triples every week. The number of insects is modeled by the expression $5400 \cdot 3^w$, where w is the number of weeks after the population was measured. Evaluate the expression for $w = -2$, $w = 0$, and $w = 1$. What does each value of the expression represent in the situation?

 Lesson Check

Do you know HOW?

Simplify each expression.

1. 2^{-5}

2. m^0

3. $5s^2t^{-1}$

4. $\frac{4}{x^{-3}}$

Evaluate each expression for $a = 2$ and $b = -4$.

5. a^3b^{-1}

6. $2a^{-4}b^0$

Do you UNDERSTAND?

7. Vocabulary A positive exponent shows repeated multiplication. What repeated operation does a negative exponent show?

8. Error Analysis A student incorrectly simplified $\frac{x^n}{a^{-n}b^0}$ as shown below. Find and correct the student's error.

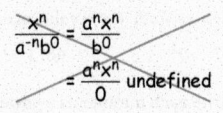

 Practice and Problem-Solving Exercises

A Practice Simplify each expression. *See Problem 1.*

9. 3^{-2} **10.** $(-4.25)^0$ **11.** $(-5)^{-2}$

12. -5^{-2} **13.** $(-4)^{-2}$ **14.** 2^{-6}

15. -3^0 **16.** -12^{-1} **17.** $\frac{1}{2^0}$

18. 58^{-1} **19.** 1.5^{-2} **20.** $(-5)^{-3}$

Simplify each expression. *See Problem 2.*

21. $4ab^0$ **22.** $\frac{1}{x^{-7}}$ **23.** $5x^{-4}$ **24.** $\frac{1}{c^{-1}}$

25. $\frac{3^{-2}}{n}$ **26.** $k^{-4}j^0$ **27.** $\frac{3x^{-2}}{y}$ **28.** $\frac{7ab^{-2}}{3w}$

29. $c^{-5}d^{-7}$ **30.** $c^{-5}d^7$ **31.** $\frac{8}{2s^{-3}}$ **32.** $\frac{7s}{5t^{-3}}$

33. $\frac{6a^{-1}c^{-3}}{d^0}$ **34.** $2^{-3}x^2z^{-7}$ **35.** $12^0t^7u^{-11}$ **36.** $\frac{7s^0t^{-5}}{2^{-1}m^2}$

Got It?

Q What effect does a greater value of w have on the population? **[A greater value of w results in a larger population.]**

Q What happens to the population as the value of w decreases? **[The size of the population approaches zero but never reaches it.]**

3 Lesson Check

Do you know HOW?
• If students have difficulty with Exercise 5, then have them review Problem 3.

Do you UNDERSTAND?
• If students have difficulty with Exercise 8, then have them review the definition of zero as an exponent.

Close

Q How can you describe the Property of Negative Exponents in your own words? **[Answers may vary. Sample: A term raised to a negative exponent can be written as the reciprocal of the term raised to the opposite of the negative exponent.]**

Got It? (continued)

4. 600 represents the number of insects 2 weeks before the population was measured; 5400 represents the population when it was measured; 16,200 represents the number of insects 1 week after the population was measured.

Lesson Check

1. $\frac{1}{32}$ **2.** 1, $m \neq 0$ **3.** $\frac{5s^2}{t}$

4. $4x^3$ **5.** -2 **6.** $\frac{1}{8}$

7. division

8. b^0 is equal to 1, not 0; $\frac{x^n}{a^{-n}b^0} = \frac{a^nx^n}{1} = a^nx^n$

Practice and Problem-Solving Exercises

9. $\frac{1}{9}$ **10.** 1 **11.** $\frac{1}{25}$

12. $-\frac{1}{25}$ **13.** $\frac{1}{16}$ **14.** $\frac{1}{64}$

15. -1 **16.** $-\frac{1}{12}$ **17.** 1

18. $\frac{1}{58}$ **19.** $0.\overline{4}$ or $\frac{4}{9}$ **20.** $-\frac{1}{125}$

21. $4a$, $b \neq 0$ **22.** x^7 **23.** $\frac{5}{x^4}$

24. c **25.** $\frac{1}{9n}$ **26.** $\frac{1}{k^4}$, $j \neq 0$

27. $\frac{3}{x^2y}$ **28.** $\frac{7a}{3b^2w}$ **29.** $\frac{1}{c^5d^7}$

30. $\frac{d^7}{c^5}$ **31.** $4s^3$ **32.** $\frac{7st^3}{5}$

33. $\frac{6}{ac^3}$, $d \neq 0$ **34.** $\frac{x^2}{8z^7}$ **35.** $\frac{t^7}{u^{11}}$

36. $\frac{14}{m^2t^5}$

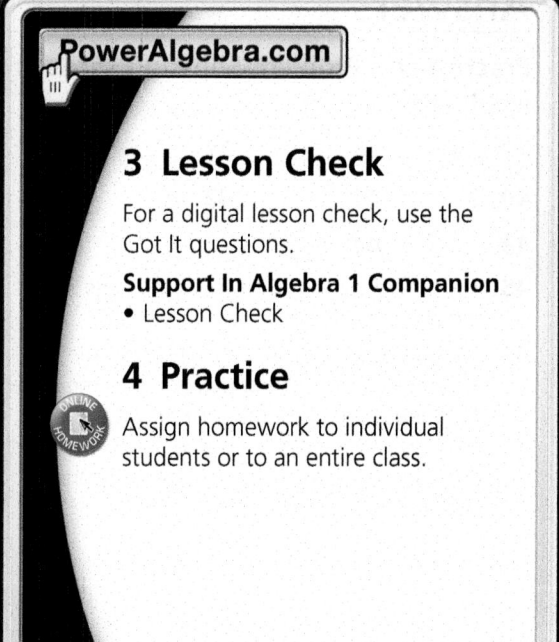

PowerAlgebra.com

3 Lesson Check

For a digital lesson check, use the Got It questions.

Support In Algebra 1 Companion
• Lesson Check

4 Practice

Assign homework to individual students or to an entire class.

4 Practice

ASSIGNMENT GUIDE

Basic: 9–46 all, 48–58 even, 60, 62, 64

Average: 9–45 odd, 47–65

Advanced: 9–45 odd, 47–72

Standardized Test Prep: 73–77

Mixed Review: 78–91

Reasoning exercises have blue headings.

Applications exercises have red headings.

EXERCISE 64: Use the Think About a Plan worksheet in the Practice and Problem Solving Workbook (also available in the Teaching Resources in print and online) to further support students' development in becoming independent learners.

HOMEWORK QUICK CHECK

To check students' understanding of key skills and concepts, go over Exercises 23, 45, 60, 62, and 64.

Evaluate each expression for $r = -3$ and $s = 5$.

See Problem 3.

37. r^{-3}

38. s^{-3}

39. $\dfrac{3r}{s^{-2}}$

40. $\dfrac{s^0}{r^{-2}}$

41. $4s^{-1}$

42. $r^0 s^{-2}$

43. $r^{-4} s^2$

44. $2^{-4} r^3 s^{-2}$

45. Internet Traffic The number of visitors to a certain Web site triples every month. The number of visitors is modeled by the expression $8100 \cdot 3^m$, where m is the number of months after the number of visitors was measured. Evaluate the expression $m = -4$. What does the value of the expression represent in the situation?

See Problem 4.

46. Population Growth A Galápagos cactus finch population increases by half every decade. The number of finches is modeled by the expression $45 \cdot 1.5^d$, where d is the number of decades after the population was measured. Evaluate the expression for $d = -2$, $d = 0$, and $d = 1$. What does each value of the expression represent in the situation?

Galápagos cactus finch

B Apply

Mental Math Is the value of each expression *positive* or *negative*?

47. -2^2

48. $(-2)^2$

49. $(-2)^3$

50. $(-2)^{-3}$

Write each number as a power of 10 using negative exponents.

51. $\dfrac{1}{10}$

52. $\dfrac{1}{100}$

53. $\dfrac{1}{1000}$

54. $\dfrac{1}{10,000}$

55. a. Patterns Complete the pattern using powers of 5.

$\dfrac{1}{5^2} = \blacksquare$ $\qquad$ $\dfrac{1}{5^1} = \blacksquare$ $\qquad$ $\dfrac{1}{5^0} = \blacksquare$ $\qquad$ $\dfrac{1}{5^{-1}} = \blacksquare$ $\qquad$ $\dfrac{1}{5^{-2}} = \blacksquare$

b. Write $\dfrac{1}{5^{-4}}$ using a positive exponent.

c. Rewrite $\dfrac{1}{a^{-n}}$ as a power of a.

Rewrite each fraction with all the variables in the numerator.

56. $\dfrac{a}{b^{-2}}$

57. $\dfrac{4g}{h^3}$

58. $\dfrac{5m^6}{3n}$

59. $\dfrac{8c^5}{11d^4 e^{-2}}$

60. Think About a Plan Suppose your drama club's budget doubles every year. This year the budget is $500. How much was the club's budget 2 yr ago?
- What expression models what the budget of the club will be in 1 yr? In 2 yr? In y years?
- What value of y can you substitute into your expression to find the budget of the club 2 yr ago?

61. Copy and complete the table at the right.

62. a. Simplify $a^n \cdot a^{-n}$.

b. Reasoning What is the mathematical relationship between a^n and a^{-n}? Explain.

n	3	$\blacksquare$	$\blacksquare$	$\frac{5}{8}$	$\blacksquare$
n^{-1}	$\blacksquare$	6	$\frac{1}{7}$	$\blacksquare$	0.5

Answers

Practice and Problem-Solving Exercises
(continued)

37. $-\dfrac{1}{27}$ **38.** $\dfrac{1}{125}$ **39.** -225

40. 9 **41.** $\dfrac{4}{5}$ **42.** $\dfrac{1}{25}$

43. $\dfrac{25}{81}$ **44.** $-\dfrac{27}{400}$

45. 100; there were 100 visitors 4 months before the number of visitors was measured.

46. 20 represents the cactus finch population 2 decades before the population was measured; 45 represents the number of finches when the population was measured; 67.5 represents the number of finches 1 decade after the population was measured.

47. negative **48.** positive

49. negative **50.** negative

51. 10^{-1} **52.** 10^{-2}

53. 10^{-3} **54.** 10^{-4}

55. a. $5^{-2}, 5^{-1}, 5^0, 5^1, 5^2$

b. 5^4 **c.** a^n

56. ab^2 **57.** $4gh^{-3}$

58. $\dfrac{5m^6 n^{-1}}{3}$ **59.** $\dfrac{8c^5 d^{-4} e^2}{11}$

60. $125

61.

n	3	$\frac{1}{6}$	7	$\frac{5}{8}$	2
n^{-1}	$\frac{1}{3}$	6	$\frac{1}{7}$	$\frac{8}{5}$	0.5

62 a. 1

b. They are reciprocals.

63. Open-Ended Choose a fraction to use as a value for the variable a. Find the values of a^{-1}, a^2, and a^{-2}.

64. Manufacturing A company is making metal rods with a target diameter of 1.5 mm. A rod is acceptable when its diameter is within 10^{-3} mm of the target diameter. Write an inequality for the acceptable range of diameters.

65. Reasoning Are $3x^{-2}$ and $3x^2$ reciprocals? Explain.

 **Challenge** Simplify each expression.

66. $\left(\frac{r^{-7}b^{-8}}{t^{-4}w^1}\right)^0$ **67.** $(-5)^2 - (0.5)^{-2}$ **68.** $\frac{6}{m^2} + \frac{5m^{-2}}{3^{-3}}$

69. $2^3(5^0 - 6m^2)$ **70.** $\frac{2x^{-5}y^3}{n^2} \div \frac{r^2y^5}{2n}$ **71.** $2^{-1} - \frac{1}{3^{-2}} + 5\left(\frac{1}{2^2}\right)$

72. For what value or values of n is $n^{-3} = \left(\frac{1}{n}\right)^5$?

Standardized Test Prep

GRIDDED RESPONSE

SAT/ACT

73. What is the simplified form of $-6(-6)^{-1}$?

74. Segment CD represents the flight of a bird that passes through the points $(1, 2)$ and $(5, 4)$. What is the slope of a line that represents the flight of a second bird that flew perpendicular to the first bird?

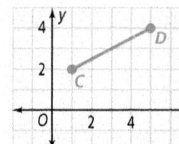

75. What is the solution of the equation $1.5(x - 2.5) = 3$?

76. What is the simplified form of $|3.5 - 4.7| + 5.6$?

77. What is the y-intercept of the graph of $3x - 2y = -8$?

Mixed Review

Solve each system by graphing.   **See Lesson 6-6.**

78. $y > 3x + 4$
$y \leq -3x + 1$

79. $y \leq -2x + 1$
$y < 2x - 1$

80. $y \geq 0.5x$
$y \leq x + 2$

Write an equation in slope-intercept form for the line with the given slope m and y-intercept b.   **See Lesson 5-3.**

81. $m = -1$, $b = 4$ **82.** $m = 5$, $b = -2$ **83.** $m = \frac{2}{5}$, $b = -3$

84. $m = -\frac{3}{11}$, $b = -17$ **85.** $m = \frac{5}{9}$, $b = \frac{1}{3}$ **86.** $m = 1.25$, $b = -3.79$

Get Ready! To prepare for Lesson 7-2, do Exercises 87–91.

Simplify each expression.   **See Lesson 7-1.**

87. $6 \cdot 10^4$ **88.** $7 \cdot 10^{-2}$ **89.** $8.2 \cdot 10^5$ **90.** $3 \cdot 10^{-3}$ **91.** $3.4 \cdot 10^5$

---

63. Answers may vary. Sample: Let $a = \frac{2}{3}$, then $a^{-1} = \frac{3}{2}$, $a^2 = \frac{4}{9}$, and $a^{-2} = \frac{9}{4}$.

64. $1.499 < d < 1.501$

65. No; answers may vary. Sample: $3x^{-2} = \frac{3}{x^2}$ which is not the reciprocal of $3x^2$.

66. 1   **67.** 21

68. $\frac{141}{m^2}$ **69.** $8 - 48m^2$

70. $\frac{4}{nr^2x^5y^2}$ **71.** $-7\frac{1}{4}$

72. -1 and 1 **73.** 1

74. -2 **75.** 4.5

76. 6.8   **77.** 4

78.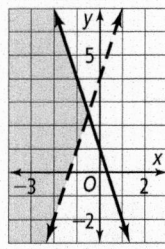

79.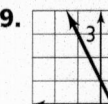

80.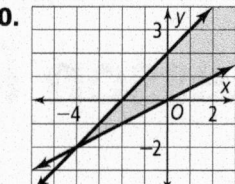

81. $y = -x + 4$ **82.** $y = 5x - 2$

83. $y = \frac{2}{5}x - 3$ **84.** $y = -\frac{3}{11}x - 17$

85. $y = \frac{5}{9}x + \frac{1}{3}$ **86.** $y = 1.25x - 3.79$

87. 60,000   **88.** 0.07

89. 820,000   **90.** 0.003

91. 340,000

Additional Instructional Support

Algebra 1 Companion

Students can use the **Algebra 1 Companion** worktext (4 pages) as you teach the lesson. Use the Companion to support

- New Vocabulary
- Key Concepts
- Got It for each Problem
- Lesson Check

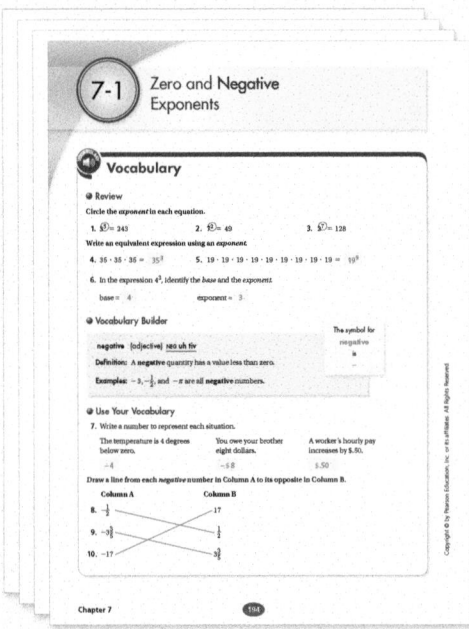

ELL Support

Focus on Communication Have students make a two-column table. Label one column "Zero Exponent" and the other "Negative Exponent." Have students write an example of each in the columns. Ask volunteers for their examples to put on the board. Repeat the property each time you simplify the power. For example, say: A value with a zero exponent always equals 1 so $-9^0 = -1$. Continue with examples, allowing students a chance to explain the property used to simplify the powers. Use both numeric and algebraic bases.

5 Assess & Remediate

Lesson Quiz

1. What is the simplified form of each expression?

   a. 2^{-3}

   b. $(5.5)^0$

2. What is the simplified form of each expression?

   a. $-6a^2b^{-1}$

   b. $\dfrac{5}{y^{-3}}$

3. What is the value of $-6a^{-3}b^2$ for $a = -2$ and $b = 4$?

4. **Do you UNDERSTAND?** The number of hits on a website doubles every month. About 10,600 people visited the website during May. The expression $10{,}600 \cdot 2^t$ models the number of visitors after t months. Evaluate the expression for $t = 0$ and $t = -2$. Describe what each value of the expression represents in the situation.

ANSWERS TO LESSON QUIZ

1. **a.** $\dfrac{1}{8}$ **b.** 1

2. **a.** $\dfrac{-6a^2}{b}$ **b.** $5y^3$

3. 12

4. 10,600; 2,650; About 10,600 people visited the website in May. About 2,650 people visited the website in March.

PRESCRIPTION FOR REMEDIATION

Use the student work on the Lesson Quiz to prescribe a differentiated review assignment.

Points	Differentiated Remediation
0–2	Intervention
3	On-level
4	Extension

PowerAlgebra.com

5 Assess & Remediate

Assign the Lesson Quiz. Appropriate intervention, practice, or enrichment is automatically generated based on student performance.

Intervention

- **Reteaching** (2 pages) Provides reteaching and practice exercises for the key lesson concepts. Use with struggling students or absent students.

- **English Language Learner Support** Helps students develop and reinforce mathematical vocabulary and key concepts.

All-in-One Resources/Online
Reteaching

7-1 Reteaching
Zero and Negative Exponents

For every nonzero number a, $a^0 = 1$.

For every nonzero number a and integer n, $a^{-n} = \dfrac{1}{a^n}$. In other words, when the exponent is negative, raise the reciprocal of the base to the opposite of the exponent.

Problem

What is the simplified form of each expression?

a. $3.9^0 = 1$ — Since the exponent is 0 but the base of the expression is 3.9, which is not 0, the expression has a value of 1.

b. $9^{-2} = \dfrac{1}{9^2}$ — The exponent is negative, so raise the reciprocal of 9, or $\frac{1}{9}$, to the exponent $-(-2)$, or 2.

$= \dfrac{1}{81}$ — Simplify.

Problem

What is the simplified form of $\dfrac{7b^{-3}}{a^2}$ using only positive exponents?

$\dfrac{7b^{-3}}{a^2} = \dfrac{7}{a^2} \cdot b^{-3}$ — Rewrite the expression as a product of factors with positive exponents and factors with negative exponents.

$= \dfrac{7}{a^2} \cdot \dfrac{1}{b^3}$ — Rewrite the factor with the negative exponent by raising the reciprocal of the base to a positive exponent.

$= \dfrac{7}{a^2 b^3}$ — Simplify by multiplying.

All-in-One Resources/Online
English Language Learner Support

7-1 ELL Support
Zero and Negative Exponents

Complete the vocabulary chart by filling in the missing information.

Word or Word Phrase	Definition	Picture or Example
base	A number used as a repeated factor	$6^3 = 6 \times 6 \times 6$ The base is 6.
exponent	The number that tells how many times a base is to be used as a repeated factor	$6^3 = 6 \times 6 \times 6$ The exponent is 3.
zero as an exponent	For every nonzero number a, $a^0 = 1$.	$5^0 = 1$
negative exponent	For every nonzero number a and integer n, $a^{-n} = \dfrac{1}{a^n}$.	$6^{-2} = \dfrac{1}{6^2}$
exponential expression	A mathematical expression consisting of a constant raised to a power	5^x
reciprocal	A number and its reciprocal have a product of 1.	$\dfrac{1}{x^2}, x^2$ $\frac{2}{3}, \frac{3}{2}$
simplest form	An algebraic expression is in simplest form when it has no like terms, negative exponents, or parentheses.	$4a^{-2}b^4 = \frac{4b^4}{a^2}$ $3a^2 + 2a - 5ab$

Differentiated Remediation *continued*

On-Level

- **Practice** (2 pages) Provides extra practice for each lesson. For simpler practice exercises, use the Form K Practice pages found in the All-in-One Teaching Resources and online.

- **Think About a Plan** Helps students develop specific problem-solving skills and strategies by providing scaffolded guiding questions.

- **Standardized Test Prep** Focuses on all major exercises, all major question types, and helps students prepare for the high-stakes assessments.

Extension

- **Enrichment** Provides students with interesting problems and activities that extend the concepts of the lesson.

- **Activities, Games, and Puzzles** Worksheets that can be used for concepts development, enrichment, and for fun!

Practice and Problem Solving WKBK/ All-in-One Resources/Online
Practice page 1

7-1 Practice — Form G
Zero and Negative Exponents

Simplify each expression.

1. 13^0 1

2. 5^{-3} $\frac{1}{125}$

3. $\frac{3}{3^{-4}}$ 243

4. $\frac{2}{4^{-1}}$ 8

5. $-(7)^{-2}$ $-\frac{1}{49}$

6. 46^{-1} $\frac{1}{46}$

7. -6^0 1

8. $-(12x)^{-2}$ $-\frac{1}{144x^2}$

9. $\frac{1}{8^0}$ 1

10. $6b e^0$ 6b

11. $-(11x)^0$ -1

12. $\left(\frac{2}{9}\right)^{-2}$ $20\frac{1}{4}$

13. $3m^{-8}p^0$ $\frac{3}{m^8}$

14. $\frac{5a^{-4}}{2c}$ $\frac{5}{2a^4 c}$

15. $\frac{-3k^{-2}(mn)^3}{p^{-8}}$ $\frac{-3p^8 m^3 n^3}{k^2}$

16. $\left(\frac{2m}{3n}\right)^{-3}$ $\frac{27n^3}{8m^3}$

17. $8^{-2}q^3 r^{-5}$ $\frac{q^3}{64r^5}$

18. $-(10a)^{-4}b^0$ $\frac{-1}{10,000a^4}$

19. $\frac{11xy^{-1}z^0}{v^{-3}}$ $\frac{11xv^3}{y}$

20. $\frac{5m^{-1}}{9(ab)^{-4}z^3}$ $\frac{5a^4 b^4}{9m z^3}$

Practice and Problem Solving WKBK/ All-in-One Resources/Online
Practice page 2

7-1 Practice (continued) — Form G
Zero and Negative Exponents

Evaluate each expression for $a = -4$, $b = 3$, and $c = 2$.

21. $3a^{-1}$ $-\frac{3}{4}$

22. b^{-3} $\frac{1}{27}$

23. $4a^2 b^{-2} c^3$ $\frac{512}{9}$

24. $9a^2 c^4$ 144

25. $-a^{-2}$ $-\frac{1}{16}$

26. $(-c)^{-2}$ $\frac{1}{4}$

Write each number as a power of 10 using negative exponents.

27. $\frac{1}{1000}$ 10^{-3}

28. $\frac{1}{10}$ 10^{-1}

Write each expression as a decimal.

29. 10^{-3} 0.001

30. $8 \cdot 10^{-4}$ 0.0008

31. The number of people who vote early doubles every week leading up to an election. This week 1200 people voted early. The expression $1200 \cdot 2^w$ models the number of people who will vote early w weeks after this week. Evaluate the expression for $w = -3$. Describe what the value of the expression represents in the situation.
150; The expression $1200 \cdot 2^{-3}$ represents the number of people who voted early three weeks ago.

32. A pizza shop makes large pizzas with a target diameter of 16 inches. A pizza is acceptable if its diameter is within $3 \cdot 2^{-2}$ in. of the target diameter. Let d represent the diameter of a pizza. Write an inequality for the range of acceptable large pizza diameters in inches.
$15\frac{1}{4} < d < 16\frac{3}{4}$

33. **Open-Ended** Choose a fraction to use as a value for the variable c. Find the values of c^{-1}, c^{-3}, and c^3.
Answers may vary. Sample: $c = \frac{2}{3}$; $c^{-1} = \frac{3}{2}$; $c^{-3} = \frac{27}{8}$; $c^3 = \frac{8}{27}$

All-in-One Resources/Online
Enrichment

7-1 Enrichment
Zero and Negative Exponents

For each exercise below, a student's answer is shown. Indicate below each exercise whether each answer is correct or incorrect. For each incorrect answer, indicate where the student made an error, and describe how to correct it. Then write the correct answer.

1. Simplify $\frac{1}{3} \cdot (2y)^0 x^{-3}$.
$\frac{1}{3} \cdot (2y)^0 x^{-3} = \frac{(2)(1)x^{-3}}{3}$
$= \frac{2}{3x^3}$
incorrect; The student simplified $(2y)^0$ as 2 instead of 1. The correct answer is $\frac{1}{3x^3}$.

2. Simplify $-5 \cdot \frac{8b^{-8}cd^{-4}}{12b^0}$.
$-5 \cdot \frac{8b^{-8}cd^{-4}}{12b^0} = \frac{-40b^{-8}cd^{-4}}{1}$
$= \frac{-40}{b^8 cd^4}$
incorrect; The student simplified cd^{-4} as $\frac{c}{d^4}$ instead of $\frac{c}{d^4}$. The correct answer is $\frac{-40c}{3b^8 d^4}$.

3. Simplify $\frac{2x}{y^{-4}} \cdot \frac{3z^{-3}}{18}$.
$\frac{2x}{y^{-4}} \cdot \frac{3z^{-3}}{18} = \frac{2x(3z^{-3})}{y^{-4}(18)}$
$= \frac{6xy^4}{18z^3}$
$= \frac{xy^4}{3z^3}$ correct

4. Simplify $-(5a^3)^{-2}$.
$-(5a^3)^{-2} = -5^{-2}a^{-9}$
$= -\frac{1}{25a^9}$
incorrect; The student simplified $(5a^3)^{-2}$ as $5^{-2}a^{-9}$ instead of $5^{-2}a^{-6}$. The correct answer is $-\frac{1}{25a^6}$.

5. Simplify $\frac{9p}{7q^{-2}} \div \frac{2r^{-3}}{5}$.
$\frac{9p}{7q^{-2}} \div \frac{2r^{-3}}{5} = \frac{9p}{7q^{-2}} \cdot \frac{5}{2r^{-3}}$
$= \frac{45p}{14q^{-2}r^{-3}}$
$= \frac{45pq^2 r^{-3}}{14}$
incorrect; The student simplified $\frac{45p}{14q^{-2}r^{-3}}$ as $\frac{45pq^2 r^{-3}}{14}$ instead of $\frac{45pq^2 r^3}{14}$. The correct answer is $\frac{45pq^2 r^3}{14}$.

Practice and Problem Solving WKBK/ All-in-One Resources/Online
Think About a Plan

7-1 Think About a Plan
Zero and Negative Exponents

Manufacturing A company is making metal rods with a target diameter of 1.5 mm. A rod is acceptable when its diameter is within 10^{-3} mm of the target diameter. Write an inequality for the acceptable range of diameters.

Understanding the Problem

1. What is the target diameter for the metal rods? ___1.5 mm___

2. How do you know if a rod is acceptable? ___within 10^{-3} of 1.5 mm___

3. What is the problem asking you to determine? ___an inequality for the acceptable range of diameters___

Planning the Solution

4. What does the word "within" tell you about the acceptable range of diameters? ___The diameter may be not greater than 1.50 + 0.001 mm or less than 1.5 − 0.001 mm.___

5. What does this tell you about the type of inequality that you should use? ___The inequality will use the symbols < and >.___

Getting an Answer

6. Write 10^{-3} as a fraction and as a decimal. $\frac{1}{10}$, 0.1

7. Find the acceptable range for the diameters of the rods. between 14.999 and 15.001 mm

8. Write your answer as a single inequality. ___14.99 < d < 15.001___

Practice and Problem Solving WKBK/ All-in-One Resources/Online
Standardized Test Prep

7-1 Standardized Test Prep
Zero and Negative Exponents

Multiple Choice

For Exercises 1–6, choose the correct letter.

1. What is the simplified form of $3a^4 b^{-2}c^3$? D
   A. $\frac{81a^4 c^3}{b^2}$ B. $\frac{81a^4}{b^2 c^3}$ C. $\frac{3a^4}{b^2 c^3}$ D. $\frac{3a^4 c^3}{b^2}$

2. What is $-a^{-2}$ if $a = -5$? H
   F. -25 G. 25 H. $-\frac{1}{25}$ I. $\frac{1}{25}$

3. Which of the following simplifies to a negative number? A
   A. -4^{-4} B. $(-4)^{-4}$ C. 4^{-4} D. $\frac{1}{4^{-4}}$

4. What is the simplified form of $-(14x)^0 y^{-7}z$? I
   F. $-\frac{14z}{y^7}$ G. $\frac{14z}{y^7}$ H. $\frac{z}{y^7}$ I. $-\frac{z}{y^7}$

5. What is $(-m)^{-3}n$ if $m = 2$ and $n = -24$? A
   A. 3 B. -3 C. 4 D. -4

6. What is the simplified form of $\left(-\frac{5a}{3}\right)^{-3}$? G
   F. $\frac{27}{125a^3}$ G. $-\frac{27}{125a^3}$ H. $\frac{125a^3}{27}$ I. $-\frac{125a^3}{27}$

Short Response

7. The number of bacteria in a culture quadruples every hour. There were 65,536 bacteria in the culture at 8:00 A.M. The expression $65,536 \cdot 4^h$ models the number of bacteria in the culture h hours after 8:00 A.M.
   a. What is the value of the expression for $h = -4$?
   b. What does the value of the expression in part a represent?
   256; the number of bacteria in the culture at 4:00 A.M.
   [2] Both parts answered correctly
   [1] One part answered correctly
   [0] Neither part answered correctly

Online Teacher Resource Center
Activities, Games, and Puzzles

7-1 Puzzle: Find the Power of 2
Zero and Negative Exponents

Answer each of the 12 clues below. Each time you find an answer, use an X to cross out the numbers in the figure below.

2^{-2} and its reciprocal	10^{-2} and 11^{-2}	2^4 and $\frac{1}{16}$	7^2 and $\frac{1}{9^2}$
2^{-5} and $1 + 3^4$	3^4 and 3^{-1}	2^{-3} and 2^{-6}	8^2 and $\frac{1}{7^2}$
$1 \div 2^{-5}$ and $1 \div 3^{-2}$	$1 + 2$ and $1 + 2^{-1}$	$1 + 5^{-1}$ and $1 + 5^{-2}$	6^2 and $\frac{1}{3^{-1}}$

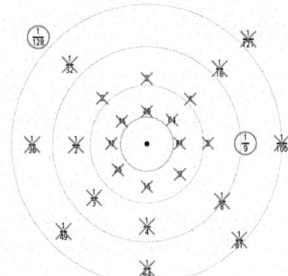

After you follow all the clues, only two fractions should remain. Circle these fractions. When you rearrange the digits of their denominators, you will find a positive power of 2. What is it? (*Hint:* Every power of 2 has an even digit as its ones digit.)

Puzzle answer: ___8192 or 2^{13}___

1 Interactive Learning

Solve It!
PURPOSE To allow students to discover the reason for using scientific notation to write and compare very large and very small numbers

PROCESS Students may use paper and pencil or a calculator to complete the calculations.

> **FACILITATE**
> Having students use paper and pencil to complete this calculation will provide motivation to learn scientific notation concepts.
>
> **Q** How can you tell that the Mirabilis pollen is somewhere between 100 and 1000 times larger than the Myosatis pollen? **[The measurement for the Mirabilis pollen has two less zeros directly after the decimal point.]**

ANSWER See Solve It in Answers on next page.

CONNECT THE MATH Explain to students that writing numbers in scientific notation improves efficiency and accuracy of various calculations involving very large and very small numbers.

2 Guided Instruction

Take Note
Remind students that a positive exponent means repeated multiplication. 8.3×10^5 means to multiply 8.3 by 10 five times. Further, a negative exponent means repeated division. 7.1×10^{-5} means to divide 7.1 by 10 five times.

Objectives To write numbers in scientific and standard notation
To compare and order numbers using scientific notation

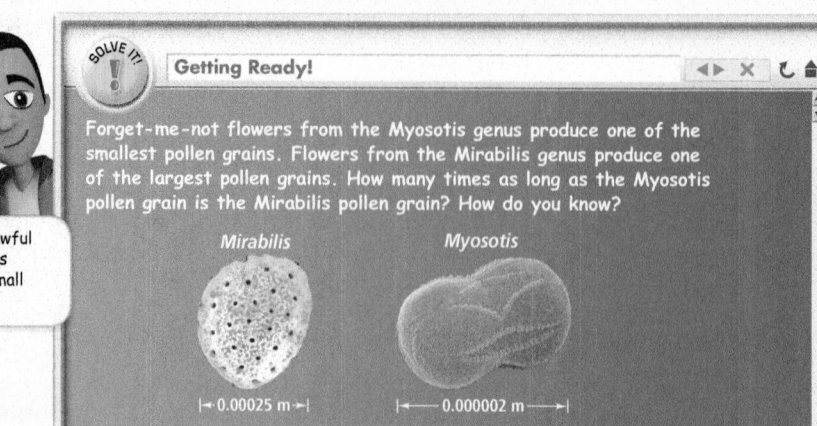

Getting Ready!

Forget-me-not flowers from the *Myosotis* genus produce one of the smallest pollen grains. Flowers from the *Mirabilis* genus produce one of the largest pollen grains. How many times as long as the Myosotis pollen grain is the Mirabilis pollen grain? How do you know?

That's an awful lot of digits for such small numbers.

Mirabilis — |← 0.00025 m →|

Myosotis — |←— 0.000002 m —→|

In the Solve It, you worked with very small numbers. Scientists and mathematicians write very small or very large numbers, such as the masses of subatomic particles or the diameters of planets, using powers of 10.

Lesson Vocabulary
• scientific notation

Essential Understanding You can use powers of 10 to write and compare very large or very small numbers more easily. *Scientific notation* is a shorthand way to write numbers using powers of 10.

> **take note**
>
> ### Key Concept   Scientific Notation
>
> A number in **scientific notation** is written as the product of two factors in the form $a \times 10^n$, where n is an integer and $1 \leq |a| < 10$.
>
> **Examples** 8.3×10^5 4.12×10^{22} 7.1×10^{-5}

You can use a scientific calculator to work with numbers in scientific notation. The E on a calculator readout stands for exponentiation. The readout 1.35E8 means 1.35×10^8, or 135,000,000. The key lets you input an exponent for a power of 10. So to enter 4×10^6, you can enter 4 6.

7-2 **Preparing to Teach**

BIG idea   **Equivalence**   **UbD**

ESSENTIAL UNDERSTANDINGS
• Powers of 10 can be used to more easily write and compare very large or very small numbers.
• *Scientific notation* is a shorthand way to write numbers using powers of 10.

Math Background
The ability to use scientific notation is an essential prerequisite skill for many subjects in science and engineering. The exponent of the power of 10 is also known as the *order of magnitude of a number*. In many circumstances, scientists and engineers are interested in the order of magnitude of some measurement. Familiarity with scientific notation also prepares students for work with common logarithms.

Support Student Learning
Use the **Algebra 1 Companion** to engage and support students during instructions. See Lesson Resources at the end of this lesson for details.

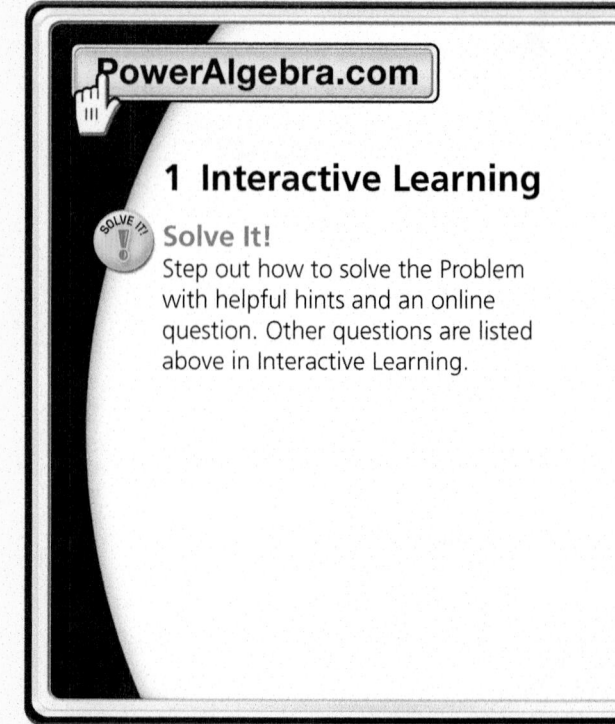

PowerAlgebra.com

1 Interactive Learning

Solve It!
Step out how to solve the Problem with helpful hints and an online question. Other questions are listed above in Interactive Learning.

Problem 1 Recognizing Scientific Notation

Is the number written in scientific notation? If not, explain.

Ⓐ 0.23×10^{-3} Ⓑ 2.3×10^7 Ⓒ 9.3×100^9

No. 0.23 is less than 1.   Yes   No. 100^9 is not in the form 10^n.

✓ **Got It?** 1. Is the number written in scientific notation? If not, explain.

     a. 53×10^4 **b.** 3.42×10^{-7} **c.** 0.35×100

With scientific notation, you use nonnegative exponents to write numbers greater than 1. Notice that $1,430,000,000 = 1.43 \times 1,000,000,000 = 1.43 \times 10^9$. Problem 2 shows you a shortcut. You use negative exponents to write numbers between 0 and 1.

 Problem 2 Writing a Number in Scientific Notation

Physical Science What is each number written in scientific notation?

Ⓐ approximate distance between the sun and Saturn: 1,430,000,000 km

$$1,430,000,000 = 1.43 \times 10^9$$

Use 9 as the exponent.

Move the decimal point 9 places to the left.   Remove the zeros after the 3.

Ⓑ the radius of an atom: 0.0000000001 m

$0.0000000001 = 1 \times 10^{-10}$ Move the decimal point 10 places to the right and use −10 as the exponent. Remove the zeros before the 1.

✓ **Got It?** 2. What is each number written in scientific notation?

     a. 678,000   **b.** 0.000032   **c.** 51,400,000   **d.** 0.0000007

Notice that $5.5 \times 10^6 = 5.5 \times 1,000,000 = 5,500,000$. Problem 3 shows you a shortcut.

 Problem 3 Writing a Number in Standard Notation

Biology What is each number written in standard notation?

Ⓐ weight of an Asian elephant: 5.5×10^6 g

$5.5 \times 10^6 = 5,500,000$ Move the decimal point 6 places to the right.

$= 5,500,000$

Ⓑ weight of an ant: 3.1×10^{-3} g

$3.1 \times 10^{-3} = 0.0031$ Move the decimal point 3 places to the left.

$= 0.0031$

Problem 1

Q What two conditions must be true for a number to be written in scientific notation? [**The first factor must be between 1 and 10 and the second factor must be a power of 10.**]

Got It?   ERROR PREVENTION

Q If 1c was written as 0.35×10^2, would it be in scientific notation? Explain. [**No; the first factor is not greater than or equal to 1.**]

Problem 2

Q In 2B, how many times would you need to divide 1 by 10 in order to yield a quotient of 0.0000000001? [**ten times**]

Q Is the number 1×10^{-10} equivalent to the number 10^{-10}? Explain. [**Yes; 1 is the multiplicative identity.**]

Got It?   ERROR PREVENTION

If students give an answer of 6.78×10^3 for 2a or an answer of 5.14×10^5 for 2c, then they are likely counting only the zeros when determining the exponent.

Problem 3

Q In 3A, what part of the weight indicates to move the decimal point to the right? [**the positive exponent**]

Q In 3B, what part of the weight indicates to move the decimal point to the left? [**the negative exponent**]

2 Guided Instruction

 Each Problem is worked out and supported online.

Problem 1
Recognizing Scientific Notation

Problem 2
Writing a Number in Scientific Notation
Animated

Problem 3
Writing a Number in Standard Notation
Animated

Problem 4
Comparing Numbers in Scientific Notation

Problem 5
Using Scientific Notation to Order Numbers
Animated

Support in Algebra 1 Companion
• Vocabulary
• Key Concepts
• Got It?

Answers

Solve It!

About 125 times as long; $\frac{0.00025}{0.000002} = 125$

Got It?

1. a. No; 53 is not less than 10.
     b. yes
     c. No; 0.35 is not greater than or equal to 1 and 100 is not in the form 10^n.

2. a. 6.78×10^5 **b.** 3.2×10^{-5}
     c. 5.14×10^7 **d.** 7×10^{-7}

Got It?
VISUAL LEARNERS

Have students write the first factor in each scientific notation and then draw curved arrows as they move the decimal point in the direction indicated by the exponent on the power of 10. Ensure they place a zero above each arrow.

Problem 4

> **Q** Is each ocean size written in scientific notation? Explain. **[Yes; each first factor is between 1 and 10 and each second factor is a power of 10.]**
>
> **Q** When two numbers written in scientific notation have the same power of 10, what determines the lesser number? **[the first factor]**

Got It?
ERROR PREVENTION

Point out to students that even though the scientific notation forms of these masses have negative powers of 10, their standard forms are positive numbers.

 Got It? 3. What is each number in parts (a)–(d) written in standard notation?
  a. 5.23×10^7 **b.** 4.6×10^{-5} **c.** 2.09×10^{-4} **d.** 3.8×10^{12}
  e. Reasoning How do you write a number of the form $a \times 10^0$ in standard notation?

You can compare and order numbers in scientific notation. First compare the powers of 10. If numbers have the same power of 10, then compare the decimals.

 **Problem 4** Comparing Numbers in Scientific Notation

Geography The map below shows four major world oceans and their surface areas. What is the order of the oceans from least to greatest surface area?

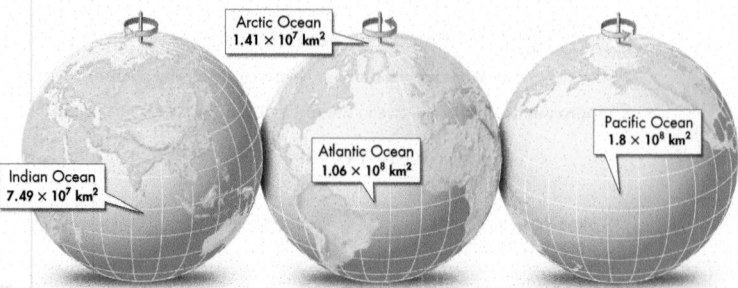

Arctic Ocean 1.41×10^7 km²
Pacific Ocean 1.8×10^8 km²
Atlantic Ocean 1.06×10^8 km²
Indian Ocean 7.49×10^7 km²

Think

Why do you arrange the numbers by the powers of 10 first?
If two numbers written in scientific notation have different powers of 10, then the number with the greater power of 10 is greater.

Order the numbers by the powers of 10. Arrange the numbers with the same power of 10 in order by their decimal parts.

1.41×10^7	7.49×10^7	1.06×10^8	1.8×10^8
Arctic	Indian	Atlantic	Pacific

From least to greatest surface area, the order of the oceans is the Arctic, the Indian, the Atlantic, and the Pacific.

 Got It? 4. What is the order of the following parts of an atom from least to greatest mass?
  neutron: 1.675×10^{-24} g, electron: 9.109×10^{-28} g, proton: 1.673×10^{-24} g

You can write numbers like 815×10^5 and 0.078×10^{-2} in scientific notation.

$$815 \times 10^5 = 81{,}500{,}000 = 8.15 \times 10^7 \qquad 0.078 \times 10^{-2} = 0.00078 = 7.8 \times 10^{-4}$$

The problems above show a pattern. When you move a decimal point n places to the left, the exponent of 10 increases by n. When you move a decimal point n places to the right, the exponent of 10 decreases by n.

Additional Problems

1. Is the number written in scientific notation? If not, explain.

  a. 8.15×10^{-6}

  b. 12.9×10^8

  c. 1.003×10^7

  ANSWER a. yes **b.** No; 12.9 is greater than 10. **c.** yes

2. What is each number written in scientific notation?

  a. population of Florida: 18,000,000

  b. diameter of an atom: 0.0000000002 m

  ANSWER a. 1.8×10^7 **b.** 2×10^{-10}

3. What is each number written in standard notation?

  a. weight of a truck: 2.8×10^6 g

  b. weight of a paperclip: 2×10^{-3} lb

  ANSWER a. 2,800,000 g **b.** 0.002 lb

4. The table shows the areas of four states. What is the order of the states from least to greatest area?

Areas of States

State	Area (mi²)
Georgia	5.9×10^4
Montana	1.5×10^6
Ohio	4.5×10^4
Rhode Island	1.5×10^3

ANSWER Rhode Island, Ohio, Georgia, Montana

5. What is the order of 18.6×10^{-3}, 1.84×10^3, 0.034×10^2, and 21.3×10^{-2} from least to greatest?

ANSWER 18.6×10^{-3}, 21.3×10^{-2}, 0.034×10^2, 1.84×10^3

Answers

Got It? (continued)

3. a. 52,300,000

  b. 0.000046

  c. 0.000209

  d. 3,800,000,000,000

  e. a

4. electron, proton, neutron

What is the order of 49.7×10, 4.17×10^7, 0.047×10^9, and 495 from least to greatest?

Know	Need	Plan
49.7×10, 4.17×10^7, 0.047×10^9, and 495	The order of the numbers from least to greatest	Write each number in scientific notation. Then compare them.

Think

How do you write 49.7×10 in scientific notation?
Move the decimal point one place to the left. Increase the exponent of 10 by 1.

Step 1 Write each number in scientific notation.

49.7×10 $\quad$ 4.17×10^7 $\quad$ 0.047×10^9 $\quad$ 495
$\downarrow$ $\qquad\qquad$ $\downarrow$ $\qquad\qquad$ $\downarrow$ $\qquad\qquad$ $\downarrow$
4.97×10^2 $\quad$ 4.17×10^7 $\quad$ 4.7×10^7 $\quad$ 4.95×10^2

Step 2 Order the numbers by the powers of 10. Arrange the numbers with the same power of 10 in order by their decimal parts.

4.95×10^2 $\qquad$ 4.97×10^2 $\qquad$ 4.17×10^7 $\qquad$ 4.7×10^7

Step 3 Write the original numbers in order.

495 $\qquad$ 49.7×10 $\qquad$ 4.17×10^7 $\qquad$ 0.047×10^9

 Got It? 5. What is the order of 24.8×10^{-4}, 28×10^3, 0.025×10^4, and 258×10^{-5} from least to greatest?

Lesson Check

Do you know HOW?

Write each number in scientific notation.

1. 0.0007 $\qquad\qquad$ **2.** 32,000,000

Write each number in standard notation.

3. 3.5×10^6 $\qquad\qquad$ **4.** 1.27×10^{-4}

Order the numbers in each list from least to greatest.

5. $10^5, 10^{-3}, 10^0, 10^{-1}, 10^1$

6. $5 \times 10^{-3}, 2 \times 10^4, 3 \times 10^0, 7 \times 10^{-1}$

7. $2.5 \times 10^7, 2.1 \times 10^7, 3.5 \times 10^6, 3.6 \times 10^6$

Do you UNDERSTAND?

8. Open-Ended Describe a situation in which it is easier to use numbers written in scientific notation than to use numbers written in standard form.

9. Error Analysis A student wrote 1.88×10^{-5} in standard notation as shown below. Describe and correct the student's mistake.

$$1.88 \times 10^{-5} = 0.00188$$

10. Reasoning A student claims that 3.5×10^{11} is greater than 1.4×10^{13} because $3.5 > 1.4$. Is the student correct? Explain.

Q Why can't the numbers given be ordered at first glance? **[The numbers are not all in scientific notation.]**

Q When 0.047×10^9 is written in scientific notation, why does the exponent on the power of 10 decrease by 2? **[Because the first factor in the expression is multiplied by 100 to get it between 1 and 10, the second factor must be divided by 100.]**

Got It?

Q What is each number written in scientific notation? **[2.48×10^{-3}, 2.8×10^4, 2.5×10^2, 2.58×10^{-3}]**

3 Lesson Check

Do you know HOW?
- If students have difficulty with Exercise 7, then have them review Problem 4.

Do you UNDERSTAND?
- If students have difficulty with Exercise 10, then have them write the numbers in standard form.

Close

Q Why is it important to understand how to write numbers in scientific notation? **[Scientific notation is a shorthand way to write very small or very large numbers using powers of 10.]**

Got It? (continued)

5. 24.8×10^{-4}, 258×10^{-5}, 0.025×10^4, 28×10^3

Lesson Check

1. 7×10^{-4} $\qquad$ **2.** 3.2×10^7

3. 3,500,000 $\qquad$ **4.** 0.000127

5. $10^{-3}, 10^{-1}, 10^0, 10^1, 10^5$

6. $5 \times 10^{-3}, 7 \times 10^{-1}, 3 \times 10^0, 2 \times 10^4$

7. $3.5 \times 10^6, 3.6 \times 10^6, 2.1 \times 10^7, 2.5 \times 10^7$

8. Answers may vary. Sample: When numbers are very large or very small. An example of a very large distance may be the distance from Earth to the nearest star.

9. The student interpreted the negative exponent of −5 to represent the number of decimal places when it represents how many places to move the decimal point to the left; $1.88 \times 10^{-5} = 0.0000188$.

10. No; the difference between two numbers with different powers of 10 is more significant than the difference between two numbers with the same power of 10.

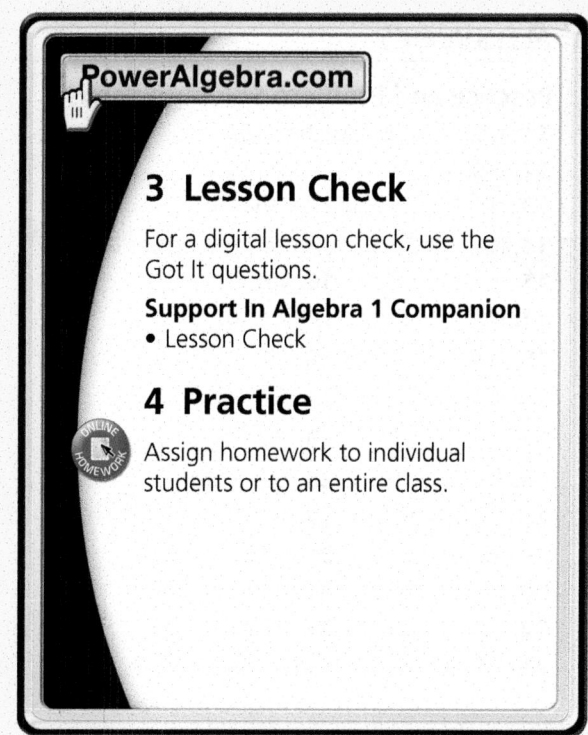

PowerAlgebra.com

3 Lesson Check

For a digital lesson check, use the Got It questions.

Support In Algebra 1 Companion
- Lesson Check

4 Practice

Assign homework to individual students or to an entire class.

4 Practice

ASSIGNMENT GUIDE

Basic: 11–39 all, 40–44 even, 46, 48–49

Average: 11–39 odd, 40–49

Advanced: 11–39 odd, 40–51

Standardized Test Prep: 52–55

Mixed Review: 56–70

Reasoning exercises have blue headings.

Applications exercises have red headings.

EXERCISE 48: Use the Think About a Plan worksheet in the **Practice and Problem Solving Workbook** (also available in the Teaching Resources in print and online) to further support students' development in becoming independent learners.

HOMEWORK QUICK CHECK

To check students' understanding of key skills and concepts, go over Exercises 21, 37, 46, 48, and 49.

Practice and Problem-Solving Exercises

 A Practice

Is the number written in scientific notation? If not, explain.

See Problem 1.

11. 44×10^8 **12.** 3.2×10^6 **13.** 0.9×10^{-2} **14.** 6.7×1000^9

15. 7.3×10^{-5} **16.** 1.12×10^1 **17.** 457×10^7 **18.** 9.54×10^{15}

Write each number in scientific notation.

See Problem 2.

19. 9,040,000,000 **20.** 0.02 **21.** 9.3 million **22.** 21,700

23. 0.00325 **24.** 8,003,000 **25.** 0.00092 **26.** 0.0156

Write each number in standard notation.

See Problem 3.

27. 5×10^2 **28.** 7.45×10^2 **29.** 2.04×10^3 **30.** 7.2×10^6

31. 8.97×10^{-1} **32.** 1.3×10^0 **33.** 2.74×10^5 **34.** 4.8×10^{-3}

Order the numbers in each list from least to greatest.

See Problems 4 and 5.

35. $9 \times 10^{-7}, 8 \times 10^{-8}, 7 \times 10^{-6}, 6 \times 10^{-10}$

36. $8.2 \times 10^5, 7.9 \times 10^5, 2.7 \times 10^5, 8.1 \times 10^5$

37. $50.1 \times 10^{-3}, 4.8 \times 10^{-3}, 0.52 \times 10^{-3}, 56 \times 10^{-3}$

38. $0.53 \times 10^7, 5300 \times 10^{-1}, 5.3 \times 10^5, 530 \times 10^8$

39. Physics The half-life of a radioactive isotope is the amount of time it takes one half of a sample of the isotope to decay. What is the order of the following radioactive isotopes of uranium from shortest to longest half-life?

Isotope	^{232}U	^{234}U	^{235}U	^{236}U
Half-life (years)	68.9	2.45×10^5	7.04×10^8	2.34×10^7

 B Apply

Simplify. Write each answer using scientific notation.

40. $4(2 \times 10^{-3})$ **41.** $8(3 \times 10^{14})$ **42.** $0.2(3 \times 10^2)$

43. $6(5.3 \times 10^{-4})$ **44.** $0.3(8.2 \times 10^{-3})$ **45.** $0.5(6.8 \times 10^5)$

46. Think About a Plan A light-year is the distance light travels in one year. One light-year is about 5,878,000,000,000 mi. The table shows the estimated distance, in light-years, of several stars from Earth. How many miles is each star from Earth?
- How do you convert from light-years to miles?
- What notation is easier to use for writing long distances?

47. Writing You write 1 billion in scientific notation as 10^9. Explain why you write 436 billion in scientific notation as 4.36×10^{11} rather than as 436×10^9.

Distance From Earth

Star	Distance (light-years)
Proxima Centauri	4.2
Sirius	8.7
Vega	27
Polaris	431

SOURCE: NASA

Answers

Practice and Problem-Solving Exercises

11. No; 44 is not less than 10.

12. yes

13. No; 0.9 is not greater than 1.

14. No; 1000^9 is not written as a power of 10.

15. yes   **16.** yes

17. No; 457 is not less than 10.

18. yes   **19.** 9.04×10^9

20. 2×10^{-2} **21.** 9.3×10^6

22. 2.17×10^4 **23.** 3.25×10^{-3}

24. 8.003×10^6 **25.** 9.2×10^{-4}

26. 1.56×10^{-2} **27.** 500

28. 745   **29.** 2040

30. 7,200,000   **31.** 0.897

32. 1.3   **33.** 274,000

34. 0.0048

35. $6 \times 10^{-10}, 8 \times 10^{-8}, 9 \times 10^{-7}, 7 \times 10^{-6}$

36. $2.7 \times 10^5, 7.9 \times 10^5, 8.1 \times 10^5, 8.2 \times 10^5$

37. $0.52 \times 10^{-3}, 4.8 \times 10^{-3}, 50.1 \times 10^{-3}, 56 \times 10^{-3}$

38. $5300 \times 10^{-1}, 5.3 \times 10^5, 0.53 \times 10^7, 530 \times 10^8$

39. $^{232}U, {}^{234}U, {}^{236}U, {}^{235}U$

40. 8×10^{-3} **41.** 2.4×10^{15}

42. 6×10^1 **43.** 3.18×10^{-3}

44. 2.46×10^{-3} **45.** 3.4×10^5

46. Proxima Centauri: 2.46876×10^{13} mi;
Sirius: 5.11386×10^{13} mi;
Vega: 1.58706×10^{14} mi;
Polaris: 2.533418×10^{15} mi

47. 436 billion is 436,000,000,000 so in scientific notation it becomes 4.36×10^{11}. It must be the product of a number greater than or equal to 1 and less than 10, and a power of 10.

48. Physics The radius of a water molecule is about 1.4 angstroms. One angstrom is 0.00000001 cm. What is the diameter of a water molecule in centimeters? Use scientific notation.

49. Reasoning Explain how the exponent of 10 changes when you multiply a number written in scientific notation by 100. Show an example.

Challenge **50. Economics** Gross domestic product (GDP) is a measure of the economic output of a country. The GDP of the United States was about 1.2×10^{13} dollars in 2005. This is about 3 times the U.S. GDP in 1985. What was the U.S. GDP in 1985?

51. Write $\frac{1}{300}$ in scientific notation.

Standardized Test Prep

SAT/ACT

52. A lab sample has a mass of 0.000345 g. What is this amount written in scientific notation?

Ⓐ 0.345×10^3 Ⓑ 0.345×10^{-3} Ⓒ 3.45×10^{-4} Ⓓ 3.45×10^4

53. What is the union of $\{1, 3, 5, 7\}$ and $\{3, 4, 5\}$?

Ⓕ $\{\}$ Ⓖ $\{1, 7\}$ Ⓗ $\{3, 5\}$ Ⓘ $\{1, 3, 4, 5, 7\}$

54. What is the equation of the graph at the right?

Ⓐ $y = 2x - \frac{1}{2}$ Ⓒ $y = \frac{1}{2}x - \frac{1}{2}$

Ⓑ $y = -2x - \frac{1}{2}$ Ⓓ $y = -\frac{1}{2}x + 2$

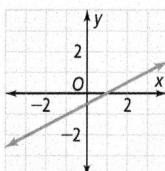

Short Response

55. A student is collecting cans to raise money for a class trip. Each week the student collects 150 cans. Make a graph of the situation. How many weeks will it take the student to collect 1200 cans?

Mixed Review

Simplify each expression.   ◀ See Lesson 7-1.

56. cd^{-6} **57.** $a^0 b^3$ **58.** $9w^{-3}$ **59.** $\frac{4m}{n^{-5}}$ **60.** $\frac{3^{-2}}{k^{-5}}$

Graph each linear inequality.   ◀ See Lesson 6-5.

61. $y < -\frac{1}{4}x + 2$ **62.** $y \geq \frac{2}{3}x$ **63.** $y < 3x - 4$ **64.** $y > -3x + \frac{1}{2}$

Get Ready! To prepare for Lesson 7-3, do Exercises 65–70.

Rewrite each expression using exponents.   ◀ See page 794.

65. $t \cdot t \cdot t \cdot t \cdot t \cdot t \cdot t$ **66.** $(6 - m)(6 - m)(6 - m)$ **67.** $(r + 2)(r + 2)(r + 2)(r + 2)$

68. $5 \cdot 5 \cdot 5 \cdot s \cdot s \cdot s$ **69.** $2 \cdot 2 \cdot 2 \cdot 2 \cdot 2 \cdot x \cdot x \cdot x$ **70.** $8 \cdot 8 \cdot (x - 1)(x - 1)(x - 1)$

PowerAlgebra.com | Lesson 7-2 Scientific Notation   **425**

64.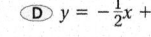

65. t^7

66. $(6 - m)^3$

67. $(r + 2)^4$

68. $5^3 s^3$

69. $2^5 x^3$

70. $8^2(x - 1)^3$

---

48. 2.8×10^{-8} cm

49. It increases by 2 because 100 is 10^2. Sample: $100(3.46 \times 10^5) = 346 \times 10^5 = 3.46 \times 10^7$

50. 4×10^{12} **51.** $3.\overline{3} \times 10^{-3}$

52. C   **53.** I

54. C

55. [2]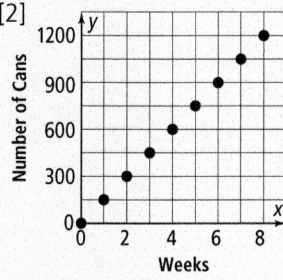

8 weeks

[1] Graph correct but with error in number of weeks

56. $\frac{c}{d^6}$ **57.** b^3 **58.** $\frac{9}{w^3}$

59. $4mn^5$ **60.** $\frac{k^5}{9}$

61.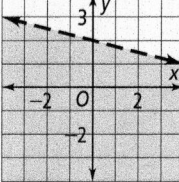

62.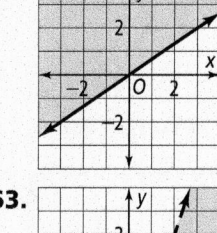

63.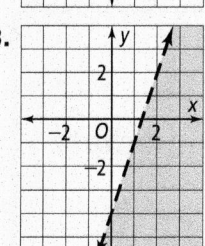

Additional Instructional Support

Algebra 1 Companion

Students can use the **Algebra 1 Companion** worktext (4 pages) as you teach the lesson. Use the Companion to support

- New Vocabulary
- Key Concepts
- Got It for each Problem
- Lesson Check

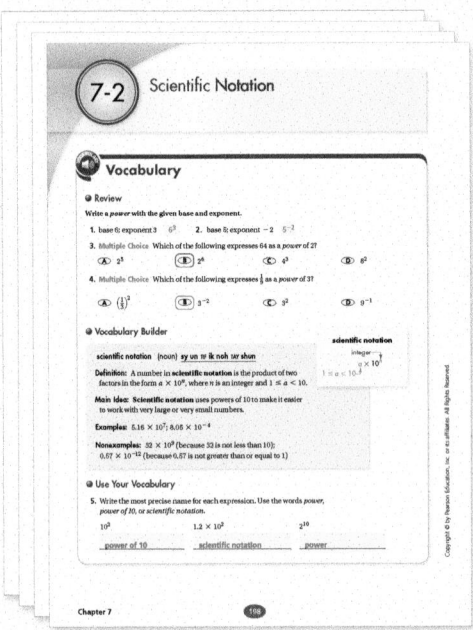

ELL Support

Assess Understanding Many students rely on their calculators to provide them with the correct answer to any computation. Have students explain how to multiply 715,000 and 32,000. Then have them explain how to use their calculators to multiply 715,000 and 32,000. Many calculators will display 2.288×10^{10}. Ask students to identify this notation and how it helps when operating with large numbers.

Connect to Prior Knowledge Arrange the class into pairs, with more proficient students working with less proficient students. Have one student write an example of a number written in scientific notation. Have the other student read the number. Then have students reverse roles and repeat. Have pairs discuss real-world situations in which numbers are written in scientific notation.

5 Assess & Remediate

Lesson Quiz

1. Is the number written in scientific notation? If not, explain.
   a. 0.15×10^4
   b. 7.06×10^{-8}
   c. 3.3×100^{12}
2. What is 37,200,000,000 written in scientific notation?
3. What is 0.000000000065 written in scientific notation?
4. **Do you UNDERSTAND?** How do you order two numbers written in scientific notation?

ANSWERS TO LESSON QUIZ

1. **a.** no, 0.15 is less than 1 **b.** yes
   c. No, 100 is not 10.
2. 3.72×10^{10}
3. 6.5×10^{-11}
4. The number in which 10 is raised to the highest power is the greater number. If the powers are the same, then the number with the greater first factor is greater.

PRESCRIPTION FOR REMEDIATION
Use the student work on the Lesson Quiz to prescribe a differentiated review assignment.

Points	Differentiated Remediation
0–2	Intervention
3	On-level
4	Extension

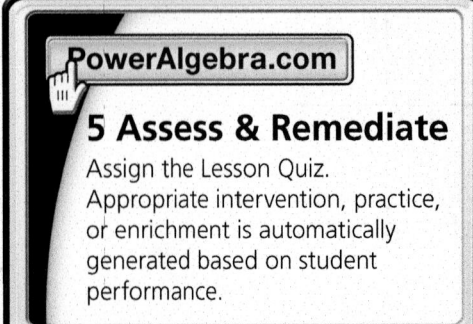

PowerAlgebra.com

5 Assess & Remediate
Assign the Lesson Quiz. Appropriate intervention, practice, or enrichment is automatically generated based on student performance.

Intervention

- **Reteaching** (2 pages) Provides reteaching and practice exercises for the key lesson concepts. Use with struggling students or absent students.
- **English Language Learner Support** Helps students develop and reinforce mathematical vocabulary and key concepts.

All-in-One Resources/Online
Reteaching

7-2 Reteaching
Scientific Notation

Scientific notation is used to write very large numbers and very small numbers in a more compact form.

Scientific notation makes use of the fact that our number system is a base 10 system.

The number 10,000 can be expanded as $10 \times 10 \times 10 \times 10$. It can be written as a power of 10 as 10^4. The exponent 4 is the number of places the decimal point moves to the left when the number is written in scientific notation. In scientific notation, 10,000 is written as 1×10^4. The number 0.0001 can be written as a power of 10 as 10^{-4}.

Problem What is 0.0034 written in scientific notation?

In scientific notation, numbers are written in the form $a \times 10^n$, where a is at least 1, but less than 10. Move the decimal point 3 places to the right. The exponent of 10 in scientific notation will be -3. Since 0.0034 is smaller than 3.4, the exponent must be negative.

$0.0034 = 3.4 \times 10^{-3}$

Problem What is 35,100,000 written in scientific notation?

To write 35,100,000 in scientific notation first identify a. The value of a must be greater than or equal to 1 and less than 10. So $a = 3.51$. Now determine what power of 10 you need to multiply a by to get 35,100,000.

$$3.51 \times 10,000,000 = 35,100,000$$

Because $10,000,000 = 10^7$, $35,100,000 = 3.51 \times 10^7$.

To change a number from scientific notation to standard notation, start with the value of a. Then move the decimal point to the left or right depending on the exponent of 10. For example, $4.72 \times 10^4 = 47,200$. The decimal point is moved 4 places to the right, and zeros are added as placeholders.

All-in-One Resources/Online
English Language Learner Support

7-2 ELL Support
Scientific Notation

Problem

Write 0.00062 in scientific notation. Justify your steps. Then check your solution.

0.00062	Copy the number.
0.00062	Move the decimal place 4 places to the right.
6.2×10^7	Multiply the new number by a power of 10.
6.2×10^{-7}	Decide if the exponent is positive or negative.
6.2×10^{-4}	Write the exponent.
Check	6.2×10^{-4}	Copy the answer.
	00006.2	Move the decimal place 4 places to the left.
	0.00062 ✓	Simplify.

Exercise

Write 0.0024 in scientific notation. Justify your steps. Then check your solution.

0.0024	Copy the number.
0.0024	Move the decimal place 3 places to the right.
2.4×10^7	Multiply the new number by a power of 10.
2.4×10^{-7}	Decide if the exponent is positive or negative.
2.4×10^{-3}	Write the exponent.
Check	2.4×10^{-3}	Copy the answer.
	0002.4	Move the decimal place __3__ places to the left.
	0.0024 ✓	Simplify.

Differentiated Remediation *continued*

On-Level

- **Practice** (2 pages) Provides extra practice for each lesson. For simpler practice exercises, use the Form K Practice pages found in the All-in-One Teaching Resources and online.

- **Think About a Plan** Helps students develop specific problem-solving skills and strategies by providing scaffolded guiding questions.

- **Standardized Test Prep** Focuses on all major exercises, all major question types, and helps students prepare for the high-stakes assessments.

Extension

- **Enrichment** Provides students with interesting problems and activities that extend the concepts of the lesson.

- **Activities, Games, and Puzzles** Worksheets that can be used for concepts development, enrichment, and for fun!

Practice and Problem Solving WKBK/All-in-One Resources/Online
Practice page 1

7-2 Practice   Form G
Scientific Notation

Is the number written in scientific notation? If not, explain.

1. 32.1×10^5 no; 32 is greater than 10   2. 5.6×10^{12} yes

3. 4.6×10^{-5} yes   4. 0.7×10^{34} no; 0.7 is less than 1

Write each number in scientific notation.

5. 3,200,000,000,000 3.2×10^{12} 6. 0.00000802 8.02×10^{-6}

7. 70,030,000 7.003×10^7 8. 8.7 billion 8.7×10^9

Write each number in standard notation.

9. 3.37×10^{12} 3,370,000,000,000   10. 3.060×10^7 30,600,000

11. 4.2×10^{-6} 0.0000042   12. 4.56×10^0 4.56

Simplify. Write each answer using scientific notation.

13. $5(3.2 \times 10^{-4})$ 1.6×10^{-3} 14. $0.7(8.54 \times 10^4)$ 5.978×10^4

15. $87(6.4 \times 10^5)$ 5.568×10^7 16. $0.03(6 \times 10^{-7})$ 1.8×10^{-8}

17. **Writing** Scientific notation is often used for working with very small or very large numbers. Describe two situations where using scientific notation might be appropriate. Answers may vary. Sample: Scientific notation is appropriate for describing the distances between stars and the distances between parts of a molecule.

18. **Reasoning** How does a number in scientific notation change when you multiply it by 100? The exponent of 10 increases by 2.

19. Country A has a population of 8.7×10^9. You hear that country B has twice as many people as country A and country C has twice as many people as country B. How many people live in country C? 3.48×10^{10}

Practice and Problem Solving WKBK/All-in-One Resources/Online
Practice page 2

7-2 Practice (continued)   Form G
Scientific Notation

Write a number in scientific notation that is between the two given numbers.

20. $6.2 \times 10^5, 9.6 \times 10^4$ 21. $3.7 \times 10^{-3}, 9.4 \times 10^{-2}$
Sample: 2.4×10^5 Sample: 8.6×10^{-2}

22. $7.94 \times 10^6, 7.93 \times 10^7$ 23. $9 \times 10^{-6}, 6 \times 10^{-7}$
Sample: 5.27×10^7 Sample: 5.3×10^{-7}

Write a number in standard notation that is between the two given numbers.

24. $3.42 \times 10^8, 3.421 \times 10^8$ 25. $1.3 \times 10^{-4}, 1 \times 10^{-3}$
Sample: 342,070,000   Sample: 0.000256

26. $5.708 \times 10^{-6}, 5.7008 \times 10^{-6}$ 27. $1.2 \times 10^0, 1.3 \times 10^0$
Sample: 0.000005707   Sample: 1.25

Write a number in words that is between the two given numbers.

28. $6.52 \times 10^7, 1.2 \times 10^8$ 29. $3.9 \times 10^{-5}, 2.8 \times 10^{-4}$
seventy-seven million, seven hundred thousand   forty-one millionths

30. **Open-Ended** Write two factors that, when multiplied together, produce a product of 3.6×10^8. One of the factors should be written in scientific notation. $2 \times 1.8 \times 10^8$

31. Light travels at 1.86×10^5 miles per second. If a particle is traveling at half the speed of light, how fast is it moving? 9.3×10^4 mi/s

32. An atom of carbon has a mass of 1.99×10^{-23} grams.
   a. What is the mass of two atoms of carbon? 3.98×10^{-23} g
   b. What is the mass of five atoms of carbon? 9.95×10^{-23} g

---

Practice and Problem Solving WKBK/All-in-One Resources/Online
Think About a Plan

7-2 Think About a Plan
Scientific Notation

Physics The radius of a water molecule is about 1.4 angstroms. One angstrom is 0.00000001 cm. What is the diameter of a water molecule in centimeters? Use scientific notation.

1. What geometric facts and arithmetic operation(s) are you going to need to use to solve the problem? What is the relationship between diameter and radius? How do you convert between the given units?

The diameter of a circle is twice the length of its radius.

1 angstrom = 0.00000001 cm; You multiply to convert angstrom

units to centimeters.

2. How many angstroms are there in the diameter of a water molecule? ___ 2.8
How will you turn angstroms into centimeters? ___ multiply by 0.00000001

3. Rewrite 0.00000001 in scientific notation. Recall that a number written in scientific notation is in the form $a \times 10^n$.

$a =$ ___ 1 $n =$ ___ -8 $0.00000001 =$ ___ 1×10^{-8}

4. Multiply the number of angstroms in the diameter of a water molecule by the length of an angstrom in centimeters to find the number of centimeters in the diameter of a water molecule.

2.8×10^{-8} cm

Practice and Problem Solving WKBK/All-in-One Resources/Online
Standardized Test Prep

7-2 Standardized Test Prep
Scientific Notation

Multiple Choice

For Exercises 1–6, choose the correct letter.

1. Which of the following expressions is written in scientific notation? D
   A. 73.4×10^5 B. 0.09×10^7 C. 80×10^3 D. 4.22×10^{-5}

2. Which of the following is 0.0000000708 written in scientific notation? F
   F. 7.08×10^{-8} G. 7.8×10^{-8} H. 708×10^{-10} I. 70.8×10^{-9}

3. Which expression represents the largest number? A
   A. 40.1×10^{-6} B. 4.1×10^{-7} C. 0.411×10^{-6} D. 0.04001×10^{-5}

4. Which expression is equal to $\frac{1}{8000}$ written in scientific notation? G
   F. 8.0×10^3 G. 1.25×10^{-4} H. 125×10^{-5} I. 1.25×10^4

5. Which of the following statements is *not* true regarding an expression written in scientific notation in the form $a \times 10^n$? C
   A. The value of a must be greater than or equal to 1 and smaller than 10.
   B. The value of n must be an integer.
   C. Doubling n results in a doubling of the value of the expression.
   D. Doubling a results in a doubling of the value of the expression.

6. Which number is equal to $7(3.5 \times 10^4)$ written in scientific notation? G
   F. 24.5×10^4 G. 2.45×10^5 H. 24.5×10^4 I. 1.05×10^5

Short Response

7. A state government has 5.7×10^7 dollars invested in a pension fund for retired employees. It expects this investment to double in value every 8 years. What is the value of the investment after 8 years, 16 years and 24 years? Write your response in scientific notation.
8 yr: 1.14×10^8; 16 yr: 2.28×10^8; 24 yr: 4.56×10^8
[2] Correct answer for each period in correct scientific notation
[1] Correct answers for most periods with a few computational errors
[0] Significant errors in answers for most of all the periods

---

All-in-One Resources/Online
Enrichment

7-2 Enrichment
Scientific Notation

We often encounter numbers that are very small or very large. Writing those numbers in words or in standard notation can be cumbersome, so instead we use scientific notation.

Prepare a report or a presentation on situations that involve using very small or very large numbers.

- The first situation should involve very large numbers (think distances between stars, national debt, number of grains of sand on a beach).

- The second should involve very small numbers (think atomic weights, the time it takes for the flash of a lightning strike to reach your eye, the length of a grain of sand).

After you decide on two different situations you would like to investigate, consider the numeric question you want to answer regarding each situation.

Write a brief report (1 page) or prepare a brief (5 minute) presentation for each of your situations. The report should include the actual numbers that describe the situations you are dealing with, so be sure to cite the sources you used to find those numbers. Check students' work.

Online Teacher Resource Center
Activities, Games, and Puzzles

7-2 Game: From Very Small to Very Large
Scientific Notation

This game can be played in groups of three or more students. A student or your teacher can play host.

Part 1

The host assigns one of the nine problems below to a player. The host can choose the problems in any order and also enforce a limit on response time, if necessary. Players must use mental math to determine if the answer is small, medium, or large according to the information at the right. The host takes turns assigning the problems. Each correct response is worth 1 point.

	small	medium	large
	$x < 0.5$	$0.5 \leq x < 0.5$	$x \geq 50$

1. 3.27×10^{-2} small   2. 3.27×10^2 large   3. 1.65 medium

4. 3.27×10^3 large   5. 9.99×10^1 large   6. 1.00001×10^{-3} small

7. 9.9999 medium   8. 7.07×10^{10} large   9. 3.00001 medium

Part 2

The same rules from Part 1 apply here. After being assigned a problem from below, the player must use mental math to determine the direction *and* number of decimal places needed to move the decimal point in order to write the number in scientific notation.

10. 0.00348 right 3   11. 9.486 no moves   12. 123,985 left 5

13. 0.35 right 1   14. 19.444 left 1   15. 1,850,000 left 6

16. 7 no moves   17. 85,000 left 4   18. 0.1567 right 1

My Score Sheet
1	2	3	4	5	6	7	8	9	10	11	12	13	14	15	16	17	18

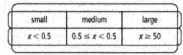

Here is the final part of the game. You may risk as many points as you have on the question below. If you are correct, add the number of points you risked. If you are incorrect, subtract the number of points you risked. The highest score wins the game!

Total number of points (from 0 to 18): Check students' work.

Final risk value (number of points): Check students' work.

Write 0.0101435 *in scientific notation:* 1.01435×10^{-2}

Final game score: Check students' work.

1 Interactive Learning

Solve It!
PURPOSE To present students with a problem that can be modeled by multiplying powers with the same base

PROCESS Students may use a calculator to complete the calculations. Students may write the numbers as powers of ten to complete the calculations.

FACILITATE

Q How can you determine the number of cubic meters of sand on all of the world's beaches? **[Find the volume of the beach in the diagram.]**

Q What is the first step in calculating the volume? **[Convert 100,000 km to meters.]**

Q Once you know the volume, how can you determine the total number of grains of sand? **[Multiply the volume by 10^9.]**

ANSWER See Solve It in Answers on next page.

CONNECT THE MATH Show students that the problem can be modeled with the numerical expression $1 \times 10^2 \times 10^8 \times 10^9$. Remind students that an exponent means repeated multiplication. Ask them to determine the number of times that 1 is multiplied by 10 in the expression.

2 Guided Instruction

Take Note   ERROR PREVENTION
While students usually successfully apply this property to algebraic expressions, they often incorrectly apply this property to numerical expressions and will often state that $4^3 \cdot 4^5 = 16^8$.

Objective To multiply powers with the same base

All of the numbers in the Solve It are powers of 10. In this lesson, you will learn a method for multiplying powers that have the same base.

Essential Understanding You can use a property of exponents to multiply powers with the same base.

You can write a product of powers with the same base, such as $3^4 \cdot 3^2$, using one exponent.

$$3^4 \cdot 3^2 = (3 \cdot 3 \cdot 3 \cdot 3) \cdot (3 \cdot 3) = 3^6$$

Notice that the sum of the exponents in the expression $3^4 \cdot 3^2$ equals the exponent of 3^6.

Property Multiplying Powers With the Same Base
Words To multiply powers with the same base, add the exponents.
Algebra $a^m \cdot a^n = a^{m+n}$, where $a \neq 0$ and m and n are integers
Examples $4^3 \cdot 4^5 = 4^{3+5} = 4^8$ $b^7 \cdot b^{-4} = b^{7+(-4)} = b^3$

BIG idea **Properties**   **UbD**

ESSENTIAL UNDERSTANDINGS
- A property of exponents can be used to multiply powers with the same base.
- To multiply powers with the same base, add the exponents.

Math Background
This lesson provides students with the rules to compute with numbers in scientific notation. Using the Multiply by the Same Base Property, along with the Commutative and Associative Properties, students should be able to multiply and divide very large and very small numbers. For example, students can use these properties to rewrite $(1.3 \times 10^8)(3.2 \times 10^{-2})$ as (1.3×3.2) and $(10^8 \times 10^{-2})$.

Support Student Learning
Use the **Algebra 1 Companion** to engage and support students during instructions. See Lesson Resources at the end of this lesson for details.

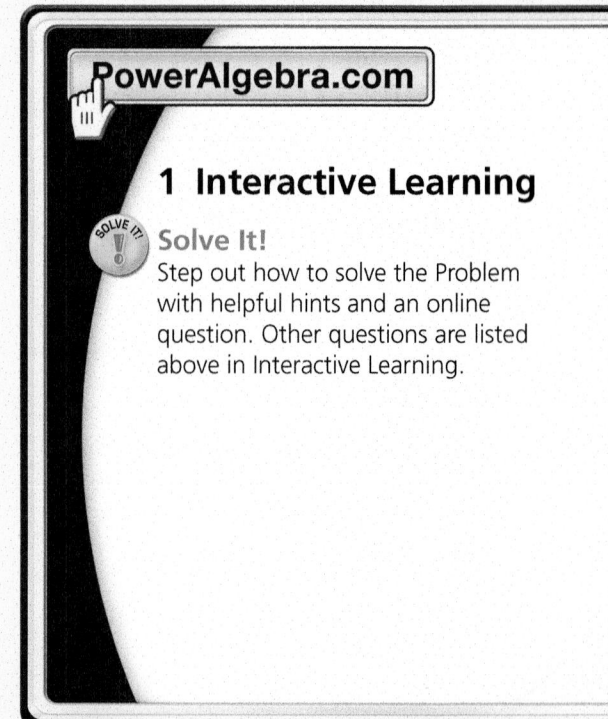

PowerAlgebra.com

1 Interactive Learning

Solve It!
Step out how to solve the Problem with helpful hints and an online question. Other questions are listed above in Interactive Learning.

Here's Why It Works You can use repeated multiplication to rewrite a product of powers.

$$a^m \cdot a^n = \underbrace{(a \cdot a \cdot \ldots \cdot a)}_{m \text{ factors of } a} \cdot \underbrace{(a \cdot a \cdot \ldots \cdot a)}_{n \text{ factors of } a} = \underbrace{a \cdot a \cdot \ldots \cdot a}_{m + n \text{ factors of } a} = a^{m+n}$$

 Problem 1 Multiplying Powers

What is each expression written using each base only once?

Ⓐ $12^4 \cdot 12^3 = 12^{4+3}$ Add the exponents of the powers with the same base.

$= 12^7$ Simplify the exponent.

Ⓑ $(-5)^{-2}(-5)^7 = (-5)^{-2+7}$ Add the exponents of the powers with the same base.

$= (-5)^5$ Simplify the exponent.

✓ **Got It? 1.** What is each expression written using each base only once?
a. $8^3 \cdot 8^6$ b. $(0.5)^{-3}(0.5)^{-8}$ c. $9^{-3} \cdot 9^2 \cdot 9^6$

When variable factors have more than one base, be careful to combine only those powers with the same base.

 Problem 2 Multiplying Powers in Algebraic Expressions

What is the simplified form of each expression?

Ⓐ $4z^5 \cdot 9z^{-12} = (4 \cdot 9)(z^5 \cdot z^{-12})$ Commutative and associative properties of multiplication

$= 36(z^{5+(-12)})$ Multiply the coefficients. Add the exponents of the powers with the same base.

$= 36z^{-7}$ Simplify the exponent.

$= \frac{36}{z^7}$ Rewrite using a positive exponent.

Ⓑ $2a \cdot 9b^4 \cdot 3a^2 = (2 \cdot 9 \cdot 3)(a \cdot a^2)(b^4)$ Commutative and associative properties of multiplication

$\underbrace{}_{a = a^1}$

$= 54(a^1 \cdot a^2)(b^4)$ Multiply the coefficients. Write a as a^1.

$= 54(a^{1+2})(b^4)$ Add exponents of powers with the same base.

$= 54a^3b^4$ Simplify.

✓ **Got It? 2.** What is the simplified form of each expression in parts (a)–(c)?
a. $5x^4 \cdot x^9 \cdot 3x$ b. $-4c^3 \cdot 7d^2 \cdot 2c^{-2}$ c. $j^2 \cdot k^{-2} \cdot 12j$
d. **Reasoning** Explain how to simplify the expression $x^a \cdot x^b \cdot x^c$.

You can help students clarify why this property works only with like bases by using a non-example such as $2^4 \cdot 3^4$ and writing out the factors.

Problem 1

Q How can you rewrite the expression in 1A using repeated multiplication? [(12 • 12 • 12 • 12) • (12 • 12 • 12)]

Q If you were to evaluate $(-5)^5$, would the product be positive or negative? Explain. [Negative; all powers with a negative base and an odd exponent yield a negative product.]

Got It?   ERROR PREVENTION

Q For 1c, does it matter in which order you add the exponents? Explain. [No; Commutative and Associative Properties of Addition]

Problem 2

Q In 2A, why is $36z^{-7}$ not considered simplified form? [An expression is not in simplified form if it contains a negative exponent.]

Q In 2B, why does the exponent on base b remain 4? [There are no other factors with base b.]

Got It?   VISUAL LEARNERS

Have students use colored highlighters to mark factors with like bases. They can use one color for coefficients and a different color for each unique base.

---

2 Guided Instruction

 Each Problem is worked out and supported online.

Problem 1
Multiplying Powers

Problem 2
Multiplying Powers in Algebraic Expressions
Animated

Alternative Problem 2
Multiplying Powers in Algebraic Expressions

Problem 3
Multiplying Numbers in Scientific Notation
Animated

Problem 4
Multiplying Numbers in Scientific Notation
Animated

Support in Algebra 1 Companion
• Vocabulary
• Key Concepts
• Got It?

Answers

Solve It!
More stars; the volume of sand is $100,000,000 \times 1 \times 100 = 10^8 \times 10^2 = 10^{10}$ m^3. Each cubic meter of sand contains 10^9 grains of sand so there are $10^{10} \times 10^9$ or 10^{19} grains of sand. $10^{19} < 10^{20}$

Got It?

1. a. 8^9 **b.** $(0.5)^{-11}$ **c.** 9^5

2. a. $15x^{14}$ **b.** $-56cd^2$ **c.** $\frac{12j^3}{k^2}$

d. Since they have like bases, you keep the same base and add the exponents;
$x^a \cdot x^b \cdot x^c = x^{(a+b+c)}$

Problem 3

> **Q** Why is the expression $15 \cdot 10^{-7}$ not in scientific notation? **[The first factor is greater than 10.]**

Got It?
Rewrite the problem using repeated multiplication and then simplify to ensure that students understand why the property for multiplying powers can be used to multiply numbers in scientific notation: $7 \cdot 10 \cdot 10 \cdot 10 \cdot 10 \cdot 10 \cdot 10 \cdot 10 \cdot 10 \cdot 4 \cdot 10 \cdot 10 \cdot 10 \cdot 10 \cdot 10$.

Problem 4
To help students understand how to find the number of molecules, write a dimensional analysis statement with the given rates. Show that when dividing by like terms, the result is a multiplication problem and the only remaining unit is molecules. The ratios to include in the statement are

1.13×10^{-7} cubic meter, $\dfrac{9.98 \times 10^5 \text{ grams}}{1 \text{ cubic meter}}$, and $\dfrac{3.34 \times 10^{22} \text{ molecules}}{1 \text{ gram}}$.

Got It?

> **Q** How can you determine the number of molecules of water if you know the mass of the water in grams? **[Multiply the mass by 3.34×10^{22}.]**

You can use the property for multiplying powers with the same base to multiply two numbers written in scientific notation.

 Problem 3 Multiplying Numbers in Scientific Notation

What is the simplified form of $(3 \times 10^5)(5 \times 10^{-12})$? Write your answer in scientific notation.

 **Plan**

Which numbers can you group to make the calculation easier?
Group 3 and 5. Group the powers of 10.

$$(3 \times 10^5)(5 \times 10^{-12}) = (3 \cdot 5)(10^5 \cdot 10^{-12}) \quad \text{Commutative and associative properties of multiplication}$$
$$= 15 \cdot 10^{-7} \quad \text{Multiply. Add exponents.}$$
$$= 1.5 \times 10^1 \cdot 10^{-7} \quad \text{Write 15 in scientific notation.}$$
$$= 1.5 \times 10^{-6} \quad \text{Add exponents.}$$

 Got It? 3. What is the simplified form of $(7 \times 10^8)(4 \times 10^5)$? Write your answer in scientific notation.

 **Problem 4** Multiplying Numbers in Scientific Notation

Chemistry At 20°C, one cubic meter of water has a mass of about 9.98×10^5 g. Each gram of water contains about 3.34×10^{22} molecules of water. About how many molecules of water does the droplet of water shown below contain?

$V = 1.13 \times 10^{-7} \text{ m}^3$

1 m^3

Plan

How do you find the number of molecules?
Use unit analysis. Divide out the common units.

$$\text{molecules of water} = \cancel{\text{cubic meters}} \cdot \frac{\text{grams}}{\cancel{\text{cubic meters}}} \cdot \frac{\text{molecules}}{\cancel{\text{grams}}} \quad \text{Use unit analysis.}$$
$$= (1.13 \times 10^{-7}) \cdot (9.98 \times 10^5) \cdot (3.34 \times 10^{22}) \quad \text{Substitute.}$$
$$= (1.13 \cdot 9.98 \cdot 3.34) \times (10^{-7} \cdot 10^5 \cdot 10^{22}) \quad \text{Commutative and associative properties of multiplication}$$
$$\approx 37.7 \times 10^{-7+5+22} \quad \text{Multiply. Add exponents.}$$
$$= 37.7 \times 10^{20} \quad \text{Simplify.}$$
$$= 3.77 \times 10^{21} \quad \text{Write in scientific notation.}$$

The droplet contains about 3.77×10^{21} molecules of water.

Got It? 4. About how many molecules of water are in a swimming pool that holds 200 m^3 of water? Write your answer in scientific notation.

Additional Problems

1. What is each expression written as a single power?

 a. $9^5 \cdot 9^3$

 b. $(-3)^{-2} \cdot (-3)^{10}$

 ANSWER a. 9^8 **b.** $(-3)^8$

2. What is the simplified form of each expression?

 a. $6b^3 \cdot 3b^{-8}$

 b. $4c \cdot 3d^5 \cdot 2c^3$

 ANSWER a. $\dfrac{18}{b^5}$ **b.** $24c^4d^5$

3. What is the simplified form of $(5 \times 10^6)(6 \times 10^{-10})$?

 ANSWER 3×10^{-3}

4. The speed of light is about 3×10^8 meters per second. How far would a beam of light travel in 8.64×10^4 seconds (1 day)?

 ANSWER 2.592×10^{13} meters

Answers

Got It? (continued)

 3. 2.8×10^{14}

 4. 6.7×10^{30} molecules of water

Lesson Check

Do you know HOW?

1. What is $8^4 \cdot 8^8$ written using each base only once?

2. What is the simplified form of $2n^3 \cdot 3n^{-2}$?

3. What is $(3 \times 10^5)(8 \times 10^4)$ written in scientific notation?

4. **Measurement** The diameter of a penny is about 1.9×10^{-5} km. It would take about 2.1×10^9 pennies placed end to end to circle the equator once. What is the approximate length of the equator?

Do you UNDERSTAND?

5. **Writing** Can $x^8 \cdot y^3$ be written as a single power? Explain your reasoning.

6. **Reasoning** Suppose $a \times 10^m$ and $b \times 10^n$ are two numbers in scientific notation. Is their product $ab \times 10^{m+n}$ *always*, *sometimes*, or *never* a number in scientific notation? Justify your answer.

7. **Error Analysis** Your friend says $4a^2 \cdot 3a^5 = 7a^7$. Do you agree with your friend? Explain.

Practice and Problem-Solving Exercises

A Practice

Rewrite each expression using each base only once.   ● See Problem 1.

8. $7^3 \cdot 7^4$

9. $(-6)^{12} \cdot (-6)^5 \cdot (-6)^2$

10. $9^6 \cdot 9^{-4} \cdot 9^{-2}$

11. $2^2 \cdot 2^7 \cdot 2^0$

12. $5^{-2} \cdot 5^{-4} \cdot 5^8$

13. $(-8)^5 \cdot (-8)^{-5}$

Simplify each expression.   ● See Problem 2.

14. $m^3 m^4$

15. $5c^4 \cdot c^6$

16. $4t^{-5} \cdot 2t^{-3}$

17. $(7x^5)(8x)$

18. $3x^2 \cdot x^2$

19. $(-2.4n^4)(2n^{-1})$

20. $b^{-2} \cdot b^4 \cdot b$

21. $(-2m^3)(3.5m^{-3})$

22. $(15a^3)(-3a)$

23. $(x^5y^2)(x^{-6}y)$

24. $(5x^5)(3y^6)(3x^2)$

25. $(4c^4)(ac^3)(-3a^5c)$

26. $x^6 \cdot y^2 \cdot x^4$

27. $a^6b^3 \cdot a^2b^{-2}$

28. $-m^2 \cdot 4r^3 \cdot 12r^{-4} \cdot 5m$

Simplify each expression. Write each answer in scientific notation.   ● See Problem 3.

29. $(2 \times 10^3)(3 \times 10^2)$

30. $(2 \times 10^6)(3 \times 10^3)$

31. $(4 \times 10^6) \cdot 10^{-3}$

32. $(1 \times 10^3)(3.4 \times 10^{-8})$

33. $(8 \times 10^{-5})(7 \times 10^{-3})$

34. $(5 \times 10^7)(3 \times 10^{14})$

Write each answer in scientific notation.   ● See Problem 4.

35. **Astronomy** The distance light travels in one second (one light-second) is about 1.86×10^5 mi. Saturn is about 475 light-seconds from the sun. About how many miles from the sun is Saturn?

36. **Biology** A human body contains about 2.7×10^4 microliters (μL) of blood for each pound of body weight. Each microliter of blood contains about 7×10^4 white blood cells. About how many white blood cells are in the body of a 140-lb person?

---

3 Lesson Check

Do you know HOW?

- If students have difficulty with Exercise 4, then have them draw a diagram.

Do you UNDERSTAND?

- If students have difficulty with Exercise 7, then have them write the problem as a complete string of factors, such as $4 \times a \times a \times 3 \times a \times a \times a \times a \times a$.

Close

> **Q** How can you summarize multiplying powers with the same base? **[Answers may vary. Sample: Multiply coefficients and add exponents on factors with the same base.]**

Lesson Check

1. 8^{12}

2. $6n$

3. 2.4×10^{10}

4. 39,900 km

5. No; x and y are not like bases and they do not share a common factor.

6. Sometimes; if the product ab is greater than 10, then the number will not be in scientific notation.

7. No; $4 \times 3 = 12$ so the correct result is $12a^7$.

Practice and Problem-Solving Exercises

8. 7^7

9. $(-6)^{19}$

10. 9^0

11. 2^9

12. 5^2

13. $(-8)^0$

14. m^7

15. $5c^{10}$

16. $\frac{8}{t^8}$

17. $56x^6$

18. $3x^4$

19. $-4.8n^3$

20. b^3

21. -7

22. $-45a^4$

23. $\frac{y^3}{x}$

24. $45x^7y^6$

25. $-12a^6c^8$

26. $x^{10}y^2$

27. a^8b

28. $\frac{-240m^3}{r}$

29. 6×10^5

30. 6×10^9

31. 4×10^3

32. 3.4×10^{-5}

33. 5.6×10^{-7}

34. 1.5×10^{22}

35. 8.84×10^7 mi

36. 2.6×10^{11} white blood cells

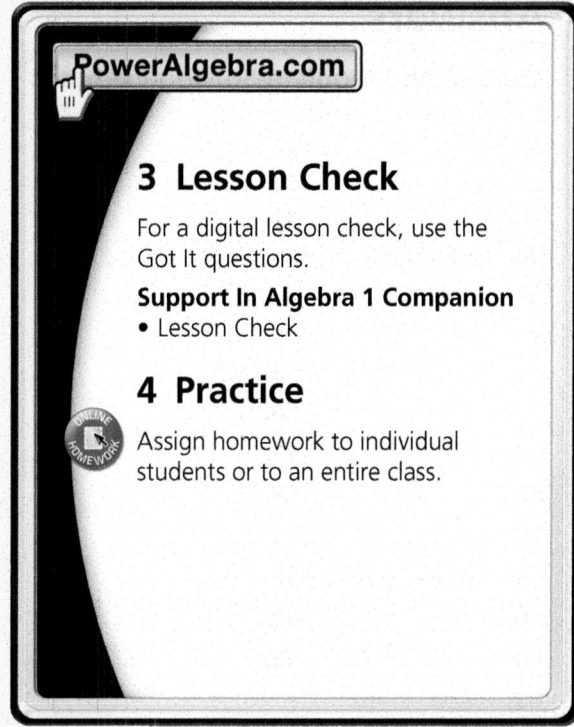

PowerAlgebra.com

3 Lesson Check

For a digital lesson check, use the Got It questions.

Support In Algebra 1 Companion
- Lesson Check

4 Practice

Assign homework to individual students or to an entire class.

4 Practice

ASSIGNMENT GUIDE

Basic: 8–36 all, 38–56 even, 57, 58–64 even

Average: 9–35 odd, 37–64

Advanced: 9–35 odd, 37–71

Standardized Test Prep: 72–76

Mixed Review: 77–87

Reasoning exercises have blue headings.

Applications exercises have red headings.

EXERCISE 57: Use the Think About a Plan worksheet in the **Practice and Problem Solving Workbook** (also available in the Teaching Resources in print and online) to further support students' development in becoming independent learners.

HOMEWORK QUICK CHECK

To check students' understanding of key skills and concepts, go over Exercises 13, 29, 46, 57, and 64.

B Apply

Complete each equation.

37. $5^2 \cdot 5^{\blacksquare} = 5^{11}$

38. $5^7 \cdot 5^{\blacksquare} = 5^3$

39. $2^{\blacksquare} \cdot 2^4 = 2^1$

40. $c^{-5} \cdot c^{\blacksquare} = c^6$

41. $m^{\blacksquare} \cdot m^{-4} = m^{-9}$

42. $a \cdot a \cdot a^3 = a^{\blacksquare}$

43. $a^{\blacksquare} \cdot a^4 = 1$

44. $a^{12} \cdot a^{\blacksquare} = a^{12}$

45. $x^3 y^{\blacksquare} \cdot x^{\blacksquare} = y^2$

46. Think About a Plan A liter of water contains about 3.35×10^{25} molecules. The Mississippi River discharges about 1.7×10^7 L of water every second. About how many molecules does the Mississippi River discharge every minute? Write your answer in scientific notation.
- How can you use unit analysis to help you find the answer?
- What properties can you use to make the calculation easier?

Geometry Find the area of each figure.

47.

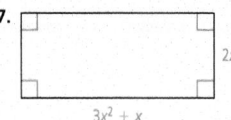

48.

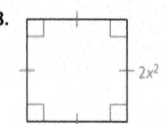

49.

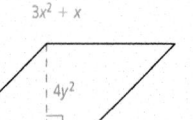

50.

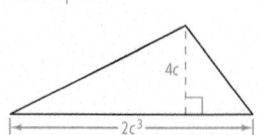

Simplify each expression. Write each answer in scientific notation.

51. $(9 \times 10^7)(3 \times 10^{-16})$

52. $(8 \times 10^{-3})(0.1 \times 10^9)$

53. $(0.7 \times 10^{-12})(0.3 \times 10^8)$

54. $(0.4 \times 10^0)(3 \times 10^{-4})$

55. $(0.2 \times 10^5)(4 \times 10^{-12})$

56. $(0.5 \times 10^{13})(0.3 \times 10^{-4})$

57. Chemistry In chemistry, a *mole* is a unit of measure equal to 6.02×10^{23} atoms of a substance. The mass of a single neon atom is about 3.35×10^{-23} g. What is the mass of 2 moles of neon atoms? Write your answer in scientific notation.

Simplify each expression.

58. $\dfrac{1}{x^3 \cdot x^{-7}}$

59. $\dfrac{1}{a^4 \cdot a^{-3}}$

60. $\dfrac{4}{c \cdot c^{-5}}$

61. $2a^3(3a + 1)$

62. $8m^3(m^4 + 2)$

63. $-4x^3(3x^3 - 10x)$

64. a. Open-Ended Write y^6 as a product of two powers with the same base in four different ways. Use only positive exponents.
- **b.** Write y^6 as a product of two powers with the same base in four different ways, using negative or zero exponents in each product.
- **c. Reasoning** How many ways can you write y^6 as the product of two powers? Explain your reasoning.

---

64. a. Answers may vary. Sample:
$y^5 \cdot y, \ y^4 \cdot y^2, \ y^3 \cdot y^3, \ y^2 \cdot y^4$

b. Answers may vary. Sample:
$y^7 \cdot y^{-1}, \ y^8 \cdot y^{-2}, \ y^9 \cdot y^{-3}, \ y^6 \cdot y^0$

c. Infinitely many; there are infinitely many ways to add to get 6.

Answers

Practice and Problem-Solving Exercises
(continued)

37. 9

38. −4

39. −3

40. 11

41. −5

42. 5

43. −4

44. 0

45. 2; −3

46. 3.42×10^{34} molecules

47. $6x^3 + 2x^2$

48. $4x^4$

49. $4y^5 + 8y^2$

50. $4c^4$

51. 2.7×10^{-8}

52. 8×10^5

53. 2.1×10^{-5}

54. 1.2×10^{-4}

55. 8×10^{-8}

56. 1.5×10^8

57. 4.0334×10^1 g

58. x^4

59. $\frac{1}{a}$

60. $4c^4$

61. $6a^4 + 2a^3$

62. $8m^7 + 16m^3$

63. $-12x^6 + 40x^4$

Challenge **Simplify each expression.**

65. $3^x \cdot 3^{2-x} \cdot 3^2$

66. $2^n \cdot 2^{n+2} \cdot 2$

67. $3^x \cdot 2^y \cdot 3^2 \cdot 2^x$

68. $(a + b)^2(a + b)^{-3}$

69. $(t + 3)^7(t + 3)^{-5}$

70. $5^{x+1} \cdot 5^{1-x}$

71. Nature A book shows an enlarged photo of a carpenter bee. A carpenter bee is about 6×10^{-3} m long. The photo is 13.5 cm long. About how many times as long as a carpenter bee is the photo?

Standardized Test Prep

 SAT/ACT

72. What is the simplified form of $(2x^2y^3)(4xy^{-2})$?

Ⓐ $6x^3y^5$ Ⓑ $6x^2y^6$ Ⓒ $8x^2y$ Ⓓ $8x^3y$

73. What is the x-intercept of the graph of $5x - 3y = 30$?

Ⓕ -10 Ⓖ -6 Ⓗ 6 Ⓘ 10

74. At the Athens Olympics, the winning time for the women's 100-m hurdles was 2.06×10^{-1} min. Which number is another way to express this time in minutes?

Ⓐ 0.206 Ⓑ 20.6 Ⓒ 206×10^1 Ⓓ 206×10^{-2}

75. What is the solution of $4x - 5 = 2x + 13$?

Ⓕ 3 Ⓖ 4 Ⓗ 9 Ⓘ 32

Extended Response

76. Bill's company packages its circular mirrors in boxes with square bottoms, as shown at the right. Show your work for each answer.
  a. What is an expression for the area of the bottom of the box?
  b. If the mirror has a radius of 4 in., what is the area of the bottom of the box?
  c. The area of the bottom of a second box is 196 in.^{2}. What is the diameter of the largest mirror the box can hold?

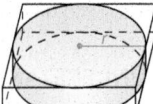

Mixed Review

Write each number in scientific notation.   ◀ See Lesson 7-2.

77. 2,358,000   **78.** 0.00465   **79.** 0.00007   **80.** 5.1 billion

Find the third, seventh, and tenth terms of the sequence described by each rule.   ◀ See Lesson 4-7.

81. $A(n) = 10 + (n - 1)(4)$ **82.** $A(n) = -5 + (n - 1)(2)$ **83.** $A(n) = 1.2 + (n - 1)(-4)$

Get Ready! **To prepare for Lesson 7-4, do Exercises 84–87.**

Simplify each expression.   ◀ See Lesson 7-1.

84. $(-2)^{-4}$ **85.** $5xy^0$ **86.** $4m^{-1}n^2$ **87.** $-3x^3y^{-2}z^6$

---

65. 3^4

66. 2^{2n+3}

67. $2^{x+y} \cdot 3^{x+2}$

68. $\frac{1}{a + b}$

69. $(t + 3)^2$

70. 5^2

71. 22.5 times

72. D

73. H

74. A

75. H

76. [4] **a.** $(2r)^2$
     b. $A = (2 \cdot 4)^2 = 8^2 = 64$ in.^{2}
     c. $196 = (2r)^2$, so $(2r) = 14$, so $d = 14$.
   [3] appropriate methods, but with one computational error
   [2] correct formula but either part a or part b incorrect
   [1] correct answers with no work shown

77. 2.358×10^6 **78.** 4.65×10^{-3}

79. 7×10^{-5} **80.** 5.1×10^9

81. 18, 34, 46   **82.** -1, 7, 13

83. -6.8, -22.8, -34.8

84. $\frac{1}{16}$ **85.** $5x$

86. $\frac{4n^2}{m}$ **87.** $\frac{-3x^3z^6}{y^2}$

Additional Instructional Support

Algebra 1 Companion

Students can use the **Algebra 1 Companion** worktext (4 pages) as you teach the lesson. Use the Companion to support

- New Vocabulary
- Key Concepts
- Got It for each Problem
- Lesson Check

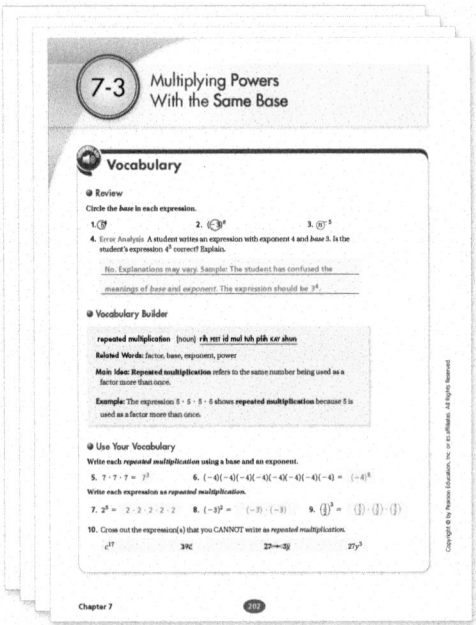

ELL Support

Focus on Communication Write the Essential Understanding of this lesson on the board. Ask students to give the meaning of each keyword in their own words. Have students rephrase the Essential Understanding in their own words.

Assess Understanding Have students work in groups. Ask each student to create one expression of a power multiplied by a power with the same base and simplify their own expression. Then, have students check each others' work. Discuss these examples at the end of the lesson as practice problems.

5 Assess & Remediate

Lesson Quiz

1. What is each expression written as a single power?
   a. $20^7 \cdot 20^6$
   b. $(-4)^8 \cdot (-4)^{-5}$

2. What is the simplified form of each expression?
   a. $2n^{-2} \cdot 5n^7$
   b. $-2r \cdot 5s^3 \cdot 4r^8$

3. What is the simplified form of $(7 \times 10^{-12})(4 \times 10^5)$?

4. **Do you UNDERSTAND?** The length of a 1-inch paperclip is about 1.6×10^{-5} miles. It takes about 1.5×10^{10} paperclips to reach from the east coast to the west coast of the United States. What is the approximate distance from the east coast to the west coast of the United States?

ANSWERS TO LESSON QUIZ

1. **a.** 20^{13} **b.** $(-4)^3$
2. **a.** $10n^5$ **b.** $-40r^9s^3$
3. 2.8×10^{-6}
4. 2.4×10^5 mi

PRESCRIPTION FOR REMEDIATION
Use the student work on the Lesson Quiz to prescribe a differentiated review assignment.

Points	Differentiated Remediation
0–2	Intervention
3	On-level
4	Extension

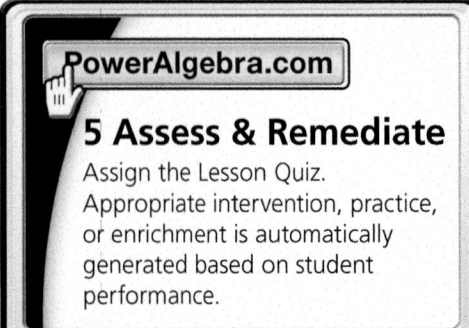

PowerAlgebra.com

5 Assess & Remediate
Assign the Lesson Quiz. Appropriate intervention, practice, or enrichment is automatically generated based on student performance.

Intervention

- **Reteaching** (2 pages) Provides reteaching and practice exercises for the key lesson concepts. Use with struggling students or absent students.

- **English Language Learner Support** Helps students develop and reinforce mathematical vocabulary and key concepts.

All-in-One Resources/Online
Reteaching

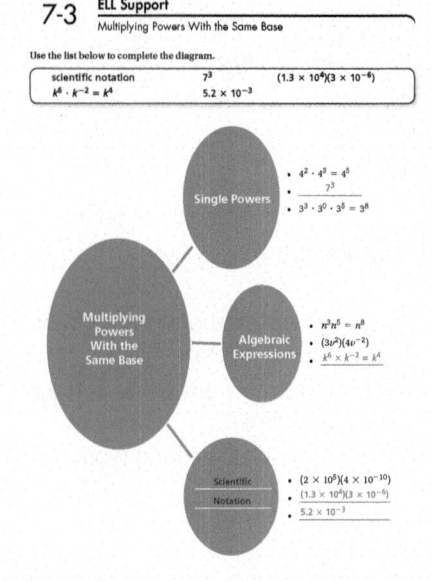

All-in-One Resources/Online
English Language Learner Support

Differentiated Remediation *continued*

On-Level

- **Practice** (2 pages) Provides extra practice for each lesson. For simpler practice exercises, use the Form K Practice pages found in the All-in-One Teaching Resources and online.

- **Think About a Plan** Helps students develop specific problem-solving skills and strategies by providing scaffolded guiding questions.

- **Standardized Test Prep** Focuses on all major exercises, all major question types, and helps students prepare for the high-stakes assessments.

Extension

- **Enrichment** Provides students with interesting problems and activities that extend the concepts of the lesson.

- **Activities, Games, and Puzzles** Worksheets that can be used for concepts development, enrichment, and for fun!

Practice and Problem Solving WKBK/All-in-One Resources/Online
Practice page 1

Practice and Problem Solving WKBK/All-in-One Resources/Online
Practice page 2

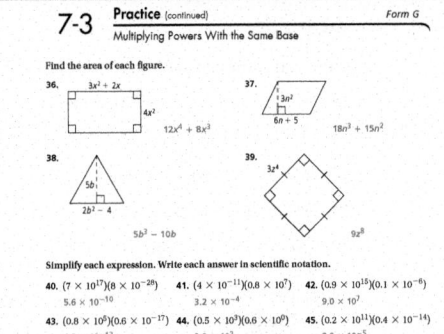

All-in-One Resources/Online
Enrichment

Practice and Problem Solving WKBK/All-in-One Resources/Online
Think About a Plan

Practice and Problem Solving WKBK/All-in-One Resources/Online
Standardized Test Prep

Online Teacher Resource Center
Activities, Games, and Puzzles

Guided Instruction

PURPOSE To discover rules for powers of powers and powers of products

PROCESS Students will
- use patterns to complete statements of powers of powers and powers of products.
- simplify powers of powers and powers of products.

DISCUSS Early steps of the first few Exercises in each set are started for students. Fewer steps are given later on so that students can find and apply the patterns.

Activity 1
In this Activity, students use patterns to complete statements involving powers of powers.

> **Q** What does the 2 indicate in the term $(4^5)^2$? **[It indicates that 4^5 is raised to the exponent 2.]**
>
> **Q** Why does $4^5 \cdot 4^5 = 4^{5+5}$? **[Exponents are added when multiplying powers with the same base.]**

Activity 2
In this Activity, students focus on completing statements involving powers of products using patterns.

> **Q** Are the expressions $3n^2$ and $(3n)^2$ equivalent? Explain. **[No; in $3n^2$, only n is raised to the exponent 2 and in $(3n)^2$, $3n$ is raised to the exponent 2.]**
>
> **Q** How do the parentheses affect the exponent? **[When the exponent is to the right of the parentheses, it applies to everything within the parentheses.]**

You can use patterns to find a shortcut for simplifying a power raised to a power or a product raised to a power.

Activity 1

Copy and complete each statement in Exercises 1–6.

1. $(4^5)^2 = 4^5 \cdot 4^5 = 4^{\blacksquare + \blacksquare} = 4^{5 \cdot \blacksquare} = 4^{\blacksquare}$

2. $(3^6)^3 = 3^6 \cdot 3^6 \cdot 3^6 = 3^{\blacksquare + \blacksquare + \blacksquare} = 3^{6 \cdot \blacksquare} = 3^{\blacksquare}$

3. $(5^8)^4 = 5^8 \cdot 5^8 \cdot 5^8 \cdot 5^8 = 5^{\blacksquare + \blacksquare + \blacksquare + \blacksquare} = 5^{8 \cdot \blacksquare} = 5^{\blacksquare}$

4. $(a^4)^2 = a^4 \cdot a^4 = a^{\blacksquare + \blacksquare} = a^{4 \cdot \blacksquare} = a^{\blacksquare}$

5. $(n^2)^3 = \blacksquare \cdot \blacksquare \cdot \blacksquare = n^{\blacksquare + \blacksquare + \blacksquare} = n^{2 \cdot \blacksquare} = n^{\blacksquare}$

6. $(x^5)^4 = \blacksquare \cdot \blacksquare \cdot \blacksquare \cdot \blacksquare = x^{\blacksquare + \blacksquare + \blacksquare + \blacksquare} = x^{5 \cdot \blacksquare} = x^{\blacksquare}$

7. **a.** Look for a Pattern What pattern do you see in your answers to Exercises 1–6?
   b. Predict Use your pattern to simplify $(y^{11})^{33}$.

Activity 2

Copy and complete each statement in Exercises 8–12.

8. $(3n)^2 = 3n \cdot 3n = (3 \cdot 3)(n \cdot n) = 3^{\blacksquare} n^{\blacksquare}$

9. $(2x)^3 = 2x \cdot 2x \cdot 2x = (2 \cdot 2 \cdot 2)(x \cdot x \cdot x) = 2^{\blacksquare} x^{\blacksquare}$

10. $(ab)^2 = ab \cdot ab = (a \cdot a)(b \cdot b) = a^{\blacksquare} b^{\blacksquare}$

11. $(xy)^3 = xy \cdot xy \cdot xy = (\blacksquare \cdot \blacksquare \cdot \blacksquare)(\blacksquare \cdot \blacksquare \cdot \blacksquare) = x^{\blacksquare} y^{\blacksquare}$

12. $(pq)^4 = \blacksquare \cdot \blacksquare \cdot \blacksquare \cdot \blacksquare = (\blacksquare \cdot \blacksquare \cdot \blacksquare \cdot \blacksquare)(\blacksquare \cdot \blacksquare \cdot \blacksquare \cdot \blacksquare) = p^{\blacksquare} q^{\blacksquare}$

13. **a.** Look for a Pattern What pattern do you see in your answers to Exercises 8–12?
    b. Predict Use your pattern to simplify $(rs)^{20}$.

Answers

Activity 1
1. 5, 5, 2, 10
2. 6, 6, 6, 3, 18
3. 8, 8, 8, 8, 4, 32
4. 4, 4, 2, 8
5. n^2, n^2, n^2, 2, 2, 2, 3, 6
6. x^5, x^5, x^5, x^5, 5, 5, 5, 5, 4, 20
7. **a.** When you raise a power to a power you can multiply the exponents.
   b. y^{363}

Activity 2
8. 2, 2   9. 3, 3   10. 2, 2
11. x, x, x, y, y, y, 3, 3
12. pq, pq, pq, pq, p, p, p, p, q, q, q, q, 4, 4
13. **a.** When you raise a product to a power, each factor is raised to that power.
    b. $r^{20} s^{20}$

7-4 More Multiplication Properties of Exponents

Objectives To raise a power to a power
To raise a product to a power

Be careful! Multiplying r by 2.5 doesn't multiply the volume by 2.5.

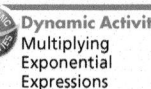
Dynamic Activity
Multiplying
Exponential
Expressions

SOLVE IT

Getting Ready!

The radius of a bubble made by the bubble machine on the right is 2.5 times as large as the radius of a bubble made by the bubble machine on the left. What is the volume of a bubble made by the machine on the right? Explain your reasoning. (Hint: $V = \frac{4}{3}\pi r^3$)

radius = x in.

In the Solve It, the expression for the volume of the larger bubble involves a product raised to a power. In this lesson, you will use properties of exponents to simplify similar expressions.

Essential Understanding You can use properties of exponents to simplify a power raised to a power or a product raised to a power.

You can use repeated multiplication to simplify a power raised to a power.

$$(x^5)^2 = x^5 \cdot x^5 = x^{5+5} = x^{5 \cdot 2} = x^{10}$$

Notice that $(x^5)^2 = x^{5 \cdot 2}$. Raising a power to a power is the same as raising the base to the product of the exponents.

Property Raising a Power to a Power

Words To raise a power to a power, multiply the exponents.

Algebra $(a^m)^n = a^{mn}$, where $a \neq 0$ and m and n are integers

Examples $(5^4)^2 = 5^{4 \cdot 2} = 5^8$ $(m^3)^5 = m^{3 \cdot 5} = m^{15}$

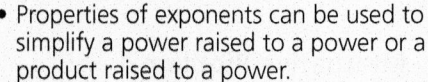

| PowerAlgebra.com | Lesson 7-4   More Multiplication Properties of Exponents | 433 |

7-4 Preparing to Teach

BIG idea Properties

ESSENTIAL UNDERSTANDINGS

- Properties of exponents can be used to simplify a power raised to a power or a product raised to a power.
- To raise a power to a power, multiply the exponents.
- To raise a product to a power, raise each factor to the power and multiply.

Math Background

It is important for students to understand that the properties of exponents are shortcuts for repeated multiplication. For example, write $(2b^5)^3$ as $2b^5 \cdot 2b^5 \cdot 2b^5 = 2 \cdot 2 \cdot 2 \cdot b^5 \cdot b^5 \cdot b^5 = 8b^{15}$. Students who understand the mathematics behind the properties will be able to derive the properties for themselves by writing an expression using repeated multiplication.

UbD Support Student Learning

Use the **Algebra 1 Companion** to engage and support students during instructions. See Lesson Resources at the end of this lesson for details.

---

1 Interactive Learning

Solve It!

PURPOSE To present students with a problem that can be modeled by the power of a product
PROCESS Students may

- use prior knowledge of the formula for the volume of a sphere.
- use repeated multiplication to simplify a product raised to an exponent.

FACILITATE

Q What expression represents the length of the radius of a bubble made by the machine on the right? **[2.5x]**

Q How many times greater is the volume of a bubble made by the machine on the right compared to the volume of a bubble made by the machine on the left? **[2.5³, or 15.625]**

ANSWER See Solve It in Answers on next page.
CONNECT THE MATH Emphasize to students that the reason they will learn properties for power of a power and power of a product are to expedite calculations in ways that will avoid repeated multiplication.

2 Guided Instruction

Take Note

Q Does the property for power of a power apply to positive and negative exponents? Explain. **[Yes; the property states that m and n can be any integer.]**

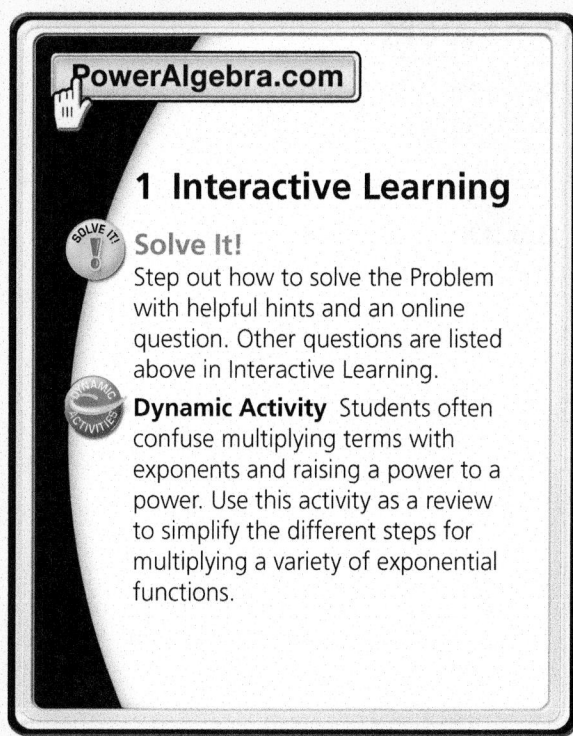

PowerAlgebra.com

1 Interactive Learning

SOLVE IT! **Solve It!**
Step out how to solve the Problem with helpful hints and an online question. Other questions are listed above in Interactive Learning.

Dynamic Activity Students often confuse multiplying terms with exponents and raising a power to a power. Use this activity as a review to simplify the different steps for multiplying a variety of exponential functions.

Problem 1

> **Q** How can you use repeated multiplication to simplify this expression? $[(n^4) \cdot (n^4) \cdot (n^4) \cdot (n^4) \cdot (n^4) \cdot (n^4) \cdot (n^4) = n^{4+4+4+4+4+4+4} = n^{28}]$

Got It?

> **Q** Why are the simplified forms of the expressions in 1a and 1b equivalent? **[According to the property used, exponents are multiplied. The Commutative Property of Multiplication shows that 5 • 4 is the same as 4 • 5.]**

Problem 2

> **Q** Which part of the expression is being raised to the exponent -2? Explain. **[y^5; it is inside of the parentheses.]**
>
> **Q** How would the simplification process be the same if the original expression for Problem 2 were $x^3(y^5)^{-2}$? How would it be different? **[The first step of raising a power to a power would be the same. The second step would not be the same because the bases are not the same.]**

Got It?   SYNTHESIZING

> **Q** Why did you learn the property for multiplying bases with the same power prior to learning the property for power of a power? **[The property for raising a power to a power is a shortcut for multiplying bases with the same power.]**

Think

Should you add or multiply the exponents to simplify the expression?
You multiply the exponents when raising a power to a power.

What is the simplified form of $(n^4)^7$?

$(n^4)^7 = n^{4 \cdot 7}$ Multiply exponents when raising a power to a power.

$= n^{28}$ Simplify.

Got It? 1. What is the simplified form of each expression in parts (a)–(c)?

    a. $(p^5)^4$ **b.** $(p^4)^5$ **c.** $(p^{-5})^4$

    d. Reasoning Is $(a^m)^n = (a^n)^m$ true for all integers m and n? Explain.

Use the order of operations when you simplify an exponential expression.

 **Problem 2** Simplifying an Expression With Powers

What is the simplified form of $y^3(y^5)^{-2}$?

Plan

What is the first step in simplifying the expression?
By the order of operations, you simplify powers before you multiply.

Think

You multiply exponents when raising a power to a power.

You add exponents when multiplying powers with the same base.

Write the expression using only positive exponents.

Write

$y^3(y^5)^{-2} = y^3 y^{5 \cdot (-2)}$

$= y^3 y^{-10}$

$= y^{3+(-10)}$

$= y^{-7}$

$= \dfrac{1}{y^7}$

Got It? 2. What is the simplified form of each expression?

    a. $x^2(x^6)^{-4}$ **b.** $w^{-2}(w^7)^3$ **c.** $(r^{-5})^{-2}r^3$

You can use repeated multiplication to simplify an expression like $(4m)^3$.

$(4m)^3 = 4m \cdot 4m \cdot 4m$

$= 4 \cdot 4 \cdot 4 \cdot m \cdot m \cdot m$

$= 4^3 m^3$

$= 64m^3$

Notice that $(4m)^3 = 4^3m^3$. This example illustrates another property of exponents.

Answers

Solve It!

$\dfrac{125\pi r^3}{6}$; the radius of the larger bubble is $2.5r$.

$V = \dfrac{4}{3}\pi\left(\dfrac{5}{2}r\right)\left(\dfrac{5}{2}r\right)\left(\dfrac{5}{2}r\right) = \dfrac{500\pi r^3}{24} = \dfrac{125\pi r^3}{6}$.

Got It?

1. a. p^{20} **b.** p^{20}

    c. $\dfrac{1}{p^{20}}$ **d.** yes; $(a^m)^n = a^{mn} = (a^n)^m$

2. a. $\dfrac{1}{x^{22}}$ **b.** w^{19}

    c. r^{13}

 PowerAlgebra.com

2 Guided Instruction

Each Problem is worked out and supported in the Student Online Center.

Problem 1
Simplifying a Power Raised to a Power

Problem 2
Simplifying an Expression With Powers

Problem 3
Simplifying a Product Raised to a Power
Animated

Problem 4
Simplifying an Expression With Products
Animated

Alternative Problem 4
Simplifying an Expression With Products
Animated

Problem 5
Raising a Number in Scientific Notation to a Power

Support in the Algebra 1 Companion
• Vocabulary
• Key Concepts
• Got It?

Property Raising a Product to a Power

Words To raise a product to a power, raise each factor to the power and multiply.

Algebra $(ab)^n = a^n b^n$, where $a \neq 0$, $b \neq 0$, and n is an integer

Example $(3x)^4 = 3^4 x^4 = 81x^4$

 Problem 3 Simplifying a Product Raised to a Power

Multiple Choice Which expression represents the area of the square?

Ⓐ $10x^3$ Ⓒ $25x^5$

Ⓑ $5x^6$ Ⓓ $25x^6$

$5x^3$

$(5x^3)^2 = 5^2(x^3)^2$ Raise each factor to the second power.

$\quad\quad\quad = 5^2 x^6$ Multiply the exponents of a power raised to a power.

$\quad\quad\quad = 25x^6$ Simplify.

The correct answer is D.

Got It? 3. What is the simplified form of each expression?

a. $(7m^9)^3$ **b.** $(2z)^{-4}$ **c.** $(3g^4)^{-2}$

 Problem 4 Simplifying an Expression With Products

What is the simplified form of $(n^5)^2 (4mn^{-2})^3$?

$(n^5)^2(4mn^{-2})^3 = (n^5)^2 4^3 m^3 (n^{-2})^3$ Raise each factor of $4mn^{-2}$ to the third power.

$\quad\quad\quad\quad\quad = n^{10} 4^3 m^3 n^{-6}$ Multiply the exponents of a power raised to a power.

$\quad\quad\quad\quad\quad = 4^3 m^3 n^{10} n^{-6}$ Commutative Property of Multiplication

$\quad\quad\quad\quad\quad = 4^3 m^3 n^{10+(-6)}$ Add the exponents of powers with the same base.

$\quad\quad\quad\quad\quad = 64m^3 n^4$ Simplify.

Got It? 4. What is the simplified form of each expression?

a. $(x^{-2})^2 (3xy^5)^4$ **b.** $(3c^5)^4 (c^2)^3$ **c.** $(6ab)^3 (5a^{-3})^2$

You can use the property of raising a product to a power to solve problems involving scientific notation. For example, to simplify the expression $(3 \times 10^8)^2$, you raise both 3 and 10^8 to the second power. Then multiply the two powers.

Plan

How do you find the area of the square?
The area of a square with side length s is s^2. Square the side length of the square to find the area.

Think

What is the exponent of m?
It has an implied exponent of 1. Similar to coefficients, exponents of 1 don't need to be written.

Take Note
Students will eventually operate with polynomials and will need to simplify expressions such as $(a + b)^3$. Emphasize now, that while $(ab)^3 = a^3 b^3$, $(a + b)^3 \neq a^3 + b^3$.

Problem 3

Q If a student indicates an answer of "A," what mistake did they likely make? **[The student likely added $5x^3$ to itself.]**

Q If a student indicates an answer of "B," what mistake did they likely make? **[The student likely neglected to apply the exponent to the coefficient.]**

Q If a student indicates an answer of "C," what mistake did they likely make? **[The student likely added, instead of multiplying the exponents.]**

Got It?
Remind students that coefficients have an implied exponent of 1.

Problem 4
Ask these questions prior to completing the problem.

Q How many factors will the simplified form of the expression have? Explain. **[3; there will be a constant factor, a factor of m, and a factor of n.]**

Got It?

Q In 4a, why is x eliminated from the simplified form? **[After applying the power of a power property and multiplying factors with the same base, the exponent of base x is 0, and $x^0 = 1$.]**

Additional Problems

1. What is the simplified form of $(b^3)^5$?

ANSWER b^{15}

2. What is the simplified form of $h^{-2}(h^4)^{-3}$?

ANSWER $\frac{1}{h^{14}}$

3. Which expression represents the area of the square?

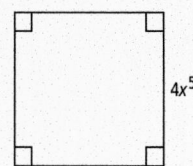

$4x^5$

A. $4x^{10}$

B. $8x^5$

C. $16x^{10}$

D. $16x^{25}$

ANSWER C

4. What is the simplified form of $(b^6)^3 (8ab^{-4})^2$?

ANSWER $64a^2 b^{10}$

5. The formula for the volume of a sphere is $V = \frac{4}{3}\pi r^3$, where r is the radius. What is the volume of a sphere with a radius of 10^2 millimeter? Give your answer in terms of π.

ANSWER $(\frac{4}{3} \times 10^6)\pi$ cubic millimeters

Answers

Got It? (continued)

3. a. $343m^{27}$ **b.** $\frac{1}{16z^4}$

c. $\frac{1}{9g^8}$

4. a. $81y^{20}$ **b.** $81c^{26}$

c. $\frac{5400b^3}{a^3}$

Problem 5

Q What property of exponents is illustrated in the first step? **[Raising a Product to a Power]**

Q What property of exponents is illustrated in the fifth line? **[Multiplying Powers With the Same Base]**

Got It?

Q What factors are multiplied to get the answer's first factor in scientific notation? **[$\frac{1}{2}$, 2.5, and 3^2]**

3 Lesson Check

Do you know HOW?
- If students have difficulty with Exercise 6, then make sure they raised each factor to the fifth power.

Do you UNDERSTAND?
- If students think the first student is correct, have them look at the Take Note on page 433.

Close

Q What is the difference between a "power of a power" and "product of a power"? **[The power expression is the base of the exponent in a "power of a power". The factors of an expression raised to a single exponent are each a base of the exponent in a "product of a power".]**

 **Problem 5** Raising a Number in Scientific Notation to a Power

Aircraft The expression $\frac{1}{2}mv^2$ gives the kinetic energy, in joules, of an object with a mass of m kg traveling at a speed of v meters per second. What is the kinetic energy of an experimental unmanned jet with a mass of 1.3×10^3 kg traveling at a speed of about 3.1×10^3 m/s?

Plan

How do you raise a number in scientific notation to a power?
A number written in scientific notation is a product. Use the property for raising a product to a power.

$$\frac{1}{2}mv^2 = \frac{1}{2} \cdot (1.3 \times 10^3)(3.1 \times 10^3)^2$$ Substitute the values for m and v into the expression.

$$= \frac{1}{2} \cdot 1.3 \cdot 10^3 \cdot 3.1^2 \cdot (10^3)^2$$ Raise the two factors to the second power.

$$= \frac{1}{2} \cdot 1.3 \cdot 10^3 \cdot 3.1^2 \cdot 10^6$$ Multiply the exponents of a power raised to a power.

$$= \frac{1}{2} \cdot 1.3 \cdot 3.1^2 \cdot 10^3 \cdot 10^6$$ Use the Commutative Property of Multiplication.

$$= \frac{1}{2} \cdot 1.3 \cdot 3.1^2 \cdot 10^{3+6}$$ Add exponents of powers with the same base.

$$= 6.2465 \times 10^9$$ Simplify. Write in scientific notation.

The aircraft has a kinetic energy of about 6.2×10^9 joules.

 Got It? 5. What is the kinetic energy of an aircraft with a mass of 2.5×10^5 kg traveling at a speed of 3×10^2 m/s?

 Lesson Check

Do you know HOW?
Simplify each expression.

1. $(n^3)^6$ **2.** $(b^{-7})^3$

3. $(3a)^4$ **4.** $(9x^5)^2(x^2)^5$

Simplify each expression. Write each answer in scientific notation.

5. $(4 \times 10^5)^2$ **6.** $(2 \times 10^{-3})^5$

Do you UNDERSTAND?
7. Vocabulary Compare and contrast the property for raising a power to a power and the property for multiplying powers with the same base.

8. Error Analysis One student simplified $x^5 + x^5$ to x^{10}. A second student simplified $x^5 + x^5$ to $2x^5$. Which student is correct? Explain.

9. Open-Ended Write four different expressions that are equivalent to $(x^4)^3$.

 Practice and Problem-Solving Exercises

Ⓐ **Practice** Simplify each expression.   See Problems 1 and 2.

10. $(n^8)^4$ **11.** $(n^4)^8$ **12.** $(c^2)^5$ **13.** $(q^{10})^{10}$

14. $(w^7)^{-1}$ **15.** $(x^3)^{-5}$ **16.** $d(d^{-2})^{-9}$ **17.** $(z^8)^0 z^5$

18. $(a^5)^3 c^4$ **19.** $(c^3)^5(d^3)^0$ **20.** $(t^2)^{-2}(t^2)^{-5}$ **21.** $(m^3)^{-1}(x^2)^5$

Answers

Got It? (continued)
5. about 1.125×10^{10} joules of energy

Lesson Check
1. n^{18} **2.** $\frac{1}{b^{21}}$

3. $81a^4$ **4.** $81x^{20}$

5. 1.6×10^{11} **6.** 3.2×10^{-14}

7. Answers may vary. Sample: When you raise a power to a power, you multiply the exponents. When you multiply powers with the same base, you add the exponents.

8. The second student; when you add like terms, you add the coefficients and keep the same variable part.

9. Answers may vary. Sample: x^{12}, $(x^3)^4$, $(x^6)^2$, $(x^2)^6$

Practice and Problem-Solving Exercises

10. n^{32} **11.** n^{32} **12.** c^{10}

13. q^{100} **14.** $\frac{1}{w^7}$ **15.** $\frac{1}{x^{15}}$

16. d^{19} **17.** z^5 **18.** $a^{15}c^4$

19. c^{15} **20.** $\frac{1}{t^{14}}$ **21.** $\frac{x^{10}}{m^3}$

Simplify each expression.

See Problems 3 and 4.

22. $(4m)^5$ **23.** $(7a)^{-2}$ **24.** $(5y)^4$ **25.** $(12g^4)^{-1}$

26. $(3n^{-6})^{-4}$ **27.** $(2y^4)^{-3}$ **28.** $(xy)^0$ **29.** $(r^2s)^5$

30. $(2x)^3x^2$ **31.** $(y^2z^{-3})^5(y^3)^2$ **32.** $(mg^4)^{-1}(mg^4)$ **33.** $p(p^{-7}q^3)^{-2}q^{-3}$

34. $(3b^{-2})^2(a^2b^4)^3$ **35.** $c^{-12}(c^{-2}d)^3d^5$ **36.** $(2j^2k^4)^{-5}(k^{-1}j^7)^6$ **37.** $4j^2k^6(2j^{11})^3k^5$

Simplify. Write each answer in scientific notation.

See Problem 5.

38. $(3 \times 10^5)^2$ **39.** $(4 \times 10^2)^5$ **40.** $(2 \times 10^{-10})^3$ **41.** $(2 \times 10^{-3})^3$

42. $(7.4 \times 10^4)^2$ **43.** $(6.25 \times 10^{-12})^{-2}$ **44.** $(3.5 \times 10^{-4})^3$ **45.** $(2.37 \times 10^8)^3$

46. Geometry The radius of a cylinder is 7.8×10^{-4} m. The height of the cylinder is 3.4×10^{-2} m. What is the volume of the cylinder? Write your answer in scientific notation. (*Hint:* $V = \pi r^2 h$)

 Apply

Complete each equation.

47. $(b^2)^{\blacksquare} = b^8$ **48.** $(m^{\blacksquare})^3 = m^{-12}$ **49.** $(x^{\blacksquare})^7 = x^6$

50. $(n^9)^{\blacksquare} = 1$ **51.** $(y^{-4})^{\blacksquare} = y^{12}$ **52.** $7(c^1)^{\blacksquare} = 7c^8$

53. $(5x^{\blacksquare})^2 = 25x^{-4}$ **54.** $(3x^3y^{\blacksquare})^3 = 27x^9$ **55.** $(m^2n^3)^{\blacksquare} = \frac{1}{m^6n^9}$

56. Think About a Plan How many times the volume of the small cube is the volume of the large cube?
- What expression can you write for the volume of the small cube? For the volume of the large cube?
- What property of exponents can you use to simplify the volume expressions?

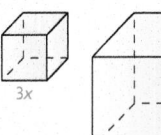

Simplify each expression.

57. $3^2(3x)^3$ **58.** $(4.1)^5(4.1)^{-5}$ **59.** $(b^5)^3b^2$

60. $(-5x)^2 + 5x^2$ **61.** $(-2a^2b)^3(ab)^3$ **62.** $(2x^{-3})^2(0.2x)^2$

63. $4xy^20^4(-y)^{-3}$ **64.** $(10^3)^4(4.3 \times 10^{-8})$ **65.** $(3^7)^2(3^{-4})^3$

66. Reasoning Simplify $(x^2)^3$ and x^{2^3}. Are the expressions equivalent? Explain.

67. Measurement How many cubic millimeters are in a cubic meter? Write your answer as a power of 10.

68. Wind Energy The power generated by a wind turbine depends on the wind speed. The expression $800v^3$ gives the power in watts for a certain wind turbine at wind speed v in meters per second. If the wind speed triples, by what factor does the power generated by the wind turbine increase?

69. Can you write the expression $49x^2y^2z^2$ using only one exponent? Show how or explain why not.

---

22. $1024m^5$ **23.** $\frac{1}{49a^2}$ **24.** $625y^4$

25. $\frac{1}{12g^4}$ **26.** $\frac{n^{24}}{81}$ **27.** $\frac{1}{8y^{12}}$

28. 1 **29.** $r^{10}s^5$ **30.** $8x^5$

31. $\frac{y^{16}}{z^{15}}$ **32.** 1 **33.** $\frac{p^{15}}{q^9}$

34. $9a^6b^8$ **35.** $\frac{d^8}{c^{18}}$ **36.** $\frac{j^{32}}{32k^{26}}$

37. $32j^{35}k^{11}$ **38.** 9×10^{10}

39. 1.024×10^{13} **40.** 8×10^{-30}

41. 8×10^{-9} **42.** 5.476×10^9

43. 2.56×10^{22} **44.** 4.2875×10^{-11}

45. 1.3312053×10^{25}

46. 6.499×10^{-8} m³

47. 4 **48.** -4 **49.** $\frac{6}{7}$

50. 0 **51.** -3 **52.** 8

53. -2 **54.** 0 **55.** -3

56. 8 **57.** $243x^3$ **58.** 1

59. b^{17} **60.** $30x^2$ **61.** $-8a^9b^6$

62. $\frac{4}{25x^4}$ **63.** 0 **64.** $43{,}000$

65. 9

66. x^6, x^8; no; $(x^2)^3 = (x^2)(x^2)(x^2) = x^6$ while $x^{2^3} = x^{2 \cdot 2 \cdot 2} = x^8$

67. 10^9 **68.** 27

69. yes; $(7xyz)^2$

ASSIGNMENT GUIDE

Basic: 10–46 all, 48–66 even, 70

Average: 11–45 odd, 47–70

Advanced: 11–45 odd, 47–77

Standardized Test Prep: 78–80

Mixed Review: 81–93

Reasoning exercises have blue headings.

Applications exercises have red headings.

EXERCISE 70: Use the Think About a Plan worksheet in the **Practice and Problem Solving Workbook** (also available in the Teaching Resources in print and online) to further support students' development in becoming independent learners.

HOMEWORK QUICK CHECK

To check students' understanding of key skills and concepts, go over Exercises 19, 35, 56, 66, and 70.

Answers

Practice and Problem-Solving Exercises
(continued)

70. a. about 5.1×10^{14} m^2
  b. about 3.6×10^{14} m^2
  c. about 1.4×10^{18} m^3

71. 3

72. 12

73. 6

74. 3

75. 4

76. -5

77. 10; $(2x)^4$, $(4x^2)^2$, $(16x^4)^1$, $(-2x)^4$, $(-4x^2)^2$, $\left(\frac{1}{2x}\right)^{-4}$, $\left(\frac{1}{4x^2}\right)^{-2}$, $\left(\frac{1}{16x^4}\right)^{-1}$, $\left(\frac{1}{-2x}\right)^{-4}$, $\left(\frac{1}{-4x^2}\right)^{-2}$

78. C

79. F

80. [2] 31.68 in./min;
$\frac{3 \times 10^{-2} \text{ mi}}{1 \text{ h}} \times \frac{5280 \text{ ft}}{1 \text{ mi}} \times \frac{12 \text{ in.}}{1 \text{ ft}} \times \frac{1 \text{ h}}{60 \text{ min}} =$
31.68 in./min
[1] Appropriate methods with one minor computational error

81. $\frac{b^4}{c^6}$

82. $a^8 b^3$

83. $54m^5 n^4$

84. $-4t^5$

85. $-\frac{3}{4}$

86. 6

87. $-\frac{3}{2}$

88. -9

89. $\frac{1}{4}$

90. 31

91. $\frac{2}{5}$

92. $\frac{y}{3}$

93. $\frac{c}{4}$

---

70. a. Geography Earth has a radius of about 6.4×10^6 m. What is the approximate surface area of Earth? Use the formula for the surface area of a sphere, S.A. $= 4\pi r^2$. Write your answer in scientific notation.
  b. Oceans cover about 70% of the surface of the Earth. About how many square meters of Earth's surface are covered by ocean water?
  c. The oceans have an average depth of 3790 m. Estimate the volume of water in Earth's oceans.

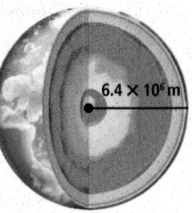
6.4 × 10⁶ m

Challenge Solve each equation. Use the fact that if $a^x = a^y$, then $x = y$.

71. $5^6 = 25^x$

72. $3^x = 27^4$

73. $8^2 = 2^x$

74. $4^x = 2^6$

75. $3^{2x} = 9^4$

76. $2^x = \frac{1}{32}$

77. Reasoning How many different ways are there to rewrite the expression $16x^4$ using only the property of raising a product to a power? Show the ways.

Standardized Test Prep

SAT/ACT

78. Which expression does NOT equal $25n^{12}$?
  Ⓐ $(5n^6)^2$ Ⓑ $(5n^3)(5n^9)$ Ⓒ $25(n^3)^9$ Ⓓ $5^2(n^2)^6$

79. One morning an employee washed 4 cars and 2 vans in less than 115 min. That afternoon it took the employee more than 150 min to wash 3 cars and 5 vans. The information can be represented by the inequalities $4x + 2y < 115$ and $3x + 5y > 150$, where x is the time it takes to wash one car and y is the time it takes to wash one van. Which region of the graph at the right represents the possible numbers of minutes it takes to wash a car and a van?
  Ⓕ A   Ⓖ B   Ⓗ C   Ⓘ D

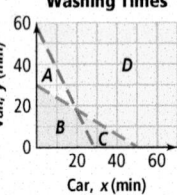
Washing Times

Short Response

80. A snail travels at a speed of 3×10^{-2} mi/h. What is the snail's speed in inches per minute? Show your work.

Mixed Review

Simplify each expression.   ◆ See Lesson 7-3.

81. $bc^{-6}b^3$

82. $(a^2 b^3)(a^6)$

83. $9m^3(6m^2 n^4)$

84. $2t(-2t^4)$

Find the slope of the line that passes through each pair of points.   ◆ See Lesson 5-1.

85. $(0, 3)$, $(4, 0)$

86. $(2, -5)$, $(3, 1)$

87. $(-3, 6)$, $(1, 0)$

88. $(0, 0)$, $(1, -9)$

Get Ready! **To prepare for Lesson 7-5, do Exercises 89–93.**

Write each fraction in simplest form.   ◆ See page 789.

89. $\frac{5}{20}$

90. $\frac{124}{4}$

91. $\frac{6}{15}$

92. $\frac{5xy}{15x}$

93. $\frac{3ac}{12a}$

Differentiated Remediation

Additional Instructional Support

Algebra 1 Companion

Students can use the **Algebra 1 Companion** worktext (4 pages) as you teach the lesson. Use the Companion to support

- New Vocabulary
- Key Concepts
- Got It for each Problem
- Lesson Check

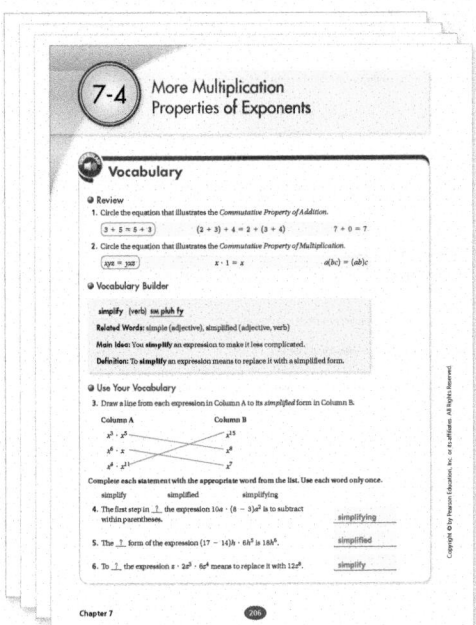

ELL Support

Focus on Language While presenting the properties covered in this lesson, focus on the names of the properties. Emphasize the words "power" and "product" and point to examples as you demonstrate "power of a power" and "power of a product."

Explain that a product usually means something you make by doing something. In math, a product is what you get by multiplying. If students confuse powers and products, it may help them to remember that powers are more "powerful" than products because they usually involve multiplying more than once.

Use a visual aid such as:
$(Pro\bullet duct)^{Power}$

5 Assess & Remediate

Lesson Quiz

1. What is the simplified form of $(a^7)^3$?
2. What is the simplified form of $c^{-3}(c^8)^{-1}$?
3. **Do you UNDERSTAND?** Write an expression for the area of the rectangle.

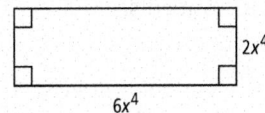

4. What is the simplified form of $(z^{-2})^{-3}(7yz^3)^{-2}$?

ANSWERS TO LESSON QUIZ

1. a^{21}
2. $\dfrac{1}{c^{11}}$
3. $12x^8$
4. $\dfrac{1}{49y^2}$

PRESCRIPTION FOR REMEDIATION
Use the student work on the Lesson Quiz to prescribe a differentiated review assignment.

Points	Differentiated Remediation
0–2	Intervention
3	On-level
4	Extension

5 Assess & Remediate

Assign the Lesson Quiz. Appropriate intervention, practice, or enrichment is automatically generated based on student performance.

Intervention

- **Reteaching** (2 pages) Provides reteaching and practice exercises for the key lesson concepts. Use with struggling students or absent students.
- **English Language Learner Support** Helps students develop and reinforce mathematical vocabulary and key concepts.

All-in-One Resources/Online
Reteaching

7-4 **Reteaching**
More Multiplication Properties of Exponents

All-in-One Resources/Online
English Language Learner Support

7-4 **ELL Support**
More Multiplication Properties of Exponents

Differentiated Remediation *continued*

On-Level

- **Practice (2 pages)** Provides extra practice for each lesson. For simpler practice exercises, use the Form K Practice pages found in the All-in-One Teaching Resources and online.

- **Think About a Plan** Helps students develop specific problem-solving skills and strategies by providing scaffolded guiding questions.

- **Standardized Test Prep** Focuses on all major exercises, all major question types, and helps students prepare for the high-stakes assessments.

Extension

- **Enrichment** Provides students with interesting problems and activities that extend the concepts of the lesson.

- **Activities, Games, and Puzzles** Worksheets that can be used for concepts development, enrichment, and for fun!

Practice and Problem Solving WKBK/ All-in-One Resources/Online
Practice page 1

7-4 Practice — Form G
More Multiplication Properties of Exponents

Simplify each expression.

1. $(z^5)^3$
z^{15}

2. $(m^4)^{10}$
m^{40}

3. $(v^7)^2$
v^{14}

4. $(k^4)^3$
k^{12}

5. $(x^7)^{-2}$
$\frac{1}{x^{14}}$

6. $(r^4)^{-6}$
$\frac{1}{r^{24}}$

7. $b(b^{-8})^{-3}$
b^{25}

8. $h^2(h^7)^0$
h^2

9. $(m^2)^7 n^5$
$m^{14} n^5$

10. $(x^6)^2(y^2)^0$
x^{12}

11. $(g^5)^{-2}(g^6)^{-3}$
$\frac{1}{g^{37}}$

12. $(v^2)^3(w^4)^{-3}$
$\frac{v^6}{w^{12}}$

13. $(6a)^4$
$1296a^4$

14. $(5f)^{-3}$
$\frac{1}{125f^3}$

15. $(9z)^{-4}$
$\frac{1}{6561z^4}$

16. $(10m^2)^{-2}$
$\frac{1}{100m^4}$

17. $(6j^{-2})^{-3}$
$\frac{j^6}{216}$

18. $(9d^{10})^{-2}$
$\frac{1}{18d^{20}}$

19. $(gh)^0$
1

20. $(qr^6)^4$
$q^4 r^{24}$

21. $(4a^3)^2 a^5$
$16a^{11}$

22. $(m^4 n^3)^7 (m^4)^3$
$m^{40} n^{21}$

23. $(xy^2)(xy^2)^{-1}$
1

24. $z(y^{-5}z^7)^{-1} y^{-5}$
$\frac{1}{z^6 y^{10}}$

25. $(7r^{-3})^3(5^2 r^4)^2$
$\frac{343r^{59}}{r^{11}}$

26. $m^{-8}(m^{-1}n)^8 n^8$
$\frac{n^{16}}{m^{11}}$

27. $(3b^{-4}c^{-2})^8 c^3$
$\frac{729}{b^{32}c^{13}}$

28. $5x^{-5} y^2(2x^{-14})^2$
$\frac{20y^2}{x^{33}}$

Simplify. Write each answer in scientific notation.

29. $(5 \times 10^7)^2$
2.5×10^{15}

30. $(2 \times 10^4)^6$
6.4×10^{25}

31. $(9 \times 10^{-12})^2$
8.1×10^{-23}

32. $(3 \times 10^{-8})^3$
2.7×10^{-23}

33. $(3.6 \times 10^5)^2$
1.296×10^{11}

34. $(9.3 \times 10^{-6})^{-2}$
1.16×10^{10}

35. $(1.7 \times 10^{-8})^3$
4.913×10^{-29}

36. $(6.24 \times 10^{13})^3$
2.4297×10^{41}

37. The radius of a cylinder is 5.4×10^6 cm. The height of the cylinder is 2.5×10^3 cm. What is the volume of the cylinder? (Hint: $V = \pi r^2 h$)
$2.28906 \times 10^{11} \text{ cm}^3$

38. The side length of a square is 9.6×10^5 in. What is the area of the square?
$9.216 \times 10^{13} \text{ in}^2$

39. The side length of a cube is 3.78×10^3 ft. What is the volume of the cube?
$5.401 \times 10^{10} \text{ ft}^3$

Practice and Problem Solving WKBK/ All-in-One Resources/Online
Practice page 2

7-4 Practice *(continued)* — Form G
More Multiplication Properties of Exponents

Complete each equation.

40. $(p^4)^{\square} = p^8$
2

41. $(z^{\square})^6 = z^{-24}$
−4

42. $(t^{12})^{\square} = 1$
0

43. $(w^{\square})^3 = w^{-12}$
−4

44. $(n^{-8})^{\square} = n^8$
−1

45. $10(g^2)^{\square} = 10g^6$
3

46. $(3d^{\square})^3 = 27d^{-9}$
−3

47. $(6q^4)^{\square} = 36q^8$
2

48. $(x^4 y^3)^{\square} = \frac{1}{x^8 y^6}$
−2

49. **Writing** Is $(y^m)^n = (y^n)^m$ a true statement? Explain your reasoning.
yes; $(y^m)^n = (y^n)^m$ because $y^{mn} = y^{nm}$. The product $mn = nm$ because of the commutative property.

50. **Reasoning** What is the difference between $x^4 x^3$ and $(x^4)^3$? Justify your answer.
The product of x^4 and x^3 is $x^{4+3} = x^7$. The expression $(x^4)^3$ means x^4 times x^4 times x^4 or x^{12}, a product of three terms.

Simplify each expression.

51. $2^3(2m)^2$
$32 m^2$

52. $(68.68)^8(68.68)^{-8}$
1

53. $(d^8)^{-5} d^0$
$\frac{1}{d^{40}}$

54. $(-7p)^3 + 7p^3$
$-336p^3$

55. $4a(0^8)b^4(-b)^{-7}$
0

56. $(10^{-5})^3(9.9 \times 10^{-12})^3$
9.801×10^{-98}

57. The volume of a circular cone can be determined by the formula $V = \frac{1}{3} 3.14 r^2 h$, where r is the radius of the base and h is the height of the cone. Find the volume of the cone shown at the right in terms of x.
$251.2x^6$

58. The volume of a sphere can be determined by the formula $V = \frac{4}{3} 3.14 r^3$, where r is the radius. Find the volume of the sphere shown at the right in terms of t.
$904.32t^4$

All-in-One Resources/Online
Enrichment

7-4 Enrichment
More Multiplication Properties of Exponents

In this lesson you learned that when you have a product raised to a power, each factor in the product must be raised to the power and the exponents get multiplied.

$$(2x^2 y^3)^4 = (2)^4 \cdot (x^2)^4 \cdot (y^3)^4$$
$$= 16x^8 y^{12}$$

In this activity we will investigate to see if the same rule holds true for the sum of two numbers that are raised to a power.

1. Do you think that the sum of two numbers raised to a power can be simplified by raising each addend to the power?
no; $(2 + 3)^2 = 25$; $2^2 + 3^2 = 13$

To investigate if the rule will work, look at an expression containing only numerals.

2. Simplify $(3 + 4)^2$ by adding the numbers in the parentheses and then squaring. 49

3. Now, square each number separately and then add. 25

4. Do your results in Exercises 2 and 3 match? no

To simplify an expression involving variables, you must use the distributive property twice. You distribute the first term and the second term throughout the second expression. For example,

$$(a + b)^2 = (a + b)(a + b) = a \cdot a + a \cdot b + b \cdot a + b \cdot b = a^2 + 2ab + b^2$$

Use a double distribution to simplify each expression.

5. $(x + 3)^2$
$x^2 + 6x + 9$

6. $(y + 1)^2$
$y^2 + 2y + 1$

7. $(a + 4)^2$
$a^2 + 8a + 16$

8. $(s - 5)^2$
$z^2 - 10z + 25$

9. $(t - 10)^2$
$t^2 - 20t + 100$

10. $(b - 2)^2$
$b^2 - 4b + 4$

Practice and Problem Solving WKBK/ All-in-One Resources/Online
Think About a Plan

7-4 Think About a Plan
More Multiplication Properties of Exponents

a. **Geography** Earth has a radius of 6.4×10^6 m. What is the approximate surface area of Earth? Use the formula for the surface area of a sphere, $S = 4\pi r^2$. Write your answer in scientific notation.
b. Oceans cover about 70% of the surface of the Earth. About how many square meters of Earth's surface are covered by ocean water?
c. The oceans have an average depth of 3790 m. Estimate the volume of water in Earth's oceans.

1. What can you substitute into the formula?
substitute 6.4×10^6 for r.

2. What numbers need to be squared?
$(6.4 \times 10^6)^2$ so 6.4 and 10^6 need to be squared

3. Calculate the surface area using 3.14 for π. Show your work. Write your answer in scientific notation.
$5.57056 \times 10^{14} \text{ m}^2$

4. For part b, set up a percent proportion with the appropriate units.
$\frac{w}{5.144576 \times 10^{14}} = \frac{70}{100}$

5. Solve your proportion. Show your work. Leave your answer in scientific notation.
$\frac{705.144576 \times 10^{14}}{10^2} = 3.6012032 \times 10^{12}$

6. Since you calculated the surface area of the ocean, how can you use your calculation to determine the volume of the water?
multiply the surface area by the average depth

7. Determine the volume. Show your work. Write your answer in scientific notation.
$1.949794304 \times 10^{18} \text{ m}^3$

Practice and Problem Solving WKBK/ All-in-One Resources/Online
Standardized Test Prep

7-4 Standardized Test Prep
More Multiplication Properties of Exponents

Gridded Response

Solve each exercise and enter your answer on the grid provided.

1. What is the simplified form of $(2 \times 10^2)^2$ in standard notation?
40,000; check students' grids

2. What is the simplified form of $(0.00038 \times 10^3)^2$ in standard notation?
0.1444; check students' grids

3. The side of a square measures $2x^2 y^3$. What is the area of the square if $x = -2$ and $y = 2$?
4096; check students' grids

4. The side of a square measures $3mn^2$. What is the area of the square if $m = 4$ and $n = -2$?
11,664; check students' grids

5. The radius of a circle is 0.00012×10^5 ft. What is the area of the circle? Use the formula $A = \pi r^2$.
452.16; check students' grids

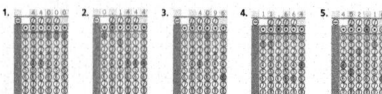

Online Teacher Resource Center
Activities, Games, and Puzzles

7-4 Activity: Playing with Properties
More Multiplication Properties of Exponents

You can raise a product ab to a power n by finding the product of the factors a and b each to the nth power, so that $(ab)^n = a^n b^n$.

Is there a rule, similar to the rule for finding a power of a product, for finding a power of a sum or difference? Work with a partner to find out. Your teacher may decide to have the entire class discuss some or all of the questions when everyone is finished.

Evaluate each pair of expressions.

$(5 + 2)^2 = $ 49 and $5^2 + 2^2 = $ 29 $(4 + 4)^2 = $ 64 and $4^2 + 4^2 = $ 32

$(2 + 3)^3 = $ 125 and $2^3 + 3^3 = $ 35 $(1 + 2)^4 = $ 81 and $1^4 + 2^4 = $ 17

Discuss whether the following statement is true: The nth power of a sum is the sum of the nth powers of the numbers.

In general, the nth power of a sum of numbers is not the sum of the nth powers of the numbers.

Give examples of two numbers a and b such that $(a + b)^2 = a^2 + b^2$ and explain why the equation is only true in those cases.

If a, b, or both a and b are 0, then the statement is true. For example, if $a = 3$ and $b = 0$, then $(3 + 0)^2 = 3^2 + 0^2$, because $(3 + 0)^2 = 3^2 + 9$ and $3^2 + 0^2 = 9$.

You can extend the Power of a Product Property correctly to products that involve three factors, a, b, and c. Complete the reasoning for each step below to write a rule for $(abc)^n$.

$(abc)^n = ((ab)c)^n$ — Associative Property of Multiplication

$(abc)^n = (ab)^n c^n$ — Power of a Product Property

$(abc)^n = a^n b^n c^n$ — Power of a Product Property

Explain how to find the product $(3 \times 2 \times 5)^2$ without multiplying the factors in the base.
Square each of 3, 2, and 5. Then find the product of the squares. $9 \times 4 \times 25 = 900$

Explain how to find the value of $((2^3)^2)^2$.
Use the Power of a Power Property twice. $(2^{3 \times 2})^2 = 2^{3 \times 2 \times 2} = 2^{12}$

Explain in words how to evaluate $((x^a)^b)^c$.
Write the base x and use the product abc as a single exponent.

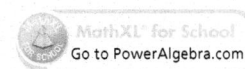

MathXL for School
Go to PowerAlgebra.com

Do you know HOW?

Simplify each expression.

1. $5^{-1}(3^{-2})$

2. $(r^{-5})^{-4}$

3. $(2x^5)(3x^{12})$

4. $\dfrac{mn^{-4}}{p^0 q^{-2}}$

5. $a^2 b^0 (a^{-3})$

6. $(3^2)^{-1}(4m^2)^3$

7. $(2m^3)^0 (3m^6)^{-1}$

8. $(3t^2)^3 (2t^0)^{-3}$

Write each number in scientific notation.

9. 48,030,000,000

10. 0.0042

11. 0.0000312

12. 76 million

Write each number in standard notation.

13. 8.3×10^9

14. 6.12×10^3

15. 1.2×10^{-4}

16. 4.326×10^{-1}

Simplify. Write each answer in scientific notation.

17. $0.5(8 \times 10^5)$

18. $(4 \times 10^7)(3 \times 10^{-1})$

19. $(6 \times 10^5)(1.2 \times 10^8)$

20. $(9 \times 10^{-3})^2$

21. **Astronomy** The radius of Mars is about 3.4×10^3 km.

   a. What is the approximate surface area of Mars? Use the formula for the surface area of a sphere, S.A. $= 4\pi r^2$. Write your answer in scientific notation.

   b. Write your answer from part (a) in standard form.

22. **Geometry** A box has a square bottom with sides of length $3x^2$ cm. The height of the box is $4xy$ cm. What is the volume of the box?

23. Evaluate $\frac{1}{2}a^{-4}b^2$ for $a = -2$ and $b = 4$.

Do you UNDERSTAND?

24. **Reasoning** A population of bacteria triples every week in a laboratory. The number of bacteria is modeled by the expression $900 \cdot 3^x$, where x is the number of weeks after a scientist measures the population size. When $x = -2$, what does the value of the expression represent?

25. Use the properties of exponents to explain whether each of the following expressions is equal to 64.

   a. $2^5 \cdot 2$ b. $2^2 \cdot 2^3$ c. $(2^2)(2^2)^2$

26. **Reasoning** Is the number 10^5 written in scientific notation? Explain.

27. **Writing** Is the following statement *always, sometimes,* or *never* true? Explain your choice.

   A number raised to a negative exponent is negative.

28. **Error Analysis** Identify and correct the error in the student's work below.

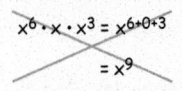

Answers

Mid-Chapter Quiz

1. $\frac{1}{45}$ 2. r^{20} 3. $6x^{17}$

4. $\frac{mq^2}{n^4}$ 5. $\frac{1}{a}$ 6. $\frac{64m^6}{9}$

7. $\frac{1}{3m^6}$ 8. $\frac{27t^6}{8}$

9. 4.803×10^{10} 10. 4.2×10^{-3}

11. 3.12×10^{-5} 12. 7.6×10^7

13. 8,300,000,000   14. 6120

15. 0.00012   16. 0.4326

17. 4×10^5 18. 1.2×10^7

19. 7.2×10^{13} 20. 8.1×10^{-5}

21. a. about 1.45×10^8 km²

   b. about 145,000,000 km²

22. $36x^5y$ cm³   23. $\frac{1}{2}$

24. the number of bacteria two weeks before the population was measured

25. a. yes; $2^5 = 2 \cdot 2 \cdot 2 \cdot 2 \cdot 2 = 32$ and $32 \cdot 2 = 64$

   b. no; $2^2 \cdot 2^3 = 2^{2+3} = 2^5 \neq 64$

   c. yes; $(2^2)(2^2)^2 = 2^2 \cdot 2^4 = 2^6 = 64$

26. No; a number written in scientific notation must have two factors.

27. Sometimes; a number raised to a negative exponent is negative only when a negative number is raised to an odd negative number. Sample: $(-3)^{-3} = \frac{1}{(-3)^3} = -\frac{1}{27}$. Otherwise, it will be positive. Sample: $(-3)^{-2} = \frac{1}{(-3)^2} = \frac{1}{9}$

28. When there is no exponent written, it is raised to the first power, not the 0 power. So $x^6 \cdot x \cdot x^3 = x^{6+1+3} = x^{10}$.

1 Interactive Learning

Solve It!

PURPOSE To present a problem that can be modeled by the power of a quotient

PROCESS Students may pick values for the dimensions of the wood block. Students may write an algebraic expression for the volume of the block and the dowel, and use the expressions to answer the question.

FACILITATE

Q How can the expression representing the volume of the wooden dowel be written without parentheses? $\left[\frac{x^2\pi\ell}{4}\right]$

Q What expression represents the volume of the wood that is removed? $\left[\left(1 - \frac{\pi}{4}\right)x^2\ell\right]$

Q Does the percent of wood remaining depend on the dimensions of the original piece of wood? Explain. **[No; the ratio of the amount of wood used for the dowel and the amount of original wood is constant.]**

ANSWER See Solve It in Answers on next page.
CONNECT THE MATH As students write the numerator and denominator as repeated multiplication, terms will be able to be divided out as factors of one, which is the foundation of the Property of Dividing Powers with the Same Base.

2 Guided Instruction

Take Note

Q How can this property be used to show that $x^0 = 1$? **[Applying the property to an expression like $\frac{x^4}{x^4}$ gives $x^{4-4} = x^0 = 1$.]**

7-5 Division Properties of Exponents

Objectives To divide powers with the same base
To raise a quotient to a power

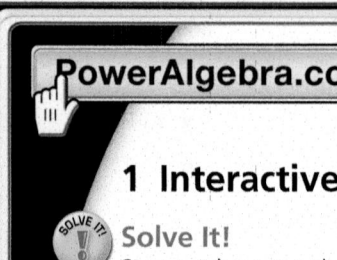

SOLVE IT! Getting Ready!

A machine makes wooden dowels by removing material from a block of wood as shown in the diagram. What percent of the wood does the machine remove from the original piece of wood to form the dowel? Explain how you found your answer. (Hint: What is the volume of the dowel?)

To review percents, go to Lesson 2-9.

Dynamic Activity
Dividing Exponential Expressions

In the Solve It, the expression for the volume of the dowel involves a quotient raised to a power.

Essential Understanding You can use properties of exponents to divide powers with the same base.

You can use repeated multiplication to simplify quotients of powers with the same base. Expand the numerator and the denominator. Then divide out the common factors.

$$\frac{4^5}{4^3} = \frac{4 \cdot 4 \cdot 4 \cdot 4 \cdot 4}{4 \cdot 4 \cdot 4} = 4^2$$

This example illustrates the following property of exponents.

take note

Property   Dividing Powers With the Same Base

Words	To divide powers with the same base, subtract the exponents.
Algebra	$\frac{a^m}{a^n} = a^{m-n}$, where $a \neq 0$ and m and n are integers
Examples	$\frac{2^6}{2^2} = 2^{6-2} = 2^4$ $\frac{x^4}{x^7} = x^{4-7} = x^{-3} = \frac{1}{x^3}$

7-5 Preparing to Teach

BIG idea Properties   **UbD**

ESSENTIAL UNDERSTANDINGS
- Properties of exponents can be used to divide powers with the same base.
- To divide powers with the same base, subtract the exponents.
- To raise a quotient to a power, raise the numerator and the denominator to the power and simplify.

Math Background

How can the division properties of exponents be used to reinforce student understanding of negative and zero exponents? Students know that a number divided by itself has a quotient of 1, and thus can see that an expression such as $\frac{x^4}{x^4}$ is equal to 1. Applying the Dividing Powers With the Same Base Property to $\frac{x^4}{x^4}$ will result in a simplified expression of x^0. Thus, x^0 must equal 1. Further, a problem such as $\frac{x^3}{x^7}$ can be used to show that

x^{-4} is equal to $\frac{1}{x^4}$. If $\frac{x^3}{x^7}$ is written using repeated multiplication, students can see that the expression reduces to $\frac{1}{x^4}$. Applying the Dividing Powers With the Same Base Property to $\frac{x^3}{x^7}$ will result in a simplified expression of x^{-4}. Thus, $x^{-4} = \frac{1}{x^4}$.

Support Student Learning
Use the **Algebra 1 Companion** to engage and support students during instructions. See Lesson Resources at the end of this lesson for details.

PowerAlgebra.com

1 Interactive Learning

Solve It!
Step out how to solve the Problem with helpful hints and an online question. Other questions are listed above in Interactive Learning.

Dynamic Activity This activity involves selecting the appropriate solution steps for dividing an exponential function. When students choose the correct step, it appears immediately on the screen.

Think

How are the properties for dividing powers and multiplying powers similar?

For both properties, the bases of the powers must be the same. Dividing a power is the same as multiplying by a negative exponent.

 Problem 1 Dividing Algebraic Expressions

What is the simplified form of each expression?

A $\dfrac{x^8}{x^3}$

$\dfrac{x^8}{x^3} = x^{8-3}$ Subtract exponents when dividing powers with the same base.

$= x^5$ Simplify.

B $\dfrac{m^2 n^4}{m^5 n^3}$

$\dfrac{m^2 n^4}{m^5 n^3} = m^{2-5} n^{4-3}$ Subtract exponents when dividing powers with the same base.

$= m^{-3} n^1$ Simplify the exponents.

$= \dfrac{n}{m^3}$ Rewrite using positive exponents.

 Got It? **1.** What is the simplified form of each expression?

a. $\dfrac{y^5}{y^4}$ **b.** $\dfrac{d^3}{d^9}$ **c.** $\dfrac{k^6 j^2}{k j^5}$ **d.** $\dfrac{a^{-3} b^7}{a^5 b^2}$ **e.** $\dfrac{x^4 y^{-1} z^8}{x^4 y^{-5} z}$

You can use the property of dividing powers with the same base to divide numbers in scientific notation.

 Problem 2 Dividing Numbers in Scientific Notation

Demographics Population density describes the number of people per unit area. During one year, the population of Angola was 1.21×10^7 people. The area of Angola is 4.81×10^5 mi². What was the population density of Angola that year?

Know	Need	Plan
• The population • The area	The population density	Write the ratio of population to area.

$\dfrac{1.21 \times 10^7}{4.81 \times 10^5} = \dfrac{1.21}{4.81} \times 10^{7-5}$ Subtract exponents when dividing powers with the same base.

$= \dfrac{1.21}{4.81} \times 10^2$ Simplify the exponent.

$\approx 0.252 \times 10^2$ Divide. Round to the nearest thousandth.

$= 25.2$ Write in standard notation.

The population density of Angola was about 25.2 people per square mile.

 Got It? **2.** During one year, Honduras had a population of 7.33×10^6 people. The area of Honduras is 4.33×10^4 mi². What was the population density of Honduras that year?

Problem 1

Q How can the expression in 1A be written as a product rather than a quotient? [$x^8 \cdot x^{-3}$]

Q Does using the Multiplying Powers With the Same Base Property yield the same simplified form? Explain. [yes; since $8 - 3$ is the same as $8 + (-3)$]

Got It?

If students have difficulty with the negative exponents in 1c and 1d, suggest that they rewrite the expressions using only positive exponents prior to finding the simplified form.

Problem 2

Q Which number is greater: 1.21×10^7 or 4.81×10^5? What impact does that have on the quotient? [1.21×10^7 is greater, which indicates the quotient will be a number greater than 1.]

Q Why is the final answer written in standard notation rather than scientific notation? [The final answer is neither a very large nor a very small number.]

Got It?   SYNTHESIZING

Show students two alternate methods for solving this problem.

Method 1: $7,330,000 \div 43,300 \approx 169$

Method 2:

$\dfrac{7.33 \cdot 10 \cdot 10 \cdot 10 \cdot 10 \cdot 10 \cdot 10}{4.33 \cdot 10 \cdot 10 \cdot 10 \cdot 10} \approx 169$

---

2 Guided Instruction

Each Problem is worked out and supported online.

Problem 1
Dividing Algebraic Expressions

Problem 2
Dividing Numbers in Scientific Notation
        Animated

Problem 3
Raising a Quotient to a Power

Problem 4
Simplifying an Exponential Expression
        Animated

Alternative Problem 4
Simplifying an Exponential Expression
        Animated

Support in Algebra 1 Companion
• Vocabulary
• Key Concepts
• Got It?

Answers

Solve It!

about 21.46% of the wood removed

Got It?

1. a. y **b.** $\dfrac{1}{d^6}$ **c.** $\dfrac{k^5}{j^3}$

    d. $\dfrac{b^5}{a^8}$ **e.** $y^4 z^7$

2. about 169 people per mi²

Take Note

Ask students to compare and contrast the Power of a Quotient Property with the Power of a Product Property.

Problem 3

Q What other property must be used to simplify the numerator in this expression? **[Power of a Power]**

Q If a student gives an answer of "B," what mistake did they likely make? **[The student likely found the product of 5 and 3 rather than raising 5 to the exponent 3.]**

Got It?

Q What is the benefit of applying the Dividing Powers With the Same Base Property before the Power of a Quotient Property? **[Answers may vary. Sample: Subtracting the exponents first gives you less cumbersome numbers to multiply.]**

You can use repeated multiplication to simplify a quotient raised to a power.

$$\left(\frac{x}{y}\right)^3 = \frac{x}{y} \cdot \frac{x}{y} \cdot \frac{x}{y} = \frac{x \cdot x \cdot x}{y \cdot y \cdot y} = \frac{x^3}{y^3}$$

This illustrates another property of exponents.

take note

Property	**Raising a Quotient to a Power**
Words	To raise a quotient to a power, raise the numerator and the denominator to the power and simplify.
Algebra	$\left(\frac{a}{b}\right)^n = \frac{a^n}{b^n}$, where $a \neq 0$, $b \neq 0$, and n is an integer
Examples	$\left(\frac{3}{5}\right)^3 = \frac{3^3}{5^3} = \frac{27}{125}$ $\qquad$ $\left(\frac{x}{y}\right)^5 = \frac{x^5}{y^5}$

Problem 3 **Raising a Quotient to a Power**

Multiple Choice What is the simplified form of $\left(\frac{z^4}{5}\right)^3$?

Ⓐ $\frac{z^7}{15}$ $\qquad$ Ⓑ $\frac{z^{12}}{15}$ $\qquad$ Ⓒ $\frac{z^7}{125}$ $\qquad$ Ⓓ $\frac{z^{12}}{125}$

Think

How can you check your answer?
Substitute the same number for the variable in the original expression and the simplified expression. The expressions should be equal.

$\left(\frac{z^4}{5}\right)^3 = \frac{(z^4)^3}{5^3}$ $\qquad$ Raise the numerator and the denominator to the third power.

$= \frac{z^{4 \cdot 3}}{5^3}$ $\qquad$ Multiply the exponents in the numerator.

$= \frac{z^{12}}{125}$ $\qquad$ Simplify.

The correct answer is D.

✓ **Got It?** **3. a.** What is the simplified form of $\left(\frac{4}{x^3}\right)^2$?

b. Reasoning Describe two different ways to simplify the expression $\left(\frac{a^7}{a^5}\right)^3$. Which method do you prefer? Explain.

You can write an expression of the form $\left(\frac{a}{b}\right)^{-n}$ using positive exponents.

$\left(\frac{a}{b}\right)^{-n} = \frac{1}{\left(\frac{a}{b}\right)^n}$ $\qquad$ Use the definition of negative exponent.

$= \frac{1}{\left(\frac{a^n}{b^n}\right)}$ $\qquad$ Raise the quotient to a power.

$= 1 \cdot \frac{b^n}{a^n}$ $\qquad$ Multiply by the reciprocal of $\frac{a^n}{b^n}$ which is $\frac{b^n}{a^n}$.

$= \frac{b^n}{a^n} = \left(\frac{b}{a}\right)^n$ $\qquad$ Simplify. Write the quotient using one exponent.

So, $\left(\frac{a}{b}\right)^{-n} = \left(\frac{b}{a}\right)^n$ for all nonzero numbers a and b and positive integers n.

Additional Problems

1. What is the simplified form of each expression?

a. $\frac{c^{12}}{c^9}$

b. $\frac{a^4 b^8}{a^6 b^3}$

ANSWER a. c^3 $\qquad$ **b.** $\frac{b^5}{a^2}$

2. The population of Pennsylvania is about 1.24×10^7. The population of North Dakota is about 6.4×10^5. About how many times greater is the population of Pennsylvania than North Dakota?

ANSWER about 19 times greater

3. What is the simplified form of $\left(\frac{w^5}{4}\right)^3$?

a. $\frac{w^{15}}{64}$ $\qquad$ **b.** $\frac{w^8}{64}$

c. $\frac{w^8}{4}$ $\qquad$ **d.** $\frac{w^{15}}{4}$

ANSWER a

4. What is the simplified form of $\left(\frac{3c^3}{d^2}\right)^{-4}$?

ANSWER $\frac{d^8}{81c^{12}}$

Answers

Got It?

3. a. $\frac{16}{x^6}$

b. Answers may vary. Sample: You can simplify within the parentheses first to give you $(a^2)^3 = a^6$ or you can raise the quotient to a power first, $\left(\frac{a^{21}}{a^{15}}\right) = a^6$.

 **Problem 4** Simplifying an Exponential Expression

What is the simplified form of $\left(\frac{2x^6}{y^4}\right)^{-3}$?

$$\left(\frac{2x^6}{y^4}\right)^{-3} = \left(\frac{y^4}{2x^6}\right)^3 \quad \text{Rewrite using the reciprocal of } \frac{2x^6}{y^4}.$$

$$= \frac{(y^4)^3}{(2x^6)^3} \quad \text{Raise the numerator and denominator to the third power.}$$

$$= \frac{y^{12}}{8x^{18}} \quad \text{Simplify.}$$

 Plan

How do you write an expression in simplified form?
Use the properties of exponents to write each variable with a single positive exponent.

Got It? 4. What is the simplified form of $\left(\frac{a}{5b}\right)^{-2}$?

Lesson Check

Do you know HOW?

Simplify each expression.

1. $\frac{y^3}{y^{10}}$

2. $\left(\frac{x^4}{3}\right)^3$

3. $\left(\frac{m}{n}\right)^{-3}$

4. $\left(\frac{3x^2}{5y^4}\right)^{-4}$

5. A large cube is made up of many small cubes. The volume of the large cube is 7.506×10^5 mm^3. The volume of each small cube is 2.78×10^4 mm^3. How many small cubes make up the large cube?

Do you UNDERSTAND?

6. **Vocabulary** How is the property for raising a quotient to a power similar to the property for raising a product to a power?

7. **a. Reasoning** Ross simplifies $\frac{a^3}{a^7}$ as shown at the right. Explain why Ross's method works.

$$\frac{a^3}{a^7} = \frac{1}{a^{7-3}} = \frac{1}{a^4}$$

  b. Open-Ended Write a quotient of powers and use Ross's method to simplify it.

Practice and Problem-Solving Exercises

A Practice   Copy and complete each equation.   **See Problem 1.**

8. $\frac{5^9}{5^2} = 5^{\blacksquare}$

9. $\frac{2^4}{2^3} = 2^{\blacksquare}$

10. $\frac{3^2}{3^5} = 3^{\blacksquare}$

11. $\frac{5^2 5^3}{5^3 5^2} = 5^{\blacksquare}$

Simplify each expression.

12. $\frac{3^8}{3^6}$

13. $\frac{3^6}{3^8}$

14. $\frac{d^{14}}{d^{17}}$

15. $\frac{n^{-1}}{n^{-4}}$

16. $\frac{5s^{-7}}{10s^{-9}}$

17. $\frac{x^{11}y^3}{x^{11}y}$

18. $\frac{c^3 d^{-5}}{c^4 d^{-1}}$

19. $\frac{10m^6n^3}{5m^2n^7}$

20. $\frac{m^3n^2}{m^{-1}n^3}$

21. $\frac{3^2 m^5 t^6}{3^5 m^7 t^{-5}}$

22. $\frac{x^5 y^{-8} z^3}{xy^{-4}z^3}$

23. $\frac{12a^{-1}b^6c^{-3}}{4a^5 b^{-1}c^5}$

Lesson 7-5   443

Problem 4

Q Would you have the same simplified form of the expression had you first applied the Power of a Quotient Property? Explain. **[yes; as long as the properties are all applied correctly and the order of operations is followed]**

Got It?

Q How would you explain to another student the process of simplifying this expression? **[Answers will vary. Sample: Square the reciprocal of the original expression.]**

3 Lesson Check

Do you know HOW?
• If students have difficulty with Exercise 4, then have them review Problem 4.

Do you UNDERSTAND?
• If students have difficulty with Exercise 7, then have them review the property for dividing powers with the same base.

Close

Q If you could not remember the property for the power of a quotient, how could you find the simplified form? **[Use repeated multiplication to rewrite the expression, and then simplify.]**

Got It? (continued)

4. $\frac{25b^2}{a^2}$

Lesson Check

1. $\frac{1}{y^7}$

2. $\frac{x^{12}}{27}$

3. $\frac{n^3}{m^3}$

4. $\frac{625y^{16}}{81x^8}$ 5. 27 cubes

6. In raising a quotient to a power, the exponent goes to all the factors of both the numerator and the denominator and in raising a product to a power, the exponent goes to all the factors.

7. **a.** Answers may vary. Sample: a^3 can be rewritten as $\frac{1}{a^{-3}}$, so $\frac{a^3}{a^7} = \frac{1}{a^7} \cdot \frac{1}{a^{-3}}$.

  b. Check students' work.

Practice and Problem-Solving Exercises

8. 7

9. 1

10. −3

11. 0

12. 9

13. $\frac{1}{9}$

14. $\frac{1}{d^3}$

15. n^3

16. $\frac{s^2}{2}$

17. y^2

18. $\frac{1}{cd^4}$

19. $\frac{2m^4}{n^4}$

20. $\frac{m^4}{n}$

21. $\frac{t^{11}}{27m^2}$

22. $\frac{x^4}{y^4}$

23. $\frac{3b^7}{a^6 c^8}$

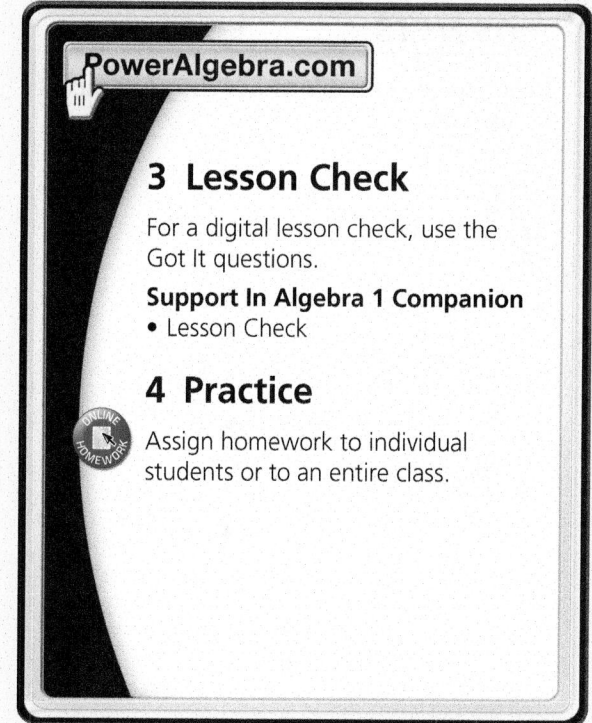

PowerAlgebra.com

3 Lesson Check

For a digital lesson check, use the Got It questions.

Support In Algebra 1 Companion
• Lesson Check

4 Practice

Assign homework to individual students or to an entire class.

4 Practice

ASSIGNMENT GUIDE

Basic: 8–48 all, 50–54 even, 60–72 even, 78–80 all, 84, 86

Average: 9–47 odd, 49–87

Advanced: 9–47 odd, 49–93

Standardized Test Prep: 94–97

Mixed Review: 98–110

Reasoning exercises have blue headings.

Applications exercises have red headings.

EXERCISE 79: Use the Think About a Plan worksheet in the Practice and Problem Solving Workbook (also available in the Teaching Resources in print and online) to further support students' development in becoming independent learners.

HOMEWORK QUICK CHECK

To check students' understanding of key skills and concepts, go over Exercises 21, 25, 54, 79, and 80.

Simplify each quotient. Write each answer in scientific notation. 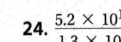 **See Problem 2.**

24. $\dfrac{5.2 \times 10^{13}}{1.3 \times 10^7}$

25. $\dfrac{3.6 \times 10^{-10}}{9 \times 10^{-6}}$

26. $\dfrac{6.5 \times 10^4}{5 \times 10^6}$

27. $\dfrac{8.4 \times 10^{-5}}{2 \times 10^{-8}}$

28. $\dfrac{4.65 \times 10^{-4}}{3.1 \times 10^2}$

29. $\dfrac{3.5 \times 10^6}{5 \times 10^8}$

30. **Computers** The average time it takes a computer to execute one instruction is measured in picoseconds. There are 3.6×10^{15} picoseconds per hour. What fraction of a second is a picosecond?

31. **Wildlife** Data from a deer count in a forested area show that an estimated 3.16×10^3 deer inhabit 7.228×10^4 acres of land. What is the density of the deer population?

32. **Astronomy** The sun's mass is 1.998×10^{30} kg. Saturn's mass is 5.69×10^{26} kg. How many times as great as the mass of Saturn is the mass of the sun?

Simplify each expression. **See Problems 3 and 4.**

33. $\left(\dfrac{3}{8}\right)^2$

34. $\left(\dfrac{1}{a}\right)^3$

35. $\left(\dfrac{3x}{y}\right)^4$

36. $\left(\dfrac{2x}{3y}\right)^5$

37. $\left(\dfrac{6}{5^2}\right)^3$

38. $\left(\dfrac{2^2}{2^3}\right)^5$

39. $\left(\dfrac{8}{n^5}\right)^6$

40. $\left(\dfrac{2p}{9}\right)^3$

41. $\left(\dfrac{2}{5}\right)^{-1}$

42. $\left(\dfrac{5}{4}\right)^{-4}$

43. $\left(-\dfrac{7x^5}{5y^4}\right)^{-2}$

44. $\left(-\dfrac{2x^3}{3y^4}\right)^{-3}$

45. $\left(\dfrac{3x^3}{15}\right)^2$

46. $\left(\dfrac{6n^2}{3n}\right)^{-3}$

47. $\left(\dfrac{b^4}{b^7}\right)^{-5}$

48. $\left(\dfrac{3}{5c^2}\right)^0$

Ⓑ Apply **Explain why each expression is *not* in simplest form.**

49. $5^3 m^3$

50. $x^5 y^{-2}$

51. $(2c)^4$

52. $x^0 y$

53. $\dfrac{d^7}{d}$

54. **Think About a Plan** During one year, about 163 million adults over 18 years old in the United States spent a total of about 93 billion hours online at home. On average, how many hours per day did each adult spend online at home?
- How do you write each number in scientific notation?
- How do you convert the units to hours per day?

55. **Television** During one year, people in the United States older than 18 years old watched a total of 342 billion hours of television. The population of the United States older than 18 years old was about 209 million people.
   a. On average, how many hours of television did each person older than 18 years old watch that year? Round to the nearest hour.
   b. On average, how many hours per week did each person older than 18 years old watch that year? Round to the nearest hour.

Which property or properties of exponents would you use to simplify each expression?

56. 2^{-3}

57. $\dfrac{2^2}{2^5}$

58. $\dfrac{1}{2^{-4} 2^7}$

59. $\dfrac{(2^4)^3}{2^{15}}$

Answers

Practice and Problem-Solving Exercises
(continued)

24. 4×10^6

25. 4×10^{-5}

26. 1.3×10^{-2}

27. 4.2×10^3

28. 1.5×10^{-6}

29. 7×10^{-3}

30. 1×10^{-12} s

31. about 4.4×10^{-2} deer per acre

32. about 3511 times as great

33. $\dfrac{9}{64}$

34. $\dfrac{1}{a^3}$

35. $\dfrac{81x^4}{y^4}$

36. $\dfrac{32x^5}{243y^5}$

37. $\dfrac{216}{15,625}$

38. $\dfrac{1}{32}$

39. $\dfrac{262,144}{n^{30}}$

40. $\dfrac{8p^3}{729}$

41. $\dfrac{5}{2}$

42. $\dfrac{256}{625}$

43. $\dfrac{25y^8}{49x^{10}}$

44. $-\dfrac{27y^{12}}{8x^9}$

45. $\dfrac{x^6}{25}$

46. $\dfrac{1}{8n^3}$

47. b^{15}

48. 1

49. 5^3 should be 125.

50. y^{-2} contains a negative exponent.

51. Each factor should be raised to the fourth power and simplified.

52. x^0 needs to be simplified to 1.

53. The base d should appear only once.

54. about 1.6 hours per day

55. a. about 1636 h
   b. about 31 h

56. definition of negative exponent

57. dividing powers with the same base, definition of negative exponent

58. multiply powers with the same base

59. raising a power to a power, dividing powers with the same base, definition of negative exponent

Simplify each expression.

60. $\dfrac{3n^2(5^0)}{2n^3}$ **61.** $\left(\dfrac{2m^4}{m^2}\right)^{-4}$ **62.** $\dfrac{3x^3}{(3x)^3}$ **63.** $\dfrac{(2a^6)(4a)}{8a^3}$

64. $\left(\dfrac{9t^2}{36t}\right)^3$ **65.** $\left(\dfrac{a^4a}{a^2}\right)^{-3}$ **66.** $\left(\dfrac{2x^2}{5x^3}\right)^{-2}$ **67.** $\dfrac{4x^{-2}y^4}{8x^3(y^{-2})^3}$

68. a. Open-Ended Write three numbers greater than 1000 in scientific notation.
  b. Divide each number by 2.
  c. Reasoning Is the exponent of the power of 10 divided by 2 when you divide a number in scientific notation by 2? Explain.

69. Simplify the expression $\left(\dfrac{3}{x^2}\right)^{-3}$ in three different ways. Justify each step.

70. Geometry The area of the rectangle is $72a^3b^4$. What is the length of the rectangle?

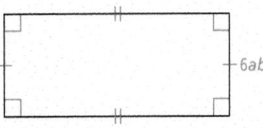

  Ⓐ $\dfrac{a^3b^4}{12}$ Ⓒ $\dfrac{12}{a^3b^4}$
  Ⓑ $12a^2b^3$ Ⓓ $12a^3b^4$

Simplify each expression.

71. $\left(\dfrac{3xy^5}{x^4y}\right)^{-2}$ **72.** $\dfrac{m^4n^3p^{-3}}{m^{-2}n^7p^{-8}}$ **73.** $\dfrac{\left(\frac{1}{4}\right)^{-2}}{\left(\frac{1}{6}\right)^{-3}}$ **74.** $\dfrac{0.2^3 \cdot 0.2^4}{0.2^7}$

75. $\left(\dfrac{a^{-1}b^3c}{a^2b^4}\right)^6$ **76.** $\left(\dfrac{(-4)^2}{(-3)^{-3}}\right)^2$ **77.** $\left(\dfrac{(4x)^2y}{xy^4}\right)^{-2}$ **78.** $\dfrac{(6a^3)(8b^4)}{(2a^4)(36b^{-1})}$

79. Physics The wavelength of a radio wave is defined as speed divided by frequency. An FM radio station has a frequency of 9×10^7 waves per second. The speed of the waves is about 3×10^8 meters per second. What is the wavelength of the station?

80. a. Error Analysis What mistake did the student make in simplifying the expression at the right?
  b. What is the correct simplified form of the expression?

81. Writing Suppose $\dfrac{a^x}{a^y} = a^3$ and $\dfrac{a^x}{a^{3y}} = a^{-5}$. Find the values of x and y. Explain how you found your answer.

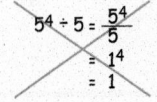

82. a. Finance In 2000, the United States government owed about $5.63 trillion to its creditors. The population of the United States was 282.4 million people. How much did the government owe per person in 2000? Round to the nearest dollar.
  b. In 2005, the debt had grown to $7.91 trillion, with a population of 296.9 million. How much did the government owe per person? Round to the nearest dollar.
  c. What was the percent increase in the average amount owed per person from 2000 to 2005?

Write each expression with only one exponent. You may need to use parentheses.

83. $\dfrac{m^7}{n^7}$ **84.** $\dfrac{10^7 \cdot 10^0}{10^{-3}}$ **85.** $\dfrac{27x^3}{8y^3}$ **86.** $\dfrac{4m^2}{169m^4}$

82. a. about $19,936
  b. about $26,642
  c. about 33.6%

83. $\left(\dfrac{m}{n}\right)^7$ **84.** 10^{10}

85. $\left(\dfrac{3x}{2y}\right)^3$ **86.** $\left(\dfrac{2}{13m}\right)^2$

60. $\dfrac{3}{2n}$ **61.** $\dfrac{1}{16m^8}$ **62.** $\dfrac{1}{9}$ **63.** a^4

64. $\dfrac{t^3}{64}$ **65.** $\dfrac{1}{a^9}$ **66.** $\dfrac{25x^2}{4}$ **67.** $\dfrac{y^{10}}{2x^5}$

68. a.–b. Check students' work.
  c. No; the factor a is divided by 2. The power will remain the same or be one less.

69. Answers may vary. Samples are given.

I. $\left(\dfrac{3}{x^2}\right)^{-3} = \left(\dfrac{x^2}{3}\right)^3$ Rewrite using the reciprocal.
  $= \dfrac{(x^2)^3}{3^3}$ Raise the numerator and denominator to the third power.
  $= \dfrac{x^6}{27}$ Simplify.

II. $\left(\dfrac{3}{x^2}\right)^{-3} = \dfrac{3^{-3}}{(x^2)^{-3}}$ Raise the quotient to a power rule.
  $= \dfrac{3^{-3}}{x^{-6}}$ Power to a power rule
  $= \dfrac{x^6}{3^3}$ Definition of negative exponent
  $= \dfrac{x^6}{27}$ Simplify.

III. $\left(\dfrac{3}{x^2}\right)^{-3} = \left(\dfrac{x^2}{3}\right)^3$ Rewrite using the reciprocal.
  $= \dfrac{x^2}{3} \cdot \dfrac{x^2}{3} \cdot \dfrac{x^2}{3}$ Definition of an exponent
  $= \dfrac{x^6}{27}$ Simplify.

70. B **71.** $\dfrac{x^6}{9y^8}$ **72.** $\dfrac{m^6p^5}{n^4}$

73. $\dfrac{2}{27}$ **74.** 1 **75.** $\dfrac{c^6}{a^{18}b^6}$

76. 186,624 **77.** $\dfrac{y^6}{256x^2}$ **78.** $\dfrac{2b^5}{3a}$

79. about $3\frac{1}{3}$ m

80. a. The student simplified the bases of 5 instead of subtracting the exponents.
  b. 125

81. $x = 7$ and $y = 4$; use the two given expressions to find the system of equations, $x - y = 3$ and $x - 3y = -5$. Solve the system to find the values of x and y.

Answers

Practice and Problem-Solving Exercises
(continued)

87. a. a^{-n}

   b. $\frac{1}{a^n}$

   c. Since $\frac{a^0}{a^n}$ equals both $\frac{1}{a^n}$ and a^{-n}, $\frac{1}{a^n} = a^{-n}$.
   This is the definition of a negative exponent.

88. $0^0 = 0^{n-n} = \frac{0^n}{0^n} = \frac{0}{0}$; any expression with a
zero in the denominator is undefined.

89. n^2 **90.** n^{4x} **91.** x^6

92. $\frac{1}{m^3}$ **93.** about 1.6×10^6 g/m^3

94. B   **95.** H   **96.** C

97. [2] The domain is $0 \leq b \leq 8$ because
you can use between 0 and 8 bags.
The range is $0 \leq A(b) \leq 9600$ because
$A(0) = 0$ and $A(8) = 9600$.

   [1] either domain or range is incorrect, or no
explanation

98. $\frac{8}{m^{21}}$ **99.** $\frac{2s^6}{27}$ **100.** $\frac{1}{64c^2}$

101. $9r^{10}$ **102.** n^{15}

103. $(0, 0)$;

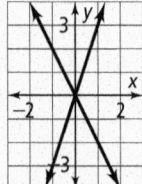

104. $(-4, -7)$;

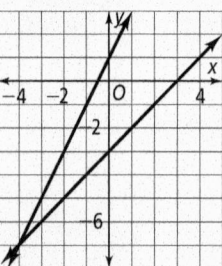

105. $(3, 5)$;

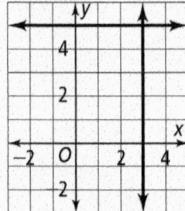

106. no solution;

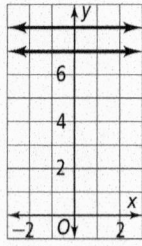

87. a. Use the property for dividing powers with the same base to write $\frac{a^0}{a^n}$ as a power of a.

   b. Use the definition of a zero exponent to simplify $\frac{a^0}{a^n}$.

   c. **Reasoning** Explain how your results from parts (a) and (b) justify the definition of a negative exponent.

 **Challenge** **88. Reasoning** Use the division property to show why 0^0 is undefined.

Simplify each expression.

89. $n^{x+2} \div n^x$ **90.** $n^{5x} \div n^x$ **91.** $\left(\frac{x^n}{x^{n-2}}\right)^3$ **92.** $\frac{\left(\frac{m^4}{m^5}\right)}{m^2}$

93. Astronomy The density of an object is the ratio of its mass to its volume. Neptune
has a mass of 1.02×10^{26} kg. The radius of Neptune is 2.48×10^4 km. What is the
density of Neptune in grams per cubic meter? (*Hint:* $V = \frac{4}{3}\pi r^3$)

Standardized Test Prep

SAT/ACT **94.** Which expression is equivalent to $\frac{(2x)^5}{x^3}$?

   Ⓐ $2x^2$ Ⓑ $32x^2$ Ⓒ $2x^8$ Ⓓ $32x^{-2}$

95. Which equation is an equation of the line that contains the point $(8, -3)$ and is
perpendicular to the line $y = -4x + 5$?

   Ⓕ $y = -\frac{1}{4}x - 1$ Ⓖ $y = \frac{1}{4}x + \frac{35}{4}$ Ⓗ $y = \frac{1}{4}x - 5$ Ⓘ $y = 4x - 35$

96. What is the solution of the system of equations $y = -3x + 5$ and $y = -4x - 1$?

   Ⓐ $(23, 6)$ Ⓑ $(6, 23)$ Ⓒ $(-6, 23)$ Ⓓ $(-6, -23)$

Short Response **97.** You have 8 bags of grass seed. Each bag covers 1200 ft^2 of ground. The function
$A(b) = 1200b$ represents the area $A(b)$, in square feet, that b bags cover. What
domain and range are reasonable for the function? Explain.

Mixed Review

Simplify each expression.   ◀ **See Lesson 7-4.**

98. $(2m^{-7})^3$ **99.** $2(3s^{-2})^{-3}$ **100.** $(4^3c^2)^{-1}$ **101.** $(-3)^2(r^5)^2$ **102.** $(7^0n^{-3})^2(n^7)^3$

Solve each system by graphing.   ◀ **See Lesson 6-1.**

103. $y = 3x$ **104.** $y = 2x + 1$ **105.** $y = 5$ **106.** $y = 7$
     $y = -2x$ $y = x - 3$ $x = 3$ $y = 8$

Get Ready!   **To prepare for Lesson 7-6, do Exercises 107–110.**

Graph each function.   ◀ **See Lesson 4-4.**

107. $y = 4x$ **108.** $y = 5x$ **109.** $y = -3x$ **110.** $y = 1.5x$

107.

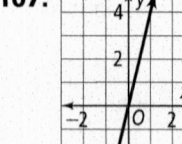

108.

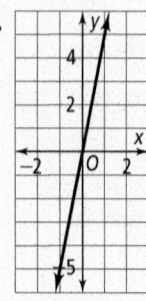

109.

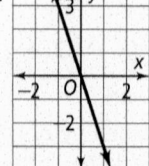

110.

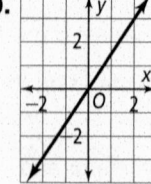

Lesson Resources

Additional Instructional Support

Algebra 1 Companion

Students can use the **Algebra 1 Companion** worktext (4 pages) as you teach the lesson. Use the Companion to support

- New Vocabulary
- Key Concepts
- Got It for each Problem
- Lesson Check

ELL Support

Focus on Language Have students write the division properties of exponents in their own words. Then provide expressions for students to write the steps to simplify. They can follow their written steps to simplify each expression.

5 Assess & Remediate

Lesson Quiz

1. What is the simplified form of $\frac{p^4}{p^6}$?

2. **Do you UNDERSTAND?** The mass of Earth is about 6×10^{24} kilograms. The mass of the moon is about 7.4×10^{22} kilograms. About how many times greater is Earth's mass than the mass of the moon?

3. What is the simplified form of $\left(\frac{t^2}{3}\right)^5$?

4. What is the simplified form of $\left(\frac{2b^4}{c^3}\right)^{-3}$?

ANSWERS TO LESSON QUIZ

1. $\frac{1}{p^2}$

2. about 81 times larger

3. $\frac{t^{10}}{243}$

4. $\frac{c^9}{8b^{12}}$

PRESCRIPTION FOR REMEDIATION
Use the student work on the Lesson Quiz to prescribe a differentiated review assignment.

Points	Differentiated Remediation
0–2	Intervention
3	On-level
4	Extension

PowerAlgebra.com

5 Assess & Remediate

Assign the Lesson Quiz. Appropriate intervention, practice, or enrichment is automatically generated based on student performance.

Intervention

- **Reteaching** (2 pages) Provides reteaching and practice exercises for the key lesson concepts. Use with struggling students or absent students.

- **English Language Learner Support** Helps students develop and reinforce mathematical vocabulary and key concepts.

All-in-One Resources/Online
Reteaching

All-in-One Resources/Online
English Language Learner Support

Differentiated Remediation *continued*

On-Level

- **Practice** (2 pages) Provides extra practice for each lesson. For simpler practice exercises, use the Form K Practice pages found in the All-in-One Teaching Resources and online.

- **Think About a Plan** Helps students develop specific problem-solving skills and strategies by providing scaffolded guiding questions.

- **Standardized Test Prep** Focuses on all major exercises, all major question types, and helps students prepare for the high-stakes assessments.

Extension

- **Enrichment** Provides students with interesting problems and activities that extend the concepts of the lesson.

- **Activities, Games, and Puzzles** Worksheets that can be used for concepts development, enrichment, and for fun!

Practice and Problem Solving WKBK/All-in-One Resources/Online
Practice page 1

Practice and Problem Solving WKBK/All-in-One Resources/Online
Practice page 2

All-in-One Resources/Online
Enrichment

Practice and Problem Solving WKBK/All-in-One Resources/Online
Think About a Plan

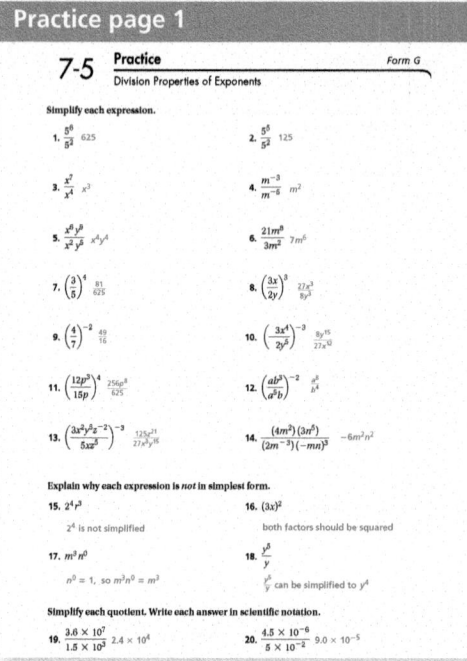

Practice and Problem Solving WKBK/All-in-One Resources/Online
Standardized Test Prep

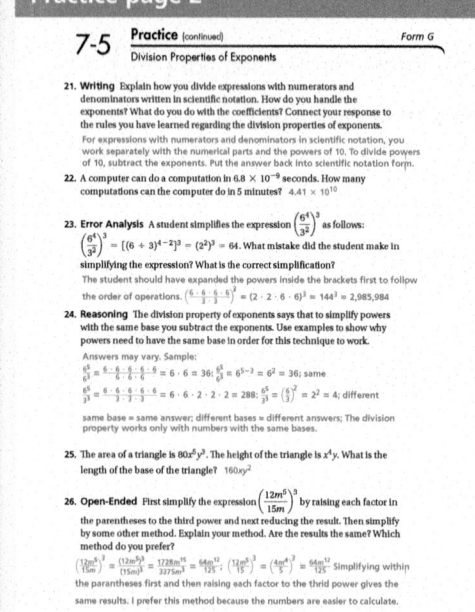

Online Teacher Resource Center
Activities, Games, and Puzzles

7-6 Exponential Functions

Objective To evaluate and graph exponential functions

Family feud! These functions don't belong in the same family of functions.

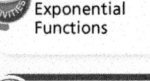
Dynamic Activity
Exponential Functions

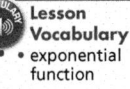
Lesson Vocabulary
• exponential function

Getting Ready!

Your soccer team wants to practice a drill for a certain amount of time each day. Which plan will give your team more total practice time over 4 days? Over 8 days? Explain your reasoning.

Plan 1
5 minutes today and then 1 minute more each day than the previous day

Plan 2
1 minute today and then twice as much time each day as the previous day

The two plans in the Solve It have different patterns of growth. You can model each type of growth with a different type of function.

Essential Understanding Some functions model an initial amount that is repeatedly multiplied by the same positive number. In the rules for these functions, the independent variable is an exponent.

take note

Key Concept   Exponential Function

Definition
An **exponential function** is a function of the form $y = a \cdot b^x$, where $a \neq 0$, $b > 0$, $b \neq 1$, and x is a real number.

Examples

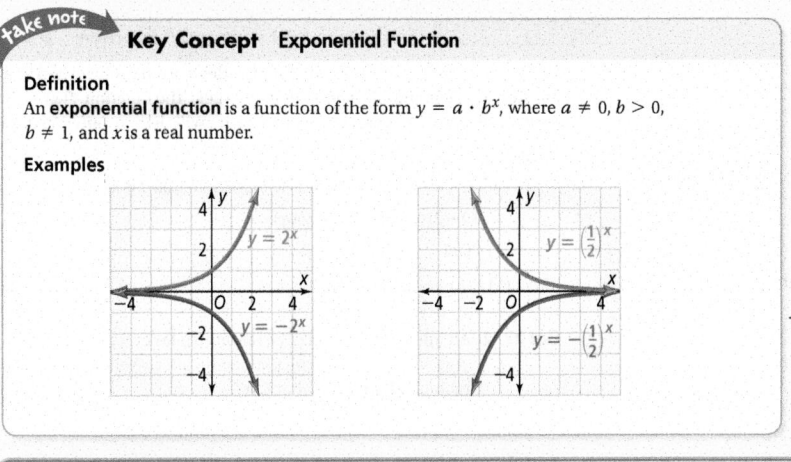

1 Interactive Learning

Solve It!
PURPOSE To present two sets of data to compare linear growth to exponential growth
PROCESS Students may create a chart to keep track of the day and the number of minutes of drill practice under each plan.

FACILITATE

Q As the days increase, what happens to the number of minutes according to Plan 1? **[The numbers of minutes increase by the same amount each day.]**

Q As the days increase, what happens to the number of minutes according to Plan 2? **[The numbers of minutes increase more and more each day.]**

Q If x represents the number of days following the plan, what expressions represent each plan? **[Plan 1: $x + 5$, Plan 2: $2^x + 1$]**

ANSWER See Solve It in Answers on next page.
CONNECT THE MATH Show graphs of Plan 1 and Plan 2. The graph showing Plan 1 is a linear relationship. The graph showing Plan 2 is an exponential relationship.

2 Guided Instruction

Take Note

Q How can you write the description of Plan 2 from the Solve It as an exponential function? What do x and y represent? **[$y = 1 \cdot 2^x$, where x is the number of days and y is the minutes practiced.]**

Q How can you use the placement of the independent variable to identify an exponential function? **[The independent variable must be an exponent in an exponential function.]**

7-6 Preparing to Teach

BIG idea Function
ESSENTIAL UNDERSTANDING

• Some functions model an initial amount that is repeatedly multiplied by the same positive number. In the rules for these functions, the independent variable is an exponent.

Math Background
As you review functions, have students recall that the graphs of linear functions are transformations of the parent function $y = x$. Quadratic functions are a group of functions that are transformations of the parent function $y = x^2$. Although linear functions and quadratic functions are different groups of functions and have different appearances, they share common characteristics of all functions; they model a relationship between an independent and dependent variable.

UbD Exponential functions are another group of functions that share the common characteristics of all functions, but have a different parent function and a different appearance. Exponential functions provide students a model for many real-world situations that they could not consider when situations are limited to linear and quadratic functions.

Support Student Learning
Use the **Algebra 1 Companion** to engage and support students during instructions. See Lesson Resources at the end of this lesson for details.

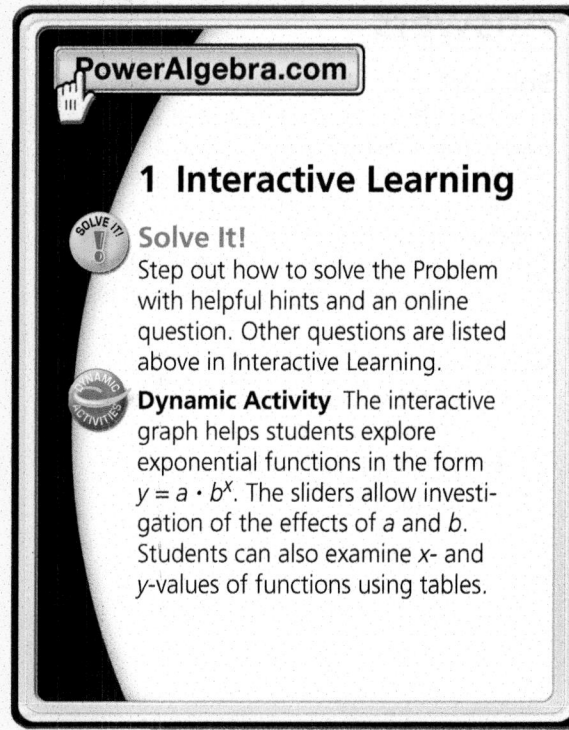

PowerAlgebra.com

1 Interactive Learning

Solve It!
Step out how to solve the Problem with helpful hints and an online question. Other questions are listed above in Interactive Learning.

Dynamic Activity The interactive graph helps students explore exponential functions in the form $y = a \cdot b^x$. The sliders allow investigation of the effects of a and b. Students can also examine x- and y-values of functions using tables.

Problem 1

> **Q** What is a pattern in the *x*-values in the table? **[Each *x*-value is the previous *x*-value plus 1.]**
>
> **Q** What is a pattern in the *y*-values in the table? **[Each *y*-value is the previous *y*-value multiplied by 3.]**

Got It?   SYNTHESIZING

If students are unsure if the equation in 1b represents an exponential function, have them make a table of values and examine it to decide whether the function is exponential.

Problem 2

> **Q** When simplifying the numerical expression $30 \cdot 2^8$, which operation is performed first? Why? **[The order of operations indicates to simplify the exponent first.]**
>
> **Q** If there are 960 beetles in the bin, how many days have passed? Explain. **[5 days; $30 \cdot 2^5 = 960$]**

Got It?   ERROR PREVENTION

If students give an answer of 1,180,980, then they likely did not account for the fact that 10 years is equal to 20 half-year periods.

If all of the *x*-values in a table of values have a constant difference and all of the *y*-values have a constant ratio, then the table represents an exponential function.

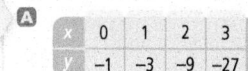 **Problem 1** Identifying an Exponential Function

Think

How can you identify a constant ratio between *y*-values?
When you multiply each *y*-value by the same constant and get the next *y*-value, there is a constant ratio between the values.

Does the table or rule represent an exponential function? Explain.

A

x	0	1	2	3
y	−1	−3	−9	−27

The difference between each *x*-value is 1.

x	0	1	2	3
y	−1	−3	−9	−27

+1 +1 +1
3 3 3

The ratio between each *y*-value is 3.

Yes, the table represents an exponential function. There is a constant difference between *x*-values and a constant ratio between *y*-values.

B $y = 3x^2$

No, the function is not in the form $y = a \cdot b^x$. The independent variable *x* is not an exponent.

Got It? **1.** Does the table or rule represent an exponential function? Explain.

a.

x	1	2	3	4
y	×1	1	3	5

b. $y = 3 \cdot 6^x$

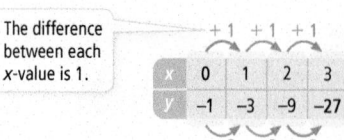 **Problem 2** Evaluating an Exponential Function **GRIDDED RESPONSE**

Population Growth Suppose 30 flour beetles are left undisturbed in a warehouse bin. The beetle population doubles each week. The function $f(x) = 30 \cdot 2^x$ gives the population after *x* weeks. How many beetles will there be after 56 days?

Think

Why is the function $30 \cdot 2^x$ not $2 \cdot 30^x$?
In an exponential function, *a* is the starting value and *b* is the rate of change.

$$f(x) = 30 \cdot 2^x$$
$$= 30 \cdot 2^8 \quad \text{56 days is equal to 8 weeks. Evaluate the function for } x = 8.$$
$$= 30 \cdot 256 \quad \text{Simplify the power.}$$
$$= 7680 \quad \text{Simplify.}$$

After 56 days, there will be 7680 beetles.

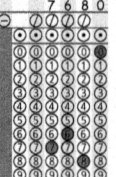

Got It? **2.** An initial population of 20 rabbits triples every half year. The function $f(x) = 20 \cdot 3^x$ gives the population after *x* half-year periods. How many rabbits will there be after 3 yr?

Answers

Solve It!

Over 4 days, Plan 1 gives $5 + 6 + 7 + 8 = 26$ min of practice time and Plan 2 gives $1 + 2 + 4 + 8 = 15$ min of practice time. Over 8 days, Plan 1 gives $5 + 6 + 7 + 8 + 9 + 10 + 11 + 12 = 68$ min of practice time, and Plan 2 gives $1 + 2 + 4 + 8 + 16 + 32 + 64 + 128 = 255$ min of practice time. Over 4 days, Plan 1 gives more practice time; over 8 days Plan 2 does.

Got It?

1. a. No; the *y*-values are not multiplied by a constant amount.

　b. Yes; it is of the form $y = a \cdot b^x$.

2. 14,580 rabbits

 PowerAlgebra.com

2 Guided Instruction

Each Problem is worked out and supported in the Student Online Center.

Problem 1
Identifying an Exponential Function
Animated

Problem 2
Evaluating an Exponential Function
Animated

Problem 3
Graphing an Exponential Function
Animated

Problem 4
Graphing an Exponential Mode

Support in the Algebra 1 Companion
- Vocabulary
- Key Concepts
- Got It?

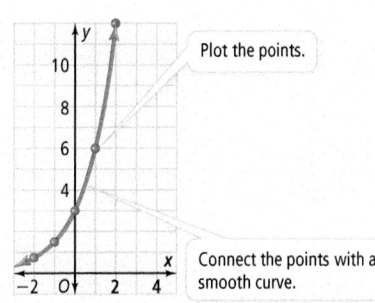

Problem 3 Graphing an Exponential Function

Think

What is the domain and range of the function?
Any value substituted for x results in a positive y-value. The domain is all real numbers. The range is all positive real numbers.

What is the graph of $y = 3 \cdot 2^x$?

Make a table of x- and y-values.

x	$y = 3 \cdot 2^x$	(x, y)
-2	$3 \cdot 2^{-2} = \frac{3}{2^2} = \frac{3}{4}$	$\left(-2, \frac{3}{4}\right)$
-1	$3 \cdot 2^{-1} = \frac{3}{2^1} = 1\frac{1}{2}$	$\left(-1, 1\frac{1}{2}\right)$
0	$3 \cdot 2^0 = 3 \cdot 1 = 3$	(0, 3)
1	$3 \cdot 2^1 = 3 \cdot 2 = 6$	(1, 6)
2	$3 \cdot 2^2 = 3 \cdot 4 = 12$	(2, 12)

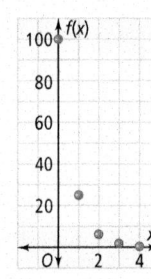

Plot the points.

Connect the points with a smooth curve.

✔ **Got It? 3.** What is the graph of each function?
a. $y = 0.5 \cdot 3^x$ **b.** $y = -0.5 \cdot 3^x$

Problem 4 Graphing an Exponential Model

Think

Should you connect the points of the graph?
No. The number of times you zoom in must be a nonnegative integer.

Maps Computer mapping software allows you to zoom in on an area to view it in more detail. The function $f(x) = 100 \cdot 0.25^x$ models the percent of the original area the map shows after zooming in x times. Graph the function.

x	$f(x) = 100 \cdot 0.25^x$	(x, f(x))
0	$100 \cdot 0.25^0 = 100$	(0, 100)
1	$100 \cdot 0.25^1 = 25$	(1, 25)
2	$100 \cdot 0.25^2 = 6.25$	(2, 6.25)
3	$100 \cdot 0.25^3 \approx 1.56$	(3, 1.56)
4	$100 \cdot 0.25^4 \approx 0.39$	(4, 0.39)

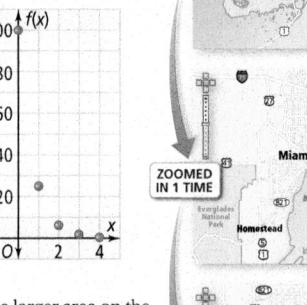

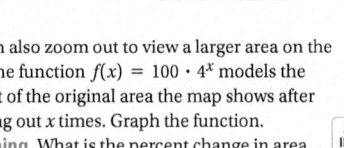

ORIGINAL AREA

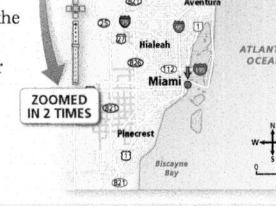

ZOOMED IN 1 TIME

ZOOMED IN 2 TIMES

✔ **Got It? 4. a.** You can also zoom out to view a larger area on the map. The function $f(x) = 100 \cdot 4^x$ models the percent of the original area the map shows after zooming out x times. Graph the function.
b. Reasoning What is the percent change in area each time you zoom out in part (a)?

Problem 3

Q What happens to the y-values as the x-values decrease? **[The y-values approach zero.]**

Got It?

Q Why does the graph of every exponential function in the form $y = a \cdot b^x$, where b is nonzero, have a y-intercept that is equal to a? **[When x = 0, b^0 is equal to 1, and a • 1 is equal to a.]**

Problem 4

Q What is a pattern in the f(x)-values in the table? **[Each f(x)-value is the previous f(x)-value divided by 4.]**

Q What does a value of −2 for x represent in this function? **[It would represent zooming out twice.]**

Got It?
Ask students to compare the two functions given for the mapping software. Point out that 0.25 is the reciprocal of 4, and thus the function $f(x) = 100 \cdot 0.25x$ represents both situations, where positive values of x are considered zooming in and negative values of x are considered zooming out.

Additional Problems

1. Does the table or rule represent an exponential function? Explain.

a.

x	y
0	2
1	6
2	10
3	14

b. $y = 2x$

ANSWER a. No, the x-values increase by a constant amount, but the y-values are not multiplied by a constant amount. **b.** yes

2. Suppose a culture of bacteria doubles each hour. There are initially 2200 bacteria. The function $f(x) = 2200 \cdot 2^x$ gives the number of bacteria after x hours. How many bacteria will there be after 5 hours?
ANSWER 70,400

3. What is the graph of $y = 0.25 \cdot 3^x$?
ANSWER

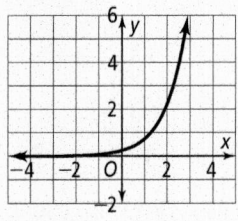

4. Suppose an investment of $7500 doubles in value every 12 years. The function $f(x) = 7500 \cdot 2^x$ models the growth of the investment, where x is the number of 12-year periods. Graph the function.
ANSWER

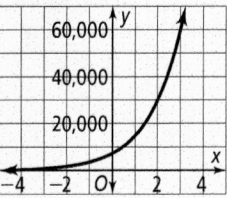

Answers

Got It? (continued)

3. a.

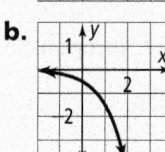

b.

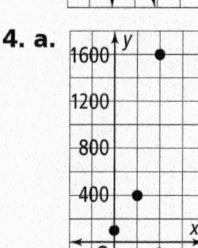

4. a.

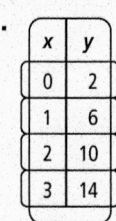

b. 300%

3 Lesson Check

Do you know HOW?
- If students have difficulty with Exercise 4, then have them review Problem 3.

Do you UNDERSTAND?
- If students have difficulty with Exercise 6, then have them review the definition of an exponential function.

Close

> **Q** How can you tell if values in a table represent an exponential function? **[If the input values in a table increase by a constant amount and the output values are obtained by multiplying the previous output value by the same factor, then the values in the table represent an exponential function.]**

 Lesson Check

Do you know HOW?
Evaluate each function for the given value.

1. $f(x) = 6 \cdot 2^x$ for $x = 3$

2. $g(w) = 45 \cdot 3^w$ for $w = -2$

Graph each function.

3. $y = 3^x$

4. $f(x) = 4\left(\frac{1}{2}\right)^x$

Do you UNDERSTAND?

5. Vocabulary Describe the differences between a linear function and an exponential function.

6. Reasoning Is $y = (-2)^x$ an exponential function? Justify your answer.

7. Error Analysis A student evaluated the function $f(x) = 3 \cdot 4^x$ for $x = -1$ as shown at the right. Describe and correct the student's mistake.

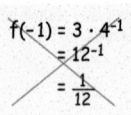

Practice and Problem-Solving Exercises

A Practice Determine whether each table or rule represents an exponential function. Explain why or why not. ◀ See Problem 1.

8.

x	1	2	3	4
y	2	8	32	128

9.

x	0	1	2	3
y	6	9	18	33

10. $y = 4 \cdot 5^x$

11. $y = 12 \cdot x^2$

12. $y = -5 \cdot 0.25^x$

13. $y = 7x + 3$

Evaluate each function for the given value. ◀ See Problem 2.

14. $f(x) = 6^x$ for $x = 2$

15. $g(t) = 2 \cdot 0.4^t$ for $t = -2$

16. $y = 20 \cdot 0.5^x$ for $x = 3$

17. $h(w) = -0.5 \cdot 4^w$ for $w = 18$

18. Finance An investment of $5000 doubles in value every decade. The function $f(x) = 5000 \cdot 2^x$, where x is the number of decades, models the growth of the value of the investment. How much is the investment worth after 30 yr?

19. Wildlife Management A population of 75 foxes in a wildlife preserve quadruples in size every 15 yr. The function $y = 75 \cdot 4^x$, where x is the number of 15-yr periods, models the population growth. How many foxes will there be after 45 yr?

Graph each exponential function. ◀ See Problem 3.

20. $y = 4^x$

21. $y = -4^x$

22. $y = \left(\frac{1}{3}\right)^x$

23. $y = -\left(\frac{1}{3}\right)^x$

24. $y = 10 \cdot \left(\frac{3}{2}\right)^x$

25. $y = 0.1 \cdot 2^x$

26. $y = \frac{1}{4} \cdot 2^x$

27. $y = 1.25^x$

Answers

Lesson Check
1. 48

2. 5

3.
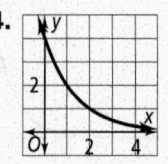

4.

5. Answers may vary. Linear functions have a constant rate of change, while an exponential function has a constant finite ratio.

6. No; the value of the base cannot be negative.

7. The student did not use the order of operations correctly. You must evaluate the exponent before you multiply:
$f(-1) = 3 \cdot 4^{-1} = 3 \cdot \frac{1}{4} = \frac{3}{4}$.

Practice and Problem-Solving Exercises

8. Exponential; the x-values have a constant difference and the y-values have a constant ratio.

9. Not exponential; the y-values do not have a constant ratio.

10. Exponential; it is of the form $y = a \cdot b^x$.

11. Not exponential; the x-value is not used as an exponent.

12. Exponential; it is of the form $y = a \cdot b^x$.

13. Not exponential; it is not of the form $y = a \cdot b^x$.

14. 36

15. 12.5

16. 2.5

17. -3.44×10^{10}

18. $40,000

19. 4800 foxes

---

28. Admissions A new museum had 7500 visitors this year. The museum curators expect the number of visitors to grow by 5% each year. The function $y = 7500 \cdot 1.05^x$ models the predicted number of visitors each year after x years. Graph the function.

◀ See Problem 4.

29. Environment A solid waste disposal plan proposes to reduce the amount of garbage each person throws out by 2% each year. This year, each person threw out an average of 1500 lb of garbage. The function $y = 1500 \cdot 0.98^x$ models the average amount of garbage each person will throw out each year after x years. Graph the function.

Apply

Evaluate each function over the domain $\{-2, -1, 0, 1, 2, 3\}$. As the values of the domain increase, do the values of the range *increase* or *decrease*?

30. $f(x) = 5^x$ **31.** $y = 2.5^x$ **32.** $h(x) = 0.1^x$ **33.** $f(x) = 5 \cdot 4^x$

34. $y = 0.5^x$ **35.** $y = 8^x$ **36.** $g(x) = 4 \cdot 10^x$ **37.** $y = 100 \cdot 0.3^x$

38. Think About a Plan Hydra are small freshwater animals. They can double in number every two days in a laboratory tank. Suppose one tank has an initial population of 60 hydra. When will there be more than 5000 hydra?
- How can a table help you identify a pattern?
- What function models the situation?

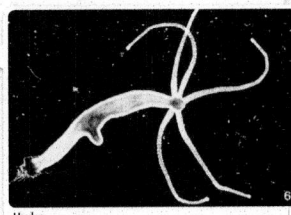
Hydra

39. a. Graph $y = 2^x$, $y = 4^x$, and $y = 0.25^x$ on the same axes.
  b. What point is on all three graphs?
  c. Does the graph of an exponential function intersect the x-axis? Explain.
  d. Reasoning How does the graph of $y = b^x$ change as the base b increases or decreases?

Which function has the greater value for the given value of x?

40. $y = 4^x$ or $y = x^4$ for $x = 2$ **41.** $f(x) = 10 \cdot 2^x$ or $f(x) = 200 \cdot x^2$ for $x = 7$

42. $y = 3^x$ or $y = x^3$ for $x = 5$ **43.** $f(x) = 2^x$ or $f(x) = 100x^2$ for $x = 10$

44. Computers A computer valued at $1500 loses 20% of its value each year.
  a. Write a function rule that models the value of the computer.
  b. Find the value of the computer after 3 yr.
  c. In how many years will the value of the computer be less than $500?

45. a. Graph the functions $y = x^2$ and $y = 2^x$ on the same axes.
  b. What do you notice about the graphs for the values of x between 1 and 3?
  c. Reasoning How do you think the graph of $y = 8^x$ would compare to the graphs of $y = x^2$ and $y = 2^x$?

46. Writing Find the range of the function $f(x) = 500 \cdot 1^x$ using the domain $\{1, 2, 3, 4, 5\}$. Explain why the definition of *exponential function* states that $b \neq 1$.

---

4 Practice

ASSIGNMENT GUIDE

Basic: 8–29 all, 30–46 even

Average: 9–29 odd, 30–46

Advanced: 9–29 odd, 30–51

Standardized Test Prep: 52–54

Mixed Review: 55–65

Reasoning exercises have blue headings.

Applications exercises have red headings.

EXERCISE 44: Use the Think About a Plan worksheet in the **Practice and Problem Solving Workbook** (also available in the Teaching Resources in print and online) to further support students' development in becoming independent learners.

HOMEWORK QUICK CHECK

To check students' understanding of key skills and concepts, go over Exercises 9, 21, 38, 44, and 46.

20.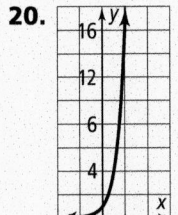

21.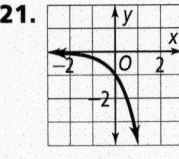

22.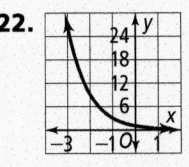

23.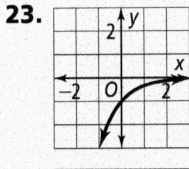

24.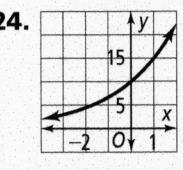

25.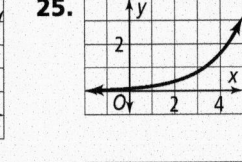

26.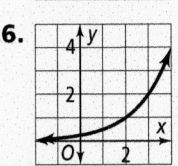

27.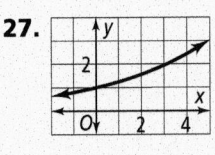

28.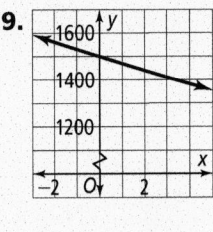

29.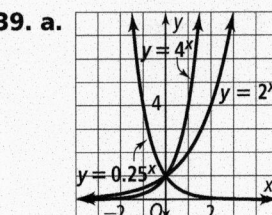

30. $\{0.04, 0.2, 1, 5, 25, 125\}$; increase

31. $\{0.16, 0.4, 1, 2.5, 6.25, 15.625\}$; increase

32. $\{100, 10, 1, 0.1, 0.01, 0.001\}$; decrease

33. $\{0.3125, 1.25, 5, 20, 80, 320\}$; increase

34. $\{4, 2, 1, 0.5, 0.25, 0.125\}$; decrease

35. $\{0.015625, 0.125, 1, 8, 64, 512\}$; increase

36. $\{0.04, 0.4, 4, 40, 400, 4000\}$; increase

37. $\{1111.\overline{11}, 333.\overline{33}, 100, 30, 9, 2.7\}$; decrease

38. after 7 two-day periods

39. a.

b. (0, 1)

c. No, the values of y are always positive.

d. When $0 < b < 1$, the graph decreases to the right, but when $b > 1$, the graph rises to the right. The larger the value of b, the faster it rises.

40. They are the same.

41. $f(x) = 200x^2$

42. $y = 3^x$

43. $f(x) = 100x^2$

44. a. $y = 1500 \cdot 0.80^x$
  b. $768
  c. a little less than 5 years

45.–46. See next page.

Answers

Practice and Problem-Solving Exercises
(continued)

45. a.

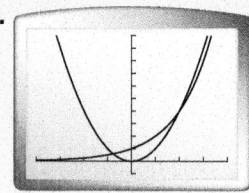

b. Answers may vary. Sample: The values are close though the exponential function is greater from 1 to 2. The two functions are equal at $x = 2$. The quadratic function is greater from 2 to 3.

c. Answers may vary. Sample: The function values increase more rapidly.

46. The range of the function consists of just 500. When b equals 1, the function is a horizontal line, $y = 500$, because 1 raised to any positive integer is 1.

47. 6   **48.** -3

49. 3   **50.** 5

51. a. 4   **b.** 3

     c. $y = 4 \cdot 3^x$ **d.** $\frac{4}{9}$; 324

52. D   **53.** I

54. [2] $11 \le |x - 2| + 4$

$7 \le |x - 2|$ or $|x - 2| \ge 7$.

Therefore, $(x - 2) \ge 7$ or $(x - 2) \le -7$

$x \ge 9$ or $x \le -5$;

[1] appropriate methods used with a minor error in either the solving or the graph

55. a^4 **56.** $\frac{n^{14}}{m^{28}}$

57. $\frac{1}{x^{10}z^{20}}$ **58.** $\frac{1}{p^{15}}$

59. $y = 5x$ **60.** $y = 3x + 1$

61. $y = 0.4x - 3.8$ **62.** 12% decrease

63. 20% increase   **64.** 31% decrease

65. 36% increase

Challenge   Solve each equation.

47. $2^x = 64$ **48.** $3^x = \frac{1}{27}$ **49.** $3 \cdot 2^x = 24$ **50.** $5 \cdot 2^x - 152 = 8$

51. Suppose $(0, 4)$ and $(2, 36)$ are on the graph of an exponential function.
   a. Use $(0, 4)$ in the general form of an exponential function, $y = a \cdot b^x$, to find the value of the constant a.
   b. Use your answer from part (a) and $(2, 36)$ to find the value of the constant b.
   c. Write a rule for the function.
   d. Evaluate the function for $x = -2$ and $x = 4$.

Standardized Test Prep

SAT/ACT

52. A population of 30 swans doubles every 10 yr. Which graph represents the population growth?

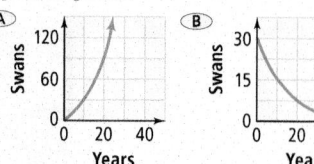
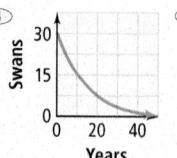
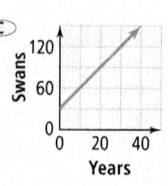
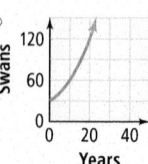

53. Which equation do you get when you solve $y = 2x - 12$ for x?

     Ⓕ $x = y - 6$ Ⓖ $x = y + 6$ Ⓗ $x = 0.5y - 6$ Ⓘ $x = 0.5y + 6$

Short Response

54. What are the solutions of the inequality $11 \le |x - 2| + 4$? Graph the solutions on a number line. Show your work.

Mixed Review

Simplify each expression.   ◀ See Lesson 7-5.

55. $\left(\frac{a^2}{a^3}\right)^{-4}$ **56.** $\left(\frac{m^4}{n^2}\right)^{-7}$ **57.** $\left(\frac{x^2 z}{z^{-3}}\right)^{-5}$ **58.** $\left(\frac{pq^0}{p^4}\right)^5$

Write an equation for the line that is parallel to the given line and passes through the given point.   ◀ See Lesson 5-6.

59. $y = 5x + 1$; $(0, 0)$ **60.** $y = 3x - 2$; $(0, 1)$ **61.** $y = 0.4x + 5$; $(2, -3)$

Get Ready!   **To prepare for Lesson 7-7, do Exercises 62–65.**

Tell whether each percent change is an increase or decrease. Then find the percent change. If necessary, round to the nearest percent.   ◀ See Lesson 2-10.

62. original price: $25; sale price: $22   **63.** height last week: 15 cm; height this week: 18 cm

64. price this year: $999; price last year: $1450   **65.** birth weight: 220 lb; weight at 1 month: 300 lb

Differentiated Remediation

Additional Instructional Support

Algebra 1 Companion

Students can use the **Algebra 1 Companion** worktext (4 pages) as you teach the lesson. Use the Companion to support

- New Vocabulary
- Key Concepts
- Got It for each Problem
- Lesson Check

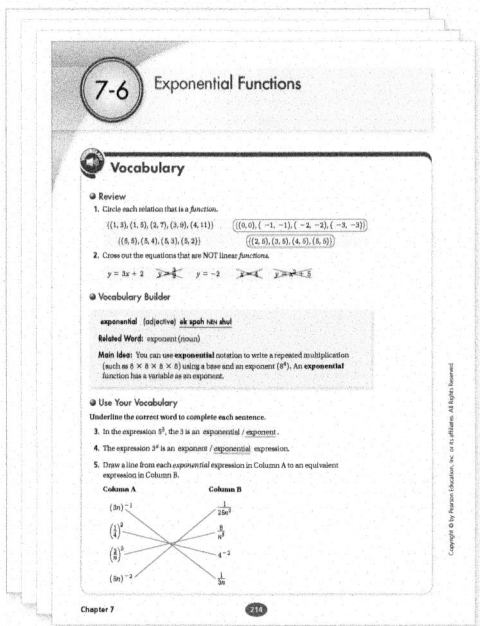

ELL Support

Focus on Language Arrange students with similar abilities into groups. Have students analyze the term *exponential function*. Ask students what word is contained in the term *exponential* that would help define *exponential function*. Encourage students to predict what an exponential function is before reading the definition. Compare student definitions with the definition presented in the text.

Use Graphic Organizers Have students draw a 3-box chain graphic organizer where each box connects to the next with an arrow. Students should write *function, table,* and *graph* in the boxes. Tell students to write in their own words the process to identify an exponential function given each form. Have students write a linked example in their graphic organizers.

5 Assess & Remediate

Lesson Quiz

1. Does the table represent an exponential function? Explain.

x	y
0	3
1	6
2	12
3	24

2. What is the graph of $y = 5 \cdot 2^x$?

3. **Do you UNDERSTAND?** Suppose the population of a species of insects doubles every year. There are 1600 insects initially. The function $f(x) = 1600 \cdot 2^x$ gives the number of insects after x years. How many insects will there be after 3 years?

ANSWERS TO LESSON QUIZ

1. Yes, the x-values increase by a constant amount and the y-values are multiplied by a constant amount.

2.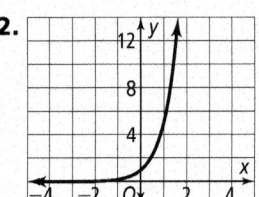

3. 12,800

PRESCRIPTION FOR REMEDIATION

Use the student work on the Lesson Quiz to prescribe a differentiated review assignment.

Points	Differentiated Remediation
0–1	Intervention
2	On-level
3	Extension

PowerAlgebra.com

5 Assess & Remediate

Assign the Lesson Quiz. Appropriate intervention, practice, or enrichment is automatically generated based on student performance.

Intervention

- **Reteaching** (2 pages) Provides reteaching and practice exercises for the key lesson concepts. Use with struggling students or absent students.

- **English Language Learner Support** Helps students develop and reinforce mathematical vocabulary and key concepts.

All-in-One Resources/Online
Reteaching

7-6 **Reteaching**
Exponential Functions

Functions that can be modeled by an equation of the form $y = a \cdot b^x$ are exponential functions. These functions have properties that are different from the properties of linear and quadratic functions.

Consider the three function tables below.

Notice that in each table, the x-value increases by a constant amount. If these functions were linear, the y-values would also increase by a constant amount. You used these values to find the slope of linear equations.

This does not hold true for exponential functions. See if you can determine the property that holds true for all exponential functions by:

a. Finding the sum of some random pairs of consecutive y-values in each table.
b. Finding the difference between some random pairs of consecutive y-values in each table.
c. Finding the product of some random pairs of consecutive y-values in each table.
d. Finding the quotient of some random pairs of consecutive y-values in each table.

You should have noticed that, for each table, the quotients remain the same.

Exponential functions model an initial amount, a, that is repeatedly multiplied by the same positive number, b. The number of times the multiplication occurs is determined by the independent variable, x, which is the exponent in the power b^x.

All-in-One Resources/Online
English Language Learner Support

7-6 **ELL Support**
Exponential Functions

Choose the word from the list that best matches each phrase.

constant	exponential	function	independent

1. A term that does not contain a variable — constant
2. Not depending on another for its value — independent
3. A relation between two sets in which one element of the second set is assigned to each element of the first set — function
4. A pattern of growth with a constant multiplier — exponential

Use a word from the list to complete each sentence.

5. In the equation $y = 4 + x^2$, 4 is a(n) constant
6. The equation $y = 5^x$ is a(n) exponential function.
7. In the function $y = 2^x - 3$, the exponent is independent
8. $f(x)$ is the notation for a function

Circle the constant and underline the independent variable.

9. $\left(\frac{1}{2}\right)^x$
10. 1.5^x
11. 2^x
12. 3^x

Multiple Choice

13. Which of the following is *not* an exponential function? B
Ⓐ $y = 5^x$　Ⓑ $y = 5x - 1$　Ⓒ $y = 5^{x-1}$　Ⓓ $y = 5^{x+1}$

Differentiated Remediation *continued*

On-Level

- **Practice** (2 pages) Provides extra practice for each lesson. For simpler practice exercises, use the Form K Practice pages found in the All-in-One Teaching Resources and online.

- **Think About a Plan** Helps students develop specific problem-solving skills and strategies by providing scaffolded guiding questions.

- **Standardized Test Prep** Focuses on all major exercises, all major question types, and helps students prepare for the high-stakes assessments.

Extension

- **Enrichment** Provides students with interesting problems and activities that extend the concepts of the lesson.

- **Activities, Games, and Puzzles** Worksheets that can be used for concepts development, enrichment, and for fun!

Practice and Problem Solving WKBK/ All-in-One Resources/Online
Practice page 1

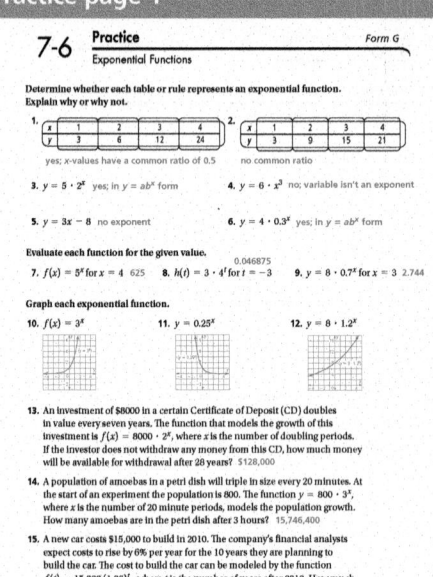

Practice and Problem Solving WKBK/ All-in-One Resources/Online
Practice page 2

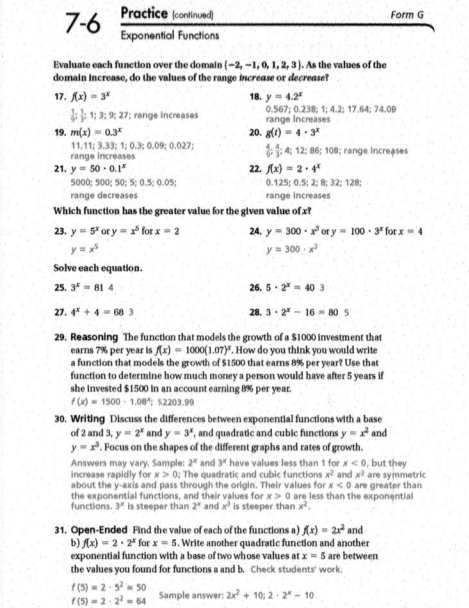

All-in-One Resources/Online
Enrichment

Practice and Problem Solving WKBK/ All-in-One Resources/Online
Think About a Plan

Practice and Problem Solving WKBK/ All-in-One Resources/Online
Standardized Test Prep

Online Teacher Resource Center
Activities, Games, and Puzzles

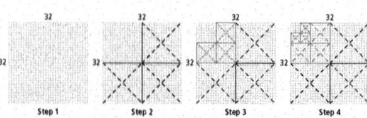

Guided Instruction

PURPOSE To explore geometric sequences, find rules for geometric sequences and extend geometric sequences.

PROCESS Students will
• determine common ratios.
• determine rules for geometric sequences.
• determine certain terms within a geometric sequence.

Recall that a sequence is a list of numbers that often forms a pattern. Each number in a sequence is a term of the sequence.

In Chapter 4 you studied arithmetic sequences, where you found each new term by adding the same number to the previous term. Another kind of sequence is a *geometric sequence*. In a geometric sequence, the ratio between consecutive terms is constant. This ratio is called the *common ratio*.

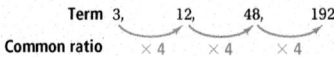

DISCUSS Give students 2 sequences to discuss.

$$5, 10, 15, 20, \ldots$$
$$5, 20, 80, 320, \ldots$$

Have them explain why both lists are considered sequences. Discuss the differences between arithmetic and geometric sequences. Challenge students to calculate the rule for each sequence.

Activity 1

1. a. What is the common ratio of the sequence 2, 4, 8, 16, . . . ?
   b. What are the next three terms in the sequence?

2. a. What is the common ratio of the sequence 80, 20, 5, $\frac{5}{4}$, . . . ?
   b. What are the next three terms in the sequence?

3. a. What is the common ratio of the sequence 2, −6, 18, −54, . . . ?
   b. What are the next three terms in the sequence?

Activity 1

In this activity, students will discover how to find a common ratio.

Q What operation is used to find the common ratio? **[division]**

Q How is the operation used to determine the common ratio? **[Divide the second term by the first term, the third term by the second term, and so on.]**

You can use the common ratio of a geometric sequence to write a function rule for the sequence.

Activity 2

Consider the sequence 2, 6, 18, 54, . . .
Let n = the term number in the sequence.
Let $A(n)$ = the value of the nth term of the sequence.

4. What is the common ratio of the sequence?

5. Complete each statement.
   a. $A(1) = 2 = 2 \cdot 3^{\blacksquare}$
   b. $A(2) = 6 = 2 \cdot 3 = 2 \cdot 3^{\blacksquare}$
   c. $A(3) = 18 = 2 \cdot 3 \cdot 3 = 2 \cdot 3^{\blacksquare}$
   d. $A(4) = 54 = 2 \cdot 3 \cdot 3 \cdot 3 = 2 \cdot 3^{\blacksquare}$

6. What is the relationship between the exponent of the base 3 and the value of n?

7. Complete the statement: $A(n) = 2 \cdot 3^{\blacksquare}$.

Activity 2

Q Why do you suppose the number 2 is the first number in each rule? **[It is the first term in the sequence.]**

Q Why do you suppose the number 3 is the second number in each rule? **[It is the common ratio.]**

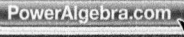
Answers

Activity 1
1. a. 2   **b.** 32, 64, 128
2. a. $\frac{1}{4}$ **b.** $\frac{5}{16}, \frac{5}{64}, \frac{5}{256}$
3. a. −3   **b.** 162, −486, 1458

Activity 2
4. 3
5. a. 0   **b.** 1
   c. 2   **d.** 3
6. The exponent of 3 is 1 less than the value of n.
7. $n - 1$

Activity 3

In this activity, students will explore data in a table that will lead them to create the rule for a geometric sequence.

Q In 8e, in the geometric sequence rule, what does 12 replace? **[n, or the term number]**

Q In 8f, in the geometric sequence rule, what does 256 replace? **[A(n), or the value of the nth term]**

ERROR PREVENTION

When students are writing a rule for a geometric sequence, have them first write the rule using words rather than symbols. Have them determine if the rule works for each term in the table. Once the students have a good understanding of the rule, have them transfer it into algebraic symbols.

In general, you can write a function rule for a geometric sequence using the first term, the term number, and the common ratio.

Geometric Sequence Rule

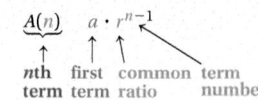

$$\underline{A(n)} \quad a \cdot r^{n-1}$$

nth term   first term   common ratio   term number

For example, the rule for the sequence 5, 15, 45, 135, ... is $A(n) = 5 \cdot 3^{n-1}$.

Activity 3

8. a. Fold a piece of paper in half. How many layers are there?
  b. Continue folding the paper in half. Copy and complete the table.
  c. Rewrite each entry in the Number of Layers column from the table in the form $2^{\blacksquare}$.
  d. Write a rule for the geometric sequence. (*Hint:* The first term is 2, not 1.)
  e. Use the rule to find the number of layers after 12 folds.
  f. If there were 256 layers, how many folds would there be?
  g. Reasoning Is it possible to fold a piece of paper in halves and get 144 layers? Explain.

Number of Folds	Number of Layers
1	2
2	■
3	■
4	■
5	■

Exercises

Find the common ratio of each sequence. Then find the next three terms of the sequence.

9. 1, 3, 9, 27, ...
10. 256, 64, 16, 4, ...
11. −3, −6, −12, −24, ...

12. 70, 7, 0.7, 0.07, ...
13. 8, −20, 50, −125, ...
14. 0.45, 0.9, 1.8, 3.6, ...

Determine whether each sequence is *arithmetic* or *geometric*.

15. 2, 4, 6, 8, ...
16. 6, 1, −4, −9, ...
17. 0.04, 0.12, 0.36, 1.08, ...

18. 14, 21, 28, 35, ...
19. 7, −21, 63, −189, ...
20. 18, 9, 4.5, 2.25, ...

Find the first, fourth, and eighth terms of each sequence.

21. $A(n) = 4 \cdot 2^{n-1}$
22. $A(n) = -2 \cdot 5^{n-1}$
23. $A(n) = 5(-0.8)^{n-1}$

24. $A(n) = 0.5 \cdot 3^{n-1}$
25. $A(n) = 1.1(0.5)^{n-1}$
26. $A(n) = 0.25(-4)^{n-1}$

27. Reasoning Can zero be a term of a geometric sequence where the first three terms are not zero? Explain.

28. Compare and Contrast How are an exponential function and a geometric sequence rule alike? How are they different? Can you use an exponential function to describe a geometric sequence? Explain.

Answers

Activity 3

8 a. 2

b.

Number of Folds	Number of Layers
1	2
2	4
3	8
4	16
5	32

c. $2^1, 2^2, 2^3, 2^4, 2^5$ **d.** $A(n) = 2^n$
e. 4096 layers   **f.** 8 folds
g. No; 144 is not a power of 2.

Exercises

9. 3; 81, 243, 729   **10.** $\frac{1}{4}$; 1, $\frac{1}{4}$, $\frac{1}{16}$
11. 2; −48, −96, −192
12. 0.1; 0.007, 0.0007, 0.00007
13. −2.5; 312.5, −781.25, 1953.125
14. 2; 7.2, 14.4, 28.8
15. arithmetic   **16.** arithmetic
17. geometric   **18.** arithmetic

19. geometric   **20.** geometric
21. 4, 32, 512   **22.** −2, −250, −156,250
23. 5, −2.56, −1.048576
24. 0.5, 13.5, 1093.5
25. 1.1, 0.1375, 0.00859375
26. 0.25, −16, −4096
27. No; if one term were 0, then all the terms would be 0. You multiply a term to get the next term. To get a product of zero, one of the factors must be zero.
28. Answers may vary. Sample: Both involve multiplying an initial value by a power of a base. In an exponential function, $y = a \cdot b^x$, a represents the initial value when $x = 0$, so graphically it is the y-intercept. In a geometric sequence, $A(n) = a \cdot r^{n-1}$, a represents the first term with $n = 1$. You can change a sequence to a function equation by rewriting it as $a \cdot r^{n-1} = a \cdot \frac{r^n}{r} = \frac{a}{r} \cdot r^n$, where the value of $\frac{a}{r}$ corresponds to the value when $n = 0$.

7-7 Exponential Growth and Decay

Objective To model exponential growth and decay

Many things decay—some just decay faster than others.

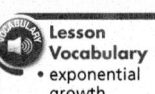
Dynamic Activity
Exponential Growth and Decay

Lesson Vocabulary
- exponential growth
- growth factor
- compound interest
- exponential decay
- decay factor

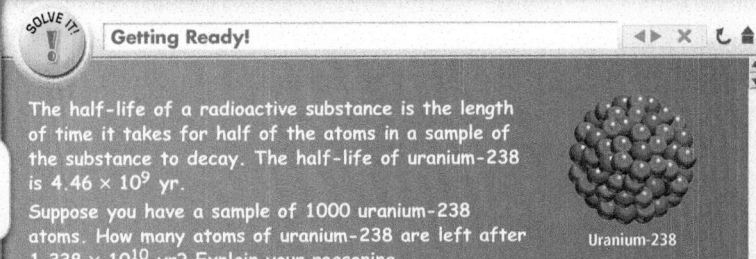

Getting Ready!

The half-life of a radioactive substance is the length of time it takes for half of the atoms in a sample of the substance to decay. The half-life of uranium-238 is 4.46×10^9 yr.

Suppose you have a sample of 1000 uranium-238 atoms. How many atoms of uranium-238 are left after 1.338×10^{10} yr? Explain your reasoning.

Uranium-238

In the Solve It, the number of uranium-238 atoms decreases exponentially. In this lesson, you will use exponential functions to model similar situations.

Essential Understanding An exponential function can model growth or decay of an initial amount.

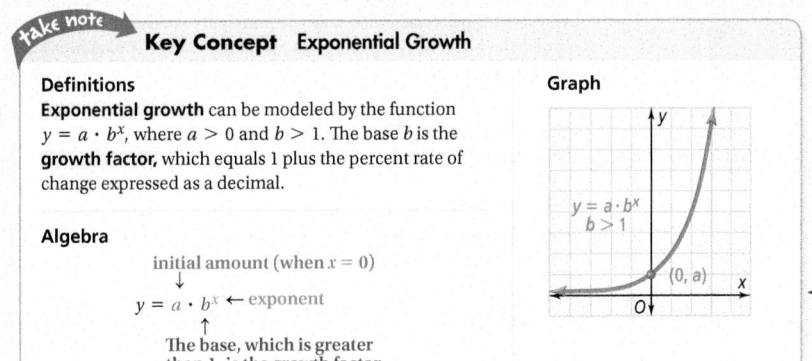

take note

Key Concept Exponential Growth

Definitions
Exponential growth can be modeled by the function $y = a \cdot b^x$, where $a > 0$ and $b > 1$. The base b is the **growth factor,** which equals 1 plus the percent rate of change expressed as a decimal.

Algebra

initial amount (when $x = 0$)
$$y = a \cdot b^x \leftarrow \text{exponent}$$
The base, which is greater than 1, is the growth factor.

Graph

$y = a \cdot b^x$
$b > 1$
$(0, a)$

Solve It!
PURPOSE To familiarize students with the recursive patterns found in a set of data that can be modeled with an exponential decay function
PROCESS Students may make a table to keep track of the years passed and the number of atoms. Students may use recursion to extend the table until they are able to answer the question.

FACILITATE
Q How many atoms of uranium-238 will be in the sample after 4.46×10^9 years have passed? **[500]**
Q How can you determine the length of time required for two half-lives to occur? For three half-lives? **[Multiply 4.46×10^9 by 2; multiply 4.46×10^9 by 3.]**

ANSWER See Solve It in Answers on next page.
CONNECT THE MATH Point out that the number of atoms for each half-life can be determined recursively by dividing the previous number of atoms by 2, or by multiplying the previous number of atoms by $\frac{1}{2}$.

2 Guided Instruction

Take Note

Q Why does an exponential growth function not exist when $b \leq 1$? **[When $b = 1$, the growth is linear and when $0 < b < 1$, the function values will decrease as x increases.]**

7-7 Preparing to Teach

BIG idea Function
ESSENTIAL UNDERSTANDINGS
- An exponential function can model growth or decay of an initial amount.

Math Background
In this lesson, students model real-world situations involving exponential growth and decay using explicit exponential functions. Growth and decay functions are generally the same format but the differences lie in the value restrictions on the base b. Students will likely become proficient at recognizing the differences in growth and decay functions by examining their graphs. For students who struggle to understand the behavior of the functions without the aid of the graphs, students can experiment with these types of exponential functions using a spreadsheet or graphing calculator.

UbD Support Student Learning
Use the **Algebra 1 Companion** to engage and support students during instructions. See Lesson Resources at the end of this lesson for details.

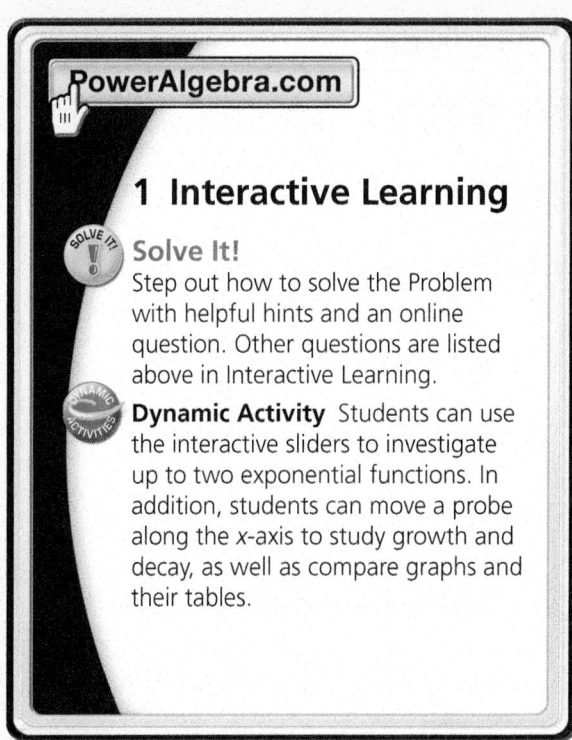

PowerAlgebra.com

1 Interactive Learning

Solve It!
Step out how to solve the Problem with helpful hints and an online question. Other questions are listed above in Interactive Learning.

Dynamic Activity Students can use the interactive sliders to investigate up to two exponential functions. In addition, students can move a probe along the x-axis to study growth and decay, as well as compare graphs and their tables.

Problem 1

> **Q** What amount of money was spent at restaurants in 2006? Explain. **[$385 billion; 360 × 1.07 ≈ 385]**
>
> **Q** In what year is the amount of money spent at restaurants approximately $472 billion? **[2009]**
>
> **Q** What three methods can be used to show the exponential growth pattern? **[an equation, a table, a graph]**

Got It?   ERROR PREVENTION

If students approximate the population to be 631,279,207 people, then they likely used 1.5 as the growth factor rather than 1.015.

Problem 1   Modeling Exponential Growth

Economics Since 2005, the amount of money spent at restaurants in the United States has increased about 7% each year. In 2005, about $360 billion was spent at restaurants. If the trend continues, about how much will be spent at restaurants in 2015?

Think

When can you use an exponential growth function?
You can use an exponential growth function when an initial amount increases by a fixed percent each time period.

Relate $y = a \cdot b^x$ Use an exponential function.

Define   Let x = the number of years since 2005.
Let y = the annual amount spent at restaurants (in billions of dollars).
Let a = the initial amount spent (in billions of dollars), 360.
Let b = the growth factor, which is $1 + 0.07 = 1.07$.

Write $y = 360 \cdot 1.07^x$

Use the equation to predict the annual spending in 2015.

$$y = 360 \cdot 1.07^x$$
$$= 360 \cdot 1.07^{10} \quad \text{2015 is 10 yr after 2005, so substitute 10 for } x.$$
$$\approx 708 \quad \text{Round to the nearest billion dollars.}$$

About $708 billion will be spent at restaurants in the United States in 2015 if the trend continues.

 Got It? 1. Suppose the population of a town was 25,000 people in 2000. If the population grows about 1.5% each year, what will the approximate population be in 2025?

When a bank pays interest on both the principal *and* the interest an account has already earned, the bank is paying **compound interest.** Compound interest is an example of exponential growth.

You can use the following formula to find the balance of an account that earns compound interest.

$$A = P\left(1 + \frac{r}{n}\right)^{nt}$$

A = the balance
P = the principal (the initial deposit)
r = the annual interest rate (expressed as a decimal)
n = the number of times interest is compounded per year
t = the time in years

Answers

Solve It!

125 atoms; $\frac{1.338 \times 10^{10}}{4.46 \times 10^9} = 3$. The sample loses half the atoms every 4.46×10^9 years, so the sample cuts in half 3 times. $\frac{1000}{2^3} = \frac{1000}{8} = 125$

Got It?

1. about 36,274 people

PowerAlgebra.com

2 Guided Instruction

Each Problem is worked out and supported in the Student Online Center.

Problem 1
Modeling Exponential Growth
Animated

Problem 2
Compound Interest
Animated

Problem 3
Modeling Exponential Decay
Animated

Support in the Algebra 1 Companion
• Vocabulary
• Key Concepts
• Got It?

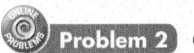

Problem 2 Compound Interest

Finance **Suppose that when your friend was born, your friend's parents deposited $2000 in an account paying 4.5% interest compounded quarterly. What will the account balance be after 18 yr?**

Know	Need	Plan
• $2000 principal • 4.5% interest • interest compounded quarterly, 4 times per year	Account balance in 18 yr	Use the compound interest formula.

Think

Is the formula an exponential growth function?
Yes. You can rewrite the formula as $A = P\left[\left(1 + \frac{r}{n}\right)^n\right]^t$. So it is an exponential function with initial amount P and growth factor $\left(1 + \frac{r}{n}\right)^n$.

$A = P\left(1 + \frac{r}{n}\right)^{nt}$	Use the compound interest formula.
$= 2000\left(1 + \frac{0.045}{4}\right)^{4 \cdot 18}$	Substitute the values for P, r, n, and t.
$= 2000(1.01125)^{72}$	Simplify.
≈ 4475.53	Use a calculator. Round to the nearest cent.

The balance will be $4475.53 after 18 yr.

Got It? **2.** Suppose the account in Problem 2 pays interest compounded monthly. What will the account balance be after 18 yr?

The function $y = a \cdot b^x$ can model *exponential decay* as well as exponential growth. In both cases, b is determined by the percent rate of change. The value of b tells if the equation models exponential growth or decay.

take note

Key Concept Exponential Decay

Definitions

Exponential decay can be modeled by the function $y = a \cdot b^x$, where $a > 0$ and $0 < b < 1$. The base b is the **decay factor,** which equals 1 minus the percent rate of change expressed as a decimal.

Algebra

initial amount (when $x = 0$)
↓
$y = a \cdot b^x$ ← exponent
↑
The base is the decay factor.

Graph

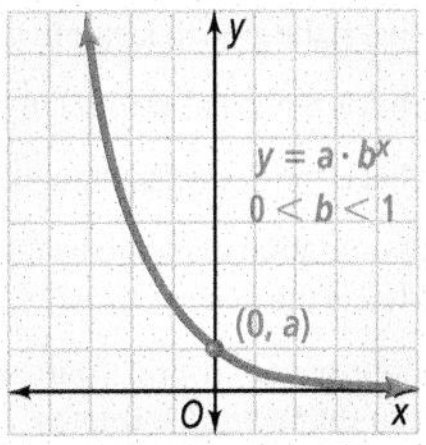

Problem 2

Q Do the parents make any other deposits to the account during the 18 years? Explain. **[No; they only make an initial deposit; the rest is interest.]**

Q How many times is interest compounded on the account? Explain. **[72 times; it is compounded 4 times a year for 18 years.]**

Q What is the growth factor in the exponential function? **[1.01125]**

Got It?

Ask students to make a chart of the account balance for each compounding frequency for 18 years. Then have them make a statement concerning the effect that the frequency of compounding has on the account.

Take Note

Q If the growth factor, b, is 0.54, what is the percent rate of change? **[decrease by 46%]**

Q How does the graph of an exponential decay function differ from the graph of an exponential growth function? How are they the same? **[Answers may vary. Sample: An exponential decay graph decreases from left to right, while an exponential growth graph increases from left to right. Both graphs approach the *x*-axis. Both graphs have a *y*-intercept of (0, *a*).]**

Additional Problems

1. Suppose the population of deer in a region was 3500 in the year 2000. Since then the population has grown by 3.5% annually. What will the approximate population be in the year 2020?

ANSWER about 6964 deer

2. Michelle invests $8000 in a money market account that pays 3.25% interest compounded monthly. How much will be in the account after 12 years?

ANSWER $11,809.62

3. The population of New Haven was 148,220 in 2005. Since then the population has been decreasing at an annual rate of 2.9%. If this rate of decline continues, what will the population be in the year 2015?

ANSWER about 110,433

Answers

Got It? (continued)

2. $4489.01

Problem 3

Q Why is 3 substituted for the value of *x*? [An altitude of 3000 m is three 1000 m increments above sea level.]

Q What is the domain of this exponential function? [positive altitudes in increments of 1000 m]

Q At what altitude is the atmospheric pressure approximately 43 kilopascals? [7000 m]

Got It?

Ask students to compare and contrast the exponential decay function in this Got It with the exponential growth function in Problem 1.

3 Lesson Check

Do you know HOW?

• If students have difficulty with Exercise 4, then have them review the definition of decay factor.

Do you UNDERSTAND?

• If students have difficulty with Exercise 8, then have them review Problem 2.

Close

Q What is the difference between an exponential growth function and an exponential decay function? [In an exponential growth function, as *x*-values increase, corresponding *y*-values increase exponentially. In an exponential decay function, as *x*-values increase, corresponding *y*-values decrease exponentially.]

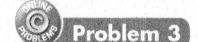 **Problem 3** Modeling Exponential Decay

Physics The kilopascal is a unit of measure for atmospheric pressure. The atmospheric pressure at sea level is about 101 kilopascals. For every 1000-m increase in altitude, the pressure decreases about 11.5%. What is the approximate pressure at an altitude of 3000 m?

Relate $y = a \cdot b^x$ Use an exponential function.

Define Let x = the altitude (in thousands of meters).
Let y = the atmospheric pressure (in kilopascals).
Let a = the initial pressure (in kilopascals), 101.
Let b = the decay factor, which is $1 - 0.115 = 0.885$.

Write $y = 101 \cdot 0.885^x$

Use the equation to estimate the pressure at an altitude of 3000 m.

$y = 101 \cdot 0.885^x$

$= 101 \cdot 0.885^3$ Substitute 3 for *x*.

≈ 70 Round to the nearest kilopascal.

The pressure at an altitude of 3000 m is about 70 kilopascals.

 Got It? **3. a.** What is the atmospheric pressure at an altitude of 5000 m?
     b. **Reasoning** Why do you subtract the percent decrease from 1 to find the decay factor?

Think

Will the pressure ever be negative?
No. The range of an exponential decay function is all positive real numbers. The graph of an exponential decay function approaches but does not cross the *x*-axis.

 Lesson Check

Do you know HOW?

1. What is the growth factor in the equation $y = 34 \cdot 4^x$?

2. What is the initial amount in the function $y = 15 \cdot 3^x$?

3. What is the decay factor in the function $y = 17 \cdot 0.2^x$?

4. A population of fish in a lake decreases 6% annually. What is the decay factor?

5. Suppose your friend's parents invest $20,000 in an account paying 5% interest compounded annually. What will the balance be after 10 yr?

Do you UNDERSTAND?

6. **Vocabulary** How can you tell if an exponential function models growth or decay?

7. **Reasoning** How can you simplify the compound interest formula when the interest is compounded annually? Explain.

8. **Error Analysis** A student deposits $500 into an account that earns 3.5% interest compounded quarterly. Describe and correct the student's error in calculating the account balance after 2 yr.

$$A = 500\left(1 + \frac{3.5}{4}\right)^{4 \cdot 2}$$
$$= 500\,(1.875)^8$$
$$\approx 76{,}380.09$$

---

3 Lesson Check

For a digital lesson check, use the Got It questions.

Support In Algebra 1 Companion
• Lesson Check

4 Practice

Assign homework to individual students or to an entire class.

Answers

Got It? (continued)

3. a. about 55 kilopascals
     b. The decimal equivalent of 100% is 1.

Lesson Check

1. 4   **2.** 15

3. 0.2   **4.** 0.94

5. $32,577.89

6. If $b > 1$, then it is exponential growth.
If $0 < b < 1$, then it is exponential decay.

7. The value of $n = 1$ so the formula becomes
$A = P(1 + r)^t$.

8. The student did not convert 3.5% to a decimal;
$A = 500\left(1 + \frac{0.035}{4}\right)^{(4 \cdot 2)} = 500(1.00875)^8$
≈ 536.09.

A Practice   Identify the initial amount a and the growth factor b in each exponential function.
See Problem 1.

  9. $g(x) = 14 \cdot 2^x$ **10.** $y = 150 \cdot 1.0894^x$

11. $y = 25{,}600 \cdot 1.01^x$ **12.** $f(t) = 1.4^t$

13. College Enrollment The number of students enrolled at a college is 15,000 and grows 4% each year.
  a. The initial amount a is ■.
  b. The percent rate of change is 4%, so the growth factor b is $1 +$ ■ $=$ ■.
  c. To find the number of students enrolled after one year, you calculate $15{,}000 \cdot$ ■.
  d. Complete the equation $y =$ ■ $\cdot$ ■ to find the number of students enrolled after x years.
  e. Use your equation to predict the number of students enrolled after 25 yr.

14. Ecology A town has 10 acres of conservation land. The town plans to increase the amount of conservation land about 5% every 10 yr. If the town continues to follow their plan, how much conservation land will there be after 50 yr?

Find the balance in each account after the given period.
See Problem 2.

15. $4000 principal earning 6% compounded annually, after 5 yr

16. $12,000 principal earning 4.8% compounded annually, after 7 yr

17. $500 principal earning 4% compounded quarterly, after 6 yr

18. $20,000 deposit earning 3.5% compounded monthly, after 10 yr

19. $5000 deposit earning 1.5% compounded quarterly, after 3 yr

20. $13,500 deposit earning 3.3% compounded monthly, after 1 yr

21. $775 deposit earning 4.25% compounded annually, after 12 yr

22. $3500 deposit earning 6.75% compounded monthly, after 6 months

Identify the initial amount a and the decay factor b in each exponential function.
See Problem 3.

23. $y = 5 \cdot 0.5^x$ **24.** $f(x) = 10 \cdot 0.1^x$ **25.** $g(x) = 100\left(\frac{2}{3}\right)^x$ **26.** $y = 0.1 \cdot 0.9^x$

27. Population The population of a city is 45,000 and decreases 2% each year. If the trend continues, what will the population be after 15 yr?

B Apply   State whether the equation represents *exponential growth, exponential decay,* or *neither.*

  28. $y = 0.93 \cdot 2^x$ **29.** $y = 2 \cdot 0.68^x$ **30.** $y = 68 \cdot x^2$ **31.** $y = 68 \cdot 0.2^x$

---

4 Practice

ASSIGNMENT GUIDE

Basic: 9–27 all, 28–42 even

Average: 9–27 odd, 28–43

Advanced: 9–27 odd, 28–45

Standardized Test Prep: 46–50

Mixed Review: 51–61

Reasoning exercises have blue headings.

Applications exercises have red headings.

EXERCISE 42: Use the Think About a Plan worksheet in the **Practice and Problem Solving Workbook** (also available in the Teaching Resources in print and online) to further support students' development in becoming independent learners.

HOMEWORK QUICK CHECK

To check students' understanding of key skills and concepts, go over Exercises 17, 23, 34, 40, and 42.

Practice and Problem-Solving Exercises

  9. 14, 2   **10.** 150, 1.0894

11. 25,600, 1.01   **12.** 1, 1.4

13 a. 15,000
   b. 0.04, 1.04
   c. 1.04
   d. 15,000, 1.04, x
   e. about 39,988

14. 12.76 acres   **15.** $5352.90

16. $16,661.35   **17.** $634.87

18. $28,366.90   **19.** $5229.70

20. $13,952.30   **21.** $1277.07

22. $3619.80   **23.** 5, 0.5

24. 10, 0.1   **25.** 100, $\frac{2}{3}$

26. 0.1, 0.9

27. about 33,236

28. exponential growth

29. exponential decay

30. neither

31. exponential decay

Answers

Practice and Problem-Solving Exercises
(continued)

32. 4 teams

33. No; the value of the car is about $5243.

34. about 9 years

35. Answers may vary. Sample: $y = -4 \cdot 1.05^x$; this is an exponential function, but it models neither exponential growth nor decay because $a < 0$.

36. exponential growth

37. neither

38. exponential decay

39. neither

40. Answers may vary. Sample: By looking at a table of values or a graph for these two accounts, I would rather have the second account if I planned to keep it less than 17 years because it has more money. If I was keeping the account for more than 17 years, I would choose the first account because from that point on, it has more money in it.

41. 3 millicuries

42 a. $P = 400(1.05)^n$, where n is the number of years and P is the profit.

  b. $5031.16

---

32. Sports In a single-elimination tournament, half of the remaining teams are eliminated in each round. If the tournament starts with 128 teams, how many teams will be left after 5 rounds?

33. Car Value A family buys a car for $20,000. The value of the car decreases about 20% each year. After 6 yr, the family decides to sell the car. Should they sell it for $4000? Explain.

34. Think About a Plan You invest $100 and expect your money to grow 8% each year. About how many years will it take for your investment to double?
- What function models the growth of your investment?
- How can you use a table to find the approximate amount of time it takes for your investment to double?

35. Reasoning Give an example of an exponential function in the form $y = a \cdot b^x$ that is neither an exponential growth function nor an exponential decay function. Explain your reasoning.

State whether each graph shows an *exponential growth function,* an *exponential decay function,* or *neither.*

36.
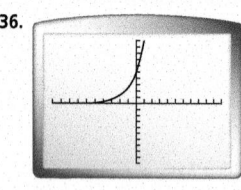

37.
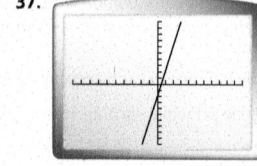

38.
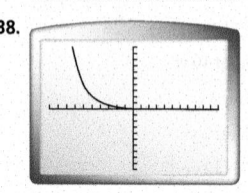

39.
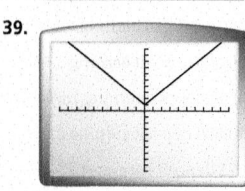

40. Writing Would you rather have $500 in an account paying 6% interest compounded quarterly or $600 in an account paying 5% interest compounded annually? Explain your reasoning.

41. Medicine Doctors can use radioactive iodine to treat some forms of cancer. The half-life of iodine-131 is 8 days. A patient receives a treatment of 12 millicuries of iodine-131. (A millicurie is a unit of radioactivity.) How much iodine-131 remains in the patient 16 days later?

42. Business Suppose you start a lawn-mowing business and make a profit of $400 in the first year. Each year, your profit increases 5%.
  a. Write a function that models your annual profit.

43. Medicine Cesium-137 is a radioisotope used in radiology where levels are measured in millicuries (mci). Use the graph at the right. What is a reasonable estimate of the half-life of cesium-137?

Cesium-137 Decay

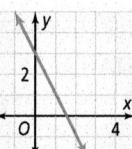

 **Challenge**

44. Credit Suppose you use a credit card to buy a new suit for $250. If you do not pay the entire balance after one month, you are charged 1.8% monthly interest on your account balance. Suppose you can make a $30 payment each month.
  a. What is your balance after your first monthly payment?
  b. How much interest are you charged on the remaining balance after your first payment?
  c. What is your balance just before you make your second payment?
  d. What is your balance after your second payment?
  e. How many months will it take for you to pay off the entire bill?
  f. How much interest will you have paid in all?

45. Open-Ended Write two exponential growth functions $f(x)$ and $g(x)$ such that $f(x) < g(x)$ for $x < 3$ and $f(x) > g(x)$ for $x > 3$.

Standardized Test Prep

GRIDDED RESPONSE

 SAT/ACT

46. A new fitness center opens with 120 members. Every month the fitness center increases the number of members by 40 members. How many members will the fitness center have after being open for 3 months?

47. What is the slope of the line at the right?

48. What is the simplified form of 8^0?

49. What is the simplified form of 5^{-2}?

50. A manufacturing company is making metal sheets with a thickness of 5.4×10^{-2} mm. What is 5.4×10^{-2} written in standard form?

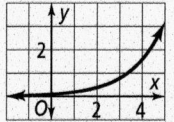

Mixed Review

Graph each function.

See Lesson 7-6.

51. $y = 2 \cdot 10^x$
52. $f(x) = 100 \cdot 0.9^x$
53. $g(x) = \frac{1}{10} \cdot 2^x$

Solve each inequality.

See Lesson 3-4.

54. $7x + 2 < 16$
55. $\frac{3}{4}t - 4 \geq 5$
56. $-0.08 > 0.35k - 0.15$

Get Ready! To prepare for Lesson 8-1, do Exercises 57–61.

Simplify each expression.

See Lesson 1-7.

57. $6t + 13t$
58. $7k - 15k$
59. $2b - 6 + 9b$
60. $4n^2 - 7n^2$
61. $8x^2 + x^2$

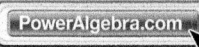 | **Lesson 7-7** Exponential Growth and Decay | 461

---

43. 30 years

44. a. $220 **b.** $3.96
  c. $223.96 **d.** $193.96
  e. 9 months **f.** $18.07

45. Answers may vary. Sample:
  $f(x) = 10(0.8)^x$ and $g(x) = 80(0.4)^x$

46. 240 **47.** −2

48. 1 **49.** $\frac{1}{25}$

50. 0.054

51.

52.

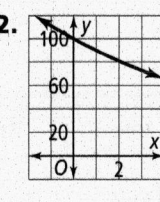

53.

54. $x < 2$ **55.** $t \geq 12$ **56.** $k < 0.2$
57. $19t$ **58.** $-8k$ **59.** $11b - 6$
60. $-3n^2$ **61.** $9x^2$

Additional Instructional Support

Algebra 1 Companion

Students can use the **Algebra 1 Companion** worktext (4 pages) as you teach the lesson. Use the Companion to support

- New Vocabulary
- Key Concepts
- Got It for each Problem
- Lesson Check

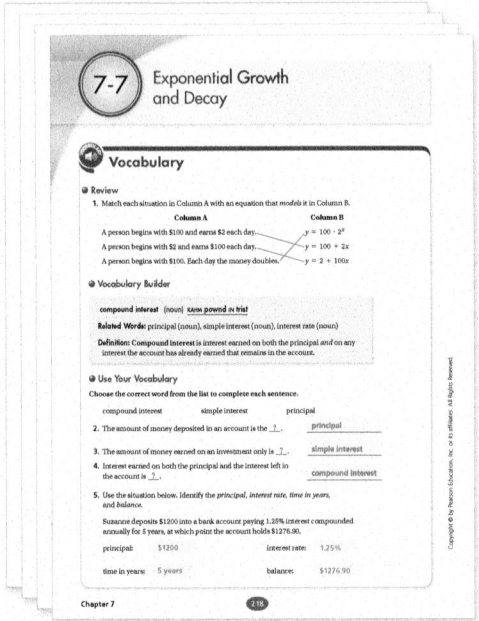

ELL Support

Focus on Communication Given below is a modified version of a famous mathematical choice. Read the following scenario to the students. Use coins as you read the scenario.

Suppose you are given the option to receive $1,000,000 at the end of a month, or to receive one penny on the first day of the month, two pennies on the second day, four pennies on the third day, eight pennies on the fourth day, and double the amount of the previous day for one month.

Have students make a table and a graph of the function $y = 2^x$ to visualize the exponential growth that occurs when the pennies are doubled each day.

Then, have them discuss the result of the exponential growth and the option they chose before and after they made the table and graph.

5 Assess & Remediate

Lesson Quiz

1. A species of frog on an island initially had a population of about 350 when scientists first began studying it. Since then the population has increased by 5.5% each year. If this trend continues, how many of the frogs in the species will there be after 18 years?

2. Alex invests $12,500 in a savings account that pays 2.75% interest compounded quarterly. How much money will he have in the account after 10 years?

3. **Do you UNDERSTAND?** The air pressure inside Jason's bike tires decreases by about 6% each week. The original pressure was 45 pounds per square inch (psi). What is the tire pressure after 6 weeks?

ANSWERS TO LESSON QUIZ

1. about 918
2. $16,441.15
3. about 31 psi

PRESCRIPTION FOR REMEDIATION
Use the student work on the Lesson Quiz to prescribe a differentiated review assignment.

Points	Differentiated Remediation
0–1	Intervention
2	On-level
3	Extension

PowerAlgebra.com

5 Assess & Remediate

Assign the Lesson Quiz. Appropriate intervention, practice, or enrichment is automatically generated based on student performance.

Intervention

- **Reteaching** (2 pages) Provides reteaching and practice exercises for the key lesson concepts. Use with struggling students or absent students.

- **English Language Learner Support** Helps students develop and reinforce mathematical vocabulary and key concepts.

All-in-One Resources/Online
Reteaching

7-7 Reteaching
Exponential Growth and Decay

Exponential functions can model the growth or decay of an initial amount.

The basic exponential function is $y = a \cdot b^x$ where

    a represents the initial amount

    b represents the growth (or decay) factor. The growth factor equals 100% plus the percent rate of change. The decay factor equals 100% minus the percent rate of decay.

    x represents the number of times the growth or decay factor is applied.

    y represents the result of applying the growth or decay factor x times.

Problem

A gym currently has 2000 members. It expects to grow 12% per year. How many members will it have in 6 years?

There are 2000 members to start, so $a = 2000$.
The growth per year is 12%, or 0.12, so $b = 1 + 0.12$ or 1.12.
The desired time period is 6 years, so $x = 6$.
The function is $y = 2000 \cdot 1.12^x$.
When $x = 6$, $y = 2000 \cdot 1.12^6 \approx 3948$. So, the gym will have about 3948 members in 6 years.

In Exercises 1–3, identify a, b, and x. Then use them to write the exponential function that models each situation. Finally use the function to answer the question.

1. When a new baby is born to the Johnsons, the family decides to invest $5000 in an account that earns 7% interest as a way to start the baby's college fund. If they do not touch that investment for 18 years, how much will there be in the college fund?
    $a = 5000$, $b = 1.07$, $x = 18$; $y = 5000(1.07)^{18}$; $16,899.66$

2. The local animal rescue league is trying to reduce the number of stray dogs in the county. They estimate that there are currently 400 stray dogs and that through their efforts they can place about 8% of the animals each month. How many stray dogs will remain in the county 12 months after the animal control effort has started?
    $a = 400$, $b = 0.92$, $x = 12$; $y = 400(0.92)^{12}$; 147 stray dogs

3. A basket of groceries costs $96.50. Assuming an inflation rate of 1.8% per year, how much will that same basket of groceries cost in 20 years?
    $a = 96.5$, $b = 1.018$, $x = 20$; $y = 96.5(1.018)^{20}$; 137.87

All-in-One Resources/Online
English Language Learner Support

7-7 ELL Support
Exponential Growth and Decay

Problem

What is the account balance on $800 at a 3.5% interest rate compounded quarterly after 2 years? Justify and explain your work.

Explain	Work	Justify
First, write the compound interest formula.	$A = P\left(1 + \frac{r}{n}\right)^{nt}$	Compound interest formula
Second, label the known values.	$P = 800$, $r = 0.035$ $n = 4$, $t = 2$	Given information
Third, substitute values into the formula.	$A = 800\left(1 + \frac{0.035}{4}\right)^{4 \cdot 2}$	Substitution
Then, simplify to get the answer.	$800(1.00875)^8 = 857.75$	Order of operations

Solution
$857.75

Exercise

What is the account balance on $550 at a 4.5% interest rate compounded quarterly after 2 years? Justify and explain your work.

Explain	Work	Justify
First, write the compound interest formula.	$A = P\left(1 + \frac{r}{n}\right)^{nt}$	Compound interest formula
Second, label the known values.	$P = 550$, $r = 0.045$ $n = 4$, $t = 2$	Given information
Third, substitute values into the formula.	$A = 550\left(1 + \frac{0.045}{4}\right)^{4 \cdot 2}$	Substitution
Then, simplify to get the answer.	$550(1.01125)^8 = 601.49$	Order of operations

Solution
$601.49

Differentiated Remediation *continued*

On-Level

- **Practice** (2 pages) Provides extra practice for each lesson. For simpler practice exercises, use the Form K Practice pages found in the All-in-One Teaching Resources and online.
- **Think About a Plan** Helps students develop specific problem-solving skills and strategies by providing scaffolded guiding questions.
- **Standardized Test Prep** Focuses on all major exercises, all major question types, and helps students prepare for the high-stakes assessments.

Extension

- **Enrichment** Provides students with interesting problems and activities that extend the concepts of the lesson.
- **Activities, Games, and Puzzles** Worksheets that can be used for concepts development, enrichment, and for fun!

Practice and Problem Solving WKBK/ All-in-One Resources/Online
Practice page 1

7-7 **Practice** *Form G*
Exponential Growth and Decay

Identify the initial amount *a* and the growth factor *b* in each exponential function.

1. $f(x) = 3 \cdot 5^x$ — $a = 3, b = 5$
2. $y = 250 \cdot 1.065^x$ — $a = 250, b = 1.065$
3. $g(t) = 3.5^t$ — $a = 1, b = 3.5$
4. $h(x) = 5 \cdot 1.02^x$ — $a = 5, b = 1.02$

Find the balance in each account after the given period.

5. $8000 principal earning 5% compounded annually, after 6 yr $10,770.77
6. $2000 principal earning 5.4% compounded annually, after 4 yr $2468.27
7. $500 principal earning 4% compounded quarterly, after 10 yr $744.43
8. $6500 principal earning 2.8% compounded monthly, after 2 yr $6819.28

Identify the initial amount *a* and the decay factor *b* in each exponential function.

9. $y = 8 \cdot 0.8^x$ $a = 8, b = 0.8$
10. $f(x) = 12 \cdot 0.1^x$ $a = 12, b = 0.1$

State whether the equation represents *exponential growth, exponential decay,* or *neither.*

11. $y = 0.82 \cdot 3^x$ exponential growth
12. $f(x) = 5 \cdot 0.3^x$ exponential decay
13. $f(x) = 18 \cdot x^2$ neither
14. $y = 0.9^x$ exponential decay
15. The town manager reports that revenue for a given year is $2.5 million. The budget director predicts that revenue will increase by 4% per yr. If the director's prediction holds true, how much revenue will the town have available 10 years from the date of the town manager's report? $3.7 million
16. A wildlife manager determines that there are approximately 200 deer in a certain state park.
    a. The population is growing at a rate of 7% per year. How many deer will live in the park after 4 years? approximately 262
    b. If the carrying capacity of this park is 350 deer, how long will it take for the deer population to reach carrying capacity? between 8 and 9 years

Practice and Problem Solving WKBK/ All-in-One Resources/Online
Practice page 2

7-7 **Practice** (continued) *Form G*
Exponential Growth and Decay

17. **Open-Ended** Write an exponential function that begins its rapid increase when $2 \le x \le 3$. Write another that begins its rapid increase when $3 \le x \le 4$. Write a third that begins its rapid increase when $6 \le x \le 8$. Check students' work.
18. A business purchases a computer system for $3000. If the value of the system decreases at a rate of 15% per year, how much is the computer worth after 4 years? $1566.02
19. **Writing** Explain the difference in how you would model the following situations. Person A puts $1000 in a safe in his home, and puts in an additional $50 per year. Person B puts $1000 in an investment that earns 5% per year. Why is one exponential and the other linear? How would their graphs compare? How would their values compare over time?
    For person A: $y = 1000 + 50x$, where y = total savings and x = number of years. This is linear because x and y both have a constant difference. For person B: $y = 1000(1.05)^x$, where y = total savings and x = number of years. This is an exponential function because x has a constant difference and y has a constant ratio. The graph for Person A is a straight line; the graph for Person B is an exponential curve. Person B's values will increase faster.

State whether each graph shows an *exponential growth function,* an *exponential decay function,* or *neither.*

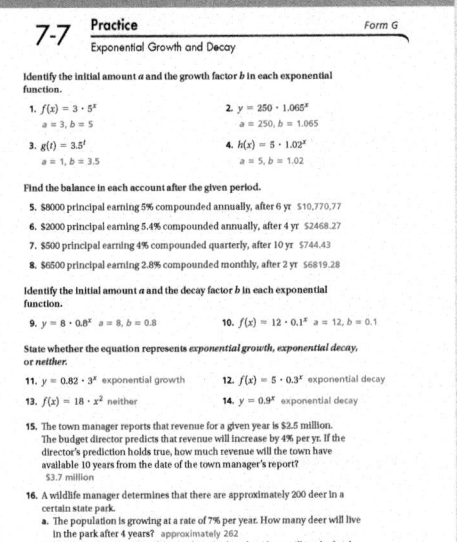

20.
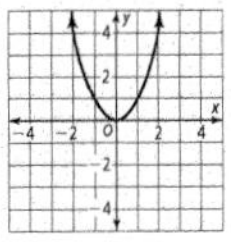
neither

21.
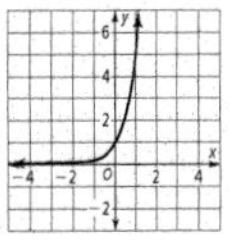
exponential growth

22.
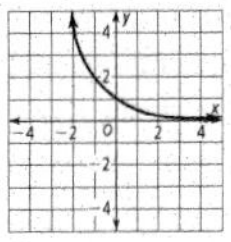
exponential decay

23.
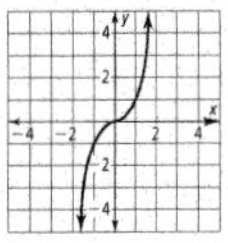
neither

24. **Reasoning** Can the graph of an exponential function ever have a *y*-intercept of 0? Why or why not?
    Answers may vary. Sample: no, because $a > 0$ and b^x is always positive

All-in-One Resources/Online
Enrichment

7-7 **Enrichment**
Exponential Growth and Decay

In this Enrichment you will consider how the compounding interval affects the final value of an investment.

For each situation outlined below, list the number of compounding intervals in 10 years, the compound interval, the percent interest at each interval, the amount earned at each interval, and the value of the investment after 10 years.

1. You have $10,000 you want to invest. Your bank will double your money after 10 years. So, after 10 years you will receive 100% interest.
2. You realize that you might want your money before 10 years. You ask your banker if he would be willing to give you a proportional part of the interest each year. The banker, eager for your business, says yes. Instead of providing 100% once over 10 years, he will provide 10% each year for 10 years.
3. You get a bit giddy with the results and wonder how much your investment would be worth if the banker gave you a proportional amount of interest compounded every six months. (If you have not done so yet, consider organizing your data in a table.)
4. Continue the table by compounding every month, every week, every day and every hour. What do you notice about the final values as the compounding interval gets small and the number of compounding periods gets large?

	Compounding intervals in 10 yrs	Compound interval	Percent interest at each interval	Amount earned at each interval	Value of the investment after 10 yrs
1.	1	10 yr	100%	$10,000	$20,000
2.	10	1 yr	10%	$1000	$25,937.42
3.	20	6 mo	5%	$500	$26,532.98
4.	120	1 mo	0.83%	$83.33	$27,070.42
	520	1 wk	0.19%	$19	$27,156.73
	3650	1 day	0.00027%	$2.70	$27,179.10
	87,600	1 hr	0.0000114%	$0.11	$27,182.66

5. What is the exponential equation that models the situation outlined above?
   $y = 10{,}000\left(1 + \frac{1}{n}\right)^n$, where n = the number of compounding intervals in 10 years
6. What happens to the value of $\left(1 + \frac{1}{x}\right)^x$ as x gets very large? What does this have to do with the situation outlined above?
   $\left(1 + \frac{1}{n}\right)^x$ gets very close to 2.72; this expression is similar to the expression used to determine the compounding for various intervals;

Practice and Problem Solving WKBK/ All-in-One Resources/Online
Think About a Plan

7-7 **Think About a Plan**
Exponential Growth and Decay

Business You open a bank account to save for college and deposit $400 in the account. Each year, the balance in your account will increase 5%.
a. Write a function that models your annual balance.
b. What will be the *total* amount in your account after 7 yr?

1. Make a table that has one column representing the number of years the account has been open, a second column representing the balance in the given year, and a third column representing the *total* balance.

Years Account Open	Balance this Year	Total Balance
0	400	400
1	420	820
2	441	1261
3	463.05	1724.05

2. The first row of the table represents year 0. Year 0 is the start up year, the year with a balance of $400. If you want to know how much you have after three years, you will read your balance from the fourth line of the table, which starts with the number 3. In order to answer the question in part b, what line of the table should you use? What number would start that line? Why?
   use the eighth row of the table; the row would start with the number 7 to represent 7 years since the account opened.
3. Recall that the general form of an exponential function is $f(x) = a \cdot b^x$. Given the situation described, what is *a*? What is *b*? Write the function that models your annual balance. Check to make sure the function you created provides the same values you put into your table for years 1, 2 and 3.
   $a =$ 400 $b =$ 1.05 $f(x) =$ $400 \cdot 1.05^x$
4. Use the exponential function and extend the table to answer part b.

Years Account Open	Balance this Year	Total Balance
0	400	400
1	420	820
2	441	1261
3	463.05	1724.05
4	486.20	2210.25
5	510.51	2720.76
6	536.04	3256.80
7	562.84	3819.64

After 7 years the account will have $3819.64

Practice and Problem Solving WKBK/ All-in-One Resources/Online
Standardized Test Prep

7-7 **Standardized Test Prep**
Exponential Growth and Decay

Multiple Choice

For Exercises 1–5, choose the correct letter.

1. Which of the following functions models exponential decay? B
   A. $f(x) = 12 \cdot 3^x$ B. $y = 2 \cdot 0.8^x$ C. $y = -3x^2$ D. $f(x) = 1.8^x$
2. Suppose you deposit $500 into an account earning 7.8% interest compounded annually. How long will it take for the account to be worth $1000? I
   F. between 6 and 7 years H. between 8 and 9 years
   G. between 7 and 8 years I. between 9 and 10 years
3. What is always true regarding functions that model exponential growth?
   A. Their graphs are always symmetric about the *y*-axis. B
   B. The range depends on the growth factor.
   C. The value of *y* is always greater than the value of *x*.
   D. The value of *y* decreases as *x* gets more negative.
4. What is $3 \cdot 2^x$ if $x = 3$? G
   F. 18 G. 24 H. 125 I. 216
5. Where will the graphs of $y = 4^x$, $y = 1.2^x$ and $y = 0.6^x$ intersect? C
   A. (0, 0) B. (1, 0) C. (0, 1) D. (1, 1)

Short Response

6. Suppose you deposit $2000 into an account earning 5% interest compounded quarterly. To the nearest dollar, what is the balance after 4 years? $2440
   [2] Correct answer given with work shown
   [1] Correct answer given with no work shown
   [0] Incorrect answer or no attempt made

Online Teacher Resource Center
Activities, Games, and Puzzles

7-7 **Game: Getting Larger or Getting Smaller?**
Exponential Growth and Decay

This is a game for three students. Decide on a host and two players.

- The host will take turns giving players items from the first group, then the second group, and then the third group.
- The host will enforce a time limit for responses, if necessary.
- Players record their scores in the columns at the right.
- The player who earns the most points wins. See Teacher Instructions page.

	An example of growth or decay? (5 points each)	Player 1	Player 2
1.	2, 4, 8, . . .		
2.	30, 15, 7.5, . . .		
3.	$y = 0.7(1.2)^x$		
4.	$y = 0.4(0.2)^x$		

	What's the multiplier? (6 points each)	Player 1	Player 2
1.	1.5, 4.5, 13.5, . . .		
2.	0.25, 1.25, 6.25, . . .		
3.	144, 36, 9, 2.25, . . .		
4.	4, 0.8, 0.16, 0.32, . . .		
5.	0.07, 0.7, 7.0, 70, . . .		
6.	$y = 0.5(1.3)^x$		

	What's the value of the function? (7 points each)	Player 1	Player 2
1.	$y = 2(5)^x$ when $x = 2$		
2.	$y = 0.1(3)^x$ when $x = 3$		
3.	$y = 10(0.1)^x$ when $x = 4$		
4.	$y = 0.5(6)^x$ when $x = 2$		
5.	$y = 2.5(2.5)^x$ when $x = 1$		
6.	$y = 3(10)^x$ when $x = 3$		
7.	$y = 4(2)^x$ when $x = 5$		
8.	$y = 0.2(10)^x$ when $x = 3$		

Performance Task UbD

Pull it All Together

The concepts and skills required to solve these problems are from several lessons within this chapter and from the previous chapter. As students solve these problems, they will demonstrate their reasoning strategies and their growth as independent problem solvers.

The following questions are designed for you to:
- Help support students as they do the Tasks.
- Gauge the amount of support a student needs as they progress to becoming an independent problem solver.

Task 1
- How can you write 1000 using an exponent?
- What property can you use to multiply the expressions with exponents?
- How can you compare numbers written in scientific notation?

Task 2
- What operation can you use to determine the number of bits in a megabyte?
- What operation can you use to determine the number of bits in a gigabyte?

Task 3
- What do you know? What do you need?
- What function models the situation?
- How can you find the year that one population will surpass the other?

> To solve these problems you will pull together many concepts and skills that you have studied about exponents and exponential functions.

BIG idea Equivalence

One way to represent numbers is in scientific notation. This form uses powers of ten to write very large or very small numbers.

Task 1

Medical X-rays, with a wavelength of about 10^{-10} m, can penetrate completely through your skin.

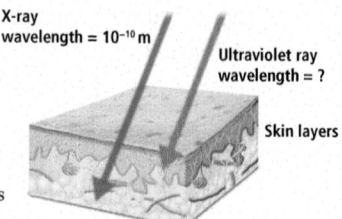

X-ray wavelength = 10^{-10} m

Ultraviolet ray wavelength = ?

Skin layers

  a. Ultraviolet rays, which cause sun burn by penetrating only the top level of skin, have a wavelength about 1000 times the wavelength of an X-ray. Find the wavelength of ultraviolet rays. Show your work.
  b. The wavelengths of visible light are between 3.8×10^{-7} m and 7.6×10^{-7} m. Are these wavelengths longer or shorter than those of ultraviolet rays? Explain.

BIG idea Properties

Just as there are properties that describe how to rewrite expressions involving addition and multiplication, there are properties that describe how to rewrite and simplify exponential expressions.

Task 2

Write each answer as a power of 2. Show your work and explain your steps.

  a. Computer capacity is often measured in bits and bytes. A bit is the smallest unit, which is a 1 or 0, in the computer's memory. A byte is 2^3 bits. A megabyte (MB) is 2^{20} bytes. How many bits are in a megabyte?
  b. A gigabyte (GB) is 2^{30} bytes. How many megabytes are in a gigabyte? How many bits are in a gigabyte?

BIG idea Functions

The family of exponential functions has equations of the form $y = a \cdot b^x$. They can be used to model exponential growth or decay.

Task 3

On January 1, 2010, Chessville has a population of 50,000 people. Chessville then enters a period of population growth. Its population increases 7% each year. On the same day, Checkersville has a population of 70,000 people. Checkersville starts to experience a population decline. Its population decreases 4% each year. During what year will the population of Chessville first exceed that of Checkersville? Show all of your work and explain your steps.

Assess Performance UbD

Pull It All Together

See p. 67 for a holistic scoring rubric to gauge a student's progress on Understanding the Problem, Planning a Solution, Getting an Answer, and Assessing Autonomy.

SOLUTION OUTLINES

1. a. Possible plan: Find the wavelength of ultraviolet rays by multiplying the wavelength of an X-ray by $1000(10^{-10} \cdot 1000 = 10^{-10} \cdot 10^3 = 10^{-10+3} = 10^{-7})$.

   b. First step: Write the wavelength of ultraviolet rays in scientific notation $(10^{-7} = 1 \times 10^{-7})$.

   Second step: Order the wavelength of ultraviolet rays and the range of wavelengths of visible light by arranging the decimals in order $(1 \times 10^{-7} < 3.8 \times 10^{-7} < 7.6 \times 10^{-7})$.

Third step: Recognize that the wavelengths of visible light are longer than those of ultraviolet rays.

2. a. Possible plan: To find the number of bits in 1 megabyte, multiply the number of bits in 1 byte by the number of bytes in 1 megabyte $(1 \text{ MB} = 2^3 \times 2^{20}, \text{ or } 2^{23} \text{ bits})$.

   b. First step: To find the number of megabytes in 1 gigabyte, divide the number of bytes in 1 gigabyte by the number of bytes in 1 megabyte $\left(\dfrac{2^{30}}{2^{20}} = 2^{10} \text{ MB}\right)$.

   Second step: To find the number of bits in 1 gigabyte, multiply the number of bytes in 1 gigabyte by the number of bits in 1 byte $(2^{30} \cdot 2^3 = 2^{33} \text{ bits})$.

3. First step: Model the population growth of Chessville with an exponential function $(y = 50,000 \cdot 1.07^x)$.

Second step: Use the function from the first step to find the population of Chessville in 2011, 2012, 2013, 2014 (53,500; 57,245; 61,252; 65,540).

Third step: Model the population decline of Checkersville with an exponential function $(y = 70,000 \cdot 0.96^x)$.

Fourth step: Use the function from the third step to find the population of Checkersville in 2011, 2012, 2013, 2014 (67,200; 64,512; 61,932; 59,454).

Fifth step: Compare the results from the Second step and the Fourth step. Determine when the population of Chessville first exceeds that of Checkersville. (On January 1, 2014, the population of Chessville is 65,540, and the population of Checkersville is 59,454. So the population of Chessville will exceed that of Checkersville sometime during the year 2013.)

7 Chapter Review

Connecting BIG ideas and Answering the Essential Questions

1 Equivalence
One way to represent numbers is in scientific notation. This form uses powers of ten to write very large or very small numbers.

Zero and Negative Exponents (Lesson 7-1)
$10^0 = 1$
$10^{-3} = \dfrac{1}{10^3}$

Scientific Notation (Lesson 7-2)
175,000,000,000,000
$= 1.75 \times 10^{14}$
$0.0000568 = 5.68 \times 10^{-5}$

2 Properties
Just as there are properties that describe how to rewrite expressions involving addition and multiplication, there are properties that describe how to rewrite and simplify exponential expressions.

Properties of Exponents (Lessons 7-3, 7-4, and 7-5)
$5^2 \cdot 5^4 = 5^{2+4} = 5^6$
$(3^7)^4 = 3^{7 \cdot 4} = 3^{28}$
$(6x)^4 = 6^4 x^4$
$\dfrac{7^8}{7^5} = 7^{8-5} = 7^3$
$\left(\dfrac{y}{2}\right)^5 = \dfrac{y^5}{2^5}$

3 Function
The family of exponential functions has equations of the form $y = a \cdot b^x$. They can be used to model exponential growth or decay.

Exponential Functions (Lesson 7-6)
$y = 2 \cdot \left(\dfrac{5}{4}\right)^x$
$y = 3 \cdot \left(\dfrac{1}{4}\right)^x$

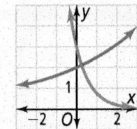

Exponential Growth and Decay (Lesson 7-7)
Exponential growth is modeled by the function $y = a \cdot b^x$, where $a > 0$ and $b > 1$. Exponential decay is modeled by the function $y = a \cdot b^x$, where $a > 0$ and $0 < b < 1$.

Chapter Vocabulary

- compound interest (p. 456)
- decay factor (p. 457)
- exponential decay (p. 457)
- exponential function (p. 447)
- exponential growth (p. 455)
- growth factor (p. 455)
- scientific notation (p. 420)

Choose the correct term to complete each sentence.

1. _?_ is a shorthand way to write very large and very small numbers.

2. For a function $y = a \cdot b^x$, where $a > 0$ and $b > 1$, b is the _?_.

3. For a function $y = a \cdot b^x$, where $a > 0$ and $0 < b < 1$, b is the _?_.

4. The function $y = a \cdot b^x$ models _?_ for $a > 0$ and $b > 1$.

5. The function $y = a \cdot b^x$ models _?_ for $a > 0$ and $0 < b < 1$.

PowerAlgebra.com | Chapter 7 Chapter Review | 463

Answers

Chapter Review

1. scientific notation
2. growth factor
3. decay factor
4. exponential growth
5. exponential decay

Essential Questions UbD

BIG idea Equivalence
ESSENTIAL QUESTION How can you represent very large and very small numbers?
ANSWER One way to represent numbers is in scientific notation. This form uses powers of ten to write very large or very small numbers.

BIG idea Properties
ESSENTIAL QUESTION How can you simplify expressions involving exponents?
ANSWER Just as there are properties that describe how to rewrite expressions involving addition and multiplication, there are properties that describe how to rewrite and simplify exponential expressions.

BIG idea Function
ESSENTIAL QUESTION What are the characteristics of exponential functions?
ANSWER The family of exponential functions has equations of the form $y = a \cdot b^x$. They can be used to model exponential growth or decay.

Summative Questions UbD

Use the following prompts as you review this chapter with your students. The prompts are designed to help you assess your students' understanding of the Big Ideas they have studied.

- How do you know when an expression with exponents is completely simplified? Give examples of expressions that need to be simplified and explain how to simplify them.

- Give examples of exponential growth and exponential decay functions. What are the differences in the equations and graphs of your examples?

- Make a graph of $y = (1)^{2x}$. Explain what happens to the graph when you change the **1** to a proper fraction, a large number, or a negative number. What happens when you change the **2** to a larger number or a fraction?

Answers

Chapter Review (continued)

6. 1 **7.** $\frac{1}{49}$ **8.** $\frac{4y^8}{x^2}$

9. $\frac{q^4}{p^2}$ **10.** 9 **11.** $\frac{9}{16}$

12. 1 **13.** 45 **14.** $\frac{25}{9}$

15. $-\frac{20}{9}$

16. No; -3 should be raised to the fourth power instead of being multiplied by 4.

17. No; 950 is not between 1 and 10.

18. No; 100 is not written as a power of 10.

19. yes

20. No; 0.84 is not between 1 and 10.

21. 2.793×10^6 **22.** 1.89×10^8

23. 4.3×10^{-5} **24.** 2.7×10^{-9}

25. 3.86×10^{12} **26.** 4.78×10^{-6}

7-1 Zero and Negative Exponents

Quick Review

You can use zero and negative integers as exponents. For every nonzero number a, $a^0 = 1$. For every nonzero number a and any integer n, $a^{-n} = \frac{1}{a^n}$. When you evaluate an exponential expression, you can simplify the expression before substituting values for the variables.

Example

What is the value of $a^2b^{-4}c^0$ for $a = 3$, $b = 2$, and $c = -5$?

$$a^2b^{-4}c^0 = \frac{a^2c^0}{b^4} \quad \text{Use the definition of negative exponents.}$$

$$= \frac{a^2(1)}{b^4} \quad \text{Use the definition of zero exponent.}$$

$$= \frac{3^2}{2^4} \quad \text{Substitute.}$$

$$= \frac{9}{16} \quad \text{Simplify.}$$

Exercises

Simplify each expression.

6. 5^0 **7.** 7^{-2}

8. $\frac{4x^{-2}}{y^{-8}}$ **9.** $\frac{1}{p^2q^{-4}r^0}$

Evaluate each expression for $x = 2$, $y = -3$, and $z = -5$.

10. x^0y^2 **11.** $(-x)^{-4}y^2$

12. x^0z^0 **13.** $\frac{5x^0}{y^{-2}}$

14. $y^{-2}z^2$ **15.** $\frac{2x}{y^2z^{-1}}$

16. Reasoning Is it true that $(-3b)^4 = -12b^4$? Explain why or why not.

7-2 Scientific Notation

Quick Review

You can use **scientific notation** to write very large or very small numbers. A number is written in scientific notation if it has the form $a \times 10^n$, where $1 \le |a| < 10$ and n is an integer.

Example

What is each number written in scientific notation?

a. 510,000,000,000

$510{,}000{,}000{,}000 = 5.1 \times 10^{11}$ Move the decimal point 11 places to the left.

b. 0.0000087

$0.0000087 = 8.7 \times 10^{-6}$ Move the decimal point 6 places to the right.

Exercises

Is the number written in scientific notation? If not, explain why not.

17. 950×10^5 **18.** 7.23×100^8

19. 1.6×10^{-6} **20.** 0.84×10^{-5}

Write each number in scientific notation.

21. 2,793,000 **22.** 189,000,000

23. 0.000043 **24.** 0.0000000027

25. 3,860,000,000,000 **26.** 0.00000478

7-3 and 7-4 Multiplication Properties of Exponents

Quick Review

To multiply powers with the same base, add the exponents.

$a^m \cdot a^n = a^{m+n}$, where $a \neq 0$ and m and n are integers

To raise a power to a power, multiply the exponents.

$(a^m)^n = a^{mn}$, where $a \neq 0$ and m and n are integers

To raise a product to a power, raise each factor in the product to the power.

$(ab)^n = a^n b^n$, where $a \neq 0$, $b \neq 0$, and n is an integer

Example

What is the simplified form of each expression?

a. $3^{10} \cdot 3^4 = 3^{10+4} = 3^{14}$

b. $(x^5)^7 = x^{5 \cdot 7} = x^{35}$

c. $(pq)^8 = p^8 q^8$

Exercises

Complete each equation.

27. $3^2 \cdot 3^{\blacksquare} = 3^{10}$

28. $a^6 \cdot a^{\blacksquare} = a^8$

29. $x^2 y^5 \cdot x^{\blacksquare} y^{\blacksquare} = x^5 y^{11}$

30. $(5^5)^{\blacksquare} = 5^{15}$

31. $(b^{-4})^{\blacksquare} = b^{20}$

32. $(4x^3 y^5)^{\blacksquare} = 16x^6 y^{10}$

Simplify each expression.

33. $2d^2 \cdot d^3$

34. $(q^3 r)^4$

35. $(5c^{-4})(-4m^2 c^8)$

36. $(1.34^2)^5 (1.34)^{-8}$

37. $(12x^2 y^{-2})^5 (4xy^{-3})^{-7}$

38. $(-2r^{-4})^2 (-3r^2 z^8)^{-1}$

39. **Estimation** Each square inch of your body has about 6.5×10^2 pores. Suppose the back of your hand has an area of about 0.12×10^2 in.^{2}. About how many pores are on the back of your hand? Write your answer in scientific notation.

7-5 Division Properties of Exponents

Quick Review

To divide powers with the same base, subtract the exponents.

$\frac{a^m}{a^n} = a^{m-n}$, where $a \neq 0$ and m and n are integers

To raise a quotient to a power, raise the numerator and the denominator to the power.

$\left(\frac{a}{b}\right)^n = \frac{a^n}{b^n}$, where $a \neq 0$, $b \neq 0$, and n is an integer

Example

What is the simplified form of $\left(\frac{5x^4}{z^2}\right)^3$?

$\left(\frac{5x^4}{z^2}\right)^3 = \frac{(5x^4)^3}{(z^2)^3} = \frac{5^3 x^{4 \cdot 3}}{z^{2 \cdot 3}} = \frac{125 x^{12}}{z^6}$

Exercises

Simplify each expression.

40. $\frac{w^2}{w^5}$

41. $\frac{21x^3}{3x^{-1}}$

42. $\left(\frac{n^5}{v^3}\right)^7$

43. $\left(\frac{3c^3}{e^5}\right)^{-4}$

Simplify each quotient. Write your answer in scientific notation.

44. $\frac{4.2 \times 10^8}{2.1 \times 10^{11}}$

45. $\frac{3.1 \times 10^4}{1.24 \times 10^2}$

46. $\frac{4.5 \times 10^3}{9 \times 10^7}$

47. $\frac{5.1 \times 10^5}{1.7 \times 10^2}$

48. **Writing** List the steps that you would use to simplify $\left(\frac{5a^8}{10a^6}\right)^{-3}$.

---

27. 8

28. 2

29. 3; 6

30. 3

31. −5

32. 2

33. $2d^5$

34. $q^{12} r^4$

35. $-20c^4 m^2$

36. 1.7956

37. $\frac{243x^3 y^{11}}{16}$

38. $-\frac{4}{3r^{10} z^8}$

39. 7.8×10^3 pores

40. $\frac{1}{w^3}$

41. $7x^4$

42. $\frac{n^{35}}{v^{21}}$

43. $\frac{e^{20}}{81c^{12}}$

44. 2×10^{-3}

45. 2.5×10^2

46. 5×10^{-5}

47. 3×10^3

48. Answers may vary. Sample:

   1) Simplify the expression within the parentheses.

   2) Take the reciprocal of the rational expression raised to the third power.

   3) Use the quotient raised to a power rule by applying the exponent to both the numerator and denominator.

   4) Simplify the numerator.

   5) Simplify the denominator using the power rule.

Answers

Chapter Review (continued)

49. 4, 16, 64

50. 0.01, 0.0001, 0.000001

51. 20, 10, 5   **52.** 6, 12, 24

53. 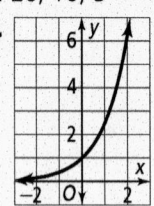   **54.**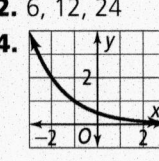

55. 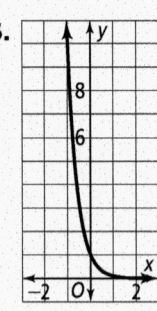   **56.**

57. a. 800 bacteria

    b. about 1.4×10^{16} bacteria

58. exponential growth; 3

59. exponential decay; 0.32

60. exponential growth; $\frac{3}{2}$

61. exponential decay; $\frac{1}{4}$

62. $2697.20

63. 463 people

7-6 Exponential Functions

Quick Review

An **exponential function** involves repeated multiplication of an initial amount a by the same positive number b. The general form of an exponential function is $y = a \cdot b^x$, where $a \neq 0$, $b > 0$, and $b \neq 1$.

Example

What is the graph of $y = \frac{1}{2} \cdot 5^x$?

Make a table of values. Graph the ordered pairs.

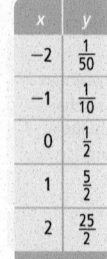

x	y
-2	$\frac{1}{50}$
-1	$\frac{1}{10}$
0	$\frac{1}{2}$
1	$\frac{5}{2}$
2	$\frac{25}{2}$

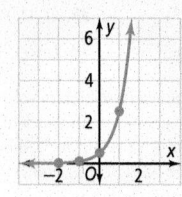

Exercises

Evaluate each function for the domain $\{1, 2, 3\}$.

49. $f(x) = 4^x$ **50.** $y = 0.01^x$

51. $y = 40\left(\frac{1}{2}\right)^x$ **52.** $f(x) = 3 \cdot 2^x$

Graph each function.

53. $f(x) = 2.5^x$ **54.** $y = 0.5(0.5)^x$

55. $f(x) = \frac{1}{2} \cdot 3^x$ **56.** $y = 0.1^x$

57. Biology A population of 50 bacteria in a laboratory culture doubles every 30 min. The function $p(x) = 50 \cdot 2^x$ models the population, where x is the number of 30-min periods.

    a. How many bacteria will there be after 2 h?

    b. How many bacteria will there be after 1 day?

7-7 Exponential Growth and Decay

Quick Review

When $a > 0$ and $b > 1$, the function $y = a \cdot b^x$ models **exponential growth**. The base b is called the **growth factor**. When $a > 0$ and $0 < b < 1$, the function $y = a \cdot b^x$ models **exponential decay**. In this case the base b is called the **decay factor**.

Example

The population of a city is 25,000 and decreases 1% each year. Predict the population after 6 yr.

$$y = 25,000 \cdot 0.99^x \quad \text{Exponential decay function}$$

$$= 25,000 \cdot 0.99^6 \quad \text{Substitute 6 for } x.$$

$$\approx 23,537 \quad \text{Simplify.}$$

The population will be about 23,537 after 6 yr.

Exercises

Tell whether the function represents *exponential growth* or *exponential decay*. Identify the growth or decay factor.

58. $y = 5.2 \cdot 3^x$ **59.** $f(x) = 7 \cdot 0.32^x$

60. $y = 0.15\left(\frac{3}{2}\right)^x$ **61.** $g(x) = 1.3\left(\frac{1}{4}\right)^x$

62. Finance Suppose $2000 is deposited in an account paying 2.5% interest compounded quarterly. What will the account balance be after 12 yr?

63. Music A band performs a free concert in a local park. There are 200 people in the crowd at the start of the concert. The number of people in the crowd grows 15% every half hour. How many people are in the crowd after 3 h? Round to the nearest person.

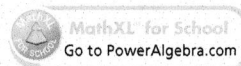
MathXL for School
Go to PowerAlgebra.com

Do you know HOW?

Simplify each expression.

1. $\frac{r^3 t^{-7}}{t^5}$

2. $\left(\frac{a^3}{5m}\right)^{-4}$

3. $c^3 v^9 c^{-1} c^0$

4. $2y^{-9} h^2 (2y^0 h^{-4})^{-6}$

5. $(1.2)^5 (1.2)^{-2}$

6. $(-3q^{-1})^3 q^2$

Write each number in scientific notation.

7. 79,500,000,000

8. 0.0000000405

Write each number in standard notation.

9. 8.4×10^{-6}

10. 9.52×10^{11}

Simplify each expression. Write each answer in scientific notation.

11. $(6 \times 10^4)(4.8 \times 10^2)$

12. $\frac{1.5 \times 10^7}{5 \times 10^{-2}}$

13. Medicine The human body normally produces about 2×10^6 red blood cells per second.

a. Use scientific notation to express how many red blood cells your body produces in one day.

b. One pint of blood contains about 2.4×10^{12} red blood cells. How many seconds will it take your body to replace the red blood cells lost by donating one pint of blood? How many days?

Evaluate each function for $x = -1, 2,$ and 3.

14. $y = 3 \cdot 5^x$

15. $f(x) = \frac{1}{2} \cdot 4^x$

16. $f(x) = 4(0.95)^x$

Graph each function.

17. $y = \frac{1}{2} \cdot 2^x$ **18.** $y = 2 \cdot \left(\frac{1}{2}\right)^x$

19. Banking A customer deposits $2000 in a savings account that pays 5.2% interest compounded quarterly. How much money will the customer have in the account after 2 yr? After 5 yr?

20. Automobiles Suppose a new car is worth $30,000. You can use the function $y = 30,000(0.85)^x$ to estimate the car's value after x years.

a. What is the decay factor? What does it mean?

b. Estimate the car's value after 1 yr.

c. Estimate the car's value after 4 yr.

Do you UNDERSTAND?

21. Error Analysis Find and correct the error in the work shown below.

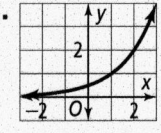
$3^4 \cdot 3^3 = 9^7$

22. Open-Ended Write two equivalent expressions. Use a negative exponent in one of the expressions.

23. Writing Explain when a function in the form $y = a \cdot b^x$ models exponential growth and when it models exponential decay.

24. Simplify the expression $\left(\frac{a^6}{a^4}\right)^2$ in two different ways. Justify each step.

25. Reasoning Explain how you can use the property for dividing powers with the same base to justify the definition of a zero exponent.

23. The function $y = a \cdot b^x$ models exponential growth when the value of b is greater than 1. It models exponential decay when $0 < b < 1$.

24. I. Simplify within the parentheses first using the quotient rule, $\left(\frac{a^6}{a^4}\right)^2 = (a^2)^2$. Then use the product rule to get a^4.

II. Apply the quotient raised to a power rule first, $\left(\frac{a^6}{a^4}\right)^2 = \frac{(a^6)^2}{(a^4)^2} = \frac{a^{12}}{a^8}$. Then use the quotient rule to get a^4.

25. Any number divided by itself equals 1. When you have a quotient of $\frac{a^n}{a^n}$, the quotient rule says that you can subtract the exponents. $\frac{a^n}{a^n} = a^{n-n} = a^0$. Therefore, a^0 must equal 1.

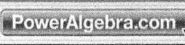
Answers

Chapter Test

1. $\frac{r^3}{t^{12}}$

2. $\frac{625m^4}{a^{12}}$

3. $c^2 v^9$

4. $\frac{h^{26}}{32y^9}$

5. 1.728

6. $\frac{-27}{q}$

7. 7.95×10^{10}

8. 4.05×10^{-8}

9. 0.0000084

10. 952,000,000,000

11. 2.88×10^7

12. 3×10^8

13. a. 1.728×10^{11} red blood cells per day

b. 1.2×10^6 s; about 13.9 days

14. 0.6, 75, 375

15. $\frac{1}{8}$, 8, 32

16. 4.2105, 3.61, 3.4295

17.

18.

19. $2217.71; $2589.52

20. a. 0.85; A car depreciates 15% per year.

b. $25,500

c. $15,660.19

21. When the bases are the same, you add the exponents and keep the same base; $3^4 \cdot 3^3 = 3^{4+3} = 3^7$

22. Answers may vary. Sample: $a^{-6}, \frac{1}{a^6}$

Item Number	Lesson
1	7-3
2	5-3
3	1-2
4	4-1
5	1-6
6	4-3
7	7-2
8	5-5
9	2-8
10	7-3
11	5-5
12	2-8
13	3-4
14	4-2
15	5-5
16	5-3
17	1-6
18	2-5
19	1-2
20	1-1
21	2-9
22	6-2
23	6-3
24	3-8
25	2-5
26	2-2
27	7-7
28	6-3

TIPS FOR SUCCESS

Some questions on tests ask you to solve problems involving exponents. Read the sample question at the right. Then follow the tips to answer it.

If the side length of a square can be represented by the expression $4x^2y^6$, which expression could represent the area of the square?

A $2xy^3$

B $8x^4y^{12}$

C $16x^4y^{12}$

D $16x^4y^{36}$

TIP 1

Look to eliminate answer choices. You need to square 4, so you can eliminate A and B.

TIP 2

Use properties of exponents to help you solve the problem.

Think It Through

The side length of the square is $4x^2y^6$, so the area is $(4x^2y^6)^2$. Multiply the exponents when you are raising a power to a power.

$$(4x^2y^6)^2 = 4^2x^{2\cdot2}y^{6\cdot2}$$
$$= 16x^4y^{12}$$

The correct answer is C.

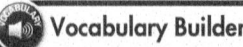 **Vocabulary Builder**

As you solve test items, you must understand the meanings of mathematical terms. Choose the correct term to complete each sentence.

A. The values of the (*independent, dependent*) variable are the output values of the function.

B. The (*base, exponent*) of a power is the number that is multiplied repeatedly.

C. A number in (*scientific, standard*) notation is a shorthand way to write numbers using powers of 10.

D. The (*slope, y-intercept*) of a line is the ratio of the vertical change to the horizontal change.

E. A system of two equations has exactly one solution if the lines are (*parallel, intersecting*) lines.

Multiple Choice

Read each question. Then write the letter of the correct answer on your paper.

1. Which expression is equivalent to $(j^2k^3)(jk^2)$?

A j^2k^2 C j^2k^6

B j^3k^5 D j^3k^6

2. Which equation has $(2, -6)$ and $(-3, 4)$ as solutions?

F $y = \frac{1}{2}x - 7$ H $y = -\frac{1}{2}x - 5$

G $y = 2x - 10$ I $y = -2x - 2$

3. Which equation best represents the statement *two more than twice a number is the number tripled*?

A $2 + n = 3n$ C $2(2 + n) = 3n$

B $2n + 2 = 3n$ D $2n + 2 = 3 + n$

Answers

Cumulative Test Prep

A. dependent

B. base

C. scientific

D. slope

E. intersecting

1. B

2. I

3. B

4. The graph at the right shows how Manuel's height changed during the past year. Which conclusion can you make from the graph?

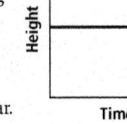

Height / Time

- Ⓕ His height is average.
- Ⓖ He will grow more next year.
- Ⓗ His height did not change during the year.
- Ⓘ His height steadily increased during the year.

5. All of the students in Haley's class received between 36 and 48 points on the last quiz. Each question was worth 2 points. There was no partial credit. How many questions could Haley have answered correctly?

- Ⓐ 12
- Ⓑ 21
- Ⓒ 44
- Ⓓ 72

6. Which *cannot* be represented by a linear function?

- Ⓕ the area of a square, given its side length
- Ⓖ the price of fruit, given the weight of the fruit
- Ⓗ the number of steps on a ladder, given the height
- Ⓘ the number of inches, given the number of yards

7. A light-year is the distance light travels in one year. One light-year is about 5.9×10^{12} mi. If it takes light 3 months to travel from one star to another, about how far apart are the stars?

- Ⓐ 2×10^3 mi
- Ⓑ 1.5×10^4 mi
- Ⓒ 1.5×10^{12} mi
- Ⓓ 2×10^{12} mi

8. Use the graph at the right. Suppose the y-intercept increases by 2 and the slope stays the same. What will the x-intercept be?

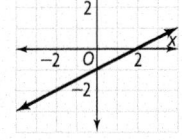

- Ⓕ -3
- Ⓖ -2
- Ⓗ 1
- Ⓘ 4

9. At lunchtime, Mitchell makes his own salad. The salad bar costs $1.25 per pound. Suppose Mitchell's salad weighs 1.8 lb, what is the cost of his salad?

- Ⓐ $1.44
- Ⓑ $2.25
- Ⓒ $2.50
- Ⓓ $22.50

10. The dimensions of a rectangular prism are shown in the diagram at the right. Which expression represents the volume of the rectangular prism?

a^2b, ab^3, ab^2

- Ⓕ a^2b^5
- Ⓖ a^2b^6
- Ⓗ a^4b^5
- Ⓘ a^4b^6

11. Suppose you are buying apples and bananas. The price of apples is $.40 each and the price of bananas is $.25 each. Which equation models the number of apples and bananas you can buy for $2?

- Ⓐ $40x + 25y = 200$
- Ⓑ $40x - 25y = 2$
- Ⓒ $5x + 8y = 200$
- Ⓓ $5x + 8y = 2$

12. At lunchtime, Mitchell cast a shadow 0.5 ft long while a nearby flagpole cast a shadow 2.5 ft long. If Mitchell is 5 ft 3 in. tall, how tall is the flagpole?

- Ⓕ 26 ft 3 in.
- Ⓖ 26 ft 4 in.
- Ⓗ 26 ft 5 in.
- Ⓘ 26 ft 6 in.

13. Laura rented a car that cost $20 for the day plus $.12 for each mile driven. She returned the car later that day. Laura gave the salesperson $50 and received change. Which inequality represents the possible numbers of miles m that she could have driven?

- Ⓐ $50 > 0.12m + 20$
- Ⓑ $50 < 0.12m + 20$
- Ⓒ $50 > 0.12m - 20$
- Ⓓ $50 < 0.12m - 20$

14. A doctor did a 6-month study on resting heart rate and exercise in healthy adults. The doctor found that for every 20 min of exercise added to a daily routine, the resting heart rate decreased by 1 beat per minute. According to the doctor's study, what does the resting heart rate depend on?

- Ⓕ the 6-month study
- Ⓖ minutes of exercise
- Ⓗ a daily routine
- Ⓘ diet

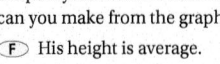
4. H
5. B
6. F
7. C
8. G
9. B
10. I
11. A
12. F
13. A
14. G

Answers

Cumulative Test Prep (continued)

15. B

16. F

17. D

18. 40.5

19. 1165

20. 36

21. 2

22. 38

23. 2.39

24. $\frac{13}{25}$

25. 35

26. [2] The six integers are 25, 26, 27, 28, 29, 30;
$n + (n + 1) + (n + 2) + (n + 3) + (n + 4)$
$+ (n + 5) = 165$
$6n + 15 = 165$
$6n = 150$
$n = 25$
[1] Appropriate method but with one computational error.

27. [2] $(1.132)x = 281,421,906$
$x = 248,605,924$
about 248,605,924 people
[1] no work shown

28. [4] **a.** (1, 2), (8, 2), (3, 4); Since $y = 2$ and $x - y = -1$, then $x - 2 = -1$ or $x = 1$. One vertex of the triangle is (1, 2). Since $y = 2$ and $-0.4x - y = -5.2$, then $-0.4x - 2 = -5.2$ or $x = 8$. A second vertex is (8, 2). To find the third vertex, you can solve the system $x - y = -1$, $-0.4x - y = -5.2$.
Multiplying the second equation by -1 and adding the two equations results in $1.4x = 4.2$, or $x = 3$. Now substitute 3 for x in the first equation and solve for y. This gives the third vertex of (3, 4).

b. 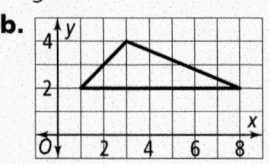 ;
The area of a triangle is given by $A = \frac{1}{2} bh$. The base has length $|8 - 1|$ or 7 and the height is $|4 - 2|$ or 2. Therefore, the area is $\frac{1}{2}(7)(2)$ or 7 units^2.
[3] appropriate methods used to find the vertices and the area, but with one computational error
[2] correct vertices with incorrect area OR incorrect vertices with but with correct corresponding area
[1] correct answers, without work shown

---

15. Which linear function has a graph that never intersects the x-axis?
Ⓐ $y = x$ Ⓒ $y = x + 1$
Ⓑ $y = -1$ Ⓓ $y = -x - 1$

16. What is the y-intercept of the graph at the right?
Ⓕ -3
Ⓖ -2
Ⓗ $-\frac{3}{2}$
Ⓘ 0

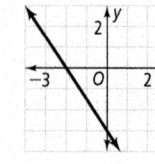

17. What is the value of $|(-3) + 7(-2)|$?
Ⓐ -17 Ⓒ 8
Ⓑ -8 Ⓓ 17

GRIDDED RESPONSE

Record your answers in a grid.

18. What is the area, in square units, of the triangle below?

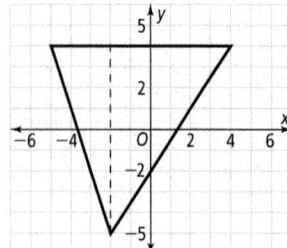

19. Charles purchased 50 shares of a stock at $23 per share. He paid a $15 commission to his broker for the purchase. How much money, in dollars, did he spend for the purchase and commission combined?

20. What is the value of the expression $9x - (4x - 1)$ when $x = 7$?

21. A designer tested 50 jackets in a clothing warehouse and found that 4% of the jackets were labeled with the wrong size. How many jackets did the designer find that were labeled the wrong size?

---

22. If $b = 2a - 16$ and $b = a + 2$, what is $a + b$?

23. Alejandro bought 6 notebooks and 2 binders for $23.52. Cassie bought 3 notebooks and 4 binders for $25.53. What was the cost, in dollars, of 1 notebook?

24. Ashley surveyed 200 students in her school to find out whether they liked mustard or mayo on a turkey sandwich. Her results are shown in the diagram below.

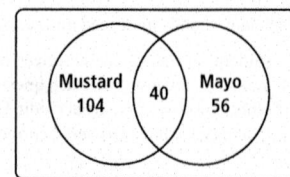

What fraction of the students surveyed liked mustard but not mayo? Write your answer in lowest terms.

25. The area of a parallelogram is $A = bh$. What is the area, in square units, of a parallelogram with vertices $(-3, 2)$, $(0, 7)$, $(7, 7)$, and $(4, 2)$?

Short Response

26. The sum of six consecutive integers is 165. What are the six integers? Show your work.

27. On April 1, 2000, the day of the 2000 national census, the population of the United States was 281,421,906 people. This was a 13.2% increase from the 1990 census. What was the 1990 population of the United States?

Extended Response

28. A triangle is enclosed by the following lines:
$$x - y = -1$$
$$y = 2$$
$$-0.4x - y = -5.2$$

a. What are the coordinates of the vertices of the triangle? Use algebraic methods to justify your answers.

b. Draw the triangle using your answers in part (a). What is the area, in square units, of the triangle?

Get Ready!

Skills
Handbook,
page 786

🔷 **Finding Factors of Composite Numbers**

List all the factors of each number.

1. 12	**2.** 18	**3.** 100	**4.** 81
5. 72	**6.** 300	**7.** 250	**8.** 207

Lesson 1-7

🔷 **Simplifying Expressions**

Simplify each expression.

9. $3x^2 - 4x - 2x^2 - 5x$ **10.** $-2d + 7 + 5d + 8$

11. $3(2r + 4r^2 - 7r + 4r^2)$ **12.** $-2(m + 1) + 9(4m - 3)$

13. $6(a - 3a^2 - 2a - 3a^2)$ **14.** $s - 4 - (s^2 - 2) - 8s$

Lessons 7-3
and 7-4

🔷 **Multiplying Expressions With Exponents**

Simplify each expression.

15. $(5x)^2$ **16.** $(-3v^2)(-3v)$ **17.** $(4c^2)^3$ **18.** $(8m^2)(7m^5)$

19. $(9b^3)^2$ **20.** $(-6pq)^2$ **21.** $7(n^2)^2$ **22.** $(-5t^4)^3$

Lesson 7-5

🔷 **Dividing Expressions With Exponents**

Simplify each expression.

23. $\dfrac{p^4q^9}{p^2q^6}$ **24.** $\dfrac{(5x)^2}{5x}$ **25.** $\dfrac{-3n}{(6n^4)(4n^2)}$ **26.** $\dfrac{(2y)(9y^4)}{6y^3}$

 Looking Ahead Vocabulary

27. Both of the words *tricycle* and *triangle* begin with the prefix *tri-*. A *trinomial* is a type of mathematical expression. How many terms do you think a trinomial has?

28. Use your knowledge of the meaning of the words *binocular* and *bicycle* to guess at the meaning of the word *binomial*.

29. Which of the following products do you think is a *perfect-square trinomial* when multiplied? Explain your reasoning.

a. $(x + 4)(x + 7)$ **b.** $(x + 4)(x + 4)$

Answers

Get Ready!

1. 1, 2, 3, 4, 6, 12

2. 1, 2, 3, 6, 9, 18

3. 1, 2, 4, 5, 10, 20, 25, 50, 100

4. 1, 3, 9, 27, 81

5. 1, 2, 3, 4, 6, 8, 9, 12, 18, 24, 36, 72

6. 1, 2, 3, 4, 5, 6, 10, 12, 15, 20, 25, 30, 50, 60, 75, 100, 150, 300

7. 1, 2, 5, 10, 25, 50, 125, 250

8. 1, 3, 9, 23, 69, 207

9. $x^2 - 9x$

10. $3d + 15$

11. $24r^2 - 15r$

12. $34m - 29$

13. $-36a^2 - 6a$

14. $-s^2 - 7s - 2$

15. $25x^2$

16. $9v^3$

17. $64c^6$

18. $56m^7$

19. $81b^6$

20. $36p^2q^2$

21. $7n^4$

22. $-125t^{12}$

23. p^2q^3

24. $5x$

25. $-\dfrac{1}{8n^5}$

26. $3y^2$

27. 3

28. A binomial is an expression with two terms.

29. b; $(x + 4)(x + 4) = (x + 4)^2$, which is a square, and $(x + 4)(x + 4) = x^2 + 8x + 16$, which is a trinomial.

Get Ready!

Assign this diagnostic assessment to determine if students have the prerequisite skills for Chapter 8.

Lesson	Skill
Skills Handbook, page T786	Finding Factors of Composite Numbers
1-7	Simplifying Expressions
7-3 and 7-4	Multiplying Expressions With Exponents
7-5	Dividing Expressions With Exponents

To remediate students, select from these resources (available for every lesson).
• Online Problems (PowerAlgebra.com)
• Reteaching (All-in-One Teaching Resources)
• Practice (All-in-One Teaching Resources)

Why Students Need These Skills

FINDING FACTORS OF COMPOSITE NUMBERS
Understanding factors of whole numbers will help students when factoring trinomials.

SIMPLIFYING EXPRESSIONS
The ability to simplify expressions is necessary for students to add and subtract polynomials.

MULTIPLYING EXPRESSIONS WITH EXPONENTS
Working with exponents will be necessary as students multiply monomials and binomials.

DIVIDING EXPRESSIONS WITH EXPONENTS
Students need to understand division of monomials in order to divide polynomials.

Looking Ahead Vocabulary

TRINOMIAL Ask students to give other examples of words with the prefix *tri-*.

BINOMIAL Ask students to give other examples of words with the prefix *bi-*.

PERFECT-SQUARE TRINOMIAL Ask students to give examples of perfect square whole numbers.

Chapter 8 Overview

UbD Understanding by Design

Chapter 8 connects and extends the BIG ideas introduced in the last chapter to polynomials. In this chapter, students will develop the answers to the Essential Questions posed on the opposite page as they learn the concepts and skills bulleted below.

BIG idea Equivalence

ESSENTIAL QUESTION Can two algebraic expressions that appear to be different be equivalent?

- Students will add and subtract polynomial expressions.
- Students will multiply polynomial expressions.
- Students will factor polynomials.

BIG idea Properties

ESSENTIAL QUESTION How are the properties of real numbers related to polynomials?

- Students will use the Commutative and Associative Properties to manipulate polynomial expressions.
- Students will use the Distributive Property to multiply polynomials and factor polynomials.

CHAPTER 8
Polynomials and Factoring

PowerAlgebra.com

Your place to get all things digital

VIDEO — Download videos connecting math to your world.

VOCABULARY — Math definitions in English and Spanish

SOLVE IT! — The online Solve It will get you in gear for each lesson.

DYNAMIC ACTIVITIES — Interactive! Vary numbers, graphs, and figures to explore math concepts.

ONLINE PROBLEMS — Download Step-by-Step Problems with Instant Replay.

ONLINE HOMEWORK — Get and view your assignments online.

MathXL FOR SCHOOL — Extra practice and review online

I bet this girl has practiced skating the half-pipe for a while! The skate park she's in has to have enough area for all the half-pipes, boxes, and rails she'll use in her tricks.

In this chapter, you'll use polynomials to describe the areas of geometric figures.

Vocabulary

English/Spanish Vocabulary Audio Online:

English	Spanish
binomial, p. 475	binomio
degree of a monomial, p. 474	grado de un monomio
degree of a polynomial, p. 475	grado de un polinomio
difference of two squares, p. 513	diferencia de dos cuadrados
factoring by grouping, p. 517	factor común por agrupación de términos
monomial, p. 474	monomio
perfect-square trinomial, p. 511	trinomio cuadrado perfecto
polynomial, p. 475	polinomio
standard form of a polynomial, p. 475	forma normal de un polinomio
trinomial, p. 475	trinomio

PowerAlgebra.com

Chapter 8 Overview

Use these online assets to engage your students. There is support for the Solve It and step-by-step solutions for Problems.

 Show the student-produced video demonstrating relevant and engaging applications of the new concepts in the chapter.

 Find online definitions for new terms in English and Spanish.

 Start each lesson with an attention-getting Problem. View the Problem online with helpful hints.

My Math Video

BIG ideas

1 Equivalence

Essential Question Can two algebraic expressions that appear to be different be equivalent?

2 Properties

Essential Question How are the properties of real numbers related to polynomials?

Chapter Preview

My Math Video

FACILITATE Use this photo to discuss area. A skate park must be built in a large area in order to accommodate the equipment. In this lesson, students will use polynomials to represent the dimensions of geometric figures. They will learn how to create expressions that represent the area of figures and volume of solids.

Q What is the equipment shown in the photo called? **[a half pipe]**

Q How much space do you think is needed for a half pipe? **[Answers may vary.]**

Q What other equipment have you seen in skate parks? **[Answers may vary. Sample: ramps, rails, benches, spine ramps]**

Q What types of geometric figures are modeled in the appearance of skate park equipment? **[Answers may vary. Sample: A pipe has a circular cross section. Benches are rectangular. Rails are linear.]**

Q If the length of a ramp is 8 feet longer than its width, how can you write an algebraic expression for the length and width? **[Let *w* represent the width of the ramp. Then *w* + 8 represents the length.]**

ERROR PREVENTION

Remind students to pay attention to units when using polynomials to represent measurements. In some problems the measurements might be given in different units so that students need to convert the measurements before they work with them. Also, remind students to label their answers with the appropriate units.

 Increase students' depth of knowledge with interactive online activities.

 Show Problems from each lesson solved step by step. Instant replay allows students to go at their own pace when studying online.

 Assign homework to individual students or to an entire class.

 Prepare students for the Mid-Chapter Quiz and Chapter Test with online practice and review.

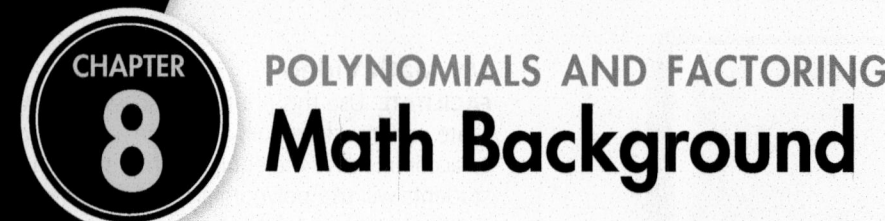

Equivalence

BIG idea A single quantity may be represented by many different expressions. The facts about a quantity may be expressed by many different equations (or inequalities).

ESSENTIAL UNDERSTANDINGS

8-1 Monomials can be used to form larger expressions called polynomials. Polynomials can be added and subtracted.

8-3 to 8-4 There are several ways to find the product of two binomials, including models, algebra, and tables.

8-5 to 8-8 Some trinomials of the form $ax^2 + bx + c$ and some polynomials of a degree greater than 2 can be factored to equivalent forms which are the product of two binomials.

Properties

BIG idea All of the facts of arithmetic and algebra follow from certain properties.

ESSENTIAL UNDERSTANDINGS

8-2 to 8-4 The properties of real numbers can be used to multiply a monomial by a polynomial or simplify the product of binomials.

8-5 to 8-8 The properties of real numbers can also be used to factor some trinomials of the form $ax^2 + bx + c$ and some polynomials of a degree greater than 2.

Adding and Subtracting Polynomials

Properties of real numbers are used to add and subtract polynomials. Grouping and adding like terms is actually a process of applying the Associative, Commutative and Distributive Properties.

Adding Polynomials

$8x^2 + (7x + 4x^2) + 2x$	
$8x^2 + (4x^2 + 7x) + 2x$	Commutative Property
$(8x^2 + 4x^2) + (7x + 2x)$	Associative Property
$(8 + 4)x^2 + (7 + 2)x$	Distributive Property
$12x^2 + 9x$	

Subtracting Polynomials

$(5x^2 + 9x) - (2x^2 + 6x)$	
$(5x^2 + 9x) + (-2x^2 + (-6x))$	Distributive Property
$5x^2 + (9x + (-2x^2)) + (-6x)$	Associative Property
$5x^2 + (-2x^2 + 9x) + (-6x)$	Commutative Property
$(5x^2 + (-2x^2)) + (9x + (-6x))$	Associative Property
$(5 + (-2))x^2 + (9 + (-6))x$	Distributive Property
$3x^2 + 3x$	

Common Errors When Adding and Subtracting Polynomials

Students might try to add and subtract exponents, especially if the coefficients of the monomials are 1.

The example below shows this common error:

$$(x^2 + x) + (x^2 + x) = x^3 + x^3 = x^6 \quad \text{(wrong!)}$$

The correct answer should be

$$(x^2 + x) + (x^2 + x)$$
$$(x^2 + x^2) + (x + x)$$
$$2x^2 + 2x$$

Multiplying Binomials

The Distributive Property is used to multiply binomials.

Multiplying a binomial by a monomial uses the Distributive Property.

$5(x + 5)$

$5(x + 5)$ Distribute the 5.

$(5 \cdot x) + (5 \cdot 5)$

$5x + 25$

Multiplying two binomials uses the Distributive Property.

$(3x - 6)(x + 5)$

$(3x - 6)(x + 5)$ Distribute the $(3x - 6)$.

$(3x - 6) \cdot x + (3x - 6) \cdot 5$

$(3x \cdot x) - (6 \cdot x) + (3x \cdot 5) - (6 \cdot 5)$

$3x^2 - 6x + 15x - 30$

$3x^2 + 9x - 30$

Common Errors With Multiplying Binomials

When multiplying binomials, students often make mistakes related to the signs of the terms.

An example of this common error is shown below:

$(2x - 6)(5x - 1)$

$(2x - 6) \cdot 5x + (2x - 6) \cdot 1$

$10x^2 + \underline{30x} + 2x \underline{+ 6}$

$10x^2 + \underline{32x + 6}$

The underlines indicate where errors were made. The correct answer is $10x^2 - 32x - 6$.

Factoring Trinomials

When a number or expression is written in factored form it is written as a product of its factors.

The factors of 8 are 2 and 4. $2 \cdot 4 = 8$

The factors of $8x$ are 2, 4, and x. $2 \cdot 4 \cdot x = 8x$

Trinomials can be factored as well. One reason factoring quadratic trinomials is useful is because the process can lead to the roots of quadratic functions. The roots are where a graph of the function crosses the x-axis.

Factoring trinomials, however, is not as simple as the factoring of whole numbers and monomials shown above.

$x^2 + x - 12$

One strategy for factoring trinomials is to start by finding all of the factors of c in the standard form $ax^2 + bx + c$. In the expression above $c = -12$.

Factors of -12 are -12, 1; -6, 2; -4, 3; -3, 4; -2, 6; and -1, 12.

Find the two factors whose sum is b. In the expression above $b = 1$.

The factors to consider are 4 and -3.

$4 + (-3) = 1$

Use these two factors to write two binomials.

$x + 4$ and $x - 3$

$x^2 + x - 12$ is the product of these two binomials.

$x^2 + x - 12 = (x + 4) \cdot (x - 3)$

Common Errors With Factoring Binomials and Trinomials

Factoring the difference of two squares follows the formula $a^2 - b^2 = (a + b)(a - b)$.

When students try to factor an expression like $x^2 - 16$, they might be confused how to proceed without the x term, not seeing that the middle term cancels itself out in the product $(a + b)(a - b)$.

$(x + 4)(x - 4) = x^2 + 4x - 4x - 16 = x^2 - 16$

Students may also expect that if there is a way to factor $x^2 - y^2$, then there must also be a way to factor $x^2 + y^2$, which is not true.

CHAPTER 8

POLYNOMIALS AND FACTORING
Pacing and Assignment Guide

		TRADITIONAL			BLOCK
Lesson	Teaching Day(s)	Basic	Average	Advanced	Block
8-1	1	Problems 1-3 Exs. 8–29, 56–67	Problems 1-3 Exs. 9–29 odd, 56–67	Problems 1-3 Exs. 9–29 odd, 56–67	**Day 1** Problems 1-3 Exs. 9–39 odd, 41–49, 56–67
	2	Problems 4-5 Exs. 30–44, 53–55	Problems 4-5 Exs. 31–39 odd, 41–49, 53–55	Problems 1-3 Exs. 31–39 odd, 41–55	
8-2	1	Problems 1-3 Exs. 9–26 all, 44–58	Problems 1-3 Exs. 9–25 odd, 44–58	Problems 1-4 Exs. 9–25 odd, 44–58	**Day 2** Problems 1-4 Exs. 9–27 odd, 29–41, 44–58
	2	Problem 4 Exs. 27–28 all, 30–34 even, 35–36, 38, 40	Problem 4 Exs. 27, 29–41	Problem 4 Exs. 27, 29–43	
8-3	1	Problems 1-3 Exs. 8–28 all, 51–61	Problems 1-3 Exs. 9–27 odd, 59–61	Problems 1-3 Exs. 9–27 odd, 51–61	**Day 3** Problems 1-5 Exs. 9–35 odd, 36–46, 51–61
	2	Problems 4-5 Exs. 29–35 all, 36–46 even	Problems 4-5 Exs. 29–35 odd, 36–46	Problems 4-5 Exs. 29–35 odd, 36–50	
8-4	1	Problems 1-3 Exs. 9–24 all, 59–71	Problems 1-3 Exs. 9–23 odd, 59–71	Problems 1-3 Exs. 9–23 odd, 59–71	**Day 4** Problems 1-5 Exs. 9–35 odd, 36–55, 59–71
	2	Problems 4-5 Exs. 25–35 all, 36–50 even, 51–52	Problems 4-5 Exs. 25–35 odd, 36–55	Problems 4-5 Exs. 25–35 odd, 36–58	
8-5	1	Problems 1-3 Exs. 10–29 all, 61–73	Problems 1-3 Exs. 11–29 odd, 61–73	Problems 1-3 Exs. 11–29 odd, 61–73	**Day 5** Problems 1-5 Exs. 11–39 odd, 41–54, 61–73
	2	Problems 4-5 Exs. 30–40 all, 42–44 all, 50–54 even	Problems 4-5 Exs. 31–39 odd, 41–54	Problems 4-5 Exs. 31–39 odd, 41–60	
8-6	1	Problems 1-2 Exs. 8–19 all, 52–67	Problems 1-2 Exs. 9–19 odd, 52–67	Problems 1-2 Exs. 9–19 odd, 52–67	**Day 6** Problems 1-4 Exs. 9–27 odd, 28–47, 52–67
	2	Problems 3-4 Exs. 20–27 all, 28–34 even, 35–36, 38–46 even	Problems 3-4 Exs. 21–27 odd, 28–47	Problems 3-4 Exs. 21–27 odd, 28–51	
8-7	1	Problems 1-2 Exs. 9–23, 60–69	Problems 1-2 Exs. 9–23 odd, 60–69	Problems 1-2 Exs. 9–23 odd, 60–69	**Day 7** Problems 1-5 Exs. 9–41 odd, 42–52, 60–69
	2	Problems 3-5 Exs. 24–42, 44–45, 51	Problems 3-5 Exs. 25–41 odd, 42–52	Problems 3-5 Exs. 25–41 odd, 42–59	
8-8	1	Problems 1-2 Exs. 9–27, 32, 34, 35	Problems 1-2 Exs. 9–27 odd, 31–36	Problems 1-3 Exs. 9–29 odd, 31–61	**Day 8** Problems 1-3 Exs. 9–29 odd, 31–40, 47–61
	2	Problem 3 Exs. 28–30, 38, 40, 47–61	Problem 3 Exs. 29, 37–40, 47–61		
Review	1	Chapter 8 Review	Chapter 8 Review	Chapter 8 Review	**Day 9** Chapter 8 Review
Assess	1	Chapter 8 Test	Chapter 8 Test	Chapter 8 Test	Chapter 8 Test
Total		**18 Days**	**18 Days**	**17 Days**	**9 Days**

Note: Pacing does not include Concept Bytes and other feature pages.

Resources

	For the Chapter	8-1	8-2	8-3	8-4	8-5	8-6	8-7	8-8
Planning									
Teacher Center Online Planner & Grade Book	I	I	I	I	I	I	I	I	I
Interactive Learning & Guided Instruction									
My Math Video	I								
Solve It!		I TM	I TM	I TM	I TM	I TM	I TM	I TM	I TM
Student Companion (SP)*		P M	P M	P M	P M	P M	P M	P M	P M
Vocabulary Support		I P M	I P M	I P M	I P M	I P M	I P M	I P M	I P M
Got It? Support		I P	I P	I P	I P	I P	I P	I P	I P
Dynamic Activity		I		I		I	I	I	
Online Problems		I	I	I	I	I	I	I	I
Additional Problems		M	M	M	M	M	M	M	M
English Language Learner Support (TR)		E P M	E P M	E P M	E P M	E P M	E P M	E P M	E P M
Activities, Games, and Puzzles		E M	E M	E M	E M	E M	E M	E M	E M
Teaching With TI Technology With CD-ROM				✓ P	✓ P				
TI-Nspire™ Support CD-ROM		✓	✓	✓	✓	✓	✓	✓	✓
Lesson Check & Practice									
Student Companion (SP)*		P M	P M	P M	P M	P M	P M	P M	P M
Lesson Check Support		I P	I P	I P	I P	I P	I P	I P	I P
Practice and Problem Solving Workbook (SP)		P	P	P	P	P	P	P	P
Think About a Plan (TR)*		E P M	E P M	E P M	E P M	E P M	E P M	E P M	E P M
Practice Form G (TR)*		E P M	E P M	E P M	E P M	E P M	E P M	E P M	E P M
Standardized Test Prep (TR)*		P M	P M	P M	P M	P M	P M	P M	P M
Practice *Form K* (TR)*		E P M	E P M	E P M	E P M	E P M	E P M	E P M	E P M
Extra Practice	E M								
Find the Errors!	M								
Enrichment (TR)		E P M	E P M	E P M	E P M	E P M	E P M	E P M	E P M
Answers and Solutions CD-ROM	✓	✓	✓	✓	✓	✓	✓	✓	✓
Assess & Remediate									
ExamView CD-ROM	✓	✓	✓	✓	✓	✓	✓	✓	✓
Lesson Quiz		I TM	I TM	I TM	I TM	I TM	I TM	I TM	I TM
Quizzes and Tests *Form G* (TR)*	E P M				E P M				E P M
Quizzes and Tests *Form K* (TR)*	E P M				E P M				E P M
Reteaching (TR)*		E P M	E P M	E P M	E P M	E P M	E P M	E P M	E P M
Performance Tasks (TR)*	P M								
Cumulative Review (TR)*	P M								
Progress Monitoring Assessments	I P M								

(TR) Available in All-In-One Teaching Resources   *Spanish available

1 Interactive Learning

Solve It!

PURPOSE To provide students with a real-world situation that involves combining like terms to simplify calculations

PROCESS Students may write and evaluate numeric expressions or algebraic expressions.

FACILITATE

Q What is the total cost of visiting the museum for m people in n cars? visiting the aquarium? **[5m + 15c; 6m + 20n]**

Q What is the total cost, per person, for admission in both places? **[$35]**

Q What is the total cost, per car, for parking at both places? **[$11]**

ANSWER See Solve It in Answers on next page.

CONNECT THE MATH Common solutions to the Solve It include combining like charges or calculating the charges for each place separately. In this lesson, students learn that combining like terms and then substituting is a more efficient method of simplifying.

2 Guided Instruction

Problem 1

Q Can you use the property for multiplying powers to simplify the expression $6x^3y^2$? Explain. **[No; x, y, and 6 are different bases.]**

Got It?   ERROR PREVENTION

If students answer 3 for 1a and 1 for 1c, then they mistakenly thought of the coefficients as having a degree of 1.

Objective To classify, add, and subtract polynomials

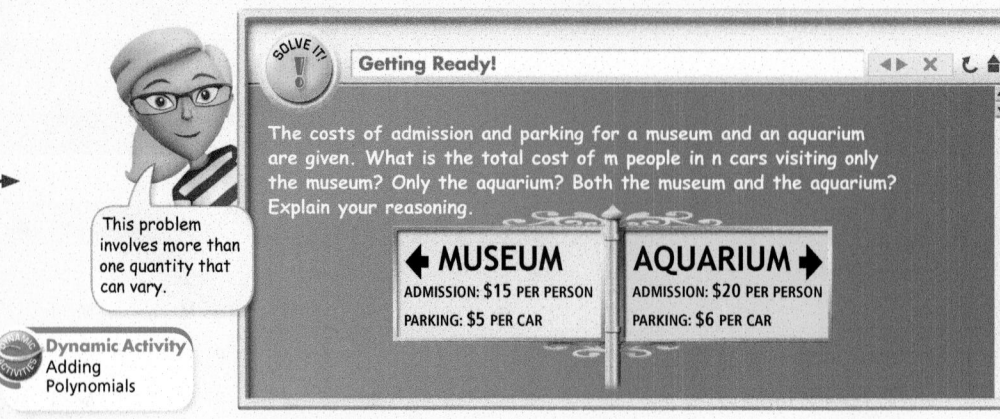

Getting Ready!

The costs of admission and parking for a museum and an aquarium are given. What is the total cost of m people in n cars visiting only the museum? Only the aquarium? Both the museum and the aquarium? Explain your reasoning.

← **MUSEUM**
ADMISSION: $15 PER PERSON
PARKING: $5 PER CAR

AQUARIUM →
ADMISSION: $20 PER PERSON
PARKING: $6 PER CAR

This problem involves more than one quantity that can vary.

Dynamic Activity Adding Polynomials

Lesson Vocabulary
• monomial
• degree of a monomial
• polynomial
• standard form of a polynomial
• degree of a polynomial
• binomial
• trinomial

In some cases, you can model a situation with an expression composed of *monomials*. A **monomial** is a real number, a variable, or a product of a real number and one or more variables with whole-number exponents. Here are some examples of monomials.

$$18 \qquad z \qquad -4x^2 \qquad 2.5xy^3 \qquad \frac{a}{3}$$

Essential Understanding You can use monomials to form larger expressions called *polynomials*. Polynomials can be added and subtracted.

The **degree of a monomial** is the sum of the exponents of its variables. The degree of a nonzero constant is 0. Zero has no degree.

Think
Why is the degree of a nonzero constant 0?
You can write a nonzero constant c as cx^0. The exponent is 0, so the degree is 0 also.

Problem 1 Finding the Degree of a Monomial

What is the degree of each monomial?

A $5x$ Degree: 1 $5x = 5x^1$. The exponent is 1.

B $6x^3y^2$ Degree: 5   The exponents are 3 and 2. Their sum is 5.

C 4 Degree: 0 $4 = 4x^0$. The degree of a nonzero constant is 0.

Got It? 1. What is the degree of each monomial?
a. $8xy$ **b.** $-7y^4z$ **c.** 11

BIG idea **Equivalence**   **UbD**

ESSENTIAL UNDERSTANDINGS
• Monomials can be used to form larger expressions called polynomials.
• Polynomials can be added and subtracted.

Math Background

So far in this text, students have worked with linear (first degree) polynomials in great detail. Students have solved linear equations and inequalities in one variable, have graphed linear equations and inequalities in two variables, and have solved systems of linear equations and inequalities in two variables. Students are now starting to study quadratic (second degree) polynomials and other higher-order polynomials. The first step in this study is to recognize and name the characteristics of such polynomials.

To define *polynomial*, first define *monomial*. Then define a polynomial as a monomial or the sum or difference of two or more monomials.

It can also be helpful to describe what a polynomial is not. The following are not polynomials: y^{-3}, $x^{\frac{1}{2}}$, and $\frac{4w^2 - 5}{w}$. Variables in a polynomial cannot have fractional exponents or negative exponents. Since a term with a negative exponent is equivalent to a term with a positive exponent placed in a denominator, a variable in a polynomial cannot be in the denominator of a fraction.

Support Student Learning

Use the **Algebra 1 Companion** to engage and support students during instructions. See Lesson Resources at the end of this lesson for details.

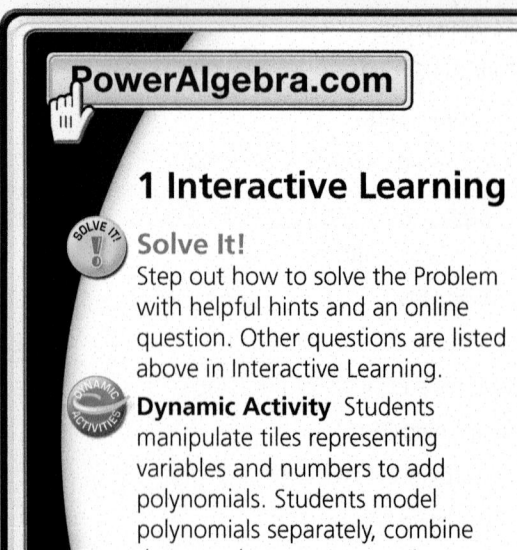

PowerAlgebra.com

1 Interactive Learning

Solve It!
Step out how to solve the Problem with helpful hints and an online question. Other questions are listed above in Interactive Learning.

Dynamic Activity Students manipulate tiles representing variables and numbers to add polynomials. Students model polynomials separately, combine them, and remove zero pairs.

You can add or subtract monomials by adding or subtracting like terms.

 Problem 2 Adding and Subtracting Monomials

Think

Will the sum of two monomials always be a monomial?

No. The monomials must be like terms.

What is the sum or difference?

Ⓐ $3x^2 + 5x^2 = 8x^2$ Combine like terms.

Ⓑ $4x^3y - x^3y = 3x^3y$ Combine like terms.

✓ **Got It? 2.** What is the sum $-6x^4 + 11x^4$? What is the difference $2x^2y^4 - 7x^2y^4$?

A **polynomial** is a monomial or a sum of monomials. The following polynomial is the sum of the monomials $3x^4$, $5x^2$, $-7x$, and 1.

$$3x^4 + 5x^2 - 7x + 1$$
$$\uparrow \quad \uparrow \quad \uparrow \quad \uparrow$$

Degree of each monomial   4   2   1   0

The polynomial shown above is in *standard form*. **Standard form of a polynomial** means that the degrees of its monomial terms decrease from left to right. The **degree of a polynomial** in one variable is the same as the degree of the monomial with the greatest exponent. The degree of $3x^4 + 5x^2 - 7x + 1$ is 4.

You can name a polynomial based on its degree or the number of monomials it contains.

Polynomial	Degree	Name Using Degree	Number of Terms	Name Using Number of Terms
6	0	Constant	1	Monomial
$5x + 9$	1	Linear	2	**Binomial**
$4x^2 + 7x + 3$	2	Quadratic	3	**Trinomial**
$2x^3$	3	Cubic	1	Monomial
$8x^4 - 2x^3 + 3x$	4	Fourth degree	3	Trinomial

 Problem 3 Classifying Polynomials

Think

Why do you need to combine like terms in part (B)?

To name a polynomial correctly based on its number of terms, you must first combine all like terms.

Write each polynomial in standard form. What is the name of the polynomial based on its degree and number of terms?

Ⓐ $3x + 4x^2$

$4x^2 + 3x$ Place terms in order.

This is a quadratic binomial.

Ⓑ $4x - 1 + 5x^3 + 7x$

$5x^3 + 4x + 7x - 1$ Place terms in order.

$5x^3 + 11x - 1$ Combine like terms.

This is a cubic trinomial.

✓ **Got It? 3. a.** Write $2x - 3 + 8x^2$ in standard form. What is the name of the polynomial based on its degree and number of terms?

   b. Reasoning How does writing a polynomial in standard form help you name the polynomial?

Problem 2

Q How can the Distributive Property be used to justify the answer for 2A? **[$3x^2 + 5x^2 = (3 + 5)x^2 = 8x^2$]**

Q How do you rewrite 2B so that each term has a coefficient? **[$4x^3y - 1x^3y$]**

Got It?   ERROR PREVENTION

If students answer $5x^8$ for the first question, then they are confusing the rules for dealing with the exponents when adding or subtracting like terms with the rules for the exponents for multiplying powers.

Problem 3

Q What is the degree of the polynomial in 3A? Explain. **[2; the monomial $4x^2$ has the greatest exponent.]**

Q If a classmate stated that the standard form of the polynomial in 3B contains four monomials, what advice would you give him or her? **[Answers may vary. Sample: Simplify a polynomial before counting the number of monomials.]**

Got It?   ERROR PREVENTION

Q How does writing a polynomial in standard form help you to simplify a polynomial by combining like terms? **[Writing the polynomial in standard form may help you recognize like terms because they will be written next to each other. Each term should have a unique exponent.]**

---

2 Guided Instruction

 Each Problem is worked out and supported online.

Problem 1
Finding the Degree of a Monomial

Problem 2
Adding and Subtracting Monomials

Problem 3
Classifying Polynomials

Alternative Problem 3
Classifying Polynomials
                              Animated

Problem 4
Adding Polynomials
                              Animated

Problem 5
Subtracting Polynomials
                              Animated

Support in Algebra 1 Companion
• Vocabulary
• Key Concepts
• Got It?

Answers

Solve It!

$15m + 5n$; $20m + 6n$; $35m + 11n$; explanations may vary.

Got It?

1. a. 2

   b. 5

   c. 0

2. $5x^4$, $-5x^2y^4$

3. a. $8x^2 + 2x - 3$, quadratic trinomial

   b. Answers may vary. Sample: Writing a polynomial in standard form allows you to see which monomial term has the greatest degree and how many terms the polynomial has.

Problem 4

Q What names would you give to each of the original polynomials? **[quadratic trinomials]**

Q What name would you give to the sum of the original polynomials? **[quadratic trinomial]**

Q Will the sum of two quadratic trinomials always be a quadratic trinomial? Explain. **[No, because some of the terms may cancel each other out when they are added together.]**

Q Do you prefer the horizontal method or the vertical method for combining the like terms? Explain. **[Answers may vary. Sample: I prefer the vertical method because like terms are lined up and it reminds me of the elimination method for solving systems of equations.]**

Got It?

Q When you arrange the polynomials in a vertical format, which term does not have another term added to it? **[$12x^3$]**

Show students that they can check the addition of polynomials by picking a test value for x and evaluating both the sum of the original polynomials and the combined polynomial. If students do not arrive at the same answer, then they likely made a mistake when adding the polynomials.

You can add polynomials by adding like terms.

 **Problem 4** Adding Polynomials

Travel A researcher studied the number of overnight stays in U.S. National Park Service campgrounds and in the backcountry of the national park system over a 5-yr period. The researcher modeled the results, in thousands, with the following polynomials.

Campgrounds: $-7.1x^2 - 180x + 5800$

Backcountry: $21x^2 - 140x + 1900$

In each polynomial, $x = 0$ corresponds to the first year in the 5-yr period. What polynomial models the total number of overnight stays in both campgrounds and backcountry?

Know	Need	Plan
• Overnight stays in campgrounds: $-7.1x^2 - 180x + 5800$ • Overnight stays in backcountry: $21x^2 - 140x + 1900$	A polynomial for the total number of overnight stays in campgrounds and backcountry	The word *both* implies addition, so add the two polynomials to find a polynomial that represents the total.

Method 1 Add vertically.
Line up like terms. Then add the coefficients.

$$\begin{array}{r} -7.1x^2 - 180x + 5800 \\ + \ 21x^2 - 140x + 1900 \\ \hline 13.9x^2 - 320x + 7700 \end{array}$$

Method 2 Add horizontally.
Group like terms. Then add the coefficients.

$$(-7.1x^2 - 180x + 5800) + (21x^2 - 140x + 1900)$$
$$= (-7.1x^2 + 21x^2) + (-180x - 140x) + (5800 + 1900)$$
$$= 13.9x^2 - 320x + 7700$$

A polynomial that models the number of stays (in thousands) in campgrounds and backcountry over the 5-yr period is $13.9x^2 - 320x + 7700$.

 Got It? 4. A nutritionist studied the U.S. consumption of carrots and celery and of broccoli over a 6-yr period. The nutritionist modeled the results, in millions of pounds, with the following polynomials.

Carrots and celery: $-12x^3 + 106x^2 - 241x + 4477$

Broccoli: $14x^2 - 14x + 1545$

In each polynomial, $x = 0$ corresponds to the first year in the 6-yr period. What polynomial models the total number of pounds, in millions, of carrots, celery, and broccoli consumed in the United States during the 6-yr period?

Additional Problems

1. What is the degree of the monomial?

a. $8x$

b. $4x^2y^5$

c. 7

ANSWER a. 1 **b.** 7 **c.** 0

2. What is the sum or difference?

a. $2x^2 + 7x^2$

b. $8x^2y - 3x^2y$

ANSWER a. $9x^2$ **b.** $5x^2y$

3. Write each polynomial in standard form. What is the name of the polynomial based on its degree and number of terms?

a. $6x + 2x^2$

b. $2 - 3x^2 + x^2 - 4x^3$

ANSWER a. $2x^2 + 6x$, quadratic binomial

b. $-4x^3 - 2x^2 + 2$, cubic trinomial

4. The revenue generated by a company and the cost of producing x units can be modeled by the polynomials below.

Revenue: $2x^2 + 120x$

Cost: $-0.5x^2 - 300x - 8000$

Add the functions to determine the net profit or loss polynomial.

ANSWER

$1.5x^2 - 180x - 8000$

5. What is the simplified form of $(2x^3 + 4x^2 - 3x) - (6x^3 + 5x^2 - 4)$?

ANSWER

$-4x^3 - x^2 - 3x + 4$

Recall that subtraction means to add the opposite. So when you subtract a polynomial, change each of the terms to its opposite. Then add the coefficients.

 Problem 5 Subtracting Polynomials

What is a simpler form of $(x^3 - 3x^2 + 5x) - (7x^3 + 5x^2 - 12)$?

Method 1 Subtract vertically.

$$x^3 - 3x^2 + 5x \qquad \text{Line up like terms.}$$
$$- (7x^3 + 5x^2 \qquad - 12)$$

$$\begin{array}{l} x^3 - 3x^2 + 5x \\ \underline{-7x^3 - 5x^2 \qquad + 12} \\ -6x^3 - 8x^2 + 5x + 12 \end{array}$$

Then add the opposite of each term in the polynomial being subtracted.

Method 2 Subtract horizontally.

$$(x^3 - 3x^2 + 5x) - (7x^3 + 5x^2 - 12)$$
$$= x^3 - 3x^2 + 5x - 7x^3 - 5x^2 + 12 \qquad \text{Write the opposite of each term in the polynomial being subtracted.}$$
$$= (x^3 - 7x^3) + (-3x^2 - 5x^2) + 5x + 12 \qquad \text{Group like terms.}$$
$$= -6x^3 - 8x^2 + 5x + 12 \qquad \text{Simplify.}$$

Got It? 5. What is a simpler form of $(-4m^3 - m + 9) - (4m^2 + m - 12)$?

Lesson Check

Do you know HOW?

Find the degree of each monomial.

1. $-7x^4$ **2.** $8y^2z^3$

Simplify each sum or difference.

3. $(5r^3 + 8) + (6r^3 + 3)$

4. $(x^2 - 2) - (3x + 5)$

Do you UNDERSTAND?

Vocabulary Name each polynomial based on its degree and number of terms.

5. $5x^2 + 2x + 1$ **6.** $3z - 2$

7. Compare and Contrast How are the processes of adding monomials and adding polynomials alike? How are the processes different?

Practice and Problem-Solving Exercises

A Practice   Find the degree of each monomial.   ◀ See Problem 1.

8. $3x$ **9.** $8a^3$ **10.** 20 **11.** $2b^8c^2$

12. $-7y^3z$ **13.** -3 **14.** $12w^4$ **15.** 0

Problem 5

Q Which terms do not have a like term in the other polynomial? **[the x term in the first polynomial and the constant in the second polynomial]**

Q Can you change the order of the subtraction of the two polynomials and still arrive at the same answer? **[No, because subtraction is not a commutative operation.]**

Q How can you check your work? **[Substitute the same value for x into both original polynomials and the simpler form to make sure you get the same answer.]**

Got It?
Show students that subtracting a polynomial can be thought of as using the Distributive Property with -1: $(-4m^3 - m + 9) + (-1)(4m^2 + m - 12)$.

3 Lesson Check

Do you know HOW?
• If students have difficulty with Exercise 4, then have them write the opposite of each term in the polynomial being subtracted.

Do you UNDERSTAND?
• If students have difficulty with Exercises 5 and 6, then refer them to the chart on page 475 to review naming conventions.

Close

Q What is the rule for simplifying like terms when you are adding and subtracting polynomials? **[Match the terms with the same variables, raised to the same exponents. Add or subtract their coefficients and leave their exponents the same.]**

Answers

Got It? (continued)
4. $-12x^3 + 120x^2 - 255x + 6022$
5. $-4m^3 - 4m^2 - 2m + 21$

Lesson Check
1. 4
2. 5
3. $11r^3 + 11$
4. $x^2 - 3x - 7$
5. quadratic trinomial
6. linear binomial
7. The coefficient of the sum of like monomials is the sum of the coefficients. To add polynomials, you group like terms and add their coefficients. A monomial has only one term and a polynomial can have more than one term.

Practice and Problem-Solving Exercises
8. 1
9. 3
10. 0
11. 10
12. 4
13. 0
14. 4
15. no degree

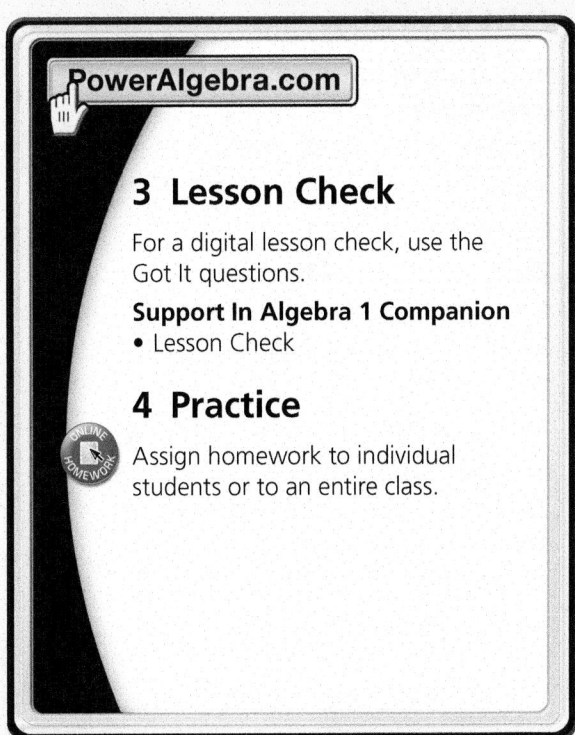

PowerAlgebra.com

3 Lesson Check
For a digital lesson check, use the Got It questions.

Support In Algebra 1 Companion
• Lesson Check

4 Practice
Assign homework to individual students or to an entire class.

4 Practice

ASSIGNMENT GUIDE

Basic: 8–44

Average: 9–39 odd, 41–49

Advanced: 9–39 odd, 41–52

Standardized Test Prep: 53–55

Mixed Review: 56–67

Reasoning exercises have blue headings.

Applications exercises have red headings.

EXERCISE 42: Use the Think About a Plan worksheet in the **Practice and Problem Solving Workbook** (also available in the Teaching Resources in print and online) to further support students' development in becoming independent learners.

HOMEWORK QUICK CHECK

To check students' understanding of key skills and concepts, go over Exercises 11, 23, 41, 42, and 43.

Simplify.   ◆ See Problem 2.

16. $12p^2 + 8p^2$ **17.** $2m^3n^3 + 9m^3n^3$ **18.** $8w^2x + w^2x$ **19.** $3t^4 + 11t^4$

20. $x^3 - 9x^3$ **21.** $30v^4w^3 - 12v^4w^3$ **22.** $7x^2 - 2x^2$ **23.** $5bc^4 - 13bc^4$

Write each polynomial in standard form. Then name each polynomial based   ◆ See Problem 3.
on its degree and number of terms.

24. $5y - 2y^2$ **25.** $-2q + 7$ **26.** $x^2 + 4 - 3x$

27. $6x^2 - 13x^2 - 4x + 4$ **28.** $c + 8c^3 - 3c^7$ **29.** $3z^4 - 5z - 2z^2$

Simplify.   ◆ See Problem 4.

30. $\begin{aligned} 4w - 5 \\ + 9w + 2 \end{aligned}$ **31.** $\begin{aligned} 6x^2 + 7 \\ + 3x^2 + 1 \end{aligned}$ **32.** $\begin{aligned} 2k^2 - k + 3 \\ + 5k^2 + 3k - 7 \end{aligned}$

33. $(5x^2 + 3) + (15x^2 + 2)$ **34.** $(2g^4 - 3g + 9) + (-g^3 + 12g)$

35. Education The number of students at East High School and the number of students at Central High School over a 10-year period can be modeled by the following polynomials.

  East High School: $-11x^2 + 133x + 1200$
  Central High School: $-7x^2 + 95x + 1100$

In each polynomial, $x = 0$ corresponds to the first year in the 10-year period. What polynomial models the total number of students at both high schools?

Simplify.   ◆ See Problem 5.

36. $\begin{aligned} 5n - 2 \\ -(3n + 8) \end{aligned}$ **37.** $\begin{aligned} 6x^3 + 17 \\ -(4x^3 + 9) \end{aligned}$ **38.** $\begin{aligned} 2c^2 + 7c - 1 \\ -(c^2 - 10c + 4) \end{aligned}$

39. $(14h^4 + 3h^3) - (9h^4 + 2h^3)$ **40.** $(-6w^4 + w^2) - (-2w^3 + 4w^2 - w)$

B Apply

41. Think About a Plan The perimeter of a triangular park is $16x + 3$. What is the missing length?
  • What is the sum of the two given side lengths?
  • What operation should you use to find the remaining side length?

42. Geometry The perimeter of a trapezoid is $39a - 7$. Three sides have the following lengths: $9a$, $5a + 1$, and $17a - 6$. What is the length of the fourth side?

43. Error Analysis Describe and correct the error in finding the difference of the polynomials.

$(4x^2 - x + 3) - (3x^2 - 5x - 6) = 4x^2 - x + 3 - 3x^2 - 5x - 6$
$= 4x^2 - 3x^2 - x - 5x + 3 - 6$
$= x^2 - 6x - 3$

Answers

Practice and Problem-Solving Exercises
(continued)

16. $20p^2$ **17.** $11m^3n^3$

18. $9w^2x$ **19.** $14t^4$

20. $-8x^3$ **21.** $18v^4w^3$

22. $5x^2$ **23.** $-8bc^4$

24. $-2y^2 + 5y$; quadratic binomial

25. $-2q + 7$; linear binomial

26. $x^2 - 3x + 4$; quadratic trinomial

27. $-7x^2 - 4x + 4$; quadratic trinomial

28. $-3c^7 + 8c^3 + c$; seventh degree trinomial

29. $3z^4 - 2z^2 - 5z$; fourth degree trinomial

30. $13w - 3$

31. $9x^2 + 8$

32. $7k^2 + 2k - 4$

33. $20x^2 + 5$

34. $2g^4 - g^3 + 9g + 9$

35. $-18x^2 + 228x + 2300$

36. $2n - 10$

37. $2x^3 + 8$

38. $c^2 + 17c - 5$

39. $5h^4 + h^3$

40. $-6w^4 + 2w^3 - 3w^2 + w$

41. $9x - 1$

42. $8a - 2$

43. The student forgot to distribute the negative sign to all the terms in the second set of parentheses.

$(4x^2 - x + 3) - (3x^2 - 5x - 6) =$
$4x^2 - x + 3 -$
$3x^2 - (-5x) - (-6) =$
$4x^2 - 3x^2 - x + 5x + 3 + 6 =$
$x^2 + 4x + 9$

Simplify. Write each answer in standard form.

44. $(5x^2 - 3x + 7x) + (9x^2 + 2x^2 + 7x)$

45. $(y^3 - 4y^2 - 2) - (6y^3 + 4 - 6y^2)$

46. $(-9r^3 + 2r - 1) - (-5r^2 + r + 8)$

47. $(3z^3 - 4z + 7z^2) + (8z^2 - 6z - 5)$

48. Reasoning Is it possible to write a trinomial with degree 0? Explain.

49. Writing Is the sum of two trinomials always a trinomial? Explain.

 **Challenge**

50. a. Write the equations for line p and line q. Use slope-intercept form.

    b. Use your equations from part (a) to write a function for the vertical distance $D(x)$ between points on lines p and q with the same x-value.

    c. For what value of x does $D(x)$ equal zero?

    d. Reasoning How does the x-value in part (c) relate to the graph?

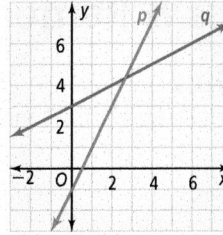

Simplify each expression.

51. $(ab^2 + ba^3) + (4a^3b - ab^2 - 5ab)$

52. $(9pq^6 - 11p^4q) - (-5pq^6 + p^4q^4)$

Standardized Test Prep

SAT/ACT

53. What is a simpler form of $(3x^2 + 6x - 1) + (4x^2 + 5x + 9)$?

  Ⓐ $-x^2 + x - 10$ Ⓑ $x^2 - x + 10$ Ⓒ $7x^2 + 11x + 8$ Ⓓ $7x^2 + 11x + 10$

54. The price of a gift basket of food can be modeled by a linear equation. You can use the graph at the right to find the price of the basket y, based on pounds of food x. What is the equation of the line?

  Ⓕ $y = 5x + 10$ Ⓗ $y = 10x + 5$

  Ⓖ $y = x + 10$ Ⓘ $y = 10x + 10$

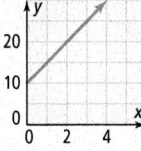

Short Response

55. Simplify $(8x^3 - 5x + 1) - (x^2 + 4)$. Show your work.

Mixed Review

Identify the growth factor in each exponential function.   ◀ **See Lesson 7-7.**

56. $y = 7 \cdot 3^x$ **57.** $y = 0.3 \cdot 2.1^x$ **58.** $y = 3 \cdot 4^x$ **59.** $y = 0.2 \cdot 5^x$

Find the slope of the line that passes through each pair of points.   ◀ **See Lesson 5-1.**

60. $(0, 2), (5, 0)$ **61.** $(3, -7), (4, 1)$ **62.** $(-2, 8), (1, 0)$ **63.** $(9, -6), (0, 0)$

Get Ready!   **To prepare for Lesson 8-2, do Exercises 64–67.**

Simplify each expression.   ◀ **See Lesson 7-3.**

64. $a^{-3}a^8$ **65.** $6r^2 \cdot 3r$ **66.** $(4x^5)(7x^3)$ **67.** $(2t^4)(-5t^2)$

---

44. $16x^2 + 11x$

45. $-5y^3 + 2y^2 - 6$

46. $-9r^3 + 5r^2 + r - 9$

47. $3z^3 + 15z^2 - 10z - 5$

48. No. Only a nonzero constant has a degree of 0, and a nonzero constant is a monomial.

49. No. Answers may vary. Sample: $(x^2 - x + 3) + (x - x^2 + 1) = 4$, which is a monomial.

50. a. p: $y = 2x - 1$; q: $y = \frac{1}{2}x + 3$

    b. $D(x) = \frac{3}{2}x - 4$

    c. $\frac{8}{3}$

    d. It is the x-coordinate of the point of intersection of the two lines.

51. $5a^3b - 5ab$

52. $14pq^6 - 11p^4q - p^4q^4$

53. C

54. F

55. [2] $(8x^3 - 5x + 1) - (x^2 + 4) =$
$8x^3 - 5x + 1 - x^2 - 4 =$
$8x^3 - x^2 - 5x - 3$

  [1] correct polynomial without work shown

56. 3

57. 2.1

58. 4

59. 5

60. $-\frac{2}{5}$

61. 8

62. $-\frac{8}{3}$

63. $-\frac{2}{3}$

64. a^5

65. $18r^3$

66. $28x^8$

67. $-10t^6$

Differentiated Remediation

Additional Instructional Support

Algebra 1 Companion

Students can use the **Algebra 1 Companion** worktext (4 pages) as you teach the lesson. Use the Companion to support

- New Vocabulary
- Key Concepts
- Got It for each Problem
- Lesson Check

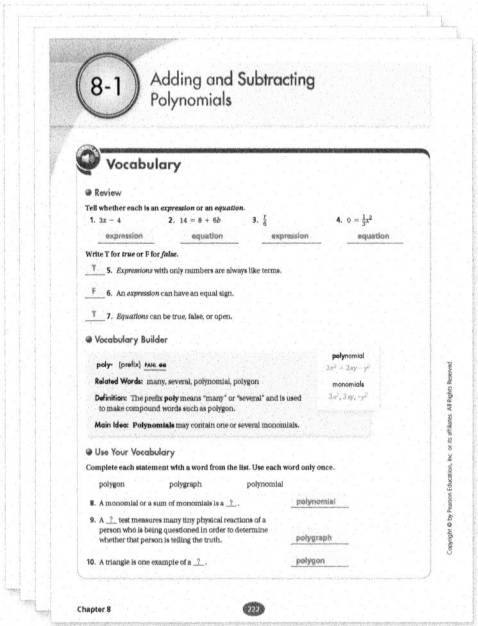

ELL Support

Use Graphic Organizers Model a three-column chart on the board titled *Polynomials*. Label the columns *monomial, binomial*, and *trinomial*. Write examples of each as you think aloud of the conditions each example must meet. Encourage student volunteers to provide both examples and nonexamples. Engage students in instructional conversation by asking, "Why is this a trinomial and not a binomial?" and "What is the difference between these two expressions?"

As an alternative, divide students into groups of mixed abilities and instruct them to arrive at four examples of each to share with the class. Students in each group will take turns explaining their reasoning.

5 Assess & Remediate

Lesson Quiz

1. What is the degree of the monomial?

   a. $6x^2$

   b. $-x^3y^3$

   c. $7x$

2. What is the sum or difference?

   a. $5x^4 + 4x^4$

   b. $12x^5y - 9x^5y$

3. **Do you UNDERSTAND?** Write each polynomial in standard form. What is the name of the polynomial based on its degree and number of terms?

   a. $3 + 5x - 4x^2$

   b. $8x + x + 5 + x^3$

4. What is the simplified form of $(-7x^3 + 5x^2 - x + 6) - (-8x^3 + x^2 + 3)$?

ANSWERS TO LESSON QUIZ

1. **a.** 2; **b.** 6; **c.** 1
2. **a.** $9x^4$; **b.** $3x^5y$
3. **a.** $-4x^2 + 5x + 3$, quadratic trinomial; **b.** $x^3 + 9x + 5$, cubic trinomial
4. $x^3 + 4x^2 - x + 3$

PRESCRIPTION FOR REMEDIATION
Use the student work on the Lesson Quiz to prescribe a differentiated review assignment.

Points	Differentiated Remediation
0–2	Intervention
3	On-level
4	Extension

PowerAlgebra.com

5 Assess & Remediate

Assign the Lesson Quiz. Appropriate intervention, practice, or enrichment is automatically generated based on student performance.

Intervention

- **Reteaching** (2 pages) Provides reteaching and practice exercises for the key lesson concepts. Use with struggling students or absent students.

- **English Language Learner Support** Helps students develop and reinforce mathematical vocabulary and key concepts.

All-in-One Resources/Online
Reteaching

All-in-One Resources/Online
English Language Learner Support

Differentiated Remediation continued

On-Level

- **Practice** (2 pages) Provides extra practice for each lesson. For simpler practice exercises, use the Form K Practice pages found in the All-in-One Teaching Resources and online.

- **Think About a Plan** Helps students develop specific problem-solving skills and strategies by providing scaffolded guiding questions.

- **Standardized Test Prep** Focuses on all major exercises, all major question types, and helps students prepare for the high-stakes assessments.

Extension

- **Enrichment** Provides students with interesting problems and activities that extend the concepts of the lesson.

- **Activities, Games, and Puzzles** Worksheets that can be used for concepts development, enrichment, and for fun!

Practice and Problem Solving WKBK/All-in-One Resources/Online
Practice page 1

8-1 Practice — Form G
Adding and Subtracting Polynomials

Find the degree of each monomial.
1. $2b^2c^2$ 4   2. $5x$ 1   3. $7y^6$ 5   4. $19ab$ 2
5. 12 0   6. $\frac{1}{2}z^2$ 2   7. 1 1   8. $4d^4e$ 5

Simplify.
9. $2a^3b + 4a^3b$ $6a^3b$ 10. $5x^3 - 4x^3$ x^3 11. $3m^6n^3 - 5m^6n^3$ $-2m^6n^3$
12. $-6ab + 3ab$ $-3ab$ 13. $4c^2d^6 - 7c^2d^6$ $-3c^2d^6$ 14. $315x^2 - 30x^2$ $285x^2$

Write each polynomial in standard form. Then name each polynomial based on its degree and number of terms.
15. $15x - x^3 + 3$ $-x^3 + 15x + 3$
16. $5x + 2x^2 - x + 3x^4$ $3x^4 + 2x^2 + 4x$
17. $9x^3$ $9x^3$
18. $7b^2 + 4b$ $7b^2 + 4b$
19. $-3x^2 + 11 + 10x$ $-3x^2 + 10x + 11$
20. $12t^2 + 1 - 3x + 8 - 2x$ $12t^2 - 5x + 9$

Simplify.
21. $8z - 12$ $+ 6z + 9$ $14z - 3$
22. $9x^3 + 3$ $+ 4x^3 + 7$ $13x^3 + 10$
23. $6j^2 - 2j + 5$ $+ 3j^2 + 4j - 6$ $9j^2 + 2j - 1$
24. $(3k^2 + 5) + (16x^2 + 7)$ $3k^2 + 16x^2 + 12$
25. $(g^4 - 4g^2 + 11) + (-g^3 + 8g)$ $g^4 - g^3 - 4g^2 + 8g + 11$
26. A local deli kept track of the sandwiches it sold for three months. The polynomials below model the number of sandwiches sold, where s represents days.

Ham and Cheese: $4s^3 - 28s^2 + 33s + 250$
Pastrami: $-7.4s^2 + 32s + 180$

Write a polynomial that models the total number of these sandwiches that were sold. $4s^3 - 35.4s^2 + 65s + 430$

Practice and Problem Solving WKBK/All-in-One Resources/Online
Practice page 2

8-1 Practice (continued) — Form G
Adding and Subtracting Polynomials

Simplify.
27. $11n - 4$ $- (5n + 2)$ $6n - 6$
28. $7x^4 + 9$ $- (8x^4 + 2)$ $x^4 + 7$
29. $3d^2 + 8d - 2$ $- (2d^2 - 7d + 6)$ $d^2 + 15d - 8$
30. $(28e^3 + 3e^2) + (19e^3 + e^2)$ $47e^3 + 4e^2$
31. $(-12h^4 + h) - (-6h^4 + 3h^2 - 4h)$ $-6h^4 - 3h^2 + 5h$
32. A small town wants to compare the number of students enrolled in public and private schools. The polynomials below show the enrollment for each:

Public School: $-19c^2 + 980c + 48,989$
Private School: $40c + 4046$

Write a polynomial for how many more students are enrolled in public school than private school. $-19c^2 + 940c + 53,035$

Simplify. Write each answer in standard form.
33. $(3a^2 + a + 5) - (2a - 5)$ $3a^2 - a + 10$
34. $(6d - 10d^3 + 3d^2) - (5d^3 + 3d - 4)$ $-15d^3 + 3d^2 + 3d + 4$
35. $(-4s^3 - 2s - 3) + (-2s^2 + s + 7)$ $-4s^3 - 2s^2 + 3s + 4$
36. $(8p^3 - 6p + 2p^2) + (9p^2 - 5p - 11)$ $8p^3 + 11p^2 - 11p - 11$
37. The fence around a quadrilateral-shaped pasture is $3a^2 + 15a + 9$ long. Three sides of the fence have the following lengths: $5a$, $10a - 2$, $a^2 - 7$. What is the length of the fourth side of the fence? $2a^2 + 18$

38. **Error Analysis** Describe and correct the error in simplifying the sum shown at the right.
two unlike terms, $6x^3$ and $-3x^2$, were added; $6x^3 - 3x^2 + 4x - 2$

$6x^3 + 4x - 10$
$+ (-3x^2 + 2x + 8)$
$3x^3 + 6x - 2$

39. **Open-Ended** Write three different examples of the sum of a quadratic trinomial and a cubic monomial.

Answers may vary. Sample: $(x^2 + 2x + 1) + x^3$;
$(2x^2 + 5x + 6) + 3x^3$; $(r^2 + r + 1) + 8r^3$

Practice and Problem Solving WKBK/All-in-One Resources/Online
Think About a Plan

8-1 Think About a Plan
Adding and Subtracting Polynomials

Geometry The perimeter of a trapezoid is $39a - 7$. Three sides have the following lengths: $9a$, $5a + 1$, and $17a - 6$. What is the length of the fourth side?

Understanding the Problem
1. What is the perimeter of the trapezoid? $39a - 7$
2. What are the lengths of the sides you are given? $9a$ $5a + 1$ $17a - 6$
3. How many sides does a trapezoid have? 4 sides
4. How do you find the perimeter of a trapezoid? add the side lengths
5. What is the problem asking you to determine? the length of the fourth side

Planning the Solution
6. Draw a diagram of the trapezoid and label the information you know.

7. Write an equation that can be used to determine the length of the fourth side.
$s = (39a - 7) - (9a + 5a + 1 + 17a - 6)$

Getting an Answer
8. Solve your equation to find the length of the fourth side of the trapezoid.
$8a - 2$

Practice and Problem Solving WKBK/All-in-One Resources/Online
Standardized Test Prep

8-1 Standardized Test Prep
Adding and Subtracting Polynomials

Multiple Choice
For Exercises 1–6, choose the correct letter.
1. What is the degree of the monomial $3x^2y^2$? C
A. 2   B. 3   C. 5   D. 6

2. What is the simplified form of $8b^3c^2 + 4b^3c^2$? G
F. $12bc$ G. $12b^3c^2$ H. $12b^6c^4$ I. $12b^9c^4$

3. How is $6d - 8 + 4d^2$ written in standard form? A
A. $4d^2 + 6d - 8$ B. $4d^2 + 6d + 8$ C. $4d^2 - 6d - 8$ D. $4d^2 - 6d + 8$

4. What is the simplified form of $(4j^2 + 6) + (2j^2 - 3)$? G
F. $6j^2 - 3$ G. $6j^2 + 3$ H. $6j^2 + 9$ I. $4j^4 + 3$

5. What is the difference of the following polynomials? D
$6x^3 - 2x^2 + 4$
$- (2x^3 + 4x^2 - 5)$
A. $4x^3 - 2x^2 - 1$ B. $8x^3 + 6x^2 - 1$ C. $4x^3 - 2x^2 + 1$ D. $4x^3 - 6x^2 + 9$

6. What is the simplified form of $(3x^2 - 4x + 6x) + (5x^3 + 2x^2 - 3x)$ in standard form? I
F. $5x^3 + 10x^2 - x$ G. $8x^3 - 2x^2 + 3x$ H. $5x^3 + 10x^2 - 5x$ I. $5x^3 + 5x^2 - x$

Short Response
7. Suppose you have been given this polynomial.
$5b + 4b^2 - 3b^5 + 3$
a. How can you write this polynomial in standard form?
$-3b^5 + 4b^2 + 5b + 3$
b. What is the degree of this polynomial? Explain.
4; b^5 is the term with the greatest degree
[2] Both parts answered correctly with full explanations
[1] One part answered correctly or both parts answered correctly with incomplete explanations
[0] Neither part answered correctly

All-in-One Resources/Online
Enrichment

8-1 Enrichment
Adding and Subtracting Polynomials

Packing boxes and packing sheets in different sizes are given by the expressions below. To find the number of packing boxes and sheets that will fit in a larger shipping box, add or subtract the polynomials. Tell the total number of boxes and sheets. Then tell how many medium and large boxes and sheets you could fit into the shipping box. The first one has been started for you.

Boxes	a^3 = small box	b^3 = medium box	c^3 = large box
	6 small boxes = 1 medium box	4 medium boxes = 1 large box	
Sheets	a^2 = small sheet	b^2 = medium sheet	c^2 = large sheet
	4 small sheets = 1 medium sheet	8 medium sheets = 1 large sheet	

1. $7a^3 + 5b^3 + 5a^3 - 3b^3 = 12a^3 - 2b^3$
= 12 small boxes and 2 medium boxes
= 4 medium boxes
= 1 large box(es)

2. $6a^2 + 3b^2 - 8c^2 + 12b^2 - 2a^2 + 10c^2 = 4a^2 + 15b^2 + 2c^2$
= 4 small sheets, 15 medium sheets, and 2 large sheets
= 16 medium sheets and 2 large sheets
= 4 large sheets

3. $(8a^3 - 3b^3 + 6c^3) - (2a^3 - 14b^3 + 2c^3) = 6a^3 + 11b^3 + 4c^3$
= 6 small boxes, 11 medium boxes, and 4 large boxes
= 12 medium boxes and 4 large boxes
= 7 large boxes

4. $(15c^2 + 12a^2 - 9b^2) + (-14c^2 + 6a^2 + 5b^2 + 25b^2) = 18$ small boxes,
= 5 medium boxes, 16 medium boxes, and 1 large sheet $18a^3 + 5b^3 + 16b^2 + c^2$
= 8 medium boxes   16 medium sheets, and 1 large sheets
= 2 large boxes and 3 large sheets

Online Teacher Resource Center
Activities, Games, and Puzzles

8-1 Puzzle: Polynomial Search
Adding and Subtracting Polynomials

You will find the answers to the problems below somewhere in the grid. An answer may appear straight across, straight down, or on a diagonal. Circle each problem and answer you find. The first one has been done for you.

a. $4x^2 + 7x + 9 - (2x^2 + 10x + 4)$
b. $x^5 - x^3 - x^2 + 3 + (x^4 - 2x^2 - 2x^2 + 4x - 3)$
c. $-2x^4 - x + 3 + (8x^2 + 8x^4 - 3x + 1)$
d. $7x^4 - 2x^2 + 5x + 4 - (x^2 - 2x^4 - 6x^3 + 4x)$
e. $6x^5 - x^4 + 5x^3 + (3x^3 + 8x^4 - 6x^2 + 3)$
f. $x^5 - 3x^3 + 6x^2 + x - (x^5 + 5x^3 - x^2 + x)$
g. $-2x^4 - x^2 + 5 - (2x^8 + 3x^4 - 6x^2 + x)$
h. $3x^4 - 4x^4 + 3x^2 + 7 + (-4x^4 - 4x^2 - x + 1)$
i. $2x^4 + x^2 + 6 - (2x^4 + 5x^2 - x^2 + 3x + 7)$
j. $-x^5 - x^2 + 3x - 1 - (2x^5 + x^2 + x^2 + 5x - 4)$
k. $-x^4 + 4x^2 + 6x^2 + 1 + (2x^4 - 4x^3 - x^2 + 3x + 3)$
l. $-x^5 - x^4 + x^3 + 4x^2 + 2 - (x^4 - 4x^3 + 2x^2 + x - 3)$

---

1 Interactive Learning

Solve It!
PURPOSE To use the Distributive Property to simplify an expression and equation that involve the product of polynomials
PROCESS Students may write, simplify, and evaluate numeric expressions; write and solve an algebraic equation; or use trial and error.

FACILITATE
Q What expression represents the area of the plot covered with grass? [$45(x - 10)$]
Q How can you determine the width of the lawn you can plant with $50 worth of seed? [**Write and solve an equation that sets the expression for the total cost of the seed equal to 50.**]

ANSWER See Solve It in Answers on next page.
CONNECT THE MATH In the Solve It, an expression that contains a monomial is multiplied by a binomial. This operation is an application of the Distributive Property.

2 Guided Instruction

Problem 1

Q Are any of the monomials in $-9x^7 + 2x^6 - 7x^3$ like terms that can be combined? Explain. [**No, there are no like terms because the exponents do not match.**]

Got It?   **ERROR PREVENTION**
Two elements can cause issues for students. The exponent on n in the term $5n$ is 1. The second term that is subtracted can be thought of as adding $-1n^2$.

Objectives To multiply a monomial by a polynomial
To factor a monomial from a polynomial

Getting Ready!

You set aside part of a rectangular plot of land for a garden and seed the rest of the plot with grass, as shown. Grass seed costs $.03 per square foot. Write an expression for the total cost of the seed. Suppose you buy $50 worth of seed. How wide can the grassy section be? Explain your reasoning.

10 ft

45 ft

x ft

Remember the Distributive Property? It can help you here.

Essential Understanding You can use the Distributive Property to multiply a monomial by a polynomial.

For example, consider the product $2x(3x + 1)$.

$$2x(3x + 1) = 2x(3x) + 2x(1)$$
$$= 6x^2 + 2x$$

You can show why the multiplication makes sense using the area model at the right.

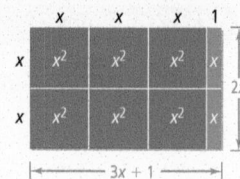

Problem 1   **Multiplying a Monomial and a Trinomial**

Multiple Choice What is a simpler form of $-x^3(9x^4 - 2x^3 + 7)$?

  (A) $-9x^{12} + 2x^9 - 7x^3$ (C) $-9x^7 - 2x^3 + 7$
  (B) $9x^7 - 2x^6 + 7x^3$ (D) $-9x^7 + 2x^6 - 7x^3$

Plan

What should I keep in mind when multiplying?
Remember to distribute $-x^3$ to *all* of the terms. Also remember to add the exponents instead of multiplying them.

$-x^3(9x^4 - 2x^3 + 7) = -x^3(9x^4) - x^3(-2x^3) - x^3(7)$ Use the Distributive Property.
$= -9x^{3+4} + 2x^{3+3} - 7x^3$ Multiply coefficients and add exponents.
$= -9x^7 + 2x^6 - 7x^3$ Simplify.

The correct answer is D.

Got It? 1. What is a simpler form of $5n(3n^3 - n^2 + 8)$?

BIG idea Properties   **UbD**
ESSENTIAL UNDERSTANDINGS
- A monomial can be multiplied by a polynomial using the Distributive Property.
- Factoring a polynomial reverses the multiplication process.
- The first step when factoring a monomial from a polynomial is finding the greatest common factor of the terms of the polynomial.

Math Background
In a sense, students already know how to factor the simplest of polynomials, namely constants. Students were taught to write out the prime factors of numbers as a preparation for reducing fractions. The idea of prime factorization is to write a number as the product of numbers which themselves cannot be factored. The idea of factoring polynomials is to write a polynomial

as the product of polynomials which themselves cannot be factored. Students should understand that every factoring problem in this lesson (this chapter, in fact) can be checked by multiplying their answers to verify that they obtain the original polynomial. However, students will use the law of exponents to multiply and factor polynomials properly.

Support Student Learning
Use the **Algebra 1 Companion** to engage and support students during instructions. See Lesson Resources at the end of this lesson for details.

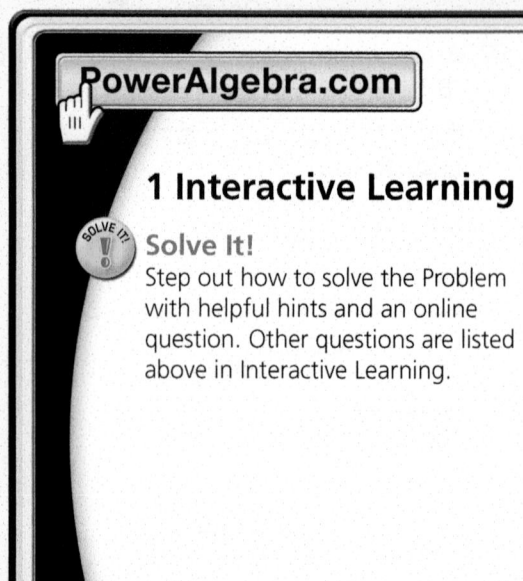

PowerAlgebra.com

1 Interactive Learning

Solve It!
Step out how to solve the Problem with helpful hints and an online question. Other questions are listed above in Interactive Learning.

Essential Understanding Factoring a polynomial reverses the multiplication process. When factoring a monomial from a polynomial, the first step is to find the greatest common factor (GCF) of the polynomial's terms.

 Problem 2 Finding the Greatest Common Factor

What is the GCF of the terms of $5x^3 + 25x^2 + 45x$?

List the prime factors of each term. Identify the factors common to all terms.

$$5x^3 = 5 \cdot x \cdot x \cdot x$$
$$25x^2 = 5 \cdot 5 \cdot x \cdot x$$
$$45x = 3 \cdot 3 \cdot 5 \cdot x$$

> Remember to list only the prime factors of the variables.

The GCF is $5 \cdot x$, or $5x$.

Think
Why use the factors 5 and x to form the GCF, but not 3?
Both 5 and x are factors of *every* term of the polynomial, but 3 is only a factor of the last term.

Got It? 2. What is the GCF of the terms of $3x^4 - 9x^2 - 12x$?

Once you find the GCF of a polynomial's terms, you can factor it out of the polynomial.

 Problem 3 Factoring Out a Monomial

What is the factored form of $4x^5 - 24x^3 + 8x$?

Think | Write

To factor the polynomial, first factor each term.

$$4x^5 = 2 \cdot 2 \cdot x \cdot x \cdot x \cdot x \cdot x$$
$$24x^3 = 2 \cdot 2 \cdot 2 \cdot 3 \cdot x \cdot x \cdot x$$
$$8x = 2 \cdot 2 \cdot 2 \cdot x$$

Find the GCF of the three terms.

The GCF is $2 \cdot 2 \cdot x$, or $4x$.

Factor out the GCF from each term. Then factor it out of the polynomial.

$$4x^5 - 24x^3 + 8x = 4x(x^4) + 4x(-6x^2) + 4x(2)$$
$$= 4x(x^4 - 6x^2 + 2)$$

The factored form of the polynomial is $4x(x^4 - 6x^2 + 2)$.

Got It? 3. a. What is the factored form of $9x^6 + 15x^4 + 12x^2$?
b. Reasoning What is $-6x^4 - 18x^3 - 12x^2$ written as the product of a polynomial with positive coefficients and a monomial?

Problem 2

Q How can you rewrite the terms x^3 and x^2 using repeated multiplication? $[x^3 = x \cdot x \cdot x \text{ and } x^2 = x \cdot x]$

Q What variable factor(s) do all three terms have in common? $[x]$

Q What constant factor(s) do all three terms have in common? **[5]**

Got It? VISUAL LEARNERS

Tell students that to find the GCF, they should first find the greatest number that divides evenly into the coefficients of each term. Then determine the least exponent for each variable.

Problem 3

Q What monomial, when multiplied by $4x$, has a product of $4x^5$? $[x^4]$

Q What monomial, when multiplied by $4x$, has a product of $-24x^3$? $[-6x^2]$

Q What monomial, when multiplied by $4x$, has a product of $8x$? **[2]**

Q How can you check to see that your factored form is correct? **[You can multiply the monomial by the polynomial factor to see if you get the original polynomial.]**

Got It? ERROR PREVENTION

Q Why is the expression $3x(3x^5 + 5x^3 + 4x)$ not the correct factored form for 1a? **[3x is not the greatest common factor.]**

Q What visual clue indicates that the GCF was not factored out in the preceding question? **[There is still an x in each term of the trinomial.]**

---

2 Guided Instruction

 Each Problem is worked out and supported online.

Problem 1
Multiplying a Monomial and a Trinomial
Animated

Problem 2
Finding the Greatest Common Factor

Problem 3
Factoring Out a Monomial
Animated

Problem 4
Factoring a Polynomial Model
Animated

Support in Algebra 1 Companion
• Vocabulary
• Key Concepts
• Got It?

Answers

Solve It!
Total cost in dollars is $45(x - 10)(0.03)$; about 37 ft wide; explanations may vary.

Got It?
1. $15n^4 - 5n^3 + 40n$
2. $3x$
3. a. $3x^2(3x^4 + 5x^2 + 4)$
   b. $-6x^2(x^2 + 3x + 2)$

Problem 4

> **Q** What is the length of the side of the square? **[2x]**
> **Q** What is the length of the radius of the circle? **[x]**

Got It?   ERROR PREVENTION

If students provide an answer of $6x^2(2 - \pi)$, then they likely did not use the Power of a Product rule properly.

> **Q** What is the GCF of the expression representing the difference in the area of the square and the area of the circle? **[$9x^2$]**

3 Lesson Check

Do you know HOW?

• If students have difficulty with Exercises 3 and 4, then tell them to write out and determine the common factors of each term as is demonstrated in the text.

Do you UNDERSTAND?

• If students have difficulty with Exercise 7, explain that polynomials can be prime just as numbers can be prime.

Close

> **Q** How are the multiplication of polynomials and the factoring of polynomials related? **[Factoring polynomials is the reverse, or inverse, of multiplying polynomials.]**

Plan

How can you find the shaded region's area?
The shaded region is the entire square except for the circular portion. So, subtract the area of the circle from the area of the square.

 **Problem 4** Factoring a Polynomial Model

Helipads A helicopter landing pad, or helipad, is sometimes marked with a circle inside a square so that it is visible from the air. What is the area of the shaded region of the helipad at the right? Write your answer in factored form.

Step 1 Find the area of the shaded region.

$$A_1 = s^2 \qquad \text{Area of a square}$$
$$= (2x)^2 \qquad \text{Substitute } 2x \text{ for } s.$$
$$= 4x^2 \qquad \text{Simplify.}$$
$$A_2 = \pi r^2 \qquad \text{Area of a circle}$$
$$= \pi x^2 \qquad \text{Substitute } x \text{ for } r.$$

The area of the shaded region is
$A_1 - A_2$, or $4x^2 - \pi x^2$.

Step 2 Factor the expression.

First find the GCF.

$$4x^2 = 2 \cdot 2 \cdot x \cdot x$$
$$\pi x^2 = \pi \cdot x \cdot x$$

The GCF is $x \cdot x$, or x^2.

Step 3 Factor out the GCF.

$$4x^2 - \pi x^2 = x^2(4) + x^2(-\pi)$$
$$= x^2(4 - \pi)$$

The factored form of the area of the shaded region is $x^2(4 - \pi)$.

 Got It? **4.** In Problem 4, suppose the side length of the square is $6x$ and the radius of the circle is $3x$. What is the factored form of the area of the shaded region?

 Lesson Check

Do you know HOW?

1. What is a simpler form of $6x(2x^3 + 7x)$?

2. What is the GCF of the terms in $4a^4 + 6a^2$?

Factor each polynomial.

3. $6m^2 - 15m$

4. $4x^3 + 8x^2 + 12x$

Do you UNDERSTAND?

Match each pair of monomials with its GCF.

5. $14n^2, 35n^4$ **A.** 1

6. $21n^3, 18n^2$ **B.** $7n^2$

7. $7n^2, 9$ **C.** $3n^2$

8. Reasoning Write a binomial with $9x^2$ as the GCF of its terms.

Additional Problems

1. What is the simplified form of $x^2(3x^3 - 2x^2 + 8)$?

A. $3x^5 + 2x^4 - 8x^2$

B. $3x^5 - 2x^4 + 8x^2$

C. $3x^6 - 2x^4 + 8x^2$

D. $3x^6 + 2x^4 - 8x^2$

ANSWER B

2. What is the GCF of the terms of $6x^3 + 12x^2 + 18x$?

ANSWER $6x$

3. What is the factored form of $6x^3 - 15x^2 + 12x$?

ANSWER $3x(2x^2 - 5x + 4)$

4. A circle with radius r is cut from a square that has side length $3r$. Write an expression in factored form for the shaded area.

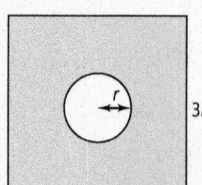

ANSWER $r^2(9 - \pi)$

Answers

Got It? (continued)

4. $9x^2(4 - \pi)$

Lesson Check

1. $12x^4 + 42x^2$

2. $2a^2$

3. $3m(2m - 5)$

4. $4x(x^2 + 2x + 3)$

5. B

6. C

7. A

8. Answers may vary. Sample: $18x^3 + 27x^2$

Practice and Problem-Solving Exercies

A Practice

Simplify each product.

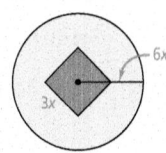 See Problem 1.

9. $7x(x + 4)$

10. $(b + 11)2b$

11. $3m^2(10 + m)$

12. $-w^2(w - 15)$

13. $4x(2x^3 - 7x^2 + x)$

14. $-8y^3(7y^2 - 4y - 1)$

Find the GCF of the terms of each polynomial.

See Problem 2.

15. $12x + 20$

16. $8w^2 - 18w$

17. $45b + 27$

18. $a^3 + 6a^2 - 11a$

19. $4x^3 + 12x - 28$

20. $14z^4 - 42z^3 + 21z^2$

Factor each polynomial.

See Problem 3.

21. $9x - 6$

22. $t^2 + 8t$

23. $14n^3 - 35n^2 + 28$

24. $5k^3 + 20k^2 - 15$

25. $14x^3 - 2x^2 + 8x$

26. $g^4 + 24g^3 + 12g^2 + 4g$

27. Art A circular mirror is surrounded by a square metal frame. The radius of the mirror is $5x$. The side length of the metal frame is $15x$. What is the area of the metal frame? Write your answer in factored form.

See Problem 4.

28. Design A circular table is painted yellow with a red square in the middle. The radius of the tabletop is $6x$. The side length of the red square is $3x$. What is the area of the yellow part of the tabletop? Write your answer in factored form.

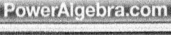

B Apply

Simplify. Write in standard form.

29. $-2x(5x^2 - 4x + 13)$

30. $-5y^2(-3y^3 + 8y)$

31. $10a(-6a^2 + 2a - 7)$

32. $p(p + 2) - 3p(p - 5)$

33. $t^2(t + 1) - t(2t^2 - 1)$

34. $3c(4c^2 - 5) - c(9c)$

35. Think About a Plan A rectangular wooden frame has side lengths $5x$ and $7x + 1$. The rectangular opening for a picture has side lengths $3x$ and $5x$. What is the area of the wooden part of the frame? Write your answer in factored form.
- How can drawing a diagram help you solve the problem?
- How can you express the area of the wooden part of the frame as a difference of areas?

36. Error Analysis Describe and correct the error made in multiplying.

$-3x(2x - 5) = -3x(2x) - 3x(5)$
$= -6x^2 - 15x$

Factor each polynomial.

37. $17xy^4 + 51x^2y^3$

38. $9m^4n^5 - 27m^2n^3$

39. $31a^6b^3 + 63a^5$

40. a. Factor $n^2 + n$.
b. Writing Suppose n is an integer. Is $n^2 + n$ always, sometimes, or never an even integer? Justify your answer.

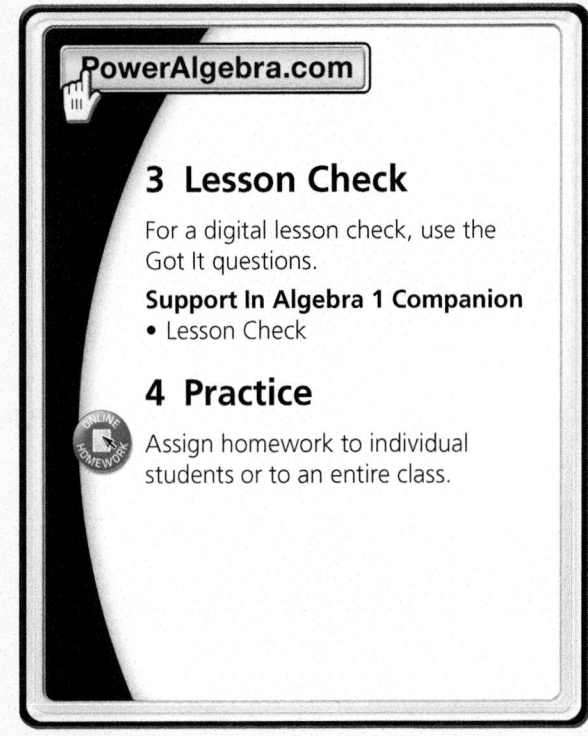

Answers

Practice and Problem-Solving Exercises

9. $7x^2 + 28x$

10. $2b^2 + 22b$

11. $30m^2 + 3m^3$

12. $-w^3 + 15w^2$

13. $8x^4 - 28x^3 + 4x^2$

14. $-56y^5 + 32y^4 + 8y^3$

15. 4

16. $2w$

17. 9

18. a

19. 4

20. $7z^2$

21. $3(3x - 2)$

22. $t(t + 8)$

23. $7(2n^3 - 5n^2 + 4)$

24. $5(k^3 + 4k^2 - 3)$

25. $2x(7x^2 - x + 4)$

26. $g(g^3 + 24g^2 + 12g + 4)$

27. $25x^2(9 - \pi)$

28. $9x^2(4\pi - 1)$

29. $-10x^3 + 8x^2 - 26x$

30. $15y^5 - 40y^3$

31. $-60a^3 + 20a^2 - 70a$

32. $-2p^2 + 17p$

33. $-t^3 + t^2 + t$

34. $12c^3 - 9c^2 - 15c$

35. $20x^2 + 5x; 5x(4x + 1)$

36. The student applied the Distributive Property incorrectly.
$a(b - c) = ab - ac$, so
$-3x(2x - 5) =$
$-3x(2x) - (-3x)5 = -6x^2 + 15x$.

37. $17xy^3(y + 3x)$

38. $9m^2n^3(m^2n^2 - 3)$

39. $a^5(31ab^3 + 63)$

40. a. $n(n + 1)$

b. Always; integers are closed under multiplication and addition, so $n(n + 1)$ is always an integer. Consider two cases: (1) n is even and (2) n is odd.(1) If n is even, then $n(n + 1) = $ (even)(odd) = even.

3 Lesson Check

For a digital lesson check, use the Got It questions.

Support In Algebra 1 Companion
- Lesson Check

4 Practice

Assign homework to individual students or to an entire class.

4 Practice

ASSIGNMENT GUIDE

Basic: 9–28 all, 30–34 even, 35–36, 38, 40

Average: 9–27 odd, 29–41

Advanced: 9–27 odd, 29–43

Standardized Test Prep: 44–48

Mixed Review: 49–58

Reasoning exercises have blue headings.

Applications exercises have red headings.

EXERCISE 40: Use the Think About a Plan worksheet in the **Practice and Problem Solving Workbook** (also available in the Teaching Resources in print and online) to further support students' development in becoming independent learners.

HOMEWORK QUICK CHECK

To check students' understanding of key skills and concepts, go over Exercises 13, 25, 35, 36, and 40.

Answers

Practice and Problem-Solving Exercises (continued)

41. 49; $p = 7a$ and $q = 7b$ where a and b have no common factors other than 1, so $p^2 = 49a^2$ and $q^2 = 49b^2$. Since a^2 and b^2 have no common factors other than 1, the GCF of p^2 and q^2 is 49.

42. a. $V = 64s^3$

   b. $V = 48\pi s^2$

   c. $V = 64s^3 - 48\pi s^2$

   d. $V = 16s^2(4s - 3\pi)$

   e. about 182,088 in.^{3}

43. a. 6; 3

   b. $n - 3$

   c. $\frac{1}{2}n^2 - \frac{3}{2}n$

   d. 20

44. $20x^3 + 12x^2 + 28x$; 12

45. $\frac{1}{3}$

46. 2

47. $16x^5$; 5

48. 3

49. $8x^2 + 4x + 5$

50. $7x^4 + 3x^2 - 1$

51. $-5x^3 - 6x$

52. $7x^4 + 2x^3 - 8x^2 + 4$

53. $y \leq \frac{4}{5}x - 2$

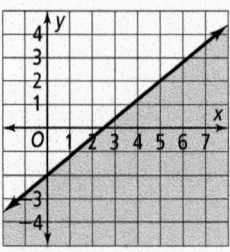

54. $y \geq \frac{7}{2}x - 4$

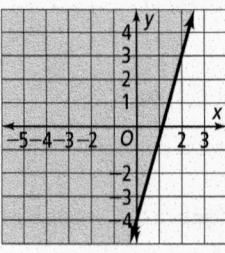

55. $y < -\frac{1}{3}x - 3$

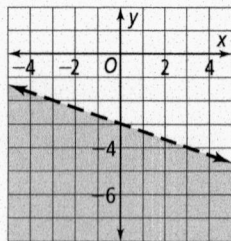

56. $8x - 40$

57. $-3w - 12$

58. $1.5c + 4$

---

41. Reasoning The GCF of two numbers p and q is 7. What is the GCF of p^2 and q^2? Justify your answer.

 **Challenge** **42. Manufacturing** The diagram shows a cube of metal with a cylinder cut out of it. The formula for the volume of a cylinder is $V = \pi r^2 h$, where r is the radius and h is the height.

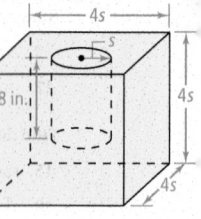

   a. Write a formula for the volume of the cube in terms of s.

   b. Write a formula for the volume of the cylinder in terms of s.

   c. Write a formula in terms of s for the volume V of the metal left after the cylinder has been removed.

   d. Factor your formula from part (c).

   e. Find V in cubic inches for $s = 15$ in. Use $\pi = 3.14$.

43. a. Geometry How many sides does the polygon have? How many of its diagonals come from one vertex?

   b. A polygon has n sides. How many diagonals will it have from one vertex?

   c. The number of diagonals from all the vertices is $\frac{n}{2}(n - 3)$. Write this polynomial in standard form.

   d. A polygon has 8 sides. How many diagonals does it have?

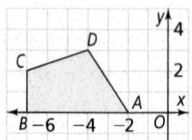

Standardized Test Prep

GRIDDED RESPONSE

SAT/ACT

44. Simplify the product $4x(5x^2 + 3x + 7)$. What is the coefficient of the x^2-term?

45. What is the slope of the line that passes through $\overline{CD}$?

46. What is the solution of the equation $7x - 11 = 3$?

47. Simplify the product $8x^3(2x^2)$. What is the exponent?

48. The expression $9x^3 - 15x$ can be factored as $ax(3x^2 - 5)$. What is the value of a?

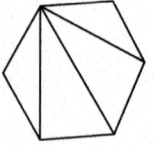

Mixed Review

Simplify each sum or difference.   *See Lesson 8-1.*

49. $(5x^2 + 4x - 2) + (3x^2 + 7)$ **50.** $(4x^4 - 3x^2 - 1) + (3x^4 + 6x^2)$

51. $(3x^3 - 2x) - (8x^3 + 4x)$ **52.** $(7x^4 + 3x^3 - 5x + 1) - (x^3 + 8x^2 - 5x - 3)$

Solve each inequality for y. Then graph the inequality.   *See Lesson 6-5.*

53. $4x - 5y \geq 10$ **54.** $7x - 2y \leq 8$ **55.** $-3y - x > 9$

Get Ready! To prepare for Lesson 8-3, do Exercises 56–58.

Use the Distributive Property to simplify each expression.   *See Lesson 1-7.*

56. $8(x - 5)$ **57.** $-3(w + 4)$ **58.** $0.25(6c + 16)$

Additional Instructional Support

Algebra 1 Companion

Students can use the **Algebra 1 Companion** worktext (4 pages) as you teach the lesson. Use the Companion to support

- New Vocabulary
- Key Concepts
- Got It for each Problem
- Lesson Check

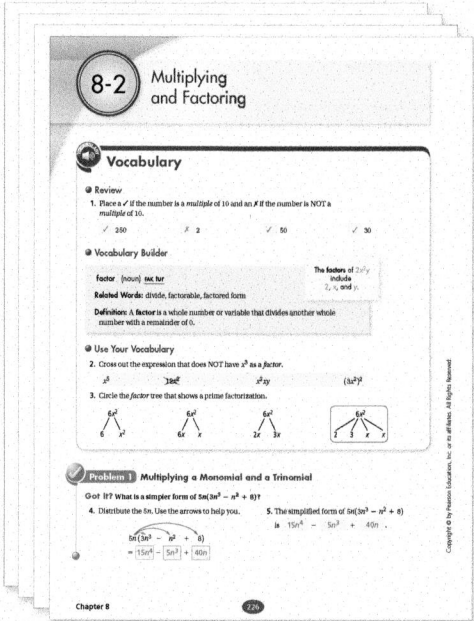

ELL Support

Assess Understanding Place Problem 2 on the overhead projector and read aloud as you point to each term or phrase. Model another example to find the GCF, and use the prompts from the text so the steps are repetitive. Then ask students to describe orally how they will find the GCF. Provide an example for students to work independently. Monitor and assist as needed. Repeat these steps for Problem 3.

5 Assess & Remediate

Lesson Quiz

1. What is the simplified form of $-x^2(2x^3 + 5x^2 + 6x)$?

2. What is the GCF of the terms of $8x^3 - 12x^2 + 4x$?

3. What is the factored form of $5x^4 + 15x^3 - 10x^2$?

4. **Do you UNDERSTAND?** Write an expression for the area of a triangle with a height of $2x^2$ units and a base of $5x^2 + 4x$ units.

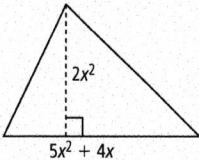

ANSWERS TO LESSON QUIZ

1. $-2x^5 - 5x^4 - 6x^3$
2. $4x$
3. $5x^2(x^2 + 3x - 2)$
4. $5x^4 + 4x^3$

PRESCRIPTION FOR REMEDIATION
Use the student work on the Lesson Quiz to prescribe a differentiated review assignment.

Points	Differentiated Remediation
0–2	Intervention
3	On-level
4	Extension

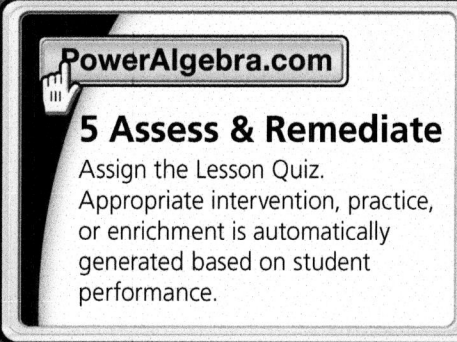

PowerAlgebra.com

5 Assess & Remediate

Assign the Lesson Quiz. Appropriate intervention, practice, or enrichment is automatically generated based on student performance.

Intervention

- **Reteaching** (2 pages) Provides reteaching and practice exercises for the key lesson concepts. Use with struggling students or absent students.

- **English Language Learner Support** Helps students develop and reinforce mathematical vocabulary and key concepts.

All-in-One Resources/Online
Reteaching

8-2 Reteaching
Multiplying and Factoring

You can multiply a monomial and a trinomial by solving simpler problems. You can use the Distributive Property to make three simpler multiplication problems.

Problem

What is the simplified form of $3x(2x^2 + 4x - 1)$?

Use the Distributive Property to rewrite the problem as three separate multiplication problems.

$$3x(2x^2 + 4x - 1) = (3x \cdot 2x^2) + (3x \cdot 4x) + (3x \cdot (-1))$$

Remember that to multiply with exponents that you add them.

Solve	$3x \cdot 2x^2 = 6x^3$	Multiply inside the first pair of parentheses.
	$3x \cdot 4x = 12x^2$	Multiply inside the second pair of parentheses.
	$3x \cdot (-1) = -3x$	Multiply inside the third pair of parentheses.
	$6x^3 + 12x^2 - 3x$	Add the products.
Check	$6x^3 + 2x^2 = 3x$	Check your solution using division.
	$12x^2 + 4x = 3x$	
	$-3x + (-1) = 3x$	

Solution: $3x(2x^2 + 4x - 1) = 6x^3 + 12x^2 - 3x$

Exercises

Simplify each product.

1. $4x(2x - 7)$
   $8x^2 - 28x$
2. $3y(3y + 4)$
   $9y^2 + 12y$
3. $2x^2(2x - 3)$
   $4x^3 - 6x^2$
4. $3a(-4a - 6)$
   $-12a^2 - 18a$
5. $6b(3b^2 + 2b - 4)$
   $18b^3 + 12b^2 - 24b$
6. $3x^2(2x^2 - 4c + 3)$
   $6c^4 - 12c^3 + 9c^2$
7. $-2d(4d^2 + 3d - 2)$
   $-8d^3 - 6d^2 + 4d$
8. $5e^2(-3e^2 - 2e - 3)$
   $-15e^4 - 10e^3 - 15e^2$
9. $4f(-3f^3 + 2f^2 + 6)$
   $-12f^4 + 8f^3 + 24f$

All-in-One Resources/Online
English Language Learner Support

8-2 ELL Support
Multiplying and Factoring

There are two sets of note cards below that show how Brittany factors the polynomial $5x^5 + 15x^3 + 4x^2$. The set on the left explains the thinking. The set on the right shows the steps. Write the thinking and the steps in the correct order.

Think Cards

- Factor each term of the polynomial.
- Simplify.
- Find the GCF of the three terms.
- Factor out the GCF from each term.

Write Cards

- $x^2(5x^3 + 15x + 4)$
- The GCF is $x \cdot x$, or x^2.
- $5x^5 + 15x^3 + 4x^2 =$ $x^2(5x^3) + x^2(15x) + x^2(4)$
- $5x^5 = 5 \cdot x \cdot x \cdot x \cdot x \cdot x$
  $15x^3 = 3 \cdot 5 \cdot x \cdot x \cdot x$
  $4x^2 = 2 \cdot 2 \cdot x \cdot x$

Think

First, she should factor each term of the polynomial.	**Step 1** $5x^5 = 5 \cdot x \cdot x \cdot x \cdot x \cdot x$ $15x^3 = 3 \cdot 5 \cdot x \cdot x \cdot x$ $4x^2 = 2 \cdot 2 \cdot x \cdot x$
Second, she should find the GCF of the three terms.	**Step 2** The GCF is $x \cdot x$, or x^2.
Next, she should factor out the GCF from each term. Then factor it out of the polynomial.	**Step 3** $5x^5 + 15x^3 + 4x^2 =$ $x^2(5x^3) + x^2(15) + x^2(4)$
Finally, she should simplify.	**Step 4** $x^2(5x^3 + 15x + 4)$

Write

Differentiated Remediation *continued*

On-Level

- **Practice** (2 pages) Provides extra practice for each lesson. For simpler practice exercises, use the Form K Practice pages found in the All-in-One Teaching Resources and online.

- **Think About a Plan** Helps students develop specific problem-solving skills and strategies by providing scaffolded guiding questions.

- **Standardized Test Prep** Focuses on all major exercises, all major question types, and helps students prepare for the high-stakes assessments.

Extension

- **Enrichment** Provides students with interesting problems and activities that extend the concepts of the lesson.

- **Activities, Games, and Puzzles** Worksheets that can be used for concepts development, enrichment, and for fun!

Practice and Problem Solving WKBK/ All-in-One Resources/Online
Practice page 1

Practice and Problem Solving WKBK/ All-in-One Resources/Online
Practice page 2

All-in-One Resources/Online
Enrichment

Practice and Problem Solving WKBK/ All-in-One Resources/Online
Think About a Plan

Practice and Problem Solving WKBK/ All-in-One Resources/Online
Standardized Test Prep

Online Teacher Resource Center
Activities, Games, and Puzzles

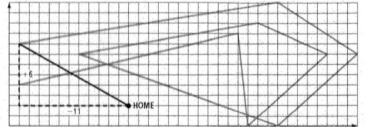

Using Models to Multiply

You can use algebra tiles to model the multiplication of two binomials.

Activity

Find the product $(x + 4)(2x + 3)$.

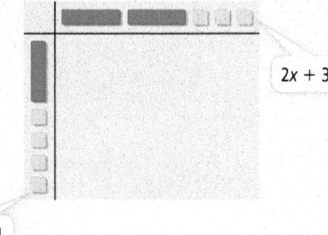

$2x + 3$

$x + 4$

$2x^2 + 3x + 8x + 12$
$2x^2 + 11x + 12$ Add coefficients of like terms.

The product is $2x^2 + 11x + 12$.

You can also model products that involve subtraction. Red tiles indicate negative variables and negative numbers.

Activity

Find the product $(x - 1)(2x + 1)$.

$2x + 1$

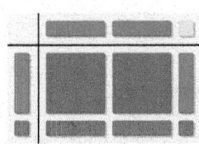

$x - 1$

$2x^2 + x - 2x - 1$
$2x^2 - x - 1$ Add coefficients of like terms.

The product is $2x^2 - x - 1$.

Exercises

Use algebra tiles to find each product.

1. $(x + 4)(x + 2)$ **2.** $(x + 2)(x - 3)$ **3.** $(x + 1)(3x - 2)$ **4.** $(3x + 2)(2x + 1)$

Guided Instruction

PURPOSE To use models to multiply binomials
PROCESS Students will
- use algebra tiles to multiply two binomials in which the terms involve addition.
- use algebra tiles to multiply two binomials in which the terms may involve subtraction.

DISCUSS This Activity and its exercises will enable students to multiply two binomials using algebra tiles. Let students know that eventually they will multiply binomials without algebra tiles.

Activity
In this Activity students multiply two binomials in which the terms involve only addition.

Q When is a blue x^2 tile placed in the product? **[when the factors are two green x tiles]**
Q When is a green x tile placed in the product? **[when the factors are a green x tile and a yellow unit tile]**
Q When is a yellow unit tile placed in the product? **[when the factors are two yellow unit tiles]**

Activity
In this Activity students multiply two binomials in which the terms may involve subtraction.

Q When is a red x tile placed in the product? **[when one of the factors is a negative x tile or a negative unit tile]**

Answers

Exercises

1. $x^2 + 6x + 8$
2. $x^2 - x - 6$
3. $3x^2 + x - 2$
4. $6x^2 + 7x + 2$

1 Interactive Learning

Solve It!

PURPOSE To explore the product of two binomials using an area model

PROCESS Students may use the area formula, geometric reasoning, and combining like terms to create the expression for the area of the run.

FACILITATE

Q What is the area of the original dog run? Explain. **[600 ft², 30 · 20 = 600]**

Q What is the total area of the four square corner pieces being added? **[4x²]**

Q What is the area of each of the top and bottom rectangles being added? of each of the side rectangles? **[30x; 20x]**

Q How can you find the area for the new dog run? **[Find the total of the original run plus the new areas.]**

ANSWER See Solve It in Answers on next page.
CONNECT THE MATH The dimensions of the dog run are expressed as binomials. When the dimensions are substituted into the formula for area, the problem is a multiplication problem of two binomials.

2 Guided Instruction

Problem 1

Q How do you get the middle term of the simplified trinomial? **[Add the like terms: $-14x$ and $12x$.]**

Got It?

Q What two monomials are distributed? **[x, -6]**

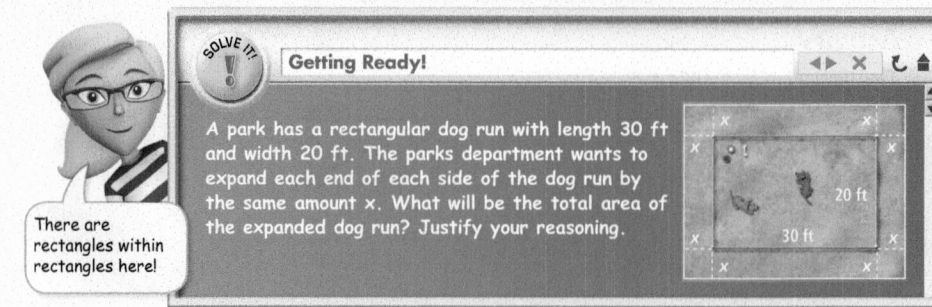
Objective To multiply two binomials or a binomial by a trinomial

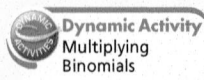

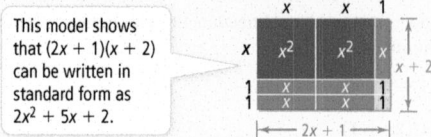

Getting Ready!

A park has a rectangular dog run with length 30 ft and width 20 ft. The parks department wants to expand each end of each side of the dog run by the same amount x. What will be the total area of the expanded dog run? Justify your reasoning.

There are rectangles within rectangles here!

Dynamic Activity Multiplying Binomials

Essential Understanding There are several ways to find the product of two binomials, including models, algebra, and tables.

One way to find the product of two binomials is to use an area model, as shown below.

This model shows that $(2x + 1)(x + 2)$ can be written in standard form as $2x^2 + 5x + 2$.

You can also use the Distributive Property to find the product of two binomials.

Problem 1 Using the Distributive Property

Plan

How can you use the Distributive Property with two binomials?
Consider the second binomial as a single variable, and distribute it to each term of the first binomial.

What is a simpler form of $(2x + 4)(3x - 7)$?

$$(2x + 4)(3x - 7) = 2x(3x - 7) + 4(3x - 7) \quad \text{Distribute the second factor, } 3x - 7.$$
$$= 6x^2 - 14x + 4(3x - 7) \quad \text{Distribute } 2x.$$
$$= 6x^2 - 14x + 12x - 28 \quad \text{Distribute } 4.$$
$$= 6x^2 - 2x - 28 \quad \text{Combine like terms.}$$

 Got It? 1. What is a simpler form of $(x - 6)(4x + 3)$?

BIG ideas Equivalence
Properties   **UbD**

ESSENTIAL UNDERSTANDINGS

- There are several ways to find the product of two binomials, including models, algebra, and tables.
- The properties of real numbers can be used to multiply two binomials.

Math Background

The set of polynomials is closed under the operations of addition, subtraction, and multiplication just as the domain of integers is closed under the operations of addition, subtraction, and multiplication. When two integers are divided, the quotient may be an integer, but may also be a rational number. Similarly, when two polynomials are divided, the quotient may be a polynomial, but may also be a rational expression.

The topic of multiplying binomials is one in which you can present multiple methods for simplifying and allow students to choose the method that works best for them and is easiest to remember. Students who like rules and definitions may prefer to use the Distributive Property. For students who benefit from mnemonic devices, encourage them to learn and use the FOIL method. Finally, for students that learn best using visual strategies or assimilating to previously learned techniques, focus on the vertical method. All three methods require students to combine like terms as the final step.

Support Student Learning

Use the **Algebra 1 Companion** to engage and support students during instructions. See Lesson Resources at the end of this lesson for details.

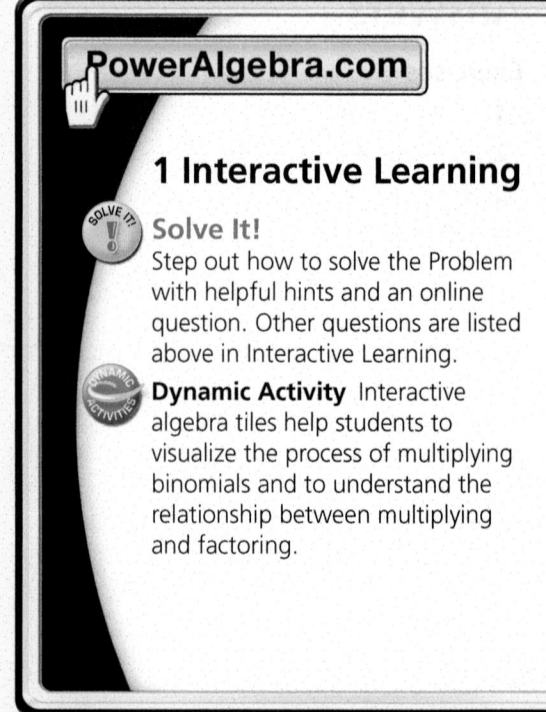

PowerAlgebra.com

1 Interactive Learning

Solve It!
Step out how to solve the Problem with helpful hints and an online question. Other questions are listed above in Interactive Learning.

Dynamic Activity Interactive algebra tiles help students to visualize the process of multiplying binomials and to understand the relationship between multiplying and factoring.

When you use the Distributive Property to multiply binomials, notice that you multiply each term of the first binomial by each term of the second binomial. A table can help you organize your work.

 Problem 2 Using a Table

What is a simpler form of $(x - 3)(4x - 5)$?

Know	Need	Plan
Binomial factors	Product of binomials written in standard form	Use a table.

Think

Is this the only table you can make?
No. You can write the terms of $x - 3$ in a row and the terms of $4x - 5$ in a column.

Make a table of products.

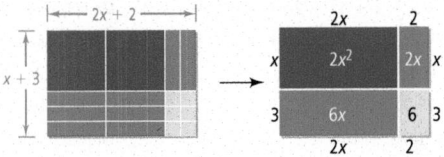

When labeling the rows and columns, think of $x - 3$ as $x + (-3)$. Think of $4x - 5$ as $4x + (-5)$.

The product is $4x^2 - 5x - 12x + 15$, or $4x^2 - 17x + 15$.

 Got It? 2. What is a simpler form of $(3x + 1)(x + 4)$? Use a table.

There is a shortcut you can use to multiply two binomials. Consider the product of $2x + 2$ and $x + 3$. The large rectangle below models this product. You can divide the large rectangle into four smaller rectangles.

The area of the large rectangle is the sum of the areas of the four smaller rectangles.

$$(2x + 2)(x + 3) = (2x)(x) + (2x)(3) + (2)(x) + (2)(3)$$
$$= 2x^2 + 6x + 2x + 6$$
$$= 2x^2 + 8x + 6$$

The area of each rectangle is the product of one term of $2x + 2$ and one term of $x + 3$.

This model illustrates another way to find the product of two binomials. You find the sum of the products of the First terms, the Outer terms, the Inner terms, and the Last terms of the binomials. The acronym FOIL may help you remember this method.

Problem 2

Q How is multiplying using a table different from multiplying using an area model? **[In an area model, each binomial is written as the sum or difference of units of x and 1. In the table method, they are not.]**

Got It? VISUAL LEARNERS

It may help students to draw arrows to indicate which monomials produce the four products shown in the table. For example:

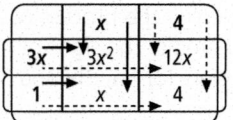

2 Guided Instruction

Each Problem is worked out and supported online.

Problem 1
Using the Distributive Property

Problem 2
Using a Table

Problem 3
Using FOIL
Animated

Problem 4
Applying Multiplication of Binomials
Animated

Problem 5
Multiplying a Trinomial and a Binomial
Animated

Support in Algebra 1 Companion
• Vocabulary
• Key Concepts
• Got It?

Answers

Solve It!
$4x^2 + 100x + 600$; explanations may vary.

Got It?
1. $4x^2 - 21x - 18$
2. $3x^2 + 13x + 4$

Problem 3

Q Which two words name the products that are like terms and therefore combined? **[outer and inner]**

Q Is the product of two binomials always a trinomial? Explain. **[Answers may vary. Sample: No, it is possible that there are no like terms to combine and the answer will have four terms. It is also possible the two like terms will add to zero and the answer will have two terms.]**

Got It?   SYNTHESIZING

Have students examine the process of using the FOIL method and predict the signs of the terms in the trinomial answers for 3a, 3b, and 3c.

Problem 4

Q What does the net of a cylinder look like? **[The net of a cylinder is made up of two circles and a rectangle.]**

Q What is the formula for the area of a rectangle? for the area of a circle? **[$A = b \cdot h$; $A = \pi r^2$]**

Q What property allows you to multiply $(x + 1)$ by $(x + 1)$ prior to multiplying 2π by $(x + 1)$? **[Associative Property of Multiplication]**

Q What is the greatest common factor of $2\pi(x^2 + 2x + 1)$ and $2\pi(x^2 + 5x + 4)$? **[$2\pi(x + 1)$]**

Got It?

Tell students that they can check the expression for the total surface area by picking a value for x and substituting it into the expression, as well as into the formula for surface area.

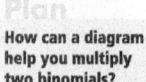 
Problem 3 Using FOIL

What is a simpler form of $(5x - 3)(2x + 1)$?

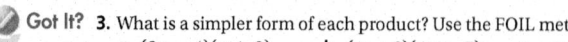

	First	Outer	Inner	Last
$(5x - 3)(2x + 1) =$	$(5x)(2x)$ +	$(5x)(1)$ +	$(-3)(2x)$ +	$(-3)(1)$
$=$	$10x^2$ +	$5x$ -	$6x$ -	3
$=$	$10x^2$ -	x -	3	

The product is $10x^2 - x - 3$.

Got It? 3. What is a simpler form of each product? Use the FOIL method.
a. $(3x - 4)(x + 2)$ **b.** $(n - 6)(4n - 7)$ **c.** $(2p^2 + 3)(2p - 5)$

Problem 4 Applying Multiplication of Binomials

Multiple Choice A cylinder has the dimensions shown in the diagram. Which polynomial in standard form best describes the total surface area of the cylinder?

Ⓐ $2\pi x^2 + 4\pi x + 2\pi$ Ⓒ $4\pi x^2 + 14\pi x + 10\pi$
Ⓑ $2\pi x^2 + 10\pi x + 8\pi$ Ⓓ $2\pi x^2 + 2\pi x + 10\pi$

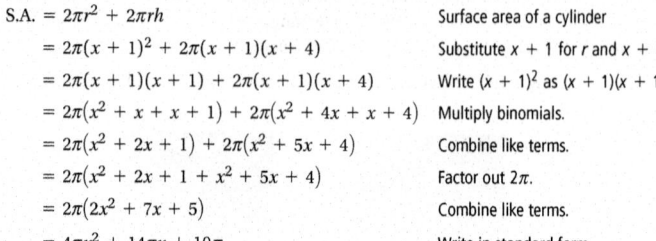

The total surface area (S.A.) of a cylinder is given by the formula
S.A. $= 2\pi r^2 + 2\pi rh$, where r is the radius of the cylinder and h is the height.

S.A. $= 2\pi r^2 + 2\pi rh$	Surface area of a cylinder
$= 2\pi(x + 1)^2 + 2\pi(x + 1)(x + 4)$	Substitute $x + 1$ for r and $x + 4$ for h.
$= 2\pi(x + 1)(x + 1) + 2\pi(x + 1)(x + 4)$	Write $(x + 1)^2$ as $(x + 1)(x + 1)$.
$= 2\pi(x^2 + x + x + 1) + 2\pi(x^2 + 4x + x + 4)$	Multiply binomials.
$= 2\pi(x^2 + 2x + 1) + 2\pi(x^2 + 5x + 4)$	Combine like terms.
$= 2\pi(x^2 + 2x + 1 + x^2 + 5x + 4)$	Factor out 2π.
$= 2\pi(2x^2 + 7x + 5)$	Combine like terms.
$= 4\pi x^2 + 14\pi x + 10\pi$	Write in standard form.

The correct answer is C.

Got It? 4. What is the total surface area of a cylinder with radius $x + 2$ and height $x + 4$? Write your answer as a polynomial in standard form.

You can use the FOIL method when you multiply two binomials, but it is not helpful when multiplying a trinomial and a binomial. In this case, you can use a vertical method to distribute each term.

Additional Problems

1. What is the simplified form of $(x + 4)(2x - 1)$?

ANSWER $2x^2 + 7x - 4$

2. What is the simplified form of $(3x + 1)(4x - 2)$?

ANSWER $12x^2 - 2x - 2$

3. What is the simplified form of $(7x + 1)(x - 4)$?

ANSWER $7x^2 - 27x - 4$

4. What is the area of a rectangle with length $2x + 1$ and width $5x - 2$?

ANSWER $10x^2 + x - 2$

5. What is the simplified form of $(2x^2 - 5x + 4)(x + 3)$?

ANSWER
$2x^3 + x^2 - 11x + 12$

Answers

Got It? (continued)

3. a. $3x^2 + 2x - 8$

   b. $4n^2 - 31n + 42$

   c. $4p^3 - 10p^2 + 6p - 15$

4. $4\pi x^2 + 20\pi x + 24\pi$

Problem 5 **Multiplying a Trinomial and a Binomial**

What is a simpler form of $(3x^2 + x - 5)(2x - 7)$?

Multiply by arranging the polynomials vertically as shown.

 Plan

How should you align the polynomials?
Write the polynomials so that like terms are vertically aligned.

$$3x^2 + x - 5$$
$$\underline{\qquad\qquad 2x - 7}$$
$$-21x^2 - 7x + 35 \qquad \text{Multiply by } -7.$$
$$\underline{6x^3 + 2x^2 - 10x \qquad\qquad} \text{Multiply by } 2x.$$
$$6x^3 - 19x^2 - 17x + 35 \qquad \text{Add like terms.}$$

The product is $6x^3 - 19x^2 - 17x + 35$.

 Got It? **5. a.** What is a simpler form of $(2x^2 - 3x + 1)(x - 3)$?
b. Reasoning How can you use the Distributive Property to find the product of a trinomial and a binomial?

Lesson Check

Do you know HOW?

Simplify each product.

1. $(x + 3)(x + 6)$

2. $(2x - 5)(x + 3)$

3. $(x + 2)(x^2 + 3x - 4)$

4. A rectangle has length $x + 5$ and width $x - 3$. What is the area of the rectangle? Write your answer as a polynomial in standard form.

Do you UNDERSTAND?

5. Reasoning Explain how to use the FOIL method to find the product of two binomials.

6. Compare and Contrast Simplify $(3x + 8)(x + 1)$ using a table, the Distributive Property, and the FOIL method. Which method is most efficient? Explain.

7. Writing How is the degree of the product of two polynomials $p(x)$ and $q(x)$ related to the degrees of $p(x)$ and $q(x)$?

Practice and Problem-Solving Exercises

A Practice   Simplify each product using the Distributive Property.   See Problem 1.

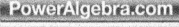

8. $(x + 7)(x + 4)$ **9.** $(y - 3)(y + 8)$ **10.** $(m + 6)(m - 7)$

11. $(c - 10)(c - 5)$ **12.** $(2r - 3)(r + 1)$ **13.** $(2x + 7)(3x - 4)$

Simplify each product using a table.   See Problem 2.

14. $(x + 5)(x - 4)$ **15.** $(a - 1)(a - 11)$ **16.** $(w - 2)(w + 6)$

17. $(2h - 7)(h + 9)$ **18.** $(x - 8)(3x + 1)$ **19.** $(3p + 4)(2p + 5)$

Problem 5
Ask students to verbalize the steps of multiplying a 3-digit whole number by a 2-digit whole number, such as 321 by 23, prior to showing them the vertical method for multiplying polynomials. Relate the steps to multiplying the trinomial by the binomial to the steps of whole number multiplication.

Got It?   SYNTHESIZING
Show students that they can also use an area model, the Distributive Property, or a table to find the product of the trinomial and binomial.

3 Lesson Check

Do you know HOW?
• If students have difficulty with Exercise 4, then have them draw a picture of the rectangle and write the formula for finding the area of a rectangle.

Do you UNDERSTAND?
• If students have difficulty with Exercise 7, then have them write several examples to find a pattern.

Close

Q What are the methods for multiplying two binomials? What do all of the methods have in common? **[Area model, table, Distributive Property, FOIL, and the vertical method; in each method, both terms of the first binomial are multiplied by both terms of the second binomial.]**

Got It? (continued)

5. a. $2x^3 - 9x^2 + 10x - 3$

b. Answers may vary. Sample: Distribute the trinomial to each term of the binomial. Then continue distributing and combining like terms as needed.

Lesson Check

1. $x^2 + 9x + 18$

2. $2x^2 + x - 15$

3. $x^3 + 5x^2 + 2x - 8$

4. $x^2 + 2x - 15$

5. Find the sum of the products of the FIRST terms, OUTER terms, INNER terms, and LAST terms.

6. $3x^2 + 11x + 8$; check students' work.

7. The degree of the product is the sum of the degrees of the two polynomials.

Practice and Problem-Solving Exercises

8. $x^2 + 11x + 28$

9. $y^2 + 5y - 24$

10. $m^2 - m - 42$

11. $c^2 - 15c + 50$

12. $2r^2 - r - 3$

13. $6x^2 + 13x - 28$

14. $x^2 + x - 20$

15. $a^2 - 12a + 11$

16. $w^2 + 4w - 12$

17. $2h^2 + 11h - 63$

18. $3x^2 - 23x - 8$

19. $6p^2 + 23p + 20$

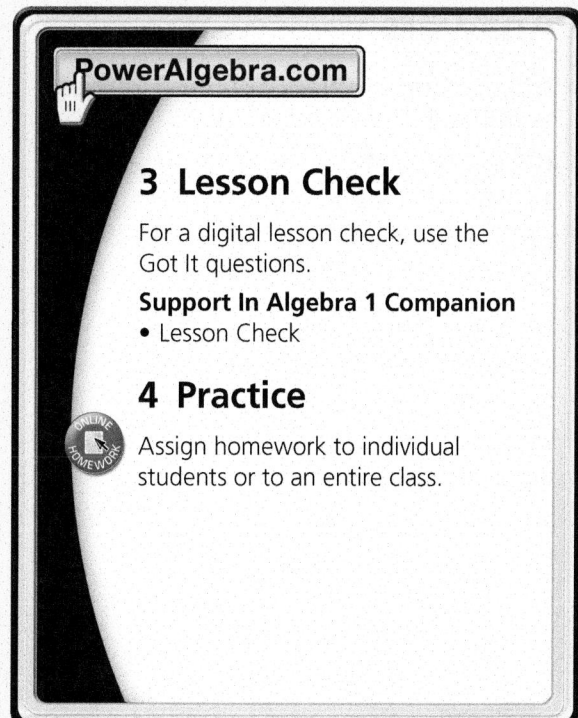

PowerAlgebra.com

3 Lesson Check

For a digital lesson check, use the Got It questions.

Support In Algebra 1 Companion
• Lesson Check

4 Practice

Assign homework to individual students or to an entire class.

4 Practice

ASSIGNMENT GUIDE

Basic: 8–35 all, 36–46 even

Average: 9–35 odd, 36–46

Advanced: 9–35 odd, 36–50

Standardized Test Prep: 51–54

Mixed Review: 55–61

Reasoning exercises have blue headings.

Applications exercises have red headings.

EXERCISE 46: Use the Think About a Plan worksheet in the Practice and Problem Solving Workbook (also available in the Teaching Resources in print and online) to further support students' development in becoming independent learners.

HOMEWORK QUICK CHECK

To check students' understanding of key skills and concepts, go over Exercises 9, 27, 42, 44, and 46.

Simplify each product using the FOIL method. ⬤ See Problem 3.

20. $(a + 8)(a - 2)$ **21.** $(x + 4)(4x - 5)$ **22.** $(k - 6)(k + 8)$

23. $(b - 3)(b - 9)$ **24.** $(5m - 2)(m + 3)$ **25.** $(9z + 4)(5z - 3)$

26. $(3h + 2)(6h - 5)$ **27.** $(4w + 13)(w + 2)$ **28.** $(8c - 1)(6c - 7)$

29. Geometry What is the total surface area of the cylinder? Write your answer as a polynomial in standard form. ⬤ See Problem 4.

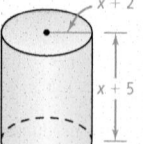

30. Design The radius of a cylindrical gift box is $(2x + 3)$ in. The height of the gift box is twice the radius. What is the surface area of the cylinder? Write your answer as a polynomial in standard form.

Simplify each product. ⬤ See Problem 5.

31. $(x + 5)(x^2 - 3x + 1)$ **32.** $(k^2 - 4k + 3)(k - 2)$

33. $(2a^2 + 4a + 5)(5a - 4)$ **34.** $(2g + 7)(3g^2 - 5g + 2)$

35. Sports A school's rectangular athletic fields currently have a length of 125 yd and a width of 75 yd. The school plans to expand both the length and the width of the fields by x yards. What polynomial in standard form represents the area of the expanded athletic field?

Ⓑ **Apply**   **Simplify each product. Write in standard form.**

36. $(x^2 + 1)(x - 3)$ **37.** $(-n^2 - 1)(n + 3)$ **38.** $(b^2 - 1)(b^2 + 3)$

39. $(2m^2 + 1)(m + 5)$ **40.** $(c^2 - 4)(2c + 3)$ **41.** $(4z^2 + 1)(z + 3z^2)$

42. Error Analysis Describe and correct the error made in finding the product.

$(x - 2)(3x + 4) = x(3x) + x(4) - 2(4)$
$= 3x^2 + 4x - 8$

43. Open-Ended Write a binomial and a trinomial. Find their product.

44. Think About a Plan You are planning a rectangular dining pavilion. Its length is three times its width x. You want a stone walkway that is 3 ft wide around the pavilion. You have enough stones to cover 396 ft² and want to use them all in the walkway. What should the dimensions of the pavilion be?
- Can you draw a diagram that represents this situation?
- How can you write a variable expression for the area of the walkway?

45. a. Simplify each pair of products.
  i. $(x + 1)(x + 1)$ **ii.** $(x + 1)(x + 2)$ **iii.** $(x + 1)(x + 3)$
  $11 \cdot 11$ $11 \cdot 12$ $11 \cdot 13$
  b. Reasoning What are the similarities between your two answers in each pair of products?

46. Geometry The dimensions of a rectangular prism are n, $n + 7$, and $n + 8$. Use the formula $V = \ell wh$ to write a polynomial in standard form for the volume of the prism.

Answers

Practice and Problem-Solving Exercises (continued)

20. $a^2 + 6a - 16$

21. $4x^2 + 11x - 20$

22. $k^2 + 2k - 48$

23. $b^2 - 12b + 27$

24. $5m^2 + 13m - 6$

25. $45z^2 - 7z - 12$

26. $18h^2 - 3h - 10$

27. $4w^2 + 21w + 26$

28. $48c^2 - 62c + 7$

29. $4\pi x^2 + 22\pi x + 28\pi$

30. $24\pi x^2 + 72\pi x + 54\pi$

31. $x^3 + 2x^2 - 14x + 5$

32. $k^3 - 6k^2 + 11k - 6$

33. $10a^3 + 12a^2 + 9a - 20$

34. $6g^3 + 11g^2 - 31g + 14$

35. $x^2 + 200x + 9375$

36. $x^3 - 3x^2 + x - 3$

37. $-n^3 - 3n^2 - n - 3$

38. $b^4 + 2b^2 - 3$

39. $2m^3 + 10m^2 + m + 5$

40. $2c^3 + 3c^2 - 8c - 12$

41. $12z^4 + 4z^3 + 3z^2 + z$

42. The student forgot to find the product $(-2)(3x)$:
$(x - 2)(3x + 4) = x(3x) + x(4) - 2(3x) - 2(4) =$
$3x^2 - 2x - 8$

43. Check students' work.

44. 15 ft by 45 ft

45. a. i. $x^2 + 2x + 1$, 121
  ii. $x^2 + 3x + 2$, 132
  iii. $x^2 + 4x + 3$, 143
  b. The digits in the product of the two integers are the coefficients of the terms in the product of the two binomials.

46. $n^3 + 15n^2 + 56n$

For Exercises 47–49, each expression represents the side length of a cube. Write a polynomial in standard form for the surface area of each cube.

47. $x + 2$ **48.** $3a + 1$ **49.** $2c^2 + 3$

50. Financial Planning Suppose you deposit $1500 for college in a savings account that has an annual interest rate r (expressed as a decimal). At the end of 3 years, the value of your account will be $1500(1 + r)^3$ dollars.

    a. Rewrite the expression $1500(1 + r)^3$ by finding the product $1500(1 + r)(1 + r)(1 + r)$. Write your answer in standard form.

    b. How much money is in the account after 3 yr if the interest rate is 3% per year?

Standardized Test Prep

51. Which expression is equivalent to $(x + 4)(x - 9)$?

    Ⓐ $x^2 + 5x - 36$ Ⓑ $x^2 - 5x - 36$ Ⓒ $x^2 - 13x - 36$ Ⓓ $x^2 - 13x - 5$

52. Malia is making a landscape drawing for her backyard. She is drawing a sidewalk. She uses the graph of the equation $y = 3x + 2$ to represent one edge of the sidewalk. She wants the other edge of the sidewalk to be parallel to the first edge through the point (3, 4). The graph of which of the following lines represents the other edge of the sidewalk?

    Ⓕ $y = x + 2$ Ⓖ $y = 4x + 2$ Ⓗ $y = 3x - 9$ Ⓘ $y = 3x - 5$

53. What is (are) the solution(s) of the equation $|x + 3| = 7$?

    Ⓐ 4 and −10   Ⓑ 4 and −4   Ⓒ 4   Ⓓ 10

54. A trapezoid is determined by the following system of inequalities.

    $y \geq 3$ $y \leq 9$ $x \leq 8$ $y \leq 2x + 3$

    a. Graph the trapezoid in the coordinate plane.

    b. The formula for the area A of a trapezoid is $A = \frac{1}{2}(b_1 + b_2)h$, where b_1 and b_2 are the bases of the trapezoid and h is its height. What is the area of the trapezoid you graphed in part (a)? Show your work.

Mixed Review

Factor each polynomial.   ◀ See Lesson 8-2.

55. $6x - 4$ **56.** $b^2 + 8b$ **57.** $10t^3 - 25t^2 + 20t$

Get Ready!   **To prepare for Lesson 8-4, do Exercises 58–61.**

Simplify each expression.   ◀ See Lesson 7-4.

58. $(6x)^2$ **59.** $(2y)^2$ **60.** $(-3m)^2$ **61.** $(-5n)^2$

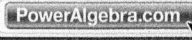

---

47. $6x^2 + 24x + 24$

48. $54a^2 + 36a + 6$

49. $24c^4 + 72c^2 + 54$

50. a. $1500r^3 + 4500r^2 + 4500r + 1500$

    b. about $1639.09

51. B

52. I

53. A

54. a.

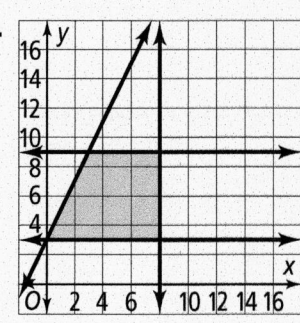

b. Area is 39 units^2.

[4] Graph is correct, lengths of sides are labeled, and area is computed correctly.

[3] Graph is correct, length of one or more sides is computed incorrectly.

[2] Graph is incorrect, but area of incorrect graph is computed correctly.

[1] correct area, but work not shown

55. $2(3x - 2)$

56. $b(b + 8)$

57. $5t(2t^2 - 5t + 4)$

58. $36x^2$

59. $4y^2$

60. $9m^2$

61. $25n^2$

Additional Instructional Support

Algebra 1 Companion

Students can use the **Algebra 1 Companion** worktext (4 pages) as you teach the lesson. Use the Companion to support

- New Vocabulary
- Key Concepts
- Got It for each Problem
- Lesson Check

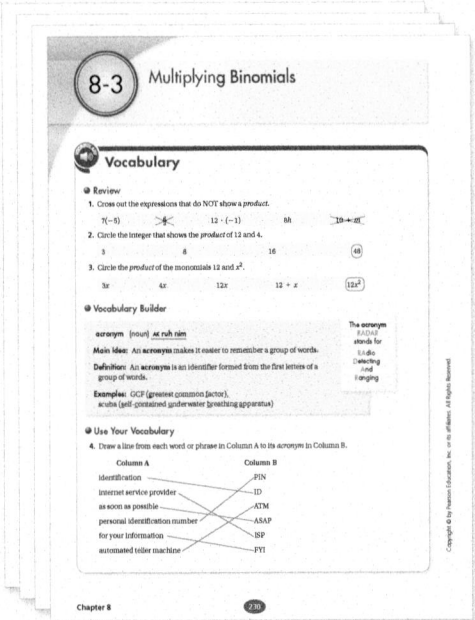

ELL Support

Focus on Language Have a word wall with important words and vocabulary words used in the chapter with their definitions. Make a separate area for the roots of words. Ask students for words that share the same word base or origin. Use an Internet site for the information if necessary. These roots can be posted on the word wall, in a separate section or using a different color, to distinguish them.

Use Multiple Representations Have other materials available of varied instructional levels which define and use the Distributive Property and FOIL methods.

5 Assess & Remediate

Lesson Quiz

1. What is the simplified form of $(x + 1)(3x - 2)$?
2. What is the simplified form of $(2x + 3)(x - 5)$?
3. What is the simplified form of $(x - 4)(3x + 1)$?
4. **Do you UNDERSTAND?** Write an expression for the area of the rectangle below.

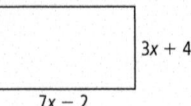

3x + 4

7x − 2

5. What is the simplified form of $(x^2 + 5x - 6)(x - 2)$?

ANSWERS TO LESSON QUIZ

1. $3x^2 + x - 2$
2. $2x^2 - 7x - 15$
3. $3x^2 - 11x - 4$
4. $21x^2 + 22x - 8$
5. $x^3 + 3x^2 - 16x + 12$

PRESCRIPTION FOR REMEDIATION
Use the student work on the Lesson Quiz to prescribe a differentiated review assignment.

Points	Differentiated Remediation
0–2	Intervention
3–4	On-level
5	Extension

PowerAlgebra.com

5 Assess & Remediate
Assign the Lesson Quiz. Appropriate intervention, practice, or enrichment is automatically generated based on student performance.

Intervention

- **Reteaching** (2 pages) Provides reteaching and practice exercises for the key lesson concepts. Use with struggling students or absent students.
- **English Language Learner Support** Helps students develop and reinforce mathematical vocabulary and key concepts.

All-in-One Resources/Online
Reteaching

8-3 **Reteaching**
Multiplying Binomials

You can multiply binomials by using the FOIL method. FOIL stands for First, Outer, Inner, and Last.

Problem

What is the simplified form of $(4x + 3)(2x + 6)$?

Use the FOIL method to simplify the binomial.

Solve	$4x \cdot 2x = 8x^2$	Multiply the First terms.
	$4x \cdot 6 = 24x$	Multiply the Outer terms.
	$3 \cdot 2x = 6x$	Multiply the Inner terms.
	$3 \cdot 6 = 18$	Multiply the Last terms.
	$8x^2 + 24x + 6x + 18$	Add the products.
	$8x^2 + 30x + 18$	Add the like terms.

Check Substitute any number for x. Try x = 2. If the two sides of the equation are equal the simplification may be correct.
$(4x + 3)(2x + 6) \stackrel{?}{=} 8x^2 + 30x + 18$
$(4 \cdot 2 + 3)(2 \cdot 2 + 6) \stackrel{?}{=} (8 \cdot 2^2) + (30 \cdot 2) + 18$
$(11)(10) \stackrel{?}{=} 32 + 60 + 18$
$110 = 110$ ✓

Solution: The simplified form of $(4x + 3)(2x + 6)$ is $8x^2 + 30x + 18$.

Exercises

Simplify each product.

1. $(a + 6)(a - 3)$ 2. $(b - 4)(b + 5)$ 3. $(c + 3)(c + 7)$
$a^2 + 3a - 18$ $b^2 + b - 20$ $c^2 + 10c + 21$
4. $(2d + 4)(3d - 2)$ 5. $(4e - 5)(3e + 3)$ 6. $(3f - 2)(2f - 4)$
$6d^2 + 8d - 8$ $12e^2 - 3e - 15$ $6f^2 - 16f + 8$
7. $(5g + 3)(g - 3)$ 8. $(4h + 4)(2h + 5)$ 9. $(3j - 5)(4j - 3)$
$5g^2 - 12g - 9$ $8h^2 + 28h + 20$ $12j^2 - 29j + 15$

All-in-One Resources/Online
English Language Learner Support

8-3 **ELL Support**
Multiplying Binomials

Use the Distributive Property to find the simplified form of $(3x + 2)(4x - 3)$.

$(3x + 2)(4x - 3)$	Write the problem.
$3x(4x - 3) + 2(4x - 3)$	Distribute the second factor, $4x - 3$.
$12x^2 - 9x + 2(4x - 3)$	Distribute 3x.
$12x^2 - 9x + 8x - 6$	Distribute 2.
$12x^2 - x - 6$	Combine like terms.

Exercises

Use the Distributive Property to find the simplified form of $(5x + 6)(2x - 4)$.

$(5x + 6)(2x - 4)$	Write the problem.
$5x(2x - 4) + 6(2x - 4)$	Distribute the second factor, $2x - 4$.
$10x^2 - 20x + 6(2x - 4)$	Distribute 5x.
$10x^2 - 20x + 12x - 24$	Distribute 6.
$10x^2 - 8x - 24$	Combine like terms.

Use the Distributive Property to find the simplified form of $(7x - 3)(4x + 6)$.

$(7x - 3)(4x + 6)$	Write the problem.
$7x(4x + 6) - 3(4x + 6)$	Distribute the second factor, $4x + 6$.
$28x^2 + 42x - 3(4x + 6)$	Distribute 7x.
$28x^2 + 42x - 12x - 18$	Distribute −3.
$28x^2 + 30x - 18$	Combine like terms.

Differentiated Remediation *continued*

On-Level

- **Practice** (2 pages) Provides extra practice for each lesson. For simpler practice exercises, use the Form K Practice pages found in the All-in-One Teaching Resources and online.

- **Think About a Plan** Helps students develop specific problem-solving skills and strategies by providing scaffolded guiding questions.

- **Standardized Test Prep** Focuses on all major exercises, all major question types, and helps students prepare for the high-stakes assessments.

Extension

- **Enrichment** Provides students with interesting problems and activities that extend the concepts of the lesson.

- **Activities, Games, and Puzzles** Worksheets that can be used for concepts development, enrichment, and for fun!

Practice and Problem Solving WKBK/ All-in-One Resources/Online
Practice page 1

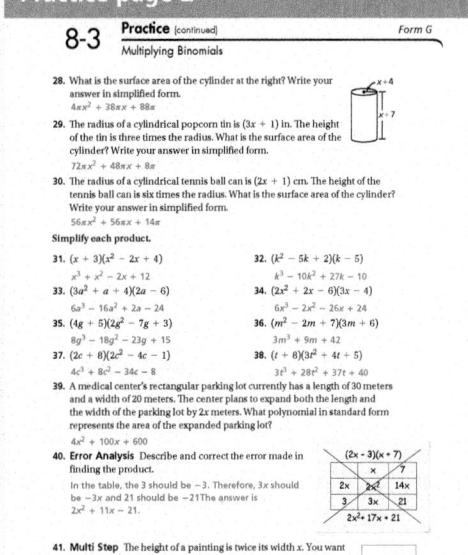

8-3 Practice — Form G
Multiplying Binomials

Simplify each product using the Distributive Property.

1. $(x + 3)(x + 8)$ $x^2 + 11x + 24$
2. $(y - 4)(y + 7)$ $y^2 + 3y - 28$
3. $(m + 9)(m - 3)$ $m^2 + 6m - 27$

4. $(c - 6)(c - 4)$ $c^2 - 10c + 24$
5. $(2r - 5)(r + 3)$ $2r^2 + r - 15$
6. $(3x + 1)(5x - 3)$ $15x^2 - 4x - 3$

7. $(d + 2)(4d - 3)$ $4d^2 + 5d - 6$
8. $(5t - 1)(3t - 2)$ $15t^2 - 13t + 2$
9. $(a + 11)(11a + 1)$ $11a^2 + 122a + 11$

Simplify each product using a table.

10. $(x + 3)(x - 5)$ $x^2 - 2x - 15$
11. $(a - 2)(a - 13)$ $a^2 - 15a + 26$
12. $(w - 4)(w + 8)$ $w^2 + 4w - 32$

13. $(5h - 3)(h + 7)$ $5h^2 + 32h - 21$
14. $(x - 3)(2x + 3)$ $2x^2 - 3x - 9$
15. $(2p + 1)(6p + 4)$ $12p^2 + 14p + 4$

Simplify each product using the FOIL method.

16. $(2x - 6)(x + 3)$ $2x^2 - 18$
17. $(n - 5)(3n - 4)$ $3n^2 - 19n + 20$
18. $(4p^2 + 2)(3p - 1)$ $12p^3 - 4p^2 + 6p - 2$

19. $(a + 7)(a - 3)$ $a^2 + 4a - 21$
20. $(x + 3)(3x - 2)$ $3x^2 + 7x - 6$
21. $(k - 9)(k + 5)$ $k^2 - 4k - 45$

22. $(b - 5)(b - 11)$ $b^2 - 16b + 55$
23. $(4m - 1)(m + 4)$ $4m^2 + 15m - 4$
24. $(7z + 3)(4z - 6)$ $28z^2 - 30z - 18$

25. $(2h + 6)(5h - 3)$ $10h^2 + 24h - 18$
26. $(3w + 12)(w + 3)$ $3w^2 + 21w + 36$
27. $(6c - 2)(9c - 8)$ $54c^2 - 66c + 16$

Practice and Problem Solving WKBK/ All-in-One Resources/Online
Practice page 2

8-3 Practice (continued) — Form G
Multiplying Binomials

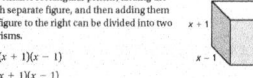
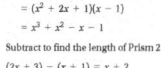

28. What is the surface area of the cylinder at the right? Write your answer in simplified form. $4\pi x^2 + 38\pi x + 88\pi$

29. The radius of a cylindrical popcorn tin is $(3x + 1)$ in. The height of the tin is three times the radius. What is the surface area of the cylinder? Write your answer in simplified form. $72\pi x^2 + 48\pi x + 8\pi$

30. The radius of a cylindrical tennis ball can is $(2x + 1)$ cm. The height of the tennis ball can is six times the radius. What is the surface area of the cylinder? Write your answer in simplified form. $56\pi x^2 + 56\pi x + 14\pi$

Simplify each product.

31. $(x + 3)(x^2 - 2x + 4)$ $x^3 + x^2 - 2x + 12$
32. $(k^2 - 5k + 2)(k - 5)$ $k^3 - 10k^2 + 27k - 10$
33. $(3a^2 + a + 4)(2a - 6)$ $6a^3 - 16a^2 + 2a - 24$
34. $(2x^2 + 2x - 6)(3x - 4)$ $6x^3 - 2x^2 - 26x + 24$
35. $(4g + 5)(2g^2 - 7g + 3)$ $8g^3 - 18g^2 - 23g + 15$
36. $(m^2 - 2m + 7)(3m + 6)$ $3m^3 + 9m + 42$
37. $(2c + 8)(2c^2 - 4c - 1)$ $4c^3 + 8c^2 - 34c - 8$
38. $(t + 6)(3t^2 + 4t + 5)$ $3t^3 + 28t^2 + 37t + 40$

39. A medical center's rectangular parking lot currently has a length of 30 meters and a width of 20 meters. The center plans to expand both the length and the width of the parking lot by 2x meters. What polynomial in standard form represents the area of the expanded parking lot? $4x^2 + 100x + 600$

40. **Error Analysis** Describe and correct the error made in finding the product.
In the table, the 3 should be −3. Therefore, 3x should be −3x and 21 should be −21 The answer is $2x^2 + 11x - 21$.

	x	7
$2x$	$2x^2$	$14x$
3	$3x$	21

41. **Multi Step** The height of a painting is twice its width x. You want a 3 inch wide wooden frame for the painting. The area of the frame alone is 216 square inches.
   a. Draw a diagram that represents this situation.
   b. Write a variable expression for the area of the frame alone. $18x + 36$
   c. What are the dimensions of the frame? length is 26; width is 16

All-in-One Resources/Online
Enrichment

8-3 Enrichment
Multiplying Binomials

You can find the volume of irregular figures by dividing the figure into smaller rectangular prisms, finding the volume of each separate figure, and then adding them together. The figure to the right can be divided into two rectangular prisms.

$V_1 = (x + 1)(x + 1)(x - 1)$
$= (x^2 + 2x + 1)(x - 1)$
$= x^3 + x^2 - x - 1$

Subtract to find the length of Prism 2.

$(2x + 3) - (x + 1) = x + 2$
$V_2 = (x + 2)(x - 1)(2x - 2)$
$= (x^2 + x - 2)(2x - 2)$
$= 2x^3 - 6x + 4$

$V_{Total} = (x^3 + x^2 - x - 1) + (2x^3 - 6x + 4)$
$= 3x^3 + x^2 - 7x + 3$

You can also find the volume of an irregular figure by finding the volume of the whole figure, as if no pieces were cut away. Next, find the volume of the cut away piece, and then subtract that volume from the whole. Prism 2 is $x - 3$ taller than Prism 1.

$V_{Whole} = (x - 1)(2x + 3)(2x - 2) = (2x^2 + x - 3)(2x - 2) = 4x^3 - 2x^2 - 8x + 6$
$V_{Piece} = (x - 1)(x + 1)(x - 3) = (x^2 - 1)(x - 3) = x^3 - 3x^2 - x + 3$
$V_{Total} = (4x^3 - 2x^2 - 8x + 6) - (x^3 - 3x^2 - x + 3) = 3x^3 + x^2 - 7x + 3$

What is the volume of each figure? Write your answer as a polynomial in standard form.

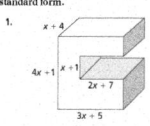
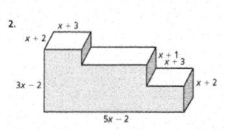

1. $10x^3 + 54x^2 + 54x - 8$
2. $10x^3 + 25x^2 - 14x - 48$

Practice and Problem Solving WKBK/ All-in-One Resources/Online
Think About a Plan

8-3 Think About a Plan
Multiplying Binomials

Geometry The dimensions of a rectangular prism are n, $n + 7$, and $n + 8$. Use the formula $V = lwh$ to write a polynomial in standard form for the volume of the prism.

Know

1. What are the dimensions of the rectangular prism? n , $n + 7$, $n + 8$
2. What is the formula for the volume of a rectangular prism? $V = lwh$
3. In the volume formula, what do l, w, and h represent? length , width , height
4. Explain how to write a polynomial in standard form. The terms are arranged in order of degree, with the highest degree first.

Need

5. To solve the problem you need to find a polynomial in standard form that represents the volume of the rectangular prism.

Plan

6. Draw a diagram of the rectangular prism and label the information you know.

7. Write an expression for the volume of the rectangular prism.
$V = n(n + 7)(n + 8)$

8. Write the volume of the rectangular prism as a polynomial in standard form.
$n^3 + 15n^2 + 56n$

Practice and Problem Solving WKBK/ All-in-One Resources/Online
Standardized Test Prep

8-3 Standardized Test Prep
Multiplying Binomials

Multiple Choice

For Exercises 1–5, choose the correct letter.

1. What is the simplified form of $(x - 2)(2x + 3)$? Use the Distributive Property. A
   A. $2x^2 - x - 6$ B. $2x^2 - 6$ C. $2x^2 - 7x - 6$ D. $2x^2 + x - 6$

2. What is the simplified form of $(3x + 2)(4x - 3)$? Use a table. I
   F. $12x^2 + 18x + 6$ G. $12x^2 + x - 6$ H. $12x^2 + 18x - 6$ I. $12x^2 - x - 6$

3. What is the simplified form of $(4p - 2)(p - 4)$? B
   A. $4p^2 + 6p - 16$ B. $4p^2 - 18p + 8$ C. $4p^2 - 14p - 6$ D. $4p^2 - 6p + 16$

4. The radius of a cylinder is $3x - 2$ cm. The height of the cylinder is $x + 3$ cm. What is the surface area of the cylinder? I
   F. $2\pi(3x^2 + 10x - 8)$
   G. $2\pi(12x^2 + 7x - 2)$
   H. $2\pi(12x^2 - 2x + 13)$
   I. $2\pi(12x^2 - 5x - 2)$

5. What is the simplified form of $(2x^2 + 4x - 3)(3x + 1)$? C
   A. $6x^3 + 10x^2 - 5x + 3$
   B. $6x^3 + 14x^2 + 5x - 3$
   C. $6x^3 + 14x^2 - 5x - 3$
   D. $6x^3 - 10x^2 - 5x - 3$

Short Response

6. A soup can that is a cylinder has a radius of $2x - 1$ and a height of $3x$. What is the surface area of the soup can? Show your work. $20\pi x^2 - 14\pi x + 2\pi$
   [2] Correct polynomial written with all work shown
   [1] Polynomial written with minor calculation error or inadequate work shown
   [0] No correct work shown

Online Teacher Resource Center
Activities, Games, and Puzzles

8-3 Puzzle: The Binomial Code
Multiplying Binomials

Multiply the binomials in the tables, then complete the columns to the right. The first one has been done for you. Translate the numbers in the *shaded* boxes to letters using the code below. Then unscramble the letters to complete the phrase at the bottom of the page.

A→1   B→2   C→3   · · ·   X→24   Y→25   Z→26

First Word		x^2	x	Constant	Letter
$(x + 1)(x + 5)$	$x^2 + 6x + 5$	1	6	5	O
$(x + 4)(x + 5)$	$x^2 + 9x + 20$	1	9	20	T
$(x + 2)(x + 7)$	$x^2 + 9x + 14$	1	9	14	N
$(x + 9)(x + 1)$	$x^2 + 10x + 9$	1	10	9	I

Second Word		x^2	x	Constant	Letter
$(9x - 1)(x + 5)$	$9x^2 + 44x - 5$	9	44	−5	I
$(x - 5)(x - 1)$	$x^2 - 6x + 5$	1	−6	5	E
$(x + 1)(x + 1)$	$x^2 + 2x + 1$	1	2	1	K

Third Word		x^2	x	Constant	Letter
$(x + 7)(x + 2)$	$x^2 + 9x + 14$	1	9	14	S
$(x + 3)(x + 3)$	$x^2 + 6x + 9$	1	6	9	S
$(3x - 2)(x - 5)$	$3x^2 - 17x + 10$	3	−17	10	C
$(x + 3)(x + 2)$	$x^2 + 5x + 6$	1	5	6	E
$(5x + 1)(7x + 3)$	$35x^2 + 22x + 3$	35	22	3	C

Fourth Word		x^2	x	Constant	Letter
$(x + 2)(x + 2)$	$x^2 + 4x + 4$	1	4	4	N
$(x + 4)(x + 5)$	$x^2 + 9x + 20$	1	9	20	I

Fifth Word		x^2	x	Constant	Letter
$(x + 2)(x + 1)$	$x^2 + 3x + 2$	1	3	2	M
$(5x + 2)(4x + 1)$	$20x^2 + 13x + 2$	20	13	2	T
$(x + 11)(x - 11)$	$x^2 - 121$	1	0	−121	A

MESSAGE: NOTHING LIKE SUCCESS IN MATH!

1 Interactive Learning

Solve It!

PURPOSE To find the product of a binomial squared using an area model

PROCESS Students may use the area formula and geometric reasoning or write and multiply binomials to determine the area.

FACILITATE

Q What is the total area of the pieces being removed? [$6x + 6x - x^2$]

Q How can you find the area for the new invitation? [**Subtract the areas to be removed from the area of the original invitation.**]

ANSWER See Solve It in Answers on next page.

CONNECT THE MATH Squares are a recurring concept in algebra, geometry, and physics. Students should understand that recognizing and generating the squares of binomials is a skill that figures in many real-world calculations.

2 Guided Instruction

Take Note

Given that students can use the FOIL method to determine the square of a binomial, they may think that memorizing the rules for simplifying $(a + b)^2$ and $(a - b)^2$ is not important. Tell students that learning these rules now will make it much easier to learn a process, used in later chapters, called "completing the square."

8-4 Multiplying Special Cases

In Lesson 8-3 you expanded an area. Now you want to reduce an area.

> **Getting Ready!**
>
> You are making square invitations for a party. You start with a square piece of paper with 6-in. sides. You reduce both its length and its width by x, as shown. What is the area of the invitation? Justify your reasoning.
>
> 6 in.
>
> 6 in.

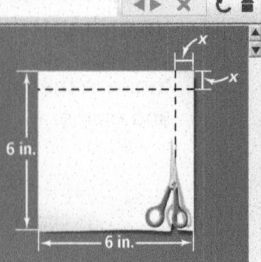

Essential Understanding There are special rules you can use to simplify the square of a binomial or the product of a sum and difference.

Squares of binomials have the form $(a + b)^2$ or $(a - b)^2$. You can algebraically simplify the product or you can use an area model to discover the rule for simplifying $(a + b)^2$, as shown below.

Simplify the product.

$$(a + b)^2 = (a + b)(a + b)$$
$$= a^2 + ab + ba + b^2 \quad \text{Multiply the binomials.}$$
$$= a^2 + 2ab + b^2 \quad \text{Simplify.}$$

Area Model

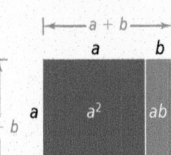

$a^2 + 2ab + b^2$

Key Concept   The Square of a Binomial

Words The square of a binomial is the square of the first term plus twice the product of the two terms plus the square of the last term.

Algebra	**Examples**
$(a + b)^2 = a^2 + 2ab + b^2$	$(x + 4)^2 = x^2 + 8x + 16$
$(a - b)^2 = a^2 - 2ab + b^2$	$(x - 3)^2 = x^2 - 6x + 9$

8-4 Preparing to Teach

BIG ideas Equivalence
Properties   **UbD**

ESSENTIAL UNDERSTANDING

- There are special rules for simplifying the square of a binomial or the product of a sum and a difference.

Math Background

While all polynomials can be multiplied using the techniques developed in the last lesson, some special cases are easy to identify and have a pattern to their products. Using these patterns makes the multiplication of these special cases quicker and easier. In addition, familiarity with the rules for the special cases will help students when they begin to factor in the next lessons.

Two special cases, the square of a binomial and the difference of squares, are patterns that students should be encouraged to recognize.

Squaring a binomial results in a perfect-square trinomial.

$$(a + b)^2 = a^2 + 2ab + b^2$$
$$(a - b)^2 = a^2 - 2ab + b^2$$

The other special case, the difference of two squares, is named by its simplified product.

$$(a + b)(a - b) = a^2 - b^2$$

Ample exposure to and practice with these special cases will enable students to easily recognize the special-case polynomials and their respective patterns.

Support Student Learning

Use the **Algebra 1 Companion** to engage and support students during instructions. See Lesson Resources at the end of this lesson for details.

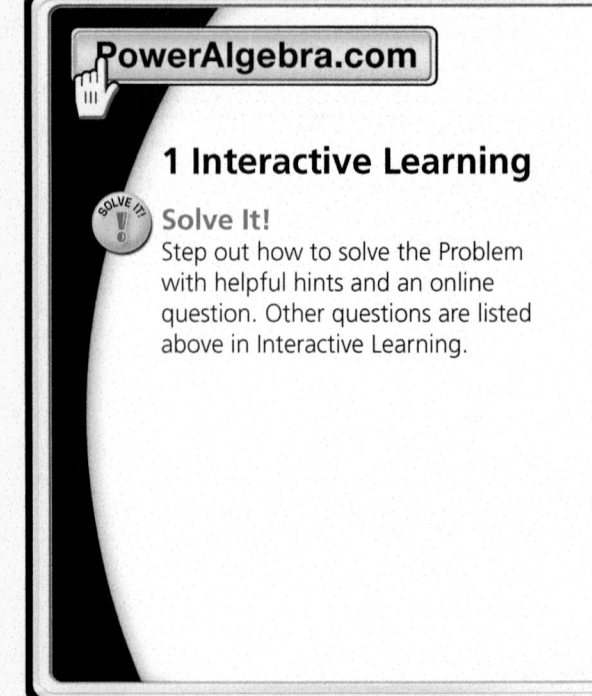

PowerAlgebra.com

1 Interactive Learning

Solve It!

Step out how to solve the Problem with helpful hints and an online question. Other questions are listed above in Interactive Learning.

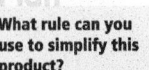 **Problem 1** Squaring a Binomial

Plan

What rule can you use to simplify this product?
$(2m - 3)^2$ may not look like $(a - b)^2$, but it has the same form. Use the rule for $(a - b)^2$ and let $a = 2m$ and $b = 3$.

What is a simpler form of each product?

A $(x + 8)^2 = x^2 + 2x(8) + 8^2$ Square the binomial.
           $= x^2 + 16x + 64$ Simplify.

B $(2m - 3)^2 = (2m)^2 - 2(2m)(3) + 3$ Square the binomial.
           $= 4m^2 - 12m + 9$ Simplify.

 Got It? **1.** What is a simpler form of each product?
   a. $(n - 7)^2$ **b.** $(2x + 9)^2$

Problem 2 Applying Squares of Binomials

Plan

How do you find the area of the walkway?
The area of the walkway is the difference of the total area and the area of the patio.

Exterior Design A square outdoor patio is surrounded by a brick walkway as shown. What is the area of the walkway?

Step 1 Find the total area of the patio and walkway.
   $(x + 6)^2 = x^2 + 2(x)(6) + 6^2$ Square the binomial.
           $= x^2 + 12x + 36$ Simplify.

Step 2 Find the area of the patio.
   The area of the patio is $x \cdot x$, or x^2.

Step 3 Find the area of the walkway.
   Area of walkway = Total area − Area of patio
                 $= (x^2 + 12x + 36) - x^2$ Substitute.
                 $= (x^2 - x^2) + 12x + 36$ Group like terms.
                 $= 12x + 36$ Simplify.

The area of the walkway is $(12x + 36)$ ft^2.

Diagram labels: 3 ft, x ft, 3 ft, (x + 6) ft, x ft, 3 ft, (x + 6) ft

 Got It? **2.** In Problem 2, suppose the brick walkway is 4 ft wide. What is its area?

Using mental math, you can square a binomial to find the square of a number.

 Problem 3 Using Mental Math

Think

What number close to 39 can you square mentally?
The nearest multiple of 10 to 39 is 40, which is a number you should be able to square mentally.

What is 39^2? Use mental math.

$39^2 = (40 - 1)^2$ Write 39^2 as the square of a binomial.
     $= 40^2 - 2(40)(1) + 1^2$ Square the binomial.
     $= 1600 - 80 + 1$ Simplify.
     $= 1521$ Simplify.

Problem 1

> **Q** How do you determine the middle term of the product of a binomial squared? **[Double the product of the first and last term.]**
>
> **Q** If the simplified form of the square of a binomial is $x^2 + 12x + 36$, what binomial was squared? **[(x + 6)]**

Got It?   ERROR PREVENTION

If students make the common error of "distributing" the exponent when simplifying an expression such as $(n - 7)^2$, their answer will be a binomial. Have them check their work by substituting a value for n to see that $(n - 7)^2 \ne n^2 + 49$.

Problem 2

> **Q** Why is the total side length of the patio with the walkway $(x + 6)$? **[The total length is x feet for the patio plus 3 feet on either side for the walkway. So, x + 3 + 3 = x + 6.]**

Got It?   VISUAL LEARNERS

Show students that the area of the brick walkway could also be determined by finding the total area of the four rectangles that form the walkway: $4(x + 8) + 4(x + 8) + 4x + 4x = 16x + 64$.

Problem 3

> **Q** If a classmate used mental math and determined that $39^2 = 1601$, what mistake did he likely make? **[He likely thought that $(40 - 1)^2 = 40^2 + (-1)^2 = 1600 + 1$.]**

---

2 Guided Instruction

 Each Problem is worked out and supported online.

Problem 1
Squaring a Binomial

Problem 2
Applying Squares of Binomials
Animated

Problem 3
Using Mental Math

Problem 4
Finding the Product of a Sum and Difference
Animated

Problem 5
Using Mental Math
Animated

Support in Algebra 1 Companion
• Vocabulary
• Key Concepts
• Got It?

Answers

Solve It!
The width is $(6 - x)$ in. and the length is $(6 - x)$ in., so the area is $(6 - x)^2 = 36 - 12x + x^2$ in.^{2}; explanations may vary.

Got It?
   1. a. $n^2 - 14n + 49$
       b. $4x^2 + 36x + 81$
   2. $(16x + 64)$ ft^2

Got It?

> **Q** What two binomials can be used to determine 85^2 using mental math? **[$(80 + 5)^2$ and $(90 - 5)^2$]**

Take Note   TACTILE LEARNERS

Some students may benefit from using algebra tiles to find the product of $(x - 2)$ and $(x + 2)$. Algebra tiles make it clear to students that the terms $2x$ and $-2x$ form a zero pair.

Problem 4

> **Q** How do you recognize when two binomials can be multiplied using the rule for the product of a sum and difference? **[Binomials look the same except one has an addition symbol and the other a subtraction symbol.]**
>
> **Q** What is the property for raising a power to a power? **[$(a^m)^n = a^{m \cdot n}$]**
>
> **Q** Would you get the same answer if you used the FOIL method to multiply the binomials? Explain. **[Yes, the middle terms would form a zero pair, leaving you with $x^6 - 64$.]**

Got It

> **Q** For each part, what are the two middle terms and what do they give when combined? **[$9x$ and $-9x$; $6m^2$ and $-6m^2$; $12c$ and $-12c$; each pair simplifies to 0.]**

 Got It? **3. a.** What is 85^2? Use mental math.

b. Reasoning Is there more than one way to find 85^2 using mental math? Explain your reasoning.

The product of the sum and difference of the same two terms also produces a pattern.

$$(a + b)(a - b) = a^2 - ab + ba - b^2$$
$$= a^2 - b^2$$

> Notice that the sum of $-ab$ and ba is 0, leaving $a^2 - b^2$.

 take note

Key Concept   The Product of a Sum and Difference

Words The product of the sum and difference of the same two terms is the difference of their squares.

Algebra
$(a + b)(a - b) = a^2 - b^2$

Examples
$(x + 2)(x - 2) = x^2 - 2^2 = x^2 - 4$

Problem 4   Finding the Product of a Sum and Difference

What is a simpler form of $(x^3 + 8)(x^3 - 8)$?

Plan

How do you choose which rule to use?
The first factor in the product is the sum of x^3 and 8. The second factor is the difference of x^3 and 8. So, use the rule for the product of a sum and difference.

Think

Write the original product.

Identify which terms correspond to a and b in the rule for the product of a sum and difference.

Substitute for a and b in the rule.

Simplify.

Write

$(x^3 + 8)(x^3 - 8)$

$a = x^3; b = 8$

$(x^3 + 8)(x^3 - 8) = (x^3)^2 - (8)^2$

$= x^6 - 64$

Got It? **4.** What is a simpler form of each product?
a. $(x + 9)(x - 9)$ **b.** $(6 + m^2)(6 - m^2)$ **c.** $(3c - 4)(3c + 4)$

Additional Problems

1. What is the simplified form of each product?

a. $(x + 5)^2$

b. $(3n - 1)^2$

ANSWER a. $x^2 + 10x + 25$
b. $9n^2 - 6n + 1$

2. What is the area of the shaded part of the figure below?

ANSWER $10x + 25$

3. What is 49^2? Use mental math.

ANSWER 2401

4. What is the simplified form of $(x^2 - 6)(x^2 + 6)$?

ANSWER $x^4 - 36$

5. What is 38×42?

ANSWER 1596

Answers

Got It? (continued)

3. a. 7225

b. Answers may vary. Sample: You could write 85 as $(80 + 5)$ or as $(100 - 15)$.

4. a. $x^2 - 81$

b. $36 - m^4$

c. $9c^2 - 16$

You can use the rule for the product of a sum and difference to calculate products using mental math.

Think

How can you write $64 \cdot 56$ as the product of a sum and difference?
Find the number halfway between the factors. 60 is 4 units from each factor. Write the factors in terms of 60 and 4.

 Problem 5 Using Mental Math

GRIDDED RESPONSE

What is $64 \cdot 56$?

$$64 \cdot 56 = (60 + 4)(60 - 4) \quad \text{Write as a product of a sum and a difference.}$$
$$= 60^2 - 4^2 \quad \text{Use } (a + b)(a - b) = a^2 - b^2.$$
$$= 3600 - 16 \quad \text{Simplify powers.}$$
$$= 3584 \quad \text{Simplify.}$$

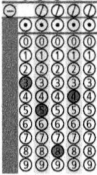

✓ **Got It? 5.** What is $52 \cdot 48$? Use mental math.

Lesson Check

Do you know HOW?

Simplify each product.

1. $(c + 3)(c + 3)$

2. $(g - 4)^2$

3. $(2r - 3)(2r + 3)$

4. A square has side length $(2x + 3)$ in. What is the area of the square?

Do you UNDERSTAND?

What rule would you use to find each product? Why?

5. $(3x - 1)^2$

6. $(4x - 9)(4x + 9)$

7. $(7x + 2)(7x + 2)$

8. Reasoning How do you know whether it is convenient to use the rule for the product of a sum and difference to mentally multiply two numbers?

Practice and Problem-Solving Exercises

Ⓐ Practice Simplify each expression.

See Problem 1.

9. $(w + 5)^2$ **10.** $(h + 2)^2$ **11.** $(3s + 9)^2$ **12.** $(2n + 7)^2$

13. $(a - 8)^2$ **14.** $(k - 11)^2$ **15.** $(5m - 2)^2$ **16.** $(4x - 6)^2$

Geometry The figures below are squares. Find an expression for the area of each shaded region. Write your answers in standard form.

See Problem 2.

17.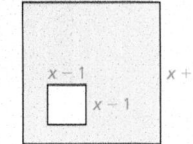

18.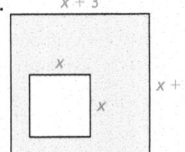

PowerAlgebra.com | Lesson 8-4 Multiplying Special Cases | 495

Problem 5

Q Would writing the product of $64 \cdot 56$ as $(70 - 6)(50 + 6)$ allow you to use a special case rule? Explain. **[No, $70 \neq 50$, so, you cannot use the rule for the product of a sum and a difference.]**

Q How is the number 60 related to the numbers 64 and 56? **[64 is 4 more than 60 and 56 is 4 less than 60.]**

Got It?   VISUAL LEARNERS

Students may benefit from seeing the product of $(50 + 2)(50 - 2)$ determined using the FOIL method.

3 Lesson Check

Do you know HOW?

• If students have difficulty with Exercise 1, then remind them that $(c + 3)(c + 3)$ could be written as $(c + 3)^2$. The product of the binomials can be determined using the rule listed on page 492.

Do you UNDERSTAND?

• If students have difficulty with Exercises 5–7, then have them condense the two Take Note sections into one that lists all three rules for multiplying special cases.

Close

Q How are the three special cases of multiplying binomials similar? How are they different? **[Each case is similar in that it involves finding the product of two identical or nearly identical binomials. Each case is different in that you use a different pattern to find the product of the two binomials.]**

Got It? (continued)

5. 2496

Lesson Check

1. $c^2 + 6c + 9$

2. $g^2 - 8g + 16$

3. $4r^2 - 9$

4. $4x^2 + 12x + 9$ in.^{2}

5. The Square of a Binomial

6. The Product of a Sum and Difference

7. The Square of a Binomial

8. Answers may vary. Sample: You can use the rule for the product of a sum and difference to multiply two numbers when one number can be written as $a + b$ and the other number can be written as $a - b$.

Practice and Problem-Solving Exercises

9. $w^2 + 10w + 25$

10. $h^2 + 4h + 4$

11. $9s^2 + 54s + 81$

12. $4n^2 + 28n + 49$

13. $a^2 - 16a + 64$

14. $k^2 - 22k + 121$

15. $25m^2 - 20m + 4$

16. $16x^2 - 48x + 36$

17. $(10x + 15)$ units^2

18. $(6x + 9)$ units^2

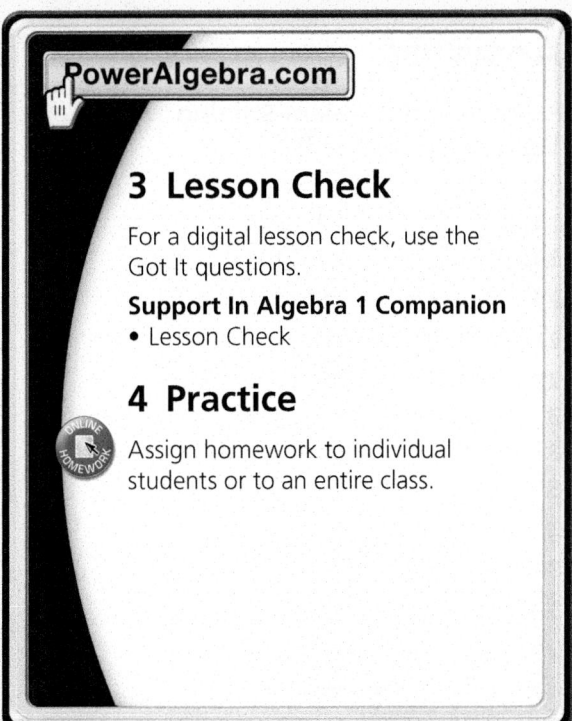

PowerAlgebra.com

3 Lesson Check

For a digital lesson check, use the Got It questions.

Support In Algebra 1 Companion
• Lesson Check

4 Practice

Assign homework to individual students or to an entire class.

Lesson 8-4 **495**

4 Practice

ASSIGNMENT GUIDE

Basic: 9–35 all, 36–50 even, 51–52

Average: 9–35 odd, 36–55

Advanced: 9–35 odd, 36–58

Standardized Test Prep: 59–61

Mixed Review: 62–71

Reasoning exercises have blue headings.

Applications exercises have red headings.

EXERCISE 52: Use the Think About a Plan worksheet in the **Practice and Problem Solving Workbook** (also available in the Teaching Resources in print and online) to further support students' development in becoming independent learners.

HOMEWORK QUICK CHECK

To check students' understanding of key skills and concepts, go over Exercises 11, 25, 50, 51, and 52.

---

19. Interior Design A square green rug has a blue square in the center. The side length of the blue square is x inches. The width of the green band that surrounds the blue square is 6 in. What is the area of the green band?

Mental Math Simplify each product.   ◀ See Problem 3.

20. 61^2 **21.** 79^2 **22.** 48^2 **23.** 403^2 **24.** 302^2

Simplify each product.   ◀ See Problem 4.

25. $(v + 6)(v - 6)$ **26.** $(b + 1)(b - 1)$ **27.** $(z - 5)(z + 5)$

28. $(x - 3)(x + 3)$ **29.** $(10 + y)(10 - y)$ **30.** $(t - 13)(t + 13)$

Mental Math Simplify each product.   ◀ See Problem 5.

31. $42 \cdot 38$ **32.** $79 \cdot 81$ **33.** $63 \cdot 57$ **34.** $399 \cdot 401$ **35.** $303 \cdot 297$

B Apply   Simplify each product.

36. $(m + 3n)^2$ **37.** $(2a + b)^2$ **38.** $(4s - t)^2$ **39.** $(g - 7h)^2$

40. $(9k + 2q)^2$ **41.** $(8r - 5s)^2$ **42.** $(s + 6t^2)^2$ **43.** $(p^4 - 9q^2)^2$

44. $(4x + 7y)(4x - 7y)$ **45.** $(a - 6b)(a + 6b)$ **46.** $(2g + 9h)(2g - 9h)$

47. $(r^2 + 3s)(r^2 - 3s)$ **48.** $(2p^2 + 7q)(2p^2 - 7q)$ **49.** $(3w^3 - z^2)(3w^3 + z^2)$

50. Error Analysis Describe and correct the error made in simplifying the product.

$$(3a - 7)^2 = 9a^2 - 21a + 49$$

51. Think About a Plan A company logo is a white square inside a red square. The side length of the white square is $x + 2$. The side length of the red square is three times the side length of the white square. What is the area of the red part of the logo? Write your answer in standard form.
- How can drawing a diagram help you solve the problem?
- How can you express the area of the red part of the logo as a difference of areas?

52. Construction A square deck has a side length of $x + 5$. You are expanding the deck so that each side is four times as long as the side length of the original deck. What is the area of the new deck? Write your answer in standard form.

53. Reasoning Use the area model at the right to write a second expression for the area of the square labeled $(a - b)^2$. Then simplify the expression to derive the rule for the square of a binomial of the form $a - b$.

54. Open-Ended Give a counterexample to show that $(x + y)^2 = x^2 + y^2$ is false.

55. Reasoning Does $\left(3\frac{1}{2}\right)^2 = 9\frac{1}{4}$? Explain.

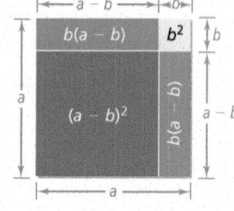

Answers

Practice and Problem-Solving Exercises (continued)

19. $36 - x^2$ in.^{2} **20.** 3721

21. 6241   **22.** 2304

23. 162,409   **24.** 91,204

25. $v^2 - 36$ **26.** $b^2 - 1$

27. $z^2 - 25$ **28.** $x^2 - 9$

29. $100 - y^2$ **30.** $t^2 - 169$

31. 1596   **32.** 6399

33. 3591   **34.** 159,999

35. 89,991

36. $m^2 + 6mn + 9n^2$

37. $4a^2 + 4ab + b^2$

38. $16s^2 - 8st + t^2$

39. $g^2 - 14gh + 49h^2$

40. $81k^2 + 36kq + 4q^2$

41. $64r^2 - 80rs + 25s^2$

42. $s^2 + 12st^2 + 36t^4$

43. $p^8 - 18p^4q^2 + 81q^4$

44. $16x^2 - 49y^2$

45. $a^2 - 36b^2$

46. $4g^2 - 81h^2$

47. $r^4 - 9s^2$

48. $4p^4 - 49q^2$

49. $9w^6 - z^4$

50. The middle term should be $-2(21a)$ because
$(a - b)^2 = a^2 - 2ab + b^2$;
$(3a - 7)^2 = 9a^2 - 42a + 49$.

51. $8x^2 + 32x + 32$

52. $16x^2 + 160x + 400$

53. Answers may vary. Sample:
$a^2 = b(a - b) + b^2 + (a - b)^2 + b(a - b)$
Area of big square = sum of areas of the 4 interior rectangles
$= 2b(a - b) + b^2 + (a - b)^2$
Combine like terms.
$= 2ab - 2b^2 + b^2 + (a - b)^2$
Distributive Property
$= 2ab - b^2 + (a - b)^2$ Combine like terms.
So, $(a - b)^2 = a^2 - 2ab + b^2$ by the Add. and Subtr. Prop. of $=$.

54. Answers will vary. Sample: Let $x = 1$ and $y = 1$. Then $(x + y)^2 = 2^2 = 4$ and $x^2 + y^2 = 1 + 1 = 2$.

55. No;
$\left(3\frac{1}{2}\right)^2 = \left(3 + \frac{1}{2}\right)^2 = \left(3 + \frac{1}{2}\right)\left(3 + \frac{1}{2}\right) = 3^2 + 2(3)\left(\frac{1}{2}\right) + \left(\frac{1}{2}\right)^2 = 9 + 3 + \frac{1}{4} = 12\frac{1}{4} \neq 9\frac{1}{4}$

Challenge

56. Simplify $(a + b + c)^2$.

57. Number Theory You can use factoring to show that the sum of two multiples of 3 is also a multiple of 3.

If m and n are integers, then $3m$ and $3n$ are multiples of three.

$3m + 3n = 3(m + n)$

Since $m + n$ is an integer, $3(m + n)$ is a multiple of three.

a. Show that if an integer is one more than a multiple of 3, then its square is also one more than a multiple of 3.

b. Reasoning If an integer is two more than a multiple of 3, is its square also two more than a multiple of 3? Explain.

58. The formula $V = \frac{4}{3}\pi r^3$ gives the volume of a sphere with radius r. Find the volume of a sphere with radius $x + 3$. Write your answer in standard form.

Standardized Test Prep

 SAT/ACT

59. What is a simpler form of $(2x + 5)(2x - 5)$?

    Ⓐ $4x^2 - 20x - 25$ Ⓑ $4x^2 + 20x + 25$ Ⓒ $4x^2 - 25$ Ⓓ $2x^2 - 5$

60. Sara and Nick sold tickets to a play. Sara sold 20 student tickets and 3 adult tickets for more than $60. Nick sold 15 student tickets and 5 adult tickets for less than $75. This information can be represented by $20x + 3y > 60$ and $15x + 5y < 75$, where x is the price of a student ticket and y is the price of an adult ticket. The inequalities are graphed at the right. Which could be the price of a student ticket?

    Ⓕ $1   Ⓗ $5.50

    Ⓖ $2.75   Ⓘ $6

Ticket Sales

Short Response

61. Graph the solutions of the system.

$$5x + 4y \geq 20$$
$$5x + 4y \leq 20$$

Mixed Review

Simplify each product.   ◀ See Lesson 8-3.

62. $(3x + 2)(2x - 5)$ **63.** $(4m - 1)(6m - 7)$ **64.** $(x + 9)(5x + 8)$

Find each percent change. Describe the percent change as an *increase* or   ◀ See Lesson 2-10.
decrease. If necessary, round to the nearest tenth.

65. $4 to $3   **66.** 4 ft to 5 ft   **67.** 12 lb to 15 lb   **68.** $40 to $35

Get Ready!   **To prepare for Lesson 8-5, do Exercises 69–71.**

Factor each polynomial.   ◀ See Lesson 8-2.

69. $12x^4 + 30x^3 + 42x$ **70.** $72x^3 + 54x^2 + 27$ **71.** $35x^3 + 7x^2 + 63x$

56. $a^2 + b^2 + c^2 + 2ab + 2ac + 2bc$

57. a. $(3m + 1)^2 = 9m^2 + 6m + 1 = 3(3m^2 + 2m) + 1$
Since $3(3m^2 + 2m)$ is a multiple of 3, the expression on the right is 1 more than a multiple of 3.

b. no; $(3m + 2)^2 = 3(3m^2 + 4m) + 4$

58. $\frac{4}{3}\pi x^3 + 12\pi x^2 + 36\pi x + 36\pi$

59. C

60. G

61. [2] The solutions are the coordinates of the points on the line with equation $5x + 4y = 20$.

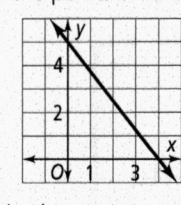

62. $6x^2 - 11x - 10$

63. $24m^2 - 34m + 7$

64. $5x^2 + 53x + 72$

65. decrease of 25%

66. increase of 25%

67. increase of 25%

68. decrease of 12.5%

69. $6x(2x^3 + 5x^2 + 7)$

70. $9(8x^3 + 6x^2 + 3)$

71. $7x(5x^2 + x + 9)$

[1] correct answer with a minor error in the explanation

Additional Instructional Support

Algebra 1 Companion

Students can use the **Algebra 1 Companion** worktext (4 pages) as you teach the lesson. Use the Companion to support

- New Vocabulary
- Key Concepts
- Got It for each Problem
- Lesson Check

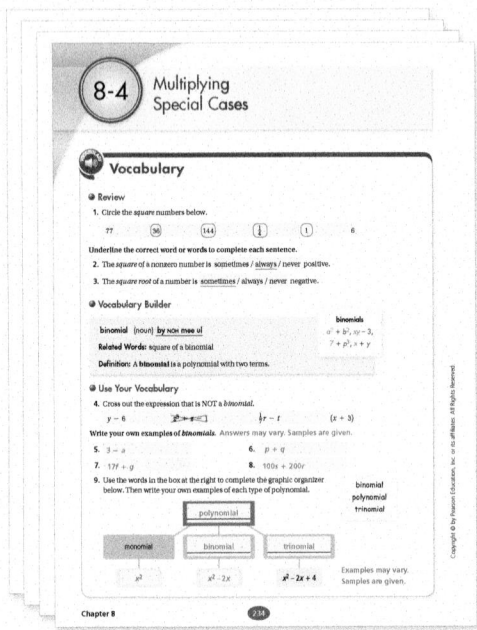

ELL Support

Use Manipulatives In small groups, draw a model to show how to represent $(a + b)^2$. Talk aloud as you demonstrate the model. Have students work through the same expression. Ask students to describe how the model for $(x + 3)^2$ can be made. Repeat their instructions aloud as you draw the model. Provide the square of other binomials for them to work through. Now, draw a model on the board to show $(x - 4)^2$. Ask students to identify the squared binomial the model represents. Discuss their justifications.

An alternative is to begin with algebra tiles to represent the square binomials. After students have handled the concrete materials, progress to the more abstract hand-drawn models.

5 Assess & Remediate

Lesson Quiz

1. Simplify $(x + 3)^2$.
2. **Do you UNDERSTAND?** What is the area of the shaded part of the figure below?

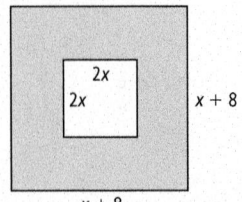

3. What is 24^2? Use mental math.
4. What is the simplified form of $(x^2 - 10)(x^2 + 10)$?
5. What is 44×56?

ANSWERS TO LESSON QUIZ

1. $x^2 + 6x + 9$
2. $-3x^2 + 16x + 64$
3. 576
4. $x^4 - 100$
5. 2464

PRESCRIPTION FOR REMEDIATION
Use the student work on the Lesson Quiz to prescribe a differentiated review assignment.

Points	Differentiated Remediation
0–2	Intervention
3–4	On-level
5	Extension

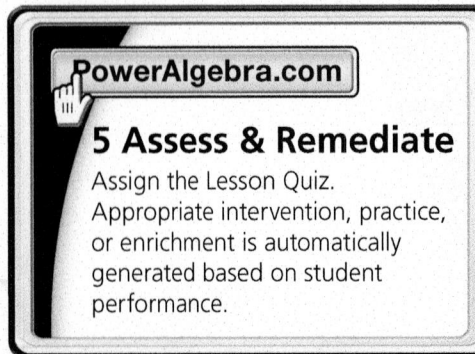

PowerAlgebra.com

5 Assess & Remediate
Assign the Lesson Quiz. Appropriate intervention, practice, or enrichment is automatically generated based on student performance.

Intervention

- **Reteaching** (2 pages) Provides reteaching and practice exercises for the key lesson concepts. Use with struggling students or absent students.

- **English Language Learner Support** Helps students develop and reinforce mathematical vocabulary and key concepts.

All-in-One Resources/Online
Reteaching

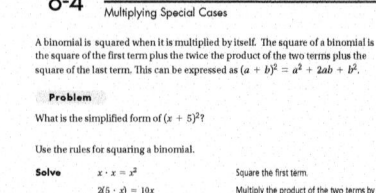

All-in-One Resources/Online
English Language Learner Support

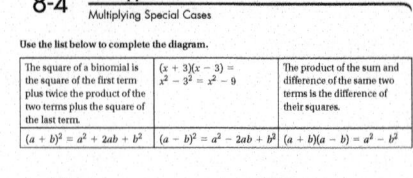

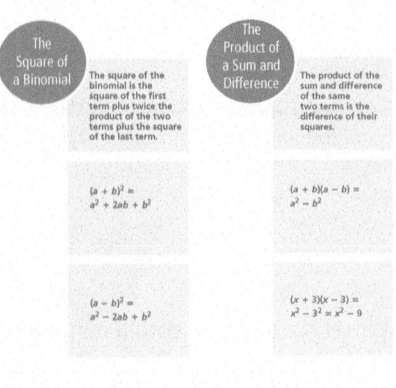

Differentiated Remediation *continued*

On-Level

- **Practice** (2 pages) Provides extra practice for each lesson. For simpler practice exercises, use the Form K Practice pages found in the All-in-One Teaching Resources and online.

- **Think About a Plan** Helps students develop specific problem-solving skills and strategies by providing scaffolded guiding questions.

- **Standardized Test Prep** Focuses on all major exercises, all major question types, and helps students prepare for the high-stakes assessments.

Extension

- **Enrichment** Provides students with interesting problems and activities that extend the concepts of the lesson.

- **Activities, Games, and Puzzles** Worksheets that can be used for concepts development, enrichment, and for fun!

Practice and Problem Solving WKBK/ All-in-One Resources/Online
Practice page 1

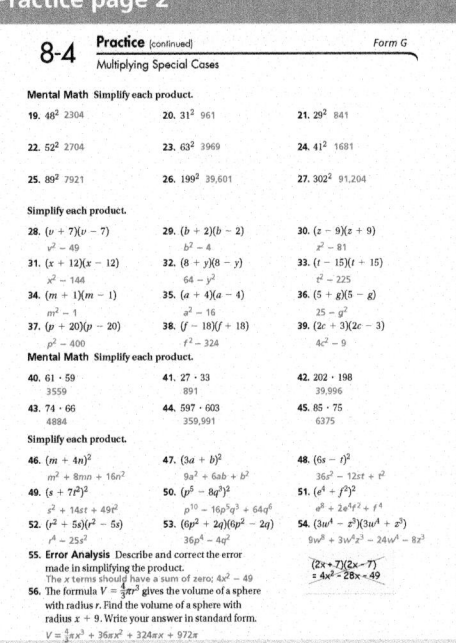

8-4 Practice *Form G*
Multiplying Special Cases

Simplify each expression.

1. $(x + 7)^2$
$x^2 + 14x + 49$
2. $(w + 9)^2$
$w^2 + 18w + 81$
3. $(h + 3)^2$
$h^2 + 6h + 9$
4. $(2s + 4)^2$
$4s^2 + 16s + 16$
5. $(3s + 1)^2$
$9s^2 + 6s + 1$
6. $(5s + 2)^2$
$25s^2 + 20s + 4$
7. $(a - 5)^2$
$a^2 - 10a + 25$
8. $(k - 10)^2$
$k^2 - 20k + 100$
9. $(n - 4)^2$
$n^2 - 8n + 16$
10. $(3m - 4)^2$
$9m^2 - 24m + 16$
11. $(6m - 2)^2$
$36m^2 - 24m + 4$
12. $(4m - 2)^2$
$16m^2 - 16m + 4$

The figures below are squares. Find an expression for the area of each shaded region. Write your answers in standard form.

13. $6x + 3$
14. $12x + 36$
15. $8x + 24$
16. $18x + 45$

17. A square brown tarp has a square green patch green in the corner. The side length of the tarp is $(x + 8)$ and the side length of the patch is x. What is the area of the brown part of the tarp? $16x + 64$

18. A square red placemat has a gold square in the center. The side length of the gold square is $(x - 2)$ inches and the width of the red region is 4 inches. What is the area of the red part of the placemat? $-x^2 + 4x + 12$ square inches

---

Practice and Problem Solving WKBK/ All-in-One Resources/Online
Practice page 2

8-4 Practice *(continued)* *Form G*
Multiplying Special Cases

Mental Math Simplify each product.

19. 48^2 2304
20. 31^2 961
21. 29^2 841
22. 52^2 2704
23. 63^2 3969
24. 41^2 1681
25. 89^2 7921
26. 199^2 39,601
27. 302^2 91,204

Simplify each product.

28. $(v + 7)(v - 7)$
$v^2 - 49$
29. $(b + 2)(b - 2)$
$b^2 - 4$
30. $(z - 9)(z + 9)$
$z^2 - 81$
31. $(x + 12)(x - 12)$
$x^2 - 144$
32. $(8 + y)(8 - y)$
$64 - y^2$
33. $(t - 15)(t + 15)$
$t^2 - 225$
34. $(m + 1)(m - 1)$
$m^2 - 1$
35. $(a + 4)(a - 4)$
$a^2 - 16$
36. $(5 + g)(5 - g)$
$25 - g^2$
37. $(p + 20)(p - 20)$
$p^2 - 400$
38. $(f - 18)(f + 18)$
$f^2 - 324$
39. $(2c + 3)(2c - 3)$
$4c^2 - 9$

Mental Math Simplify each product.

40. $61 \cdot 59$
3559
41. $27 \cdot 33$
891
42. $202 \cdot 198$
39,996
43. $74 \cdot 66$
4884
44. $597 \cdot 603$
359,991
45. $85 \cdot 75$
6375

Simplify each product.

46. $(m + 4n)^2$
$m^2 + 8mn + 16n^2$
47. $(3a + b)^2$
$9a^2 + 6ab + b^2$
48. $(6s - t)^2$
$36s^2 - 12st + t^2$
49. $(s + 7t^2)^2$
$s^2 + 14st + 49t^2$
50. $(p^5 - 8q^3)^2$
$p^{10} - 16p^5q^3 + 64q^6$
51. $(e^4 + f^2)^2$
$e^8 + 2e^4f^2 + f^4$
52. $(t^2 + 5s)(t^2 - 5s)$
$t^4 - 25s^2$
53. $(6p^2 + 2q)(6p^2 - 2q)$
$36p^4 - 4q^2$
54. $(3w^4 - z^3)(3w^4 + z^3)$
$9w^8 + 3w^4z^3 - 24w^4 - 8z^3$

55. **Error Analysis** Describe and correct the error made in simplifying the product. The x terms should have a sum of zero; $4x^2 - 49$

$(2x + 7)(2x - 7)$
$= 4x^2 - 28x - 49$

56. The formula $V = \frac{4}{3}\pi r^3$ gives the volume of a sphere with radius r. Find the volume of a sphere with radius $x + 9$. Write your answer in standard form.
$V = \frac{4}{3}\pi x^3 + 36\pi x^2 + 324\pi x + 972\pi$

All-in-One Resources/Online
Enrichment

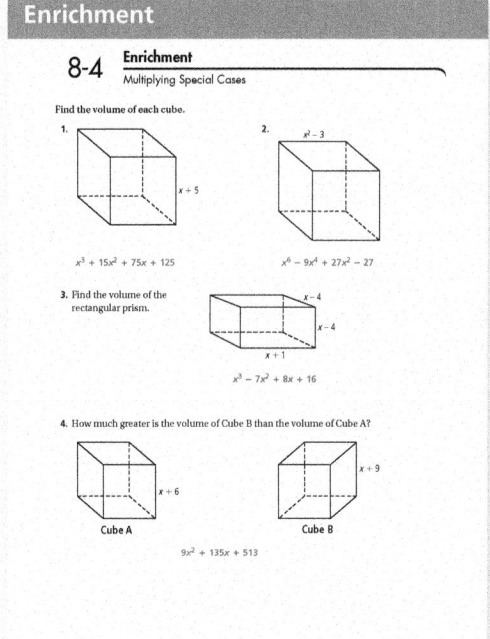

8-4 Enrichment
Multiplying Special Cases

Find the volume of each cube.

1. $x + 5$
$x^3 + 15x^2 + 75x + 125$
2. $x^2 - 3$
$x^6 - 9x^4 + 27x^2 - 27$

3. Find the volume of the rectangular prism.
$x - 4$
$x - 4$
$x + 1$
$x^3 - 7x^2 + 8x + 16$

4. How much greater is the volume of Cube B than the volume of Cube A?
Cube A $x + 6$
Cube B $x + 9$
$9x^2 + 135x + 513$

Practice and Problem Solving WKBK/ All-in-One Resources/Online
Think About a Plan

8-4 Think About a Plan
Multiplying Special Cases

Construction A square deck has a side length of $x + 5$. You are expanding the deck so that each side is four times as long as the side length of the original deck. What is the area of the new deck? Write your answer in standard form.

Understanding the Problem

1. What is the shape of the deck? __square__

2. How long is each side of the deck? __$x + 5$__

3. The new deck has sides that are __4__ times longer than the original sides.

4. What is the problem asking you to find? __area of new deck__

Planning the Solution

5. Write an expression for the new side length of the deck.
$4(x + 5)$, or $4x + 20$
6. Write an expression for the area of the new deck.
$(4x + 20)^2$

Getting an Answer

7. What is the standard form of the expression for the area of the new deck?
$16x^2 + 160x + 400$

Practice and Problem Solving WKBK/ All-in-One Resources/Online
Standardized Test Prep

8-4 Standardized Test Prep
Multiplying Special Cases

Gridded Response

Solve each exercise and enter your answer on the grid provided.

1. What is coefficient of the x-term in the simplified form of $(2x + 4)^2$? 16

2. What is 27^2? Use mental math. 729

3. What is constant in the simplified form of $(x - 6)^2$? 36

4. What is the product of 38 and 42? Use mental math. 1596

5. How much greater is the product of 73 and 67 than the product of 74 and 66? 7

Online Teacher Resource Center
Activities, Games, and Puzzles

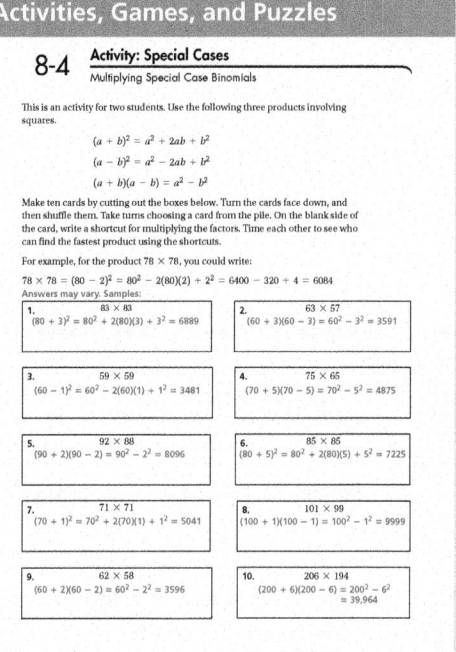

8-4 Activity: Special Cases
Multiplying Special Case Binomials

This is an activity for two students. Use the following three products involving squares.

$(a + b)^2 = a^2 + 2ab + b^2$
$(a - b)^2 = a^2 - 2ab + b^2$
$(a + b)(a - b) = a^2 - b^2$

Make ten cards by cutting out the boxes below. Turn the cards face down, and then shuffle them. Take turns choosing a card from the pile. On the blank side of the card, write a shortcut for multiplying the factors. Time each other to see who can find the fastest product using the shortcuts.

For example, for the product 78×78, you could write:
$78 \times 78 = (80 - 2)^2 = 80^2 - 2(80)(2) + 2^2 = 6400 - 320 + 4 = 6084$
Answers may vary. Samples:

1. 83×83
$(80 + 3)^2 = 80^2 + 2(80)(3) + 3^2 = 6889$
2. 63×57
$(60 + 3)(60 - 3) = 60^2 - 3^2 = 3591$
3. 59×59
$(60 - 1)^2 = 60^2 - 2(60)(1) + 1^2 = 3481$
4. 75×65
$(70 + 5)(70 - 5) = 70^2 - 5^2 = 4875$
5. 92×88
$(90 + 2)(90 - 2) = 90^2 - 2^2 = 8096$
6. 85×85
$(80 + 5)^2 = 80^2 + 2(80)(5) + 5^2 = 7225$
7. 71×71
$(70 + 1)^2 = 70^2 + 2(70)(1) + 1^2 = 5041$
8. 101×99
$(100 + 1)(100 - 1) = 100^2 - 1^2 = 9999$
9. 62×58
$(60 + 2)(60 - 2) = 60^2 - 2^2 = 3596$
10. 206×194
$(200 + 6)(200 - 6) = 200^2 - 6^2 = 39,964$

Answers

Mid-Chapter Quiz

1. 8   **2.** 5

3. $3x^2 + 4x$; quadratic binomial

4. $2p^3 + 7p^2 - 3p$; cubic trinomial

5. $4x^2 + 13x + 15$

6. $5w^3 + 10w^2 + 11w + 3$

7. $2q^2 + 3q + 2$

8. $9t^4 - 3t^2 + 11t + 12$

9. $24x^4 + 18x^2$

10. $-24c^5 - 16c^4 + 72c^3$

11. $4b(4b^3 + 2b + 5)$

12. $11(7x^3 + 2x^2 - 3x - 8)$

13. $x^2 + 11x + 18$

14. $4b^2 - 33b + 8$

15. $3h^3 + 7h^2 - 5h - 14$

16. $z^3 - 5z^2 + 13z - 9$

17. $2r^2 - 5r - 12$

18. $r^2 + 6r + 9$

19. $k^2 - 9$ **20.** $9d^2 + 60d + 100$

21. $g^2 - 100$ **22.** $4m^2 - 28m + 49$

23. $49h^2 - 4$ **24.** $9x^2 - 24x + 16$

25. No; by definition, a monomial must have a whole-number exponent.

26. $15x + 10$

27. Answers will vary. Sample: $81x^4 + 27x^3 - 9x^2$

28. Answers will vary. Sample: $x^4 + x^2y + 3$

29. $n^2 + 6n + 8$

30. Answers may vary. Sample: Rewrite the expression as a sum, then combine like terms:
$8k^2 + k - 1 - k^3 + 4k^2 + 7k - 15 = -k^3 + 12k^2 + 8k - 16$

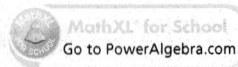
Do you know HOW?

Find the degree of each monomial.

1. $-5a^8$

2. $4x^2y^3$

Write each polynomial in standard form. Then name each polynomial based on its degree and number of terms.

3. $4x + 3x^2$

4. $7p^2 - 3p + 2p^3$

Simplify each sum or difference.

5. $(x^2 + 6x + 11) + (3x^2 + 7x + 4)$

6. $(5w^3 + 3w^2 + 8w + 2) + (7w^2 + 3w + 1)$

7. $(4q^2 + 10q + 7) - (2q^2 + 7q + 5)$

8. $(9t^4 + 5t + 8) - (3t^2 - 6t - 4)$

Simplify each product.

9. $6x^2(4x^2 + 3)$

10. $-8c^3(3c^2 + 2c - 9)$

Factor each polynomial.

11. $16b^4 + 8b^2 + 20b$

12. $77x^3 + 22x^2 - 33x - 88$

Simplify each product.

13. $(x + 2)(x + 9)$

14. $(4b - 1)(b - 8)$

15. $(h + 2)(3h^2 + h - 7)$

16. $(z - 1)(z^2 - 4z + 9)$

17. Design You are designing a rectangular rubber stamp. The length of the stamp is $2r + 3$. The width of the stamp is $r - 4$. What polynomial in standard form represents the area of the stamp?

Simplify each product.

18. $(r + 3)^2$

19. $(k - 3)(k + 3)$

20. $(3d + 10)^2$

21. $(g + 10)(g - 10)$

22. $(2m - 7)^2$

23. $(7h - 2)(7h + 2)$

24. Woodworking A birdhouse has a square base with side length $3x - 4$. What polynomial in standard form represents the area of the base?

Do you UNDERSTAND?

25. Writing Can the degree of a monomial ever be negative? Explain.

26. Geometry The figures below are rectangles. What polynomial in standard form represents the area of the shaded region?

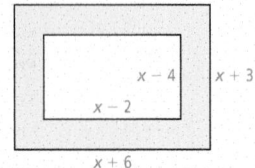

27. Open-Ended Write a trinomial that has $9x^2$ as the GCF of its terms.

28. Open-Ended Write a trinomial of degree 4 such that the GCF of its terms is 1.

29. Reasoning Suppose n represents an even number. Write a simplified expression that represents the product of the next two even numbers.

30. Writing Describe how to simplify $(8k^2 + k - 1) - (k^3 - 4k^2 - 7k + 15)$. Write your answer as a polynomial in standard form.

Concept Byte — Using Models to Factor

Use With Lesson 8-5

You can sometimes write a trinomial as the product of two binomial factors. You can use algebra tiles to find the factors by arranging all of the tiles to form a rectangle. The lengths of the sides of the rectangle are the factors of the trinomial.

Activity

Write $x^2 + 7x + 12$ as the product of two binomial factors.

Model of polynomial

$x^2 + \quad 7x \quad + \quad 12$

Use the tiles to form a rectangle.

First try:

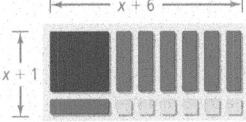

$x + 6$
$x + 1$

There are six ☐ tiles left over.

Second try:

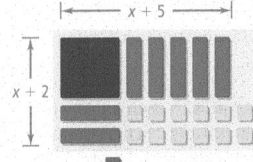

$x + 5$
$x + 2$

There is one ☐ tile too few.

Third try:

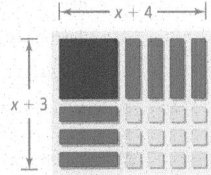

$x + 4$
$x + 3$

Correct! There is the exact number of tiles needed.

$x^2 + 7x + 12 = (x + 3)(x + 4)$

Exercises

Use algebra tiles to find binomial factors of each trinomial.

1. $x^2 + 4x + 4$ **2.** $x^2 + 5x + 6$ **3.** $x^2 + 10x + 9$

4. $x^2 + 7x + 10$ **5.** $x^2 + 9x + 14$ **6.** $x^2 + 8x + 16$

7. Reasoning Explain why you cannot use algebra tiles to represent the trinomial $x^2 + 2x + 3$ as a rectangle.

Guided Instruction

PURPOSE To use models to factor trinomials

PROCESS Students will use algebra tiles to find the binomial factors by arranging the tiles to form a rectangle.

DISCUSS This Activity and its exercises will enable students to factor two binomials using algebra tiles. This method is a trial-and-error method. Reinforce to students that they may not be able to form a rectangle until after a few attempts.

Activity

In this Activity students try to form a rectangle given a specific number of algebra tiles.

Q In the three trials shown, what algebra tile is always in the same place? **[the blue x^2 tile]**

Q On the third try, 4 green x tiles are across the top and 3 are along the left side. What is another possible rectangle? **[one with 3 green x tiles across the top and 4 along the left side]**

Q The directions state that your tiles must form a rectangle. If your tiles formed a square, would that be acceptable? Explain. **[Yes, because a square is a specific type of rectangle.]**

Answers

Exercises

1. $(x + 2)(x + 2)$

2. $(x + 2)(x + 3)$

3. $(x + 9)(x + 1)$

4. $(x + 5)(x + 2)$

5. $(x + 7)(x + 2)$

6. $(x + 4)(x + 4)$

7. You cannot make a rectangle with the tiles because you cannot write the trinomial as the product of two binomial factors.

1 Interactive Learning

Solve It!

PURPOSE To find the other binomial factor of a trinomial given one factor

PROCESS Students may use trial and error or algebraic reasoning.

FACILITATE

Q If ℓ stands for the length of the solar panel, what equation can you write to represent the area? [$\ell \cdot (x + 3) = x^2 + 4x + 3$]

Q Is it possible that ℓ is a constant? Explain. [No, multiplying $(x + 3)$ by a constant does not result in a product that includes an x^2.]

Q Is it possible that ℓ is a monomial? [No, there is no monomial that produces a product that has three terms.]

ANSWER See Solve It in Answers on next page.
CONNECT THE MATH The pair of binomial factors found in the Solve It is unique. Explain to students that when they factor a trinomial completely, they are seeking a unique set of factors.

2 Guided Instruction

Problem 1

Q Why are the numbers −3 and −5 not included in the list of factors? [The middle term has a coefficient of 8. The sum of two negative numbers cannot be 8.]

Got It?

Students should list factors by starting with 1 and proceeding in numerical order until they repeat numbers that have already appeared in a pair.

Objective To factor trinomials of the form $x^2 + bx + c$

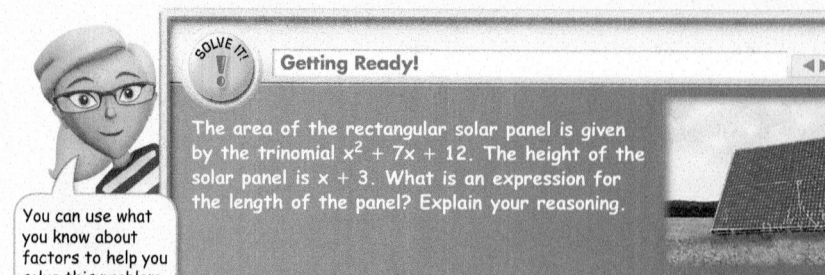

Getting Ready!

The area of the rectangular solar panel is given by the trinomial $x^2 + 7x + 12$. The height of the solar panel is $x + 3$. What is an expression for the length of the panel? Explain your reasoning.

You can use what you know about factors to help you solve this problem.

Dynamic Activity
Factoring $x^2 + bx + c$

Essential Understanding You can write some trinomials of the form $x^2 + bx + c$ as the product of two binomials.

To understand how, consider the product of binomials below.

$$(x + 3)(x + 7) = x^2 + (7 + 3)x + 3 \cdot 7 = x^2 + 10x + 21$$

The coefficient of the trinomial's x^2-term is 1. The coefficient of the trinomial's x-term, 10, is the *sum* of the numbers 3 and 7 in the binomials. The trinomial's constant term, 21, is the *product* of the same numbers, 3 and 7. To factor a trinomial of the form $x^2 + bx + c$ as the product of binomials, you must find two numbers that have a sum of b and a product of c.

Plan

What is an easy way to organize your factoring?
Use a table to list the pairs of factors of the constant term c and the sums of those pairs of factors.

Problem 1 Factoring $x^2 + bx + c$ Where $b > 0, c > 0$

What is the factored form of $x^2 + 8x + 15$?

List the pairs of factors of 15. Identify the pair that has a sum of 8.

Factors of 15	Sum of Factors
1 and 15	16
3 and 5	8 ✔

$x^2 + 8x + 15 = (x + 3)(x + 5)$

Check $(x + 3)(x + 5) = x^2 + 5x + 3x + 15$
$= x^2 + 8x + 15$ ✔

Got It? **1.** What is the factored form of $r^2 + 11r + 24$?

BIG ideas **Equivalence**
        Properties   **UbD**

ESSENTIAL UNDERSTANDINGS

- Some trinomials of the form $x^2 + bx + c$ can be factored into equivalent forms that are the product of two binomials.
- The signs and factors of the coefficients of the trinomial indicate how the trinomial can be factored.

Math Background

Students should be proficient with solving linear equations. The algebraic method for solving linear equations is to write a series of equivalent equations that isolate the variable. Because this method cannot be used to solve most polynomial equations of a higher degree, a new algebraic method must be learned. The skill of factoring is the first component of this new method and

is used to rewrite polynomials of a higher degree as the product of linear binomials.

Factoring trinomials can be reduced to a set of procedures that results in finding the integer factors if they exist.

Whenever the quadratic term has a coefficient of 1, the goal is to find factors of c that have a sum equal to b.

Support Student Learning

Use the **Algebra 1 Companion** to engage and support students during instructions. See Lesson Resources at the end of this lesson for details.

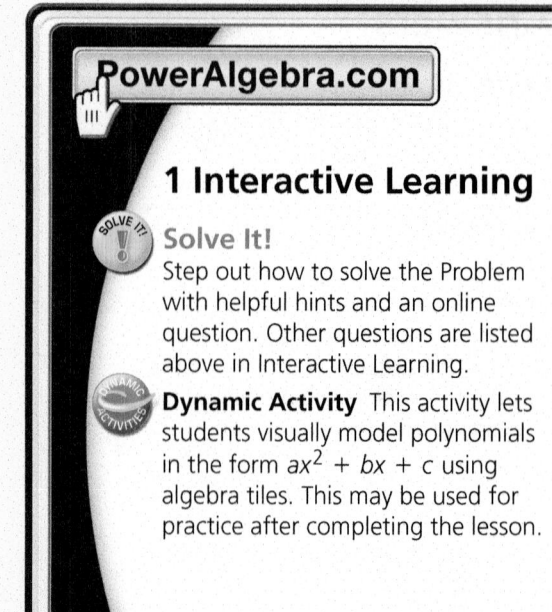

PowerAlgebra.com

1 Interactive Learning

Solve It!
Step out how to solve the Problem with helpful hints and an online question. Other questions are listed above in Interactive Learning.

Dynamic Activity This activity lets students visually model polynomials in the form $ax^2 + bx + c$ using algebra tiles. This may be used for practice after completing the lesson.

Some factorable trinomials have a negative coefficient of x and a positive constant term. In this case, you need to inspect the negative factors of c to find the factors of the trinomial.

 Problem 2 Factoring $x^2 + bx + c$ Where $b < 0$, $c > 0$

What is the factored form of $x^2 - 11x + 24$?

List the pairs of negative factors of 24. Identify the pair that has a sum of -11.

Factors of 24	Sum of Factors
-1 and -24	-25
-2 and -12	-14
-3 and -8	-11 ✔
-4 and -6	-10

$x^2 - 11x + 24 = (x - 3)(x - 8)$

Check $(x - 3)(x - 8) = x^2 - 8x - 3x + 24$
$= x^2 - 11x + 24$ ✔

 Got It? 2. a. What is the factored form of $y^2 - 6y + 8$?
b. Reasoning Can you factor $x^2 - x + 2$? Explain.

When you factor trinomials with a negative constant term, you need to inspect pairs of positive and negative factors of c.

 Problem 3 Factoring $x^2 + bx + c$ Where $c < 0$

What is the factored form of $x^2 + 2x - 15$?

Identify the pair of factors of -15 that has a sum of 2.

Factors of -15	Sum of Factors
1 and -15	-14
-1 and 15	14
3 and -5	-2
-3 and 5	2 ✔

$x^2 + 2x - 15 = (x - 3)(x + 5)$

 Got It? 3. What is the factored form of each polynomial?
a. $n^2 + 9n - 36$ **b.** $c^2 - 4c - 21$

Think

Why look at pairs of negative factors of 24?
You want the factors of 24 with a sum of -11. Only two negative numbers have a positive product *and* a negative sum.

Think

What's another way to do this problem?
Find two positive factors of 15 that *differ* by 2. The factors are 3 and 5. Then attach a negative sign to one of the factors so that their sum is positive. You get -3 and 5.

Problem 2

Q Could the factors of the trinomial be written as $(x - 8)(x - 3)$? Explain. **[Yes, multiplication is commutative.]**

Q How do the factors of $x^2 + 11x + 24$ compare to the factors of $x^2 - 11x + 24$? **[The second terms of the two binomials are opposites.]**

Got It?   ERROR PREVENTION

If students answer $(x - 2)$ and $(x + 1)$ for 2b, then they need to be reminded that when $b < 0$ and $c > 0$ both factors must be negative.

Problem 3

Q If two factors have a product that is negative, what is true of the two factors? **[One is positive and one is negative.]**

Q If you find the sum of one positive and one negative number, how do you determine the sign of the sum? **[The sign of the sum is the sign of the number with the greater absolute value.]**

Q Could the factors be written as $(x + 3)(x - 5)$? Explain. **[No, these factors would produce a middle term of $-2x$.]**

Got It?

Q By visual inspection, does the negative or the positive factor in 3a have the greater absolute value? Explain. **[Positive factor; the middle term is positive.]**

2 Guided Instruction

 Each Problem is worked out and supported online.

Problem 1
Factoring $x^2 + bx + c$
Where $b > 0$, $c > 0$
Animated

Problem 2
Factoring $x^2 + bx + c$
Where $b < 0$, $c > 0$

Problem 3
Factoring $x^2 + bx + c$ Where $c < 0$
Animated

Problem 4
Applying Factoring Trinomials
Animated

Problem 5
Factoring a Trinomial With Two Variables

Support in Algebra 1 Companion
• Vocabulary
• Key Concepts
• Got It?

Answers

Solve It!
$x + 4$; explanations may vary.

Got It?
1. $(r + 8)(r + 3)$
2. a. $(y - 4)(y - 2)$
    b. No. There are no factors of 2 with sum -1.
3. a. $(n + 12)(n - 3)$
    b. $(c - 7)(c + 3)$

Problem 4

Q What phrase describes a set of factors that meet both criteria? **[factors that have a product of −35 and a sum of −2]**

Q How can you use substitution to check your answer? **[You can substitute a value for x into the trinomial and into the factors. If your factors are correct, you will arrive at the same number for each.]**

Got It?

Q Will the factor with the greater absolute value need to be positive or negative? Explain. **[Negative, because the sum of the two factors must be negative.]**

Problem 5

Q By visual inspection, does the positive or the negative factor have a greater absolute value? Explain. **[The positive factor has a greater absolute value since the middle term of the trinomial is positive.]**

Q How will the factors in the list differ from the related terms of the trinomial? **[Each of the factors in the trinomial will also contain a y.]**

Got It?   SYNTHESIZING

If students have difficulty with factoring this trinomial, suggest that they first factor the related trinomial $m^2 + 6m - 27$. Then, when checking the answer using the FOIL method, students will note that the n must be included for the product to be correct.

 **Problem 4**   **Applying Factoring Trinomials**

Geometry The area of a rectangle is given by the trinomial $x^2 - 2x - 35$. What are the possible dimensions of the rectangle? Use factoring.

Know	Need	Plan
The area of the rectangle	Possible dimensions of the rectangle	Area = length × width, so factor the trinomial for area as the product of binomials that represent the length and width.

To factor $x^2 - 2x - 35$, identify the pair of factors of −35 that has a sum of −2.

Factors of −35	Sum of Factors
1 and −35	−34
−1 and 35	34
5 and −7	−2 ✔
−5 and 7	2

$x^2 - 2x - 35 = (x + 5)(x - 7)$

So the possible dimensions of the rectangle are $x + 5$ and $x - 7$.

 Got It? 4. A rectangle's area is $x^2 - x - 72$. What are possible dimensions of the rectangle? Use factoring.

You can also factor some trinomials that have more than one variable. Consider the product $(p + 9q)(p + 7q)$.

$(p + 9q)(p + 7q) = p^2 + 7pq + 9pq + 9q(7q)$
$= p^2 + 16pq + 63q^2$

This suggests that a trinomial with two variables may be factorable if the first term includes the square of one variable, the middle term includes both variables, and the last term includes the square of the other variable.

Plan

Is this problem similar to one you've seen before?
Yes. This problem is similar to factoring a trinomial in one variable of the form $x^2 + bx + c$, where $c < 0$.

 Problem 5   **Factoring a Trinomial With Two Variables**

What is the factored form of $x^2 + 6xy - 55y^2$?

List the pairs of factors of −55. Identify the pair that has a sum of 6.

Factors of −55	Sum of Factors
1 and −55	−54
−1 and 55	54
5 and −11	−6
−5 and 11	6 ✔

$x^2 + 6xy - 55y^2 = (x - 5y)(x + 11y)$

Got It? 5. What is the factored form of $m^2 + 6mn - 27n^2$?

Additional Problems

1. What is the factored form of $x^2 + 9x + 20$?

   ANSWER $(x + 4)(x + 5)$

2. What is the factored form of $x^2 - 6x + 8$?

   ANSWER $(x - 2)(x - 4)$

3. What is the factored form of $x^2 - 3x - 18$?

   ANSWER $(x - 6)(x + 3)$

4. The area of a picture frame is given by the trinomial $x^2 + 6x - 16$. The length of the frame is $x + 8$. What is the width of the picture frame?

   ANSWER $(x - 2)$

5. What is the factored form of $x^2 - xy - 6y^2$?

   ANSWER $(x + 2y)(x - 3y)$

Answers

Got It? (continued)

4. $x + 8$ and $x - 9$

5. $(m + 9n)(m - 3n)$

Lesson Check

Do you know HOW?

Factor each expression. Check your answer.

1. $x^2 + 7x + 12$

2. $r^2 - 13r + 42$

3. $p^2 + 3p - 40$

4. $a^2 + 12ab + 32b^2$

5. The area of a rectangle is given by the trinomial $n^2 - 3n - 28$. What are the possible dimensions of the rectangle? Use factoring.

Do you UNDERSTAND?

Tell whether the sum of the factors of the constant term should be *positive* or *negative* when you factor the trinomial.

6. $s^2 + s - 30$

7. $w^2 + 11w + 18$

8. $x^2 - x - 20$

9. **Reasoning** Under what circumstances should you look at pairs of negative factors of the constant term when factoring a trinomial of the form $x^2 + bx + c$?

Practice and Problem-Solving Exercises

A **Practice**   **Complete.**    See Problems 1 and 2.

10. $k^2 + 5k + 6 = (k + 2)(k + \blacksquare)$

11. $x^2 - 7x + 10 = (x - 5)(x - \blacksquare)$

12. $t^2 - 10t + 24 = (t - 4)(t - \blacksquare)$

13. $v^2 + 12v + 20 = (v + 10)(v + \blacksquare)$

Factor each expression. Check your answer.

14. $y^2 + 6y + 5$

15. $t^2 + 10t + 16$

16. $x^2 + 15x + 56$

17. $n^2 - 15n + 56$

18. $r^2 - 11r + 24$

19. $q^2 - 8q + 12$

Complete.   See Problem 3.

20. $q^2 + 3q - 54 = (q - 6)(q + \blacksquare)$

21. $z^2 - 2z - 48 = (z - 8)(z + \blacksquare)$

22. $n^2 - 5n - 50 = (n + 5)(n - \blacksquare)$

23. $y^2 + 8y - 9 = (y + 9)(y - \blacksquare)$

Factor each expression. Check your answer.

24. $r^2 + 6r - 27$

25. $w^2 - 7w - 8$

26. $z^2 + 2z - 8$

27. $x^2 + 5x - 6$

28. $v^2 + 5v - 36$

29. $n^2 - 3n - 10$

30. **Carpentry** The area of a rectangular desk is given by the trinomial $d^2 - 7d - 18$. See Problem 4. What are the possible dimensions of the desk? Use factoring.

31. **Design** The area of a rectangular rug is given by the trinomial $r^2 - 3r - 4$. What are the possible dimensions of the rug? Use factoring.

3 Lesson Check

Do you know HOW?
- If students have difficulty with Exercise 4, then suggest that they first factor the trinomial $a^2 + 12a + 32$.

Do you UNDERSTAND?
- If students have difficulty with Exercise 9, then ask them to create a chart in which they identify each possible circumstance for the sign of the middle and constant terms and describe the signs of the two factors that will be used for each.

Close

Q How do you determine the appropriate pair of factors to use when you factor a trinomial of the form $x^2 + bx + c = 0$? **[The pair of factors must have a product of *c* and a sum of *b*.]**

Answers

Lesson Check

1. $(x + 4)(x + 3)$
2. $(r - 7)(r - 6)$
3. $(p + 8)(p - 5)$
4. $(a + 4b)(a + 8b)$
5. $n - 7$ and $n + 4$
6. positive
7. positive
8. negative
9. when the constant term is positive and the coefficient of the second term is negative

Practice and Problem-Solving Exercises

10. 3
11. 2
12. 6
13. 2
14. $(y + 5)(y + 1)$
15. $(t + 2)(t + 8)$
16. $(x + 8)(x + 7)$
17. $(n - 7)(n - 8)$
18. $(r - 8)(r - 3)$
19. $(q - 6)(q - 2)$
20. 9
21. 6
22. 10
23. 1
24. $(r + 9)(r - 3)$
25. $(w + 1)(w - 8)$
26. $(z + 4)(z - 2)$
27. $(x + 6)(x - 1)$
28. $(v + 9)(v - 4)$
29. $(n + 2)(n - 5)$
30. $d - 9$ and $d + 2$
31. $r - 4$ and $r + 1$

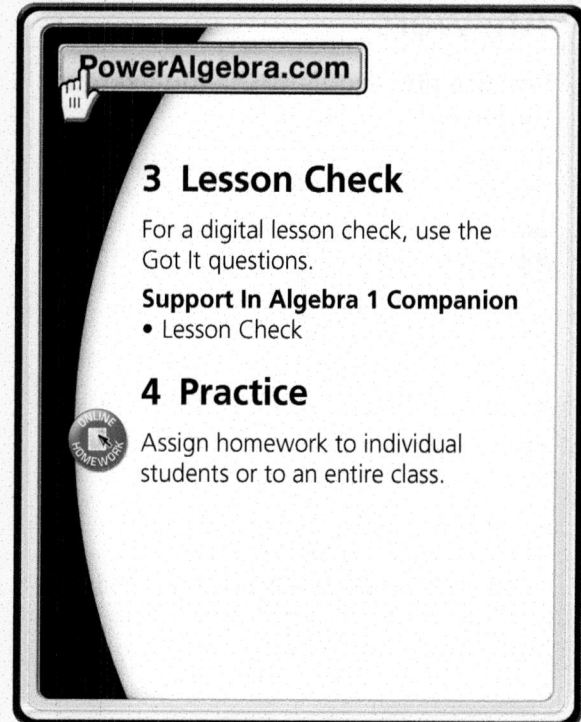

3 Lesson Check

For a digital lesson check, use the Got It questions.

Support In Algebra 1 Companion
- Lesson Check

4 Practice

Assign homework to individual students or to an entire class.

4 Practice

ASSIGNMENT GUIDE

Basic: 10–40 all, 42–44 all, 50–54 even

Average: 11–39 odd, 41–54

Advanced: 11–39 odd, 41–60

Standardized Test Prep: 61–64

Mixed Review: 65–73

Reasoning exercises have blue headings.

Applications exercises have red headings.

EXERCISE 44: Use the Think About a Plan worksheet in the **Practice and Problem Solving Workbook** (also available in the Teaching Resources in print and online) to further support students' development in becoming independent learners.

HOMEWORK QUICK CHECK

To check students' understanding of key skills and concepts, go over Exercises 15, 31, 42, 43, and 44.

See Problem 5.

Choose the correct factored form for each expression.

32. $k^2 + 5kn - 84n^2$ **A.** $(k - 7n)(k - 12n)$ **B.** $(k - 7n)(k + 12n)$

33. $p^2 - 8pq - 33q^2$ **A.** $(p + 3q)(p - 11q)$ **B.** $(p - 3q)(p + 11q)$

34. $x^2 - 16xy + 48y^2$ **A.** $(x - 4y)(x + 12y)$ **B.** $(x - 4y)(x - 12y)$

Factor each expression.

35. $r^2 + 19rs + 90s^2$ **36.** $g^2 - 12gh + 35h^2$ **37.** $m^2 - 3mn - 28n^2$

38. $x^2 + 3xy - 18y^2$ **39.** $w^2 - 14wz + 40z^2$ **40.** $p^2 + 11pq + 24q^2$

 Apply

41. Writing Suppose you can factor $x^2 + bx + c$ as $(x + p)(x + q)$.
 a. Explain what you know about p and q when $c > 0$.
 b. Explain what you know about p and q when $c < 0$.

42. Error Analysis Describe and correct the error made in factoring the trinomial.

$$\underline{x^2 - 10x - 24 = (x - 6)(x - 4)}$$

43. Think About a Plan The area of a parallelogram is given by the trinomial $x^2 - 14x + 24$. The base of the parallelogram is $x - 2$. What is an expression for the height of the parallelogram?
 • What is the formula for the area of a parallelogram?
 • How can you tell whether the binomial that represents the height has a positive or negative constant term?

44. Recreation A rectangular skateboard park has an area of $x^2 + 15x + 54$. What are the possible dimensions of the park? Use factoring.

Write the standard form of each polynomial modeled below. Then factor each expression.

45.

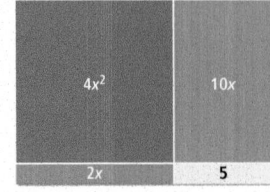

46.

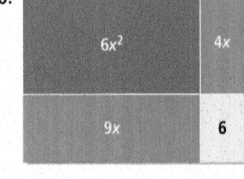

47. Reasoning Let $x^2 - 13x - 30 = (x + p)(x + q)$.
 a. What do you know about the signs of p and q?
 b. Suppose $|p| > |q|$. Which number, p or q, is a negative integer? Explain.

48. Reasoning Let $x^2 + 13x - 30 = (x + p)(x + q)$.
 a. What do you know about the signs of p and q?
 b. Suppose $|p| > |q|$. Which number, p or q, is a negative integer? Explain.

Answers

Practice and Problem-Solving Exercises
(continued)

32. B

33. A

34. B

35. $(r + 9s)(r + 10s)$

36. $(g - 7h)(g - 5h)$

37. $(m - 7n)(m + 4n)$

38. $(x + 6y)(x - 3y)$

39. $(w - 10z)(w - 4z)$

40. $(p + 8q)(p + 3q)$

41. a. p and q must have the same sign.
 b. p and q must have opposite signs.

42. The sum of -4 and -6 is -10, but their product is not -24. The factors should be $(x + 2)(x - 12)$.

43. $x - 12$

44. $x + 6$ and $x + 9$

45. $4x^2 + 12x + 5$; $(2x + 5)(2x + 1)$

46. $6x^2 + 13x + 6$; $(3x + 2)(2x + 3)$

47. a. They are opposites.
 b. Since the coefficient of the middle term is negative, the number with the greater absolute value must be negative. So, p must be a negative integer.

48. a. They are opposites.
 b. Since the coefficient of the middle term is positive, the number with the greater absolute value must be positive. So, q must be a negative integer.

Factor each expression.

49. $x^2 + 27x + 50$

50. $g^2 - 18g + 45$

51. $k^2 - 18k - 63$

52. $d^2 + 30d - 64$

53. $s^2 - 10st - 75t^2$

54. $h^2 + 9hj - 90j^2$

C Challenge   Factor each trinomial.

Sample $n^6 + n^3 - 42 = (n^3)^2 + n^3 - 42$
$$= (n^3 - 6)(n^3 + 7)$$

55. $x^{12} + 12x^6 + 35$

56. $t^8 + 5t^4 - 24$

57. $r^6 - 21r^3 + 80$

58. $m^{10} + 18m^5 + 17$

59. $x^{12} - 19x^6 - 120$

60. $p^6 + 14p^3 - 72$

Standardized Test Prep

SAT/ACT

61. What is the factored form of $x^2 + x - 42$?

    Ⓐ $(x - 7)(x - 6)$ Ⓑ $(x - 7)(x + 6)$ Ⓒ $(x + 7)(x - 6)$ Ⓓ $(x + 7)(x + 6)$

62. What is the solution of the equation $6x + 7 = 25$?

    Ⓕ 2   Ⓖ 3   Ⓗ $5\frac{1}{3}$ Ⓘ 8

63. A museum charges an admission price of $12 per person when you buy tickets online. There is also a $5 charge per order. You spend $65 purchasing p tickets online. Which equation best represents this situation?

    Ⓐ $12p + 5 = 65$ Ⓑ $5p + 12 = 65$ Ⓒ $12p - 5 = 65$ Ⓓ $65p + 12 = 5$

Short Response

64. You and your friend bike to school at the rates shown. Who is faster? Show your work.

You: 7 mi/h   Your friend: 11 ft/s

Mixed Review

Simplify each product.   ◀ See Lesson 8-4.

65. $(c + 4)^2$

66. $(2v - 9)^2$

67. $(3w + 7)(3w - 7)$

Solve each equation for x.   ◀ See Lesson 2-5.

68. $\frac{a}{b} = \frac{x}{d}$

69. $8(x - d) = x$

70. $m = \frac{(c + x)}{n}$

Get Ready!   **To prepare for Lesson 8-6, do Exercises 71–73.**

Find the GCF of the terms of each polynomial.   ◀ See Lesson 8-2.

71. $14x^2 + 7x$

72. $24x^2 - 30x + 12$

73. $6x^3 + 45x^2 + 15$

 PowerAlgebra.com   Lesson 8-5   Factoring $x^2 + bx + c$ **505**

---

49. $(x + 25)(x + 2)$

50. $(g - 3)(g - 15)$

51. $(k - 21)(k + 3)$

52. $(d + 32)(d - 2)$

53. $(s + 5t)(s - 15t)$

54. $(h + 15j)(h - 6j)$

55. $(x^6 + 7)(x^6 + 5)$

56. $(t^4 + 8)(t^4 - 3)$

57. $(r^3 - 16)(r^3 - 5)$

58. $(m^5 + 17)(m^5 + 1)$

59. $(x^6 - 24)(x^6 + 5)$

60. $(p^3 + 18)(p^3 - 4)$

61. C

62. G

63. A

64. [2] Your friend is faster at 7.5 mi/h;

     $11 \text{ ft/s} \cdot \frac{60 \text{ s}}{1 \text{ min}} \cdot \frac{60 \text{ min}}{1 \text{ h}} \cdot \frac{1 \text{ min}}{5280 \text{ ft}} = 7.5 \text{ mi/h}.$

     [1] correct answer without work shown

65. $c^2 + 8c + 16$

66. $4v^2 - 36v + 81$

67. $9w^2 - 49$

68. $\frac{ad}{b}$

69. $\frac{8d}{7}$

70. $mn - c$

71. $7x$

72. 6

73. 3

Lesson Resources

Differentiated Remediation
Available in editable format online.

Additional Instructional Support

Algebra 1 Companion
Students can use the **Algebra 1 Companion** worktext (4 pages) as you teach the lesson. Use the Companion to support

- New Vocabulary
- Key Concepts
- Got It for each Problem
- Lesson Check

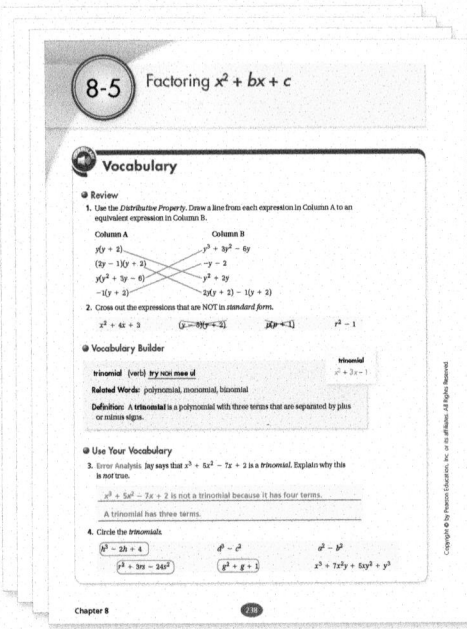

ELL Support
Focus on Communication Arrange students into pairs. Write binomials such as $(x + 4)$ and $(x - 5)$ on index cards and give one to each student. Each pair will multiply the binomials and then trade the resulting polynomial with another student pair to factor. Students will then move into groups of four with their partners and discuss their results.

Use Role Playing An alternative is to arrange students in groups of three. Have one student act as the instructor by helping with an explanation and by modeling factoring a polynomial.

5 Assess & Remediate

Lesson Quiz
1. What is the factored form of $x^2 + 13x + 40$?
2. What is the factored form of $x^2 - 7x + 12$?
3. What is the factored form of $x^2 - 4x - 12$?
4. **Do you UNDERSTAND?** The area of a rectangular envelope is given by the trinomial $x^2 + 8x + 7$. The length of the envelope is $x + 7$. What is the width of the envelope?
5. What is the factored form of $x^2 + 2xy - 8y^2$?

ANSWERS TO LESSON QUIZ
1. $(x + 5)(x + 8)$
2. $(x - 3)(x - 4)$
3. $(x + 2)(x - 6)$
4. $x + 1$
5. $(x + 4y)(x - 2y)$

PRESCRIPTION FOR REMEDIATION
Use the student work on the Lesson Quiz to prescribe a differentiated review assignment.

Points	Differentiated Remediation
0–2	Intervention
3–4	On-level
5	Extension

PowerAlgebra.com

5 Assess & Remediate
Assign the Lesson Quiz. Appropriate intervention, practice, or enrichment is automatically generated based on student performance.

Intervention

- **Reteaching** (2 pages) Provides reteaching and practice exercises for the key lesson concepts. Use with struggling students or absent students.
- **English Language Learner Support** Helps students develop and reinforce mathematical vocabulary and key concepts.

All-in-One Resources/Online
Reteaching

8-5 Reteaching
Factoring $x^2 + bx + c$

If a trinomial of the form $x^2 + bx + c$ can be written as the product of two binomials, then:
- The coefficient of the x-term in the trinomial is the sum of the constants in the binomials.
- The trinomial's constant term is the product of the constants in the binomials.

Problem

What is the factored form of $x^2 + 12x + 32$?

To write the factored form, you are looking for two factors of 32 that have a sum of 12.

Solve Make a table showing the factors of 32.

Factors of 32	Sum of Factors
1 and 32	33
2 and 16	18
4 and 8	12

$x^2 + 12x + 32 = (x + 4)(x + 8)$

Check $(x + 4)(x + 8)$
$x^2 + 8x + 4x + 32$ Use FOIL Method.
$x^2 + 12x + 32$ Combine the like terms.

Solution: The factored form of $x^2 + 12x + 32$ is $(x + 4)(x + 8)$.

Exercises

Factor each expression.
1. $x^2 + 9x + 20$ 2. $y^2 + 12y + 35$ 3. $z^2 + 8z + 15$
   $(x + 5)(x + 4)$ $(x + 7)(x + 5)$ $(x + 5)(x + 3)$
4. $a^2 + 11a + 28$ 5. $b^2 + 10b + 16$ 6. $c^2 + 12c + 27$
   $(x + 4)(x + 7)$ $(b + 8)(b + 2)$ $(c + 9)(c + 3)$
7. $d^2 + 6d + 5$ 8. $e^2 + 15e + 54$ 9. $f^2 + 11f + 24$
   $(d + 5)(d + 1)$ $(e + 9)(e + 6)$ $(f + 8)(f + 3)$

All-in-One Resources/Online
English Language Learner Support

8-5 ELL Support
Factoring $x^2 + bx + c$

For Exercises 1–5, draw a line from each term in Column A to its definition in Column B. The first one is done for you.

$(x + 4)(x + 8) = x^2 + (8 + 4)x + 4 \cdot 8 = x^2 + 12x + 32$

Column A | Column B
1. 1 — coefficient of trinomial's x^2 term
2. 12 — binomial
3. 32 — coefficient of trinomial's x term
4. $x + 4$ — product of $(x + 4)$ and $(x + 8)$
5. $x^2 + 12x + 32$ — trinomial's constant term

For Exercises 6–9, match the expression in Column A with its definition in Column B.

$n^2 - 9n - 36 = (n - 12)(n + 3)$

Column A | Column B
6. $(n - 12)(n + 3)$ — factors of -36
7. $n^2 - 9n - 36$ — sum of -12 and 3
8. -12 and 3 — trinomial
9. -9 — factored form of $n^2 - 9n - 36$

Differentiated Remediation *continued*

On-Level

- **Practice** (2 pages) Provides extra practice for each lesson. For simpler practice exercises, use the Form K Practice pages found in the All-in-One Teaching Resources and online.

- **Think About a Plan** Helps students develop specific problem-solving skills and strategies by providing scaffolded guiding questions.

- **Standardized Test Prep** Focuses on all major exercises, all major question types, and helps students prepare for the high-stakes assessments.

Extension

- **Enrichment** Provides students with interesting problems and activities that extend the concepts of the lesson.

- **Activities, Games, and Puzzles** Worksheets that can be used for concepts development, enrichment, and for fun!

Practice and Problem Solving WKBK/ All-in-One Resources/Online
Practice page 1

Practice and Problem Solving WKBK/ All-in-One Resources/Online
Practice page 2

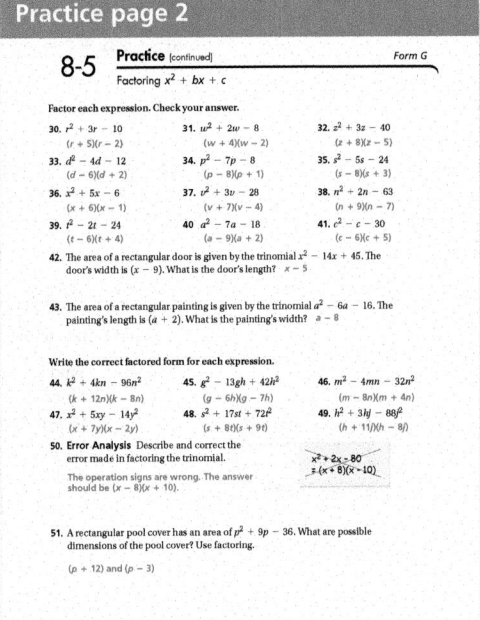

All-in-One Resources/Online
Enrichment

Practice and Problem Solving WKBK/ All-in-One Resources/Online
Think About a Plan

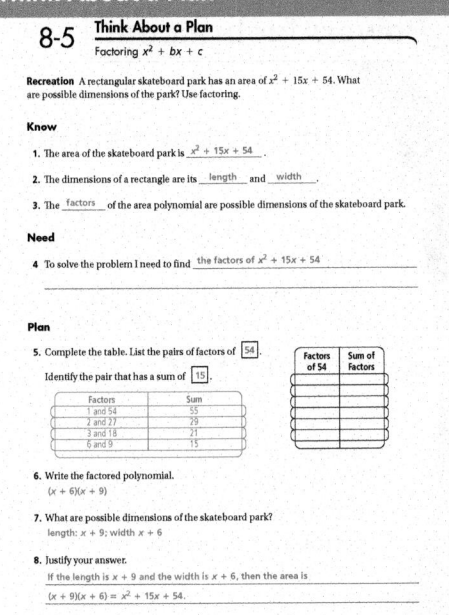

Practice and Problem Solving WKBK/ All-in-One Resources/Online
Standardized Test Prep

Online Teacher Resource Center
Activities, Games, and Puzzles

1 Interactive Learning

Solve It!
PURPOSE To find the other binomial factor of a trinomial of the form $ax^2 + bx + c$ given one factor
PROCESS Students may use trial and error or algebraic reasoning.

FACILITATE
Q If ℓ stands for the length of a solar panel, what equation can you write to represent the area? **[$3\ell(x + 3)$ or $3x\ell + 9\ell$]**

ANSWER See Solve It in Answers on next page.
CONNECT THE MATH This Solve It and the problems in this lesson differ from the previous lesson in the coefficient of the first term of the trinomial. The impact that this coefficient has is that its factors have to be considered when determining the combination of factors that yield a sum equal to the middle term.

2 Guided Instruction

Problem 1

Q Why are there only two sets of factors to consider when finding a sum of 11? **[Both 5 and 2 are prime numbers. Each has only one set of factors.]**
Q How should you check your work? **[by finding the product of the two binomials]**

Objective To factor trinomials of the form $ax^2 + bx + c$

Getting Ready!

An array of three rectangular solar panels has area $3x^2 + 21x + 36$. The height of the array is $x + 3$. What is the length of the array? Explain your reasoning.

You did this for one panel in Lesson 8-5—now there are more.

Dynamic Activity
Factoring $ax^2 + bx + c$

Essential Understanding You can write some trinomials of the form $ax^2 + bx + c$ as the product of two binomials.

Consider the trinomial $6x^2 + 23x + 7$. To factor it, think of $23x$ as $2x + 21x$.

$$6x^2 + 23x + 7 = 6x^2 + 2x + 21x + 7 \quad \text{Rewrite } 23x \text{ as } 2x + 21x.$$
$$= 2x(3x + 1) + 7(3x + 1) \quad \text{Factor out the GCF of each pair of terms.}$$
$$= (2x + 7)(3x + 1) \quad \text{Distributive Property}$$

How do you know to rewrite $23x$ as $2x + 21x$? Notice that multiplying 2 and 21 gives 42, which is the product of the x^2-coefficient 6 and the constant term 7. This example suggests that, to factor a trinomial of the form $ax^2 + bx + c$, you should look for factors of the product ac that have a sum of b.

Problem 1 Factoring When ac Is Positive

What is the factored form of $5x^2 + 11x + 2$?

Think
Will the process still work if you write $5x^2 + 10x + x + 2$?
Yes. You can rewrite this alternate expression as $5x(x + 2) + (x + 2)$, which equals $(5x + 1)(x + 2)$.

Step 1 Find factors of ac that have sum b.
Since $ac = 10$ and $b = 11$, find positive factors of 10 that have sum 11.

Step 2 To factor the trinomial, use the factors you found to rewrite bx.

$$5x^2 + 11x + 2 = 5x^2 + 1x + 10x + 2 \quad \text{Rewrite } bx: 11x = 1x + 10x.$$
$$= x(5x + 1) + 2(5x + 1) \quad \text{Factor out the GCF of each pair of terms.}$$
$$= (x + 2)(5x + 1) \quad \text{Distributive Property}$$

Factors of 10	1, 10	2, 5
Sum of Factors	11 ✔	7

BIG ideas Equivalence
Properties   **UbD**

ESSENTIAL UNDERSTANDINGS
- Some trinomials of the form $ax^2 + bx + c$ can be factored to equivalent forms which are the product of two binomials.
- Sometimes the greatest common monomial factor of the polynomial should be factored out before the remaining polynomial is factored.

Math Background

Factoring trinomials of the form $ax^2 + bx + c$ through a process of trial and error is often a tedious task. An alternate approach, which leads to success that is more consistent, is presented in this lesson. The process requires the Distributive Property to be used in reverse twice. First, the middle term of the trinomial is rewritten by "uncombining" like terms. Second, the two binomial factors are extracted from an expression

that shows one of the binomial factors being distributed to the other binomial factor.

When the quadratic term has a coefficient, the process of factoring can involve several steps, especially if the coefficient has many factors, resulting in a large number of possible combinations to be tested.

Learning to factor trinomials of the form $ax^2 + bx + c$ is a good exercise in logical reasoning, and students will improve with practice.

Support Student Learning

Use the **Algebra 1 Companion** to engage and support students during instructions. See Lesson Resources at the end of this lesson for details.

PowerAlgebra.com

1 Interactive Learning

Solve It!
Step out how to solve the Problem with helpful hints and an online question. Other questions are listed above in Interactive Learning.

Dynamic Activity Students use a geometric model to factor polynomials. Algebra tiles representing expressions are arranged into rectangles, and the lengths of the resulting sides represent the factors.

Got It? **1. a.** What is the factored form of $6x^2 + 13x + 5$?

b. Reasoning In $ax^2 + bx + c$, suppose ac is positive and b is negative. What do you know about the factors of ac? Explain.

 Problem 2 **Factoring When ac Is Negative**

What is the factored form of $3x^2 + 4x - 15$?

Step 1 Find factors of ac that have sum b. Since $ac = -45$ and $b = 4$, find factors of -45 that have sum 4.

Factors of −45	1, −45	−1, 45	3, −15	−3, 15	5, −9	−5, 9
Sum of Factors	−44	44	−12	12	−4	4 ✔

Step 2 To factor the trinomial, use the factors you found to rewrite bx.

$3x^2 + 4x - 15 = 3x^2 - 5x + 9x - 15$ Rewrite bx: $4x = -5x + 9x$.

$= x(3x - 5) + 3(3x - 5)$ Factor out the GCF of each pair of terms.

$= (3x - 5)(x + 3)$ Distributive Property

 Got It? **2.** What is the factored form of $10x^2 + 31x - 14$?

 Problem 3 **Applying Trinomial Factoring**

Geometry The area of a rectangle is $2x^2 - 13x - 7$. What are the possible dimensions of the rectangle? Use factoring.

Step 1 Find factors of ac that have sum b. Since $ac = -14$ and $b = -13$, find factors of -14 that have sum -13.

Factors of −14	1, −14	−1, 14	2, −7	−2, 7
Sum of Factors	−13 ✔	13	−5	5

Step 2 To factor the trinomial, use the factors you found to rewrite bx.

$2x^2 - 13x - 7 = 2x^2 + x - 14x - 7$ Rewrite bx: $-13x = x - 14x$.

$= x(2x + 1) - 7(2x + 1)$ Factor out the GCF of each pair of terms.

$= (2x + 1)(x - 7)$ Distributive Property

The possible dimensions of the rectangle are $2x + 1$ and $x - 7$.

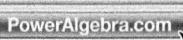 **Got It?** **3.** The area of a rectangle is $8x^2 + 22x + 15$. What are the possible dimensions of the rectangle? Use factoring.

Got It?

Q What statement describes the factors for which you are looking? **[factors of 30 that have a sum 13]**

Problem 2

Some students may wish to use trial and error to find the factors of a trinomial of the form $ax^2 + bx + c$. Students should recognize that trial and error is an acceptable method, but that the process introduced in this lesson needs to be learned because it is used in subsequent lessons.

Q How do you know that $ac = -45$? **[$a = 3$ and $c = -15$, therefore $ac = -45$.]**

Got It?   ERROR PREVENTION

If students determine factors of $(x + 35)$ and $(x - 4)$, then they are likely confusing the processes taught for factoring trinomials of the form $x^2 + bx + c$ and $ax^2 + bx + c$.

Problem 3

Q Why do you factor a GCF of -7 from $-14x - 7$ rather than a GCF of 7? **[If you were to use a GCF of 7, then the binomial left inside the parentheses would not match the binomial inside the parentheses when factored.]**

Got It?

Q By visual inspection, will the binomial representing the width of the rectangle be a sum or a difference? Explain. **[Sum; the values of b and c are both positive.]**

---

2 Guided Instruction

 Each Problem is worked out and supported online.

Problem 1
Factoring When ac is Positive

Alternative Problem 1
Factoring When ac is Positive
     Animated

Problem 2
Factoring When ac is Negative

Problem 3
Applying Trinomial Factoring
     Animated

Problem 4
Factoring Out a Monomial First
     Animated

Support in Algebra 1 Companion
- Vocabulary
- Key Concepts
- Got It?

Answers

Solve It!
$3x + 12$; explanations may vary.

Got It?
1. a. $(3x + 5)(2x + 1)$
    b. The factors are both negative.
2. $(2x + 7)(5x - 2)$
3. $2x + 3$ and $4x + 5$

Problem 4

Students should understand that they have not factored completely until the polynomial is written as the product of polynomials that themselves cannot be factored.

Q How do you determine the GCF to factor out first? [**Look at the coefficients 18, 33, and 12 and find their GCF.**]

Got It? SYNTHESIZING

Q If you do not factor the GCF first, can you still factor the polynomial completely? Explain. [**Yes; If you factor the trinomial without first factoring the GCF, then one or both of the factors will have a GCF that can be factored from it.**]
---

3 Lesson Check

Do you know HOW?

• If students have difficulty with Exercise 4, then have them check their work by calculating the area of the rectangle using both the trinomial and the factored form when $x = 3$.

Do you UNDERSTAND?

• If students have difficulty with Exercise 7, then ask them to write two example trinomials to use as a reference when writing their answers.

Close

Q How do you determine how to rewrite the middle term of a trinomial that has a leading coefficient? [**Use addends that have a product equal to the product of a and c.**]

To factor a polynomial completely, first factor out the GCF of the polynomial's terms. Then factor the remaining polynomial until it is written as the product of polynomials that cannot be factored further.

 **Problem 4** Factoring Out a Monomial First

What is the factored form of $18x^2 - 33x + 12$?

Plan

How can you simplify this problem?
Factor out the GCF of the trinomial's terms. The trinomial that remains is similar to those in Problems 1–3.

Think

Factor out the GCF.

Factor $6x^2 - 11x + 4$. Since $ac = 24$ and $b = -11$, find negative factors of 24 that have sum -11.

Rewrite the term bx. Then use the Distributive Property to finish factoring.

Write

$18x^2 - 33x + 12 = 3(6x^2 - 11x + 4)$

Factors of 24	-1, -24	-2, -12	-3, -8	-4, -6
Sum of Factors	-25	-14	-11 ✔	-10

$3(6x^2 - 3x - 8x + 4)$
$3[3x(2x - 1) - 4(2x - 1)]$
$3(3x - 4)(2x - 1)$

 Got It? **4.** What is the factored form of $8x^2 - 36x - 20$?

 Lesson Check

Do you know HOW?

Factor each expression.

1. $3x^2 + 16x + 5$

2. $10q^2 + 9q + 2$

3. $4w^2 + 4w - 3$

4. The area of a rectangle is $6x^2 - 11x - 72$. What are the possible dimensions of the rectangle? Use factoring.

Do you UNDERSTAND?

5. Reasoning Explain why you cannot factor the trinomial $2x^2 + 7x + 10$.

6. Reasoning To factor $8x^2 + bx + 3$, a student correctly rewrites the trinomial as $8x^2 + px + qx + 3$. What is the value of pq?

7. Compare and Contrast How is factoring a trinomial $ax^2 + bx + c$ when $a \neq 1$ different from factoring a trinomial when $a = 1$? How is it similar?

Practice and Problem-Solving Exercises

A Practice Factor each expression. **See Problem 1.**

8. $2x^2 + 13x + 6$

9. $3d^2 + 23d + 14$

10. $4n^2 - 8n + 3$

11. $4p^2 + 7p + 3$

12. $6r^2 - 23r + 20$

13. $8g^2 - 14g + 3$

Additional Problems

1. What is the factored form of $3x^2 + 7x + 2$?

ANSWER $(3x + 1)(x + 2)$

2. What is the factored form of $2x^2 - x - 3$?

ANSWER $(x + 1)(2x - 3)$

3. The area of a rectangle is $4x^2 - 7x - 15$. The width of the rectangle is $x - 3$. What is the length of the rectangle?

ANSWER $4x + 5$

4. What is the factored form of $30x^2 + 14x - 8$?

ANSWER $2(3x - 1)(5x + 4)$

Answers

Got It? (continued)

4. $4(2x + 1)(x - 5)$

Lesson Check

1. $(3x + 1)(x + 5)$

2. $(5q + 2)(2q + 1)$

3. $(2w - 1)(2w + 3)$

4. $3x + 8$ and $2x - 9$

5. There are no factors of 20 with sum 7.

6. 24

7. Answers may vary. Sample: If $a = 1$, you look for factors of c whose sum is b. If $a \neq 1$, you look for factors of ac whose sum is b.

Practice and Problem-Solving Exercises

8. $(2x + 1)(x + 6)$

9. $(3d + 2)(d + 7)$

10. $(2n - 3)(2n - 1)$

11. $(4p + 3)(p + 1)$

12. $(3r - 4)(2r - 5)$

13. $(2g - 3)(4g - 1)$

Factor each expression. **See Problem 2.**

14. $5z^2 + 19z - 4$ **15.** $2k^2 - 13k - 24$ **16.** $6t^2 + 7t - 5$

17. $3x^2 + 23x - 36$ **18.** $4w^2 - 5w - 6$ **19.** $4d^2 - 4d - 35$

20. Interior Design The area of a rectangular kitchen tile is $8x^2 + 30x + 7$. **See Problem 3.**
What are the possible dimensions of the tile? Use factoring.

21. Crafts The area of a rectangular knitted blanket is $15x^2 - 14x - 8$. What are the
possible dimensions of the blanket? Use factoring.

Factor each expression completely. **See Problem 4.**

22. $12p^2 + 20p - 8$ **23.** $8v^2 + 34v - 30$ **24.** $6s^2 + 57s + 72$

25. $20w^2 - 45w + 10$ **26.** $12x^2 - 46x - 8$ **27.** $9r^2 + 3r - 30$

B Apply

Open-Ended Find two different values that complete each expression so
that the trinomial can be factored into the product of two binomials. Factor
your trinomials.

28. $4s^2 + \blacksquare s + 10$ **29.** $15v^2 + \blacksquare v - 24$ **30.** $35m^2 + \blacksquare m - 16$

31. $9g^2 + \blacksquare g + 4$ **32.** $6n^2 + \blacksquare n + 28$ **33.** $8r^2 + \blacksquare r - 42$

34. Error Analysis Describe and correct the error made
in factoring the expression at the right.

35. Think About a Plan A triangle has area
$9x^2 - 9x - 10$. The base of the triangle is $3x - 5$.
What is the height of the triangle?
- What is the formula for the area of a triangle?
- How does factoring the given trinomial help you solve the problem?

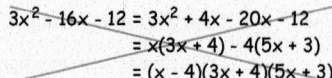
$3x^2 - 16x - 12 = 3x^2 + 4x - 20x - 12$
$= x(3x + 4) - 4(5x + 3)$
$= (x - 4)(3x + 4)(5x + 3)$

36. Carpentry The top of a rectangular table has an area of $18x^2 + 69x + 60$. The
width of the table is $3x + 4$. What is the length of the table?

37. a. Write each area as a product of two binomials.

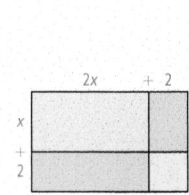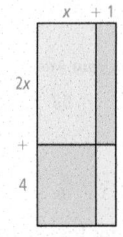

b. Are the products equal?
c. Writing Explain how the two products you found in part (a) can equal the
same trinomial.

---

14. $(5z - 1)(z + 4)$ **15.** $(2k + 3)(k - 8)$

16. $(3t + 5)(2t - 1)$ **17.** $(3x - 4)(x + 9)$

18. $(4w + 3)(w - 2)$ **19.** $(2d + 5)(2d - 7)$

20. $2x + 7$ and $4x + 1$

21. $5x + 2$ and $3x - 4$

22. $4(3p - 1)(p + 2)$ **23.** $2(4v - 3)(v + 5)$

24. $3(2s + 3)(s + 8)$

25. $5(w - 2)(4w - 1)$

26. $2(6x + 1)(x - 4)$

27. $3(3r - 5)(r + 2)$

28–33. Answers may vary. Samples are given.

28. 41, $(4s + 1)(s + 10)$; 13, $(4s + 5)(s + 2)$

29. -31, $(5v + 3)(3v - 8)$; 31, $(5v - 3)(3v + 8)$

30. -26, $(7m - 8)(5m + 2)$; 8, $(7m - 4)(5m + 4)$

31. 20, $(3g + 2)(3g + 2)$; 15, $(3g + 1)(3g + 4)$

32. 31, $(6n + 7)(n + 4)$; 29, $(3n + 4)(2n + 7)$

33. 41, $(8r - 7)(r + 6)$; -5, $(8r - 21)(r + 2)$

34. The student should find the factors of -36
whose sum is -16. They are 2 and -18.

$3x^2 - 16x - 12 = 3x^2 - 18x + 2x - 12 =$
$3x(x - 6) + 2(x - 6) = (3x + 2)(x - 6)$

35. $6x + 4$

36. $6x + 15$

37. a. $(2x + 2)(x + 2)$; $(x + 1)(2x + 4)$

b. yes

c. Answers may vary. Sample:
Neither factoring is complete.
Each one has a common
factor, 2.

---

4 Practice

ASSIGNMENT GUIDE

Basic: 8–27 all, 28–34 even, 35–36, 38–46 even

Average: 9–27 odd, 28–47

Advanced: 9–27 odd, 28–51

Standardized Test Prep: 52–56

Mixed Review: 57–67

Reasoning exercises have blue headings.

Applications exercises have red headings.

EXERCISE 36: Use the Think About a Plan
worksheet in the **Practice and Problem Solving
Workbook** (also available in the Teaching
Resources in print and online) to further support
students' development in becoming independent
learners.

HOMEWORK QUICK CHECK

To check students' understanding of key skills and
concepts, go over Exercises 9, 23, 34, 35, and 36.

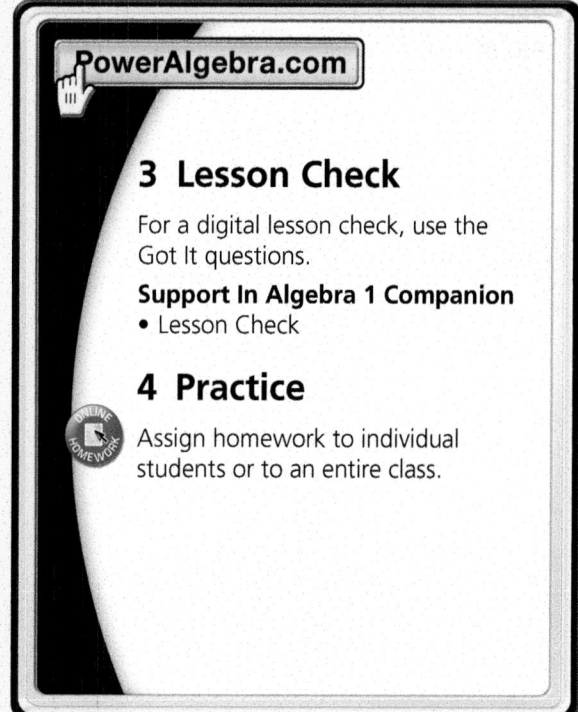

PowerAlgebra.com

3 Lesson Check

For a digital lesson check, use the
Got It questions.

Support In Algebra 1 Companion
- Lesson Check

4 Practice

Assign homework to individual
students or to an entire class.

Answers

Practice and Problem-Solving Exercises
(continued)

38. $(9x + 4)(6x + 7)$

39. $3(11k + 4)(2k + 1)$

40. $(7z - 2)(2z - 7)$

41. $28(h - 1)(h + 2)$

42. $3(7y - 4)(y + 4)$

43. $(11n - 6)(5n - 2)$

44. $2(6p - 1)(3p + 10)$

45. $(9g - 5)(7g - 6)$

46. $(9v - 1)(11v - 9)$

47. 2; explanations may vary. Sample:
$ax^2 + bx + c$ factors to $(ax + 1)(x + c)$ or
$(ax + c)(x + 1)$ so $b = ac + 1$ or $b = a + c$.

48. $x(8x + 5)(7x + 1)$

49. $(7p - 3q)(7p + 12q)$

50. $54h(2g - 1)(g - 1)$

51. a. $-2, -3$

    b. $(x + 2)(x + 3)$

    c. Answers may vary. Sample: If you set each
factor equal to 0 and solve the resulting
equations, you get the x-intercepts.

52. 9

53. 1

54. 13

55. 0.043

56. 4.4

57. $(w + 4)(w + 11)$

58. $(t - 7)(t + 4)$

59. $(x - 5)(x - 12)$

60. 12.5

61. 12

62. 37.5

63. 21

64. $a^2 + 18a + 81$

65. $q^2 - 30q + 225$

66. $h^2 - 100$

67. $4x^2 - 49$

Factor each expression.

38. $54x^2 + 87x + 28$

39. $66k^2 + 57k + 12$

40. $14z^2 - 53z + 14$

41. $28h^2 + 28h - 56$

42. $21y^2 + 72y - 48$

43. $55n^2 - 52n + 12$

44. $36p^2 + 114p - 20$

45. $63g^2 - 89g + 30$

46. $99v^2 - 92v + 9$

47. Reasoning If a and c in $ax^2 + bx + c$ are prime numbers and the trinomial is factorable, how many positive values are possible for b? Explain your reasoning.

 **Challenge**   Factor each expression.

48. $56x^3 + 43x^2 + 5x$

49. $49p^2 + 63pq - 36q^2$

50. $108g^2h - 162gh + 54h$

51. The graph of the function $y = x^2 + 5x + 6$ is shown at the right.

    a. What are the x-intercepts?

    b. Factor $x^2 + 5x + 6$.

    c. Reasoning Describe the relationship between the binomial factors you found in part (b) and the x-intercepts.

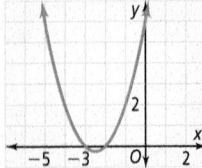

Standardized Test Prep   GRIDDED RESPONSE

SAT/ACT

52. What is the missing value in the statement $7x^2 - 61x - 18 = (7x + 2)(x - \blacksquare)$?

53. What is the y-intercept of the graph of $-3x + y = 1$?

54. What is the absolute value of the negative solution of the equation $|x + 4| = 9$?

55. A book has a spine 4.3×10^{-2} m thick. What is 4.3×10^{-2} written in standard form?

56. The number of tourists who visit a certain country is expected to be 440% greater in the year 2020 than in the year 2000. What is 440% written as a decimal?

Mixed Review

Factor each expression. Check your answer.   ◀ See Lesson 8-5.

57. $w^2 + 15w + 44$

58. $t^2 - 3t - 28$

59. $x^2 - 17x + 60$

Solve each proportion.   ◀ See Lesson 2-7.

60. $\frac{5}{6} = \frac{x}{15}$

61. $\frac{2}{3} = \frac{d}{18}$

62. $\frac{5}{8} = \frac{a}{60}$

63. $\frac{6}{10} = \frac{z}{35}$

Get Ready!   **To prepare for Lesson 8-7, do Exercises 64–67.**

Simplify each product.   ◀ See Lesson 8-4.

64. $(a + 9)^2$

65. $(q - 15)^2$

66. $(h - 10)(h + 10)$

67. $(2x - 7)(2x + 7)$

Additional Instructional Support

Algebra 1 Companion

Students can use the **Algebra 1 Companion** worktext (4 pages) as you teach the lesson. Use the Companion to support

- New Vocabulary
- Key Concepts
- Got It for each Problem
- Lesson Check

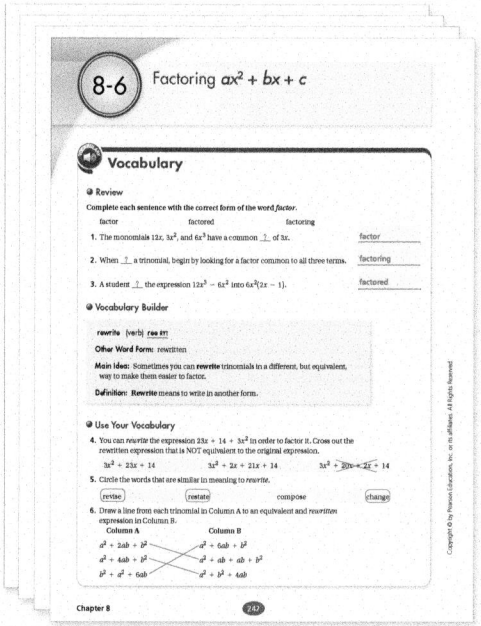

ELL Support

Use Role Playing Arrange students into equal-sized groups of five or six. Assign a leader to act as an instructor. Have a student from each group form a temporary group with one student from each of the other groups. Assign each group a trinomial in the form $ax + bx + c$ from the lesson. Students in the temporary groups factor the trinomial, writing and discussing each step. Have them practice teaching before returning to their original groups. Each student will peer-teach the others the factoring of their polynomial.

5 Assess & Remediate

Lesson Quiz

1. What is the factored form of $2x^2 + 9x + 10$?
2. What is the factored form of $6x^2 - 23x - 4$?
3. **Do you UNDERSTAND?** The area of a rectangle is $8x^2 + 2x - 1$. The width of the rectangle is $4x - 1$. What is the length of the rectangle?
4. What is the factored form of $24x^2 + 52x - 20$?

ANSWERS TO LESSON QUIZ

1. $(2x + 5)(x + 2)$
2. $(6x + 1)(x - 4)$
3. $2x + 1$
4. $4(3x - 1)(2x + 5)$

PRESCRIPTION FOR REMEDIATION
Use the student work on the Lesson Quiz to prescribe a differentiated review assignment.

Points	Differentiated Remediation
0–2	Intervention
3	On-level
4	Extension

PowerAlgebra.com

5 Assess & Remediate

Assign the Lesson Quiz. Appropriate intervention, practice, or enrichment is automatically generated based on student performance.

Intervention

- **Reteaching** (2 pages) Provides reteaching and practice exercises for the key lesson concepts. Use with struggling students or absent students.
- **English Language Learner Support** Helps students develop and reinforce mathematical vocabulary and key concepts.

All-in-One Resources/Online
Reteaching

8-6 **Reteaching**
Factoring $ax^2 + bx + c$

You can use your knowledge of prime numbers to help you factor some trinomials as two binomials. A prime number has only 1 and itself as factors. For trinomials of the form $ax^2 + bx + c$, if a is a prime number then you already know the first term of each binomial: ax and $1x$. Then list the factors that will multiply to produce c. Use guess and check to find the factor pair that will add to b.

Problem

What is the factored form of $7x^2 + 31x + 12$?

$7x^2 + 31x + 12 = (7x\ \ )(1x\ \ )$ a is 7, which is prime, so the factors are 7 and 1.
$= (7x\ \ )(x\ \ )$ You don't need the 1 in front of the variable, so drop it.

$7x^2 + 31x + 12 = (7x +\ \ )(x +\ \ )$ The trinomial has two plus signs, so the binomials also have plus signs.

Because c is 12, find factor pairs that multiply to 12: (1 and 12), (2 and 6), (3 and 4).

Try each pair in the expression to see if the INNER and OUTER products add to b, or 31.
$(7x + 1)(x + 12) = 7x^2 + x + 84x = 7x^2 + 85x + 12$ (NO)
$(7x + 2)(x + 6) = 7x^2 + 2x + 42x = 7x^2 + 44x + 12$ (NO)
$(7x + 3)(x + 4) = 7x^2 + 3x + 28x = 7x^2 + 31x + 12$ (YES)
The factored form of $7x^2 + 31x + 12$ is $(7x + 3)(x + 4)$.

Exercises

Factor each expression.

1. $3x^2 + 14x + 8$
$(3x + 2)(x + 4)$
2. $5y^2 + 43y + 24$
$(5y + 3)(y + 8)$
3. $2z^2 + 19z + 42$
$(2z + 7)(z + 6)$
4. $11a^2 + 39a + 18$
$(11a + 6)(a + 3)$
5. $13b^2 + 58b + 24$
$(13b + 6)(b + 4)$
6. $23c^2 + 56c + 20$
$(23c + 10)(c + 2)$
7. $7d^2 + d - 8$
$(7d + 8)(d - 1)$
8. $3x^2 + 20x - 32$
$(3x - 4)(x + 8)$
9. $19f^2 + 10f - 9$
$(19f - 9)(f + 1)$
10. $5s^2 - 18s + 16$
$(5s - 8)(s - 2)$
11. $17t^2 - 12t - 5$
$(17t + 5)(t - 1)$
12. $29u^2 + 48u - 20$
$(29u - 10)(u + 2)$

All-in-One Resources/Online
English Language Learner Support

8-6 **ELL Support**
Factoring $ax^2 + bx + c$

A student is trying to factor $3x^2 + 13x + 4$. She wrote these steps to solve the problem on note cards, but they got mixed up.

| Find factors of ac that have sum b. | | Since ac = 12 and b = 13, find positive factors of 12 that have sum 13. |

$(3x + 1)(x + 4)$

| To factor the trinomial, use the factors you found to rewrite bx as $1x + 12x$. | | Make a table. |

| | Factors of 12 | 2, 6 | 3, 4 | 1, 12 |
| | Sum of factors | 8 | 7 | 13 ✓ |

Use the note cards to complete the steps below.

1. First, find factors of ac that have sum b.

2. Second, since ac = 12 and b = 13, find positive factors of 12 that have sum 13.

3. Third,

| Factors of 12 | 2, 6 | 3, 4 | 1, 12 |
| Sum of factors | 8 | 7 | 13 ✓ |

4. Then, to factor the trinomial, use the factors you found to rewrite bx.

5. Finally, $(3x + 1)(x + 4)$

Differentiated Remediation *continued*

On-Level

- **Practice** (2 pages) Provides extra practice for each lesson. For simpler practice exercises, use the Form K Practice pages found in the All-in-One Teaching Resources and online.

- **Think About a Plan** Helps students develop specific problem-solving skills and strategies by providing scaffolded guiding questions.

- **Standardized Test Prep** Focuses on all major exercises, all major question types, and helps students prepare for the high-stakes assessments.

Extension

- **Enrichment** Provides students with interesting problems and activities that extend the concepts of the lesson.

- **Activities, Games, and Puzzles** Worksheets that can be used for concepts development, enrichment, and for fun!

Practice and Problem Solving WKBK/All-in-One Resources/Online
Practice page 1

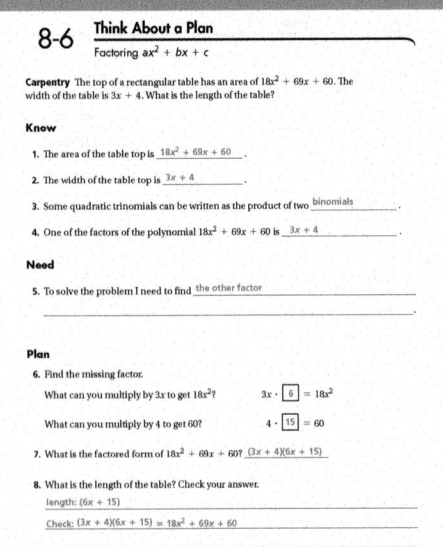

Practice and Problem Solving WKBK/All-in-One Resources/Online
Practice page 2

All-in-One Resources/Online
Enrichment

Practice and Problem Solving WKBK/All-in-One Resources/Online
Think About a Plan

Practice and Problem Solving WKBK/All-in-One Resources/Online
Standardized Test Prep

Online Teacher Resource Center
Activities, Games, and Puzzles

8-7 Factoring Special Cases

Objective To factor perfect-square trinomials and the differences of two squares

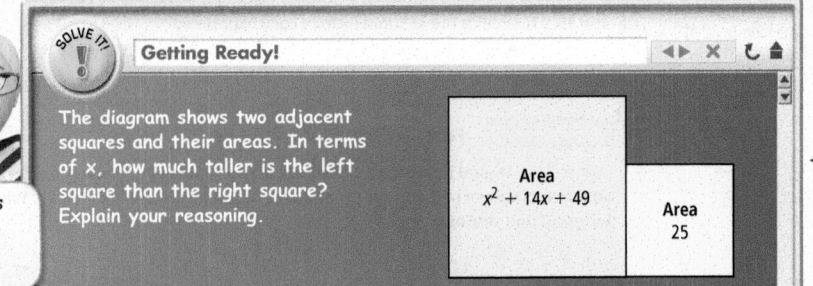

Getting Ready!

The diagram shows two adjacent squares and their areas. In terms of x, how much taller is the left square than the right square? Explain your reasoning.

Area $x^2 + 14x + 49$

Area 25

This problem is about the difference of squares!

Dynamic Activity
Factoring Special Products

Lesson Vocabulary
• perfect-square trinomial
• difference of two squares

Essential Understanding You can factor some trinomials by "reversing" the rules for multiplying special case binomials that you learned in Lesson 8-4.

For example, recall the rules for finding squares of binomials.

$$(a + b)^2 = (a + b)(a + b) = a^2 + 2ab + b^2$$
$$(a - b)^2 = (a - b)(a - b) = a^2 - 2ab + b^2$$

Any trinomial of the form $a^2 + 2ab + b^2$ or $a^2 - 2ab + b^2$ is a **perfect-square trinomial** because it is the result of squaring a binomial. Reading the equations above from right to left gives you rules for factoring perfect-square trinomials.

Key Concept Factoring Perfect-Square Trinomials
Algebra For every real number a and b:
$a^2 + 2ab + b^2 = (a + b)(a + b) = (a + b)^2$
$a^2 - 2ab + b^2 = (a - b)(a - b) = (a - b)^2$
Examples $x^2 + 8x + 16 = (x + 4)(x + 4) = (x + 4)^2$
$4n^2 - 12n + 9 = (2n - 3)(2n - 3) = (2n - 3)^2$

Here is how to recognize a perfect-square trinomial:

• The first and the last terms are perfect squares.
• The middle term is twice the product of one factor from the first term and one factor from the last term.

Solve It!
PURPOSE To find the difference of two squares
PROCESS Students may use the formula for the area of a square, knowledge of multiplying and simplifying polynomials, or geometric reasoning.

FACILITATE
Q A square with an area of x^2 has a side length of x. What is the side length of the square on the right? On the left? **[5; $x + 7$]**

ANSWER See Solve It in Answers on next page.
CONNECT THE MATH The Solve It presents multiplying two identical binomials. In this lesson students study the products of special binomials, namely identical binomials and binomials that only differ by the operation sign between their terms. Students will learn of a pattern that can be used for finding their products.

2 Guided Instruction

Take Note

Q Is $x^2 - 10x - 25$ a perfect square trinomial? Explain. **[No, because a perfect square trinomial will always have a positive c value.]**

Q Is $x^2 - 10xy + 25y^2$ a perfect square trinomial? Explain. **[Yes, because the first and last terms are perfect squares and the middle term is twice the product of x and 5y.]**

8-7 Preparing to Teach

BIG ideas Equivalence
         Properties
UbD

ESSENTIAL UNDERSTANDING
• Some trinomials, such as squares of binomials or differences of two squares, can be factored by reversing the rules for multiplying special-case binomials.

Math Background

The patterns learned for multiplying the special cases in Lesson 8-4 shortened the process of multiplying binomials. In this lesson, these same patterns are reexamined and are used in reverse order to shorten the process of factoring when the polynomial being factored is either a perfect-square trinomial or a difference of two squares.

While the main benefit of being familiar with these patterns is to make factoring as efficient as possible, an added benefit is

that it helps to develop students' abilities to recognize patterns, which is a key skill in many academic disciplines.

Recognizing perfect-square trinomials and the difference of two squares that have leading coefficients other than 1 can be challenging to students. A key to success with such problems is to teach students always to check whether they can factor out a GCF before deciding if the polynomial is one of the two special cases.

Support Student Learning

Use the **Algebra I Companion** to engage and support students during instruction. See Lesson Resources at the end of this lesson for details.

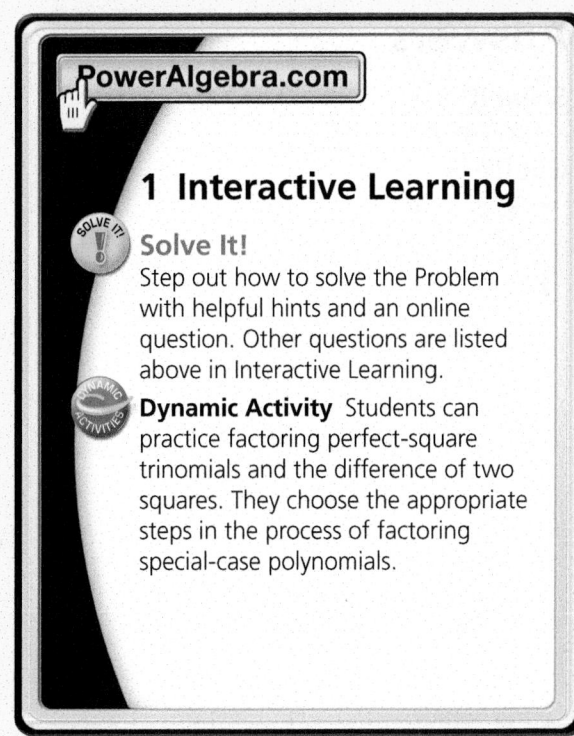

PowerAlgebra.com

1 Interactive Learning

Solve It!
Step out how to solve the Problem with helpful hints and an online question. Other questions are listed above in Interactive Learning.

Dynamic Activity Students can practice factoring perfect-square trinomials and the difference of two squares. They choose the appropriate steps in the process of factoring special-case polynomials.

Problem 1

Q Can you identify a relationship between 36 and 12 that involves the square root of 36? Explain. **[Yes, 12 is 2 times the square root of 36, or 2 × 6.]**

Q What indicates the operation sign to use in the factored form? What is that sign? **[the sign of the middle term; negative]**

Got It?

Point out that although students can also use the processes described in Lessons 8-5 and 8-6 to factor these trinomials, being able to recognize the special cases will be beneficial later.

Problem 2

Q What expression squared is equal to $4x^2$? **[2x]**

Q What number squared is equal to 25? **[5]**

Q Will the factored form be $(a + b)^2$ or $(a - b)^2$? Explain. **[$(a + b)^2$, because the middle term is positive.]**

Got It?   ERROR PREVENTION

Common mistakes students make when factoring a trinomial in this format are:

- $(16m - 9)^2$; they only took the square root of m^2 instead of $16m^2$.
- $(8m - 9)^2$; they divided 16 by 2 instead of taking its square root.
- $(4m + 9)^2$; they did not pay attention to the sign of the middle term.
- $(2m - 3)^2$; they took the square root two times because they recognized 4 and 9 as also being perfect squares.

Think

Will the answer have the form $(a + b)^2$ or $(a - b)^2$?
The middle term $-12x$ has a negative coefficient, so the factored expression will have the form $(a - b)^2$.

Problem 1 — Factoring a Perfect-Square Trinomial

What is the factored form of $x^2 - 12x + 36$?

$$x^2 - 12x + 36 = x^2 - 12x + 6^2 \quad \text{Write the last term as a square.}$$
$$= x^2 - 2(x)(6) + 6^2 \quad \text{Does middle term equal } -2ab? \ -12x = -2(x)(6) \ ✔$$
$$= (x - 6)^2 \quad \text{Write as the square of a binomial.}$$

Got It? 1. What is the factored form of each expression?

    a. $x^2 + 6x + 9$ **b.** $x^2 - 14x + 49$

Problem 2 — Factoring to Find a Length

Computers Digital images are composed of thousands of tiny pixels rendered as squares, as shown below. Suppose the area of a pixel is $4x^2 + 20x + 25$. What is the length of one side of the pixel?

Plan

How can you find the side length?
Since the pixel's area is its side length squared, factor the expression for area as the square of a binomial. The binomial is the side length.

One Pixel
$A = 4x^2 + 20x + 25$

$$4x^2 + 20x + 25 = (2x)^2 + 20x + 5^2 \quad \text{Write first and last terms as squares.}$$
$$= (2x)^2 + 2(2x)(5) + 5^2 \quad \text{Does middle term equal } 2ab? \ 20x = 2(2x)(5) \ ✔$$
$$= (2x + 5)^2 \quad \text{Write as the square of a binomial.}$$

The length of one side of the pixel is $2x + 5$.

Got It? 2. You are building a square patio. The area of the patio is $16m^2 - 72m + 81$. What is the length of one side of the patio?

Answers

Solve It!
$x + 2$; explanations may vary.

Got It?
1. a. $(x + 3)^2$

   b. $(x - 7)^2$

2. $4m - 9$

PowerAlgebra.com

2 Guided Instruction

Each Problem is worked out and supported online.

Problem 1
Factoring a Perfect-Square Trinomial
Animated

Problem 2
Factoring to Find a Length

Problem 3
Factoring a Difference of Two Squares

Problem 4
Factoring a Difference of Two Squares
Animated

Problem 5
Factoring Out a Common Factor
Animated

Support in Algebra 1 Companion
- Vocabulary
- Key Concepts
- Got It?

Recall from Lesson 8-4 that $(a + b)(a - b) = a^2 - b^2$. So you can factor a **difference of two squares**, $a^2 - b^2$, as $(a + b)(a - b)$.

Key Concept Factoring a Difference of Two Squares

Algebra For all real numbers a and b:
$$a^2 - b^2 = (a + b)(a - b)$$

Examples $x^2 - 64 = (x + 8)(x - 8)$
$25x^2 - 36 = (5x + 6)(5x - 6)$

Problem 3 Factoring a Difference of Two Squares

What is the factored form of $z^2 - 9$?

Think   *Write*

Plan
Can you use the rule for the difference of two squares?
Yes. The binomial is a difference *and* both its terms are perfect squares.

Rewrite 9 as a square.
$$z^2 - 9 = z^2 - 3^2$$

Factor using the rule for a difference of two squares.
$$= (z + 3)(z - 3)$$

Check your answer by multiplying the factored form.
$$(z + 3)(z - 3) = z^2 - 3z + 3z - 9$$
$$= z^2 - 9 ✔$$

Got It? **3.** What is the factored form of each expression?
    a. $v^2 - 100$ **b.** $s^2 - 16$

Problem 4 Factoring a Difference of Two Squares

What is the factored form of $16x^2 - 81$?
$$16x^2 - 81 = (4x)^2 - 9^2 \qquad \text{Write each term as a square.}$$
$$= (4x + 9)(4x - 9) \qquad \text{Use the rule for the difference of squares.}$$

Think
When is a term of the form ax^2 a perfect square?
ax^2 is a perfect square when a is a perfect square. For example, $16x^2$ is a perfect square but $17x^2$ is not.

Got It? **4. a.** What is the factored form of $25d^2 - 64$?
     b. **Reasoning** The expression $25d^2 + 64$ contains two perfect squares. Can you use the method in Problem 4 to factor it? Explain your reasoning.

Take Note

A common error in factoring occurs when students assume that a binomial such as $a^2 + b^2$ is also a special case and therefore can be factored. Show students that $a^2 + b^2$ may appear similar to $a^2 - b^2$ but is not factorable.

Point out that the word *difference* should remind them that a subtraction sign is necessary. Difference means subtraction.

Problem 3

Q How do you recognize a difference of two squares? **[It is a binomial in which both terms are perfect squares and the second term is subtracted from the first term.]**

Q How can you tell if a variable is a perfect square? **[The exponent is an even number.]**

Got It?   SYNTHESIZING

Show students that $v^2 - 100$ can be factored using the techniques introduced in Lesson 8-5 by rewriting it as the trinomial $v^2 + 10v - 10v - 100$.

Problem 4

Q When you take the square root of $16x^2$, what square roots are you actually calculating? **[The square root of 16, which is 4, and the square root of x^2, which is x.]**

Q How can you check that the factored form is correct? **[Multiply the binomials of the factored form to get the original binomial.]**

Got It?   SYNTHESIZING

Q How can you rewrite the binomial such that each term is written as a square? **[$(5d)^2 - 8^2$]**

Additional Problems

1. What is the factored form of $x^2 - 4x + 4$?
ANSWER $(x - 2)^2$

2. Suppose the area of a square can be represented by the expression $9x^2 + 24x + 16$. What is an expression for the length of one side of the square?
ANSWER $3x + 4$

3. What is the factored form of $x^2 - 64$?
ANSWER $(x - 8)(x + 8)$

4. What is the factored form of $9x^2 - 25$?
ANSWER $(3x - 5)(3x + 5)$

5. What is the factored form of $12x^2 - 3$?
ANSWER $3(2x + 1)(2x - 1)$

Answers

Got It? (continued)

3. a. $(v - 10)(v + 10)$
    b. $(s - 4)(s + 4)$
4. a. $(5d + 8)(5d - 8)$
    b. No; $25d^2 + 64$ is not a difference of two squares.

Problem 5

Explain that at first look, students would notice that $24g^2$ and 6 are not perfect squares. But, they should ask themselves the following questions.

> **Q** Do 24 and 6 have a GCF? What is it? **[yes; 6]**
>
> **Q** When the GCF is factored out, is the resulting binomial a difference of two squares? Explain **[Yes, 4 is a perfect square because $2 \cdot 2 = 4$ and 1 is a perfect square because $1 \cdot 1 = 1$. The terms are separated by a subtraction sign.]**

Got It?

Remind students that they should look for a GCF before deciding that either polynomial is not a special case.

> **Q** Is there a GCF for 5a? for 5b? If so, name it. **[Yes, the GCF of 5a is 12; the GCF of 5b is 3.]**

3 Lesson Check

Do you know HOW?

- If students have difficulty with Exercises 1–3, then ask them to justify why each polynomial is an example of one of the special cases introduced in the lesson.

Do you UNDERSTAND?

- If students have difficulty with Exercise 8, then have them make a list of the squares of whole numbers and variables to use as a reference when factoring.

Close

> **Q** What special cases did you learn to factor in this lesson? Give an example of each. **[Perfect-square trinomials and difference of two squares; check students' work for examples.]**

When you factor out the GCF of a polynomial, sometimes the expression that remains is a perfect-square trinomial or the difference of two squares. You can then factor this expression further using the rules from this lesson.

Think

Is $24g^2 - 6$ a difference of two squares?

No. $24g^2$ and 6 are not perfect squares. To get a difference of squares, you must first factor out the GCF.

 **Problem 5** Factoring Out a Common Factor

What is the factored form of $24g^2 - 6$?

$$24g^2 - 6 = 6(4g^2 - 1) \qquad \text{Factor out the GCF, 6.}$$
$$= 6[(2g)^2 - 1^2] \qquad \text{Write the difference as } a^2 - b^2.$$
$$= 6(2g + 1)(2g - 1) \qquad \text{Use the rule for the difference of squares.}$$

 Got It? 5. What is the factored form of each expression?

    a. $12t^2 - 48$ **b.** $12x^2 + 12x + 3$

 Lesson Check

Do you know HOW?

Factor each expression.

1. $y^2 - 16y + 64$

2. $9q^2 + 12q + 4$

3. $p^2 - 36$

4. The area of a square is $36w^2 + 60w + 25$. What is the side length of the square?

Do you UNDERSTAND?

Identify the rule you would use to factor each expression.

5. $81r^2 - 90r + 25$

6. $k^2 + 12k + 36$

7. $9h^2 - 64$

8. **Reasoning** Explain how to determine whether a binomial is a difference of two squares.

 **Practice and Problem-Solving Exercises**

(A) Practice   Factor each expression.   **See Problems 1 and 2.**

9. $h^2 + 8h + 16$	**10.** $v^2 - 10v + 25$	**11.** $d^2 - 20d + 100$
12. $m^2 + 18m + 81$	**13.** $q^2 + 2q + 1$	**14.** $p^2 - 4p + 4$
15. $64x^2 + 112x + 49$	**16.** $4r^2 + 36r + 81$	**17.** $9n^2 - 42n + 49$
18. $36s^2 - 60s + 25$	**19.** $25z^2 + 40z + 16$	**20.** $49g^2 - 84g + 36$

The given expression represents the area. Find the side length of the square.

21.

$100r^2 - 220r + 121$

22.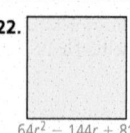

$64r^2 - 144r + 81$

23.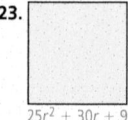

$25r^2 + 30r + 9$

PowerAlgebra.com

3 Lesson Check

For a digital lesson check, use the Got It questions.

Support in Algebra 1 Companion

- Lesson Check

4 Practice

Assign homework to individual students or to an entire class.

Answers

Got It? (continued)

5. a. $12(t + 2)(t - 2)$

    b. $3(2x + 1)^2$

Lesson Check

1. $(y - 8)^2$

2. $(3q + 2)^2$

3. $(p + 6)(p - 6)$

4. $6w + 5$

5. perfect-square trinomial

6. perfect-square trinomial

7. difference of two squares

8. In a difference of two squares, both terms are perfect squares separated by a subtraction symbol.

Practice and Problem-Solving Exercises

9. $(h + 4)^2$

10. $(v - 5)^2$

11. $(d - 10)^2$

12. $(m + 9)^2$

13. $(q + 1)^2$

14. $(p - 2)^2$

15. $(8x + 7)^2$

16. $(2r + 9)^2$

17. $(3n - 7)^2$

18. $(6s - 5)^2$

19. $(5z + 4)^2$

20. $(7g - 6)^2$

21. $10r - 11$

22. $8r - 9$

23. $5r + 3$

Factor each expression.

See Problems 3–5.

24. $w^2 - 144$ **25.** $a^2 - 49$ **26.** $y^2 - 121$

27. $t^2 - 25$ **28.** $k^2 - 64$ **29.** $m^2 - 225$

30. $4p^2 - 49$ **31.** $81r^2 - 1$ **32.** $36v^2 - 25$

33. $64q^2 - 81$ **34.** $16x^2 - 121$ **35.** $9n^2 - 400$

36. $2h^2 - 2$ **37.** $27w^2 - 12$ **38.** $80g^2 - 45$

39. $27x^2 + 90x + 75$ **40.** $8p^2 + 56p + 98$ **41.** $8s^2 - 64s + 128$

 Apply

42. Error Analysis Describe and correct the error made in factoring.

$$9x^2 - 49 = (9x + 7)(9x - 7)$$

43. Writing Summarize the procedure for factoring a difference of two squares. Give at least two examples.

44. Think About a Plan Two square windows and their areas are shown at the right. What is an expression that represents the difference of the areas of the windows? Show two different ways to find the solution.
- How can you solve the problem without factoring?
- How can you use the factored forms of the areas to find the difference of the areas of the windows?

45. Interior Design A square rug has an area of $49x^2 - 56x + 16$. A second square rug has an area of $16x^2 + 24x + 9$. What is an expression that represents the difference of the areas of the rugs? Show two different ways to find the solution.

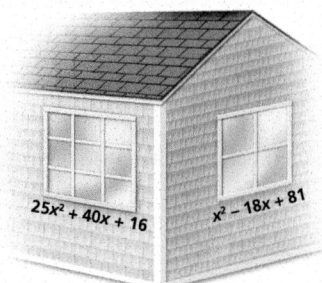

$25x^2 + 40x + 16$ $x^2 - 18x + 81$

Mental Math For Exercises 46–50, find a pair of factors for each number by using the difference of two squares.

Sample	$117 = 121 - 4$	Write 117 as the difference of two squares.
	$= 11^2 - 2^2$	Write each term as a square.
	$= (11 + 2)(11 - 2)$	Use the rule for the difference of squares.
	$= (13)(9)$	Simplify.

46. 143   **47.** 99   **48.** 224   **49.** 84   **50.** 91

51. a. Open-Ended Write an expression that is a perfect-square trinomial.
    b. Explain how you know your trinomial is a perfect-square trinomial.

4 Practice

ASSIGNMENT GUIDE

Basic: 9–42, 44–45, 51

Average: 9–41 odd, 42–52

Advanced: 9–41 odd, 42–59

Standardized Test Prep: 60–63

Mixed Review: 64–69

Reasoning exercises have blue headings.

Applications exercises have red headings.

EXERCISE 45: Use the Think About a Plan worksheet in the **Practice and Problem Solving Workbook** (also available in the Teaching Resources in print and online) to further support students' development in becoming independent learners.

HOMEWORK QUICK CHECK

To check students' understanding of key skills and concepts, go over Exercises 19, 35, 42, 44, and 45.

---

24. $(w + 12)(w - 12)$

25. $(a + 7)(a - 7)$

26. $(y + 11)(y - 11)$

27. $(t + 5)(t - 5)$

28. $(k + 8)(k - 8)$

29. $(m + 15)(m - 15)$

30. $(2p + 7)(2p - 7)$

31. $(9r + 1)(9r - 1)$

32. $(6v + 5)(6v - 5)$

33. $(8q + 9)(8q - 9)$

34. $(4x + 11)(4x - 11)$

35. $(3n + 20)(3n - 20)$

36. $2(h + 1)(h - 1)$

37. $3(3w + 2)(3w - 2)$

38. $5(4g + 3)(4g - 3)$

39. $3(3x + 5)^2$

40. $2(2p + 7)^2$

41. $8(s - 4)^2$

42. The square root of $9x^2$ is $(3x)$, so the factorization should be $9x^2 - 49 = (3x + 7)(3x - 7)$.

43. Answers may vary. Sample: Rewrite the absolute value of both terms as squares. The factorization is the product of two binomials. The first is the sum of square roots of the squares. The second is the difference of the square roots of the squares.
Example 1: $x^2 - 4 = (x + 2)(x - 2)$;
Example 2: $4y^2 - 25 = (2y + 5)(2y - 5)$

44. (1) Subtract by combining like terms.
$(25x^2 + 40x + 16) - (x^2 - 18x + 81) =$
$(25x^2 - x^2) + (40x + 18x) + (16 - 81) =$
$24x^2 + 58x - 65$
(2) Factor each expression, then use the rule for factoring the difference of two squares.
$(25x^2 + 40x + 16) - (x^2 - 18x + 81) =$
$(5x + 4)^2 - (x - 9)^2 =$
$[(5x + 4) + (x - 9)][(5x + 4) - (x - 9)] =$
$(6x - 5)(4x + 13) = 24x^2 + 58x - 65$

45. [1] Subtract by combining like terms.
$(49x^2 - 56x + 16) - (16x^2 + 24x + 9) =$
$(49x^2 - 16x^2) + (-56x - 24x) + (16 - 9) =$
$33x^2 - 80x + 7$

[2] Factor each expression, then use the rule for factoring the difference of two squares.
$(49x^2 - 56x + 16) - (16x^2 + 24x + 9) =$
$(7x - 4)^2 - (4x + 3)^2 =$
$[(7x - 4) - (4x + 3)] - [(7x - 4) + (4x + 3)] =$
$(3x - 7)(11x - 1) = 33x^2 - 80x + 7$

46. 13, 11

47. 11, 9

48. 16, 14

49. 14, 6

50. 13, 7

51. a. Answers may vary. Sample: $x^2 + 6x + 9$

    b. because the first term x^2 is a square, the last term 3^2 is a square, and the middle term is $2(x)(3)$

Answers

Practice and Problem-Solving Exercises
(continued)

52. a. $4x^2 - 100 = 4(x^2 - 25) = 4(x + 5)(x - 5)$

  b. $4x^2 - 100 = (2x + 10)(2x - 10) =$
  $2(x + 5)(2)(x - 5) = 4(x + 5)(x - 5)$

  c. The polynomial has a GCF that has two
  equal factors.

  d. No; the GCF of the polynomial is 3, and 3
  does not have two equal factors.

53. $(8r^3 - 9)^2$

54. $(p^3 + 20q)^2$

55. $(6m^2 + 7)^2$

56. $3(6n^3 + 7)(6n^3 - 7)$

57. $(x^{10} - 2y^5)^2$

58. $4(8g^2 - 5h^3)(8g^2 + 5h^3)$

59. a. $(4 + 9n^2)(2 + 3n)(2 - 3n)$

  b. They are squares of square terms.

  c. Answers may vary. Sample: $16x^4 - 1$

60. B

61. H

62. A

63. [2] **a.** $c = 190 - 2p$

  b.

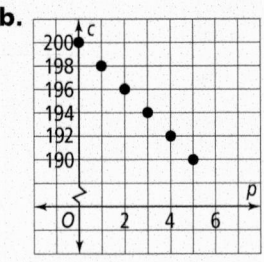

[1] minor error in computation or graph

64. $(6x + 7)(3x - 2)$

65. $(2x + 3)(4x + 3)$

66. $(4x - 7)(3x - 5)$

67. 2

68. $3m$

69. $4h^2$

---

52. a. Factor $4x^2 - 100$ by removing the common monomial factor and then using the difference-of-squares rule to factor the remaining expression.

  b. Factor $4x^2 - 100$ by using the difference-of-squares rule and removing the common monomial factors.

  c. Reasoning Why can you factor $4x^2 - 100$ in two different ways?

  d. Can you factor $3x^2 - 75$ in the two ways you factored $4x^2 - 100$ in parts (a) and (b)? Explain your answer.

 **Challenge**   Factor each expression.

53. $64r^6 - 144r^3 + 81$ **54.** $p^6 + 40p^3q + 400q^2$ **55.** $36m^4 + 84m^2 + 49$

56. $108n^6 - 147$ **57.** $x^{20} - 4x^{10}y^5 + 4y^{10}$ **58.** $256g^4 - 100h^6$

59. The binomial $16 - 81n^4$ can be factored twice using the difference-of-squares rule.

  a. Factor $16 - 81n^4$ completely.

  b. Reasoning What characteristics do 16 and $81n^4$ share that make this possible?

  c. Open-Ended Write another binomial that can be factored twice using the difference of squares rule.

Standardized Test Prep

SAT/ACT

60. What is the factored form of $4x^2 - 20x + 25$?

  Ⓐ $(2x + 5)(2x - 5)$ Ⓑ $(2x - 5)(2x - 5)$ Ⓒ $(4x - 5)(4x - 5)$ Ⓓ $(4x + 5)(4x - 5)$

61. Which equation has -2 as its solution?

  Ⓕ $x + 3 = 2x + 1$ Ⓖ $x - 5 = 2x - 7$ Ⓗ $2x + 5 = 5x + 11$ Ⓘ $3x + 1 = x - 5$

62. Which equation illustrates the Commutative Property of Multiplication?

  Ⓐ $ab = ba$ Ⓑ $a(bc) = (ab)c$ Ⓒ $ab = ab$ Ⓓ $a(b + c) = ab + ac$

Short Response

63. A film club sponsors a film fest at a local movie theater. Renting the theater costs $190. The admission is $2 per person.

  a. Write an equation that relates the film club's total cost c and the number of people p who attend the film fest.

  b. Graph the equation you wrote in part (a).

Mixed Review

Factor each expression.   ◀ See Lesson 8-6.

64. $18x^2 + 9x - 14$ **65.** $8x^2 + 18x + 9$ **66.** $12x^2 - 41x + 35$

Get Ready!   To prepare for Lesson 8-8, do Exercises 67–69.

Find the GCF of the terms of each polynomial.   ◀ See Lesson 8-2.

67. $6t^2 + 12t - 4$ **68.** $9m^3 + 15m^2 - 21m$ **69.** $16h^4 - 12h^3 - 36h^2$

Additional Instructional Support

Algebra 1 Companion

Students can use the **Algebra 1 Companion** worktext (4 pages) as you teach the lesson. Use the Companion to support

- New Vocabulary
- Key Concepts
- Got It for each Problem
- Lesson Check

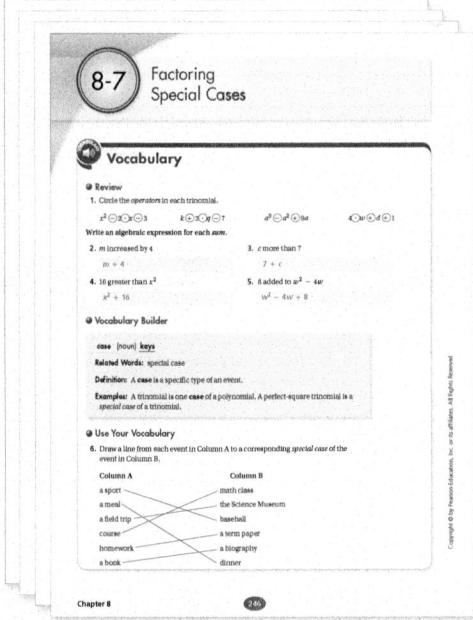

ELL Support

Connect to Prior Knowledge Review perfect squares. Write 1, 4, and 9 on the board. Ask students what they have in common. Then encourage students to guide you as you list more perfect squares on the board.

Use Manipulatives Model to students how to use grid paper to show a trinomial is a perfect square. One unit on the grid paper is "1", two vertical units is x, and a 2×2 square unit is x^2. $4x^2 + 4x + 1$ can be arranged into a perfect square. Challenge students to arrange other trinomials into squares and write the factors.

5 Assess & Remediate

Lesson Quiz

1. What is the factored form of $x^2 - 12x + 36$?

2. **Do you UNDERSTAND?** Suppose the area of a square can be represented by the expression $25x^2 + 80x + 64$. What is an expression for the length of one side of the square?

3. What is the factored form of $x^2 - 49$?

4. What is the factored form of $16x^2 - 25$?

5. What is the factored form of $18x^2 - 2$?

ANSWERS TO LESSON QUIZ

1. $(x - 6)^2$
2. $5x + 8$
3. $(x - 7)(x + 7)$
4. $(4x - 5)(4x + 5)$
5. $2(3x - 1)(3x + 1)$

PRESCRIPTION FOR REMEDIATION
Use the student work on the Lesson Quiz to prescribe a differentiated review assignment.

Points	Differentiated Remediation
0–2	Intervention
3–4	On-level
5	Extension

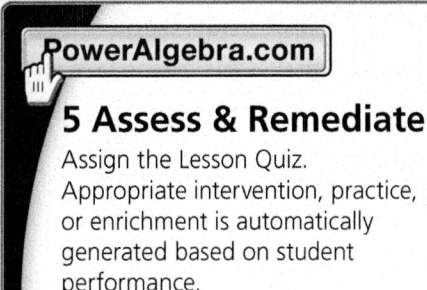

PowerAlgebra.com

5 Assess & Remediate

Assign the Lesson Quiz. Appropriate intervention, practice, or enrichment is automatically generated based on student performance.

Intervention

- **Reteaching** (2 pages) Provides reteaching and practice exercises for the key lesson concepts. Use with struggling students or absent students.

- **English Language Learner Support** Helps students develop and reinforce mathematical vocabulary and key concepts.

All-in-One Resources/Online
Reteaching

All-in-One Resources/Online
English Language Learner Support

Differentiated Remediation *continued*

On-Level

- **Practice** (2 pages) Provides extra practice for each lesson. For simpler practice exercises, use the Form K Practice pages found in the All-in-One Teaching Resources and online.

- **Think About a Plan** Helps students develop specific problem-solving skills and strategies by providing scaffolded guiding questions.

- **Standardized Test Prep** Focuses on all major exercises, all major question types, and helps students prepare for the high-stakes assessments.

Extension

- **Enrichment** Provides students with interesting problems and activities that extend the concepts of the lesson.

- **Activities, Games, and Puzzles** Worksheets that can be used for concepts development, enrichment, and for fun!

Practice and Problem Solving WKBK/ All-in-One Resources/Online
Practice page 1

8-7 Practice Form G
Factoring Special Cases

Factor each expression.

1. $h^2 + 10h + 25$ $(h + 5)^2$
2. $v^2 - 14v + 49$ $(v - 7)^2$
3. $d^2 - 22d + 121$ $(d - 11)^2$
4. $m^2 + 4m + 4$ $(m + 2)^2$
5. $q^2 + 6q + 9$ $(q + 3)^2$
6. $p^2 - 24p + 144$ $(p - 12)^2$
7. $36x^2 + 60x + 25$ $(6x + 5)^2$
8. $64x^2 + 48x + 9$ $(8x + 3)^2$
9. $49n^2 + 14n + 1$ $(7n + 1)^2$
10. $16x^2 - 72x + 81$ $(4x - 9)^2$
11. $25x^2 - 80x + 64$ $(5x - 8)^2$
12. $9g^2 - 24g + 16$ $(3g - 4)^2$
13. $81w^2 + 144w + 64$ $(9w + 8)^2$
14. $16e^2 - 88e + 121$ $(4e - 11)^2$
15. $25f^2 + 100f + 100$ $(5f + 10)^2$
16. $144f^2 - 24f + 1$ $(12f - 1)^2$
17. $4a^2 - 36a + 81$ $(2a - 9)^2$
18. $49d^2 - 84d + 36$ $(7d - 6)^2$

The given expression represents the area. Find the side length of the square.

19. $64x^2 + 80x + 25$ $8x + 5$
20. $9y^2 - 24y + 16$ $3y - 4$
21. $4t^2 + 36t + 81$ $2t + 9$
22. $36r^2 + 84n + 49$ $6n + 7$
23. $100w^2 + 20w + 1$ $10w + 1$
24. $16t^2 + 104t + 169$ $4t + 13$

25. **Error Analysis** Describe and correct the error made in factoring the expression at the right.
$175x^2 - 28 = 7(25x^2 - 4)$
$= 7(5x - 2)(5x - 2)$
$= 7(5x - 2)^2$
$(25x^2 - 4)$ factors to $(5x - 2)(5x + 2)$, not $(5x - 2)^2$

Practice and Problem Solving WKBK/ All-in-One Resources/Online
Practice page 2

8-7 Practice *(continued)* Form G
Factoring Special Cases

Factor each expression.

26. $m^2 - 49$ $(m + 7)(m - 7)$
27. $c^2 - 100$ $(c + 10)(c - 10)$
28. $p^2 - 16$ $(p + 4)(p - 4)$
29. $4a^2 - 25$ $(2a + 5)(2a - 5)$
30. $64n^2 - 1$ $(8n + 1)(8n - 1)$
31. $25x^2 - 144$ $(5x + 12)(5x - 12)$
32. $50g^2 - 8$ $2(5g + 2)(5g - 2)$
33. $8d^2 - 8$ $8(d + 1)(d - 1)$
34. $27x^2 - 48$ $3(3x + 4)(3x - 4)$
35. $24d^2 - 54$ $6(2a + 3)(2a - 3)$
36. $245k^2 - 20$ $5(7k + 2)(7k - 2)$
37. $112h^2 - 63$ $7(4h + 3)(4h - 3)$
38. $48w^2 + 72x + 27$ $3(4x + 3)(4x + 3)$
39. $8b^2 + 80b + 200$ $8(b + 5)^2$
40. $48w^2 + 48w + 12$ $12(2w + 1)^2$
41. $45r^2 - 210s + 245$ $5(3s - 7)^2$
42. $45t^2 - 72t + 24$ $3(15t^2 - 24t + 8)$
43. $100x^2 - 120x + 36$ $4(5x - 3)^2$

44. **Writing** Explain how to recognize a perfect-square trinomial.
The coefficient of the squared term and the constant will be perfect squares. Twice the product of these numbers is the coefficient of the middle term. The sign before the constant will be positive.

45. a. **Open-Ended** Write an expression that shows the factored form of a difference of two squares. Answers may vary. Sample: $(2x + 3)(2x - 3)$
b. Explain how you know that your expression is a difference of two squares.
Answers may vary. Sample: $4x^2 - 9$; $4x^2$ and 9 are squares

Factor each expression.

46. $36p^8 - 60x^4 + 25$ $(6x^4 - 5)^2$
47. $c^{10} - 30c^5d^6 + 225d^4$ $(c^5 - 15d^2)^2$
48. $25n^6 + 40n^3 + 16$ $(5n^3 + 4)^2$

Mental Math For Exercises 49–51, find a pair of factors for each number by using the difference of two squares.

49. 24 $24 = 5^2 - 1^2$ $= (5 + 1)(5 - 1) = (6)(4)$
50. 28 $28 = 8^2 - 6^2$ $= (8 + 6)(8 - 6) = (2)(14)$
51. 72 $72 = 9^2 - 3^2$ $= (9 + 3)(9 - 3) = (12)(6)$

52. **Reasoning** Explain how reversing the rules for multiplying squares of binomials can help you factor a perfect-square trinomial.
When the b term in a trinomial is exactly twice the product of a and c, you can factor it as $(a + b)^2$ or as $(a - b)^2$.

53. **Writing** The area of a square parking lot is $49p^4 - 84p^2 + 36$. Explain how you would find the length of the parking lot.
Factor $49p^4 - 84p^2 + 36$ to find the length. You get $(7p^2 - 6)^2$ so each side has a length of $(7p^2 - 6)$.

Practice and Problem Solving WKBK/ All-in-One Resources/Online
Think About a Plan

8-7 Think About a Plan
Factoring Special Cases

Interior Design A square rug has an area of $49x^2 - 56x + 16$. A second square rug has an area of $16x^2 + 24x + 9$. What is an expression that represents the difference of the areas of the rugs? Show two different ways to find the solution.

1. What are two methods you could use to solve this problem? _____
subtraction; factoring before subtracting

2. How would you find the difference without factoring? subtract the polynomials

3. What polynomial do you get when you use this method? $33x^2 - 80x + 7$

4. Can you factor that polynomial? yes ; $(11x - 1)(3x - 7)$

5. How could you use factoring to solve the problem? Factoring gives you a second way to find the difference. You can represent the difference in the form $a^2 - b^2$.

6. What do the shape of the rug and the polynomials tell you about how to factor the polynomials for the area of the rugs? The factors of each square polynomial will be the same.

7. Factor each trinomial.
$49x^2 - 56x + 16 = (\square - \square)(\square - \square) = (\square\square\square)^2$ $(7x - 4)(7x - 4) = (7x - 4)^2$
$16x^2 + 24x + 9 = (\square + \square)(\square + \square) = (\square\square\square)^2$ $(4x + 3)(4x + 3) = (4x - 3)^2$

8. Use your results from Exercise 7 to write an expression for the difference in the areas.
$(7x - 4)^2 - (4x + 3)^2$

9. Factor the expression from Exercise 8 using the difference of two squares. Simplify the expressions within each set of parentheses.
$[(7x - 4) + (4x + 3)][(7x - 4) - (4x + 3)] = (11x - 1)(3x - 7)$

10. Do the two methods give you the same result?
yes

Practice and Problem Solving WKBK/ All-in-One Resources/Online
Standardized Test Prep

8-7 Standardized Test Prep
Factoring Special Cases

Multiple Choice

For Exercises 1–6, choose the correct letter.

1. What is the factored form of $q^2 - 12q + 36$? B
A. $(q + 6)(q - 6)$ B. $(q - 6)(q - 6)$ C. $(q - 9)(q + 4)$ D. $(q + 4)(q + 9)$

2. What is the factored form of $9x^2 + 12x + 4$? F
F. $(3x + 2)^2$ G. $(3x + 3)^2$ H. $(3x - 2)^2$ I. $(3x - 3)^2$

3. What is the factored form of $x^2 - 196$? D
A. $(x - 14)^2$ B. $(x + 14)^2$ C. $(x - 28)(4x + 7)$ D. $(x - 14)(x + 14)$

4. What is the factored form of $9x^2 - 64$? H
F. $(3x - 8)^2$ G. $(3x + 8)^2$ H. $(3x - 8)(3x + 8)$ I. $(9x - 8)(x + 8)$

5. What is the factored form of $12m^2 - 75$? B
A. $3(2m - 5)^2$ B. $3(2m + 5)(2m - 5)$ C. $3(2m + 5)^2$ D. $(6m - 25)(2m + 3)$

6. What is the factored form of $49x^2 - 56x + 16$? F
F. $(7x - 4)^2$ G. $(7x + 4)(7x - 4)$ H. $(7x + 4)^2$ I. $(7x - 8)^2$

Extended Response

7. A four-sided building has an area of $36x^2 + 48x + 16$. Explain how to find a possible length and width of the building. What is a possible shape of the building?
$(6x + 4)^2$; The length and width could be the same, so the shape is a square.
[4] Answer correctly factors the polynomial and indicates the building could be a square with sides $6x + 4$. Complete explanation is provided.
[3] Minor calculation error in the answer or incomplete explanation
[2] Polynomial correctly factored but not related to length and width of the building
[1] Some steps in solution of problem completed correctly
[0] No correct work shown

All-in-One Resources/Online
Enrichment

8-7 Enrichment
Factoring Special Cases

The surface area of a cube is determined by the formula $SA = 6s^2$, where s is the length of a side of the cube. You can use this formula to analyze a polynomial that represents the surface area of a cube.

Start by dividing the polynomial by 6. This will leave an expression for the area of one face of the cube. You can see that the area is a perfect-square trinomial. Reverse the rules for multiplying squares of binomials to factor the trinomial.

For example, a cube with a surface area of $24x^2 + 24x + 6$ has a side measure of $2x + 1$.

$6s^2 = 24x^2 + 24x + 6$
$s^2 = \frac{24x^2 + 24x + 6}{6} = 4x^2 + 4x + 1$
$s^2 = (2x + 1)(2x + 1)$
$s = 2x + 1$

The surface area of a rectangular prism with two square faces is determined by the formula $SA = 4ls + 2s^2$, where l is the length and s is the measure of the side of the square face. If you are given the surface area and the area of the square face, you can determine the dimensions of the rectangular prism.

Suppose a rectangular prism has a surface area of $24x + 30$ and each square face measures 9 cm^2.

$24x + 30 - 18 = 24x + 12$ Subtract the area of the square faces.
$\frac{24x + 12}{4} = 6x + 3$ Divide by 4 to get the area of each remaining side.
$\frac{6x + 3}{3} = 2x + 1$ Divide by the side length of the square base, or the square root of the base's area.

1. The surface area of a cube is $96x^2 + 144x + 54$. What is the measure of each side?
$4x + 3$

2. The surface area of a cube is $54x^2 - 36x + 6$. What is the measure of each side?
$3x - 1$

3. The surface area of a cube is $864x^2 + 720x + 150$. What is the measure of each side?
$12x + 5$

4. The surface area of a rectangular prism is $100x + 90$. The areas of the two square faces of the prism are 25 m^2 each. What are the dimensions of the rectangular prism?
$5, 5,$ and $5x + 4$

5. The surface area of a rectangular prism is $2x^2 + 48x + 88$. The areas of the two square faces of the prism are $x^2 + 4x + 4$ each. What are the dimensions of the rectangular prism?
$40, x + 2,$ and $x + 2$

Online Teacher Resource Center
Activities, Games, and Puzzles

8-7 Activity: Grid-Paper Factoring
Factoring Special Cases

You can solve factoring problems with paper and scissors.

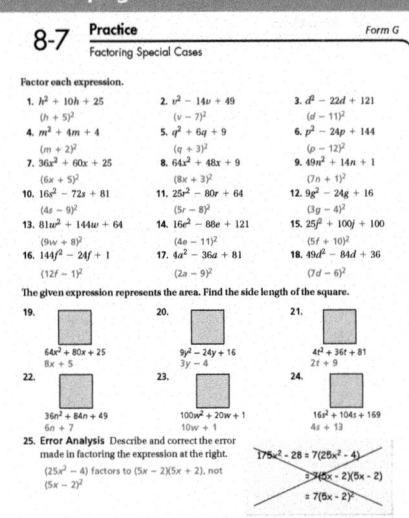

What is the area of the lightly shaded parts in the grid at the right in terms of 20 and 12?

- Use the graph paper to draw a square 20 units by 20 units and, inside it, a square 12 units by 12 units.
- Cut out the three lightly shaded regions and the darkly shaded region. Put the darkly shaded region aside.
- Tape the three remaining shapes together to form a single rectangle like the one below. Be sure to label your figure.
- Write expressions for the length and width of this rectangle in terms of 20 and 12.
$(20 + 12)(20 - 12)$
- Use the formula for the area of a rectangle to find the area of the three combined rectangles.
256 units^2

- On a separate piece of grid paper (units must be the same size as the one used above), cut out a rectangle whose length is $20 + 12$ units and whose width is $20 - 12$ units. Use the formula for the area of a rectangle to find the area of this rectangle.
256 units^2

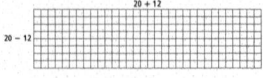

- How does this expression relate to the expression you wrote for the area of the lightly shaded region?
Regardless of the rearrangement, the nonshaded region has an area of 256 units^2.

Write $20^2 - 12^2$ as a product of a sum and a difference.
$(20 + 12)(20 - 12)$

8-8 Factoring by Grouping

Objective To factor higher-degree polynomials by grouping

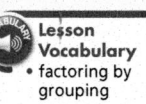

Getting Ready!

◄ ► ✕ ↺ ⌂

A packaging company sells two kinds of boxes, Box A and Box B. The company is designing a new box, Box C, that will have the same volume as Boxes A and B combined. Suppose one dimension of Box C is *x*. What could be the other two dimensions? Explain your reasoning.

Hmm . . . you know one dimension, so factoring might help.

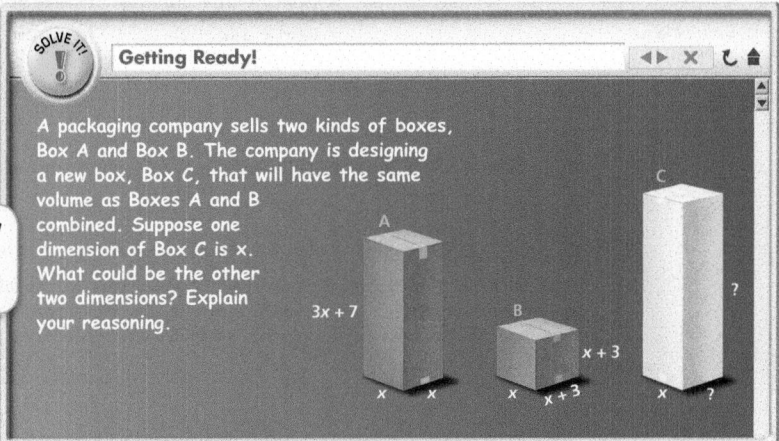

3x + 7

x + 3

x   x   x   x + 3   x   ?

Lesson Vocabulary
• factoring by grouping

Essential Understanding Some polynomials of a degree greater than 2 can be factored.

In Lesson 8-6, you factored trinomials of the form $ax^2 + bx + c$ by rewriting bx as a sum of two monomials. You then grouped the terms in pairs, factored the GCF from each pair, and looked for a common binomial factor. This process is called **factoring by grouping.** You can extend this technique to higher-degree polynomials.

Plan

How should you group the terms of the polynomial?
First group the two terms with the highest degrees. If that doesn't work, try another grouping. Your goal is to find a common binomial factor.

Problem 1 Factoring a Cubic Polynomial

What is the factored form of $3n^3 - 12n^2 + 2n - 8$?

$$3n^3 - 12n^2 + 2n - 8 = 3n^2(n - 4) + 2(n - 4)$$ Factor out the GCF of each group of two terms.

$$= (3n^2 + 2)(n - 4)$$ Factor out the common factor $n - 4$.

Check $(3n^2 + 2)(n - 4) = 3n^3 - 12n^2 + 2n - 8$ ✔

 Got It? 1. a. What is the factored form of $8t^3 + 14t^2 + 20t + 35$?
  b. Reasoning How is the factoring method used in Problem 1 like the method used in Lesson 8-6? How is it different?

8-8 Preparing to Teach

BIG ideas **Equivalence**   **UbD**
Properties
ESSENTIAL UNDERSTANDINGS
• Some polynomials of a degree greater than 2 can be factored.
• If a polynomial has 4 or more terms, it may be possible to group the terms and factor binomials from the groups.

Math Background

Learning to factor higher-degree polynomials will be an important skill for students in higher mathematics courses. Students will use factoring to both graph and solve higher-degree polynomial equations. Students will expand their factoring capabilities and thus their abilities to solve higher-degree polynomials by learning the Factor Theorem and synthetic division.

Factoring by grouping can be frustrating to students. Once students learn that grouping

terms differently can still lead to correct factors, they are more open to trying this skill. As in the previous lesson, emphasize that students should factor out any GCF. Give students this guide for making decisions about factoring after the GCF is factored out.

If a polynomial has:
• two terms, look to see if it is the difference of two squares.
• three terms, look to see if it is a perfect-square trinomial. If not, use trial-and-error methods presented in earlier lessons.
• four terms, look for ways to group factors.

Support Student Learning

Use the **Algebra I Companion** to engage and support students during instruction. See Lesson Resources at the end of this lesson for details.

1 Interactive Learning

Solve It!
PURPOSE To factor a cubic polynomial
PROCESS Students may use the volume formula for a rectangular solid, algebraic reasoning, or factoring techniques.

FACILITATE
Q What expression represents the volume of the first two boxes combined? $[4x^3 + 13x^2 + 9x]$
Q Does the expression representing the combined volume have a common factor? Explain. **[Yes, *x* is common to all terms.]**

ANSWER See Solve It in Answers on next page.
CONNECT THE MATH Show students that the polynomial $4x^3 + 13x^2 + 9x$ can be factored by removing the common factor *x* and then factoring the trinomial, or alternately, by using the grouping technique.

2 Guided Instruction

Problem 1

Q Can you still factor the polynomial if it is rewritten as $3n^3 + 2n - 12n^2 - 8$? Explain. **[Yes, the common factors are *n* and −4 and the common binomial is $(3n^2 + 2)$.]**

Got It?   **VISUAL LEARNERS**
It may help students to understand the grouping process if you write the steps for grouping side by side with the steps for using the Distributive Property to multiply $(2t^2 + 5)$ by $(4t + 7)$. Students can see that the two processes use the same steps in reverse.

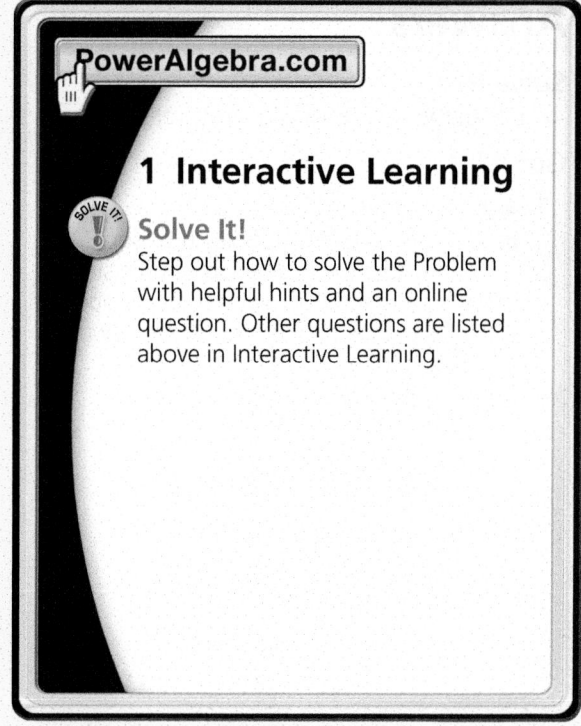

PowerAlgebra.com

1 Interactive Learning

Solve It!
Step out how to solve the Problem with helpful hints and an online question. Other questions are listed above in Interactive Learning.

Problem 2

> **Q** What is the greatest number that divides evenly into all four coefficients? **[4]**
>
> **Q** What degree of the variable q do all terms have in common? **[q^1]**

Got It?

ERROR PREVENTION

Have students draw a long vertical arrow from where the common factor is first factored out to where it will be placed in the final answer to include the common term.

Problem 3

> **Q** How many dimensions does a rectangular prism have? Explain. **[3: length, width, and height]**
>
> **Q** How many polynomials will constitute the final factorization of $6x^3 + 19x^2 + 15x$? Explain. **[3, because there are three dimensions.]**
>
> **Q** Do the coefficients have a common factor that can be factored out? Explain. **[No, the greatest number that divides evenly into all coefficients is 1.]**

Before factoring by grouping, you may need to factor out the GCF of all the terms.

 **Problem 2** Factoring a Polynomial Completely

Think

Do the terms share any numerical or variable factors?
Yes. The terms have a common numerical factor of 4 and a common variable factor of q. The GCF is $4q$.

What is the factored form of $4q^4 - 8q^3 + 12q^2 - 24q$? Factor completely.

$$\begin{aligned}
4q^4 - 8q^3 + 12q^2 - 24q &= 4q(q^3 - 2q^2 + 3q - 6) &&\text{Factor out the GCF.}\\
&= 4q[q^2(q - 2) + 3(q - 2)] &&\text{Factor by grouping.}\\
&= 4q(q^2 + 3)(q - 2) &&\text{Factor again.}
\end{aligned}$$

✓ **Got It? 2.** What is the factored form of $6h^4 + 9h^3 + 12h^2 + 18h$? Factor completely.

You can sometimes factor to find possible expressions for the length, width, and height of a rectangular prism.

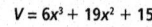 **Problem 3** Finding the Dimensions of a Rectangular Prism

Entertainment The toy shown below is made of several bars that can fold together to form a rectangular prism or unfold to form a "ladder." What expressions can represent the dimensions of the toy when it is folded up? Use factoring.

$V = 6x^3 + 19x^2 + 15x$

Plan

How can you find the prism's dimensions?
Factor the cubic expression for the volume of the prism as the product of three linear expressions. Each linear expression is a dimension.

Step 1 Factor out the GCF.
$$6x^3 + 19x^2 + 15x = x(6x^2 + 19x + 15)$$

Step 2 To factor the trinomial, find factors of ac that have sum b.
Since $ac = 90$ and $b = 19$, find factors of 90 that have sum 19.

Factors of 90	1, 90	2, 45	3, 30	5, 18	6, 15	9, 10
Sum of Factors	91	47	33	23	21	19 ✔

Step 3 To factor the trinomial, use the factors you found to rewrite bx.
$$\begin{aligned}
x(6x^2 + 19x + 15) &= x(6x^2 + 9x + 10x + 15) &&\text{Rewrite } bx: 19x = 9x + 10x.\\
&= x[3x(2x + 3) + 5(2x + 3)] &&\text{Factor by grouping.}\\
&= x(3x + 5)(2x + 3) &&\text{Distributive Property}
\end{aligned}$$

The possible dimensions are x, $3x + 5$, and $2x + 3$.

Answers

Solve It!
$4x + 9$ and $x + 1$; explanations may vary.

Got It?

1. a. $(2t^2 + 5)(4t + 7)$

  b. Answers may vary. Sample: In Lesson 8-6, you rewrote the middle term as the sum of two terms and then factored by grouping. In this problem, there were already two middle terms.

2. $3h(h^2 + 2)(2h + 3)$

 PowerAlgebra.com

2 Guided Instruction

Each Problem is worked out and supported online.

Problem 1
Factoring a Cubic Polynomial
Animated

Problem 2
Factoring a Polynomial Completely

Alternative Problem 2
Factoring a Polynomial Completely
Animated

Problem 3
Finding the Dimensions of a Rectangular Prism
Animated

Support in Algebra 1 Companion
• Vocabulary
• Key Concepts
• Got It?

Got It? **3. Geometry** A rectangular prism has volume $60x^3 + 34x^2 + 4x$. What expressions can represent the dimensions of the prism? Use factoring.

Here is a summary of what to remember as you factor polynomials.

 take note

Summary Factoring Polynomials

1. Factor out the greatest common factor (GCF).

2. If the polynomial has two terms or three terms, look for a difference of two squares, a perfect-square trinomial, or a pair of binomial factors.

3. If the polynomial has four or more terms, group terms and factor to find common binomial factors.

4. As a final check, make sure there are no common factors other than 1.

Lesson Check

Do you know HOW?

Factor each expression.

1. $20r^3 + 8r^2 + 15r + 6$

2. $6d^3 + 3d^2 - 10d - 5$

3. $24x^3 + 60x^2 + 36x + 90$

4. A rectangular prism has a volume of $36x^3 + 36x^2 + 8x$. What expressions can represent the dimensions of the prism? Use factoring.

Do you UNDERSTAND?

Vocabulary Tell whether you would factor the polynomial by grouping. Explain your answer.

5. $x^2 - 6x + 9$

6. $4w^2 + 23w + 15$

7. $24t^3 - 42t^2 - 28t + 49$

8. Reasoning Can you factor the polynomial $6q^3 + 2q^2 + 12q - 3$ by grouping? Explain.

Practice and Problem-Solving Exercises

A Practice Find the GCF of the first two terms and the GCF of the last two terms for each polynomial.
See Problem 1.

9. $2z^3 + 6z^2 + 3z + 9$

10. $10g^3 - 25g^2 + 4g - 10$

11. $2r^3 + 12r^2 - 5r - 30$

12. $6p^3 + 3p^2 + 2p + 1$

Factor each expression.

13. $15q^3 + 40q^2 + 3q + 8$

14. $14y^3 + 8y^2 + 7y + 4$

15. $14z^3 - 35z^2 + 16z - 40$

16. $11w^3 - 9w^2 + 11w - 9$

17. $8m^3 + 12m^2 - 2m - 3$

18. $12k^3 - 27k^2 - 40k + 90$

19. $20v^3 + 24v^2 - 25v - 30$

20. $18h^3 + 45h^2 - 8h - 20$

21. $12y^3 + 4y^2 - 9y - 3$

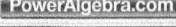
Got It?

Q How should you rewrite bx when factoring the trinomial? Explain. [$15x + 2x$, because $15 \cdot 2 = 30$ and $15 + 2 = 17$.]

Take Note   VISUAL LEARNERS

Encourage students to create a graphic organizer in the form of a flow chart that incorporates the five summary points as well as any personal tips for factoring.

3 Lesson Check

Do you know HOW?

• If students have difficulty with Exercises 2 and 3, then have them review Problem 2. For Exercise 3, ask them what is the greatest number that is a factor of 24, 60, 36, and 90.

Do you UNDERSTAND?

• If students have difficulty with Exercise 5, then have them factor the trinomial using both grouping and the simpler process taught in Lesson 8-5.

Close

Q What should be your first and last steps when completing the factorization of a polynomial? [Your first step should be to check for common factors; your last step should be to make sure that none of the factors in the final answer can be factored further.]

Additional Problems

1. What is the factored form of $4n^3 + 12n^2 - n - 3$?

ANSWER $(n + 3)(2n + 1)(2n - 1)$

2. What is the factored form of $3n^4 - 12n^3 + 15n^2 - 60n$?

ANSWER $3n(n^2 + 5)(n - 4)$

3. A rectangular prism has volume $4x^3 + 12x^2 + 5x$. What expressions can represent the dimensions of the prism?

ANSWER $x, 2x + 1, 2x + 5$

Answers

Got It? (continued)

3. Answers may vary. Sample: $2x, 5x + 2,$ and $6x + 1$

Lesson Check

1. $(4r^2 + 3)(5r + 2)$

2. $(3d^2 - 5)(2d + 1)$

3. $6(2x^2 + 3)(2x + 5)$

4. Answers may vary. Sample: $4x, 3x + 1,$ and $3x + 2$

5. No; the polynomial is a perfect square.

6. Yes; when you write $23w$ as $20w + 3w$, the resulting two groups of terms have the same factor, $w + 5$.

7. Yes; two groups of terms have the same factor, $4t - 7$.

8. No; when you factor out the GCF from each pair of terms, there is no common factor.

Practice and Problem-Solving Exercises

9. $2z^2, 3$

10. $5g^2, 2$

11. $2r^2, -5$

12. $3p^2, 1$

13. $(5q^2 + 1)(3q + 8)$

14. $(2y^2 + 1)(7y + 4)$

15. $(7z^2 + 8)(2z - 5)$

16. $(w^2 + 1)(11w - 9)$

17. $(2m + 1)(2m - 1)(2m + 3)$

18. $(3k^2 - 10)(4k - 9)$

19. $(4v^2 - 5)(5v + 6)$

20. $(3h + 2)(3h - 2)(2h + 5)$

21. $(4y^2 - 3)(3y + 1)$

4 Practice

ASSIGNMENT GUIDE

Basic: 9–30, 32, 34, 35, 38, 40

Average: 9–29 odd, 31–40

Advanced: 9–29 odd, 31–46

Standardized Test Prep: 47–51

Mixed Review: 52–61

Reasoning exercises have blue headings.

Applications exercises have red headings.

EXERCISE 40: Use the Think About a Plan worksheet in the **Practice and Problem Solving Workbook** (also available in the Teaching Resources in print and online) to further support students' development in becoming independent learners.

HOMEWORK QUICK CHECK

To check students' understanding of key skills and concepts, go over Exercises 11, 23, 35, 38, and 40.

Factor completely. 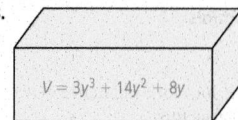 See Problem 2.

22. $8p^3 - 32p^2 + 28p - 112$ **23.** $3w^4 - 2w^3 + 18w^2 - 12w$ **24.** $5g^4 - 5g^3 + 20g^2 - 20g$

25. $6q^4 + 3q^3 - 24q^2 - 12q$ **26.** $36v^3 - 126v^2 + 48v - 168$ **27.** $4d^3 - 6d^2 + 16d - 24$

Find expressions for the possible dimensions of each rectangular prism. See Problem 3.

28.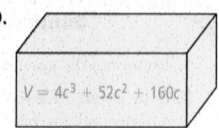

$V = 3y^3 + 14y^2 + 8y$

29.

$V = 4c^3 + 52c^2 + 160c$

30. Carpentry A trunk in the shape of a rectangular prism has a volume of $6x^3 + 38x^2 - 28x$. What expressions can represent the dimensions of the trunk?

B Apply

Factor completely.

31. $9t^3 - 90t^2 + 144t$

32. $60y^4 - 300y^3 - 42y^2 + 210y$

33. $8m^3 + 32m^2 + 40m + 160$

34. $10p^2 - 5pq - 180q^2$

35. Error Analysis Describe and correct the error made in factoring completely.

$$4x^4 + 12x^3 + 8x^2 + 24x = 4(x^4 + 3x^3 + 2x^2 + 6x)$$
$$= 4[x^3(x + 3) + 2x(x + 3)]$$
$$= 4(x^3 + 2x)(x + 3)$$

36. a. Factor $(20x^3 - 5x^2) + (44x - 11)$.

   b. Factor $(20x^3 + 44x) + (-5x^2 - 11)$.

   c. Reasoning Why can you factor the same polynomial using different pairs of terms?

37. Writing Describe how to factor the expression $6x^5 + 4x^4 + 12x^3 + 8x^2 + 9x + 6$.

38. Think About a Plan Bat houses, such as the one at the right, are large wooden structures that people mount on buildings to attract bats. What expressions can represent the dimensions of the bat house?

   • Into how many factors should you factor the expression for the volume?

   • What is the first step in factoring this expression?

39. Open-Ended Write a four-term polynomial that you can factor by grouping. Factor your polynomial.

40. Art The pedestal of a sculpture is a rectangular prism with a volume of $63x^3 - 28x$. What expressions can represent the dimensions of the pedestal? Use factoring.

$V = 4x^3 + 22x^2 + 24x$

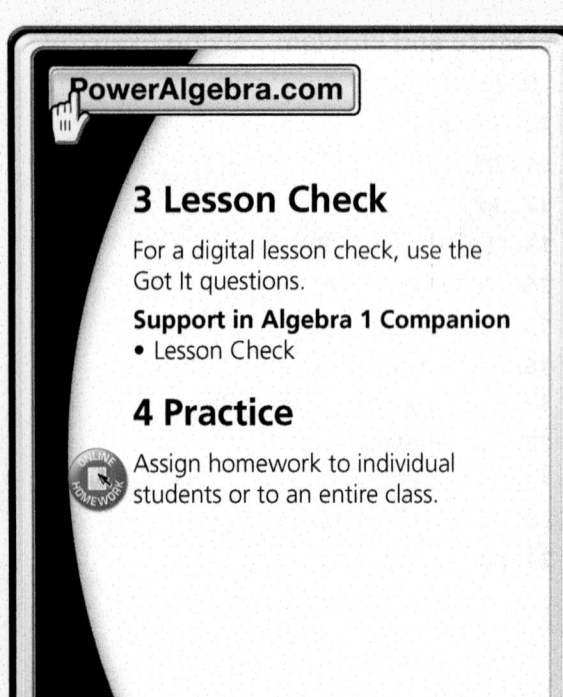

PowerAlgebra.com

3 Lesson Check

For a digital lesson check, use the Got It questions.

Support in Algebra 1 Companion
• Lesson Check

4 Practice

Assign homework to individual students or to an entire class.

Answers

Practice and Problem-Solving Exercises (continued)

22. $4(2p^2 + 7)(p - 4)$

23. $w(w^2 + 6)(3w - 2)$

24. $5g(g^2 + 4)(g - 1)$

25. $3q(q + 2)(q - 2)(2q + 1)$

26. $6(3v^2 + 4)(2v - 7)$

27. $2(d^2 + 4)(2d - 3)$

28–30. Answers may vary. Samples are given.

28. $y, 3y + 2,$ and $y + 4$

29. $4c, c + 8,$ and $c + 5$

30. $2x, 3x - 2, x + 7$

31. $9t(t - 8)(t - 2)$

32. $6y(10y^2 - 7)(y - 5)$

33. $8(m^2 + 5)(m + 4)$

34. $5(2p - 9q)(p + 4q)$

35. The factorization is correct, but it is not complete.

The GCF of all the terms is $4x$, not 4.
$$4x^4 + 12x^3 + 8x^2 + 24x =$$
$$4x(x^3 + 3x^2 + 2x + 6) =$$
$$4x[x^2(x + 3) + 2(x + 3)] =$$
$$4x(x^2 + 2)(x + 3)$$

36. a. $(5x^2 + 11)(4x - 1)$

   b. $(4x - 1)(5x^2 + 11)$

   c. Answers may vary. Sample: The associative and commutative properties of addition tell us that the nonfactored polynomials in parts (a) and (b) are equivalent.

37. Answers may vary. Sample: Split the expression into three binomials. Find the GCF of each binomial, then factor again.

38. $2x, 2x + 3, x + 4$

39. Answers may vary. Sample:
$$30x^3 + 36x^2 + 40x + 48 =$$
$$2(3x^2 + 4)(5x + 6)$$

40. Answers may vary. Sample:
$7x, 3x + 2, 3x - 2$

Factor by grouping.

41. $y^3 + 11y^2 - 4y - 44$ **42.** $p^2m + p^2n^5 + qm + qn^5$ **43.** $30g^5 + 24g^3h - 35g^2h^2 - 28h^3$

44. Geometry The polynomial $2\pi x^3 + 12\pi x^2 + 18\pi x$ represents the volume of a
cylinder. The formula for the volume V of a cylinder with radius r and height h
is $V = \pi r^2 h$.
   a. Factor $2\pi x^3 + 12\pi x^2 + 18\pi x$.
   b. Based on your answer to part (a), write an expression for a possible radius of
      the cylinder.

You can write the number 63 as $2^5 + 2^4 + 2^3 + 2^2 + 2^1 + 2^0$. For Exercises
45 and 46, factor each expression by grouping. Then simplify the powers of 2 to
write 63 as the product of two numbers.

45. $(2^5 + 2^4 + 2^3) + (2^2 + 2^1 + 2^0)$ **46.** $(2^5 + 2^4) + (2^3 + 2^2) + (2^1 + 2^0)$

Standardized Test Prep

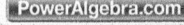 **SAT/ACT**

47. What is $30z^3 - 12z^2 + 120z - 48$ factored completely?
   Ⓐ $2(15z^3 - 6z^2 + 60z - 24)$ Ⓒ $6(5z^3 - 2z^2 + 20z - 8)$
   Ⓑ $(6z^2 + 24)(5z - 2)$ Ⓓ $6(z^2 + 4)(5z - 2)$

48. What is the simplified form of $2x^3 \cdot x^8$?
   Ⓕ $2x^{11}$ Ⓖ $8x^{11}$ Ⓗ $2x^{24}$ Ⓘ $8x^{24}$

49. Which equation represents the line with slope -3 that passes through $(2, 5)$?
   Ⓐ $y = -3x + 17$ Ⓑ $y = -3x + 11$ Ⓒ $y = 4x - 3$ Ⓓ $y = x - 3$

50. What is the solution of the inequality $7 < -2x + 5$?
   Ⓕ $x > -1$ Ⓖ $x < -1$ Ⓗ $x > 1$ Ⓘ $x < 1$

Short Response

51. Factor $10r^4 + 30r^3 + 5r^2 + 15r$ completely. Show your work.

Mixed Review

Factor each expression.   **See Lesson 8-7.**

52. $m^2 + 12m + 36$ **53.** $64x^2 - 144x + 81$ **54.** $49p^2 - 4$

Use a mapping diagram to determine whether each relation is a function.   **See Lesson 4-6.**

55. $\{(4, 3), (3, 4), (4, 7), (7, 4)\}$ **56.** $\{(-1, 8), (1, 8), (3, 8), (5, 8)\}$ **57.** $\{(2, 7), (4, -7), (6, 7), (8, -7)\}$

Get Ready!   To prepare for Lesson 9-1, do Exercises 58–61.

Use the slope and y-intercept to graph each equation.   **See Lesson 5-3.**

58. $y = \frac{1}{2}x + 3$ **59.** $y = -4x - 1$ **60.** $y = 2x - 3$ **61.** $y = -\frac{5}{3}x + 2$

---

41. $(y + 2)(y - 2)(y + 11)$

42. $(p^2 + q)(m + n^5)$

43. $(6g^3 - 7h^2)(5g^2 + 4h)$

44. a. $2\pi x(x + 3)^2$
   b. Answers may vary. Sample: $x + 3$

45. $(2^3 + 2^0)(2^2 + 2^1 + 2^0); 9(7)$

46. $(2^4 + 2^2 + 2^0)(2^1 + 2^0); 21(3)$

47. D

48. F

49. B

50. G

51. [2] $5r(2r^2 + 1)(r + 3)$
   [1]   Student finds correct GCF, $5r$.

52. $(m + 6)^2$

53. $(8x - 9)^2$

54. $(7p + 2)(7p - 2)$

55. not a function

56. function

57. function

58.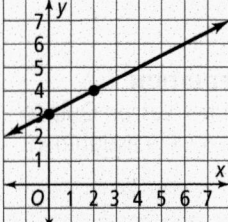

59.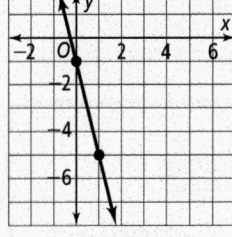

60.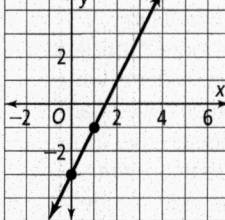

61.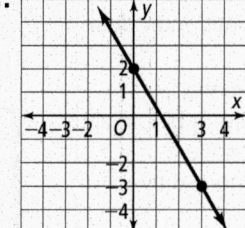

Additional Instructional Support

Algebra 1 Companion

Students can use the **Algebra 1 Companion** worktext (4 pages) as you teach the lesson. Use the Companion to support

- New Vocabulary
- Key Concepts
- Got It for each Problem
- Lesson Check

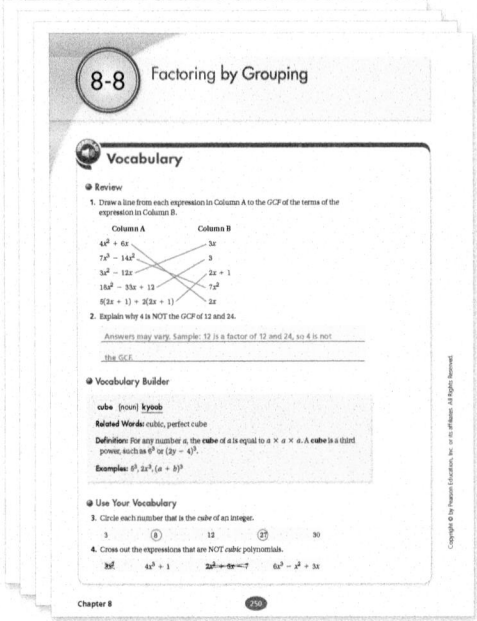

5 Assess & Remediate

Lesson Quiz

1. What is the factored form of $5n^3 - 10n^2 + 3n - 6$?
2. What is the factored form of $2n^4 + 14n^3 - 4n^2 - 28n$?
3. **Do you UNDERSTAND?** A rectangular prism has volume $12x^3 - 11x^2 - 5x$. What expressions can represent the dimensions of the prism?

ANSWERS TO LESSON QUIZ

1. $(5n^2 + 3)(n - 2)$
2. $2n(n^2 - 2)(n + 7)$
3. $x, 3x + 1, 4x - 5$

Intervention

- **Reteaching** (2 pages) Provides reteaching and practice exercises for the key lesson concepts. Use with struggling students or absent students.
- **English Language Learner Support** Helps students develop and reinforce mathematical vocabulary and key concepts.

All-in-One Resources/Online
Reteaching

8-8 **Reteaching**
Factoring by Grouping

All-in-One Resources/Online
English Language Learner Support

8-8 **ELL Support**
Factoring by Grouping

ELL Support

Assess Understanding Place students in heterogeneous groups, a mix of more proficient and less proficient students. Have students write the key topics from the chapter on one side of an index card. Have student pairs discuss the "how to" of each topic. Next, tell students to write a summary of the process on the reverse side of the card in their own words. Students can quiz one another on the topics learned in this chapter and keep the cards for later individual review.

Key topics include adding polynomials, subtracting polynomials, multiplying binomials, factoring quadratic and perfect-square trinomials, and factoring a polynomial by grouping.

PRESCRIPTION FOR REMEDIATION
Use the student work on the Lesson Quiz to prescribe a differentiated review assignment.

Points	Differentiated Remediation
0–1	Intervention
2	On-level
3	Extension

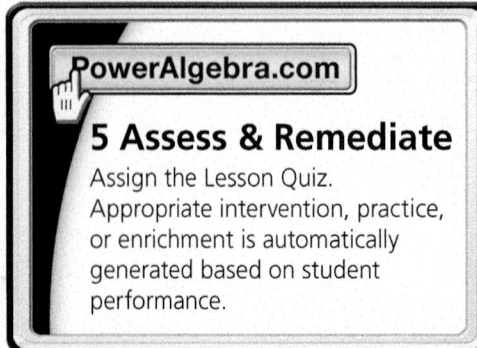

5 Assess & Remediate

Assign the Lesson Quiz. Appropriate intervention, practice, or enrichment is automatically generated based on student performance.

Differentiated Remediation *continued*

On-Level

- **Practice** (2 pages) Provides extra practice for each lesson. For simpler practice exercises, use the Form K Practice pages found in the All-in-One Teaching Resources and online.

- **Think About a Plan** Helps students develop specific problem-solving skills and strategies by providing scaffolded guiding questions.

- **Standardized Test Prep** Focuses on all major exercises, all major question types, and helps students prepare for the high-stakes assessments.

Extension

- **Enrichment** Provides students with interesting problems and activities that extend the concepts of the lesson.

- **Activities, Games, and Puzzles** Worksheets that can be used for concepts development, enrichment, and for fun!

Practice and Problem Solving WKBK/ All-in-One Resources/Online
Practice page 1

8-8 Practice — Form G
Factoring by Grouping

Find the GCF of the first two terms and the GCF of the last two terms for each polynomial.

1. $12x^3 + 3x^2 + 20x + 5$ 2. $6t^3 + 42t^2 + 5v + 35$
3. $8t^3 + 36t^2 + 2t + 9$ 4. $10g^3 + 35g^2 + 6s + 21$
5. $9m^3 - 6m^2 + 12m - 8$ 6. $8w^3 + 6w^2 - 28w - 21$
7. $7t^3 + 16t^2 - 9r - 72$ 8. $21x^3 - 28x^2 - 6x + 8$

Factor each expression.

9. $8f^3 + 4f^2 + 10f + 5$ 10. $2m^3 + 8m^2 + 9m + 36$
11. $10s^3 + 25s^2 + 8s + 20$ 12. $6x^3 + 9x^2 + 2x + 3$
13. $21x^3 + 6x^2 - 28x - 8$ 14. $8w^3 + 12w^2 + 10w + 15$
15. $18r^3 - 12r^2 + 21r - 14$ 16. $36n^3 - 27n^2 - 8n + 6$
17. $110b^3 + 77b^2 - 60b - 42$ 18. $64d^3 - 40d^2 - 24d + 15$
19. $10s^3 + 80s^2 - 7s - 56$ 20. $25f^3 + 15f^2 - 5f - 3$
21. $24c^3 - 84c^2 + 10c - 35$ 22. $27f^3 + 9f^2 - 24f - 8$

Practice and Problem Solving WKBK/ All-in-One Resources/Online
Practice page 2

8-8 Practice (continued) — Form G
Factoring by Grouping

Factor completely.

23. $32x^3 + 8x^2 + 48x + 12$ 24. $45w^4 - 36w^2 + 15w^2 - 12w$
25. $32k^4 - 16k^3 + 12k^2 - 6k$ 26. $6g^4 + 18g^2 + 60g + 180$
27. $30b^4 - 45b^3 - 10b^2 + 15b$ 28. $32m^3 + 72m^2 - 80m - 180$
29. $63j^3 + 84j^3 - 18j^2 - 24j$ 30. $6u^3 - 240m^2 - 168n + 420$
31. $12e^4 + 18e^3 + 36e^2 + 54e$ 32. $60a^6 - 72a^4 - 210a^3 + 252a^2$

Find linear expressions for the possible dimensions of each rectangular prism.

33. $V = 15x^3 + 52x^2 + 32x$
34. $V = 18d^3 + 84d^2 + 48d$
35. $V = 24y^3 + 54y^2 - 15y$
36. $V = 32p^3 - 224p^2 + 360p$

37. A shipping box in the shape of a rectangular prism has a volume of $12x^3 + 32x^2 + 20x$. What linear expressions can represent possible dimensions of the box?

38. **Error Analysis** Describe and correct the error made in factoring completely.

39. **Open-Ended** Write a 3-term expression for the volume of a rectangular prism that you can factor by grouping. Factor your polynomial.

All-in-One Resources/Online
Enrichment

8-8 Enrichment
Factoring by Grouping

Pascal's triangle is named after French mathematician Blaise Pascal, but this special number pattern had been studied in India, China, Persia, and Italy long before Pascal. To generate Pascal's triangle, start with the number 1 in Row 0. Each successive row has a 1 at both ends. Add the numbers directly above-left and above-right to find the new value.

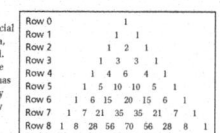

You can use Pascal's triangle to quickly expand a binomial expression. The exponent tells you the row number to choose. The numbers in the correct row are the coefficients to use in the expansion.

To expand $(a + b)^4$, look to Row 4. The coefficients are 1, 4, 6, 4, 1. Expand the variables, raising the first variable to 4 and decreasing by one for each term. Raise the second variable to 0 and increase by 1 at each new term. Multiply each term by the coefficients:
$a^4 + 4a^3b + 6a^2b^2 + 4ab^3 + b^4$.

You can also use Pascal's triangle to factor polynomials that are expansions of binomial expressions. Arrange the polynomial in standard form. Check to see if the coefficients correspond to a row in Pascal's triangle. Work backwards to factor.

To factor $15xy^2 - y^3 + 125x^3 - 75x^2y$, first rearrange the terms in standard form:
$125x^3 - 75x^2y + 15xy^2 - y^3$. In expansions of binomial expressions the x-exponents decrease by one in every term and y-exponents increase by one. Since the first and last terms have exponents of 3, the binomial is raised to the third power. Find the cube root of 125 to find the coefficient of x: 5. The final term is negative and has a coefficient of one, so the expression is $(5x - y)^3$. Expand the binomial to check your answer:
$(5x - y)^3 = 1(5x)^3 + 3(5x)^2(-y) + 3(5x)(-y)^2 + 1(-y)^3 = 125x^3 - 75x^2y + 15xy^2 - y^3$

Expand the binomial using Pascal's triangle.

1. $(4k + f)^4$
2. $(7x - y)^7$
Factor using Pascal's triangle. Then expand the binomial to check your answer.
3. $8a^3 + 12a^2b + 6ab^2 + b^3$
4. $40x^2y^3 + 32x^5 + 10xy^4 + 80x^4y + y^5 + 80x^3y^2$
5. $1215x^4y^2 + 135x^2y^4 + 729x^6 + 18xy^5 + y^6 + 1458x^3y^3$

Practice and Problem Solving WKBK/ All-in-One Resources/Online
Think About a Plan

8-8 Think About a Plan
Factoring by Grouping

Art The pedestal of a sculpture is a rectangular prism with a volume of $63x^3 - 28x$. What expressions can represent the dimensions of the pedestal? Use factoring.

KNOW

1. The pedestal of the sculpture is shaped like a ___rectangular prism___.

2. The volume of the pedestal is ___$63x^3 - 28x$___.

3. The formula you can use to find the dimensions of the pedestal is ___$V = lwh$___.

NEED

4. To solve the problem you need to find ___3 factors___

PLAN

5. Factor out the GCF from the volume of the pedestal. ___$7x(9x^2 - 4)$___

6. What type of expression is of the remaining expression? ___difference of two squares___

7. Factor the expression completely. ___$7x(3x - 2)(3x + 2)$___

8. What expressions represent possible dimensions of the pedestal?
___$7x$, $(3x - 2)$, and $(3x + 2)$___

Practice and Problem Solving WKBK/ All-in-One Resources/Online
Standardized Test Prep

8-8 Standardized Test Prep
Factoring by Grouping

Multiple Choice

For Exercises 1–5, choose the correct letter.

1. What is the GCF of the first two terms of the polynomial $4y^3 + 8y^2 + 5y + 10$? B
A. $4y$ B. $4y^2$ C. $4y^3$ D. 4

2. What is the factored form of $4x^3 + 3x^2 + 8x + 6$? I
F. $(2x^2 + 3)(2x + 3)$
G. $(2x^2 + 2)(2x + 3)$
H. $(x^2 + 2)(2x + 3)$
I. $(x^2 + 2)(4x + 3)$

3. What is the factored form of $9x^4 - 6x^3 + 18x^2 - 12x$? C
A. $3x(x^2 - 2x)(x - 4)$
B. $3x(x^2 - 2)(3x + 2)$
C. $3x(x^2 + 2)(3x - 2)$
D. $3x(3x^2 - 2x)(6x - 4)$

4. What is the factored form of $20p^3 + 40p^2 + 15p + 30$? H
F. $5(2p^2 + 3)(p + 2)$
G. $5(2p^2 + 6)(p + 4)$
H. $5(4p^2 + 3)(p + 2)$
I. $5(4p^2 + 8p)(3p + 6)$

5. A box in the shape of a rectangular prism has a volume of $9x^3 + 24x^2 + 12x$. Which is not one of the possible dimensions? (Its dimensions are all linear expressions with integer coefficients.) A
A. $2x + 3$ B. $3x + 2$ C. $3x$ D. $x + 2$

Short Response

6. The polynomial $3\pi x^3 + 24\pi x^2 + 48\pi x$ represents the volume of a cylinder. The formula for the volume of a cylinder with radius r and height h is $V = \pi r^2 h$.
a. Factor $3\pi x^3 + 24\pi x^2 + 48\pi x$. $3\pi x(x + 4)^2$
b. Write a linear expression for a possible radius of the cylinder. Explain.
$x + 4$ because that is the term that is squared
[2] Both parts answered correctly with full explanation
[1] One part answered correctly or both parts answered correctly with incomplete explanation

---

Online Teacher Resource Center
Activities, Games, and Puzzles

8-8 Game: Common Binomial Factors
Factoring by Grouping

In this game, each player is competing against the clock. Your teacher will choose a time limit for each of the parts below. Each correct answer completed within the time limit is worth two points. When everyone has finished, review the answers and compare your scores with the rest of the class.

Part 1
Each expression in the left column can be factored by grouping into the product of two binomials. One of these binomials can be found in the right column. Write the correct letter next to each polynomial.

1. $2x^3 - 6x^2 + x - 3$ B   A. $(x - 5)$
2. $x^3 + 4x^2 + 4x + 16$ G   B. $(x - 3)$
3. $x^3 - 5x^2 + 5x - 25$ A   C. $(x - 7)$
4. $x^3 - 7x^2 + 4x - 28$ C   D. $(x + 7)$
5. $3x^3 - 18x^2 + 2x - 12$ F   E. $(x + 1)$
6. $7x^3 + 49x^2 + 2x + 14$ D   F. $(x - 6)$
7. $4x^3 + 4x^2 + 2x + 2$ E   G. $(x + 4)$

Part 2
Fill in the missing coefficients in the right column in order to factor each expression by grouping.

8. $2x^3 + 2x^2 + 3x + 3$ $(\_2\_ x^2 + \_3\_)(x + \_1\_)$
9. $3x^3 - 12x^2 + 2x - 8$ $(\_3\_ x^2 + \_2\_)(x + \_-4\_)$
10. $2x^3 + 14x^2 + 2x + 14$ $(\_2\_ x^2 + \_2\_)(x + \_7\_)$
11. $7x^3 - 7x^2 + x - 1$ $(\_7\_ x^2 + \_1\_)(x + \_-1\_)$
12. $4x^3 + 36x^2 + 5x + 18$ $(\_4\_ x^2 + \_1\_)(x + \_9\_)$
13. $11x^3 - 11x^2 + 11x - 11$ $(\_11\_ x^2 + \_11\_)(x + \_-1\_)$
14. $-3x^3 - 9x^2 - 3x - 9$ $(\_-3\_ x^2 + \_-3\_)(x + \_3\_)$

My score: ☐

Performance Task

Pull It All Together

The concepts and skills required to solve these problems are from several lessons within this chapter and from the previous chapter. As students solve these problems, they will demonstrate their reasoning strategies and their growth as independent problem solvers.

The following questions are designed to:
- Help support students as they do the Tasks.
- Gauge the amount of support students need as they become independent problem solvers.

Task 1
- What is the formula for the area of a circle?
- What is the radius of the entire target?
- How can you find the area of the outermost ring?

Task 2
- How many faces of the box are there?
- What do you substitute for w? for ℓ? for h?
- How can you check your answer?

Task 3
- What is the formula for the volume of a prism?
- Can you factor the GCF out of the expression?
- What does the GCF represent?

To solve these problems you will pull together many concepts and skills that you have studied about polynomials and factoring.

BIG idea Equivalence

You can represent algebraic expressions in many ways. When you add, subtract, multiply, divide, and factor polynomials, you replace one expression with an equivalent expression.

BIG idea Properties

The properties of real numbers are the basis of the laws of algebra. You can apply properties of real numbers, such as the Distributive Property, to polynomials.

Task 1

Solve. Show all of your work and explain your steps.

An archery target consists of a circular bull's-eye with radius x, surrounded by four rings with width y. What is the area of the outermost ring in terms of x and y?

Task 2

Solve. Show all of your work and explain your steps.

You are painting the outside of a jewelry box, including the bottom. To find the surface area (S.A.) of the jewelry box, you can use the formula S.A. $= 2w\ell + 2\ell h + 2wh$, where ℓ is the length, w is the width, and h is the height. What is the surface area of the jewelry box in terms of x?

Task 3

Solve. Show all of your work and explain your steps.

The volume of a square prism is $144x^3 + 216x^2 + 81x$. What is an expression that could describe the perimeter of one of the prism's square faces?

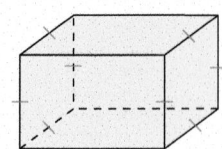

Assess Performance

Pull It All Together

See p. 67 for a holistic scoring rubric to gauge a student's progress on Understanding the Problem, Planning a Solution, Getting an Answer, and Assessing Autonomy.

SOLUTION OUTLINES

Task 1

Possible Plan: Subtract the area enclosed by the outermost ring from the total area of the target.

First Step: Find the radius of the target:
$(y + y + y + y + x$, or $4y + x)$

Second Step: Find the total area of the target:
$A = \pi(4y + x)^2 = 16\pi y^2 + 8\pi xy + \pi x^2$

Third Step: Find the inner radius of the largest ring:
$(y + y + y + x$, or $3y + x)$

Fourth Step: Find the area enclosed by the largest ring: $A = \pi(3y + x)^2 = 9\pi y^2 + 6\pi xy + \pi x^2$

Fifth Step: To find the area of the outermost ring, subtract the area enclosed by the largest ring from the area of the target.
$[(16\pi y^2 + 8\pi xy + \pi x^2) -$
$(9\pi y^2 + 6\pi xy + \pi x^2)] =$
$16\pi y^2 + 8\pi xy + \pi x^2 - 9\pi y^2 - 6\pi xy -$
$\pi x^2 = 7\pi y^2 + 2\pi xy$

Task 2

First Step: Use the formula for the surface area of a rectangular prism.
(S.A. $= 2w\ell + 2\ell h + 2wh$)

Second Step: Substitute measures into formula:
(S.A. $= 2(x)(2x + 5) +$
$2(2x + 5)(x + 3) + 2(x)(x + 3))$

Third Step: Multiply polynomials:
(S.A. $= 4x^2 + 10x + 4x^2 +$
$22x + 30 + 2x^2 + 6x)$

Fourth Step: Combine like terms:
(S.A. $= 10x^2 + 38x + 30)$

Task 3

Possible Plan: Find all perfect-square factors of the polynomial. For each perfect square factor, take the square root and multiply by 4 to find the perimeter of a square face having that area.

First step: Factor the polynomial:
$3 \cdot 3 \cdot x \cdot (4x + 3) \cdot (4x + 3)$.

Second step: There are two sets of equal factors, 3^2 and $(4x + 3)^2$. Either pair of factors or their product could represent dimensions of a square face. So there are possible square faces with sides of 3, $(4x + 3)$, and $(12x + 9)$, with corresponding perimeters of 12, $16x + 12$, and $48x + 36$. Other solutions are possible.

8 Chapter Review

Connecting BIG ideas and Answering the Essential Questions

1 Equivalence
You can represent algebraic expressions in many ways. When you add, subtract, multiply, divide, and factor polynomials, you replace one expression with an equivalent expression.

Adding and Subtracting Polynomials (Lesson 8-1)
$(3x^2 + 4x + 1) + (2x^2 + 5x + 8)$
$= (3x^2 + 2x^2) + (4x + 5x) + (1 + 8)$
$= 5x^2 + 9x + 9$

Multiplying Binomials (Lesson 8-3)
$(m + 4)(2m - 5) = 2m^2 - 5m + 8m - 20$
$= 2m^2 + 3m - 20$

Multiplying Special Cases (Lesson 8-4)
$(2x + 3)(2x - 3) = 4x^2 - 9$

2 Properties
The properties of real numbers are the basis of the laws of algebra. You can apply properties of real numbers, such as the Distributive Property, to polynomials.

Factoring Trinomials (Lessons 8-5 and 8-6)
$x^2 - 6x + 8 = (x - 2)(x - 4)$

Factoring Special Cases (Lesson 8-7)
$49p^2 - 16 = (7p + 4)(7p - 4)$

Factoring by Grouping (Lesson 8-8)
$3x^2 - 10x - 8 = 3x^2 - 12x + 2x - 8$
$= (3x^2 - 12x) + (2x - 8)$
$= 3x(x - 4) + 2(x - 4)$
$= (3x + 2)(x - 4)$

Chapter Vocabulary

- binomial (p. 475)
- degree of a monomial (p. 474)
- degree of a polynomial (p. 475)
- difference of two squares (p. 513)
- factoring by grouping (p. 517)
- monomial (p. 474)
- perfect-square trinomial (p. 511)
- polynomial (p. 475)
- standard form of a polynomial (p. 475)
- trinomial (p. 475)

Choose the correct term to complete each sentence.

1. A polynomial that has two terms is a(n) ? .

2. A monomial or the sum of two or more monomials is a(n) ? .

3. A(n) ? is an expression that is a number, a variable, or a product of a number and one or more variables.

4. A polynomial that is the product of two identical binomial factors is a(n) ? .

5. The sum of the exponents of the variables in a monomial is the ? .

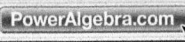

BIG idea Equivalence
ESSENTIAL QUESTION Can two algebraic expressions that appear to be different be equivalent?
ANSWER You can represent algebraic expressions in many ways. When you add, subtract, multiply, divide, and factor polynomials, you replace one expression with an equivalent expression.

BIG idea Properties
ESSENTIAL QUESTION How are the properties of real numbers related to polynomials?
ANSWER The properties of real numbers are the basis of the laws of algebra. You can apply properties of real numbers, such as the Distributive Property, to polynomials, because they represent real numbers in variable form.

Answers

Chapter Review

1. binomial
2. polynomial
3. monomial
4. perfect-square trinomial
5. degree of the monomial

Summative Questions

Use the following prompts as you review this chapter with your students. The prompts are designed to help you assess your students' understanding of the BIG Ideas they have studied.
- How do you add and subtract polynomials?
- How do you multiply polynomials?
- How do you factor polynomials?

Answers

Chapter Review (continued)

6. $-9r^2 + 11r + 3$; quadratic trinomial

7. $b^3 + b^2 + 3$; cubic trinomial

8. $8t^2 + 3$; quadratic binomial

9. $4n^5 + n$; fifth degree binomial

10. $6x + 8$; linear binomial

11. p^3q^3; sixth degree monomial

12. $v^3 + 5$

13. $14s^4 - 4s^2 + 9s + 7$

14. $9h^3 - 3h + 3$

15. $7z^3 - 2z^2 - 16$

16. $-20k^2 + 15k$

17. $36m^3 + 8m^2 - 24m$

18. $6g^3 - 48g^2$

19. $3d^3 + 18d^2$

20. $-8n^4 - 10n^3 + 18n^2$

21. $-2q^3 + 8q^2 + 11q$

22. $4p(3p^3 + 4p^2 + 2)$

23. $3b(b^3 - 3b + 2)$

24. $9c(5c^4 - 7c^2 + 3)$

25. $4g(g + 2)$

26. $3(t^4 - 2t^3 - 3t + 4)$

27. $3h^3(10h^2 - 2h - 5)$

28. 30; if the GCF of p and q is 5, then the GCF of $6p$ and $6q$ is $6(5) = 30$.

8-1 Adding and Subtracting Polynomials

Quick Review

A **monomial** is a number, a variable, or a product of a number and one or more variables. A **polynomial** is a monomial or the sum of two or more monomials. The **degree of a polynomial** in one variable is the same as the degree of the monomial with the greatest exponent. To add two polynomials, add the like terms of the polynomials. To subtract a polynomial, add the opposite of the polynomial.

Example

What is the difference of $3x^3 - 7x^2 + 5$ and $2x^2 - 9x - 1$?

$$(3x^3 - 7x^2 + 5) - (2x^2 - 9x - 1)$$
$$= 3x^3 - 7x^2 + 5 - 2x^2 + 9x + 1$$
$$= 3x^3 + (-7x^2 - 2x^2) + 9x + (1 + 5)$$
$$= 3x^3 - 9x^2 + 9x + 6$$

Exercises

Write each polynomial in standard form. Then name each polynomial based on its degree and number of terms.

6. $4r + 3 - 9r^2 + 7r$ **7.** $3 + b^3 + b^2$

8. $3 + 8t^2$ **9.** $n^3 + 4n^5 + n - n^3$

10. $7x^2 + 8 + 6x - 7x^2$ **11.** p^3q^3

Simplify. Write each answer in standard form.

12. $(2v^3 - v + 8) + (-v^3 + v - 3)$

13. $(6s^4 + 7s^2 + 7) + (8s^4 - 11s^2 + 9s)$

14. $(4h^3 + 3h + 1) - (-5h^3 + 6h - 2)$

15. $(8z^3 - 3z^2 - 7) - (z^3 - z^2 + 9)$

8-2 Multiplying and Factoring

Quick Review

You can multiply a monomial and a polynomial using the Distributive Property. You can factor a polynomial by finding the greatest common factor (GCF) of the terms of the polynomial.

Example

What is the factored form of $10y^4 - 12y^3 + 4y^2$?

First find the GCF of the terms of the polynomial.

$$10y^4 = 2 \cdot 5 \cdot y \cdot y \cdot y \cdot y$$
$$12y^3 = 2 \cdot 2 \cdot 3 \cdot y \cdot y \cdot y$$
$$4y^2 = 2 \cdot 2 \cdot y \cdot y$$

The GCF is $2 \cdot y \cdot y$ or $2y^2$.

Then factor out the GCF.

$$10y^4 - 12y^3 + 4y^2 = 2y^2(5y^2) + 2y^2(-6y) + 2y^2(2)$$
$$= 2y^2(5y^2 - 6y + 2)$$

Exercises

Simplify each product. Write in standard form.

16. $5k(3 - 4k)$ **17.** $4m(2m + 9m^2 - 6)$

18. $6g^2(g - 8)$ **19.** $3d(6d + d^2)$

20. $-2n^2(5n - 9 + 4n^2)$ **21.** $q(11 + 8q - 2q^2)$

Find the GCF of the terms of each polynomial. Then factor the polynomial.

22. $12p^4 + 16p^3 + 8p$ **23.** $3b^4 - 9b^2 + 6b$

24. $45c^5 - 63c^3 + 27c$ **25.** $4g^2 + 8g$

26. $3t^4 - 6t^3 - 9t + 12$ **27.** $30h^5 - 6h^4 - 15h^3$

28. Reasoning The GCF of two numbers p and q is 5. Can you find the GCF of $6p$ and $6q$? Explain your answer.

8-3 and 8-4 Multiplying Binomials

Quick Review

You can use algebra tiles, tables, or the Distributive Property to multiply polynomials. The FOIL method (First, Outer, Inner, Last) can be used to multiply two binomials. You can also use rules to multiply special case binomials.

Example

What is the simplified form of $(4x + 3)(3x + 2)$?

Use FOIL to multiply the binomials. Find the product of the first terms, the outer terms, the inner terms, and the last terms. Then add.

$$(4x + 3)(3x + 2) = (4x)(3x) + (4x)(2) + (3)(3x) + (3)(2)$$
$$= 12x^2 + 8x + 9x + 6$$
$$= 12x^2 + 17x + 6$$

Exercises

Simplify each product. Write in standard form.

29. $(w + 1)(w + 12)$ **30.** $(2s - 3)(5s + 4)$

31. $(3r - 2)^2$ **32.** $(6g + 7)(g - 8)$

33. $(7q + 2)(3q + 8)$ **34.** $(4n^3 + 5)(3n + 5)$

35. $(t + 9)(t - 3)$ **36.** $(6c + 5)^2$

37. $(7h - 3)(7h + 3)$ **38.** $(y - 6)(3y + 7)$

39. $(4a - 7)(8a + 3)$ **40.** $(4b - 3)(4b + 3)$

41. Geometry A rectangle has dimensions $3x + 5$ and $x + 7$. Write an expression for the area of the rectangle as a product and as a polynomial in standard form.

8-5 and 8-6 Factoring Quadratic Trinomials

Quick Review

You can write some quadratic trinomials as the product of two binomial factors. When you factor a polynomial, be sure to factor out the GCF first.

Example

What is the factored form of $x^2 + 7x + 12$?

List the pairs of factors of 12. Identify the pair with a sum of 7.

Factors of 12	Sum of Factors
1, 12	13
2, 6	8
3, 4	7 ✔

$x^2 + 7x + 12 = (x + 3)(x + 4)$

Exercises

Factor each expression.

42. $g^2 - 5g - 14$ **43.** $2n^2 + 3n - 2$

44. $6k^2 - 10k\ell + 4\ell^2$ **45.** $p^2 + 8p + 12$

46. $r^2 + 6r - 40$ **47.** $6m^2 + 25mn + 11n^2$

48. $t^2 - 13t - 30$ **49.** $2g^2 - 35g + 17$

50. $3x^2 + 3x - 6$ **51.** $d^2 - 18d + 45$

52. $w^2 - 15w - 54$ **53.** $21z^2 - 70z + 49$

54. $-2h^2 + 4h + 70$ **55.** $x^2 + 21x + 38$

56. $10v^2 + 11v - 8$ **57.** $5g^2 + 15g + 10$

58. Reasoning Can you factor the expression $2x^2 + 15x + 9$? Explain why or why not.

29. $w^2 + 13w + 12$

30. $10s^2 - 7s - 12$

31. $9r^2 - 12r + 4$

32. $6g^2 - 41g - 56$

33. $21q^2 + 62q + 16$

34. $12n^4 + 20n^3 + 15n + 25$

35. $t^2 + 6t - 27$

36. $36c^2 + 60c + 25$

37. $49h^2 - 9$

38. $3y^2 - 11y - 42$

39. $32a^2 - 44a - 21$

40. $16b^2 - 9$

41. $(3x + 5)(x + 7)$; $3x^2 + 26x + 35$

42. $(g - 7)(g + 2)$

43. $(2n - 1)(n + 2)$

44. $2(3k - 2\ell)(k - \ell)$

45. $(p + 6)(p + 2)$

46. $(r + 10)(r - 4)$

47. $(2m + n)(3m + 11n)$

48. $(t + 2)(t - 15)$

49. $(2g - 1)(g - 17)$

50. $3(x + 2)(x - 1)$

51. $(d - 3)(d - 15)$

52. $(w + 3)(w - 18)$

53. $7(3z - 7)(z - 1)$

54. $-2(h - 7)(h + 5)$

55. $(x + 2)(x + 19)$

56. $(5v + 8)(2v - 1)$

57. $5(g + 2)(g + 1)$

58. Answers may vary. Sample: If the expression is factorable then there must be factors of 18 whose sum is $b = 15$. The factors of 18 are 1 and 18, 2 and 9, 3 and 6. None of these have a sum equal to 15, so the expression is not factorable.

Answers

Chapter Review (continued)

59. $(s - 10)^2$

60. $(4q + 7)^2$

61. $(r + 8)(r - 8)$

62. $(3z + 4)(3z - 4)$

63. $(5m + 8)^2$

64. $(7n + 2)(7n - 2)$

65. $(g + 15)(g - 15)$

66. $(3p - 7)^2$

67. $(6h - 1)^2$

68. $(w + 12)^2$

69. $8(2v + 1)(2v - 1)$

70. $(5x - 6)(5x + 6)$

71. $3n + 9$

72. It is a perfect-square trinomial.

73. $3y^2$; 1

74. $8m^2$; 3

75. $2d(d + 1)(d - 1)(3d + 2)$

76. $(b^2 + 1)(11b - 6)$

77. $(5z^2 + 1)(9z + 4)$

78. $3(a^2 + 2)(3a - 4)$

8-7 Factoring Special Cases

Quick Review

When you factor a perfect-square trinomial, the two binomial factors are the same.

$$a^2 + 2ab + b^2 = (a + b)(a + b) = (a + b)^2$$
$$a^2 - 2ab + b^2 = (a - b)(a - b) = (a - b)^2$$

When you factor a difference of squares of two terms, the two binomial factors are the sum and the difference of the two terms.

$$a^2 - b^2 = (a + b)(a - b)$$

Example

What is the factored form of $81t^2 - 90t + 25$?

First rewrite the first and last terms as squares. Then determine if the middle term equals $-2ab$.

$$81t^2 - 90t + 25 = (9t)^2 - 90t + 5^2$$
$$= (9t)^2 - 2(9t)(5) + 5^2$$
$$= (9t - 5)^2$$

Exercises

Factor each expression.

59. $s^2 - 20s + 100$

60. $16q^2 + 56q + 49$

61. $r^2 - 64$

62. $9z^2 - 16$

63. $25m^2 + 80m + 64$

64. $49n^2 - 4$

65. $g^2 - 225$

66. $9p^2 - 42p + 49$

67. $36h^2 - 12h + 1$

68. $w^2 + 24w + 144$

69. $32v^2 - 8$

70. $25x^2 - 36$

71. Geometry Find an expression for the length of a side of a square with an area of $9n^2 + 54n + 81$.

72. Reasoning Suppose you are using algebra tiles to factor a quadratic trinomial. What do you know about the factors of the trinomial when the tiles form a square?

8-8 Factoring by Grouping

Quick Review

When a polynomial has four or more terms, you may be able to group the terms and find a common binomial factor. Then you can use the Distributive Property to factor the polynomial.

Example

What is the factored form of $2r^3 - 12r^2 + 5r - 30$?

First factor out the GCF from each group of two terms. Then factor out a common binomial factor.

$$2r^3 - 12r^2 + 5r - 30 = 2r^2(r - 6) + 5(r - 6)$$
$$= (2r^2 + 5)(r - 6)$$

Exercises

Find the GCF of the first two terms and the GCF of the last two terms for each polynomial.

73. $6y^3 - 3y^2 + 2y - 1$

74. $8m^3 + 40m^2 + 6m + 15$

Factor completely.

75. $6d^4 + 4d^3 - 6d^2 - 4d$

76. $11b^3 - 6b^2 + 11b - 6$

77. $45z^3 + 20z^2 + 9z + 4$

78. $9a^3 - 12a^2 + 18a - 24$

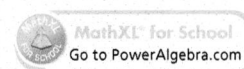

Do you know HOW?

Write each polynomial in standard form.

1. $2x - 3x^2 + 6 + 5x^3$

2. $7 + 9x + 2x^2 + 8x^5$

Simplify. Write each answer in standard form.

3. $(4x^2 + 9x + 1) + (2x^2 + 7x + 13)$

4. $(8x^2 + 5x + 7) - (5x^2 + 8x - 6)$

5. $(5x^4 + 7x + 2) - (3x^2 - 2x + 9)$

6. $(-7x^3 + 4x - 6) + (6x^3 + 10x^2 + 3)$

Simplify each product. Write in standard form.

7. $-p(8p^2 + 3p)$

8. $(r + 8)(r + 6)$

9. $(5w - 6)(2w + 7)$

10. $(4s + 5)(7s^2 - 4s + 3)$

11. $(q - 1)^2$

12. $(3g - 5)(3g + 5)$

13. Camping A rectangular campground has length $4x + 7$ and width $3x - 2$. What is the area of the campground?

Find the GCF of the terms of each polynomial.

14. $16x^6 + 22x^2 + 30x^5$

15. $7v^3 - 10v^2 + 9v^4$

Factor each expression.

16. $x^2 + 17x + 72$

17. $4v^2 - 16v + 7$

18. $n^2 - 16n + 64$

19. $6t^2 - 54$

20. $y^2 - 121$

Factor completely.

21. $7h^4 - 4h^3 + 28h^2 - 16h$

22. $15t^3 + 2t^2 - 45t - 6$

23. $6n^4 + 15n^3 - 9n^2$

24. $9v^4 + 12v^3 - 18v^2 - 24v$

25. Art The area of a square painting is $81p^2 + 90p + 25$. What is the side length of the painting?

Do you UNDERSTAND?

26. Open-Ended Write a trinomial with degree 5.

27. Writing Explain how to use the Distributive Property to multiply two binomials. Include an example.

28. Geometry What is an expression for the area of the figure? Write your answer as a polynomial in standard form.

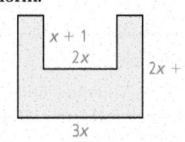

29. Open-Ended What are three different values that complete the expression $x^2 + \blacksquare x + 24$ so that you can factor it into the product of two binomials? Show each factorization.

Write the missing value in each perfect-square trinomial.

30. $n^2 + \blacksquare n + 81$

31. $16y^2 - 56y + \blacksquare$

32. $\blacksquare p^2 + 30p + 25$

33. Reasoning The expression $(x - 2)^2 - 9$ has the form $a^2 - b^2$.
  a. Identify a and b.
  b. Factor $(x - 2)^2 - 9$. Then simplify.

Answers

Chapter Test

1. $5x^3 - 3x^2 + 2x + 6$

2. $8x^5 + 2x^2 + 9x + 7$

3. $6x^2 + 16x + 14$

4. $3x^2 - 3x + 13$

5. $5x^4 - 3x^2 + 9x - 7$

6. $-x^3 + 10x^2 + 4x - 3$

7. $-8p^3 - 3p^2$

8. $r^2 + 14r + 48$

9. $10w^2 + 23w - 42$

10. $28s^3 + 19s^2 - 8s + 15$

11. $q^2 - 2q + 1$ **12.** $9g^2 - 25$

13. $12x^2 + 13x - 14$ **14.** $2x^2$

15. v^2 **16.** $(x + 9)(x + 8)$

17. $(2v - 7)(2v - 1)$ **18.** $(n - 8)^2$

19. $6(t + 3)(t - 3)$

20. $(y - 11)(y + 11)$

21. $h(7h - 4)(h^2 + 4)$

22. $(15t + 2)(t^2 - 3)$

23. $3n^2(2n - 1)(n + 3)$

24. $3v(v^2 - 2)(3v + 4)$

25. $9p + 5$

26. Answers may vary. Sample: $x^5 + 3x + 2$

27. Answers may vary. Sample:
The Distributive Property says
$a(b + c) = ab + ac$. Let $a =$ the
first binomial, and apply the property.
Example: $(x + 3)(x + 4) =$
$(x + 3)x + (x + 3)4 =$
$x^2 + 3x + 4x + 12 = x^2 + 7x + 12$

28. $4x^2 + x$

29. Answers may vary. Sample:
11, $(x + 3)(x + 8)$;
14, $(x + 2)(x + 12)$; 25, $(x + 24)(x + 1)$

30. 18   **31.** 49   **32.** 9

33. a. $a = x - 2, b = 3$

    b. $(x + 1)(x - 5)$

Item Number	Lesson
1	5-5
2	6-2
3	1-7
4	5-2
5	2-5
6	2-2
7	2-8
8	8-3
9	5-5
10	8-3
11	5-3
12	5-5
13	6-4
14	4-1
15	8-6
16	1-2
17	7-5
18	2-5
19	2-8
20	2-8
21	7-6b
22	1-6
23	3-7
24	5-6
25	5-3
26	1-6
27	1-6
28	8-3
29	1-2
30	2-9

TIPS FOR SUCCESS

Some questions on tests ask you to use polynomials to represent perimeter, area, and volume. Read the sample question at the right. Then follow the tips to answer it.

The figure below is a rectangular prism.

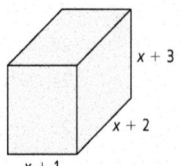

$x + 3$

$x + 2$

$x + 1$

Which expression represents the volume of the prism?

Ⓐ $x^3 + 6$

Ⓑ $x^2 + 2x + 2$

Ⓒ $x^3 + x^2 + 10x + 6$

Ⓓ $x^3 + 6x^2 + 11x + 6$

TIP 1

Make sure you look at the figure and understand it. This figure is a rectangular prism. The expressions $x + 1$, $x + 2$, and $x + 3$ represent the lengths of its edges.

TIP 2

Be sure to answer the question being asked. In this problem, you need to find the volume of the prism.

Think It Through

The volume of a rectangular prism is given by $V = \ell wh$. Substitute the edge lengths into the formula. Then simplify the product.

$V = \ell wh$
$= (x + 1)(x + 2)(x + 3)$
$= (x^2 + 3x + 2)(x + 3)$
$= x^3 + 6x^2 + 11x + 6$

The correct answer is D.

Vocabulary Builder

As you solve test items, you must understand the meanings of mathematical terms. Match each term with its mathematical meaning.

A. polynomial

B. power

C. area

D. volume

E. scale

I. an expression of the form a^n, where a is the base and n is the exponent

II. the ratio of a distance in a drawing and the actual distance

III. the number of cubic units contained in a space figure

IV. a monomial or the sum of two or more monomials

V. the number of square units contained in a planar figure

Multiple Choice

Read each question. Then write the letter of the correct answer on your paper.

1. What is $y = \frac{2}{7}x - 4$ written in standard form?

Ⓐ $2x + 7y = -28$ Ⓒ $-2x - 7y = -28$

Ⓑ $2x - 7y = 28$ Ⓓ $-2x + 7y = 28$

2. Suppose $b = 2a - 16$ and $b = a + 2$. What is the value of a?

Ⓕ 5   Ⓗ 14

Ⓖ 6   Ⓘ 18

3. Which expression is equivalent to $10x - (5x - 1)$?

Ⓐ $2x - 1$ Ⓒ $5x - 1$

Ⓑ $2x + 1$ Ⓓ $5x + 1$

Answers

Cumulative Test Prep

A. IV

B. I

C. V

D. III

E. II

1. B

2. I

3. D

4. A student's score on a history test varies directly with the number of questions the student correctly answers. A student who correctly answers 14 questions receives a score of 70. What score would a student receive for correctly answering 15 questions?

   Ⓕ 72   Ⓗ 85

   Ⓖ 75   Ⓘ 90

5. The areas of three squares are shown in the figure at the right. What is the area of the triangle?

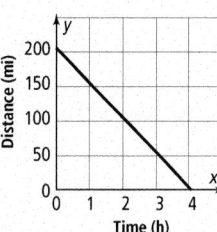

   Ⓐ 6 m^2

   Ⓑ 8 m^2

   Ⓒ 12 m^2

   Ⓓ 72 m^2

6. You bought a candlestick holder for $11.78 and several candles for $.62 each. You spent a total of $18.60. How many candles did you buy?

   Ⓕ 11   Ⓗ 25

   Ⓖ 19   Ⓘ 30

7. You are using a map to find the distance between your house and a friend's house. On the map, the distance is 2.5 in. Suppose the map's scale is $\frac{1}{8}$ in. = 1.5 mi. How far do you live from your friend?

   Ⓐ 0.08 mi   Ⓒ 3.75 mi

   Ⓑ 0.2 mi   Ⓓ 30 mi

8. Which expression represents the volume of the prism?

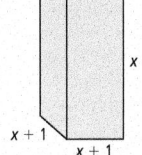

   Ⓕ $x^3 + 4$

   Ⓖ $x^3 + 6x^2 + 9x + 4$

   Ⓗ $x^3 + 9x^2 + 6x + 4$

   Ⓘ $x^3 + 4x^2 + x + 4$

9. Which equation models a line with positive slope and a positive x-intercept?

   Ⓐ $5x - 2y = 14$

   Ⓑ $-5x - 2y = 14$

   Ⓒ $-5x + 2y = 14$

   Ⓓ $5x + 2y = -14$

10. You can represent the width of a certain rectangle with the expression $x + 2$. The length of the rectangle is twice the width. What is the area of the rectangle?

   Ⓕ $2x + 4$ Ⓗ $2x^2 + 8x + 8$

   Ⓖ $2x^2 + 8$ Ⓘ $4x^2 + 16x + 16$

11. Which equation represents a line with slope that is greater than the slope of the line with equation $y = \frac{3}{4}x - 1$?

   Ⓐ $y = -\frac{3}{4}x - 2$ Ⓒ $y = \frac{2}{3}x - 1$

   Ⓑ $y = \frac{4}{3}x - 2$ Ⓓ $y = \frac{3}{4}x + 2$

12. What is the x-intercept of the line that passes through $(0, -4)$ and $(1, 4)$?

   Ⓕ -4 Ⓗ $\frac{1}{2}$

   Ⓖ $\frac{1}{4}$ Ⓘ 2

13. Megan earns $20,000 per year plus 5% commission on her sales. Laurie earns $32,000 per year plus 1% commission on her sales. Which system of equations can you use to determine the amounts that Megan and Laurie must sell s to receive equal pay p?

   Ⓐ $p = 5s + 20{,}000$ Ⓒ $p + 0.5s = 20{,}000$
       $p = s + 32{,}000$ $p + 0.1s = 32{,}000$

   Ⓑ $p + 5s = 20{,}000$ Ⓓ $p = 0.05s + 20{,}000$
       $p + s = 32{,}000$ $p = 0.01s + 32{,}000$

14. Your family is driving to the beach. The graph at the right relates your distance from the beach to the amount of time you spend driving.

What does the y-intercept of the graph represent?

   Ⓕ a stop on the way to the beach

   Ⓖ your average speed in miles per hour

   Ⓗ your distance from the beach before you started driving

   Ⓘ the amount of time it takes to get to the beach

4. G

5. A

6. F

7. D

8. G

9. A

10. H

11. B

12. H

13. D

14. H

Answers

Cumulative Test Prep (continued)

15. D

16. I

17. C

18. F

19. 12

20. 6.5

21. $\frac{1}{9}$

22. 4

23. 14

24. 5

25. 8 ft

26. 16

27. 10.5

28. [2] $2x^2 - 4x$

[1] correct expression but not written in standard form

29. [2] $15.60

[1] correct method but with computational error

30. a. $160,000

b. $44,800

[4] both answers are correct and work is shown

[3] amount of home loan, closing costs, and down payment are correct, but student forgot to add the down payment and closing costs

[2] 2 out of 3 correct: amount of home loan, closing costs, down payment

[1] 1 out of 3 correct: amount of home loan, closing costs, down payment

---

15. The area of a rectangle is $6n^2 + n - 2$. Which expression could represent the perimeter of the rectangle?

Ⓐ $2n - 1$ Ⓒ $5n + 1$
Ⓑ $3n + 2$ Ⓓ $10n + 2$

16. A company sells calculators for $35 each. Businesses must order a minimum of 100 calculators, and they must pay a shipping cost of $50. Which amount of money represents a reasonable sum that a business might spend to purchase calculators?

Ⓕ $750 Ⓗ $2990
Ⓖ $1070 Ⓘ $3585

17. Which expression is equivalent to $\frac{3x^3y}{(3y)^{-2}}$?

Ⓐ $9x^3y^3$ Ⓒ $27x^3y^3$
Ⓑ $\frac{x^3}{y}$ Ⓓ $\frac{x^3y^3}{3}$

18. The formula for the volume V of a pyramid is $V = \frac{1}{3}Bh$, where B is the area of the base of the pyramid and h is the height of the pyramid. Which equation represents the height of the pyramid in terms of V and B?

Ⓕ $h = \frac{3V}{B}$ Ⓗ $h = 3VB$
Ⓖ $h = \frac{V}{3B}$ Ⓘ $h = \frac{B}{3V}$

GRIDDED RESPONSE

19. An artist is making a scale model of a ladybug for an insect museum. What is the length in millimeters of the actual ladybug that the artist is using to make this model?

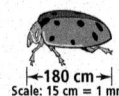
←180 cm→
Scale: 15 cm = 1 mm

20. A flagpole casts a shadow that is 9.1 m long. At the same time, a meter stick casts a shadow that is 1.4 m long. How tall is the flagpole in meters?

21. What is the seventh term in the following sequence?

81, 27, 9, 3, 1, . . .

22. Suppose you have $200. Sweaters cost $45 each. What is the greatest number of sweaters you can buy?

23. How many whole-number solutions does the inequality $|x - 5| \le 8$ have?

24. Line m passes through $(-9, 4)$ and $(9, 6)$. What is the y-intercept of line m?

25. You made a graph to model the height of a tree each year since you planted it.

Suppose the tree had been 5 ft tall when you planted it. How tall would the tree be in 6 yr? Assume its growth rate did not change.

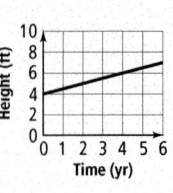

26. A laundromat charges $2.25 to wash one load of clothes and $1.75 to dry one load. The machines accept only quarters. To wash and dry one load of clothes, how many quarters would you need?

27. Suppose that $xy = 0$ and $y = 3\frac{1}{2}$. What is the value of $x + 3y$?

Short Response

28. The formula for the area A of a trapezoid is $A = \frac{1}{2}h(b_1 + b_2)$, where h is the height of the trapezoid and b_1 and b_2 are the lengths of its two bases.

Suppose the height of a trapezoid is $x - 2$. The lengths of the bases are $x + 2$ and $3x - 2$. What polynomial in standard form represents the area of the trapezoid? Show your work.

29. A monthly subway pass costs $60. A one-ride ticket costs $1.80. You plan to ride the subway to school and back for 21 days this month. How much more money would you spend to buy one-way tickets than to buy a monthly pass? Show your work.

Extended Response

30. Jeremy purchases a home for $200,000. He pays a down payment equal to 20% of the purchase price. He gets a home loan for the remainder of the purchase price.

a. What is the amount of Jeremy's home loan?

b. In addition, Jeremy pays closing costs that equal 3% of the amount of the home loan. How much does Jeremy pay altogether for the down payment and the closing costs?

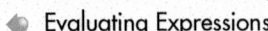

Get Ready!

sson 1-2 ◆ **Evaluating Expressions**

Evaluate each expression for $a = -1$, $b = 3$, and $c = -2$.

1. $2a - b^2 + c$

2. $\dfrac{c^2 - ab}{2a}$

3. $bc - 3a^2$

4. $\dfrac{b^2 - 4ac}{2a}$

5. $5a + 2b(c - 1)$

6. $c^2 + 2ab - 1$

sson 4-4 ◆ **Graphing Functions**

Graph each function.

7. $y = x$

8. $y = -x^2$

9. $y = |x|$

10. $y = 2x - 5$

11. $y = 2|x|$

12. $y = -4x + 3$

sson 4-6 ◆ **Evaluating Function Rules**

Evaluate each function rule for $x = -6$.

13. $f(x) = -3x^2$

14. $h(x) = x^2 + 6x$

15. $g(x) = (x - 1)^2$

16. $f(x) = (1 + x)^2$

17. $g(x) = \frac{2}{3}x^2$

18. $h(x) = (2x)^2$

ssons 8-5
d 8-6 ◆ **Factoring**

Factor each expression.

19. $4x^2 + 4x + 1$

20. $5x^2 + 32x - 21$

21. $8x^2 - 10x + 3$

22. $x^2 - 18x + 81$

23. $12y^2 + 8y - 15$

24. $m^2 - 7m - 18$

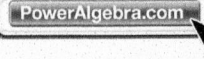

Looking Ahead Vocabulary

25. Use your knowledge of the definition of a quadratic polynomial to make a conjecture about the definition of a *quadratic function*.

26. The graph of a quadratic function is a U-shaped curve that has an *axis of symmetry*. What do you think this means?

27. The following is an example of the *Zero-Product Property*.
$(x + 3)(x - 4) = 0$, so $x + 3 = 0$ or $x - 4 = 0$.
What do you think this means?

Get Ready!

Assign this diagnostic assessment to determine if students have the prerequisite skills for Chapter 9.

Lesson	Skill
1-2	Evaluating Expressions
4-4	Graphing Functions
4-6	Evaluating Function Rules
8-5 and 8-6	Factoring

To remediate students, select from these resources (available for every lesson).
- Online Problems (PowerAlgebra.com)
- Reteaching (All-in-One Teaching Resources)
- Practice (All-in-One Teaching Resources)

Why Students Need These Skills

EVALUATING EXPRESSIONS
Students will find the value of the discriminant of a quadratic function.

GRAPHING FUNCTIONS
Students will graph quadratic functions.

EVALUATING FUNCTION RULES
Students will find the coordinate of the vertex and axis of symmetry of a quadratic function.

FACTORING
Students will solve quadratic functions by factoring.

Looking Ahead Vocabulary

QUADRATIC FUNCTION Ask students to identify what conditions make a quadratic polynomial quadratic.

AXIS OF SYMMETRY Have students draw the line(s) of symmetry of several geometric figures.

ZERO-PRODUCT PROPERTY Have students solve the equations in 27A and 27B to verify their answer.

Answers

Get Ready!

1. -13 **2.** -3.5 **3.** -9

4. -0.5 **5.** -23 **6.** -3

7–12. See back of book.

13. -108 **14.** 0 **15.** 49

16. 25 **17.** 24 **18.** 144

19. $(2x + 1)^2$ **20.** $(5x - 3)(x + 7)$

21. $(4x - 3)(2x - 1)$ **22.** $(x - 9)^2$

23. $(6y - 5)(2y + 3)$

24. $(m - 9)(m + 2)$

25. A quadratic function is of the form $f(x) = ax^2 + bx + c$, where $a \neq 0$.

26. Answers will vary. Sample: You can fold the graph along the axis of symmetry and the two halves of the graph will match.

27. Answers will vary. Sample: the product of two factors can only be zero if at least one of the factors is zero.

Chapter 9 Overview

UbD Understanding by Design

In Chapter 9 students solve quadratic equations using a variety of methods. In this chapter, students will develop the answers to the Essential Questions posed on the opposite page as they learn the concepts and skills bulleted below.

BIG idea Function

ESSENTIAL QUESTION What are the characteristics of quadratic functions?

- Students will graph quadratic functions on the coordinate plane.
- Students will use the discriminant of a quadratic equation to analyze the number of times a function crosses the *x*-axis.

BIG idea Solving Equations and Inequalities

ESSENTIAL QUESTION How can you solve a quadratic equation?

- Students will solve quadratic equations by graphing.
- Students will solve quadratic equations by factoring.
- Students will solve quadratic equations by completing the square.
- Students will solve quadratic equations by using the quadratic formula.

BIG idea Modeling

ESSENTIAL QUESTION How can you use functions to model real-world situations?

- Students will use quadratic functions that represent real-world situations.
- Students will decide if linear, quadratic, or exponential functions appropriately model a set of data.

CHAPTER 9

Quadratic Functions and Equations

PowerAlgebra.com

Your place to get all things digital

VIDEO Download videos connecting math to your world.

VOCABULARY Math definitions in English and Spanish

SOLVE IT! The online Solve It will get you in gear for each lesson.

DYNAMIC ACTIVITIES Interactive! Vary numbers, graphs, and figures to explore math concepts.

ONLINE PROBLEMS Download Step-by-Step Problems with Instant Replay.

ONLINE HOMEWORK Get and view your assignments online.

MathXL FOR SCHOOL Extra practice and review online

This photo makes it look easy, but it takes quite a bit of practice to get good at basketball! How hard you throw the ball can mean the difference between making a basket and missing it. The player might not think about it, but there's an equation that relates the height of a ball or other object over time and the speed it's thrown. You'll use this model and other quadratic equations in this chapter.

Vocabulary

English/Spanish Vocabulary Audio Online:

English	Spanish
axis of symmetry, p. 534	eje de simetría
completing the square, p. 561	completar el cuadrado
discriminant, p. 570	discriminante
maximum, p. 535	valor máximo
minimum, p. 535	valor mínimo
parabola, p. 534	parábola
quadratic equation, p. 548	ecuación cuadrática
quadratic formula, p. 567	fórmula cuadrática
quadratic function, p. 534	función cuadrática
root of an equation, p. 548	raíz de una ecuación
vertex, p. 535	vértice

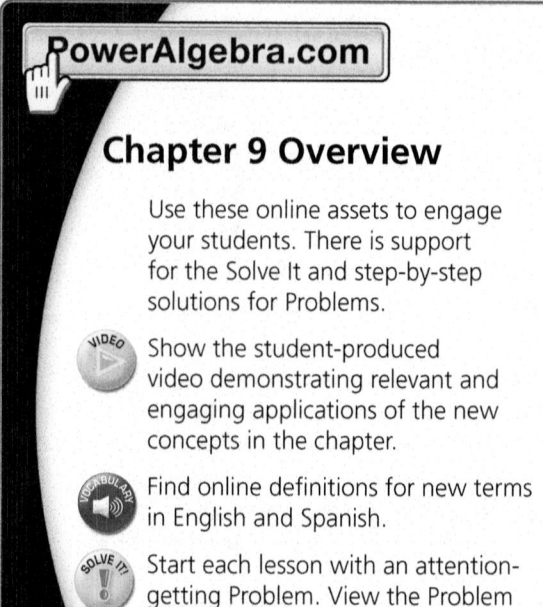

PowerAlgebra.com

Chapter 9 Overview

Use these online assets to engage your students. There is support for the Solve It and step-by-step solutions for Problems.

VIDEO Show the student-produced video demonstrating relevant and engaging applications of the new concepts in the chapter.

VOCABULARY Find online definitions for new terms in English and Spanish.

SOLVE IT! Start each lesson with an attention-getting Problem. View the Problem online with helpful hints.

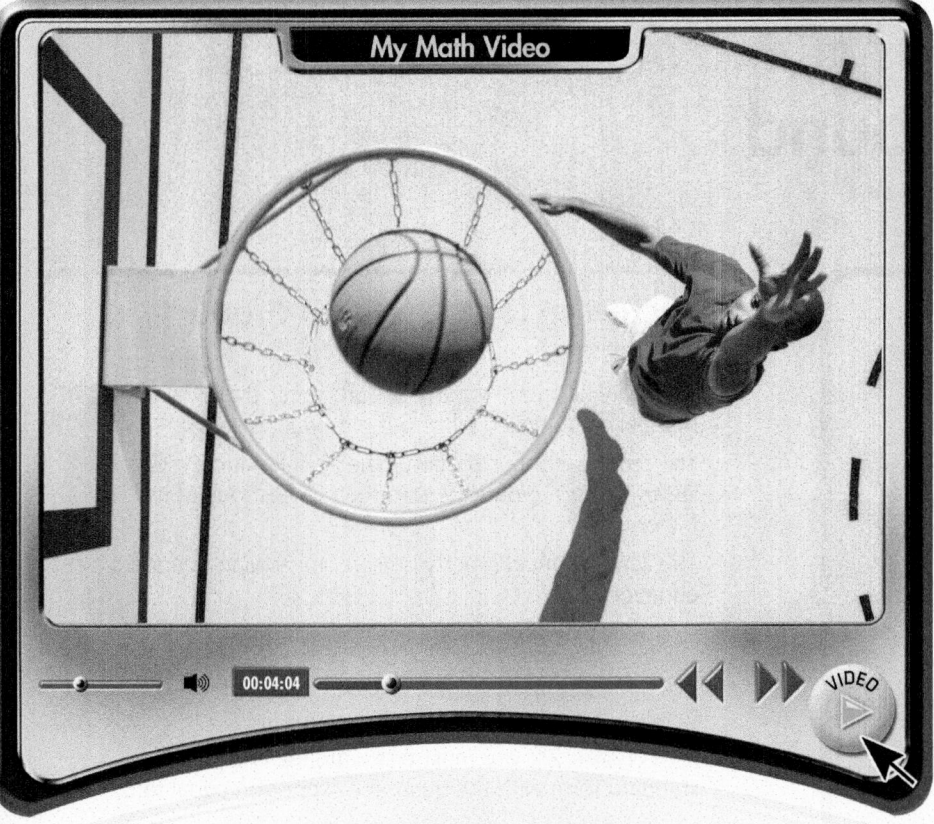

My Math Video

FACILITATE Use this photo to discuss the shape of a path of a thrown object. A basketball follows an arc that can be modeled using a quadratic equation. In this chapter, students will learn how to graph quadratic equations and find maximum or minimum values of the equation.

Q What factors play a role in making a basket in basketball? **[Answers may vary. Sample: The player must know exactly where and when to release the ball and at what angle it should be thrown.]**

Q How would you describe the path of the basketball as it leaves the player's hands and heads toward the basket? **[The ball's path is an arc.]**

Q At approximately what point is the ball at its maximum height? **[The ball reaches a maximum height about halfway between the player and the basket.]**

Q A quadratic equation has a graph that is shaped like a U. The point at which the graph turns is called the vertex. What would the vertex represent if we were to model the path of the ball with a quadratic equation? **[the point at which the ball is at its maximum height]**

EXTENSION

Students can do an experiment to find the equation for the path of a ball thrown toward a basket. They can model the situation using a ball and a trash can as a basket. Students will find a value for c in the equation $h(t) = -4.9t^2 + 3t + c$. Have students measure the height at which they begin their throw and substitute this value for c. Then, students can use a graphing calculator or software to see the graph of their equation. Ask students to identify the beginning point of the ball, the maximum height it reaches, and the time it takes to get to the basket.

BIG ideas

1 **Function**
Essential Question What are the characteristics of quadratic functions?

2 **Solving Equations and Inequalities**
Essential Question How can you solve a quadratic equation?

3 **Modeling**
Essential Question How can you use functions to model real-world situations?

Chapter Preview

PowerAlgebra.com   Chapter 9   Quadratic Functions and Equations   **533**

 Increase students' depth of knowledge with interactive online activities.

 Show Problems from each lesson solved step by step. Instant replay allows students to go at their own pace when studying online.

 Assign homework to individual students or to an entire class.

 Prepare students for the Mid-Chapter Quiz and Chapter Test with online practice and review.

Math Background

UbD

Function

BIG idea A function is a relationship between variables in which each value of the input variable is associated with a unique value of the output variable. Functions can be represented in a variety of ways, such as graphs, tables, equations, or words. Each representation is particularly useful in certain situations. Some important families of functions are developed through transformations of the simplest form of the function.

ESSENTIAL UNDERSTANDINGS

9-1 The family of quadratic functions models certain situations where the rate of change is not constant. These functions are graphed by a symmetric curve with a highest or lowest point corresponding to a maximum or minimum value.

9-2 In the quadratic function $y = ax^2 + bx + c$, the value of b translates the position of the axis of symmetry.

Solving Equations and Inequalities

BIG idea Solving an equation is the process of rewriting the equation to make what it says about its variable(s) as simple as possible. Properties of numbers and equality can be used to transform an equation (or inequality) into equivalent, simpler equations (or inequalities) in order to find solutions. Useful information about equations and inequalities (including solutions) can be found by analyzing graphs or tables. The numbers and types of solutions vary predictably, based on the type of equation.

ESSENTIAL UNDERSTANDINGS

9-3 to 9-6 Quadratic equations can be solved by a variety of methods, including graphing and finding the square root, using the Zero–Product Property, writing the equation in the form $m^2 = n$, or using the Quadratic Formula.

9-8 Systems of linear and quadratic equations can be solved graphically and algebraically. This type of system can have two solutions, one solution, or no solutions.

Modeling

BIG idea Many real-world mathematical problems can be represented algebraically. These representations can lead to algebraic solutions. A function that models a real-world situation can then be used to make estimates or predictions about future occurrences.

ESSENTIAL UNDERSTANDING

9-7 Linear, quadratic, or exponential functions can be used to model various sets of data.

Factoring (and the Zero-Product Property)

The Multiplication Property of Zero states that when a real number is multiplied by zero the product is zero.

The converse of this property, the Zero-Product Property, states that if a product is zero then at least one of its factors is zero.

The Zero-Product Property is useful for solving quadratic equations.

$$ax^2 + bx + c = 0 \qquad \text{standard form of quadratic equation}$$

When using the Zero-Product Property to solve $x^2 + 10x = 24$, you must first write the equation in standard form with the quadratic expression equal to 0.

$$x^2 + 10x - 24 = 0$$
$$(x + 12)(x - 2) = 0 \qquad \text{Factor the trinomial.}$$

Set each factor equal to zero and solve for x.

$$(x + 12) = 0 \qquad (x - 2) = 0$$
$$x = -12 \qquad\quad x = 2$$

The solutions of the quadratic equation are -12 and 2.

Common Errors With Factoring

When factoring quadratic expressions, students might not figure the factors correctly.

For the expression $x^2 + 10x - 24$, students might choose 6 and 4 as factors of -24. These two numbers have a sum of 10, but they do not have a product of -24.

$$(x + 6)(x + 4) = x^2 + 10x + 24$$

Or students might choose 8 and -3 as factors of -24. These two numbers have a product of -24, but they do not have a sum of 10.

$$(x + 8)(x - 3) = x^2 + 5x - 24$$

Completing the Square

A perfect square is the product of a number or expression multiplied by itself.

16 is the square of 4.

x^2 is the square of x.

$x^2 + 6x + 9$ is the square of $x + 3$.

The quadratic expression $x^2 + 6x + 9$ is called a perfect square trinomial because it is the product of two identical binomials, $(x + 3)(x + 3)$.

The process of creating a perfect square trinomial is called *completing the square*. Completing the square can be used to solve any quadratic equation.

You can change an expression $x^2 + bx$ into a perfect square trinomial by adding $\left(\frac{b}{2}\right)^2$ to $x^2 + bx$.

$$x^2 + bx + \left(\frac{b}{2}\right)^2$$

Equations that can be solved by factoring can also be solved by completing the square.

Given the equation $x^2 + 10x = 24$, for example, $b = 10$.

$$x^2 + 10x + \left(\frac{10}{2}\right)^2 = 24 + \left(\frac{10}{2}\right)^2$$
$$x^2 + 10x + 25 = 24 + 25$$
$$(x + 5)^2 = 49$$
$$\sqrt{(x + 5)^2} = \sqrt{49}$$
$$(x + 5) = \pm 7$$
$$x + 5 = 7 \text{ or } x + 5 = -7$$
$$x = 2 \text{ or } x = -12$$

Common Errors With Completing the Square

When completing the square to solve a quadratic equation, students might forget to add the value that completes the square to both sides.

To complete the square on the right side of $x^2 + 10x = 24$, students must remember to add 25 to both sides to get the perfect square trinomial.

$$x^2 + 10 + 25 = 24 + 25$$

The Quadratic Formula

Not all quadratic equations can be solved by factoring. Completing the square is always available, but that method sometimes leads to messy computations.

In these cases the Quadratic Formula is useful.

The Quadratic Formula: $x = \dfrac{-b \pm \sqrt{b^2 - 4ac}}{2a}$

For $3x^2 + 7x - 22 = 0$, the numbers 3, 7, and -22 are substituted into the formula for a, b, and c to yield $\dfrac{-7 \pm \sqrt{7^2 - 4(3)(-22)}}{2(3)}$, which can be simplified to give solutions of $\dfrac{-7 + \sqrt{313}}{6} \approx 1.78$ and $\dfrac{-7 - \sqrt{313}}{6} \approx -4.12$.

The Quadratic Formula works for any quadratic equation. Here is the solution, using the Quadratic Formula, of the equation previously solved by factoring:

$$x^2 + 10x - 24 = 0$$
$$x = \frac{-10 \pm \sqrt{10^2 - 4(1)(-24)}}{2(1)} = \frac{-10 \pm \sqrt{196}}{2} = \frac{-10 \pm 14}{2}$$
$$\frac{-10 + 14}{2} = \frac{4}{2} = 2$$
$$\frac{-10 - 14}{2} = \frac{-24}{2} = -12$$

These are the same two solutions as above.

Common Errors With the Quadratic Formula

Students may forget or confuse parts of the Quadratic Formula. For example, they may compute using b in place of $-b$ or divide by a instead of $2a$. They may also make a mistake when subtracting $4ac$ as part of the radical if either a or c is negative. To counter these tendencies, students should write out the formula with the substituted values, checking each sign, and simplify step by step without attempting to do any two steps at once.

CHAPTER 9

QUADRATIC FUNCTIONS AND EQUATIONS
Pacing and Assignment Guide

Lesson	Teaching Day(s)	**TRADITIONAL** Basic	Average	Advanced	**BLOCK** Block
9-1	1	Problems 1-2 Exs. 7–15 all, 52–65	Problems 1-2 Exs. 7–15 odd, 52–65	Problems 1-2 Exs. 7–15 odd, 52–65	**Day 1** Problems 1-5 Exs. 7–27 odd, 28–48, 52–65
	2	Problems 3-5 Exs. 16–28 all, 30–32 even, 33, 34–40 even, 48	Problems 3-5 Exs. 17–27 odd, 28–40	Problems 3-5 Exs. 17–27 odd, 28–42	
9-2	1	Problems 1-2 Exs. 7–27 all, 28–34 even, 35, 39, 43–54	Problems 1-2 Exs. 7–27 odd, 28–40, 43–54	Problems 1-2 Exs. 7–27 odd, 28–54	**Day 2** Problems 1-2 Exs. 7–27 odd, 28–40, 43–54
9-3	1	Problems 1-2 Exs. 8–31 all, 58–74	Problems 1-3 Exs. 9–35 odd, 37–55, 58–74	Problems 1-3 Exs. 9–35 odd, 37–74	Problems 1-3 Exs. 9–35 odd, 37–55, 58–74
	2	Problem 3 Exs. 32–36 all, 38–48 even, 51			
9-4	1	Problems 1-4 Exs. 8–28 all, 30–40 even, 46–59	Problems 1-4 Exs. 9–27 odd, 29–41, 46–59	Problems 1-4 Exs. 9–27 odd, 29–59	**Day 3** Problems 1-4 Exs. 9–27 odd, 29–41, 46–59
9-5	1	Problems 1-3 Exs. 7–24 all, 50–66	Problems 1-3 Exs. 7–23 odd, 50–66	Problems 1-3 Exs. 7–23 odd, 50–66	Problems 1-3 Exs. 7–23 odd, 50–66
	2	Problem 4 Exs. 25–33 all, 34–42 even, 43–44	Problem 4 Exs. 25–31 odd, 32–47	Problem 4 Exs. 25–31 odd, 32–49	**Day 4** Problem 4 Exs. 25–31 odd, 32–47
9-6	1	Problems 1-2 Exs. 7–22 all, 50–61	Problems 1-2 Exs. 7–21 odd, 50–61	Problems 1-2 Exs. 7–21 odd, 50–61	Problems 1-2 Exs. 7–21 odd, 50–61
	2	Problems 3-4 Exs. 23–34 all, 36–40 even, 41–44 all	Problems 3-4 Exs. 23–33 odd, 35–45	Problems 3-4 Exs. 23–33 odd, 35–49	**Day 5** Problems 3-4 Exs. 23–33 odd, 35–45
9-7	1	Problems 1-2 Exs. 6–14, 20	Problems 1-2 Exs. 7–13 odd, 20–21	Problems 1-2 Exs. 7–13 odd, 20–21	Problems 1-2 Exs. 7–13 odd, 20–21
	2	Problems 3-4 Exs. 15–19, 22–24, 28–37	Problems 3-4 Exs. 15–19 odd, 22–25, 28–37	Problems 3-4 Exs. 15–19 odd, 22–37	**Day 6** Problems 3-4 Exs. 15–19 odd, 22–25, 28–37
9-8	1	Problems 1-2 Exs. 8–17	Problems 1-4 Exs. 9–29 odd, 30–34, 37–50	Problems 1-4 Exs. 9–29 odd, 30–50	Problems 1-4 Exs. 9–29 odd, 30–34, 37–50
	2	Problems 3-4 Exs. 18–29, 31–33, 37–50			
Review	1	Chapter 9 Review	Chapter 9 Review	Chapter 9 Review	**Day 7** Chapter 9 Review
Assess	1	Chapter 9 Test	Chapter 9 Test	Chapter 9 Test	Chapter 9 Test
Total		**16 Days**	**14 Days**	**14 Days**	**7 Days**

Note: Pacing does not include Concept Bytes and other feature pages.

Resources

	For the Chapter	9-1	9-2	9-3	9-4	9-5	9-6	9-7
Planning								
Teacher Center Online Planner & Grade Book	I	I	I	I	I	I	I	I
Interactive Learning & Guided Instruction								
My Math Video	I							
Solve It!		I TM	I TM	I TM	I TM	I TM	I TM	I TM
Student Companion (SP)*		P M	P M	P M	P M	P M	P M	
Vocabulary Support		I P M	I P M	I P M	I P M	I P M	I P M	I P M
Got It? Support		I P	I P	I P	I P	I P	I P	I P
Dynamic Activity			I			I		
Online Problems		I	I	I	I	I	I	I
Additional Problems		M	M	M	M	M	M	M
English Language Learner Support (TR)		E P M	E P M	E P M	E P M	E P M	E P M	E P M
Activities, Games, and Puzzles		E M	E M	E M	E M	E M	E M	E M
Teaching With TI Technology With CD-ROM				✓ P				✓ P
TI-Nspire™ Support CD-ROM		✓	✓	✓	✓	✓	✓	✓
Lesson Check & Practice								
Student Companion (SP)*		P M	P M	P M	P M	P M	P M	P M
Lesson Check Support		I P	I P	I P	I P	I P	I P	I P
Practice and Problem Solving Workbook (SP)		P	P	P	P	P	P	P
Think About a Plan (TR)*		E P M	E P M	E P M	E P M	E P M	E P M	E P M
Practice Form G (TR)*		E P M	E P M	E P M	E P M	E P M	E P M	E P M
Standardized Test Prep (TR)*		P M	P M	P M	P M	P M	P M	P M
Practice Form K (TR)*		E P M	E P M	E P M	E P M	E P M	E P M	E P M
Extra Practice	E M							
Find the Errors!	M							
Enrichment (TR)		E P M	E P M	E P M	E P M	E P M	E P M	E P M
Answers and Solutions CD-ROM	✓	✓	✓	✓	✓	✓	✓	✓
Assess & Remediate								
ExamView CD-ROM	✓	✓	✓	✓	✓	✓	✓	✓
Lesson Quiz		I TM	I TM	I TM	I TM	I TM	I TM	I TM
Quizzes and Tests Form G (TR)*	E P M				E P M			E P M
Quizzes and Tests Form K (TR)*	E P M				E P M			E P M
Reteaching (TR)*		E P M	E P M	E P M	E P M	E P M	E P M	E P M
Performance Tasks (TR)*	P M							
Cumulative Review (TR)*	P M							
Progress Monitoring Assessments	I P M							

(TR) Available in All-In-One Teaching Resources   * Spanish available

1 Interactive Learning

Solve It!

PURPOSE To evaluate a quadratic function that represents a real-world situation

PROCESS Students may write an algebraic equation to represent the situation and may use trial and error or create a table of values to solve the equation.

FACILITATE

Q Does the speed of a falling object remain constant as it falls to the ground? Explain. **[No, the speed of the object increases as the object gets closer to the ground.]**

Q What is the height of the flowerpot at zero seconds? Explain. **[64 feet; the flowerpot is still on the railing.]**

Q What is the height of the flowerpot at 0.5 seconds? Explain. **[60 ft; $-16 \cdot (0.5)^2 + 64 = 60$]**

Q What will be the value of $h(t)$ when the flowerpot hits the ground? **[zero]**

ANSWER See Solve It in Answers on next page.

CONNECT THE MATH In the Solve It, students study the equation $y = -16 \cdot t^2 + 64$. In the lesson, students learn that quadratic equations are not linear.

2 Guided Instruction

Take Note

Compare and contrast the standard form of a quadratic equation with the slope-intercept form of a linear equation. The coefficient of x in a quadratic equation does not represent slope, but the constant term represents the y-intercept.

 **9-1** Quadratic Graphs and Their Properties

Objective To graph quadratic functions of the form $y = ax^2$ and $y = ax^2 + c$

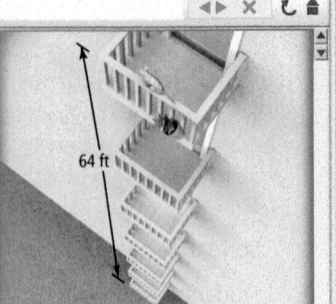

Getting Ready! ◄► ✕ ⟲ ⌂

As a cat walks along the railing of a balcony, it knocks a flowerpot off the railing. The function $h(t) = -16t^2 + c$ gives the height h of the flowerpot after t seconds when it falls from a height of c feet. How long will it take the flowerpot to reach the ground? Explain your reasoning.

A certain type of function models the motion of a falling object.

64 ft

Lesson Vocabulary
- quadratic function
- standard form of a quadratic function
- quadratic parent function
- parabola
- axis of symmetry
- vertex
- minimum
- maximum

Recall from Chapter 8 that a polynomial of degree 2, such as $-16x^2 + 64$, is called a quadratic polynomial. You can use a quadratic polynomial to define a *quadratic function* like the one in the Solve It.

Essential Understanding A quadratic function is a type of nonlinear function that models certain situations where the rate of change is not constant. The graph of a quadratic function is a symmetric curve with a highest or lowest point corresponding to a maximum or minimum value.

 take note

Key Concept   Standard Form of a Quadratic Function

A **quadratic function** is a function that can be written in the form $y = ax^2 + bx + c$, where $a \neq 0$. This form is called the **standard form of a quadratic function.**

Examples $y = 3x^2$ $y = x^2 + 9$ $y = x^2 - x - 2$

The simplest quadratic function $f(x) = x^2$ or $y = x^2$ is the **quadratic parent function.**

The graph of a quadratic function is a U-shaped curve called a **parabola.** The parabola with equation $y = x^2$ is shown at the right.

You can fold a parabola so that the two sides match exactly. This property is called *symmetry*. The fold or line that divides the parabola into two matching halves is called the **axis of symmetry.**

BIG idea Function   **UbD**

ESSENTIAL UNDERSTANDINGS
- The family of quadratic functions models certain situations where the rate of change is not constant.
- Quadratic functions are graphed by a symmetric curve with a highest or lowest point corresponding to a maximum or minimum value.

Math Background

In the study of plane geometry, a parabola is defined as the set of points in the plane that are equidistant from a point (the focus) and a line (the directrix). In the study of solid geometry, a parabola is defined as the intersection of a right circular cone with a plane parallel to a line on the surface of the cone. In the study of algebra, a parabola is defined as the graph of a quadratic function.

From visual inspection, you will be able to determine several characteristics of the graph of

the parabola when it is given in the form $y = ax^2 + bx + c$.

When a is positive the graph opens upward and has a minimum vertex. When a is negative the graph opens downward and has a maximum vertex.

When $|a|$ is less than 1, the parabola opens wide. The smaller $|a|$ is, the wider the parabola. When $|a|$ is greater than 1, the parabola is narrow. The greater $|a|$ is, the more narrow the parabola.

The value of c indicates a shift up or down from the x-axis.

Support Student Learning

Use the **Algebra 1 Companion** to engage and support students during instructions. See Lesson Resources at the end of this lesson for details.

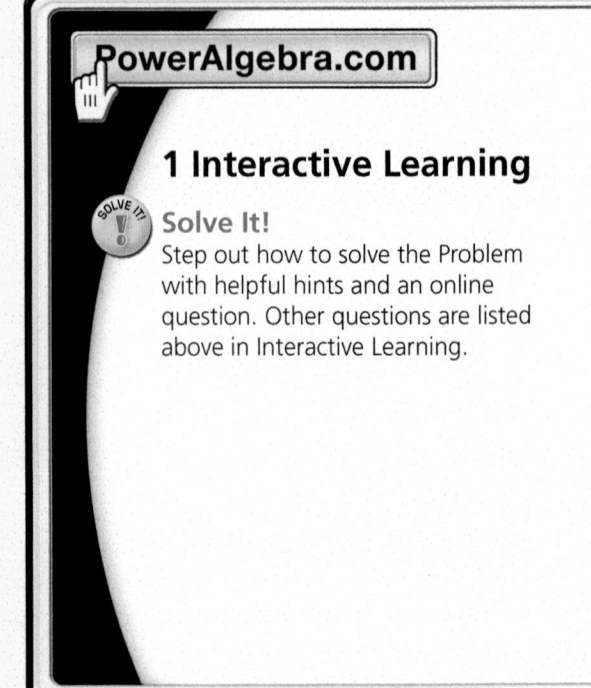

PowerAlgebra.com

1 Interactive Learning

Solve It!
Step out how to solve the Problem with helpful hints and an online question. Other questions are listed above in Interactive Learning.

The highest or lowest point of a parabola is its **vertex**, which is on the axis of symmetry.

If $a > 0$ in $y = ax^2 + bx + c$, the parabola opens upward.
$\downarrow$
The vertex is the **minimum** point, or lowest point, of the parabola.

If $a < 0$ in $y = ax^2 + bx + c$, the parabola opens downward.
$\downarrow$
The vertex is the **maximum** point, or highest point, of the parabola.

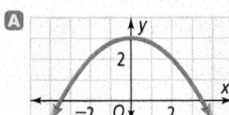

Problem 1 Identifying a Vertex

What are the coordinates of the vertex of each graph? Is it a minimum or a maximum?

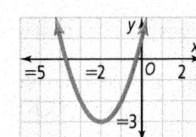

The vertex is $(0, 3)$. It is a maximum.

The vertex is $(1, -1)$. It is a minimum.

 Got It? 1. What is the vertex of the graph at the right? Is it a minimum or a maximum?

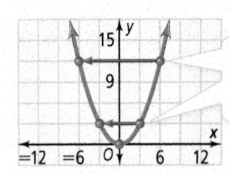

You can use the fact that a parabola is symmetric to graph it quickly. First, find the coordinates of the vertex and several points on one side of the vertex. Then reflect the points across the axis of symmetry. For graphs of functions of the form $y = ax^2$, the vertex is at the origin. The axis of symmetry is the y-axis, or $x = 0$.

Problem 2 Graphing $y = ax^2$

Graph the function $y = \frac{1}{3}x^2$. Make a table of values. What are the domain and range?

x	$y = \frac{1}{3}x^2$		(x, y)
0	$\frac{1}{3}(0)^2$	0	$(0, 0)$
3	$\frac{1}{3}(3)^2$	3	$(3, 3)$
6	$\frac{1}{3}(6)^2$	12	$(6, 12)$

Reflect the points from the table over the axis of symmetry, $x = 0$, to find more points on the graph.

The domain is all real numbers. The range is $y \geq 0$.

 Got It? 2. Graph the function $y = -3x^2$. What are the domain and range?

Think

Can a parabola have both a minimum and a maximum point?
No. A parabola either opens upward and has a minimum point or opens downward and has a maximum point.

Plan

What are good values to choose for x when making the table?
Choose values of x that make x^2 divisible by 3 so that the y-values will be integers.

Problem 1

Q Which direction does the parabola in 1A open? **[downward]**

Q What is the highest point of the parabola? **[(0, 3)]**

Q Is this vertex a maximum or a minimum? **[maximum]**

Q What is the vertex of the parabola in 1B? **[(1, −1)]**

Q Is it a maximum or a minimum? **[minimum]**

Got It?   SYNTHESIZING

Q How do you determine if a vertex is a maximum or minimum? **[A vertex is a maximum if the parabola opens downward. A vertex is a minimum if the parabola opens upward.]**

Q Does the graph of a linear function have either a minimum or maximum value? Explain. **[No, because a line does not have a vertex.]**

Problem 2

Q Does the graph of $y = \frac{1}{3}x^2$ open downward or upward? Explain. **[Upward; a is a positive number.]**

Q Do you get the same y value when $x = 3$ as when $x = -3$? Explain. **[Yes, because $(-3)^2 = 9$ and $(3)^2 = 9$.]**

Q Is the graph of $y = \frac{1}{3}x^2$ wider or more narrow than the graph of $y = x^2$? **[wider]**

Got It?

Ask students to summarize the domain and range for a quadratic function of the form $y = ax^2$. Make sure that students realize that the sign of a, but not the magnitude of a, affects the range.

---

2 Guided Instruction

 Each Problem is worked out and supported online.

Problem 1
Identifying a Vertex

Problem 2
Graphing $y = ax^2$
Animated

Problem 3
Comparing Widths of Parabolas

Problem 4
Graphing $y = ax^2 + c$
Animated

Problem 5
Using the Falling Object Model
Animated

Support in Algebra 1 Companion
• Vocabulary
• Key Concepts
• Got It?

Answers

Solve It!
2 s; explanations may vary.

Got It?
1. $(-2, -3)$; minimum

2.

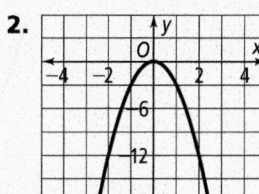

domain: all real numbers, range: $y \leq 0$

Problem 3

Q How can your knowledge of slope help you remember how the value of *a* affects the width of a parabola? **[Answers may vary. Sample: When the absolute values of *m* and *a* are greater, a line is steep and the sides of a parabola, respectively, are "steep", which makes the parabola skinny. When the absolute values of *m* and *a* are less, a line is not very steep and the sides of a parabola are not very "steep", respectively, which makes a parabola wider.]**

Got It?   ERROR PREVENTION

If students give the order of the graphs of $f(x) = -x^2$, $f(x) = -\frac{1}{3}x^2$, $f(x) = 3x^2$ from widest to narrowest, then remind them that it is the absolute value of *a* that determines the width of a parabola.

Problem 4

Q How is the graph of $y = x + 3$ different from the graph of $y = x$? How are they the same? **[The first line is shifted up 3 from the graph of the second line. They are both lines with a slope of 1.]**

Q How is the graph of $y = 2x^2 + 3$ the same as the graph of $y = 2x^2$? How are they different? **[They are both parabolas, have the same axis of symmetry, and have the same width. The first graph is shifted up three units from the graph of the second.]**

Got It?   VISUAL LEARNERS

Have students transform each point on the graph of $y = x^2$ to a new point on the graph of $y = x^2 - 3$ by translating each point down 3 units.

Think

Does the sign of the x^2-term affect the parabola's width?
No. The sign of the x^2-term affects only whether the parabola opens upward or downward.

Plan

What values should you choose for x?
Use the same values of *x* for graphing both functions so that you can see the relationship between corresponding *y*-coordinates.

The coefficient of the x^2-term in a quadratic function affects the width of a parabola as well as the direction in which it opens. When $|m| < |n|$, the graph of $y = mx^2$ is wider than the graph of $y = nx^2$.

 **Problem 3** Comparing Widths of Parabolas

Use the graphs below. What is the order, from widest to narrowest, of the graphs of the quadratic functions $f(x) = -4x^2$, $f(x) = \frac{1}{4}x^2$, and $f(x) = x^2$?

$f(x) = -4x^2$ 　　　　　 $f(x) = \frac{1}{4}x^2$ 　　　　　 $f(x) = x^2$

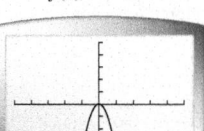　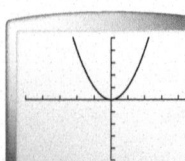

Of the three graphs, $f(x) = \frac{1}{4}x^2$ is the widest and $f(x) = -4x^2$ is the narrowest. So, the order from widest to narrowest is $f(x) = \frac{1}{4}x^2$, $f(x) = x^2$, and $f(x) = -4x^2$.

 Got It? 3. What is the order, from widest to narrowest, of the graphs of the functions $f(x) = -x^2$, $f(x) = 3x^2$, and $f(x) = -\frac{1}{3}x^2$?

The *y*-axis is the axis of symmetry for graphs of functions of the form $y = ax^2 + c$. The value of *c* translates the graph up or down.

 Problem 4 Graphing $y = ax^2 + c$

Multiple Choice How is the graph of $y = 2x^2 + 3$ different from the graph of $y = 2x^2$?

Ⓐ It is shifted 3 units up. 　　　　 Ⓒ It is shifted 3 units to the right.

Ⓑ It is shifted 3 units down. 　　　 Ⓓ It is shifted 3 units to the left.

x	$y = 2x^2$	$y = 2x^2 + 3$
$=2$	8	11
$=1$	2	5
0	0	3
1	2	5
2	8	11

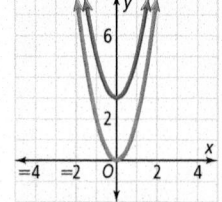

The graph of $y = 2x^2 + 3$ has the same shape as the graph of $y = 2x^2$ but is shifted up 3 units. The correct answer is A.

 Got It? 4. Graph $y = x^2$ and $y = x^2 - 3$. How are the graphs related?

Additional Problems

1. What is the vertex of the graph? Is it a minimum or a maximum?

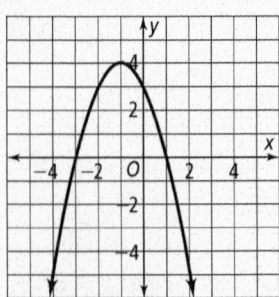

ANSWER
$(-1, 4)$, maximum

2. Graph the function $y = \frac{1}{2}x^2$ by making a table of values. What are the domain and range of the function?

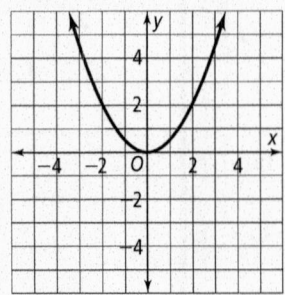

ANSWER The domain is all real numbers. The range is $y \geq 0$.

3. What is the order, from widest to narrowest graph, of the quadratic functions $f(x) = 2x^2$, $f(x) = -\frac{1}{3}x^2$, and $f(x) = 4x^2$?

ANSWER $f(x) = -\frac{1}{3}x^2$, $f(x) = 2x^2$, $f(x) = 4x^2$

4. How is the graph of $f(x) = 2x^2 + 1$ different from the graph of $f(x) = 2x^2$?

A. It is shifted 1 unit up.

B. It is shifted 1 unit down.

C. It is shifted 1 unit left.

D. It is shifted 1 unit right.

ANSWER A

5. A child drops a pebble from a height of 30 ft above a lake. The function $h = -16t^2 + 30$ gives the height *h* of the pebble (in feet) after *t* seconds. What is the graph of this quadratic function? At about what time does the pebble hit the water?

ANSWER about 1.37 s

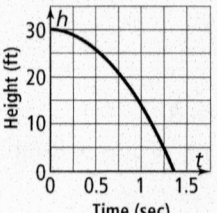

As an object falls, its speed continues to increase, so its height above the ground decreases at a faster and faster rate. Ignoring air resistance, you can model the object's height with the function $h = -16t^2 + c$. The height h is in feet, the time t is in seconds, and the object's initial height c is in feet.

Problem 5 Using the Falling Object Model

Nature An acorn drops from a tree branch 20 ft above the ground. The function $h = -16t^2 + 20$ gives the height h of the acorn (in feet) after t seconds. What is the graph of this quadratic function? At about what time does the acorn hit the ground?

Know
- The function for the acorn's height
- The initial height is 20 ft

Need
The function's graph and the time the acorn hits the ground

Plan
Use a table of values to graph the function. Use the graph to estimate when the acorn hits the ground.

Think
Can you choose negative values for t?
No. t represents time, so it cannot be negative.

t	$h = -16t^2 + 20$
0	20
0.5	16
1	4
1.5	-16

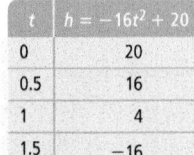

Graph the function using the first three ordered pairs from the table. Do not plot $(1.5, -16)$ because height cannot be negative.

The acorn hits the ground when its height above the ground is 0 ft. From the graph, you can see that the acorn hits the ground after slightly more than 1 s.

Got It? 5. a. In Problem 5 above, suppose the acorn drops from a tree branch 70 ft above the ground. The function $h = -16t^2 + 70$ gives the height h of the acorn (in feet) after t seconds. What is the graph of this function? At about what time does the acorn hit the ground?

b. Reasoning What are a reasonable domain and range for the original function in Problem 5? Explain your reasoning.

Lesson Check

Do you know HOW?

Graph the parabola. Identify the vertex.

1. $y = -3x^2$

2. $y = 4x^2$

3. $y = \frac{1}{2}x^2 + 2$

4. $y = -2x^2 - 1$

Do you UNDERSTAND?

5. Vocabulary When is the vertex of a parabola the minimum point? When is it the maximum point?

6. Compare and Contrast How are the graphs of $y = -\frac{1}{2}x^2$ and $y = -\frac{1}{2}x^2 + 1$ similar? How are they different?

Problem 5

Q Is it possible for the acorn's height above the ground to be a negative number? Explain. **[only if the acorn falls into a well or mineshaft below ground]**

Q Is the speed of the acorn greater at 0.25 s or at 0.75 s? Explain. **[0.75 s; speed continues to increase as the acorn falls.]**

Q What equation could be written to represent the problem situation? **[$-16t^2 + 20 = 0$]**

Got It?
Show students how they can use this process and the function to "zero" in on a more exact value for the time at which the acorn hits the ground.

3 Lesson Check

Do you know HOW?
- If students have difficulty with Exercises 1-4, then have them review Problem 2.

Do you UNDERSTAND?
- If students have difficulty with Exercise 5, then remind them when a parabola opens upward, it has a maximum point and when a parabola opens downward, it has a minimum point.

Close

Q What are two methods for graphing quadratic equations? **[One method is to graph points on one side of the axis of symmetry, using reflection, and connecting the points. Another method is using transformations of the parent quadratic function.]**

Answers

Got It? (continued)

3. $f(x) = -\frac{1}{3}x^2$, $f(x) = -x^2$, $f(x) = 3x^2$

4.

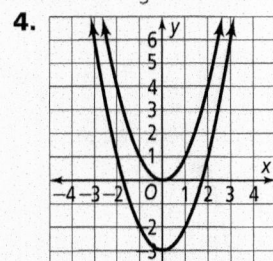

Answers will vary. Sample: They have the same shape but the second parabola is shifted down 3 units.

5. a.

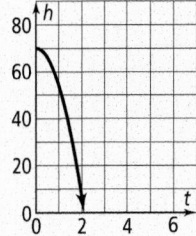

about 2 s

b. domain: $0 \le t \le 1.2$; range: $0 \le h \le 20$

Lesson Check

1.

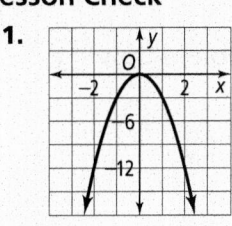

$(0, 0)$

2–6. See next page.

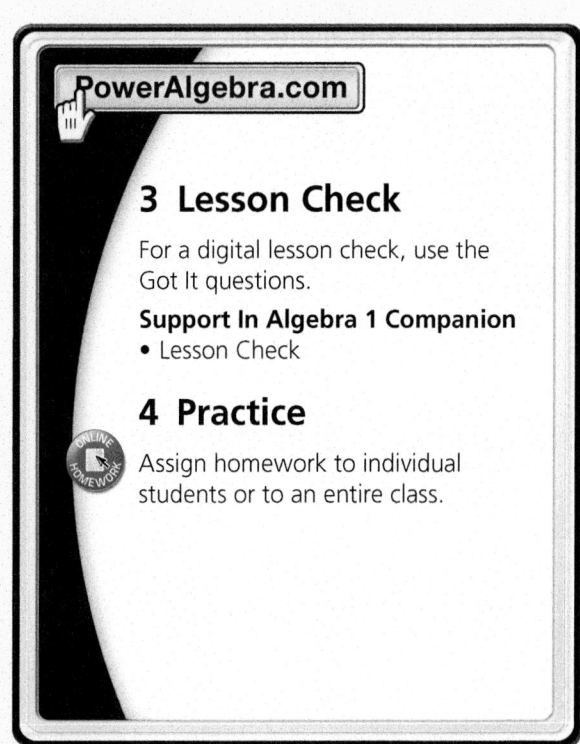

PowerAlgebra.com

3 Lesson Check

For a digital lesson check, use the Got It questions.

Support In Algebra 1 Companion
- Lesson Check

4 Practice

Assign homework to individual students or to an entire class.

4 Practice

ASSIGNMENT GUIDE

Basic: 7–28 all, 30–32 even, 33, 34–40 even, 48

Average: 7–27 odd, 28–48

Advanced: 7–27 odd, 28–51

Standardized Test Prep: 52–56

Mixed Review: 57–65

Reasoning exercises have blue headings.

Applications exercises have red headings.

EXERCISE 48: Use the Think About a Plan worksheet in the **Practice and Problem Solving Workbook** (also available in the Teaching Resources in print and online) to further support students' development in becoming independent learners.

HOMEWORK QUICK CHECK

To check students' understanding of key skills and concepts, go over Exercises 11, 19, 33, 40, and 48.

Practice and Problem-Solving Exercises

Ⓐ Practice — Identify the vertex of each graph. Tell whether it is a minimum or a maximum. ◀ See Problem 1.

7.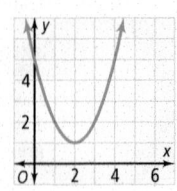

8.

9.

Graph each function. Then identify the domain and range of the function. ◀ See Problem 2.

10. $y = -4x^2$

11. $f(x) = 1.5x^2$

12. $f(x) = 3x^2$

13. $f(x) = \frac{2}{3}x^2$

14. $y = -\frac{1}{2}x^2$

15. $y = -\frac{1}{3}x^2$

Order each group of quadratic functions from widest to narrowest graph. ◀ See Problem 3.

16. $y = 3x^2, y = 2x^2, y = 4x^2$

17. $f(x) = 5x^2, f(x) = -3x^2, f(x) = x^2$

18. $y = -\frac{1}{2}x^2, y = 5x^2, y = -\frac{1}{4}x^2$

19. $f(x) = -2x^2, f(x) = -\frac{2}{3}x^2, f(x) = -4x^2$

Graph each function. ◀ See Problem 4.

20. $f(x) = x^2 + 4$

21. $y = x^2 - 7$

22. $y = \frac{1}{2}x^2 + 2$

23. $f(x) = -x^2 - 3$

24. $y = -2x^2 + 4$

25. $f(x) = 4x^2 - 5$

26. Dropped Object A person walking across a bridge accidentally drops an orange into the river below from a height of 40 ft. The function $h = -16t^2 + 40$ gives the orange's approximate height h above the water, in feet, after t seconds. Graph the function. In how many seconds will the orange hit the water? ◀ See Problem 5.

27. Nature A bird drops a stick to the ground from a height of 80 ft. The function $h = -16t^2 + 80$ gives the stick's approximate height h above the ground, in feet, after t seconds. Graph the function. At about what time does the stick hit the ground?

Ⓑ Apply

28. Error Analysis Describe and correct the error made in graphing the function $y = -2x^2 + 1$.

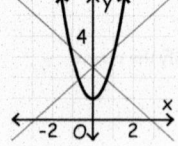

Identify the domain and range of each function.

29. $f(x) = 3x^2 + 6$

30. $y = -2x^2 - 1$

31. $y = -\frac{3}{4}x^2 - 9$

32. $y = \frac{2}{3}x^2 + 12$

33. Writing What information do the numbers a and c give you about the graph of $y = ax^2 + c$?

538 Chapter 9 Quadratic Functions and Equations

Lesson Check (continued)

2.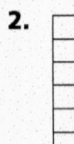

(0, 0)

3.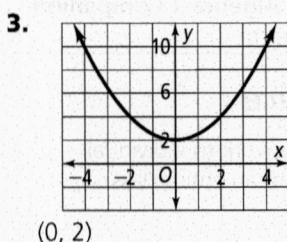

(0, 2)

4.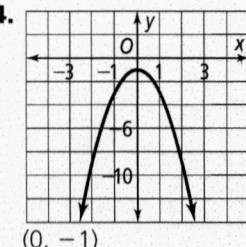

(0, −1)

5. If $a > 0$, the vertex is a minimum. If $a < 0$, the vertex is a maximum.

6. Answers will vary. Sample: They have the same shape, but the second graph is shifted up 1 unit.

Practice and Problem-Solving Exercises

7. (2, 3); maximum

8. (−3, −2); minimum

9. (2, 1); minimum

10.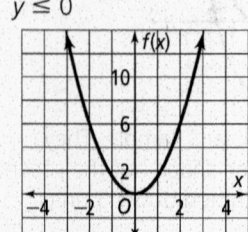

domain: all real numbers; range: $y \le 0$

11.

domain: all real numbers; range: $f(x) \ge 0$

Match each function with its graph.

34. $f(x) = x^2 - 1$

35. $f(x) = x^2 + 4$

36. $f(x) = -x^2 + 2$

37. $f(x) = 3x^2 - 5$

38. $f(x) = -3x^2 + 8$

39. $f(x) = -0.2x^2 + 5$

A.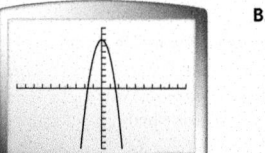

B.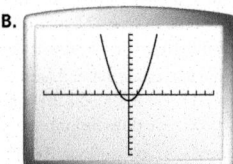

C.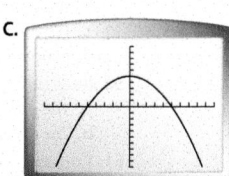

D.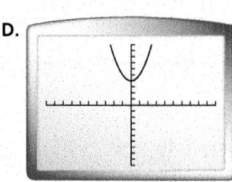

E.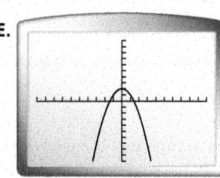

F.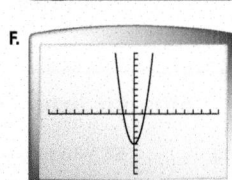

40. Think About a Plan Suppose a person is riding in a hot-air balloon, 154 ft above the ground. He drops an apple. The height h, in feet, of the apple above the ground is given by the formula $h = -16t^2 + 154$, where t is the time in seconds. To the nearest tenth of a second, at what time does the apple hit the ground?
- How can you use a table to approximate the answer between two consecutive whole numbers of seconds?
- How can you use a second table to make your approximation more accurate?

Graphing Calculator Use a graphing calculator to graph each function. Identify the vertex and axis of symmetry.

41. $y = \frac{1}{4}x^2 + 3$

42. $f(x) = -1.5x^2 + 5$

43. $y = -3x^2 - 6$

Three graphs are shown at the right. Identify the graph or graphs that fit each description.

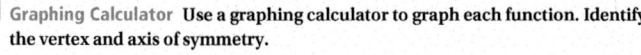

44. $a > 0$

45. $a < 0$

46. $|a|$ has the greatest value.

47. $|a|$ has the least value.

48. Physics In a physics class demonstration, a ball is dropped from the roof of a building, 72 ft above the ground. The height h, in feet, of the ball above the ground is given by the function $h = -16t^2 + 72$, where t is the time in seconds.
a. Graph the function.
b. How far has the ball fallen from time $t = 0$ to $t = 1$?
c. Reasoning Does the ball fall the same distance from time $t = 1$ to $t = 2$ as it does from $t = 0$ to $t = 1$? Explain.

12.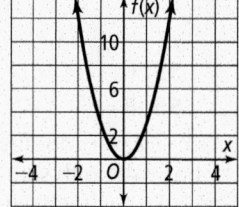

domain: all real numbers; range: $f(x) \geq 0$

13.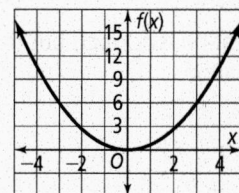

domain: all real numbers; range: $f(x) \geq 0$

14.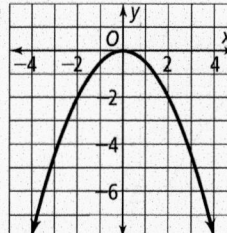

domain: all real numbers; range: $y \leq 0$

15.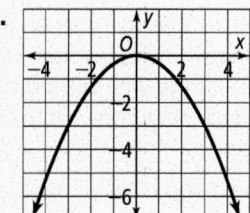

domain: all real numbers; range: $y \leq 0$

16. $y = 2x^2, y = 3x^2, y = 4x^2$

17. $f(x) = x^2, f(x) = -3x^2, f(x) = 5x^2$

18. $y = -\frac{1}{4}x^2, y = -\frac{1}{2}x^2, y = 5x^2$

19. $f(x) = -\frac{2}{3}x^2, f(x) = -2x^2, f(x) = -4x^2$

20.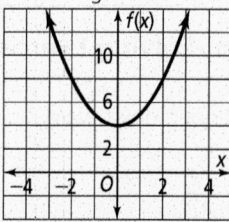

21.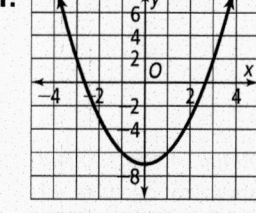

22.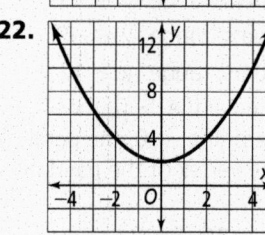

23.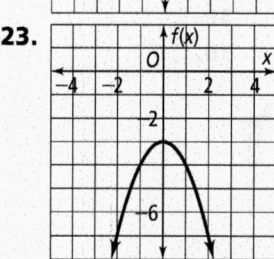

24.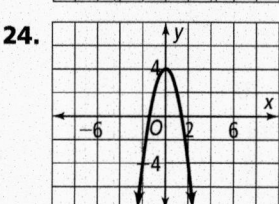

25.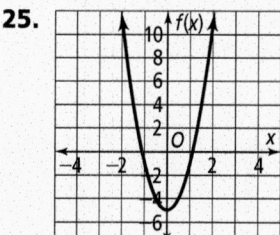

26.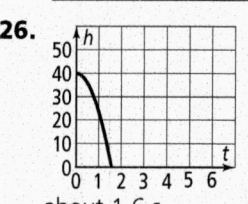

about 1.6 s

27.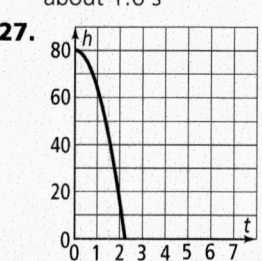

about 2.2 s

28–48. See next page.

Answers

Practice and Problem-Solving Exercises
(continued)

28. The parabola should open downward.

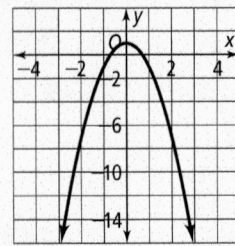

29. domain: all real numbers; range: $f(x) \geq 6$

30. domain: all real numbers; range: $y \leq -1$

31. domain: all real numbers; range: $y \leq -9$

32. domain: all real numbers; range: $y \geq 12$

33. Answers will vary. Sample: If $a > 0$, the parabola opens upward. If $a < 0$, the parabola opens downward. The vertex of the parabola is $(0, c)$.

34. B   **35.** D   **36.** E

37. F   **38.** A   **39.** C

40. 3.1 s

41.

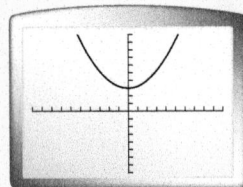

vertex: $(0, 3)$
axis of symmetry: $x = 0$

42.

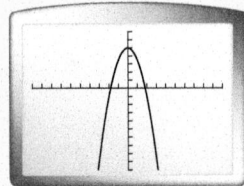

vertex: $(0, 5)$
axis of symmetry: $x = 0$

43.

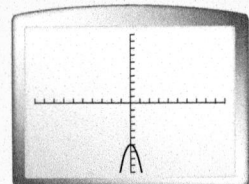

vertex: $(0, -6)$
axis of symmetry: $x = 0$

44. K, L   **45.** M

46. K   **47.** M

48. a.

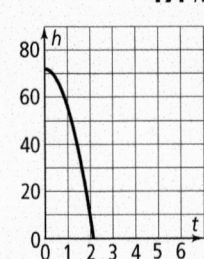

b. 16 ft

c. No, from $t = 1$ to $t = 2$ the ball falls $(72 - 16)$ ft $- (72 - 64)$ ft $= 48$ ft.

49. Construction A blueprint for a 15 ft-by-9 ft rectangular wall has a square window in the center. If each side of the window is x feet, the function $y = 135 - x^2$ gives the area (in square feet) of the wall without the window.
  a. Graph the function.
  b. What is a reasonable domain for the function? Explain.
  c. What is the range of the function? Explain.
  d. Estimate the side length of the window if the area of the wall is 117 ft^2.

50. Reasoning Complete each statement. Assume $a \neq 0$.
  a. The graph of $y = ax^2 + c$ intersects the x-axis in two places when __?__.
  b. The graph of $y = ax^2 + c$ does not intersect the x-axis when __?__.

51. Consider the graphs of $y = ax^2$ and $y = (ax)^2$. Assume $a \neq 0$.
  a. For what values of a will both graphs lie in the same quadrant(s)?
  b. For what values of a will the graph of $y = ax^2$ be wider than the graph of $y = (ax)^2$?

Standardized Test Prep

SAT/ACT

52. Which equation has a graph that is narrower than the graph of $y = 4x^2 + 5$?
  Ⓐ $y = 4x^2 - 5$
  Ⓑ $y = -5x^2 + 4$
  Ⓒ $y = 0.75x^2 + 5$
  Ⓓ $y = -0.75x^2 - 4$

53. Kristina is evaluating some formulas as part of a science experiment. One of the formulas involves the expression $24 - (-17)$. What is the value of this expression?
  Ⓕ -41 Ⓖ -7 Ⓗ 7 Ⓘ 41

54. Which expression is equivalent to $8(x + 9)$?
  Ⓐ $x + 72$ Ⓑ $8x + 72$ Ⓒ $8x + 17$ Ⓓ $8x + 9$

55. What is the solution of the equation $2(x + 3) + 7 = -11$?
  Ⓕ -12 Ⓖ -1 Ⓗ 1 Ⓘ 12

Short Response

56. A rectangular dog run has an area of $x^2 - 22x - 48$. What are possible dimensions of the dog run? Use factoring. Explain how you found the dimensions.

Mixed Review

Factor completely.   ◀ See Lesson 8-8.

57. $30r^3 + 51r^2 + 9r$
58. $15q^3 - 18q^2 - 10q + 12$
59. $7b^4 + 14b^3 + b + 2$

Get Ready! To prepare for Lesson 9-2, do Exercises 60–65.

Evaluate the expression $\frac{-b}{2a}$ for the following values of a and b.   ◀ See Lesson 1-6.

60. $a = -2, b = 3$ **61.** $a = -5, b = -4$ **62.** $a = 8, b = 6$

63. $a = 10, b = -7$ **64.** $a = -4, b = 1$ **65.** $a = -12, b = -48$

49. a.

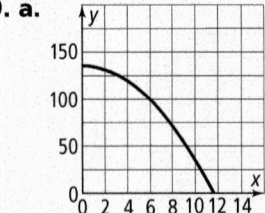

b. $0 < x < 9$; the side length of the square window must be less than the width of the wall.

c. $54 < y < 135$; as the side length of the window increases from 0 to 9, the area of the wall without the window decreases from 135 to 54.

d. about 4.2 ft

50. a. $c \neq 0$ and a and c have opposite signs.

b. $c \neq 0$ and a and c have the same sign.

51. a. $a > 0$
  b. $|a| > 1$

52. B   **53.** I

54. B   **55.** F

56. [2] To factor $x^2 - 22x - 48$, first find the factors of -48 with sum -22: -24 and 2. So the factored form of $x^2 - 22x - 48$ is $(x - 24)(x + 2)$. Possible dimensions of the dog run are $x - 24$ and $x + 2$.

[1] Factorization is correct, but there is no explanation.

57. $3r(5r + 1)(2r + 3)$

58. $(3q^2 - 2)(5q - 6)$

59. $(7b^3 + 1)(b + 2)$

60. 0.75   **61.** -0.4 **62.** $-\frac{3}{8}$

63. $\frac{7}{20}$ **64.** $\frac{1}{8}$ **65.** -2

Additional Instructional Support

Algebra 1 Companion

Students can use the **Algebra 1 Companion** worktext (4 pages) as you teach the lesson. Use the Companion to support

- New Vocabulary
- Key Concepts
- Got It for each Problem
- Lesson Check

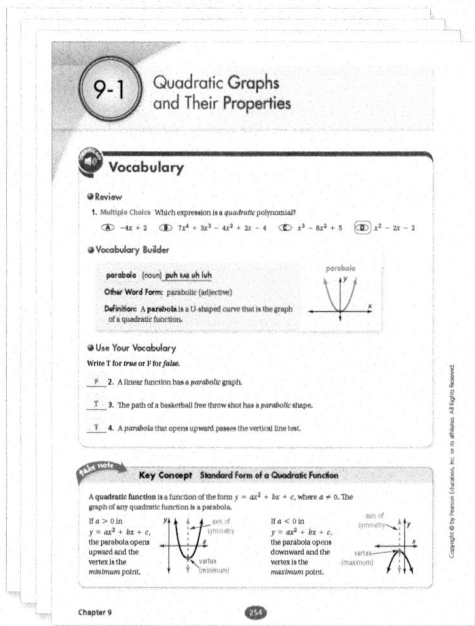

ELL Support

Connect to Prior Knowledge Write $y = 3x + 2$ on the board and ask students to guide you in graphing the function. Repeat with another example such as $y = |x|$. Make a table to find points and use the coordinates to make the graph. Invite volunteers to help find the ordered pairs and draw the graph. Now model graphing a quadratic function such as $y = 2x^2$. Think aloud as you make the table. Repeat by graphing $y = -2x^2$, but use different colored markers or chalk so students can observe the differences.

5 Assess & Remediate

Lesson Quiz

1. What is the vertex of the graph? Is it a minimum or a maximum?

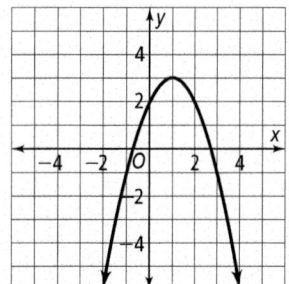

2. What is the order, from widest to narrowest graph, of the quadratic functions $f(x) = -0.5x^2$, $f(x) = \frac{1}{4}x^2$, and $f(x) = x^2$?

3. Do you UNDERSTAND? How is the graph of $f(x) = -3x^2 - 4$ different from the graph of $f(x) = -3x^2$?

4. Kyle drops a ball from a height of 15 feet above the ground. The function $h = -16t^2 + 15$ gives the height h of the ball (in feet) after t seconds. Graph the function to determine at about what time the ball hits the ground.

ANSWERS TO LESSON QUIZ

1. (1, 3), maximum

2. $f(x) = \frac{1}{4}x^2$, $f(x) = -0.5x^2$, $f(x) = x^2$

3. It is shifted 4 units down.

4. just under 1 s

PRESCRIPTION FOR REMEDIATION

Use the student work on the Lesson Quiz to prescribe a differentiated review assignment.

Points	Differentiated Remediation
0–2	Intervention
3	On-level
4	Extension

PowerAlgebra.com

5 Assess & Remediate

Assign the Lesson Quiz. Appropriate intervention, practice, or enrichment is automatically generated based on student performance.

Intervention

- **Reteaching** (2 pages) Provides reteaching and practice exercises for the key lesson concepts. Use with struggling students or absent students.

- **English Language Learner Support** Helps students develop and reinforce mathematical vocabulary and key concepts.

All-in-One Resources/Online
Reteaching

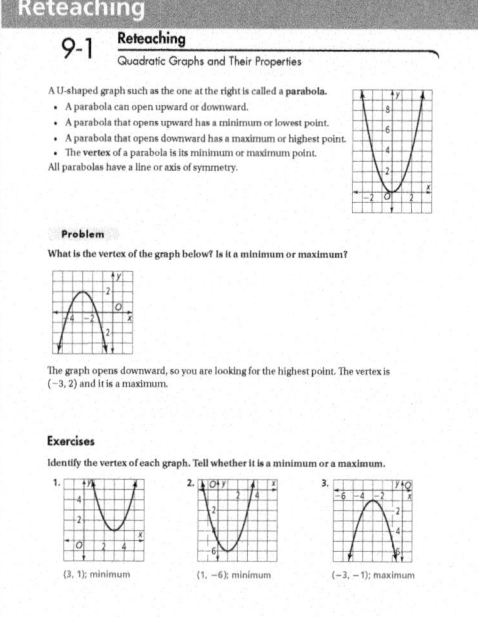

All-in-One Resources/Online
English Language Learner Support

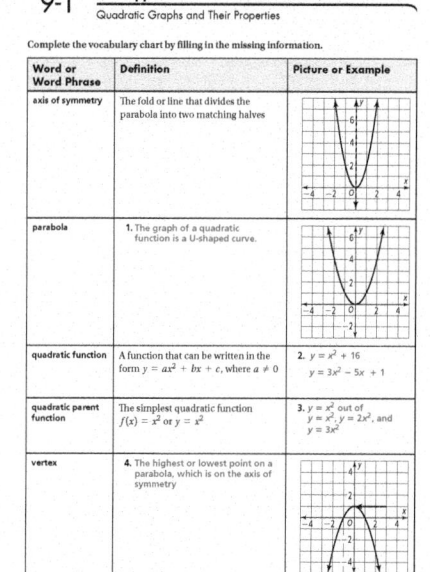

Differentiated Remediation *continued*

On-Level

- **Practice** (2 pages) Provides extra practice for each lesson. For simpler practice exercises, use the Form K Practice pages found in the All-in-One Teaching Resources and online.

- **Think About a Plan** Helps students develop specific problem-solving skills and strategies by providing scaffolded guiding questions.

- **Standardized Test Prep** Focuses on all major exercises, all major question types, and helps students prepare for the high-stakes assessments.

Extension

- **Enrichment** Provides students with interesting problems and activities that extend the concepts of the lesson.

- **Activities, Games, and Puzzles** Worksheets that can be used for concepts development, enrichment, and for fun!

Practice and Problem Solving WKBK/ All-in-One Resources/Online
Practice page 1

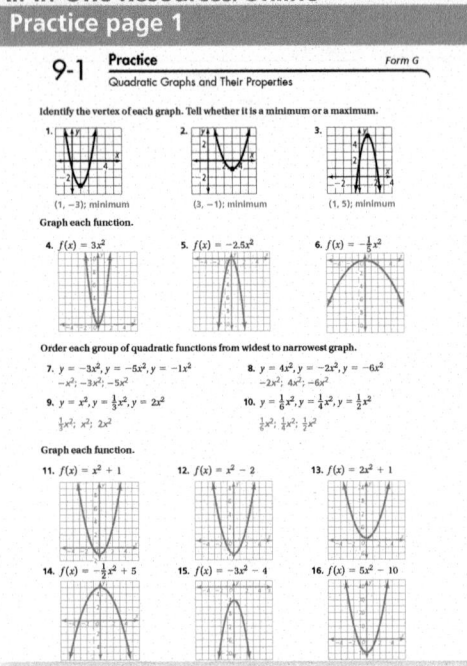

Practice and Problem Solving WKBK/ All-in-One Resources/Online
Practice page 2

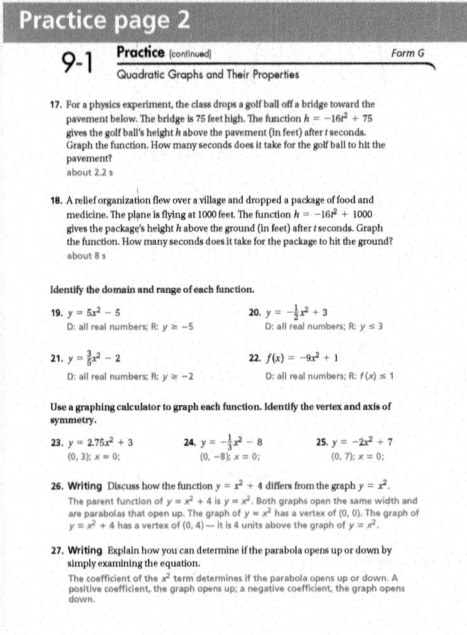

All-in-One Resources/Online
Enrichment

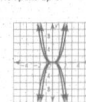

Practice and Problem Solving WKBK/ All-in-One Resources/Online
Think About a Plan

Practice and Problem Solving WKBK/ All-in-One Resources/Online
Standardized Test Prep

Online Teacher Resource Center
Activities, Games, and Puzzles

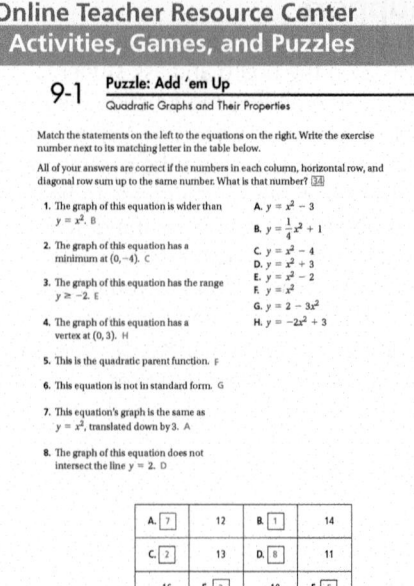

9-2 Quadratic Functions

Objective To graph quadratic functions of the form $y = ax^2 + bx + c$

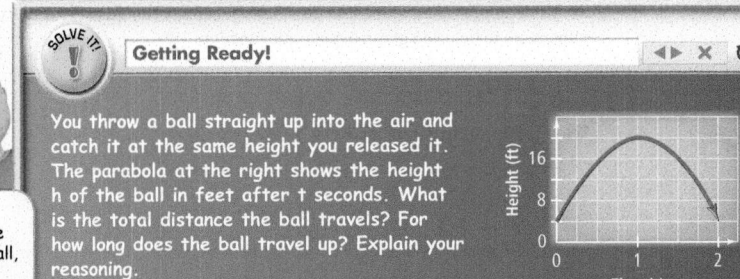

SOLVE IT!

Getting Ready!

You throw a ball straight up into the air and catch it at the same height you released it. The parabola at the right shows the height h of the ball in feet after t seconds. What is the total distance the ball travels? For how long does the ball travel up? Explain your reasoning.

Be careful! The graph shows the height of the ball, not the path of the ball.

Height (ft) vs Time (s)

Dynamic Activity
Quadratic Equations in Polynomial Form

The parabola in the Solve It has the equation $h = -16t^2 + 32t + 4$. Unlike the quadratic functions you saw in previous lessons, this function has a linear term, $32t$.

Essential Understanding In the quadratic function $y = ax^2 + bx + c$, the value of b affects the position of the axis of symmetry.

Consider the graphs of the following functions.

$y = 2x^2 + 2x$ | $y = 2x^2 + 4x$ | $y = 2x^2 + 6x$

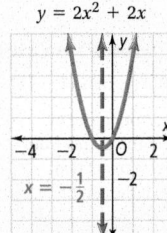 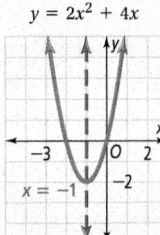 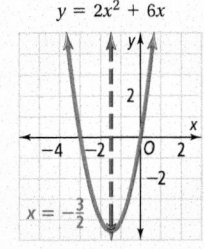

$x = -\frac{1}{2}$ | $x = -1$ | $x = -\frac{3}{2}$

Notice that the axis of symmetry changes with each change in the b-value. The equation of the axis of symmetry is related to the ratio $\frac{b}{a}$.

equation:	$y = 2x^2 + 2x$	$y = 2x^2 + 4x$	$y = 2x^2 + 6x$
$\frac{b}{a}$:	$\frac{2}{2} = 1$	$\frac{4}{2} = 2$	$\frac{6}{2} = 3$
axis of symmetry:	$x = -\frac{1}{2}$	$x = -1$, or $-\frac{2}{2}$	$x = -\frac{3}{2}$

The equation of the axis of symmetry is $x = -\frac{1}{2}\left(\frac{b}{a}\right)$, or $x = \frac{-b}{2a}$.

PowerAlgebra.com | Lesson 9-2 Quadratic Functions | 541

---

1 Interactive Learning

Solve It!

PURPOSE To analyze the graph of a quadratic function of the form $ax^2 + bx + c$

PROCESS Students may use knowledge of the symmetry of a parabola to determine the vertex and algebraic reasoning to answer the questions.

FACILITATE

Q At what height do you release and catch the ball? Explain. **[You release and catch the ball at 4 feet, because 4 feet is the height of the ball at time zero.]**

Q How many seconds is the ball in the air? Explain. **[2 seconds, because at 2 seconds it is back to a height of 4 feet.]**

Q What is the y-coordinate for the vertex of the parabola? **[The y-coordinate is 20.]**

Q How many feet has the ball traveled when it gets to its maximum value? Explain.
[16 ft; 20 − 4 = 16.]

ANSWER See Solve It in Answers on next page.

CONNECT THE MATH A quadratic function of the form $ax^2 + bx + c$ represents a parabola that has an axis of symmetry other than the y-axis. In the lesson, students learn the formula to determine the axis of symmetry.

2 Guided Instruction

Remind students that $y = ax^2 + bx + c$ is the standard form of a quadratic equation.

9-2 Preparing to Teach

BIG idea Function **UbD**

ESSENTIAL UNDERSTANDINGS

- In the quadratic function $y = ax^2 + bx + c$, the value of b translates the position of the axis of symmetry.

- The axis of symmetry for the graph of the quadratic function $y = ax^2 + bx + c$ is $x = \frac{-b}{2a}$.

- The x–coordinate of the vertex of the graph is $\frac{-b}{2a}$.

Math Background
Making a table of values to graph a parabola can be a tedious process. However, graphing a parabola of the form

$y = a^2 + bx + c$ becomes easy if the vertex of the parabola can be identified. The formula for the axis of symmetry of the parabola provides a quick method for identifying the x-element of the vertex of the parabola. The parabola can then be sketched by finding a few points on one side of the axis of symmetry and then reflecting those points across the axis of symmetry.

Support Student Learning
Use the **Algebra I Companion** to engage and support students during instruction. See Lesson Resources at the end of this lesson for details.

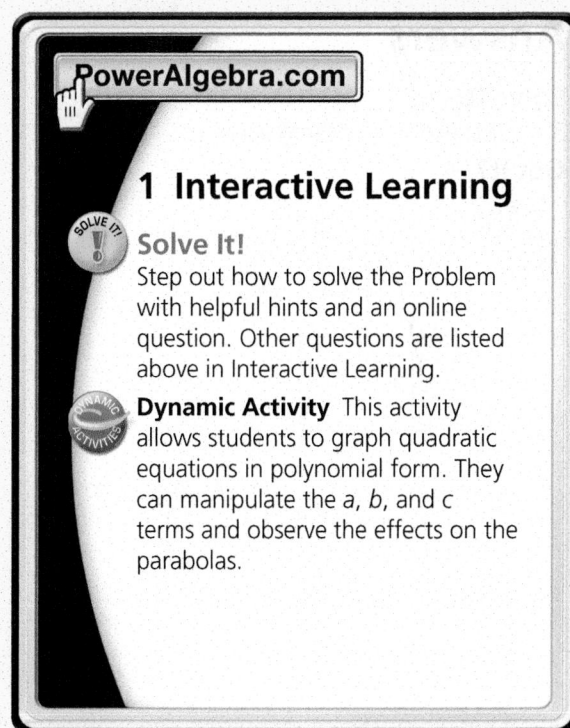

PowerAlgebra.com

1 Interactive Learning

Solve It!
Step out how to solve the Problem with helpful hints and an online question. Other questions are listed above in Interactive Learning.

Dynamic Activity This activity allows students to graph quadratic equations in polynomial form. They can manipulate the a, b, and c terms and observe the effects on the parabolas.

Take Note

Q Why is it important that *a* is not equal to zero? **[If *a* = 0, then the equation does not have a quadratic term and is not a parabola.]**

Q If *a* and *b* are both positive, will the axis of symmetry be to the left or to the right of the *y*-axis? **[It will be to the left of the *y*-axis.]**

Q If *a* and *b* are both negative, will the axis of symmetry be to the left or to the right of the *y*-axis? **[It will be to the left of the *y*-axis.]**

Q What signs of *a* and *b* are needed for the axis of symmetry to be to the right of the *y*-axis? **[One and only one will be negative.]**

Problem 1

Q What is the value of *a*? of *b*? **[1; −6]**

Q Is the vertex the minimum point or the maximum point? **[It is the minimum point because the parabola opens upward.]**

Q If an equation is written in standard form, is it necessary to substitute zero for *x* in order to determine the *y*-intercept? Explain. **[No, the constant is the *y*-intercept.]**

Q How do you determine the reflection of the point (1,−1) across the axis of symmetry? **[You determine that the horizontal distance from (1,−1) to the axis of symmetry is 2 units left, and then count 2 horizontal units right from the axis of symmetry to get to point (5, −1).]**

Got It?   SYNTHESIZING

Q What is the axis of symmetry? Explain. **[*x* = 2, since −4 ÷ 2(−1) = 2.]**

Q How do you use the axis of symmetry to locate a point on the graph? What is the significance of that point? **[Substitute 2 into the equation and solve for *y*. The point is the vertex.]**

 **Key Concept** **Graph of a Quadratic Function**

The graph of $y = ax^2 + bx + c$, where $a \neq 0$, has the line $x = \frac{-b}{2a}$ as its axis of symmetry. The *x*-coordinate of the vertex is $\frac{-b}{2a}$.

When you substitute $x = 0$ into the equation $y = ax^2 + bx + c$, you get $y = c$. So the *y*-intercept of a quadratic function is *c*. You can use the axis of symmetry and the *y*-intercept to help you graph a quadratic function.

Problem 1 **Graphing $y = ax^2 + bx + c$**

What is the graph of the function $y = x^2 - 6x + 4$?

Step 1 Find the axis of symmetry and the coordinates of the vertex.

$$x = \frac{-b}{2a} = \frac{-(-6)}{2(1)} = 3 \quad \text{Find the equation of the axis of symmetry.}$$

The axis of symmetry is $x = 3$. So the *x*-coordinate of the vertex is 3.

$$y = x^2 - 6x + 4$$
$$= 3^2 - 6(3) + 4 \quad \text{Substitute 3 for } x \text{ to find the } y\text{-coordinate of the vertex.}$$
$$= -5 \quad \text{Simplify.}$$

The vertex is $(3, -5)$.

Step 2 Find two other points on the graph.

Find the *y*-intercept. When $x = 0$, $y = 4$, so one point is $(0, 4)$.

Find another point by choosing a value for *x* on the same side of the vertex as the *y*-intercept. Let $x = 1$.

$$y = x^2 - 6x + 4$$
$$= 1^2 - 6(1) + 4 = -1 \quad \text{Substitute 1 for } x \text{ and simplify.}$$

When $x = 1$, $y = -1$, so another point is $(1, -1)$.

Step 3 Graph the vertex and the points you found in Step 2, $(0, 4)$ and $(1, -1)$. Reflect the points from Step 2 across the axis of symmetry to get two more points on the graph. Then connect the points with a parabola.

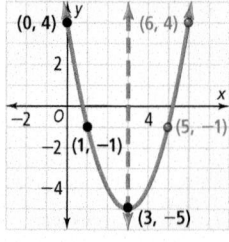

Got It? **1. a.** What is the graph of the function $y = -x^2 + 4x - 2$?
   b. Reasoning In Step 2 of Problem 1, why do you think it was useful to use the *y*-intercept as one point on the graph?

Think

How are the vertex and the axis of symmetry related?
The vertex is on the axis of symmetry. You can use the equation for the axis of symmetry to find the *x*-coordinate of the vertex.

Answers

Solve It!
32 ft; 1 s; explanations may vary.

Got It?
1. a.

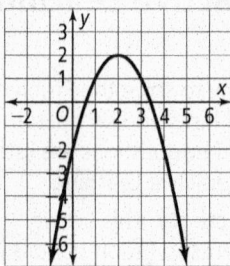

b. Answers may vary. Sample: It is easy to evaluate a quadratic function in the form $y = ax^2 + bx + c$ when $x = 0$.

 PowerAlgebra.com

2 Guided Instruction

Each Problem is worked out and supported online.

Problem 1
Graphing $y = ax^2 + bx + c$
                                    Animated

Problem 2
Using the Vertical Motion Model
                                    Animated

Support in Algebra 1 Companion
- Vocabulary
- Key Concepts
- Got It?

In Lesson 9-1, you used $h = -16t^2 + c$ to find the height h above the ground of an object falling from an initial height c at time t. If an object projected into the air given an initial upward velocity v continues with no additional force of its own, the formula $h = -16t^2 + vt + c$ gives its approximate height above the ground.

 **Problem 2** Using the Vertical Motion Model

Entertainment During halftime of a basketball game, a sling shot launches T-shirts at the crowd. A T-shirt is launched with an initial upward velocity of 72 ft/s. The T-shirt is caught 35 ft above the court. How long will it take the T-shirt to reach its maximum height? What is its maximum height? What is the range of the function that models the height of the T-shirt over time?

5 ft

Plan

What are the values of v and c?
The T-shirt is launched from a height of 5 ft, so $c = 5$. The T-shirt has an initial upward velocity of 72 ft/s, so $v = 72$.

The function $h = -16t^2 + 72t + 5$ gives the T-shirt's height h, in feet, after t seconds. Since the coefficient of t^2 is negative, the parabola opens downward, and the vertex is the maximum point.

Method 1 Use a formula.

$$t = \frac{-b}{2a} = \frac{-72}{2(-16)} = 2.25$$ Find the t-coordinate of the vertex.

$$h = -16(2.25)^2 + 72(2.25) + 5 = 86$$ Find the h-coordinate of the vertex.

The T-shirt will reach its maximum height of 86 ft after 2.25 s. The range describes the height of the T-shirt during its flight. The T-shirt starts at 5 ft, peaks at 86 ft, and then is caught at 35 ft. The height of the T-shirt at any time is between 5 ft and 86 ft, inclusive, so the range is $5 \le h \le 86$.

Method 2 Use a graphing calculator.

Enter the function $h = -16t^2 + 72t + 5$ as $y = -16x^2 + 72x + 5$ on the **Y=** screen and graph the function.

Use the **CALC** feature and select **MAXIMUM**. Set left and right bounds on the maximum point and calculate the point's coordinates. The coordinates of the maximum point are (2.25, 86).

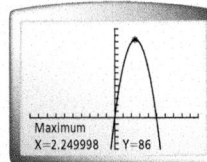

Maximum
X=2.249998   Y=86

The T-shirt will reach its maximum height of 86 ft after 2.25 s. The range of the function is $5 \le h \le 86$.

Problem 2

Q Does the velocity of a T-shirt that is shot from the air cannon remain constant? Explain. **[No, the velocity will decrease to zero as it reaches its maximum height, and then will increase as the T-shirt begins to fall.]**

Q How many times during the T-shirt's flight is it at a height of 86 ft? Explain. **[Once; 86 ft is its maximum height.]**

Q How many times during the T-shirt's flight is it at a height of 35 ft? Explain. **[Twice, once on its ascent and once on its descent.]**

Q If the T-shirt were not caught, after how many seconds would the T-shirt return to a height of 5 ft above court level? Explain. **[4.5 s; the T-shirt took 2.25 s to rise from 5 ft to 86 ft. It will take an additional 2.25 s to fall from 86 ft to 5 ft.]**

Additional Problems

1. What is the graph of the function $y = x^2 - 6x + 2$?

ANSWER

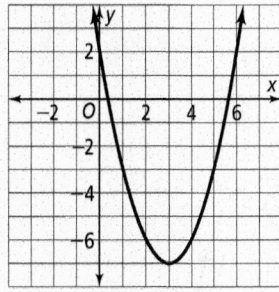

2. Daniel kicks a soccer ball up into the air with an initial upward velocity of 64 ft per second. The ball is 2 ft above the ground when it is kicked. How long will it take the ball to reach its maximum height? How high above the ground will it be? What is the range of the function?

ANSWER 2 s; 66 ft; $2 \le h \le 66$

Got It?

Allow students to use a spreadsheet to generate an extensive table of values for the quadratic function. The table of values will reflect both the vertex of the function as well as the symmetric nature of the function.

3 Lesson Check

Do you know HOW?
• If students have difficulty with Exercise 1–4, then have them review Problem 1 to identify the axis of symmetry, find the vertex of the parabola, and use the axis of symmetry to locate additional points.

Do you UNDERSTAND?
• If students have difficulty with Exercise 5, then encourage them to use the equations from Exercises 1–4 as examples.

Close

Q What are the major steps for graphing a quadratic function of the form $y = ax^2 + bx + c$? **[Use the formula to determine the axis of symmetry and x-coordinate of the vertex. Find the y-coordinate of the vertex through substitution. Determine the y-intercept and one more point. Reflect the y-intercept point and the additional point across the axis of symmetry.]**

 Got It? **2.** In Problem 2, suppose a T-shirt is launched with an initial upward velocity of 64 ft/s and is caught 35 ft above the court. How long will it take the T-shirt to reach its maximum height? How far above court level will it be? What is the range of the function that models the height of the T-shirt over time?

 ## Lesson Check

Do you know HOW?

Graph each function.

1. $y = x^2 - 4x + 1$

2. $y = -2x^2 - 8x - 3$

3. $y = 3x^2 + 6x + 2$

4. $f(x) = -x^2 + 2x - 5$

Do you UNDERSTAND?

5. **Reasoning** How does each of the numbers a, b, and c affect the graph of a quadratic function $y = ax^2 + bx + c$?

6. **Writing** Explain how you can use the y-intercept, vertex, and axis of symmetry to graph a quadratic function. Assume the vertex is not on the y-axis.

 ## Practice and Problem-Solving Exercises

 Practice

Find the equation of the axis of symmetry and the coordinates of the vertex of the graph of each function.    See Problem 1.

7. $y = 2x^2 + 3$

8. $y = -3x^2 + 12x + 1$

9. $f(x) = 2x^2 + 4x - 1$

10. $y = x^2 - 8x - 7$

11. $f(x) = 3x^2 - 9x + 2$

12. $y = -4x^2 + 11$

13. $f(x) = -5x^2 + 3x + 2$

14. $y = -4x^2 - 16x - 3$

15. $f(x) = 6x^2 + 6x - 5$

Match each function with its graph.

16. $y = -x^2 - 6x$

17. $y = -x^2 + 6$

18. $y = x^2 - 6$

19. $y = x^2 + 6x$

A.

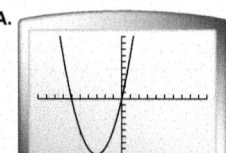

B.

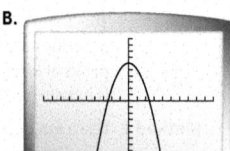

C.

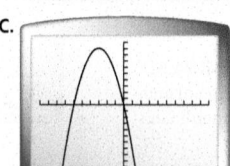

D.

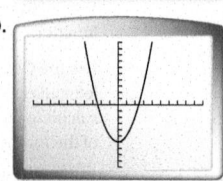

3 Lesson Check

For a digital lesson check, use the Got It questions.

Support in Algebra 1 Companion
• Lesson Check

4 Practice

Assign homework to individual students or to an entire class.

Answers

Got It? (continued)

2. 2 s; 69 ft; $5 \le h \le 69$

Lesson Check

1.

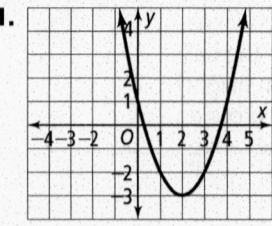

2.

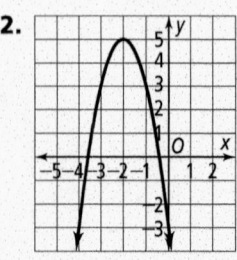

3.

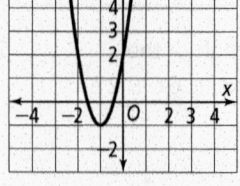

4.

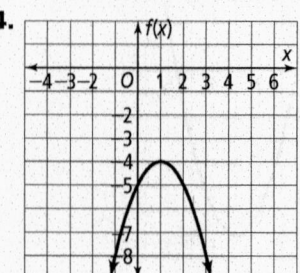

Graph each function. Label the axis of symmetry and the vertex.

20. $f(x) = x^2 + 4x - 5$ **21.** $y = 3x^2 - 20x$ **22.** $y = -2x^2 + 8x + 9$

23. $f(x) = -x^2 + 4x + 3$ **24.** $y = -2x^2 - 10x$ **25.** $y = 2x^2 - 6x + 1$

26. Sports A baseball is thrown into the air with an upward velocity of 30 ft/s. Its   See Problem 2.
height h, in feet, after t seconds is given by the function $h = -16t^2 + 30t + 6$. How
long will it take the ball to reach its maximum height? What is the ball's maximum
height? What is the range of the function?

27. School Fair Suppose you have 100 ft of string to rope off a rectangular section for a
bake sale at a school fair. The function $A = -x^2 + 50x$ gives the area of the section
in square feet, where x is the width in feet. What width gives you the maximum area
you can rope off? What is the maximum area? What is the range of the function?

 B Apply   **Graph each function. Label the axis of symmetry and the vertex.**

28. $y = \frac{1}{2}x^2 + 2x + 1$ **29.** $f(x) = -\frac{4}{3}x^2 - 8x + 8$

30. $y = \frac{1}{4}x^2 - 2x - 1$ **31.** $y = \frac{3}{2}x^2 - 3x + 2$

32. $y = \frac{1}{2}x^2 + 8x - 20$ **33.** $f(x) = -\frac{5}{2}x^2 - x + 3$

34. Think About a Plan The Riverside Geyser in Yellowstone National Park erupts
about every 6.25 h. When the geyser erupts, the water has an initial upward velocity
of 69 ft/s. What is the maximum height of the geyser? Round your answer to the
nearest foot.
• What is the initial height of the geyser?
• What function gives the geyser's height h (in feet) t seconds after it starts
erupting?

35. Business A cell phone company sells about 500 phones each week when it charges
$75 per phone. It sells about 20 more phones per week for each $1 decrease in
price. The company's revenue is the product of the number of phones sold and
the price of each phone. What price should the company charge to maximize its
revenue?

Open-Ended **Give an example of a quadratic function with the given
characteristic(s).**

36. The axis of symmetry of its graph is to the right of the y-axis.

37. Its graph opens downward and has its vertex at $(0, 0)$.

38. Its graph lies entirely above the x-axis.

39. Error Analysis Describe and correct the error made in finding the axis of
symmetry for the graph of $y = -x^2 - 6x + 2$.

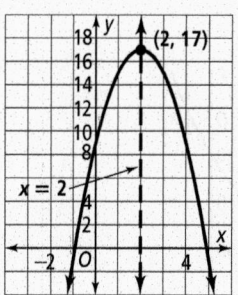

40. Reasoning What do you know about the value of b in the function
$y = ax^2 + bx + c$ when the x-coordinate of the vertex is an integer?

---

4 Practice

ASSIGNMENT GUIDE

Basic: 7–27 all, 28–34 even, 35, 39

Average: 7–27 odd, 28–40

Advanced: 7–27 odd, 28–42

Standardized Test Prep: 43–47

Mixed Review: 48–54

Reasoning exercises have blue headings.

Applications exercises have red headings.

EXERCISE 35: Use the Think About a Plan
worksheet in the **Practice and Problem Solving
Workbook** (also available in the Teaching
Resources in print and online) to further support
students' development in becoming independent
learners.

HOMEWORK QUICK CHECK

To check students' understanding of key skills and
concepts, go over Exercises 9, 27, 34, 35, and 39.

---

5. If $a > 0$, the graph opens upward and
the vertex is a minimum. If $a < 0$,
the graph opens downward, and
the vertex is a maximum. The greater
the value of $|a|$, the narrower the
parabola is. The axis of symmetry is
the line $x = -\frac{b}{2a}$. The x-coordinate
of the vertex is $-\frac{b}{2a}$. The y-intercept of
the parabola is c.

6. First graph the vertex and then graph
the y-intercept. Reflect the y-intercept
over the axis of symmetry to get a
third point. Then sketch the parabola
through these three points.

Practice and Problem-Solving Exercises

7. $x = 0; (0, 3)$

8. $x = 2; (2, 13)$

9. $x = -1; (-1, -3)$

10. $x = 4; (4, -23)$

11. $x = 1.5; (1.5, -4.75)$

12. $x = 0; (0, 11)$

13. $x = 0.3; (0.3, 2.45)$

14. $x = -2; (-2, 13)$

15. $x = -0.5; (-0.5, -6.5)$

16. C   **17.** B

18. D   **19.** A

20.
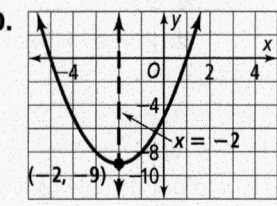

21.
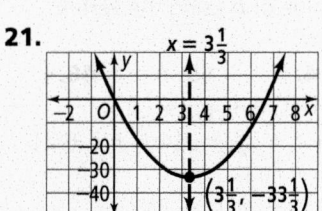

22.
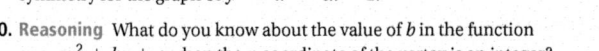

23.
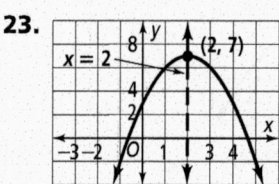

24–40. See next page.

Answers

Practice and Problem-Solving Exercises
(continued)

24.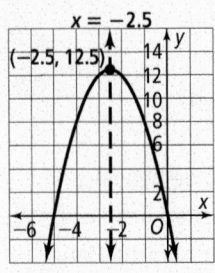

25.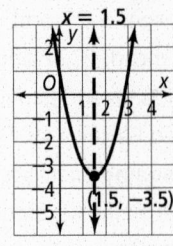

26. $\frac{15}{16}$ s; $20\frac{1}{16}$ ft; $0 \le h \le 20\frac{1}{16}$

27. 25 ft; 625 ft^2; $0 < A \le 625$

28.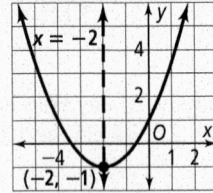

29.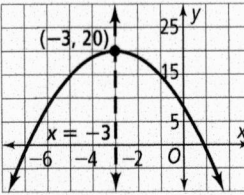

30.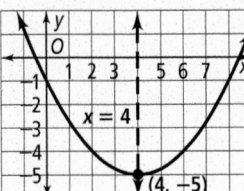

31.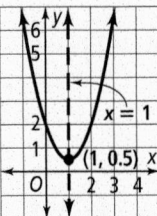

32.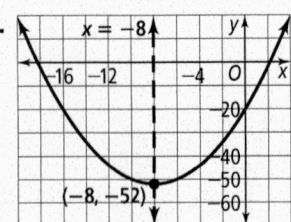

33.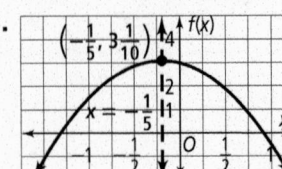

34. 74 ft   **35.** $50

36–38. Answers will vary. Samples are given.

36. $y = x^2 - 6x$ **37.** $y = -x^2$

38. $y = x^2 + 5$

39. The value of b is -6, so
$-\frac{b}{2a} = -\left(\frac{-6}{2(-1)}\right) = -\left(\frac{-6}{-2}\right) = -3$.

41. Sports Suppose a tennis player hits a ball over the net. The ball leaves the racket 0.5 m above the ground. The equation $h = -4.9t^2 + 3.8t + 0.5$ gives the ball's height h in meters after t seconds.
  a. When will the ball be at the highest point in its path? Round to the nearest tenth of a second.
  b. Reasoning If you double your answer from part (a), will you find the amount of time the ball is in the air before it hits the court? Explain.

42. The parabola at the right is of the form $y = x^2 + bx + c$.
  a. Use the graph to find the y-intercept.
  b. Use the graph to find the equation of the axis of symmetry.
  c. Use the formula $x = \frac{-b}{2a}$ to find b.
  d. Write the equation of the parabola.
  e. Test one point using your equation from part (d).
  f. Reasoning Would this method work if the value of a were not known? Explain.

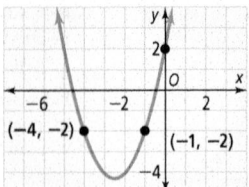

Standardized Test Prep

43. A half-pipe ramp at a skate park is approximately parabolic in shape. It can be modeled by the quadratic function $y = x^2 - 6x + 9$. At what point would a skater be at the lowest part of the ramp?
  Ⓐ $(-3, 36)$ Ⓑ $(36, -3)$ Ⓒ $(3, 0)$ Ⓓ $(0, 3)$

44. What is the simplified form of the product $4(-8)(5)(-1)$?
  Ⓕ -160 Ⓖ -80 Ⓗ 80 Ⓘ 160

45. Which of the following is equivalent to $(-4)^3$?
  Ⓐ -64 Ⓑ -12 Ⓒ 12 Ⓓ 64

46. Toby needs to write an example of the Commutative Property of Multiplication for his homework. Which of the following expressions could he use?
  Ⓕ $ab = ba$ Ⓖ $a = a$ Ⓗ $ab = ab$ Ⓘ $a(bc) = (ab)c$

47. Simplify the product $(3r - 1)(4r^2 + r + 2)$. Justify each step.

Mixed Review

Graph each function.   ◀ See Lesson 9-1.

48. $y = -x^2 - 2$ **49.** $y = -\frac{1}{2}x^2 + 1$ **50.** $y = 2x^2 + 7$

Get Ready!   To prepare for Lesson 9-3, do Exercises 51–54.

Simplify each expression.   ◀ See Lessons 1-3 and 1-6.

51. $\sqrt{25}$ **52.** $-\sqrt{64}$ **53.** $\pm\sqrt{144}$ **54.** $\sqrt{1.21}$

40. b is an even integer.

41. a. 0.4 s
  b. No, the ball does not start at height 0 m.

42. a. 2   **b.** $x = -2.5$
  c. 5   **d.** $y = x^2 + 5x + 2$
  e. Answers will vary
    Sample: Test $(-1, -2)$.
    $-2 = (-1)^2 + 5(-1) + 2 = -2$
  f. No, you would not be able to find the value of b using the vertex formula.

43. C   **44.** I   **45.** A   **46.** F

47. [2] $(3r - 1)(4r^2 + r + 2) =$
  $3r(4r^2 + r + 2) - 1(4r^2 + r + 2)$
  Distributive Prop.
  $= 3r(4r^2) + 3r(r) + 3r(2) -$
  $(4r^2 + r + 2)$
  Distributive Prop. and Mult. Prop. of -1
  $= 12r^3 + 3r^2 + 6r - 4r^2 - r - 2$
  Simplify.
  $= 12r^3 - r^2 + 5r - 2$

Comm. and Assoc. Properties of Add.
[1] correct answer, no justification or minor computational error with correct justification

48.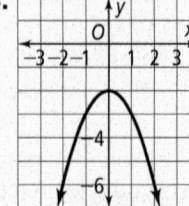

49.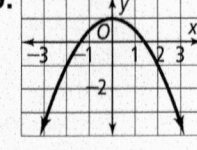

50.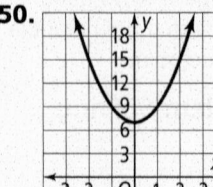

51. 5   **52.** -8
53. ± 12 **54.** 1.1

9-2 Lesson Resources

Additional Instructional Support

Algebra 1 Companion

Students can use the **Algebra 1 Companion** worktext (4 pages) as you teach the lesson. Use the Companion to support

- New Vocabulary
- Key Concepts
- Got It for each Problem
- Lesson Check

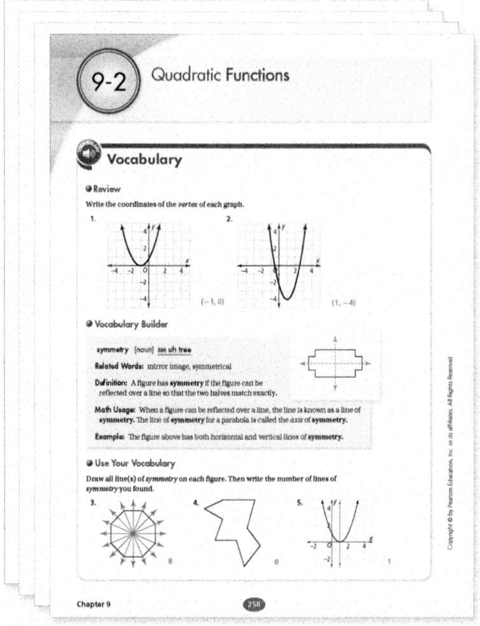

9-2 Quadratic Functions

Vocabulary

Review

Write the coordinates of the *vertex* of each graph.

1. (−1, 0)
2. (1, −4)

Vocabulary Builder

symmetry (noun) sɪm uh tree

Related Words: mirror image, symmetrical

Definition: A figure has **symmetry** if the figure can be reflected over a line so that the two halves match exactly.

Math Usage: When a figure can be reflected over a line, the line is known as a line of **symmetry.** The line of **symmetry** for a parabola is called the *axis* of **symmetry.**

Example: The figure above has both horizontal and vertical lines of **symmetry.**

Use Your Vocabulary

Draw all line(s) of *symmetry* on each figure. Then write the number of lines of *symmetry* you found.

3. 8
4. 0
5. 1

Copyright © by Pearson Education, Inc. or its affiliates. All Rights Reserved.

Chapter 9 258

ELL Support

Use Graphic Organizers Make a 3-column graphic organizer. The first column will name the steps to graph a quadratic function in standard form. The second column of the organizer will have an example using the variables of the standard form, $y = ax^2 + bx + c$. The third column will have an example such as $y = 2x^2 + 3x + 4$. As an alternative, after completing the first two columns, place the sheet into a plastic page protector. Students can work examples using dry eraser markers and following each step on the organizer. Then erase it and do a new problem.

5 Assess & Remediate

Lesson Quiz

1. What is the graph of the function $y = -x^2 + 4x + 1$?
2. **Do you UNDERSTAND?** Tyrone launches a toy rocket into the air with an initial upward velocity of 49 ft/s and an initial height of 0 ft. How long will it take the rocket to reach its maximum height? How high above the ground will it be? What is the range of the function? Why is there a maximum point on the graph of this function?

ANSWERS TO LESSON QUIZ

1. 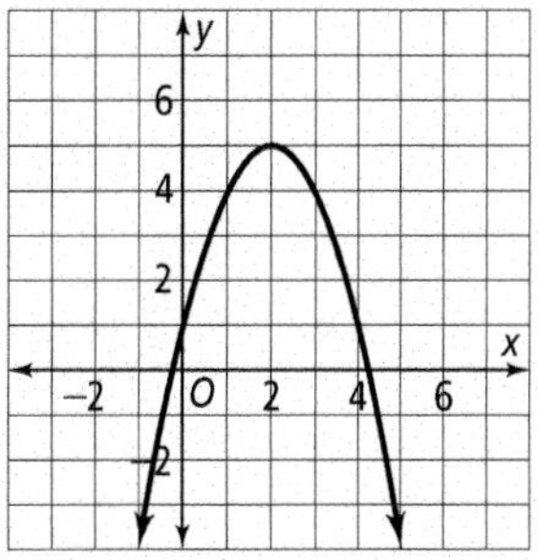

2. 1.53 s; 37.5 ft; $0 \le h \le 37.5$; The rocket will continue to travel upwards until gravity pulls it back to Earth, so there is a maximum point on the graph which opens downward.

PRESCRIPTION FOR REMEDIATION

Use the student work on the Lesson Quiz to prescribe a differentiated review assignment.

Points	Differentiated Remediation
0	Intervention
1	On-level
2	Extension

PowerAlgebra.com

5 Assess & Remediate

Assign the Lesson Quiz. Appropriate intervention, practice, or enrichment is automatically generated based on student performance.

Intervention

- **Reteaching** (2 pages) Provides reteaching and practice exercises for the key lesson concepts. Use with struggling students or absent students.
- **English Language Learner Support** Helps students develop and reinforce mathematical vocabulary and key concepts.

All-in-One Resources/Online

Reteaching

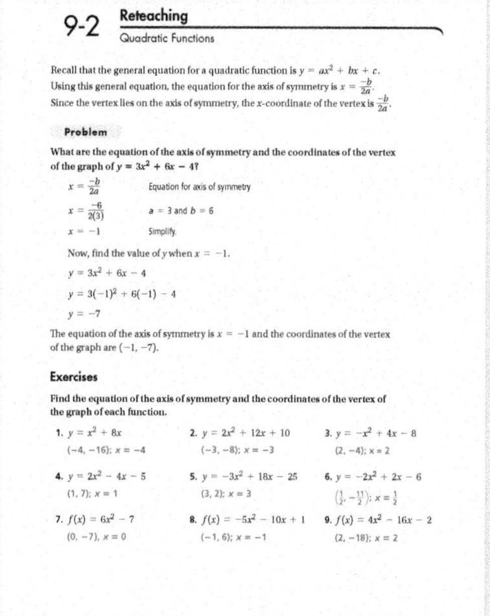

9-2 Reteaching

Quadratic Functions

Recall that the general equation for a quadratic function is $y = ax^2 + bx + c$.
Using this general equation, the equation for the axis of symmetry is $x = \frac{-b}{2a}$.
Since the vertex lies on the axis of symmetry, the x-coordinate of the vertex is $\frac{-b}{2a}$.

Problem

What are the equation of the axis of symmetry and the coordinates of the vertex of the graph of $y = 3x^2 + 6x - 4$?

$x = \frac{-b}{2a}$ Equation for axis of symmetry

$x = \frac{-6}{2(3)}$ $a = 3$ and $b = 6$

$x = -1$ Simplify.

Now, find the value of y when $x = -1$.

$y = 3x^2 + 6x - 4$

$y = 3(-1)^2 + 6(-1) - 4$

$y = -7$

The equation of the axis of symmetry is $x = -1$ and the coordinates of the vertex of the graph are $(-1, -7)$.

Exercises

Find the equation of the axis of symmetry and the coordinates of the vertex of the graph of each function.

1. $y = x^2 + 8x$ $(-4, -16)$; $x = -4$
2. $y = 2x^2 + 12x + 10$ $(-3, -8)$; $x = -3$
3. $y = -x^2 + 4x - 8$ $(2, -4)$; $x = 2$
4. $y = 2x^2 - 4x - 5$ $(1, 7)$; $x = 1$
5. $y = -3x^2 + 18x - 25$ $(3, 2)$; $x = 3$
6. $y = -2x^2 + 2x - 6$ $\left(\frac{1}{2}, -\frac{11}{2}\right)$; $x = \frac{1}{2}$
7. $f(x) = 6x^2 - 7$ $(0, -7)$, $x = 0$
8. $f(x) = -5x^2 - 10x + 1$ $(-1, 6)$; $x = -1$
9. $f(x) = 4x^2 - 16x - 2$ $(2, -18)$; $x = 2$

All-in-One Resources/Online

English Language Learner Support

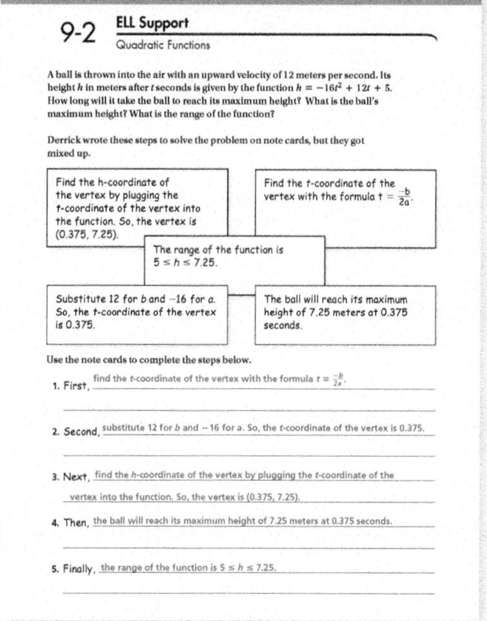

9-2 ELL Support

Quadratic Functions

A ball is thrown into the air with an upward velocity of 12 meters per second. Its height h in meters after t seconds is given by the function $h = -16t^2 + 12t + 5$. How long will it take the ball to reach its maximum height? What is the ball's maximum height? What is the range of the function?

Derrick wrote these steps to solve the problem on note cards, but they got mixed up.

Find the h-coordinate of the vertex by plugging the t-coordinate of the vertex into the function. So, the vertex is (0.375, 7.25).

Find the t-coordinate of the vertex with the formula $t = \frac{-b}{2a}$.

The range of the function is $5 \le h \le 7.25$.

Substitute 12 for b and −16 for a. So, the t-coordinate of the vertex is 0.375.

The ball will reach its maximum height of 7.25 meters at 0.375 seconds.

Use the note cards to complete the steps below.

1. First, find the t-coordinate of the vertex with the formula $t = \frac{-b}{2a}$.
2. Second, substitute 12 for b and −16 for a. So, the t-coordinate of the vertex is 0.375.
3. Next, find the h-coordinate of the vertex by plugging the t-coordinate of the vertex into the function. So, the vertex is (0.375, 7.25).
4. Then, the ball will reach its maximum height of 7.25 meters at 0.375 seconds.
5. Finally, the range of the function is $5 \le h \le 7.25$.

Differentiated Remediation *continued*

On-Level

- **Practice (2 pages)** Provides extra practice for each lesson. For simpler practice exercises, use the Form K Practice pages found in the All-in-One Teaching Resources and online.

- **Think About a Plan** Helps students develop specific problem-solving skills and strategies by providing scaffolded guiding questions.

- **Standardized Test Prep** Focuses on all major exercises, all major question types, and helps students prepare for the high-stakes assessments.

Extension

- **Enrichment** Provides students with interesting problems and activities that extend the concepts of the lesson.

- **Activities, Games, and Puzzles** Worksheets that can be used for concepts development, enrichment, and for fun!

Practice and Problem Solving WKBK/ All-in-One Resources/Online
Practice page 1

Practice and Problem Solving WKBK/ All-in-One Resources/Online
Practice page 2

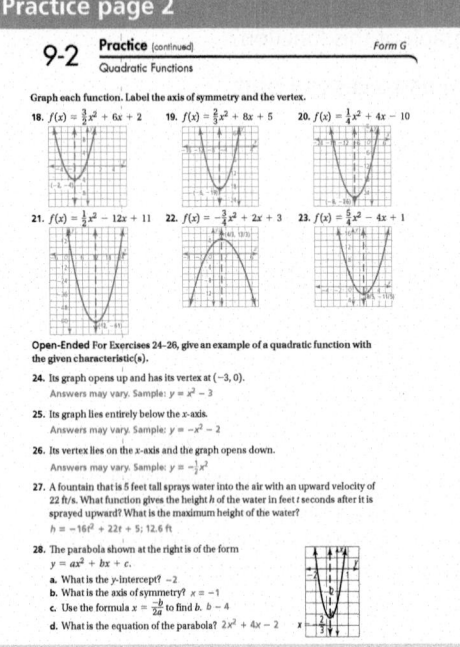

All-in-One Resources/Online
Enrichment

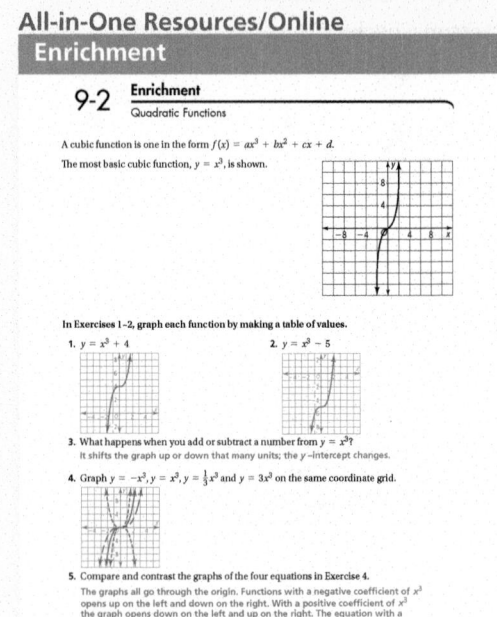

Practice and Problem Solving WKBK/ All-in-One Resources/Online
Think About a Plan

Practice and Problem Solving WKBK/ All-in-One Resources/Online
Standardized Test Prep

Online Teacher Resource Center
Activities, Games, and Puzzles

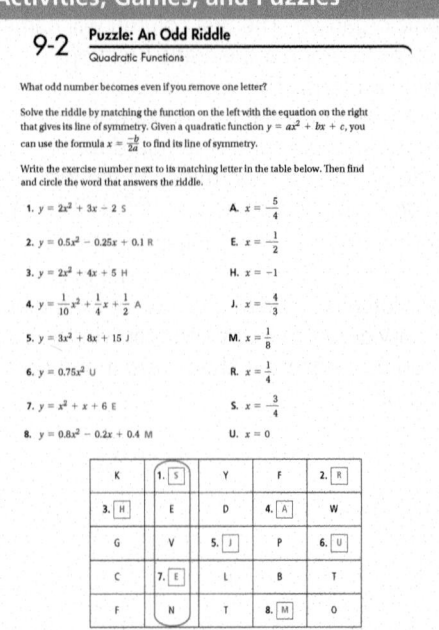

Concept Byte

Use With Lesson 9-2

Collecting Quadratic Data

In this activity, you will use a loop of string to make rectangles, record their dimensions, and explore the graph of length versus area.

Activity

Take a piece of string, no more than 40 cm long, and tie the ends to form a loop. Use your thumbs and fingers to make a rectangle with the string. Hold it over a piece of graph paper to make right angles.

Step 1 Copy the table at the right. Use the units on your graph paper to measure the length ℓ and width w of the rectangle. Record the measurements to the nearest tenth of a centimeter.

Step 2 Repeat Step 1 four more times, and complete the first two columns.

Step 3 Record the area of each rectangle in the third column of the table.

Step 4 Graph ordered pairs (length, area). Connect the points with a smooth curve.

Length (ℓ)	Width (w)	Area (A)
▪	▪	▪
▪	▪	▪
▪	▪	▪
▪	▪	▪
▪	▪	▪

Exercises

1. **Writing** Based on your graph from Step 4, explain why the data you collected in the activity cannot be modeled by a linear or exponential function.

2. **a.** Find the length of your loop of string.
   b. Write an expression for the width of any rectangle made with your loop of string in terms of the rectangle's length ℓ.
   c. Write a function for the area A of any rectangle made with your loop of string in terms of the rectangle's length ℓ.
   d. Graph the function.
   e. Find the vertex of the graph. What is the meaning of the vertex?

3. Does your graph from part (d) of Exercise 2 exactly match the graph from Step 4 of the activity? If not, explain why not.

4. Suppose you repeated the activity with a loop of string that was 140 cm long. Write a function for the area A of any rectangle made with your loop of string in terms of the rectangle's length ℓ.

Guided Instruction

PURPOSE To explore the relationship between the length and the area of rectangles

PROCESS Students will make a rectangle from a piece of string, record the lengths, widths, and areas of their rectangles in a table, and graph ordered pairs, (length, area) to see the relationship.

DISCUSS Have students work in pairs. While one student is stretching the loop into a rectangle over the graph paper, the other student will measure and record. Then, together, have them plot the graph of their data.

ACTIVITY In this Activity students explore what type of relationship exists between the length and the area of rectangles.

Q By using the same loop of string to create all of the rectangles, what measure or dimension stays constant between rectangles? **[perimeter]**

Q Using your loop, what type of rectangle do you suppose will have the greatest area? **[the square]**

Q Where will this be on your graph? **[It will be the maximum point on the graph.]**

Q As the length approaches zero, what does the area approach? **[0 cm^2]**

Answers

Exercises

1. Answers may vary. Sample: As the length of the rectangle increases, the area of the rectangle increases, and then decreases.

2–3. Check students' work.

4. $A = 70\ell - \ell^2$

1 Interactive Learning

Solve It!

PURPOSE To solve an equation of the form $ax^2 = b$

PROCESS Students may use the formula for the volume of a rectangular solid to write an equation, and may use trial and error, a table, graphing, or inverse operations to solve the equation.

FACILITATE

Q How many cubic inches of topsoil is equivalent to 1.5 cubic yards of topsoil? Explain. **[One cubic yard contains 46,656 cubic inches, so 1.5 yd³ contains 69,984 in.³ of fertilizer.]**

Q What equation represents the largest garden you can build? **[$4x^2 = 69,984$]**

Q If $4x^2 = 69,984$, what does x^2 equal? Explain. **[$x^2 = 17,496$ using the Division Property of Equality.]**

ANSWER See Solve It in Answers on next page.
CONNECT THE MATH In the Solve It, students model a situation using a quadratic equation. In the lesson, students solve quadratic equations by graphing and locating the points of intersection with the x-axis.

2 Guided Instruction

Take Note

Q If $a = 0$, $b \neq 0$, and $c \neq 0$, what kind of equation would you have? **[linear equation]**

Q Can you solve a quadratic equation such as $3x^2 + 4x - 7 = 0$ using the same methods you use to solve a linear equation? Explain. **[No, you cannot isolate x because there is both an x^2- and an x-term.]**

9-3 Solving Quadratic Equations

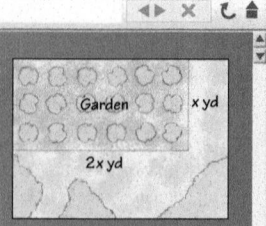

Objective To solve quadratic equations by graphing and using square roots

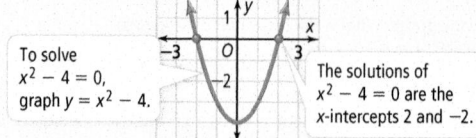

> **SOLVE IT!**
> **Getting Ready!**
>
> The diagram shows a plan for your new garden. You want to use only 1.5 yd³ of topsoil and plan to spread a layer 4 in. deep. What are the dimensions of the largest garden you can build? How do you know?
>
> Garden — x yd
> 2x yd

Need help converting units? Lesson 2-6 will help you out.

Lesson Vocabulary

- quadratic equation
- standard form of a quadratic equation
- root of an equation
- zero of a function

The situation in the Solve It can be modeled by a *quadratic equation*.

> **take note**
>
> ### Key Concept   Standard Form of a Quadratic Equation
>
> A **quadratic equation** is an equation that can be written in the form $ax^2 + bx + c = 0$, where $a \neq 0$. This form is called the **standard form of a quadratic equation**.

Essential Understanding Quadratic equations can be solved by a variety of methods, including graphing and finding square roots.

One way to solve a quadratic equation $ax^2 + bx + c = 0$ is to graph the related quadratic function $y = ax^2 + bx + c$. The solutions of the equation are the x-intercepts of the related function.

To solve $x^2 - 4 = 0$, graph $y = x^2 - 4$.

The solutions of $x^2 - 4 = 0$ are the x-intercepts 2 and -2.

A quadratic equation can have two, one, or no real-number solutions. In a future course you will learn about solutions of quadratic equations that are not real numbers. In this course, *solutions* refers to real-number solutions.

The solutions of a quadratic equation and the x-intercepts of the graph of the related function are often called **roots of the equation** or **zeros of the function**.

9-3 Preparing to Teach

BIG ideas Solving Equations and Inequalities

Function

UbD

ESSENTIAL UNDERSTANDINGS
- Quadratic equations can be solved by a variety of methods, including graphing and finding the square root.
- In many cases the negative solution of a quadratic equation will not be a reasonable solution to the original problem.

Math Background

Graphing can be used to solve quadratic equations as well as linear equations. A linear equation such as $3x - 4 = 5$ can be solved algebraically to reveal a solution of $x = 3$, or the related linear function $y + 5 = 3x - 4$ can be graphed to reveal an x-intercept of 3. A quadratic equation such as $2x^2 + 50 = 0$ can be solved algebraically to reveal solutions of $x = \pm 5$ or the related quadratic

function $y = 2x^2 + 50$ can be graphed to reveal x-intercepts of 5 and -5.

When students encounter higher-order polynomial equations in future math courses, algebraic techniques may not be appropriate, leaving graphing as the best available technique for solving an equation.

Support Student Learning

Use the **Algebra 1 Companion** to engage and support students during instructions. See Lesson Resources at the end of this lesson for details.

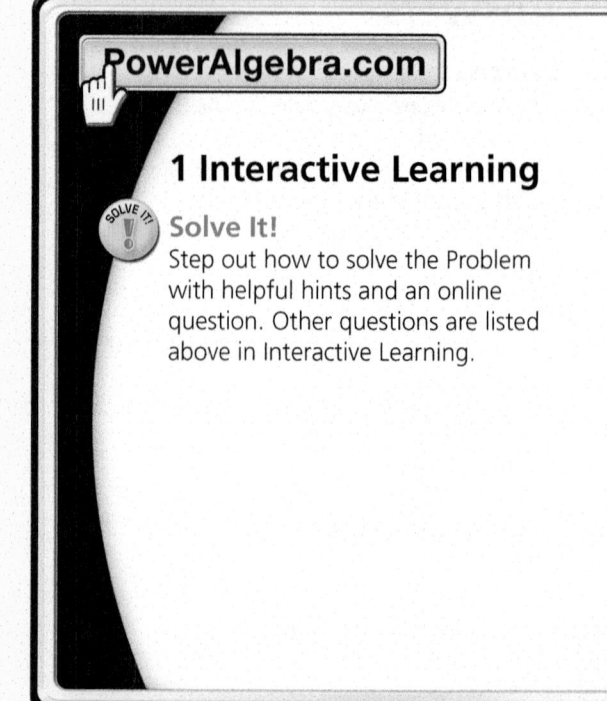

PowerAlgebra.com

1 Interactive Learning

Solve It!

Step out how to solve the Problem with helpful hints and an online question. Other questions are listed above in Interactive Learning.

 **Problem 1** Solving by Graphing

What are the solutions of each equation? Use a graph of the related function.

A $x^2 - 1 = 0$

Graph $y = x^2 - 1$.

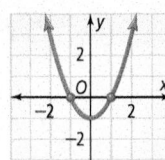

There are two solutions, ±1.

B $x^2 = 0$

Graph $y = x^2$.

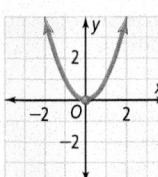

There is one solution, 0.

C $x^2 + 1 = 0$

Graph $y = x^2 + 1$.

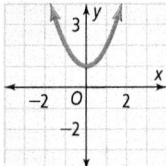

There is no real-number solution.

Think

What feature of the graph shows the solutions of the equation?

The x-intercepts show the solutions of the equation.

 Got It? **1.** What are the solutions of each equation? Use a graph of the related function.

a. $x^2 - 16 = 0$ **b.** $3x^2 + 6 = 0$ **c.** $x^2 - 25 = -25$

You can solve equations of the form $x^2 = k$ by finding the square roots of each side. For example, the solutions of $x^2 = 81$ are $\pm\sqrt{81}$, or ±9.

Problem 2 Solving Using Square Roots

What are the solutions of $3x^2 - 75 = 0$?

Think	Write
Write the original equation.	$3x^2 - 75 = 0$
Isolate x^2 on one side of the equation.	$3x^2 = 75$ $x^2 = 25$
Find the square roots of each side and simplify.	$x = \pm\sqrt{25}$ $x = \pm 5$

Plan

How do you know you can solve using square roots?

The equation has an x^2-term and a constant term, but no x-term. So, you can write the equation in the form $x^2 = k$ and then find the square roots of each side.

Got It? **2.** What are the solutions of each equation?

a. $m^2 - 36 = 0$ **b.** $3x^2 + 15 = 0$ **c.** $4d^2 + 16 = 16$

Problem 1

Q What is the axis of symmetry for each of the parabolas? Explain. [$x = 0$; for each equation $\frac{-b}{2a} = 0$.]

Q What translation of the graph of $y = x^2$ are the graphs of $y = x^2 + 1$ and $y = x^2 - 1$? **[The graph of $y = x^2 + 1$ is a vertical translation 1 unit up. The graph of $y = x^2 - 1$ is a vertical translation 1 unit down from the graph of $y = x^2$.]**

Q Without solving the equation, how can you tell that the equation $x^2 + 1 = 0$ has no real solutions? **[x^2 would have to equal -1, which is impossible.]**

Got It?   ERROR PREVENTION

If students give an answer of ±5 as the solutions to the equation in 1c, then they likely did not write the equation in standard form.

Problem 2

Q What is the quadratic equation associated with the question? [$y = 3x^2 - 75$]

Q What are the x-intercepts of the graph of $y = 3x^2 - 75$? **[The x-intercepts of the graph are 5 and -5.]**

Q How are the graphs of the equations $y = x^2 - 25$ and $y = 3x^2 - 75$ related? **[They both have x-intercepts of 5 and -5.]**

Q What can you say about the solutions of both equations $y = x^2 - 25$ and $y = 3x^2 - 75$? **[The equations have the same solutions.]**

Got It?   VISUAL LEARNERS

Ask students to describe the relationship between the graph of each related quadratic function and the x-axis.

Answers

Solve It!

2.6 yd by 5.2 yd; explanations may vary.

Got It?

1. a. ±4
   b. no solution
   c. 0

2. a. ±6
   b. no solution
   c. 0

2 Guided Instruction

 Each Problem is worked out and supported online.

Problem 1
Solving by Graphing
                    Animated

Problem 2
Solving Using Square Roots
                    Animated

Problem 3
Choosing a Reasonable Solution
                    Animated

Support in Algebra 1 Companion
• Vocabulary
• Key Concepts
• Got It?

Problem 3

> **Q** Could you also write the width in terms of the length? Explain. **[Yes, you could let the length be ℓ and the width be $\frac{1}{2}\ell$.]**
>
> **Q** How many solutions are there for the equation $w^2 = 70$? How many of the solutions make sense when interpreted in the problem situation? Explain. **[Two; one; a negative distance does not make sense.]**

Got It?   VISUAL LEARNERS

Show students how to use a graphing calculator to find the solutions to the equation in Problem 3. Emphasize that while graphing by hand might not produce an exact enough solution, using the zero function on a graphing calculator does.

3 Lesson Check

Do you know HOW?

• To show the connection between the x-intercepts of the related quadratic function and the solutions of the quadratic equation, ask students to solve Exercises 1–4 using both methods.

Do you UNDERSTAND?

• If students have difficulty with Exercise 7, then have them use the equation in Problem 1 to make generalizations about equations of the form $ax^2 + c = 0$.

Close

> **Q** How are the solutions for a quadratic equation related to the graph of its quadratic function? **[The solutions to a quadratic equation are the same as the x-intercepts of the related quadratic function.]**

You can solve some quadratic equations that model real-world problems by finding square roots. In many cases, the negative square root may not be a reasonable solution.

 **Problem 3** Choosing a Reasonable Solution   GRIDDED RESPONSE

Aquarium An aquarium is designing a new exhibit to showcase tropical fish. The exhibit will include a tank that is a rectangular prism with a length ℓ that is twice the width w. The volume of the tank is 420 ft³. What is the width of the tank to the nearest tenth of a foot?

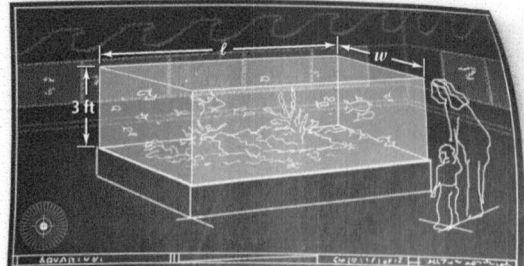

Plan

How can you write the length of the tank?
The length ℓ is twice the width w, so write the length as $2w$.

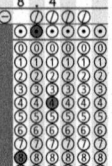

$V = \ell w h$	Use the formula for volume of a rectangular prism.
$420 = (2w)w(3)$	Substitute 420 for V, $2w$ for ℓ, and 3 for h.
$420 = 6w^2$	Simplify.
$70 = w^2$	Divide each side by 6.
$\pm\sqrt{70} = w$	Find the square roots of each side.
$\pm 8.366600265 \approx w$	Use a calculator.

A tank cannot have a negative width, so only the positive square root make sense. The tank will have a width of about 8.4 ft.

 Got It? 3. a. Suppose the tank in Problem 3 will have a height of 4 ft and a volume of 500 ft³. What is the width of the tank to the nearest tenth of a foot?
b. Reasoning What are the disadvantages of using a graph to approximate the solution to Problem 3? Explain.

Lesson Check

Do you know HOW?

Solve each equation by graphing the related function or by finding square roots.

1. $x^2 - 25 = 0$

2. $2x^2 - 8 = 0$

3. $t^2 = 144$

4. $y^2 - 225 = 0$

Do you UNDERSTAND?

5. Vocabulary What are the zeros of a function? Give an example of a quadratic function and its zeros.

6. Compare and Contrast When is it easier to solve a quadratic equation of the form $ax^2 + c = 0$ using square roots than to solve it using a graph?

7. Reasoning Consider the equation $ax^2 + c = 0$, where $a \neq 0$. What is true of a and c if the equation has two solutions? Only one solution? No solutions?

Additional Problems

1. What are the solutions of each equation? Use a graph of the related function.

a. $x^2 - 16 = 0$

b. $(x - 2)^2 = 0$

c. $x^2 + 10 = 0$

ANSWER a. $-4, 4$ **b.** 2
c. no solution

2. What are the solutions of $5x^2 - 45 = 0$?

ANSWER $-3, 3$

3. The length of a rectangular prism is three times the width. The height of the prism is 5 in. If the volume of the prism is 80 in.³, what is the length of the prism? Round to the nearest tenth of an inch.

ANSWER 6.9 in.

Answers

Got It? (continued)
3. a. 7.9 ft
   b. The solutions of the equation in Problem 3 are irrational numbers, which are difficult to approximate on a graph.

Lesson Check
1. ± 5 **2.** ± 2
3. ± 12 **4.** ± 15
5. The zeros of a function are the x-intercepts of the function. Example: $y = x^2 - 25$ has zeros ± 5.
6. Answers will vary. Sample: When an equation has noninteger solutions, it is almost always easier to use square roots to find its solutions.
7. a and c have opposite signs; $c = 0$; a and c have the same sign.

Practice and Problem-Solving Exercises

A Practice

Solve each equation by graphing the related function. If the equation has no real-number solution, write *no solution*. ◆ See Problem 1.

8. $x^2 - 9 = 0$ **9.** $x^2 + 7 = 0$ **10.** $3x^2 = 0$

11. $3x^2 - 12 = 0$ **12.** $x^2 + 4 = 0$ **13.** $\frac{1}{3}x^2 - 3 = 0$

14. $\frac{1}{2}x^2 + 1 = 0$ **15.** $x^2 + 5 = 5$ **16.** $\frac{1}{4}x^2 - 1 = 0$

17. $x^2 + 25 = 0$ **18.** $x^2 - 10 = -10$ **19.** $2x^2 - 18 = 0$

Solve each equation by finding square roots. If the equation has no real-number solution, write *no solution*. ◆ See Problem 2.

20. $n^2 = 81$ **21.** $a^2 = 324$ **22.** $k^2 - 196 = 0$

23. $r^2 + 49 = 49$ **24.** $w^2 - 36 = -64$ **25.** $4g^2 = 25$

26. $64b^2 = 16$ **27.** $5q^2 - 20 = 0$ **28.** $144 - p^2 = 0$

29. $2r^2 - 32 = 0$ **30.** $3a^2 + 12 = 0$ **31.** $5z^2 - 45 = 0$

Model each problem with a quadratic equation. Then solve. If necessary, round to the nearest tenth. ◆ See Problem 3.

32. Find the length of a side of a square with an area of 169 m².

33. Find the length of a side of a square with an area of 75 ft².

34. Find the radius of a circle with an area of 90 cm².

35. **Painting** You have enough paint to cover an area of 50 ft². What is the side length of the largest square that you could paint? Round your answer to the nearest tenth of a foot.

36. **Gardening** You have enough shrubs to cover an area of 100 ft². What is the radius of the largest circular region you can plant with these shrubs? Round your answer to the nearest tenth of a foot.

B Apply

Mental Math Tell how many solutions each equation has.

37. $h^2 = -49$ **38.** $c^2 - 18 = 9$ **39.** $s^2 - 35 = -35$

40. **Think About a Plan** A circular above-ground pool has a height of 52 in. and a volume of 1100 ft³. What is the radius of the pool to the nearest tenth of a foot? Use the equation $V = \pi r^2 h$, where V is the volume, r is the radius, and h is the height.
• How can drawing a diagram help you solve this problem?
• Do you need to convert any of the given measurements to different units?

41. **Reasoning** For what values of n will the equation $x^2 = n$ have two solutions? Exactly one solution? No solution?

Practice and Problem-Solving Exercises

8. ±3 **9.** no solution

10. 0 **11.** ±2

12. no solution **13.** ±3

14. no solution **15.** 0

16. ±2 **17.** no solution

18. 0 **19.** ±3

20. ±9 **21.** ±18

22. ±14 **23.** 0

24. no solution **25.** $\pm\frac{5}{2}$

26. $\pm\frac{1}{2}$ **27.** ±2

28. ±12 **29.** ±4

30. no solution **31.** ±3

32. Let x = length of side of a square, then $x^2 = 169$; 13 m

33. Let x = length of side of a square, then $x^2 = 75$; 8.7 ft

34. Let r = radius, then $\pi r^2 = 90$; 5.4 cm

35. 7.1 ft **36.** 5.6 ft

37. 0 **38.** 2

39. 1 **40.** 9.0 ft

41. $n > 0$; $n = 0$; $n < 0$

---

4 Practice

ASSIGNMENT GUIDE

Basic: 8–36 all, 38–48 even, 51

Average: 9–35 odd, 37–55

Advanced: 9–35 odd, 37–57

Standardized Test Prep: 58–62

Mixed Review: 63–74

Reasoning exercises have blue headings.

Applications exercises have red headings.

EXERCISE 42: Use the Think About a Plan worksheet in the **Practice and Problem Solving Workbook** (also available in the Teaching Resources in print and online) to further support students' development in becoming independent learners.

HOMEWORK QUICK CHECK

To check students' understanding of key skills and concepts, go over Exercises 15, 33, 40, 42, and 51.

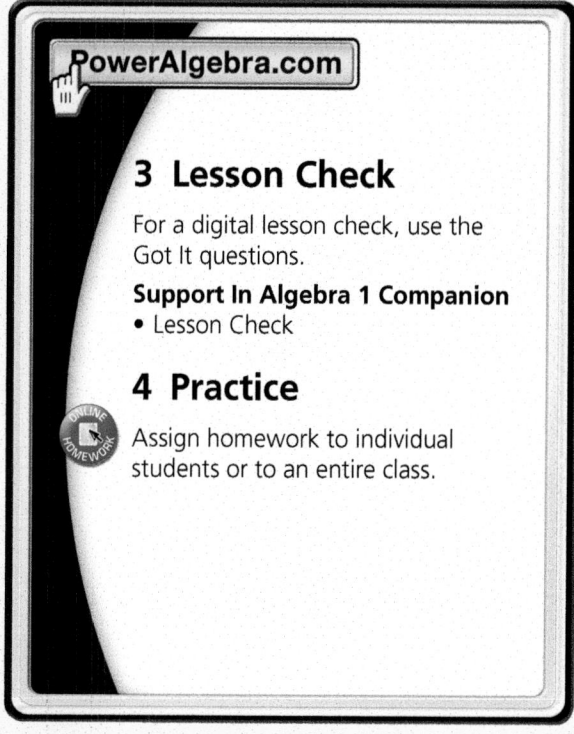

PowerAlgebra.com

3 Lesson Check

For a digital lesson check, use the Got It questions.

Support In Algebra 1 Companion
• Lesson Check

4 Practice

Assign homework to individual students or to an entire class.

Answers

Practice and Problem-Solving Exercises
(continued)

42. 4.2 ft   **43.** no solution

44. $\pm\frac{3}{7}$ **45.** $\pm\frac{1}{6}$

46. ±2.8 **47.** ±0.4

48. ±3.5 **49.** 144

50. 3.5 s

51. The student did not subtract 100 from each side of the equation. When you subtract 100 from each side, you get $x^2 = -100$, which has no solution.

52. Answers will vary. Samples are given.
   a. $2x^2 + 5 = 0$
   b. $x^2 + 0 = 0$
   c. $4x^2 - 9 = 0$

53. 6.3 ft   **54.** 11.0 cm

55. a. $= 6(A2)^2 - 24$
   b. ±2; the solution(s) of the quadratic equation is (are) the x-value(s) in column A that make(s) the value in column B equal 0.
   c. Answers may vary. Sample: Find each instance of a sign change in column B. The solution(s) lie(s) between the corresponding x-values in column A.

---

42. Quilting You are making a square quilt with the design shown at the right. Find the side length x of the inner square that would make its area equal to 50% of the total area of the quilt. Round to the nearest tenth of a foot.

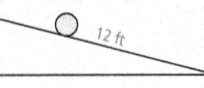

Solve each equation by finding square roots. If the equation has no real-number solution, write *no solution*. If a solution is irrational, round to the nearest tenth.

43. $1.2z^2 - 7 = -34$ **44.** $49p^2 - 16 = -7$ **45.** $3m^2 - \frac{1}{12} = 0$

46. $\frac{1}{2}t^2 - 4 = 0$ **47.** $7y^2 + 0.12 = 1.24$ **48.** $-\frac{1}{4}x^2 + 3 = 0$

49. Find the value of c such that the equation $x^2 - c = 0$ has 12 and -12 as solutions.

50. Physics The equation $d = \frac{1}{2}at^2$ gives the distance d that an object starting at rest travels given acceleration a and time t. Suppose a ball rolls down the ramp shown at the right with acceleration $a = 2$ ft/s^2. Find the time it will take the ball to roll from the top of the ramp to the bottom. Round to the nearest tenth of a second.

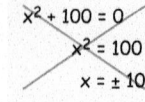

51. Error Analysis Describe and correct the error made in solving the equation.

52. Open-Ended Write and solve an equation in the form $ax^2 + c = 0$, where $a \neq 0$, that satisfies the given condition.
   a. The equation has no solution.
   b. The equation has exactly one solution.
   c. The equation has two solutions.

$$x^2 + 100 = 0$$
$$x^2 = 100$$
$$x = \pm 10$$

Geometry Find the value of h for each triangle. If necessary, round to the nearest tenth.

53.

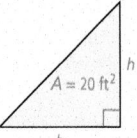

$A = 20 \text{ ft}^2$

54.

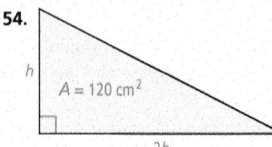

$A = 120 \text{ cm}^2$

55. You can use a spreadsheet like the one at the right to solve a quadratic equation.
   a. What spreadsheet formula would you use to find the value in cell B2?
   b. Use a spreadsheet to find the solutions of the quadratic equation $6x^2 - 24 = 0$. Explain how you used the spreadsheet to find the solutions.
   c. Reasoning Suppose a quadratic equation has solutions that are not integers. How could you use a spreadsheet to approximate the solutions?

	A	B
1	x	6x^2 − 24 = 0
2	−3	
3	−2	
4	−1	
5	0	
6	1	
7	2	
8	3	

Challenge

56. a. Solve the equation $(x - 7)^2 = 0$.
  b. Find the vertex of the graph of the related function $y = (x - 7)^2$.
  c. Open-Ended Choose a value for h and repeat parts (a) and (b) using $(x - h)^2 = 0$ and $y = (x - h)^2$.
  d. Where would you expect to find the vertex of the graph of $y = (x + 4)^2$? Explain.

57. Geometry The trapezoid has an area of 1960 cm². Use the formula $A = \frac{1}{2}h(b_1 + b_2)$, where A represents the area of the trapezoid, h represents its height, and b_1 and b_2 represent its bases, to find the value of y.

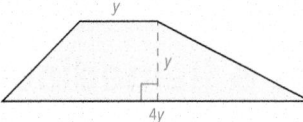

Standardized Test Prep

SAT/ACT

58. A package is shaped like a rectangular prism. The length and the width are equal. The volume of the package is 32 ft³. The height is 2 ft. What is its length?
  Ⓐ −4 ft   Ⓑ 4 ft   Ⓒ 8 ft   Ⓓ 16 ft

59. What is the y-intercept of the line with equation $y = 3x - 4$?
  Ⓕ −4   Ⓖ −3   Ⓗ 3   Ⓘ 4

60. What is the domain of the relation $\{(3, -1), (4, 2), (-2, 5), (1, 0)\}$?
  Ⓐ $\{-1, 0, 2, 5\}$ Ⓑ $\{0, 2, 5\}$ Ⓒ $\{-2, 1, 3, 4\}$ Ⓓ $\{1, 3, 4\}$

61. What is the solution of the inequality $-3x + 2 \le 14$?
  Ⓕ $x \le -4$ Ⓖ $x \ge -4$ Ⓗ $x \le 4$ Ⓘ $x \ge 4$

Extended Response

62. The surface area of a cube is 96 ft².
  a. What is the length of each edge? Show your work.
  b. Suppose you double the length of each edge. What happens to the surface area of the cube? Show your work.

Mixed Review

Graph each function. Label the axis of symmetry and the vertex.   ◀ See Lesson 9-2.

63. $y = x^2 + 4x + 3$ **64.** $y = x^2 + 5x + 4$ **65.** $y = 2x^2 - 8x - 5$
66. $y = -x^2 + 6x - 1$ **67.** $y = 6x^2 - 12x + 1$ **68.** $y = -3x^2 + 18x$

Get Ready!   To prepare for Lesson 9-4, do Exercises 69–74.

Factor each expression.   ◀ See Lesson 8-6.

69. $2c^2 + 29c + 14$ **70.** $3w^2 + 32w + 20$ **71.** $4g^2 - 21g - 18$
72. $2r^2 - 13r - 24$ **73.** $3w^2 + 16w - 12$ **74.** $5p^2 - 34p + 24$

 Lesson 9-3 Solving Quadratic Equations   553

56. a. 7
  b. (7, 0)
  c. Answers will vary. Sample: $h = 5, x = 5, (5, 0)$
  d. (−4, 0); the vertex of a quadratic function in the form $y = (x - h)^2$ is $(h, 0)$.
57. 28 cm   **58.** B
59. F   **60.** C
61. G

62. [4] **a.** Let x = length of an edge, then $6x^2 = 96$, $x^2 = 16$, and $x = 4$. Each edge is 4 ft long.
  b. If each edge is 8 ft, then the surface area is $6(8^2) = 384$ ft², which is 4 times the original surface area. The surface area is multiplied by 4.
  [3] one computational error
  [2] Student uses $4x^2$ for the surface area of a cube, otherwise all work is correct.
  [1] Answers to part (a) and (b) are correct, but no work is shown.

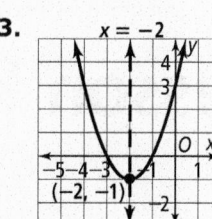
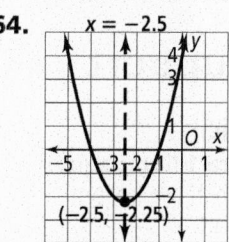
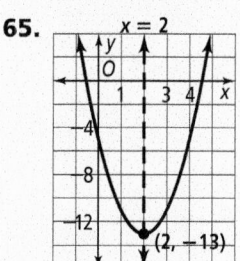
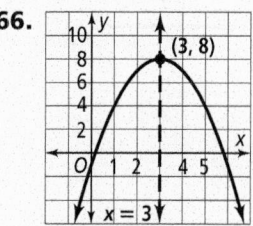
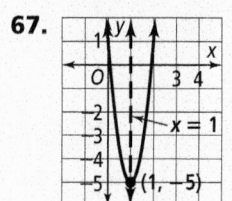
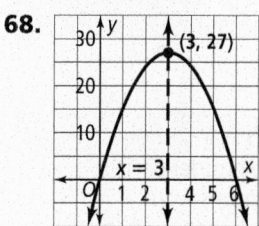

69. $(2c + 1)(c + 14)$
70. $(3w + 2)(w + 10)$
71. $(4g + 3)(g - 6)$
72. $(2r + 3)(r - 8)$
73. $(3w - 2)(w + 6)$
74. $(5p - 4)(p - 6)$

Additional Instructional Support

Algebra 1 Companion

Students can use the **Algebra 1 Companion** worktext (4 pages) as you teach the lesson. Use the Companion to support

- New Vocabulary
- Key Concepts
- Got It for each Problem
- Lesson Check

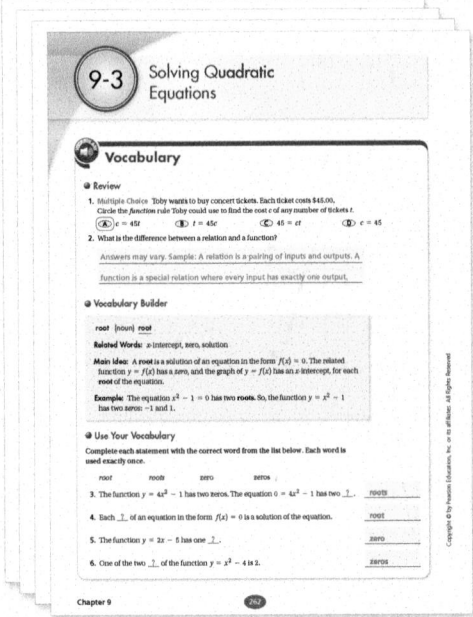

ELL Support

Focus on Communication Pair students so there is a more proficient student with a less proficient student. Write several quadratic equations on the board, such as $y = x^2$, $y = x^2 + 3$, $y = x^2 + 3x$, and $y = x^2 + 3x + 1$. Tell students to graph each equation on the same piece of graph paper using different colored pencils. Have each pair make a list of similarities and differences among the graphs. Then tell students to write a paragraph that compares each graph.

5 Assess & Remediate

Lesson Quiz

1. What are the solutions of each equation? Use a graph of the related function.

    a. $x^2 + 4 = 4$

    b. $x^2 + 16 = 0$

    c. $x^2 - 49 = 0$

2. What are the solutions of $6x^2 - 216 = 0$?

3. The length of a rectangular prism is four times the width. The height of the prism is 8 ft. If the volume of the prism is 160 ft³, what is the width of the prism? Round to the nearest tenth of a foot.

4. **Do you UNDERSTAND?** If you have an equation of the form $ax^2 + c = 0$, under what conditions will there be no real solutions?

ANSWERS TO LESSON QUIZ

1. **a.** 0   **b.** no real solutions   **c.** −7, 7

2. −6, 6

3. 2.2 ft

4. There will be no real solutions if $c > 0$.

PRESCRIPTION FOR REMEDIATION
Use the student work on the Lesson Quiz to prescribe a differentiated review assignment.

Points	Differentiated Remediation
0–2	Intervention
3	On-level
4	Extension

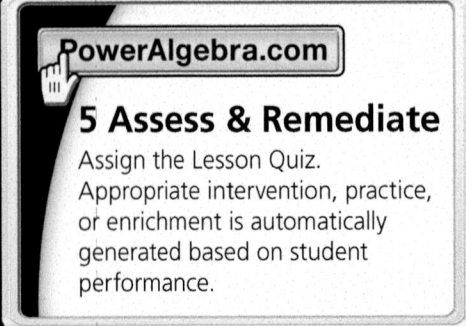

PowerAlgebra.com

5 Assess & Remediate

Assign the Lesson Quiz. Appropriate intervention, practice, or enrichment is automatically generated based on student performance.

Intervention

- **Reteaching** (2 pages) Provides reteaching and practice exercises for the key lesson concepts. Use with struggling students or absent students.

- **English Language Learner Support** Helps students develop and reinforce mathematical vocabulary and key concepts.

All-in-One Resources/Online
Reteaching

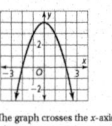

All-in-One Resources/Online
English Language Learner Support

Differentiated Remediation *continued*

On-Level

- **Practice** (2 pages) Provides extra practice for each lesson. For simpler practice exercises, use the Form K Practice pages found in the All-in-One Teaching Resources and online.
- **Think About a Plan** Helps students develop specific problem-solving skills and strategies by providing scaffolded guiding questions.
- **Standardized Test Prep** Focuses on all major exercises, all major question types, and helps students prepare for the high-stakes assessments.

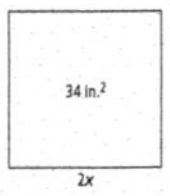

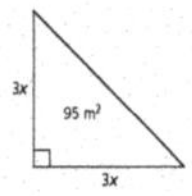

Extension

- **Enrichment** Provides students with interesting problems and activities that extend the concepts of the lesson.
- **Activities, Games, and Puzzles** Worksheets that can be used for concepts development, enrichment, and for fun!

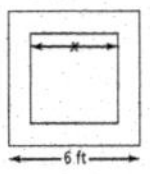

Practice and Problem Solving WKBK/ All-in-One Resources/Online
Practice page 1

9-3 Practice *Form G*
Solving Quadratic Equations

Solve each equation by graphing the related function. If the equation has no real-number solution, write *no solution*.

1. $x^2 - 16 = 0$ 4; −4
2. $x^2 + 12 = 0$ no solution
3. $2x^2 - 18 = 0$ 3; −3
4. $7x^2 = 0$ 0
5. $\frac{1}{2}x^2 - 2 = 0$ 2; −2
6. $x^2 + 49 = 0$ no solution
7. $x^2 - 15 = -15$ 0
8. $4x^2 - 36 = 0$ 3; −3
9. $x^2 + 36 = 0$ no solution

Solve each equation by finding square roots. If the equation has no real-number solution, write *no solution*.

10. $t^2 = 25$ 5; −5
11. $k^2 = 484$ 22; −22
12. $z^2 - 256 = 0$ 16; −16
13. $d^2 - 14 = -50$ no solution
14. $9y^2 - 16 = 0$ $\frac{4}{3}; -\frac{4}{3}$
15. $2g^2 - 32 = -32$ 0
16. $4a^2 = 36$ 3; −3
17. $7x^2 + 28 = 0$ no solution
18. $6n^2 - 54 = 0$ 3; −3
19. $81 - c^2 = 0$ 9; −9
20. $16x^2 - 49 = 0$ $\frac{7}{4}; -\frac{7}{4}$
21. $64 + f^2 = 0$ no solution

Model each problem with a quadratic equation. Then solve. If necessary, round to the nearest tenth.

22. Find the side length of a square with an area of 196 ft^2.
$x^2 = 196$; 14 ft
23. Find the radius of a circle with an area of 100 in^2.
$\pi r^2 = 100$; 5.6 in.^{2}
24. Find the side length of a square with an area of 50 cm^2.
$x^2 = 50$; $5\sqrt{2}$ cm or 7.1 cm

Practice and Problem Solving WKBK/ All-in-One Resources/Online
Practice page 2

9-3 Practice (continued) *Form G*
Solving Quadratic Equations

25. The square tarp you are raking leaves onto has an area of 150 ft^2. What is the side length of the tarp? Round your answer to the nearest tenth of a foot if necessary.
12.2 ft
26. There is enough mulch to spread over a flower bed with an area of 85 m^2. What is the radius of the largest circular bed that can be covered by the mulch? Round your answer to the nearest tenth of a foot if necessary.
5.2 ft

Mental Math Tell how many solutions each equation has.

27. $q^2 - 22 = -22$ one
28. $m^2 + 15 = 0$ none
29. $b^2 - 12 = 12$ two

Solve each equation by finding square roots. If the equation has no real-number solution, write *no solution*. If a solution is irrational, round to the nearest tenth.

30. $3.35z^2 + 2.75 = -14$ no solution
31. $100t^2 + 36 = 100$ 0.8; −0.8
32. $5a^2 - \frac{1}{125} = 0$ 0.04; −0.04
33. $\frac{1}{3}h^2 - 12 = 0$ 6; −6
34. $-\frac{1}{2}m^2 + 5 = -10$ 5.5; −5.5
35. $11x^2 - 0.75 = 3.21$ 0.6; −0.6
36. Find the value of n such that the equation $x^2 - n = 0$ has 24 and −24 as solutions.
576

Find the value of x for the square and triangle. If necessary, round to the nearest tenth.

37.

2.9 in.

38.

4.6 m

39. **Writing** Explain how the number of solutions for a quadratic equation relates to the graph of the function.
When there is no solution, the graph does not cross the x-axis. When there is only one solution, the vertex of the graph is on the x-axis. When the graph has two x-intercepts, the equation has two solutions.

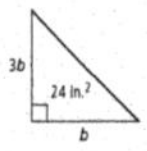

All-in-One Resources/Online
Enrichment

9-3 Enrichment
Solving Quadratic Equations

To simplify a square root, there must be no perfect square factors other than 1 in the radicand. You can use the rule below to help you simplify square roots.

The square root of a product equals the product of the square roots of the factors. For example, $\sqrt{9x} = \sqrt{9} \cdot \sqrt{x} = 3\sqrt{x}$.

Problem

Simplify $\sqrt{49a^2b^4} \cdot \sqrt{36a^6b^8}$.

$$\sqrt{49a^2b^4} \cdot \sqrt{36a^6b^8} = \left(\sqrt{49} \cdot \sqrt{a^2} \cdot \sqrt{b^4}\right) \cdot \left(\sqrt{36} \cdot \sqrt{a^6} \cdot \sqrt{b^8}\right)$$
$$= (7 \cdot a \cdot b^2) \cdot (6 \cdot a^3 \cdot b^4)$$
$$= 42a^4b^6$$

Exercises

Simplify each expression.

1. $\sqrt{64a^6b^{10}} \cdot \sqrt{81a^8b^4}$ $72a^7b^7$
2. $\sqrt{25m^{12}n^8} \cdot \sqrt{16m^6n^2}$ $20m^9n^5$
3. $\sqrt{100x^{20}y^{14}} \cdot \sqrt{121x^4y^{12}}$ $110x^{12}y^{13}$
4. $\sqrt{144r^{22}s^{14}} \cdot \sqrt{49r^6s^8}$ $84r^{14}s^{11}$
5. $\sqrt{169j^{14}k^8} \cdot \sqrt{100j^8k^{16}}$ $130j^{11}k^{12}$
6. $\sqrt{225p^{10}q^{16}} \cdot \sqrt{196p^2q^4}$ $210p^6q^{10}$
7. $\sqrt{36m^{18}n^{10}} \cdot \sqrt{81m^4n^6}$ $54m^{11}n^8$
8. $\sqrt{256x^{24}y^4} \cdot \sqrt{49x^6y^8}$ $112x^{15}y^6$
9. $\sqrt{4a^8b^6c^4} \cdot \sqrt{16a^{10}b^{12}c^6}$ $8a^9b^9c^5$
10. $\sqrt{49r^6s^{10}t^{12}} \cdot \sqrt{25r^{12}s^8t^4}$ $35r^9s^9t^8$

Practice and Problem Solving WKBK/ All-in-One Resources/Online
Think About a Plan

9-3 Think About a Plan
Solving Quadratic Equations

Quilting You are making a square quilt with the design shown at the right. Find the side length of the inner square that would make the area of the inner square equal to 50% of the total area of the quilt. Round to the nearest tenth of a foot.

1. What is an expression for the area of the inner square? x^2
2. What is the area of the entire quilt? 36 ft
3. What is 50% of the area of the entire quilt? 18 ft^2
4. Write an equation for the area of the inner square using the expressions from Steps 1 and 3. $x^2 = 18$
5. Solve the quadratic equation.
$x = \pm 3\sqrt{2}$
6. Which solution to the quadratic equation best describes the side length of the inner square? Explain.
the positive solution, because length cannot be negative

Practice and Problem Solving WKBK/ All-in-One Resources/Online
Standardized Test Prep

9-3 Standardized Test Prep
Solving Quadratic Equations

Multiple Choice

For Exercises 1–7, choose the correct letter.

1. What is the solution of $n^2 - 49 = 0$? C
A. −7 B. 7 C. ±7 D. no solution
2. What is the solution of $x^2 + 64 = 0$? I
F. −5 G. 8 H. ±8 I. no solution
3. What is the solution of $a^2 + 17 = 42$? C
A. −5 B. 5 C. ±5 D. no solution
4. What is the side length of a square with an area of $144x^2$? G
F. 12 G. $12x$ H. $\pm 12x$ I. no solution
5. What is the value of b in the triangle shown at the right? B
A. −4 in.
B. 4 in.
C. ±4 in.
D. no solution

6. What is the radius of a sphere whose surface area is 100 square centimeters? Use the formula for determining the surface area of a sphere, $S = 4\pi r^2$, and 3.14 for π. Round your answer to the nearest hundredth. F
F. 2.82 cm G. 5 cm H. 5.64 cm I. 125,600 cm
7. What is the value of z so that −9 and 9 are both solutions of $x^2 + z = 103$? C
A. −22 B. 3 C. 22 D. 184

Extended Response

8. A ball is dropped from the top of a building that is 250 feet tall. The height h of the ball in feet after t seconds is modeled by the function $h = -16t^2 + 250$. Round to the nearest tenth if necessary.
a. How long will it take for the ball to reach the ground? Show your work. 4 s
b. How long will it take for the ball to reach a height of 75 feet? Show your work. 3.3 s
[2] Both parts answered correctly.
[1] One part answered correctly.
[0] Neither part answered correctly.

Online Teacher Resource Center
Activities, Games, and Puzzles

9-3 Activity: Which Is Which?
Solving Quadratic Equations

Work in small groups of two or three students to solve the equations below.

1. $2x^2 - 25 = 7$ ±4
2. $7x^2 + 5 = 3$ no solution
3. $4x^2 - 19 = 17$ ±3
4. $10x^2 - 10 = 90$ $\pm\sqrt{10}$
5. $-3x^2 = -36$ $\pm 2\sqrt{3}$
6. $4x^2 - 20 = 5$ $\pm\frac{5}{2}$
7. $2x^2 - 5 = -5$ 0
8. $-7x^2 - 41 = 8$ no solution
9. $11x^2 = 11^2$ $\pm\sqrt{11}$
10. $16x^2 + 1 = 122$ $\pm\frac{11}{4}$
11. $2x^2 - 10 = -8$ ±1
12. $9x^2 + 11 = 12$ $\pm\frac{1}{3}$
13. $-x^2 - 1 = -1$ 0
14. $13x^2 - 16 = 10$ $\pm\sqrt{2}$
15. $7x^2 - 7 = 14$ $\pm\sqrt{3}$
16. $4 = 16x^2 - 5$ $\pm\frac{3}{4}$
17. $-3x^2 - 5 = 0$ no solution
18. $4x^2 - \frac{1}{4} = 8\frac{3}{4}$ $\pm\frac{3}{2}$

Now sort these equations by answering the following questions.

- Which equations have no solution?
- Which equations have exactly two distinct integer solutions?
- Which equations have rational solutions that are *not* integers?
- Which equations have solutions that are *not* rational?

Complete the diagram below by writing each exercise number in the appropriate space. Use each exercise number one time.

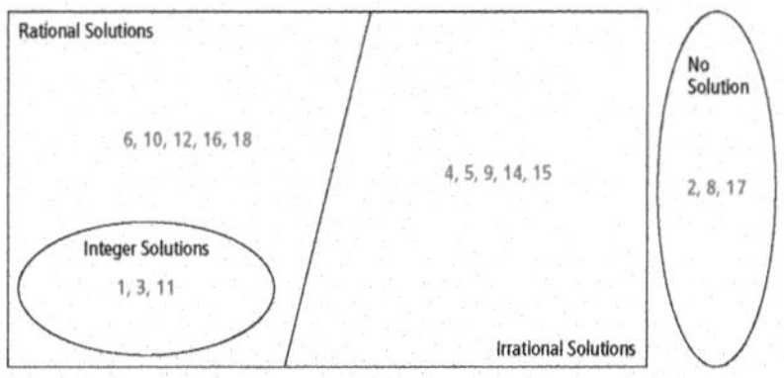

Guided Instruction

PURPOSE To use graphing calculators to find solutions of quadratic equations

PROCESS Students graph a quadratic equation using the Y= screen on their graphing calculator, and trace their graph's curve to find the *x*-intercepts or *solutions*. They also use the TABLE function on their calculators to explore solutions.

DISCUSS Three terms are synonymous when it comes to solutions of quadratic equations. *Roots*, *solutions* and *x-intercepts* all indicate the value that makes a quadratic equation true.

Activity

In this Activity, students use the graphing and TABLE features to solve a given quadratic equation.

> **Q** Where are the *x*-intercepts on a graph? **[where the graph of the function crosses the *x*-axis; this is also where the *y*-coordinates of the points of your graph are zero.]**
>
> **Q** How can you make your table more precise when using the TABLE function? **[Change the number of decimal places on the display.]**

The solutions of a quadratic equation are the *x*-intercepts of the graph of the related quadratic function. Recall that the solutions and the related *x*-intercepts are often called roots of the equation or zeros of the function.

Activity

Use a graphing calculator to solve $x^2 - 6x + 3 = 0$.

Step 1   Enter $y = x^2 - 6x + 3$ on the **Y=** screen. Use the **CALC** feature. Select **ZERO**. The calculator will graph the function.

Step 2

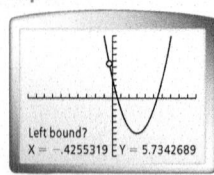

Move the cursor to the left of the first *x*-intercept. Press ⟨enter⟩ to set the left bound.

Step 3

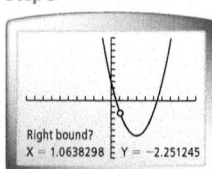

Move the cursor slightly to the right of the intercept. Press ⟨enter⟩ to set the right bound.

Step 4

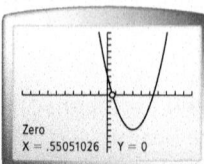

Press ⟨enter⟩ to display the first root, which is about 0.55.

Repeat Steps 2–4 for the second *x*-intercept. The second root is about 5.45. So the solutions are about 0.55 and 5.45.

Suppose you cannot see both of the *x*-intercepts on your graph. You can find the values of *y* that are close to zero by using the **TABLE** feature. Use the **TBLSET** feature to control how the table behaves. Set △**TBL** to 0.5. Set **INDPNT:** and **DEPEND:** to **AUTO**. The calculator screen at the right shows part of the table for $y = 2x^2 - 48x + 285$.

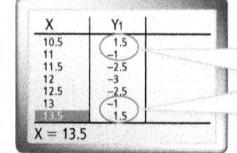

The graph crosses the *x*-axis when the values for *y* change signs. So the range of *x*-values should include 10.5 and 13.5.

Exercises

Use a graphing calculator to solve each equation. Round your solutions to the nearest hundredth.

1. $x^2 - 6x - 16 = 0$ **2.** $2x^2 + x - 6 = 0$ **3.** $\frac{1}{3}x^2 + 8x - 3 = 0$

4. $x^2 - 18x + 5 = 0$ **5.** $0.25x^2 - 8x - 45 = 0$ **6.** $0.5x^2 + 3x - 36 = 0$

554   Concept Byte   Finding Roots

Answers

Exercises

1. $-2, 8$ **2.** $-2, 1.5$

3. $-24.37, 0.37$ **4.** $0.28, 17.72$

5. $-4.88, 36.88$ **6.** $-12, 6$

9-4 Factoring to Solve Quadratic Equations

Objective To solve quadratic equations by factoring

SOLVE IT

Getting Ready!

You are finishing a stained glass hanging that your friend has started. You have enough supplies to add 6 ft² to the hanging. You are planning to add the same amount to the length and width. What will be the dimensions of the hanging when you are finished? How do you know?

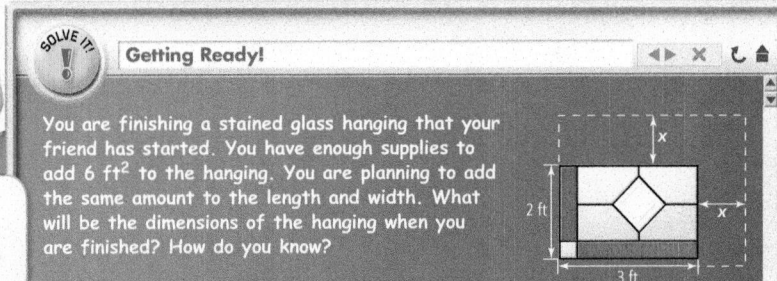

In the previous lesson, you solved quadratic equations $ax^2 + bx + c = 0$ by finding square roots. This method works if $b = 0$.

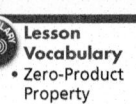

Lesson Vocabulary
• Zero-Product Property

Essential Understanding You can solve some quadratic equations, including equations where $b \neq 0$, by using the *Zero-Product Property*.

The Multiplication Property of Zero states that for any real number a, $a \cdot 0 = 0$. This is equivalent to the following statement: For any real numbers a and b, if $a = 0$ or $b = 0$, then $ab = 0$. The Zero-Product Property reverses this statement.

 **take note**

Property Zero-Product Property

For any real numbers a and b, if $ab = 0$, then $a = 0$ or $b = 0$.

Example If $(x + 3)(x + 2) = 0$, then $x + 3 = 0$ or $x + 2 = 0$.

Problem 1 Using the Zero-Product Property

What are the solutions of the equation $(4t + 1)(t - 2) = 0$?

$$(4t + 1)(t - 2) = 0$$

$4t + 1 = 0$ or $t - 2 = 0$ Use the Zero-Product Property.

$4t = -1$ or $t = 2$ Solve for t.

$t = -\frac{1}{4}$ or $t = 2$

PowerAlgebra.com | Lesson 9-4 Factoring to Solve Quadratic Equations | **555**

---

1 Interactive Learning

Solve It

PURPOSE To solve a real-world problem that can be represented using an equation of the form $ax^2 + bx + c = 0$

PROCESS Students may use the formula for the area of a rectangle to write an equation, use trial and error, or solve the equation by graphing.

FACILITATE
Some students may write expressions for the areas of the new pieces and add them together to form an equation: $x(3 + x) + 2x = 6$.

Q In terms of x, what are the dimensions of the finished stained glass hanging? [$(x + 2)$ and $(x + 3)$]

Q What equation can be used to represent the problem situation? [$(x + 2)(x + 3) - 6 = 6$]

ANSWER See Solve It in Answers on next page.
CONNECT THE MATH In Solve It, students realize that $(x + 2)(x + 3) - 6 = 6$ is equivalent to $x^2 + 5x + 6 = 12$ and $x^2 + 5x - 6 = 0$. In the lesson, students learn to solve quadratic equations by setting them equal to zero and factoring.

2 Guided Instruction

Take Note
Explore with students how the Zero-Product Property would apply to a quadratic equation whose factored form is $2(x + 3)(x + 2) = 0$.

Problem 1

Q What are the x-intercepts of the graph of the equation $y = (4x + 1)(x - 2)$? Explain. [$-\frac{1}{4}$ and 2; the x-intercepts are the same as the solutions of the equation.]

9-4 Preparing to Teach

BIG idea Solving Equations and Inequalities   **UbD**

ESSENTIAL UNDERSTANDINGS
• Some quadratic equations can be solved by using the Zero–Product Property.
• Sometimes it is useful to write a quadratic equation in standard form before solving.

Math Background
Thus far, students have learned to solve quadratic equations using several methods.

While graphing can be used to determine the solutions to any quadratic equation, it is often tedious and inexact without the aid of a graphing calculator.

Finding square roots is limited to quadratic equations of the form $ax^2 + c = 0$ in which $c < 0$. In this lesson students learn to apply the Zero-Product Property when

a quadratic equation can be factored over the set of integers. This technique combines the previously learned skills of factoring trinomials and solving linear equations.

Many quadratic equations fit none of the methods mentioned above, and therefore additional algebraic techniques will be learned in subsequent lessons.

Support Student Learning
Use the **Algebra I Companion** to engage and support students during instruction. See Lesson Resources at the end of this lesson for details.

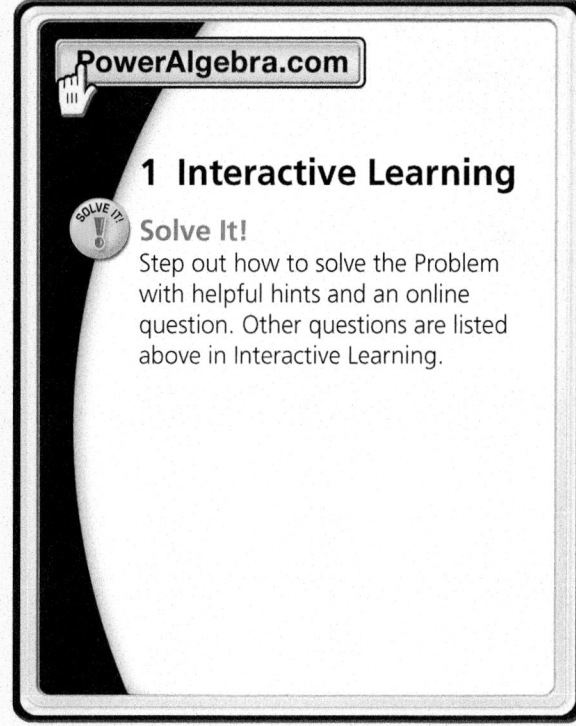

PowerAlgebra.com

1 Interactive Learning

Solve It!
Step out how to solve the Problem with helpful hints and an online question. Other questions are listed above in Interactive Learning.

Lesson 9-4   **555**

Got It?

Q Which questions have positive solutions? two negative solutions? one positive and one negative solution? **[1d; 1c; 1a and 1b]**

Problem 2

Q What is an alternate approach to determining the correct answer choice? **[Answers may vary. Sample: You could substitute the given solutions into the equation to determine which solutions are correct.]**

Q How do the solutions relate to the axis of symmetry for the graph of $y = x^2 + 8x + 15$? **[They are an equal distance from the axis of symmetry, $x = -4$.]**

Got It?   ERROR PREVENTION
If students provide solutions of -7 and 2 for 2a, then they are likely giving the integers used to factor and not solving the linear equations.

Problem 3

Q Is their a common factor that can be factored from the polynomial $4x^2 - 21x - 18$ first? Explain. **[No, there are no numbers greater than 1 that divide into each coefficient evenly, nor is there a variable shared by all terms.]**

Q What process should you use to factor the polynomial $4x^2 - 21x - 18$? **[grouping or trial and error]**

Q How should you rewrite the term $-21x$ to begin the grouping process? Explain. **[$-21x$ as $-24x + 3x$ because $3 + (-24) = -21$]**

Got It?   SYNTHESIZING
Students should recognize the trinomial as a perfect square trinomial. Review the rules for factoring a perfect square trinomial with students.

 Got It? **1.** What are the solutions of each equation?
 a. $(x + 1)(x - 5) = 0$ **b.** $(2x + 3)(x - 4) = 0$
 c. $(2y + 1)(y + 14) = 0$ **d.** $(7n - 2)(5n - 4) = 0$

You can also use the Zero-Product Property to solve equations of the form $ax^2 + bx + c = 0$ if the quadratic expression $ax^2 + bx + c$ can be factored.

 Problem 2   Solving by Factoring

Multiple Choice What are the solutions of the equation $x^2 + 8x + 15 = 0$?

 Ⓐ $-5, -3$ Ⓒ $-3, 5$
 Ⓑ $-5, 3$ Ⓓ $3, 5$

$x^2 + 8x + 15 = 0$
$(x + 3)(x + 5) = 0$ Factor $x^2 + 8x + 15$.
$x + 3 = 0$ or $x + 5 = 0$ Use the Zero-Product Property.
$x = -3$ or $x = -5$ Solve for x.

The solutions are -3 and -5. The correct answer is A.

Plan
How can you factor $x^2 + 8x + 15$?
Find two integers with a product of 15 and a sum of 8.

 Got It? **2.** What are the solutions of each equation?
 a. $m^2 - 5m - 14 = 0$ **b.** $p^2 + p - 20 = 0$ **c.** $2a^2 - 15a + 18 = 0$

Before solving a quadratic equation, you may need to add or subtract terms from each side in order to write the equation in standard form. Then factor the quadratic expression.

Problem 3   Writing in Standard Form First

What are the solutions of $4x^2 - 21x = 18$?

$4x^2 - 21x = 18$
$4x^2 - 21x - 18 = 0$ Subtract 18 from each side.
$(4x + 3)(x - 6) = 0$ Factor $4x^2 - 21x - 18$.
$4x + 3 = 0$ or $x - 6 = 0$ Use the Zero-Product Property.
$4x = -3$ or $x = 6$ Solve for x.
$x = -\frac{3}{4}$ or $x = 6$

The solutions are $-\frac{3}{4}$ and 6.

Think
Why do you need to subtract 18 from each side before you factor?
To use the Zero-Product Property, one side of the equation must be zero.

Got It? **3. a.** What are the solutions of $x^2 + 14x = -49$?
 b. Reasoning Why do quadratic equations of the form $x^2 + 2ax + a^2 = 0$ or $x^2 - 2ax + a^2 = 0$ have only one real-number solution?

Answers

Solve It!
3 ft by 4 ft; explanations may vary.

Got It?
1. a. $-1, 5$
 b. $-\frac{3}{2}, 4$
 c. $-\frac{1}{2}, -14$
 d. $\frac{2}{7}, \frac{4}{5}$
2. a. $-2, 7$
 b. $-5, 4$
 c. $\frac{3}{2}, 6$
3. a. -7
 b. The quadratic polynomials are perfect squares.

PowerAlgebra.com

2 Guided Instruction

Each Problem is worked out and supported online.

Problem 1
Using the Zero-Product Property
Animated

Problem 2
Solving by Factoring
Animated

Problem 3
Writing in Standard Form First

Problem 4
Using Factoring to Solve a Real-World Problem
Animated

Support in Algebra 1 Companion
• Vocabulary
• Key Concepts
• Got It?

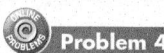 **Problem 4** Using Factoring to Solve a Real-World Problem

Photography You are constructing a frame for the rectangular photo shown. You want the frame to be the same width all the way around and the total area of the frame and photo to be 315 in.². What should the outer dimensions of the frame be?

Know	Need	Plan
The size of the photo is 11 in. by 17 in. The total area is 315 in.².	The outer dimensions of the frame	Write the frame's outer dimensions in terms of its width x. Use these dimensions to write an equation for the area of the frame and photo.

Think

Why can you ignore the factor of 4?
By the Zero-Product Property, one of the factors, 4, $x + 16$, or $x - 2$, must equal 0. Since $4 \neq 0$, either $x + 16$ or $x - 2$ equals 0.

$(2x + 11)(2x + 17) = 315$	Width × Length = Area
$4x^2 + 56x + 187 = 315$	Find the product $(2x + 11)(2x + 17)$.
$4x^2 + 56x - 128 = 0$	Subtract 315 from each side.
$4(x^2 + 14x - 32) = 0$	Factor out 4.
$4(x + 16)(x - 2) = 0$	Factor $x^2 + 14x - 32$.
$x + 16 = 0$ or $x - 2 = 0$	Use the Zero-Product Property.
$x = -16$ or $x = 2$	Solve for x.

The only reasonable solution is 2. So the outer dimensions of the frame are $2(2) + 11$ in. by $2(2) + 17$ in., or 15 in. by 21 in.

 Got It? 4. In Problem 4, suppose the total area of the frame and photo were 391 in.². What would the outer dimensions of the frame be?

 **Lesson Check**

Do you know HOW?

Solve each equation.

1. $(v - 4)(v - 7) = 0$

2. $t^2 + 3t - 54 = 0$

3. $3y^2 - 17y + 24 = 0$

4. Carpentry You are making a rectangular table. The area of the table should be 10 ft². You want the length of the table to be 1 ft shorter than twice its width. What should the dimensions of the table be?

Do you UNDERSTAND?

5. Vocabulary Give an example of how the Zero-Product Property can be used to solve a quadratic equation.

6. Compare and Contrast How is factoring the expression $x^2 - 6x + 8$ similar to solving the equation $x^2 - 6x + 8 = 0$? How is it different?

7. Reasoning Can you extend the Zero-Product Property to nonzero products of numbers? For example, if $ab = 8$, is it always true that $a = 8$ or $b = 8$? Explain.

Problem 4

Q What is the area of the photo without a frame? Explain. **[187 in.²; 11 · 17 = 187]**

Q What is the width of the photo and frame? Explain. **[11 + 2x; a length of x is added to both sides.]**

Q What is the length of the photo and frame? Explain. **[17 + 2x, since a length of x is added to both sides.]**

Q Why is a solution of −16 not reasonable? **[Length cannot be a negative number.]**

Got It?   **ERROR PREVENTION**

If students give solutions of 190 and 187 for x, then they likely did not put the equation into standard form prior to solving.

3 Lesson Check

Do you know HOW?

• If students have difficulty with Exercise 4, then remind them to express the length of the table in terms of the width.

Do you UNDERSTAND?

• If students have difficulty with Exercise 7, then have them list the factors of 8.

Close

Q What are three methods you could use to solve the equation $x^2 - 4 = 0$? **[Use square roots, graph the equation $y = x^2 - 4$ and find its x-intercepts, or factor the expression $x^2 - 4$ and use the Zero-Product Property.]**

Additional Problems

1. What are the solutions of the equation $(2x + 3)(x - 1) = 0$?

ANSWER −1.5, 1

2. What are the solutions of the equation $x^2 - x - 12$?

A. −4, −3

B. −4, 3

C. 3, 4

D. −3, 4

ANSWER D

3. What are the solutions of the equation $3x^2 + 13x = -4$?

ANSWER $-\frac{1}{3}$, −4

4. Jason has a patio of uniform width around the perimeter of his rectangular pool. The pool measures 22 ft by 12 ft. If the area of the pool and the patio is 504 ft², what is the width of the patio?

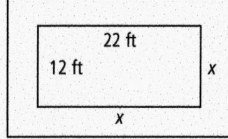

ANSWER 3 ft

Answers

Got It? (continued)

4. 17 in. by 23 in.

Lesson Check

1. 4, 7

2. −9, 6

3. $\frac{8}{3}$, 3

4. 2.5 ft by 4 ft

5. Check students' work.

6. To solve the equation, you first factor the quadratic expression, then set each factor equal to 0, and solve.

7. No, if $ab = 8$, then there are infinitely many possible values of a and b, such as $a = 2$ and $b = 4$ or $a = -1$ and $b = -8$.

4 Practice

ASSIGNMENT GUIDE

Basic: 8–28 all, 30–40 even

Average: 9–27 odd, 29–41

Advanced: 9–27 odd, 29–45

Standardized Test Prep: 46–50

Mixed Review: 51–59

Reasoning exercises have blue headings.

Applications exercises have red headings.

EXERCISE 38: Use the Think About a Plan worksheet in the **Practice and Problem Solving Workbook** (also available in the Teaching Resources in print and online) to further support students' development in becoming independent learners.

HOMEWORK QUICK CHECK

To check students' understanding of key skills and concepts, go over Exercises 13, 27, 34, 36, and 38.

Practice and Problem-Solving Exercises

A Practice

Use the Zero-Product Property to solve each equation.   ● See Problem 1.

8. $(x - 9)(x - 8) = 0$ **9.** $(4k + 5)(k + 7) = 0$ **10.** $n(n + 2) = 0$

11. $-3n(2n - 5) = 0$ **12.** $(7x + 2)(5x - 4) = 0$ **13.** $(4a - 7)(3a + 8) = 0$

Solve by factoring.   ● See Problems 2 and 3.

14. $x^2 + 11x + 10 = 0$ **15.** $g^2 + 4g - 32 = 0$ **16.** $s^2 - 14s + 45 = 0$

17. $2z^2 - 21z - 36 = 0$ **18.** $3q^2 + q - 14 = 0$ **19.** $4m^2 - 27m - 40 = 0$

20. $x^2 + 13x = -42$ **21.** $p^2 - 4p = 21$ **22.** $c^2 = 5c$

23. $2w^2 - 11w = -12$ **24.** $3h^2 + 17h = -10$ **25.** $9b^2 = 16$

26. Geometry A box shaped like a rectangular prism has a volume of 280 in.³.   ● See Problem 4.
Its dimensions are 4 in. by $(n + 2)$ in. by $(n + 5)$ in. Find n.

27. Knitting You are knitting a blanket. You want the area of the blanket to be 24 ft².
You want the length of the blanket to be 2 ft longer than its width. What should the dimensions of the blanket be?

28. Construction You are building a rectangular deck. The area of the deck should be 250 ft². You want the length of the deck to be 5 ft longer than twice its width. What should be the dimensions of the deck be?

B Apply

Use the Zero-Product Property to solve each equation. Write your solutions as a set in roster form.

29. $x^2 + 6x + 8 = 0$ **30.** $a^2 + 8a + 12 = 0$ **31.** $k^2 + 7k + 10 = 0$

Write each equation in standard form. Then solve.

32. $7n^2 + 16n + 15 = 2n^2 + 3$ **33.** $4q^2 + 3q = 3q^2 - 4q + 18$

34. Think About a Plan You have a rectangular koi pond that measures 6 ft by 8 ft. You have enough concrete to cover 72 ft² for a walkway, as shown in the diagram. What should the width of the walkway be?
• How can you write the outer dimensions of the walkway?
• How can you represent the total area of the walkway and pond in two ways?

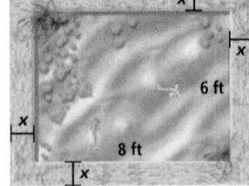

35. Open-Ended Write a quadratic equation in standard form $ax^2 + bx + c = 0$ such that a, b, and c are integers, but the solutions are rational numbers that are not integers.

36. Error Analysis Describe and correct the error made in solving the equation.

$2x^2 + 3x = 20$
$x(2x + 3) = 20$
$x = 0$ or $2x + 3 = 0$
$x = 0$ or $x = -\frac{3}{2}$

37. Reasoning How many solutions does an equation of the form $x^2 - k^2 = 0$ have? Explain.

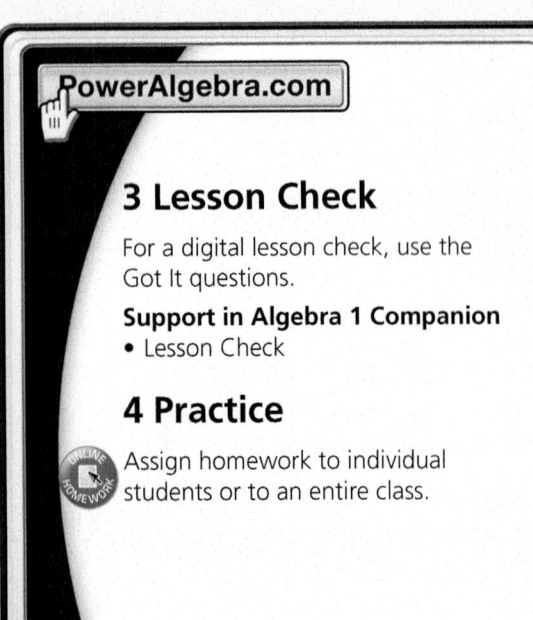

PowerAlgebra.com

3 Lesson Check

For a digital lesson check, use the Got It questions.

Support in Algebra 1 Companion
• Lesson Check

4 Practice

Assign homework to individual students or to an entire class.

Answers

Practice and Problem-Solving Exercises

8. 8, 9   **9.** $-\frac{5}{4}$, -7

10. -2, 0   **11.** 0, 2.5

12. $-\frac{2}{7}$, $\frac{4}{5}$ **13.** $\frac{7}{4}$, $-\frac{8}{3}$

14. -10, -1 **15.** -8, 4

16. 5, 9   **17.** -1.5, 12

18. $-\frac{7}{3}$, 2   **19.** $-\frac{5}{4}$, 8

20. -7, -6 **21.** -3, 7

22. 0, 5   **23.** 1.5, 4

24. -5, $-\frac{2}{3}$ **25.** $\pm\frac{4}{3}$

26. 5   **27.** 4 ft by 6 ft

28. 10 ft by 25 ft   **29.** $\{-4, -2\}$

30. $\{-2, -6\}$ **31.** $\{-5, -2\}$

32. $5n^2 + 16n + 12 = 0$; -2, $-\frac{6}{5}$

33. $q^2 + 7q - 18 = 0$; -9, 2

34. 2 ft

35. Answers will vary. Sample:
$6x^2 + 5x - 4 = 0$

36. The Zero-Product Property was applied when the product was 20, not 0. First write the equation in standard form. Begin by subtracting 20 from each side. $2x^2 + 3x - 20 = 0$, $(2x - 5)(x + 4) = 0$, $2x - 5 = 0$ or $x + 4 = 0$, $x = \frac{5}{2}$ or $x = -4$

37. 2; $\pm k$

38. Sports You throw a softball into the air with an initial upward velocity of 38 ft/s and an initial height of 5 ft.
   a. Use the vertical motion model to write an equation that gives the ball's height h, in feet, at time t, in seconds.
   b. The ball's height is 0 ft when it is on the ground. Solve the equation you wrote in part (a) for $h = 0$ to find when the ball lands.

Solve each cubic equation by factoring out the GCF first.

39. $x^3 - 10x^2 + 24x = 0$ **40.** $x^3 - 5x^2 + 4x = 0$ **41.** $3x^3 - 9x^2 = 0$

 **Challenge**   **42.** Find an equation that has the given numbers as solutions. For example, 4 and -3 are solutions of $x^2 - x - 12 = 0$.
   a. $-5, 8$ **b.** $3, -2$ **c.** $\frac{1}{2}, -10$ **d.** $\frac{2}{3}, -\frac{5}{7}$

Solve. Factor by grouping.

43. $x^3 + 5x^2 - x - 5 = 0$ **44.** $x^3 + x^2 - 4x - 4 = 0$ **45.** $x^3 + 2x^2 - 9x - 18 = 0$

Standardized Test Prep

GRIDDED RESPONSE

SAT/ACT

46. What is the negative solution of the equation $2x^2 - 13x - 7 = 0$? Round to the nearest thousandth.

47. Phil, Toby, and Sam bowled four games last weekend. Their scores are shown in the Venn diagram at the right. What is the highest score that only Toby and Sam have in common?

48. What is the y-intercept of the line with equation $3y - 4x = 9$?

49. How many elements are in the union of the two sets $M = \{1, 2, -3, 4\}$ and $N = \{1, -2, 3, 5\}$?

50. A rectangular card has a length 1 in. longer than twice the width and an area of 15 in.^{2}. What is the width of the card, in inches?

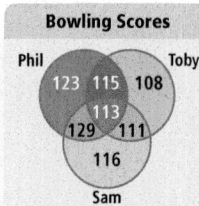

Bowling Scores

Phil — Toby
123 115 108
113
129 111
116
Sam

Mixed Review

Solve each equation by finding square roots. If the equation has no real-number solution, write *no solution*.   ◆ See Lesson 9-3.

51. $t^2 = 144$ **52.** $w^2 - 8 = -17$ **53.** $b^2 + 100 = 100$

54. $5h^2 - 80 = 0$ **55.** $49 - m^2 = 0$ **56.** $3q^2 = 27$

Get Ready!   **To prepare for Lesson 9-5, do Exercises 57–59.**

Factor each expression.   ◆ See Lesson 8-7.

57. $y^2 - 10y + 25$ **58.** $g^2 - 14g + 49$ **59.** $m^2 + 18m + 81$

---

38. a. $h = -16t^2 + 38t + 5$
   b. 2.5 s
39. 0, 4, 6   **40.** 0, 1, 4   **41.** 0, 3
42. a. $x^2 - 3x - 40 = 0$
   b. $x^2 - x - 6 = 0$
   c. $2x^2 + 19x - 10 = 0$
   d. $21x^2 + x - 10 = 0$
43. $-5, -1, 1$ **44.** $-2, -1, 2$
45. $-3, -2, 3$ **46.** -0.5
47. 111   **48.** 3
49. 7   **50.** 2.5
51. ± 12 **52.** no solution
53. 0   **54.** ± 4
55. ± 7 **56.** ± 3
57. $(y - 5)^2$ **58.** $(g - 7)^2$
59. $(m + 9)^2$

Additional Instructional Support

Algebra 1 Companion

Students can use the **Algebra 1 Companion** worktext (4 pages) as you teach the lesson. Use the Companion to support

- New Vocabulary
- Key Concepts
- Got It for each Problem
- Lesson Check

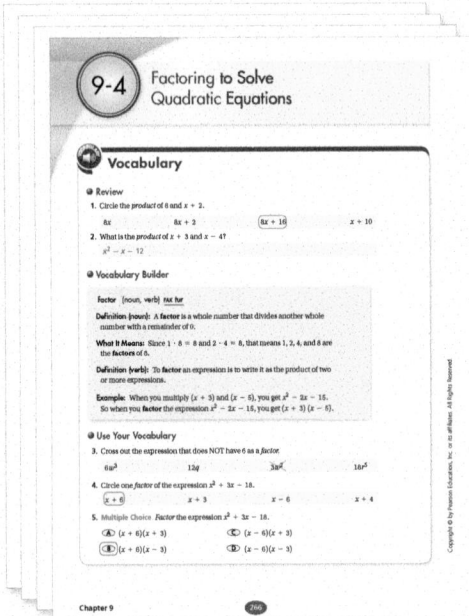

ELL Support

Focus on Language Create a word wall with vocabulary words from each lesson. Include an example and definition with each word. Whenever possible, include the roots of the words. Ask students for words that share the same word base (cognate). If students are not able to assist in providing words with the same word base, suggest they use the Internet to research some. These can be placed on the word wall on different colored paper to emphasize them.

Focus on Communication Have students work in pairs to write a letter telling a friend about quadratic equations. Students should assume their friend is eager to learn algebra and has asked them to explain the concepts in this chapter.

5 Assess & Remediate

Lesson Quiz

1. What are the solutions of the equation $(5x - 2)(x + 6) = 0$?

2. What are the solutions of the equation $x^2 + 5x + 6$?

3. What are the solutions of the equation $2x^2 + 7x = 4$?

4. The frame around a rectangular picture has a uniform width. The dimensions of the picture are 5 in. by 7 in. If the combined area of the picture and the frame is 80 in.^{2}, what is the width of the frame?

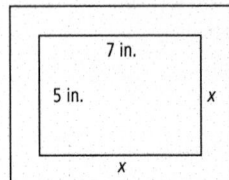

5. **Do you UNDERSTAND?** You are solving an equation to find the best length for a table you are designing. You have factored the equation as $(x + 1)(2x - 3)$. Will the solutions of the equation give you two different lengths to choose from?

ANSWERS TO LESSON QUIZ

1. 0.4, −6
2. −3, −2
3. −4, 0.5
4. 1.5 in.
5. No; one of the solutions will be negative, which will be meaningless in terms of a length.

PRESCRIPTION FOR REMEDIATION

Use the student work on the Lesson Quiz to prescribe a differentiated review assignment.

Points	Differentiated Remediation
0–2	Intervention
3–4	On-level
5	Extension

PowerAlgebra.com

5 Assess & Remediate

Assign the Lesson Quiz. Appropriate intervention, practice, or enrichment is automatically generated based on student performance.

Intervention

- **Reteaching** (2 pages) Provides reteaching and practice exercises for the key lesson concepts. Use with struggling students or absent students.

- **English Language Learner Support** Helps students develop and reinforce mathematical vocabulary and key concepts.

All-in-One Resources/Online
Reteaching

9-4 Reteaching
Factoring to Solve Quadratic Equations

If the product of two or more numbers is 0, then one of the factors must be 0. You can use this fact to solve quadratic equations.

Problem

What are the solutions of the equation $(4a + 12)(5a - 20) = 0$?
Since the product is 0, either $(4a + 12)$ or $(5a - 20)$ must equal 0.

$4a + 12 = 0$	or	$5a - 20 = 0$
$4a + 12 - 12 = 0 - 12$	or	$5a - 20 + 20 = 0 + 20$
$4a = -12$	or	$5a = 20$
$\frac{4a}{4} = \frac{-12}{4}$	or	$\frac{5a}{5} = \frac{20}{5}$
$a = -3$	or	$a = 4$

The solutions are −3 and 4.

Exercises

Solve each equation.

1. $b(b + 7) = 0$
   0; −7
2. $8y(2y - 12) = 0$
   0; 6
3. $(d - 8)(d - 2) = 0$
   8; 2

4. $(m + 1)(m - 4) = 0$
   −1; 4
5. $(2a + 14)(3a + 12) = 0$
   −7; −4
6. $(5p - 10)(2p + 20) = 0$
   2; −10

7. $(8t + 4)(3t + 6) = 0$
   −$\frac{1}{2}$; −2
8. $(4h - 1)(2h + 1) = 0$
   $\frac{1}{4}$; −$\frac{1}{2}$
9. $(8n - 16)(5n - 12) = 0$
   2; $\frac{12}{5}$

10. $(s + 6)(4s - 6) = 0$
    −6; $\frac{3}{2}$
11. $(5w - 30)(2w - 1) = 0$
    6; $\frac{1}{2}$
12. $(3g + 1)(2g - 5) = 0$
    −$\frac{1}{3}$; $\frac{5}{2}$

All-in-One Resources/Online
English Language Learner Support

9-4 ELL Support
Factoring to Solve Quadratic Equations

Problem

What are the solutions of the equation $x^2 - 6x = -8$? Justify and explain your work.

Explain	Work	Justify
First, write the equation.	$x^2 - 6x = -8$	Original equation
Second, add 8 to each side to write in standard form.	$x^2 - 6x + 8 = 0$	Write the equation in standard form.
Then, factor $x^2 - 6x + 8$.	$(x - 4)(x - 2) = 0$	Factor.
Next, use the Zero Product Property.	$x - 4 = 0$ or $x - 2 = 0$	Use the Zero-Product Property.
Finally, solve for x to get the solutions $x = 4$ and $x = 2$.	$x = 4$ or $x = 2$	Solve for x.
	Solutions $x = 4$ or $x = 2$	

What are the solutions of the equation $x^2 - 3x = 18$? Justify and explain your work.

Explain	Work	Justify
First, write the equation.	$x^2 - 3x = 18$	Original equation
Then, subtract 18 to each side to write in standard form.	$x^2 - 3x - 18 = 0$	Write the equation in standard form.
Then, factor $x^2 - 3x - 18$.	$(x + 3)(x - 6) = 0$	Factor.
Next, use the Zero-Product Property.	$x + 3 = 0$ or $x - 6 = 0$	Use the Zero-Product Property.
Finally, solve for x to get the solutions $x = -3$ and $x = 6$.	$x = -3$ or $x = 6$	Solve for x.
	Solutions	

Differentiated Remediation *continued*

On-Level

- **Practice** (2 pages) Provides extra practice for each lesson. For simpler practice exercises, use the Form K Practice pages found in the All-in-One Teaching Resources and online.

- **Think About a Plan** Helps students develop specific problem-solving skills and strategies by providing scaffolded guiding questions.

- **Standardized Test Prep** Focuses on all major exercises, all major question types, and helps students prepare for the high-stakes assessments.

Extension

- **Enrichment** Provides students with interesting problems and activities that extend the concepts of the lesson.

- **Activities, Games, and Puzzles** Worksheets that can be used for concepts development, enrichment, and for fun!

Practice and Problem Solving WKBK/All-in-One Resources/Online
Practice page 1

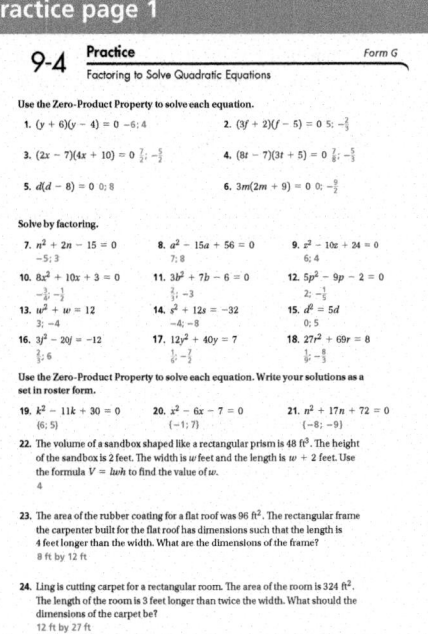

Practice and Problem Solving WKBK/All-in-One Resources/Online
Practice page 2

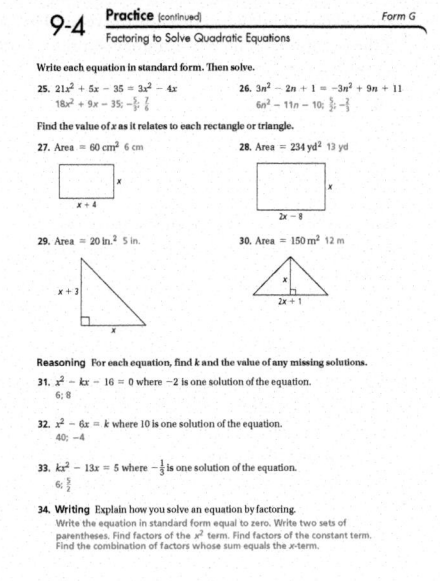

All-in-One Resources/Online
Enrichment

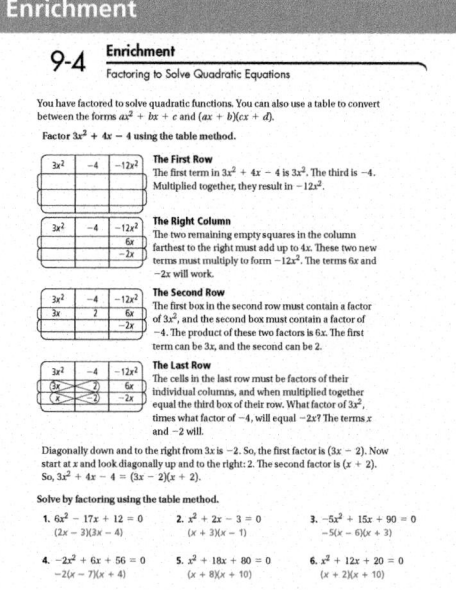

Practice and Problem Solving WKBK/All-in-One Resources/Online
Think About a Plan

9-4 Think About a Plan
Factoring to Solve Quadratic Equations

Sports You throw a softball into the air with an initial upward velocity of 38 ft/s and an initial height of 5 ft.

a. Use the vertical motion model to write an equation that gives the ball's height h (in feet) at time t (in seconds).
b. The ball's height is 0 ft when it is on the ground. Solve the equation you wrote in part (a) for $h = 0$ to find when the ball lands.

What do you know?

1. Write a vertical motion model that best describes the equation for the ball's height h at time t. What are the values of v and c?

$h = -16t^2 + v \cdot t + c$

$h = -16t^2 + \boxed{38} \cdot t + \boxed{5}$

2. How would graphing the quadratic equation help you understand the problem?

The graph would show the initial height, the maximum height (the vertex) and when the softball would reach the ground (the x-intercept).

How do you solve the problem?

3. The ball's height is 0 ft when it is on the ground. Solve the equation you wrote in part (a) for $h = 0$ to find when the ball lands.

$(8t + 1)(-2t + 5) = 0$; $\frac{5}{2}$ s

Practice and Problem Solving WKBK/All-in-One Resources/Online
Standardized Test Prep

9-4 Standardized Test Prep
Factoring to Solve Quadratic Equations

Gridded Response

Solve each exercise and enter your answer on the grid provided.

1. What is the positive solution of $3x^2 - 10x - 8 = 0$? 4

2. A triangular-shaped wall has a base of $2x + 4$ and a height of $x + 3$. The area of the triangle is 56 in.^{2}. What is the value of x? 5

3. The product of two consecutive integers, n and $n + 1$, is 42. What is the positive integer that satisfies the situation? 6

4. One more rectangular-shaped piece of metal siding needs to be cut to cover the exterior of a pole barn. The area of the piece is 30 ft^2. The length is 1 less than 3 times the width. How wide should the metal piece be? Round to the nearest hundredth of a foot. 3.33

5. What solution do $2x^2 - 31x + 21 = 0$ and $2x^2 + 9x - 56 = 0$ have in common? Round your answer to the nearest tenth if necessary. 3.5

Online Teacher Resource Center
Activities, Games, and Puzzles

9-4 Game: The Winning Factor
Factoring to Solve Quadratic Equations

This is a game for three students. Decide who will be the host and who will be the contestants.

Host

- You will receive a numbered list of quadratic expressions and their factorizations. Contestants will take turns choosing a number from the table below. Cross out the number and read the expression that corresponds to the number. Check the contestants' factorization, and award 1 point for a correct answer.
- If a contestant answers incorrectly, the other contestant has 20 seconds to factor the expression to earn the point. Keep each contestant's score.

Contestants

- Choose a number from the table below. The host will read aloud the expression that matches the number you selected.
- You will have 20 seconds to factor the expression. You are allowed to use pencil and paper, but you may be able to do some of the problems using mental math. Note that the numbers in the table do not correspond to the level of difficulty.
- The host will check your answer. A correct answer is worth 1 point. If you do not factor correctly, the other contestant has the opportunity to factor. The contestant who earns the most points wins!

1	2	3	4	5	6	7	8	9	10
11	12	13	14	15	16	17	18	19	20
21	22	23	24	25	26	27	28	29	30

See Teacher Instructions Page.

Answers

Mid-Chapter Quiz

1. $y = 0.5x^2$, $y = -x^2$, $y = 2x^2$

2. $f(x) = \frac{2}{3}x^2$, $f(x) = 3x^2$, $f(x) = 4x^2$

3. $f(x) = 0.2x^2$, $f(x) = 0.3x^2$, $f(x) = 0.6x^2$

4. $y = -0.25x^2$, $y = x^2$, $y = -2x^2$

5.
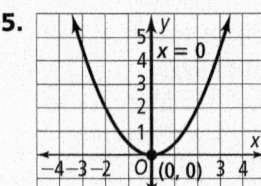

6.
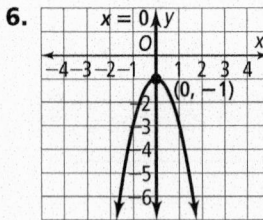

7.
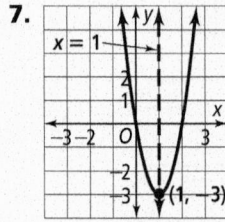

8.
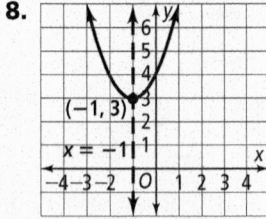

9.
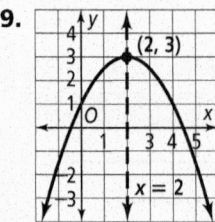

10. ± 4 **11.** no solution

12. 0   **13.** ± 9

14. no solution   **15.** ± 6

16. $\pm\frac{1}{2}$ **17.** 10.2 ft

PowerAlgebra.com

MathXL for School

Prepare students for the Mid-Chapter Quiz and Chapter Test with online practice and review.

 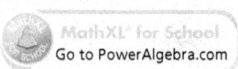

Do you know HOW?

Order each group of quadratic functions from widest to narrowest graph.

1. $y = 2x^2$, $y = 0.5x^2$, $y = -x^2$

2. $f(x) = 4x^2$, $f(x) = \frac{2}{3}x^2$, $f(x) = 3x^2$

3. $f(x) = 0.6x^2$, $f(x) = 0.3x^2$, $f(x) = 0.2x^2$

4. $y = -2x^2$, $y = x^2$, $y = -0.25x^2$

Graph each function. Label the axis of symmetry and the vertex.

5. $y = \frac{1}{2}x^2$

6. $y = -2x^2 - 1$

7. $y = 3x^2 - 6x$

8. $y = x^2 + 2x + 4$

9. $y = -0.5x^2 + 2x + 1$

Solve each equation by graphing the related function. If the equation has no real-number solution, write *no solution*.

10. $x^2 - 16 = 0$

11. $x^2 + 9 = 0$

12. $0.25x^2 = 0$

Solve each equation by finding square roots. If the equation has no real-number solution, write *no solution*.

13. $m^2 = 81$ **14.** $t^2 - 7 = -18$

15. $5r^2 - 180 = 0$ **16.** $36n^2 = 9$

17. Sewing You have 324 ft² of fabric to make a circular play parachute for kids. What is the radius of the largest parachute you could make? Round to the nearest tenth of a foot.

Solve by factoring.

18. $b^2 + 3b - 4 = 0$

19. $n^2 + n - 12 = 0$

20. $2x^2 - 5x - 3 = 0$

21. $t^2 - 3t = 28$

22. $3n^2 = 6n$

23. Construction You are building a rectangular planter for your school garden. You want the area of the bottom to be 90 ft². You want the length of the planter to be 3 ft longer than twice its width. What should the dimensions of the bottom of the planter be?

Do you UNDERSTAND?

24. Writing Describe the steps you would use to graph the function $y = 2x^2 + 5$.

25. Reasoning Does the value of c in the quadratic function $y = ax^2 + bx + c$ affect the horizontal position of the vertex of the graph? Explain why or why not.

26. Writing Describe how the graph of $y = 3x^2$ differs from the graph of $y = x^2$.

Open-Ended Give an example of a quadratic function that matches each description.

27. The axis of symmetry is to the left of the y-axis.

28. Its graph lies entirely below the x-axis.

29. Its graph opens upward and has its vertex at $(0, 0)$.

30. a. Solve $x^2 - 4 = 0$ and $2x^2 - 8 = 0$ by graphing their related functions.

     b. Reasoning Why does it make sense that the graphs have the same x-intercepts?

---

18. -4, 1   **19.** -4, 3

20. -0.5, 3   **21.** -4, 7

22. 0, 2   **23.** 6 ft by 15 ft

24. Answers will vary. Sample: Graph $y = 2x^2$ and then shift the graph up 5 units.

25. No, the values of a and b affect the x-coordinate of the vertex.

26. They have the same vertex and y-intercept, but the graph of $y = 3x^2$ is narrower than that of $y = x^2$.

27–29. Answers will vary. Samples are given.

27. $y = 2x^2 + 4x$

28. $y = -x^2 - 1$

29. $y = x^2$

30. a. ± 2

     b. Answers will vary. Sample: If you divide each side of the second equation by 2, you get the first equation, so the equations have the same solutions.

9-5 Completing the Square

Objective To solve quadratic equations by completing the square

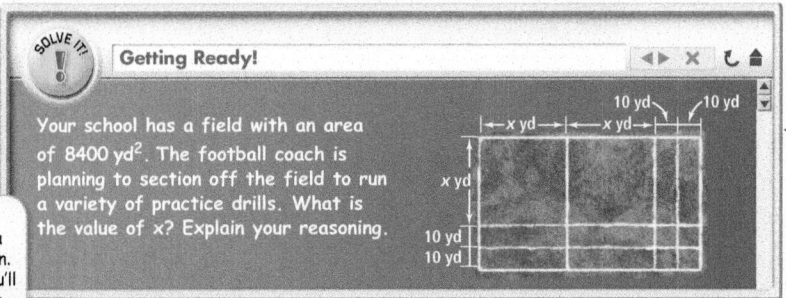

Getting Ready!

Your school has a field with an area of 8400 yd². The football coach is planning to section off the field to run a variety of practice drills. What is the value of x? Explain your reasoning.

(diagram labels: 10 yd, 10 yd, ←x yd→, ←x yd→, x yd, 10 yd, 10 yd)

> Factoring is only one way to solve a quadratic equation. In this lesson, you'll learn another way.

Lesson Vocabulary
• completing the square

In previous lessons, you solved quadratic equations by finding square roots and by factoring. These methods work in some cases, but not all.

Essential Understanding You can solve any quadratic equation by first writing it in the form $m^2 = n$.

You can model this process using algebra tiles. The algebra tiles at the right represent the expression $x^2 + 8x$.

Here is the same expression rearranged to form part of a square. Notice that the x-tiles have been split evenly into two groups of four.

You can complete the square by adding 4^2, or 16, 1-tiles. The completed square is $x^2 + 8x + 16$, or $(x + 4)^2$.

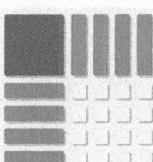

In general, you can change the expression $x^2 + bx$ into a perfect-square trinomial by adding $\left(\frac{b}{2}\right)^2$ to $x^2 + bx$. This process is called **completing the square**. The process is the same whether b is positive or negative.

 PowerAlgebra.com | Lesson 9-5 Completing the Square | **561**

9-5 Preparing to Teach

BIG idea Solving Equations and Inequalities **UbD**

ESSENTIAL UNDERSTANDING
• Any quadratic equation can be solved by first writing it in the form $m^2 = n$.

Math Background

The technique of completing the square can be used to solve any quadratic equation, unlike the technique of factoring. Further, the technique of completing the square can also be used to transform a quadratic equation from standard form to vertex form, which is a form that can be used to quickly generate the graph of a quadratic equation.

Completing the square can be a complex process for some students. It is recommended that students make a detailed list of the steps that they can follow to solve any quadratic equation by completing the square.

Understanding the process is essential to learning how and why the Quadratic Formula is derived. The Quadratic Formula is presented in Lesson 9-6.

Support Student Learning

Use the **Algebra I Companion** to engage and support students during instruction. See Lesson Resources at the end of this lesson for details.

---

1 Interactive Learning

Solve It!

PURPOSE To solve a real-world problem by a geometric representation of a quadratic expression
PROCESS Students may use the formula for the area of a rectangle to write an equation or use factoring to solve the equation.

FACILITATE
Q In terms of x, what are the dimensions of the field? **[(2x + 20) and (x + 20)]**
Q What equation can be used to represent the problem situation? **[(2x + 20)(x + 20) = 8400]**
Q What method will you use to solve the equation? What is your first step? **[Answers may vary. Sample: I will use factoring and begin by putting the equation in standard form and setting it equal to 0.]**

ANSWER See Solve It in Answers on next page.
CONNECT THE MATH Students solve a quadratic equation using a previously learned method. In the lesson, students are presented with equations that cannot be solved with previously learned methods and will be handled by another algebraic method, completing the square.

2 Guided Instruction

To verify that students understand how to complete a square using a model, have students demonstrate how to make the quadratic expression $x^2 + 9x$ into a perfect square trinomial using algebra tiles.

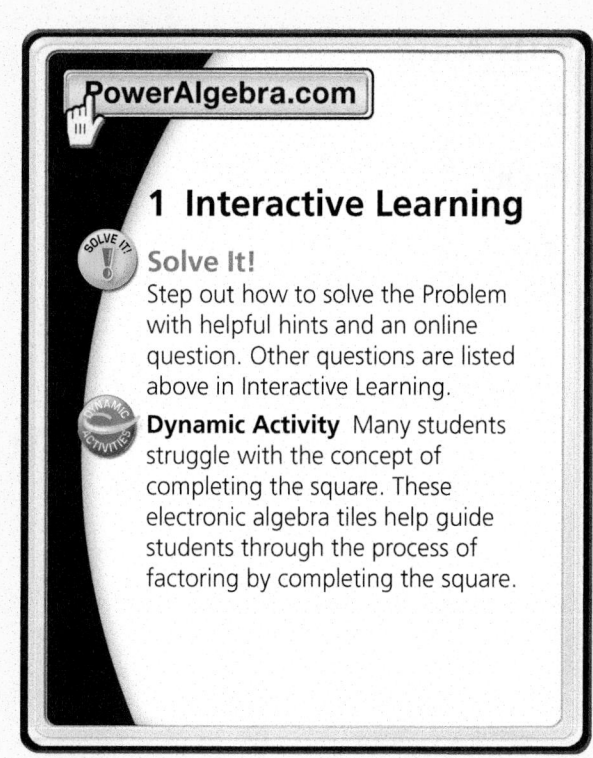

PowerAlgebra.com

1 Interactive Learning

Solve It!
Step out how to solve the Problem with helpful hints and an online question. Other questions are listed above in Interactive Learning.

Dynamic Activity Many students struggle with the concept of completing the square. These electronic algebra tiles help guide students through the process of factoring by completing the square.

Problem 1

> **Q** How can you determine the value of c in a perfect square trinomial? Explain. **[Answers may vary. Sample: Take half of the middle term and square it.]**

Got It?

> **Q** What is the length of the side of a square that has an area of $x^2 + 20x + 100$? **[$x + 10$, because $(x + 10)^2 = x^2 + 20x + 100$.]**

Problem 2

> **Q** Nine is added to the left side of the equation in order to complete the square. Why is it added to the right side of the equation? **[Nine has to be added to both sides of the equation in order to keep the new equation equivalent to the old equation.]**
>
> **Q** Why is $\sqrt{(x + 3)^2} = x + 3$? **[Squaring and taking the square root are inverse operations.]**

Got It?   ERROR PREVENTION

If students provide answers of $x \approx 18.7$ or $x \approx -12.7$, then they likely forgot to add 9 to both sides of the equation when completing the square.

Problem 3

> **Q** Is $x^2 - 14x + 16$ a perfect square trinomial? Explain. **[No, it is not in the form $a^2 + 2ab + b^2$ or $a^2 - 2ab + b^2$.]**
>
> **Q** How can you write the exact solutions to the equation rather than the decimal approximations? **[$x = \pm\sqrt{33} + 7$]**

 **Problem 1**   Finding c to Complete the Square

Think

Can c be negative?
No. c is the square of a real number, which is never negative.

What is the value of c such that $x^2 - 16x + c$ is a perfect-square trinomial?

The value of b is -16. The term to add to $x^2 - 16x$ is $\left(\frac{-16}{2}\right)^2$, or 64. So $c = 64$.

✔ **Got It? 1.** What is the value of c such that $x^2 + 20x + c$ is a perfect-square trinomial?

 **Problem 2**   Solving $x^2 + bx = c$

What are the solutions of the equation $x^2 + 6x = 216$?

Think

Why do you write $x + 3 = \pm15$ as two equations?
Recall that the symbol $\pm$ means "plus or minus." That means $x + 3$ equals 15 or -15.

$x^2 + 6x = 216$	
$x^2 + 6x + 9 = 216 + 9$	Add $\left(\frac{6}{2}\right)^2$, or 9, to each side.
$(x + 3)^2 = 216 + 9$	Write $x^2 + 6x + 9$ as a square.
$(x + 3)^2 = 225$	Simplify the right side.
$x + 3 = \pm\sqrt{225}$	Find square roots of each side.
$x + 3 = \pm15$	Simplify.
$x + 3 = 15$ or $x + 3 = -15$	Write as two equations.
$x = 12$ or $x = -18$	Subtract 3 from each side.

✔ **Got It? 2.** What are the solutions of the equation $t^2 - 6t = 247$?

To solve an equation in the form $x^2 + bx + c = 0$, first subtract the constant term c from each side of the equation.

 **Problem 3**   Solving $x^2 + bx + c = 0$

What are the solutions of the equation $x^2 - 14x + 16 = 0$?

Think

Have you seen a problem like this before?
Yes. This problem is like Problem 2, except the right side of the equation is 0. After you subtract 16 from each side, the two problems have the same form.

$x^2 - 14x + 16 = 0$	
$x^2 - 14x = -16$	Subtract 16 from each side.
$x^2 - 14x + 49 = -16 + 49$	Add $\left(\frac{-14}{2}\right)^2$, or 49, to each side.
$(x - 7)^2 = 33$	Write $x^2 - 14x + 49$ as a square.
$x - 7 = \pm\sqrt{33}$	Find square roots of each side.
$x - 7 \approx \pm5.74$	Use a calculator to approximate $\sqrt{33}$.
$x - 7 \approx 5.74$ or $x - 7 \approx -5.74$	Write as two equations.
$x \approx 5.74 + 7$ or $x \approx -5.74 + 7$	Add 7 to each side.
$x \approx 12.74$ or $x \approx 1.26$	Simplify.

Answers

Solve It!
50; explanations may vary.

Got It?
1. 100

2. -13, 19

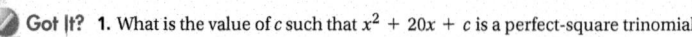

2 Guided Instruction

Each Problem is worked out and supported online.

Problem 1
Finding c to Complete the Square
Animated

Problem 2
Solving $x^2 + bx = c$
Animated

Problem 3
Solving $x^2 + bx + c = 0$

Problem 4
Completing the Square When $a \neq 1$
Animated

Support in Algebra 1 Companion
• Vocabulary
• Key Concepts
• Got It?

Got It? **3. a.** What are the solutions of the equation $x^2 + 9x + 15 = 0$?

b. Reasoning Could you use factoring to solve part (a)? Explain.

The method of completing the square works when $a = 1$ in $ax^2 + bx + c = 0$. To solve an equation when $a \neq 1$, divide each side by a before completing the square.

 Problem 4 **Completing the Square When $a \neq 1$**

Gardening You are planning a flower garden consisting of three square plots surrounded by a 1-ft border. The total area of the garden and the border is 100 ft². What is the side length x of each square plot?

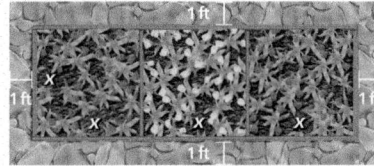

🌷 **Red tulips** 🌷 **Yellow tulips**

Know
• Area of garden and border
• Expressions for the dimensions of the garden and border.

Need
The side length x of each square plot

Plan
Write and solve an equation that relates the dimensions and area of the garden and border.

Step 1 Write an equation that you can use to solve the problem.

$(3x + 2)(x + 2) = 100$ Length × Width = Area

$3x^2 + 8x + 4 = 100$ Find the product $(3x + 2)(x + 2)$.

$3x^2 + 8x = 96$ Subtract 4 from each side.

$x^2 + \frac{8}{3}x = 32$ Divide each side by 3.

Step 2 Complete the square.

$x^2 + \frac{8}{3}x + \frac{16}{9} = 32 + \frac{16}{9}$ Add $\left(\frac{4}{3}\right)^2$, or $\frac{16}{9}$, to each side.

$\left(x + \frac{4}{3}\right)^2 = \frac{304}{9}$ Write left side as a square and right side as a fraction.

Step 3 Solve the equation.

$x + \frac{4}{3} = \pm\sqrt{\frac{304}{9}}$ Find square roots of each side.

$x + \frac{4}{3} \approx \pm 5.81$ Use a calculator to approximate $\sqrt{\frac{304}{9}}$.

$x + \frac{4}{3} \approx 5.81$ or $x + \frac{4}{3} \approx -5.81$ Write as two equations.

$x \approx 4.48$ or $x \approx -7.14$ Solve for x.

The negative answer does not make sense in this problem. So the side length of each square plot is about 4.48 ft.

Think
Why do you need to find $\frac{1}{2}\left(\frac{8}{3}\right)$?
To make $x^2 + \frac{8}{3}x = 32$ a perfect-square trinomial on the left side, find $\frac{1}{2}\left(\frac{8}{3}\right)$. Then square the result and add to each side of the equation.

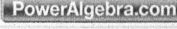

Got It?
Students may need additional guidance with this problem, as the value of $\left[\frac{b}{2}\right]^2$ is not a whole number.

Problem 4

Q Why do you divide each side of the equation by 3? **[The process learned for completing the square works only when the coefficient of the x^2-term is 1, and you must divide both sides of the equation by 3 to keep the new equation equivalent to the old equation.]**

Q What is $\frac{8}{3}$ divided by 2? Explain. **[$\frac{4}{3}$; dividing by 2 is the same as multiplying by $\frac{1}{2}$.]**

Q Why does the negative answer not make sense in the problem? **[Because length cannot be negative.]**

Additional Problems

1. What is the value of c such that $x^2 - 20x + c$ is a perfect square trinomial?

ANSWER 100

2. What are the solutions of the equation $x^2 + 2x = 8$?

ANSWER $-4, 2$

3. What are the solutions of the equation $x^2 + 12x - 20 = 0$?

ANSWER $-13.48, 1.48$

4. Eduardo has 2 square pictures surrounded by a 2-in. frame as shown below. The combined area of the pictures and frame is 126 in.². What is the side length, x, of each square picture?

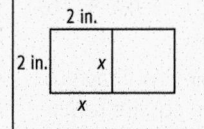

ANSWER 5 in.

Answers

Got It? (continued)

3. a. $-2.21, -6.79$

b. No, there are no factors of 15 with a sum of 9.

Got It?

Students may be tempted to approximate a decimal for the fraction that results from dividing the equation by three. Remind students that it should be left in fraction form, because the decimal form will result in a lack of accuracy due to rounding.

3 Lesson Check

Do You Know HOW?

- If students have difficulty with Exercise 4, then have them review Problem 4 to determine how to get a coefficient of 1 on the quadratic term.

Do You UNDERSTAND?

- If students have difficulty with Exercise 5, then make sure they understand that only 5a can be solved by factoring.

Close

> **Q** Why can completing the square be used to solve any quadratic equation? [The properties of algebra can be used to transform any quadratic equation into the form $m^2 = n$.]

 Got It? 4. Suppose the total area of the garden and border in Problem 4 is 150 ft². What is the side length x of each square plot? Round to the nearest hundredth.

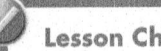 **Lesson Check**

Do you know HOW?

Solve each equation by completing the square.

1. $x^2 + 8x = 180$

2. $t^2 - 4t - 165 = 0$

3. $m^2 + 7m - 294 = 0$

4. $2z^2 + 3z = 135$

Do you UNDERSTAND?

5. **Vocabulary** Tell whether you would use square roots, factoring, or completing the square to solve each equation. Explain your choice of method.

  a. $k^2 - 3k = 304$ b. $t^2 - 6t + 16 = 0$

6. **Compare and Contrast** How is solving a quadratic equation using square roots like completing the square? How is it different?

  **Practice and Problem-Solving Exercises**

A Practice Find the value of c such that each expression is a perfect-square trinomial. See Problem 1.

7. $x^2 + 18x + c$ 8. $z^2 + 22z + c$ 9. $p^2 - 30p + c$

10. $k^2 - 5k + c$ 11. $g^2 + 17g + c$ 12. $q^2 - 4q + c$

Solve each equation by completing the square. If necessary, round to the nearest hundredth. See Problems 2 and 3.

13. $g^2 + 7g = 144$ 14. $r^2 - 4r = 30$ 15. $m^2 + 16m = -59$

16. $q^2 + 4q = 16$ 17. $x^2 + 18x = 307$ 18. $z^2 - 2z = 323$

19. $a^2 - 2a - 35 = 0$ 20. $m^2 + 12m + 19 = 0$ 21. $w^2 - 14w + 13 = 0$

22. $p^2 + 5p - 7 = 0$ 23. $t^2 + t - 28 = 0$ 24. $g^2 + 11g - 468 = 0$

Solve each equation by completing the square. If necessary, round to the nearest hundredth. See Problem 4.

25. $4a^2 - 8a = 24$ 26. $2y^2 - 8y - 10 = 0$ 27. $5n^2 - 3n - 15 = 10$

28. $4w^2 + 12w - 44 = 0$ 29. $3r^2 + 18r = 21$ 30. $2v^2 - 10v - 20 = 8$

31. **Art** The painting shown at the right has an area of 420 in.². What is the value of x?

x in.

$(2x + 5)$ in.

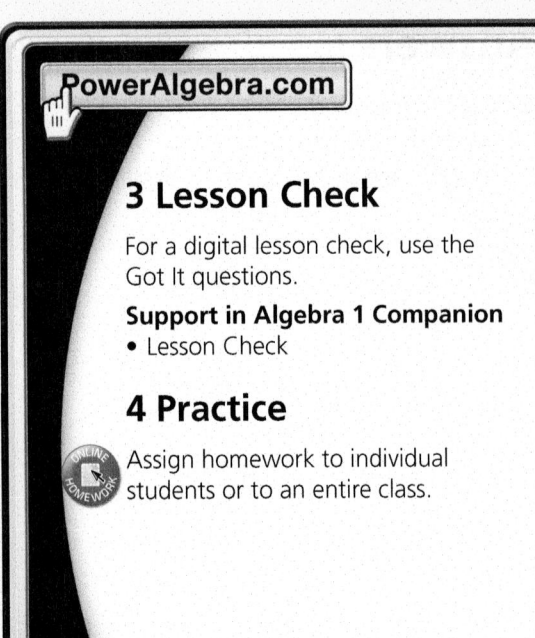

PowerAlgebra.com

3 Lesson Check

For a digital lesson check, use the Got It questions.

Support in Algebra 1 Companion

- Lesson Check

4 Practice

Assign homework to individual students or to an entire class.

Answers

Got It? (continued)

4. 5.77 ft

Lesson Check

1. −18, 10 2. −11, 15

3. −21, 14 4. −9, 7.5

5. Answers will vary. Samples are given.

  a. factoring;
    $k^2 - 3k - 304 = (k - 19)(k + 16)$

  b. completing the square

6. Answers will vary. Sample: You have to know how to solve using square roots in order to solve by completing the square. There are more steps involved in completing the square.

Practice and Problem-Solving Exercises

7. 81 8. 121

9. 225 10. $\frac{25}{4}$

11. $\frac{289}{4}$ 12. 4

13. −16, 9 14. −3.83, 7.83

15. −10.24, −5.76 16. −6.47, 2.47

17. −28.70, 10.70 18. −17, 19

19. −5, 7 20. −10.12, −1.88

21. 1, 13 22. −6.14, 1.14

23. −5.82, 4.82 24. −27.82, 16.82

25. −1.65, 3.65 26. −1, 5

27. −1.96, 2.56 28. 2.14, −5.14

29. −7, 1 30. −2, 7

31. about 13.3

Apply

32. Think About a Plan A park is installing a rectangular reflecting pool surrounded by a concrete walkway of uniform width. The reflecting pool will measure 42 ft by 26 ft. There is enough concrete to cover 460 ft² for the walkway. What is the maximum width x of the walkway?
  • How can drawing a diagram help you solve this problem?
  • How can you write an expression in terms of x for the area of the walkway?

33. Landscaping A school is fencing in a rectangular area for a playground. It plans to enclose the playground using fencing on three sides, as shown at the right. The school has budgeted enough money for 75 ft of fencing material and would like to make a playground with an area of 600 ft².
  a. Let w represent the width of the playground. Write an expression in terms of w for the length of the playground.
  b. Write and solve an equation to find the width w. Round to the nearest tenth of a foot.
  c. What should the length of the playground be?

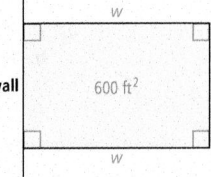

Solve each equation. If necessary, round to the nearest hundredth. If there is no real-number solution, write *no solution*.

34. $q^2 + 3q + 1 = 0$ **35.** $s^2 + 5s = -11$ **36.** $w^2 + 7w - 40 = 0$

37. $z^2 - 8z = -13$ **38.** $4p^2 - 40p + 56 = 0$ **39.** $m^2 + 4m + 13 = -8$

40. $2p^2 - 15p + 8 = 43$ **41.** $3r^2 - 27r = 3$ **42.** $s^2 + 9s + 20 = 0$

43. Error Analysis A classmate was completing the square to solve $4x^2 + 10x = 8$. For her first step she wrote $4x^2 + 10x + 25 = 8 + 25$. What was her error?

44. Reasoning Explain why completing the square is a better strategy for solving $x^2 - 7x - 9 = 0$ than graphing or factoring.

45. Open-Ended Write a quadratic equation and solve it by completing the square. Show your work.

Use each graph to estimate the values of x for which $f(x) = 5$. Then write and solve an equation to find the values of x such that $f(x) = 5$. Round to the nearest hundredth.

46. $f(x) = x^2 - 2x - 1$

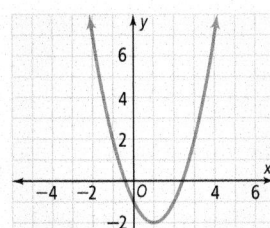

47. $f(x) = -\frac{1}{2}x^2 + 2x + 6$

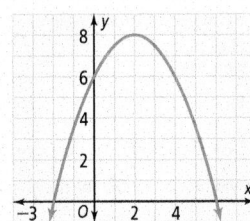

---

4 Practice

ASSIGNMENT GUIDE

Basic: 7–33 all, 34–42 even, 43–44

Average: 7–31 odd, 32–47

Advanced: 7–31 odd, 32–49

Standardized Test Prep: 50–56

Mixed Review: 57–66

Reasoning exercises have blue headings.

Applications exercises have red headings.

EXERCISE 33: Use the Think About a Plan worksheet in the **Practice and Problem Solving Workbook** (also available in the Teaching Resources in print and online) to further support students' development in becoming independent learners.

HOMEWORK QUICK CHECK

To check students' understanding of key skills and concepts, go over Exercises 11, 17, 32, 33, and 44.

---

32. about 3.1 ft

33. a. $75 - 2w$
  b. 11.6 ft or 25.9 ft
  c. 51.9 ft or 23.1 ft

34. −2.62, −0.38   **35.** no solution
36. −10.73, 3.73   **37.** 2.27, 5.73
38. 1.68, 8.32   **39.** no solution
40. −1.87, 9.37   **41.** −0.11, 9.11
42. −4, −5

43. She forgot to divide each side by 4 to make the coefficient of the x^2-term 1.

44. The solutions are irrational, which are difficult to approximate by graphing. Also, there are no integer factors of −9 with a sum of −7.

45. Check students' work.

46. −1.65, 3.65

47. −0.45, 4.45

Answers

Practice and Problem-Solving Exercises
(continued)

48. a. $6x^2 + 28x$

 b. $6x^2 + 28x = 384$

 c. 6 in. by 6 in. by 13 in.

49. a. $3 \pm \sqrt{5}$

 b. $(3, -5)$

 c. Answers will vary. Sample: p is the x-coordinate of the vertex.

50. 4.8 **51.** 0.0215 **52.** 16

53. 2 **54.** 1.5 **55.** 4.5

56. 16 **57.** $-6, -5$ **58.** $\pm\frac{8}{3}$

59. $-\frac{1}{6}, \frac{5}{2}$ **60.** m^{12} **61.** $-\frac{1}{b}$

62. t^{13} **63.** y^{29} **64.** 81

65. 0 **66.** -15

 Challenge **48. Geometry** Suppose the prism at the right has the same surface area as a cube with edges 8 in. long.

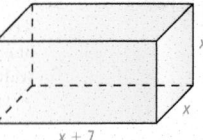

$x + 7$

 a. Write an expression for the surface area of the prism shown.

 b. Write an equation that relates the surface area of the prism to the surface area of the 8-in. cube.

 c. Solve the equation you wrote in part (b). What are the dimensions of the prism?

49. a. Solve the equation $x^2 - 6x + 4 = 0$, but leave the solutions in the form $p \pm \sqrt{q}$.

 b. Use the formula $x = \frac{-b}{2a}$ to find the coordinates of the vertex of the graph of $y = x^2 - 6x + 4$.

 c. **Reasoning** Explain the relationship between your answers to parts (a) and (b).

Standardized Test Prep

GRIDDED RESPONSE

SAT/ACT

50. The rectangular poster has an area 40 ft^2. What is the value of x to the nearest tenth of a foot?

$(x+1)$ ft

$(x+2)$ ft

51. The width of a notebook is 2.15×10^{-2} m. In decimal form, how many meters wide is the notebook?

52. What is the solution of the equation $19 + x = 35$?

53. How many elements are in the intersection of the two sets $M = \{2, 3, 4, 5\}$ and $N = \{1, 3, 5, 9\}$?

54. A ribbon with straight edges has an area of 24 $in.^2$. Its width is x and its length is $2x + 13$. What is the width of the ribbon in inches?

55. What is the x-intercept of the graph of $2x + 3y = 9$?

56. The sum of two numbers is 20. The difference between three times the larger number and twice the smaller number is 40. What is the larger number?

Mixed Review

Solve by factoring. ◀ See Lesson 9-4.

57. $n^2 + 11n + 30 = 0$ **58.** $9v^2 - 64 = 0$ **59.** $12w^2 = 28w + 5$

Simplify. ◀ See Lesson 7-4.

60. $(m^3)^4$ **61.** $-b^7(b^8)^{-1}$ **62.** $t(t^2)^6$ **63.** $y^8(y^{-7})^{-3}$

Get Ready! **To prepare for Lesson 9-6, do Exercises 64–66.**

Evaluate $b^2 - 4ac$ for the given values of a, b, and c. ◀ See Lesson 1-2.

64. $a = 2, b = 5, c = -7$ **65.** $a = 2, b = 4, c = 2$ **66.** $a = 1, b = 3, c = 6$

Additional Instructional Support

Algebra 1 Companion

Students can use the **Algebra 1 Companion** worktext (4 pages) as you teach the lesson. Use the Companion to support

- New Vocabulary
- Key Concepts
- Got It for each Problem
- Lesson Check

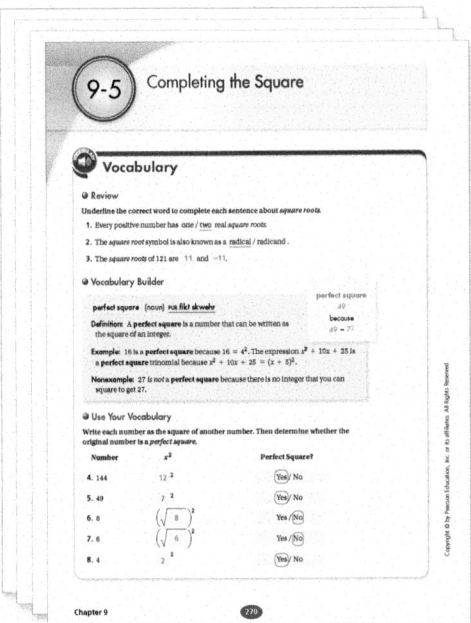

ELL Support

Use Manipulatives Write $x^2 + 4x = 0$ on the board. Use an overhead project and overhead algebra tiles to model completing the square. Think aloud as you manipulate the tiles. Write the solution, $x^2 + 4x + 4 = (x + 2)^2$ on the board. Point to the tiles and be explicit about how you arrived at the solution. Then do another example with students following along at their seats with their own tiles. Finally, write $x^2 + 2x = 0$ on the board. Monitor students as they use algebra tiles to complete the square to solve the equation.

5 Assess & Remediate

Lesson Quiz

1. What is the value of c such that $x^2 + 10x + c$ is a perfect square trinomial?

2. What are the solutions of the equation $x^2 - 6x = 27$?

3. What are the solutions of the equation $x^2 + 14x - 40 = 0$?

4. The combined area of the 3 window panes and frame shown below is 924 in.^{2}. The frame is of uniform width. What is the side length, x, of each square window frame?

5. Do you UNDERSTAND? What will happen if you try to use completing the square to solve an equation of the form $x^2 + bx + c = 0$ in which $c > \left(\frac{b}{2}\right)^2$?

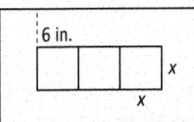

ANSWERS TO LESSON QUIZ

1. 25

2. −3, 9

3. −16.43, 2.43

4. 10 in.

5. There will be no real solutions; after you have completed the square, the right side of the equation will be negative.

PRESCRIPTION FOR REMEDIATION

Use the student work on the Lesson Quiz to prescribe a differentiated review assignment.

Points	Differentiated Remediation
0–2	Intervention
3–4	On-level
5	Extension

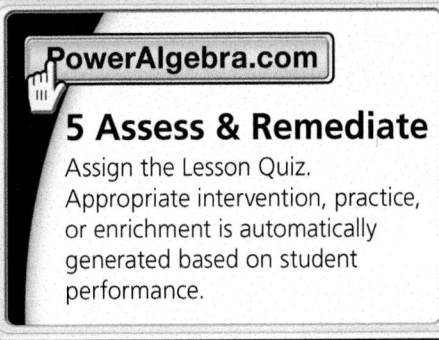

PowerAlgebra.com

5 Assess & Remediate

Assign the Lesson Quiz. Appropriate intervention, practice, or enrichment is automatically generated based on student performance.

Intervention

- **Reteaching** (2 pages) Provides reteaching and practice exercises for the key lesson concepts. Use with struggling students or absent students.

- **English Language Learner Support** Helps students develop and reinforce mathematical vocabulary and key concepts.

All-in-One Resources/Online
Reteaching

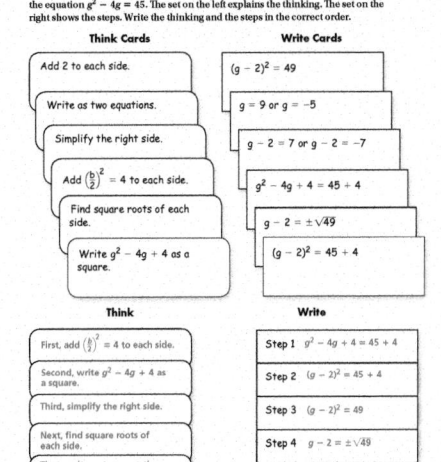

All-in-One Resources/Online
English Language Learner Support

Differentiated Remediation continued

On-Level

- **Practice (2 pages)** Provides extra practice for each lesson. For simpler practice exercises, use the Form K Practice pages found in the All-in-One Teaching Resources and online.

- **Think About a Plan** Helps students develop specific problem-solving skills and strategies by providing scaffolded guiding questions.

- **Standardized Test Prep** Focuses on all major exercises, all major question types, and helps students prepare for the high-stakes assessments.

Extension

- **Enrichment** Provides students with interesting problems and activities that extend the concepts of the lesson.

- **Activities, Games, and Puzzles** Worksheets that can be used for concepts development, enrichment, and for fun!

Practice and Problem Solving WKBK/All-in-One Resources/Online
Practice page 1

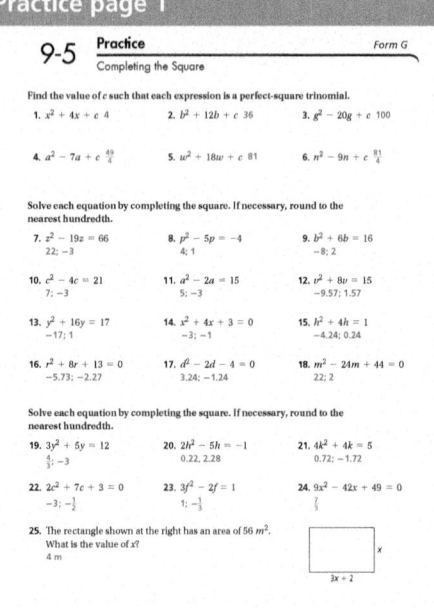

Practice and Problem Solving WKBK/All-in-One Resources/Online
Practice page 2

All-in-One Resources/Online
Enrichment

Practice and Problem Solving WKBK/All-in-One Resources/Online
Think About a Plan

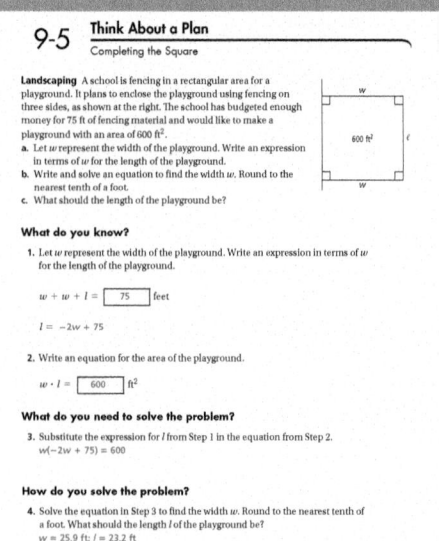

Practice and Problem Solving WKBK/All-in-One Resources/Online
Standardized Test Prep

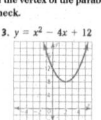

Online Teacher Resource Center
Activities, Games, and Puzzles

9-6 The Quadratic Formula and the Discriminant

Objectives To solve quadratic equations using the quadratic formula
To find the number of solutions of a quadratic equation

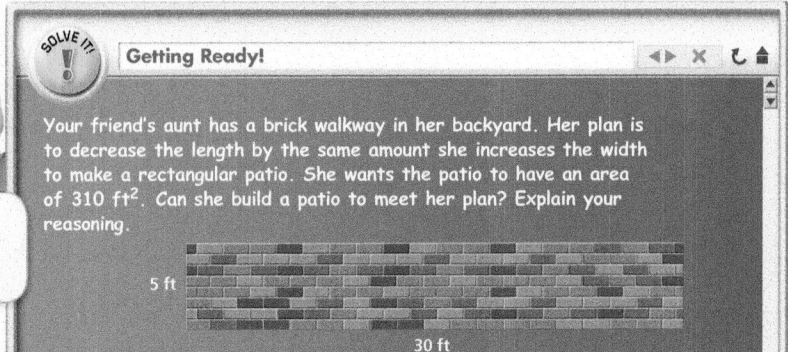

Getting Ready!

Your friend's aunt has a brick walkway in her backyard. Her plan is to decrease the length by the same amount she increases the width to make a rectangular patio. She wants the patio to have an area of 310 ft². Can she build a patio to meet her plan? Explain your reasoning.

Ever wonder how to tell if an equation has no solution?

5 ft

30 ft

Recall that quadratic equations can have two, one, or no real-number solutions. A quadratic equation can never have more than two solutions.

Essential Understanding You can find the solution(s) of *any* quadratic equation using the **quadratic formula**.

---

take note

Key Concept   Quadratic Formula

Algebra

If $ax^2 + bx + c = 0$, and $a \neq 0$, then

$$x = \frac{-b \pm \sqrt{b^2 - 4ac}}{2a}$$

Example

Suppose $2x^2 + 3x - 5 = 0$. Then $a = 2$, $b = 3$, and $c = -5$. Therefore

$$x = \frac{-(3) \pm \sqrt{(3)^2 - 4(2)(-5)}}{2(2)}$$

---

1 Interactive Learning

Solve It!

PURPOSE To show an equation of the form $ax^2 + bx + c = 0$ that has no real-number solutions

PROCESS Students may use the formula for the area of a rectangle to write an equation and/or use completing the square to solve the equation.

FACILITATE

Q What is the area of the current patio? Explain. **[150 ft²; 30 · 5 = 150]**

Q If the length is decreased by the same amount as the width is increased, what are the new dimensions of the patio? **[The length is 30 − x and the width is 5 + x.]**

Q What equation can be used to represent the problem situation? **[(30 − x)(5 + x) = 310]**

ANSWER See Solve It in Answers on next page.
CONNECT THE MATH The equation in the Solve It does not cross the x-axis, which means it has no real solutions. In the lesson, students use the quadratic formula to find solutions of quadratic equations that cannot be found by the previously taught algebraic methods.

2 Guided Instruction

Take Note

Students should note how the quadratic formula will provide two solutions for quadratic equations that have two solutions.

9-6 Preparing to Teach

BIG idea Solving Equations and Inequalities **UbD**

ESSENTIAL UNDERSTANDINGS
• Any quadratic equation can be solved using the quadratic formula.
• The discriminant of a quadratic equation can be used to determine the number of solutions an equation has.

Math Background

The technique of completing the square can be used to solve any quadratic equation, unlike the techniques of factoring or using square roots. Unfortunately, the numbers involved in the process of completing the square may become tedious to work with. The quadratic formula, which is derived by completing the square for the generic quadratic equation, $ax^2 + bx + c = 0$, can also be used to solve any quadratic equation

and is often less tedious than the process of completing the square.

One key to students' using the quadratic formula efficiently is to write the formula when they first begin the problem. Before they identify the values of *a*, *b*, and *c*, they must be certain that the equation is written in standard form. After making the substitutions, but before simplifying the solution, students should find the value of the discriminant. This tells students if they are seeking one real solution, two real solutions, or no real solutions.

Support Student Learning

Use the **Algebra I Companion** to engage and support students during instruction. See Lesson Resources at the end of this lesson for details.

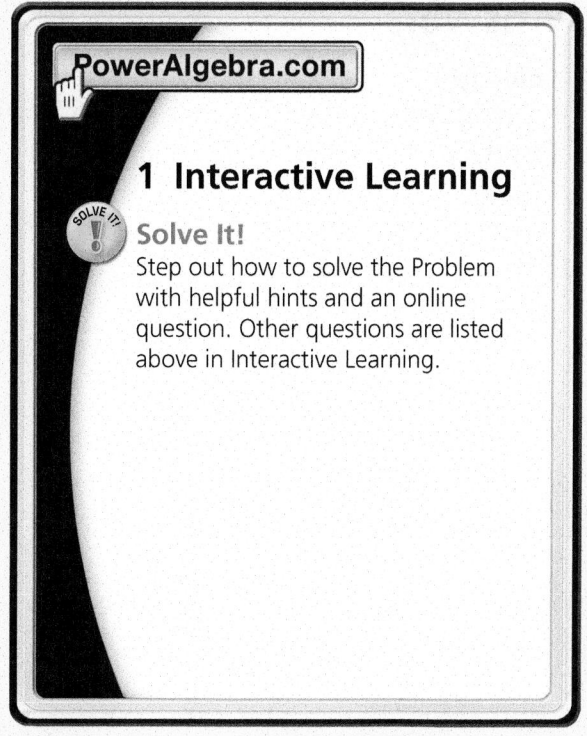

1 Interactive Learning

Solve It!
Step out how to solve the Problem with helpful hints and an online question. Other questions are listed above in Interactive Learning.

Here's Why it Works

As you show how to complete the square on the general equation, show the process on a quadratic equation such as $3x^2 + 7x + 11x = 0$ so that students can parallel the general process with a specific problem.

Problem 1

Tell students to write the quadratic formula on their paper prior to beginning each problem. This repetition will aid in their memorization of the formula.

> **Q** What are the values of a, b, and c? **[$a = 1$, $b = -2$, and $c = -8$]**
>
> **Q** What is the opposite of -2? **[2]**
>
> **Q** How can you check your solutions? **[Substitute your answers into the original equation.]**
>
> **Q** What other methods could be used to solve this quadratic equation? Explain which method might have been a preferred method and why. **[Graphing, factoring, or completing the square; factoring might have been a preferred method because the solutions are integers.]**

Got It?

ERROR PREVENTION

If students are having trouble correctly simplifying the numeric expressions in the quadratic formula, review the order of operations with them.

Here's Why It Works If you complete the square for the general equation $ax^2 + bx + c = 0$, you can derive the quadratic formula.

Step 1   Write $ax^2 + bx + c = 0$ so the coefficient of x^2 is 1.

$$ax^2 + bx + c = 0$$

$$x^2 + \frac{b}{a}x + \frac{c}{a} = 0 \qquad \text{Divide each side by } a.$$

Step 2   Complete the square.

$$x^2 + \frac{b}{a}x = -\frac{c}{a} \qquad \text{Subtract } \tfrac{c}{a} \text{ from each side.}$$

$$x^2 + \frac{b}{a}x + \left(\frac{b}{2a}\right)^2 = -\frac{c}{a} + \left(\frac{b}{2a}\right)^2 \qquad \text{Add } \left(\tfrac{b}{2a}\right)^2 \text{ to each side.}$$

$$\left(x + \frac{b}{2a}\right)^2 = -\frac{c}{a} + \frac{b^2}{4a^2} \qquad \text{Write the left side as a square.}$$

$$\left(x + \frac{b}{2a}\right)^2 = -\frac{4ac}{4a^2} + \frac{b^2}{4a^2} \qquad \text{Multiply } -\tfrac{c}{a} \text{ by } \tfrac{4a}{4a} \text{ to get like denominators.}$$

$$\left(x + \frac{b}{2a}\right)^2 = \frac{b^2 - 4ac}{4a^2} \qquad \text{Simplify the right side.}$$

Step 3   Solve the equation for x.

$$\sqrt{\left(x + \frac{b}{2a}\right)^2} = \pm\sqrt{\frac{b^2 - 4ac}{4a^2}} \qquad \text{Take square roots of each side.}$$

This step uses the property $\sqrt{\frac{m}{n}} = \frac{\sqrt{m}}{\sqrt{n}}$, which you will study in Lesson 10-2.

$$x + \frac{b}{2a} = \pm\frac{\sqrt{b^2 - 4ac}}{2a} \qquad \text{Simplify the right side.}$$

$$x = -\frac{b}{2a} \pm \frac{\sqrt{b^2 - 4ac}}{2a} \qquad \text{Subtract } \tfrac{b}{2a} \text{ from each side.}$$

$$x = \frac{-b \pm \sqrt{b^2 - 4ac}}{2a} \qquad \text{Simplify.}$$

Be sure to write a quadratic equation in standard form before using the quadratic formula.

Problem 1   Using the Quadratic Formula

Think

Why do you need to write the equation in standard form?
You can only use the quadratic formula with equations in the form $ax^2 + bx + c = 0$.

What are the solutions of $x^2 - 8 = 2x$? Use the quadratic formula.

$$x^2 - 2x - 8 = 0 \qquad \text{Write the equation in standard form.}$$

$$x = \frac{-b \pm \sqrt{b^2 - 4ac}}{2a} \qquad \text{Use the quadratic formula.}$$

$$x = \frac{-(-2) \pm \sqrt{(-2)^2 - 4(1)(-8)}}{2(1)} \qquad \text{Substitute 1 for } a, -2 \text{ for } b, \text{ and } -8 \text{ for } c.$$

$$x = \frac{2 \pm \sqrt{36}}{2} \qquad \text{Simplify.}$$

$$x = \frac{2 + 6}{2} \quad \text{or} \quad x = \frac{2 - 6}{2} \qquad \text{Write as two equations.}$$

$$x = 4 \quad \text{or} \quad x = -2 \qquad \text{Simplify.}$$

Got It?   **1.** What are the solutions of $x^2 - 4x = 21$? Use the quadratic formula.

Answers

Solve It!
No; explanations may vary.

Got It?
1. $-3, 7$

PowerAlgebra.com

2 Guided Instruction

Each Problem is worked out and supported online.

Problem 1
Using the Quadratic Formula
Animated

Problem 2
Finding Approximate Solutions

Problem 3
Choosing an Appropriate Method
Animated

Problem 4
Using the Discriminant
Animated

Support in Algebra 1 Companion
• Vocabulary
• Key Concepts
• Got It?

When the radicand in the quadratic formula is not a perfect square, you can use a calculator to approximate the solutions of an equation.

 Problem 2 Finding Approximate Solutions

Sports In the shot put, an athlete throws a heavy metal ball through the air. The arc of the ball can be modeled by the equation $y = -0.04x^2 + 0.84x + 2$, where x is the horizontal distance, in meters, from the athlete and y is the height, in meters, of the ball. How far from the athlete will the ball land?

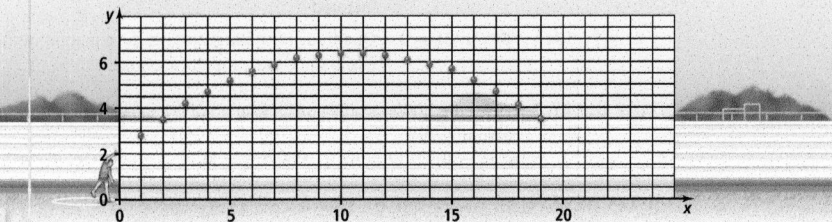

Think

Why do you substitute 0 for y?
When the ball hits the ground, its height will be 0.

$0 = -0.04x^2 + 0.84x + 2$	Substitute 0 for y in the given equation.
$x = \dfrac{-b \pm \sqrt{b^2 - 4ac}}{2a}$	Use the quadratic formula.
$x = \dfrac{-0.84 \pm \sqrt{0.84^2 - 4(-0.04)(2)}}{2(-0.04)}$	Substitute -0.04 for a, 0.84 for b, and 2 for c.
$x = \dfrac{-0.84 \pm \sqrt{1.0256}}{-0.08}$	Simplify.
$x = \dfrac{-0.84 + \sqrt{1.0256}}{-0.08}$ or $x = \dfrac{-0.84 - \sqrt{1.0256}}{-0.08}$	Write as two equations.
$x \approx -2.16$ or $x \approx 23.16$	Simplify.

Only the positive answer makes sense in this situation. The ball will land about 23.16 m from the athlete.

Got It? **2.** A batter strikes a baseball. The equation $y = -0.005x^2 + 0.7x + 3.5$ models its path, where x is the horizontal distance, in feet, the ball travels and y is the height, in feet, of the ball. How far from the batter will the ball land? Round to the nearest tenth of a foot.

There are many methods for solving a quadratic equation.

Method	When to Use
Graphing	Use if you have a graphing calculator handy.
Square roots	Use if the equation has no x-term.
Factoring	Use if you can factor the equation easily.
Completing the square	Use if the coefficient of x^2 is 1, but you cannot easily factor the equation.
Quadratic formula	Use if the equation cannot be factored easily or at all.

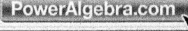
Problem 2

Q When the shotput lands on the ground, what is its height? Explain. **[Its height is zero because it is no longer in the air.]**

Q Is the equation $0 = -0.04x^2 + 0.84x + 2$ in standard form? Explain. **[Yes; the left and right sides can be reversed using the symmetric property.]**

Q What are the values of a, b, and c? **[$a = -0.04$, $b = 0.84$, and $c = 2$]**

Q Why is the negative answer not reasonable in this situation? **[The shotput is being thrown forward.]**

Got It? SYNTHESIZING

Q What is the vertex of the quadratic equation $y = -0.005x^2 + 0.7x + 3.5$? **[(70, 28)]**

Q What does the y-coordinate of the vertex represent? **[It represents the maximum height of the baseball.]**

The chart is a reference to guide students to learn when each method is the most appropriate plan to find a solution.

Although students may find it difficult to memorize the quadratic formula, it is a clear-cut method that works for all equations. The quadratic formula also makes it easy to identify when an equation has one, two, or no real solutions.

Additional Problems

1. What are the solutions of $x^2 - 3x - 10 = 0$? Use the quadratic formula.

ANSWER $-2, 5$

2. Jacob tosses a baseball across the playground. The arc of the ball can be modeled by the equation $y = -0.05x^2 + 0.75x + 4$, where x is the horizontal distance (in meters) from Jacob and y is the height (in meters) of the ball. How far from Jacob does the ball land?

ANSWER about 19.2 m

3. Which method(s) would you choose to solve each equation?

a. $2x^2 - 32 = 0$

b. $3x^2 - 17x + 11 = 0$

c. $x^2 + 7x + 10 = 0$

d. $x^2 + 4x - 15 = 0$

e. $-3x^2 + 27 = 0$

ANSWER **a.** square roots **b.** quadratic equation or graphing **c.** factoring **d.** quadratic equation, completing the square, or graphing **e.** square roots

4. What is the number of real-number solutions of $2x^2 + 7x - 15 = 0$?

ANSWER 2

Answers

Got It? (continued)

2. 144.8 ft

Problem 3

> **Q** In 3A, can the equation $3x^2 - 9 = 0$ be solved by factoring? Explain. **[No, there is a common factor of 3, but it is not a difference of two squares.]**
>
> **Q** Why is completing the square not a convenient method for 3C? **[Because the coefficient of the x^2-term is not 1.]**
>
> **Q** How would you use graphing to solve 3E? **[I would use a graphing calculator to graph the related quadratic function and use the CALC feature to locate the x-intercepts.]**

Got It?   ERROR PREVENTION

Have students use the chart on page 569 as a checklist for each equation.

Alert students that the most common error when using square roots to solve a quadratic equation is not including both solutions to the equation. Remind students that they must give both the positive and negative square root as solutions.

Take Note

> **Q** Does adding or subtracting a square root of a 0 discriminant in the quadratic formula lead to two real-number solutions? **[no]**
>
> **Q** If the discriminant is negative, is there a real square root of the discriminant? **[no]**
>
> **Q** How many solutions will you have if you add and subtract the square root of a positive discriminant? **[two]**

Think

Can you use the quadratic formula to solve part (A)?
Yes. You can use the quadratic formula with $a = 3$, $b = 0$, and $c = -9$. However, it is faster to use square roots.

 **Problem 3** **Choosing an Appropriate Method**

Which method(s) would you choose to solve each equation? Explain your reasoning.

A $3x^2 - 9 = 0$ Square roots; there is no x-term

B $x^2 - x - 30 = 0$ Factoring; the equation is easily factorable

C $6x^2 + 13x - 17 = 0$ Quadratic formula, graphing; the equation cannot be factored

D $x^2 - 5x + 3 = 0$ Quadratic formula, completing the square, or graphing; the coefficient of the x^2-term is 1, but the equation cannot be factored

E $-16x^2 - 50x + 21 = 0$ Quadratic formula, graphing; the equation cannot be factored easily since the numbers are large

✓ **Got It? 3.** Which method(s) would you choose to solve each equation? Justify your reasoning.

     a. $x^2 - 8x + 12 = 0$ **b.** $169x^2 = 36$ **c.** $5x^2 + 13x - 1 = 0$

Quadratic equations can have two, one, or no real-number solutions. Before you solve a quadratic equation, you can determine how many real-number solutions it has by using the discriminant. The **discriminant** is the expression under the radical sign in the quadratic formula.

$$x = \frac{-b \pm \sqrt{b^2 - 4ac}}{2a} \quad \text{the discriminant}$$

The discriminant of a quadratic equation can be positive, zero, or negative.

take note   **Key Concept**   **Using the Discriminant**

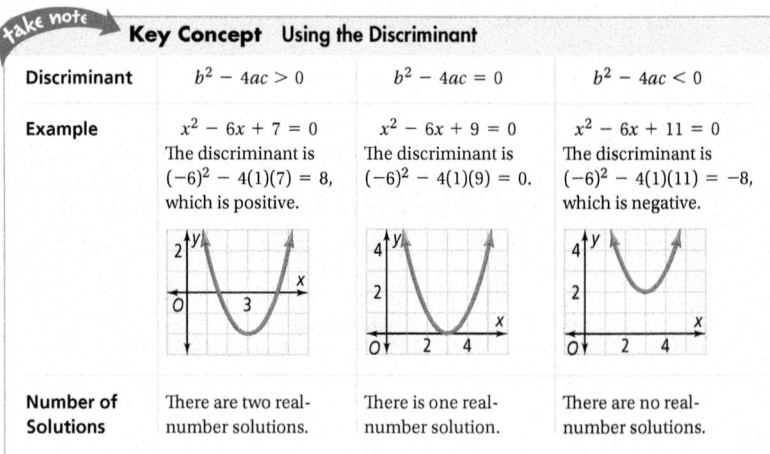

Discriminant	$b^2 - 4ac > 0$	$b^2 - 4ac = 0$	$b^2 - 4ac < 0$
Example	$x^2 - 6x + 7 = 0$ The discriminant is $(-6)^2 - 4(1)(7) = 8$, which is positive.	$x^2 - 6x + 9 = 0$ The discriminant is $(-6)^2 - 4(1)(9) = 0$.	$x^2 - 6x + 11 = 0$ The discriminant is $(-6)^2 - 4(1)(11) = -8$, which is negative.
Number of Solutions	There are two real-number solutions.	There is one real-number solution.	There are no real-number solutions.

Answers

Got It? (continued)

3. a. Factoring; the equation is easily factorable.

     b. Square roots; there is no x-term.

     c. Quadratic formula, graphing; the equation cannot be factored.

Problem 4 Using the Discriminant

How many real-number solutions does $2x^2 - 3x = -5$ have?

Think	Write
Write the equation in standard form.	$2x^2 - 3x + 5 = 0$
Evaluate the discriminant by substituting 2 for a, -3 for b, and 5 for c.	$b^2 - 4ac = (-3)^2 - 4(2)(5)$ $= -31$
Draw a conclusion.	Because the discriminant is negative, the equation has no real-number solutions.

Plan

Can you solve this problem another way?
Yes. You could actually solve the equation to find any solutions. However, you only need to know the number of solutions, so use the discriminant.

Got It? 4. a. How many real-number solutions does $6x^2 - 5x = 7$ have?
b. Reasoning If a is positive and c is negative, how many real-number solutions will the equation $ax^2 + bx + c = 0$ have? Explain.

Lesson Check

Do you know HOW?

Use the quadratic formula to solve each equation. If necessary, round answers to the nearest hundredth.

1. $-3x^2 - 11x + 4 = 0$

2. $7x^2 - 2x = 8$

3. How many real-number solutions does the equation $-2x^2 + 8x - 5 = 0$ have?

Do you UNDERSTAND?

4. Vocabulary Explain how the discriminant of the equation $ax^2 + bx + c = 0$ is related to the number of x-intercepts of the graph of $y = ax^2 + bx + c$.

5. Reasoning What method would you use to solve the equation $x^2 + 9x + c = 0$ if $c = 14$? If $c = 7$? Explain.

6. Writing Explain how completing the square is used to derive the quadratic formula.

Practice and Problem-Solving Exercises

Ⓐ Practice Use the quadratic formula to solve each equation. ◆ See Problem 1.

7. $2x^2 + 5x + 3 = 0$

8. $5x^2 + 16x - 84 = 0$

9. $4x^2 + 7x - 15 = 0$

10. $3x^2 - 41x = -110$

11. $18x^2 - 45x - 50 = 0$

12. $3x^2 + 44x = -96$

13. $3x^2 + 19x = 154$

14. $2x^2 - x - 120 = 0$

15. $5x^2 - 47x = 156$

Problem 4

Q Why does a negative discriminant indicate that the equation has no real solutions? **[When a radicand is a negative number, the square root is not a real number.]**

Q Is the vertex of the quadratic function $y = 2x^2 - 3x + 5$ above or below the x-axis? Explain. **[Above; the discriminant is a negative number, so the parabola does not intersect the x-axis. Since a is positive, the parabola opens upward and its vertex must be above the x-axis.]**

Got It? ERROR PREVENTION
If students report no solution for 4a, then they likely did not put the equation into standard form before identifying the values of a, b, and c.

3 Lesson Check

Do you know HOW?
- If students have difficulty with Exercise 3, then remind them to use the discriminant to determine the number of solutions.

Do you UNDERSTAND?
- If students have difficulty with Exercise 6, then have them review the Here's Why It Works section on page 568.

Close

Q Which methods for solving a quadratic equation can be used for any equation? only for certain equations? **[graphing, completing the square, and the quadratic formula; factoring and square roots]**

Got It? (continued)

4. a. 2
b. 2; if $a > 0$ and $c < 0$, then $-4ac > 0$ and $b^2 - 4ac > 0$.

Lesson Check

1. $-4, \frac{1}{3}$
2. $-0.94, 1.22$
3. 2
4. If the discriminant is positive, there are 2 x-intercepts. If the discriminant is 0, there is 1 x-intercept. If the discriminant is negative, there are no x-intercepts.
5. Factoring because the equation is easily factorable; quadratic formula or graphing because the equation cannot be factored.
6. If you complete the square for $ax^2 + bx + c = 0$, you will get the quadratic formula.

Practice and Problem-Solving Exercises

7. $-1.5, -1$
8. $-6, 2.8$
9. $-3, 1.25$
10. $\frac{11}{3}, 10$
11. $-\frac{5}{6}, \frac{10}{3}$
12. $-12, -2\frac{2}{3}$
13. $-11, 4\frac{2}{3}$
14. $-7.5, 8$
15. $-2.6, 12$

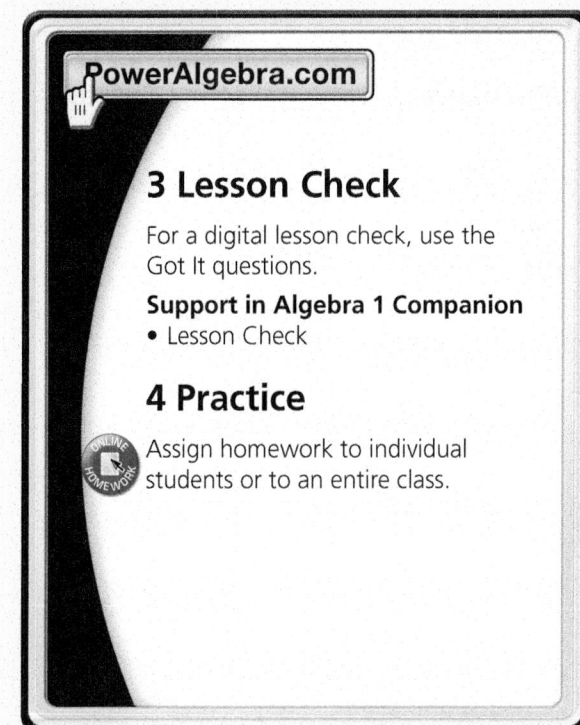

PowerAlgebra.com

3 Lesson Check
For a digital lesson check, use the Got It questions.

Support in Algebra 1 Companion
- Lesson Check

4 Practice
Assign homework to individual students or to an entire class.

4 Practice

ASSIGNMENT GUIDE

Basic: 7–34 all, 36–40 even, 41–44 all

Average: 7–33 odd, 35–45

Advanced: 7–33 odd, 35–49

Standardized Test Prep: 50–54

Mixed Review: 55–61

Reasoning exercises have blue headings.

Applications exercises have red headings.

EXERCISE 42: Use the Think About a Plan worksheet in the **Practice and Problem Solving Workbook** (also available in the Teaching Resources in print and online) to further support students' development in becoming independent learners.

HOMEWORK QUICK CHECK

To check students' understanding of key skills and concepts, go over Exercises 9, 25, 41, 42, and 44.

Use the quadratic formula to solve each equation. Round your answer to the nearest hundredth.   **See Problem 2.**

16. $x^2 + 8x + 11 = 0$ **17.** $5x^2 + 12x - 2 = 0$ **18.** $2x^2 - 16x = -25$

19. $8x^2 - 7x - 5 = 0$ **20.** $6x^2 + 9x = 32$ **21.** $3x^2 + 5x = 4$

22. Football A football player punts a ball. The path of the ball can be modeled by the equation $y = -0.004x^2 + x + 2.5$, where x is the horizontal distance, in feet, the ball travels and y is the height, in feet, of the ball. How far from the football player will the ball land? Round to the nearest tenth of a foot.

Which method(s) would you choose to solve each equation? Justify your reasoning.   **See Problem 3.**

23. $x^2 + 4x - 15 = 0$ **24.** $9x^2 - 49 = 0$ **25.** $4x^2 - 41x = 73$

26. $3x^2 - 7x + 3 = 0$ **27.** $x^2 + 4x - 60 = 0$ **28.** $-4x^2 + 8x + 1 = 0$

Find the number of real-number solutions of each equation.   **See Problem 4.**

29. $x^2 - 2x + 3 = 0$ **30.** $x^2 + 7x - 5 = 0$ **31.** $x^2 + 3x + 11 = 0$

32. $x^2 - 15 = 0$ **33.** $x^2 + 2x = 0$ **34.** $9x^2 + 12x + 4 = 0$

B Apply

Use any method to solve each equation. If necessary, round your answer to the nearest hundredth.

35. $3w^2 = 48$ **36.** $3x^2 + 2x - 4 = 0$ **37.** $6g^2 - 18 = 0$

38. $3p^2 + 4p = 10$ **39.** $k^2 - 4k = -4$ **40.** $13r^2 - 117 = 0$

41. Think About a Plan You operate a dog-walking service. You have 50 customers per week when you charge $14 per walk. For each $1 decrease in your fee for walking a dog, you get 5 more customers per week. Can you ever earn $750 in a week? Explain.
- What quadratic equation in standard form can you use to model this situation?
- How can the discriminant of the equation help you solve the problem?

42. Sports Your school wants to take out an ad in the paper congratulating the basketball team on a successful season, as shown below. The area of the photo will be half the area of the entire ad. What is the value of x?

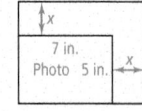

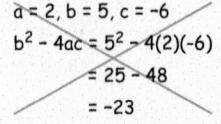

43. Writing How can you use the discriminant to write a quadratic equation that has two solutions?

44. Error Analysis Describe and correct the error at the right that a student made in finding the discriminant of $2x^2 + 5x - 6 = 0$.

Answers

Practice and Problem-Solving Exercises
(continued)

16. −6.24, −1.76   **17.** −2.56, 0.16

18. 2.13, 5.87   **19.** −0.47, 1.34

20. −3.18, 1.68   **21.** −2.26, 0.59

22. 252.5 ft

23. Quadratic formula, completing the square, or graphing; the coefficient of the x^2-term is 1, but the equation cannot be factored.

24. Square roots; there is no x-term.

25. Quadratic formula, graphing; the equation cannot be factored.

26. Quadratic formula, graphing; the equation cannot be factored.

27. Factoring; the equation is easily factorable.

28. Quadratic formula, graphing; the equation cannot be factored.

29. 0   **30.** 2

31. 0   **32.** 2

33. 2   **34.** 1

35. ±4   **36.** −1.54, 0.87

37. ±1.73   **38.** −2.61, 1.28

39. 2   **40.** ±3

41. No, there are no real-number solutions of the equation $(14 - x)(50 + 5x) = 750$.

42. about 2.43 in.

43. Find values of a, b, and c such that $b^2 - 4ac > 0$.

44. The next to the last line should be $25 + 48$. The discriminant is 73.

45. Find the discriminant and the solution of each equation in parts (a)–(c). If necessary, round to the nearest hundredth.

    a. $x^2 - 6x + 5 = 0$ **b.** $x^2 + x - 20 = 0$ **c.** $2x^2 - 7x - 3 = 0$

    d. Reasoning When the discriminant is a perfect square, are the solutions rational or irrational? Explain.

Challenge   **46. Reasoning** The solutions of any quadratic equation $ax^2 + bx + c = 0$ are $\dfrac{-b + \sqrt{b^2 - 4ac}}{2a}$ and $\dfrac{-b - \sqrt{b^2 - 4ac}}{2a}$.

    a. Find a formula for the sum of the solutions.

    b. One solution of $2x^2 + 3x - 104 = 0$ is -8. Use the formula you found in part (a) to find the second solution.

Reasoning For each condition given, tell whether $ax^2 + bx + c = 0$ will *always, sometimes,* or *never* have two solutions.

    47. $b^2 < 4ac$ **48.** $b^2 = 0$ **49.** $ac < 0$

Standardized Test Prep

50. What are the approximate solutions of the equation $x^2 - 7x + 3 = 0$?

    Ⓐ $-6.54, 0.46$ Ⓑ $-6.54, -0.46$ Ⓒ $-0.46, 6.54$ Ⓓ $0.46, 6.54$

51. Which of the following relations is a function?

    Ⓕ $\{(1, 2), (3, 5), (1, 4), (2, 3)\}$ Ⓗ $\{(8, 2), (6, 3), (6, 11), (-8, 2)\}$

    Ⓖ $\{(-5, 6), (0, 9), (-1, 2), (0, 6)\}$ Ⓘ $\{(-1, 3), (7, 3), (-7, 2), (4, 5)\}$

52. What equation do you get when you solve $3a - b = 2c$ for b?

    Ⓐ $b = -3a + 2c$ Ⓑ $b = 3a - 2c$ Ⓒ $b = 3a + 2c$ Ⓓ $b = -3a - 2c$

53. What are the approximate solutions of the equation $\frac{1}{3}x^2 - \frac{5}{4}x + 1 = 0$? Use a graphing calculator.

    Ⓕ $1.07, 2.77$ Ⓖ $1.16, 2.59$ Ⓗ $0.87, 10.38$ Ⓘ $0.19, 16.01$

54. Suppose the line through points $(n, 6)$ and $(1, 2)$ is parallel to the graph of $2x + y = 3$. Find the value of n. Show your work.

Mixed Review

Solve each equation by completing the square.   ◀ See Lesson 9-5.

55. $s^2 - 10s + 13 = 0$ **56.** $m^2 + 3m = -2$ **57.** $3w^2 + 18w - 1 = 0$

Get Ready! To prepare for Lesson 9-7, do Exercises 58–61.

Graph each function.   ◀ See Lesson 7-6.

58. $y = 2^x$ **59.** $y = 3^x$ **60.** $y = \left(\frac{1}{3}\right)^x$ **61.** $y = \left(\frac{1}{2}\right)^x$

58.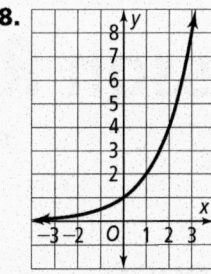

59.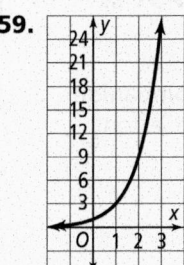

60.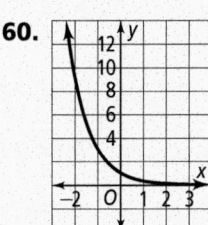

61.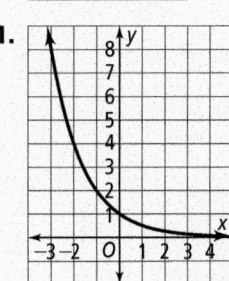

---

45. a. 16; 1, 5

    b. 81; −5, 4

    c. 73; −0.39, 3.89

    d. Rational; if the discriminant is a perfect square, then its square root is an integer, and the solutions are rational.

46. a. $-\frac{b}{a}$ **47.** never

    b. 6.5

48. sometimes   **49.** always

50. D   **51.** I

52. B   **53.** G

54. [2] The slope of $y = -2x + 3$ is −2. Parallel lines have equal slopes, so $\frac{2 - 6}{1 - n} = -2$, $-2(1 - n) = 2 - 6$, $-2 + 2n = -4$, and $n = -1$.

[1] appropriate methods with minor calculation error

55. 1.54, 8.46   **56.** −2, −1

57. −6.06, 0.06

Additional Instructional Support

Algebra 1 Companion

Students can use the **Algebra 1 Companion** worktext (4 pages) as you teach the lesson. Use the Companion to support

- New Vocabulary
- Key Concepts
- Got It for each Problem
- Lesson Check

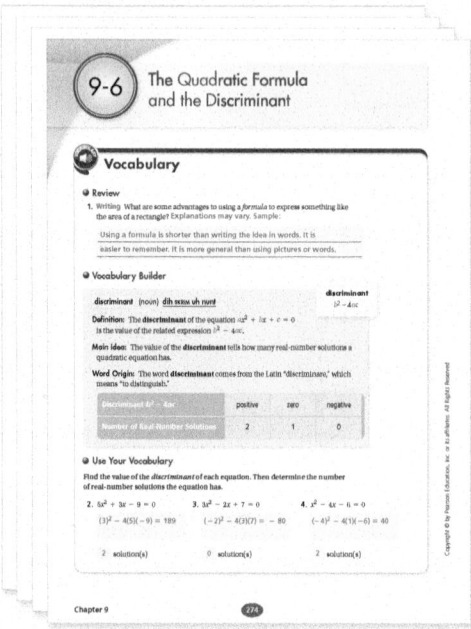

ELL Support

Assess Understanding Write this language objective on the board: Use compare and contrast to show comprehension of the methods to solve quadratic functions.

Place students into pairs of mixed abilities. Draw five ovals in a row along the board and label the ovals *graphing*, *finding the square root*, *factoring*, *completing the square*, and *quadratic formula*. Compare each method. Then list example equations on the board. Ask students to decide which equation would be best solved by which method. Discuss the results in class, allowing students to share their reasonings. Have students write the situation appropriate for each method.

5 Assess & Remediate

Lesson Quiz

1. What are the solutions of $x^2 + 12x + 32 = 0$? Use the quadratic formula.

2. Linda shoots an arrow at a target in an archery competition. The arc of the arrow can be modeled by the equation $y = -0.02x^2 + 0.65x + 4$, where x is the horizontal distance (in meters) from Linda and y is the height (in meters) of the arrow. How far from Linda does the arrow hit the ground?

3. What method(s) would you choose to solve the quadratic equation $-2x^2 + 8x + 13 = 0$? Justify your choice.

4. What is the number of solutions of $4x^2 + 12x + 9 = 0$?

5. **Do you UNDERSTAND?** A football player tosses the ball through the air to a teammate. Could the path of the ball be described by the equation $y = 0.5x^2 + 0.3x + 2$?

ANSWERS TO LESSON QUIZ

1. -8, -4
2. 37.8 m
3. quadratic formula or graphing; the equation cannot be factored, and the leading coefficient is not equal to 1.
4. 1
5. No; the graph for the path of a ball must be a parabola that opens downward, so if the equation is in the form $y = ax^2 + bx + c$, a must be negative.

PRESCRIPTION FOR REMEDIATION

Use the student work on the Lesson Quiz to prescribe a differentiated review assignment.

Points	Differentiated Remediation
0–2	Intervention
3–4	On-level
5	Extension

PowerAlgebra.com

5 Assess & Remediate

Assign the Lesson Quiz. Appropriate intervention, practice, or enrichment is automatically generated based on student performance.

Intervention

- **Reteaching** (2 pages) Provides reteaching and practice exercises for the key lesson concepts. Use with struggling students or absent students.

- **English Language Learner Support** Helps students develop and reinforce mathematical vocabulary and key concepts.

All-in-One Resources/Online
Reteaching

9-6 Reteaching
The Quadratic Formula and the Discriminant

If a quadratic equation is written in the form $ax^2 + bx + c = 0$, the solutions can be found using the following formula.

$$x = \frac{-b \pm \sqrt{b^2 - 4ac}}{2a}$$

This formula is called the **quadratic formula.**

Problem

What are the solutions of $x^2 + 7x = 60$? Use the quadratic formula.

First rewrite the equation in the form $ax^2 + bx + c = 0$.

$x^2 + 7x = 60$
$x^2 + 7x - 60 = 60 - 60$ Subtract 60 from each side.
$x^2 + 7x - 60 = 0$ Simplify.

Therefore, $a = 1$, $b = 7$, and $c = -60$.

$x = \frac{-b \pm \sqrt{b^2 - 4ac}}{2a}$

$x = \frac{-7 \pm \sqrt{7^2 - 4(1)(-60)}}{2(1)}$

$x = \frac{-7 \pm \sqrt{289}}{2}$

$x = \frac{-7 \pm 17}{2}$

The two solutions are $\frac{-7 - 17}{2}$ or -12 and $\frac{-7 + 17}{2}$ or 5.

Exercises

Use the quadratic formula to solve each equation.

1. $x^2 - 19x + 70 = 0$ 2. $x^2 + 32x + 175 = 0$ 3. $2x^2 + 37x - 19 = 0$
14; 5   −25; −7   −19; 0.5

4. $x^2 - 10x = 75$ 5. $x^2 + x = 132$ 6. $6x^2 + 13x = 28$
15; −5   −12; 11   −3.5; 1.3

7. $20x^2 + 11x = 3$ 8. $4x^2 + 24x = -35$ 9. $15x^2 + 20 = 40x$
$-\frac{3}{4}; \frac{1}{5}$ −3.5; 1.3   2; $\frac{2}{3}$

All-in-One Resources/Online
English Language Learner Support

9-6 ELL Support
The Quadratic Formula and the Discriminant

Complete the chart by filling in the missing information about when to use the given method to solve a quadratic equation.

Method	When to Use	Equation
completing the square	Use *completing the square* if the coefficient of x^2 is 1, but you cannot factor the equation easily.	$0 = x^2 - 2x + 5$
factoring	Use *factoring* if you can factor the equation easily.	1. $0 = x^2 + 8x + 15$ $= (x + 3)(x + 5)$
graphing	2. Use *graphing* if you have a graphing calculator available.	$0 = 9x^2 + 12x + 4$
quadratic formula	Use the *quadratic formula* if the equation cannot be factored easily or at all.	3. $0 = 2x^2 - 4x - 3$
square roots	4. Use *square roots* if the equation has no x-term.	$0 = 9x^2 - 36$

Differentiated Remediation *continued*

On-Level

- **Practice** (2 pages) Provides extra practice for each lesson. For simpler practice exercises, use the Form K Practice pages found in the All-in-One Teaching Resources and online.

- **Think About a Plan** Helps students develop specific problem-solving skills and strategies by providing scaffolded guiding questions.

- **Standardized Test Prep** Focuses on all major exercises, all major question types, and helps students prepare for the high-stakes assessments.

Extension

- **Enrichment** Provides students with interesting problems and activities that extend the concepts of the lesson.

- **Activities, Games, and Puzzles** Worksheets that can be used for concepts development, enrichment, and for fun!

Practice and Problem Solving WKBK/ All-in-One Resources/Online
Practice page 1

9-6 Practice   Form G
The Quadratic Formula and the Discriminant

Use the quadratic formula to solve each equation.

1. $7c^2 + 8c + 1 = 0$
$-1; -\frac{1}{7}$

2. $2w^2 - 28w = -98$
7

3. $2j^2 - 3j = -1$
$1; \frac{1}{2}$

4. $2x^2 - 6x + 4 = 0$
2; 1

5. $2n^2 - 6n = 8$
4; -1

6. $-7d^2 + 2d + 9 = 0$
$-1; \frac{9}{7}$

7. $2a^2 + 4a - 6 = 0$
$-3; 1$

8. $-3p^2 + 17p = 20$
4; $\frac{5}{3}$

9. $4d^2 - 8d + 3 = 0$
$\frac{3}{2}; \frac{1}{2}$

Use the quadratic formula to solve each equation. Round answers to the nearest hundredth.

10. $h^2 - 2h - 2 = 0$
2.75; -0.75

11. $5x^2 + 3x = 1$
$-0.84; 0.24$

12. $-z^2 - 4z = -2$
0.45; -4.45

13. $t^2 + 10t = -22$
$-3.25; -6.75$

14. $3n^2 + 10n = 5$
$-3.78; 0.44$

15. $z^2 - 10z + 14 = 0$
8.32; 1.68

16. A basketball is passed through the air. The height h of the ball in feet after the distance d in feet the ball travels horizontally is given by $h = -d^2 + 10d + 5$. How far horizontally from the player passing the ball will the ball land on the ground?
about 10.48 ft

Which method(s) would you choose to solve each equation? Justify your reasoning.

17. $h^2 + 4h + 7 = 0$
no solution

18. $a^2 - 4a - 12 = 0$
factoring is easiest

19. $24y^2 - 11y - 14 = 0$
quadratic formula

20. $2p^2 - 7p - 4 = 0$
factor

21. $4a^2 - 144 = 0$
use square roots

22. $f^2 - 2f - 35 = 0$
complete the square

23. **Writing** Explain how the discriminant can be used to determine the number of solutions a quadratic equation has.
If the discriminant is > 0, there are two real solutions. If the discriminant = 0, there is one solution. If the discriminant is < 0, there are no real solutions.

Practice and Problem Solving WKBK/ All-in-One Resources/Online
Practice page 2

9-6 Practice (continued)   Form G
The Quadratic Formula and the Discriminant

Find the number of real-number solutions of each equation.

24. $x^2 - 8x + 7 = 0$
two

25. $x^2 - 6x = 0$
two

26. $2x^2 - 5x + 16 = 0$
no real solutions

27. $-3x^2 - 4x - 8 = 0$
no real solutions

28. $7x^2 + 12x - 21 = 0$
two

29. $2x^2 + 4x + 2 = 0$
one

Use any method to solve each equation. If necessary, round answers to the nearest hundredth.

30. $5m^2 - 3m - 15 = 0$
2.06; -1.46

31. $9y^2 + 6y = -12$
no solution

32. $4a^2 = 36$
3; -3

33. $6t^2 - 96 = 0$
4; -4

34. $z^2 + 7z = -10$
$-2; -5$

35. $-g^2 + 4g + 3 = 0$
4.65; -0.65

Find the value of the discriminant and the number of real-number solutions of each equation.

36. $x^2 + 11x - 10 = 0$
161; two

37. $x^2 + 7x + 8 = 0$
17; two

38. $3x^2 + 5x - 9 = 0$
133; two

39. $-2x^2 + 10x - 1 = 0$
92; two

40. $3x^2 + 6x + 3 = 0$
0; one

41. $6x^2 + x + 12 = 0$
-287; no real solutions

42. The weekly profit of a company is modeled by the function $w = -g^2 + 120g - 28$. The weekly profit, w, is dependent on the number of gizmos, g, sold. If the break-even point is when $w = 0$, how many gizmos must the company sell each week in order to break even?
120 gizmos

43. **Reasoning** The equation $4x^2 + bx + 9 = 0$ has no real-number solutions. What must be true about b?
$-12 < b < 12$

44. **Open-Ended** Describe three different methods to solve $x^2 - x - 56 = 0$. Tell which method you prefer. Explain your reasoning.
Factor: $(x - 8)(x + 7) = 0$ using the zero products property to find that $x = 8$ or $x = -7$; graph and find x-intercepts at $x = 8$ and $x = -7$; use the quadratic formula to find solutions at 8 and -7; I prefer to factor. It is quickest.

All-in-One Resources/Online
Enrichment

9-6 Enrichment
The Quadratic Formula and the Discriminant

You have used the discriminant to find the number of solutions to a quadratic equation. You can also use the discriminant to determine the number of x-intercepts of the graph of the related function.

Discriminant	Positive Discriminant $b^2 - 4ac > 0$	Discriminant is Zero $b^2 - 4ac = 0$	Negative Discriminant $b^2 - 4ac < 0$
Example	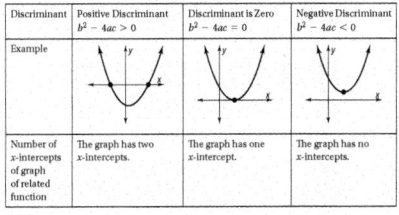		
Number of x-intercepts of graph of related function	The graph has two x-intercepts.	The graph has one x-intercept.	The graph has no x-intercepts.

Practice

Use the discriminant of the related quadratic equation to determine the number of x-intercepts of the graph of the function.

1. $y = x^2 + 4x + 5$
none

2. $y = x^2 - x - 2$
two

3. $y = x^2 - 2x + 1$
one

4. $y = x^2 - 4x + 13$
none

5. $y = 2x^2 + 11x - 5$
two

6. $y = 4x^2 - 17x - 15$
two

7. $y = x^2 - 9x$
two

8. $y = 3x^2 - 7x + 5$
none

Practice and Problem Solving WKBK/ All-in-One Resources/Online
Think About a Plan

9-6 Think About a Plan
The Quadratic Formula and the Discriminant

Sports Your school wants to take out an ad in the paper congratulating the basketball team on a successful season, as shown at the right. The area of the photo will be half the area of the entire ad. How wide will the border be?

What do you know?

1. What are the dimensions of the photo and the ad? Let $w =$ the width of the photo and $l =$ the length of the photo.
5 in. by 7 in.; $(x + 5)$ in. by $(x + 7)$ in.

What do you need to solve the problem?

2. What quadratic equation can you write that best describes the relationship between the area of the photo and the area of the ad?
$\frac{1}{2}(x + 5)(x + 7) = 35$, or $x^2 + 12x - 35 = 0$

How do you solve the problem?

3. Using the quadratic formula, how will you be able to solve for x, the width of the border? What is the width of the border?
Substitute 1 for a, 12 for b, and -35 for c; about 2.41 in.

Practice and Problem Solving WKBK/ All-in-One Resources/Online
Standardized Test Prep

9-6 Standardized Test Prep
The Quadratic Formula and the Discriminant

Multiple Choice

For Exercises 1-6, choose the correct letter.

1. Which expression gives the solutions of $-5 + 2x^2 = -6x$? C

A. $\dfrac{2 + \sqrt{4 - (4)(6)(-5)}}{12}$

B. $\dfrac{-5 \pm \sqrt{25 - (4)(2)(6)}}{-10}$

C. $\dfrac{-6 \pm \sqrt{36 - (4)(2)(-5)}}{4}$

D. $\dfrac{6 \pm \sqrt{36 - (4)(2)(5)}}{4}$

2. What are the approximate solutions of $2x^2 - x + 10 = 0$? I
F. $-2, 2.5$
G. $-1.97, 2.47$
H. $-2.5, 2$
I. no solution

3. What are the approximate solutions of $7x^2 + 4x - 9 = 0$? B
A. $-1.42, 0.85$
B. $-1.5, 0.88$
C. $-0.88, 1.5$
D. no solution

4. Which method is the best method for solving the equation $8x^2 - 13x + 3 = 0$? I
F. square roots
G. factoring
H. graphing
I. quadratic formula

5. How many solutions are there for $5x^2 + 7x - 4 = 0$? C
A. 0
B. 1
C. 2
D. 3

6. The perimeter of a rectangle is 54 cm. The area of the same rectangle is 176 cm². What are the dimensions of the rectangle? F
F. 11 cm by 16 cm
G. 8 cm by 22 cm
H. 5.5 cm by 32 cm
I. 4 cm by 44 cm

Short Response

7. The flight of a baseball that has been hit when it was 4 feet off the ground is modeled by the function $h = -16t^2 + 75t + 4$ where h is the height of the baseball in feet after t seconds. Rounding to the nearest hundredth, how long will it take before the ball lands on the ground? Show your work.
4.74 s
[2] Both parts answered correctly.
[1] One part answered correctly.
[0] Neither part answered correctly.

Online Teacher Resource Center
Activities, Games, and Puzzles

9-6 Game: Start your Engines!
The Quadratic Formula and the Discriminant

This game is for two players. Use a number cube. Each player should choose a marker to represent a race car. Decide who goes first.

Players start by choosing their lanes and placing their marker on the circle in their lane at the starting gate (number 1 on the racetrack below).

Play starts by rolling a number cube twice. The first number is the value of b, and the second number is the value of c. Compute the discriminant $d = b^2 - 4ac$ of $x^2 + bx + c$. In each case, a equals 1.

The sign of d determines how you move around the track.

- If $d > 0$, place your marker on the circle of the next point in your lane.
- If $d = 0$, place your marker on the circle of the next point on the dotted line in the middle of the track.
- If $d < 0$, place your marker on the circle of the next point in your opponent's lane.

Take turns with your opponent. You lose your turn if your opponent can prove that you have made a math error.

The first player to reach the finish line wins. Be careful—a player who is in the opponent's lane at the finish line is disqualified and loses the game. (If each player is in the other's lane at the finish, move both markers back to Point 8 and play again.) Check students' work.

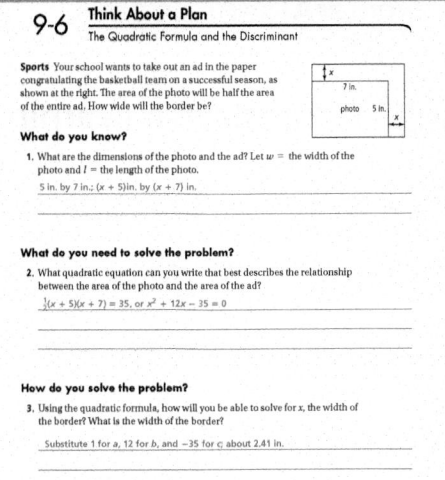

---

1 Interactive Learning

Solve It!

PURPOSE To recognize a pattern, write the correct type of function to model it, and use the function to extend the pattern

PROCESS Students may make a table of values, use inductive reasoning to write a function, or use the function to generate additional data.

FACILITATE

Q What ordered pairs of the form (stage, number of triangles) can be generated from the diagrams? **[(1, 1), (2, 4), (3, 9)]**

Q What pattern do you see to help you generate more data? **[Answers may vary. Sample: The number of triangles is the square of the stage number.]**

ANSWER See Solve It in Answers on next page.
CONNECT THE MATH In the Solve It, students look for the function that will model a pattern. In the lesson, students learn to distinguish among linear, quadratic, and exponential functions.

2 Guided Instruction

Take Note

By making a table of values for the sample functions graphed, students can note how a constant increase of the x-values affects the increase in the y-values, and how this impacts the shape of each graph.

Problem 1

Q Which two models either continually increase or continually decrease from left to right? **[linear and exponential models]**

Objective To choose a linear, quadratic, or exponential model for data

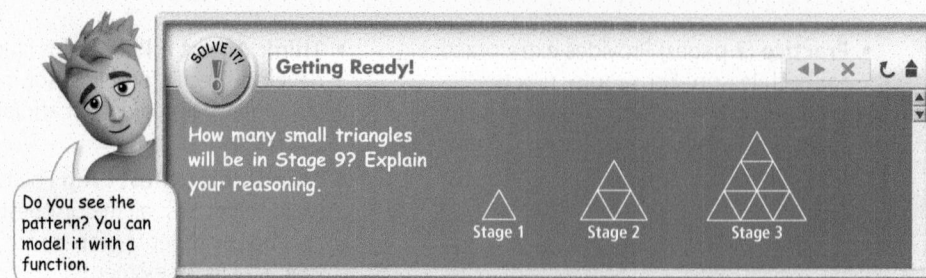

Solve It!

Getting Ready!

How many small triangles will be in Stage 9? Explain your reasoning.

Stage 1   Stage 2   Stage 3

Do you see the pattern? You can model it with a function.

Essential Understanding You can use the linear, quadratic, or exponential functions you have studied to model some sets of data.

take note

Concept Summary Linear, Quadratic, and Exponential Functions

Linear: $y = mx + b$ Quadratic: $y = ax^2 + bx + c$ Exponential: $y = a \cdot b^x$

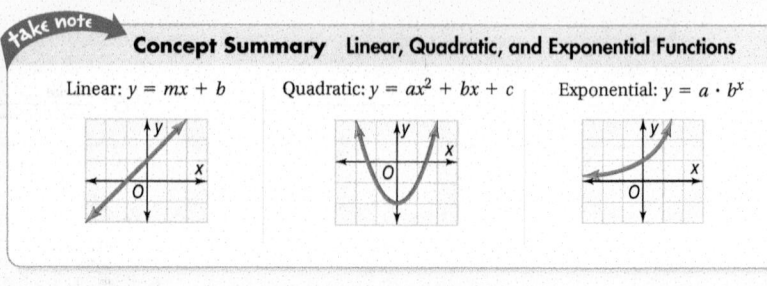

Problem 1 Choosing a Model by Graphing

Graph each set of points. Which model is most appropriate for each set?

A (1, 3), (0, 0), (−3, 3), (−1, −1), (−2, 0)

B (0, 2), (−1, 4), (1, 1), (2, 0.5)

C (−1, −2), (0, −1), (1, 0), (3, 2)

Think

Can you eliminate possibilities?
Yes. For example, you know that a linear model isn't appropriate in parts (A) and (B) because the slope between any two points is not constant.

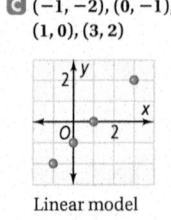

Quadratic model   Exponential model   Linear model

BIG idea Modeling   **UbD**

ESSENTIAL UNDERSTANDINGS

- Linear, quadratic, or exponential functions can be used to model various sets of data.
- Graphing and testing data can show which type of function best models the data.

Math Background

In the Solve It of this lesson, some students may note the pattern in the number of triangles in each stage and point out that since 1 + 3 = 4 and 4 + 5 = 9, the number of triangles in the next stage is 9 + 7 = 16. While students may be used to calculating second differences, the quadratic representation of this pattern is more useful. In this lesson, students learn efficient methods for identifying patterns of a function and subsequently identifying the function as linear, quadratic, or exponential.

For a line, the rate of change of the function is referred to as slope and is constant for any interval along the line. Hence, the first differences of a linear function are constant. For a parabola, the rate of change for intervals along the curve is not constant. Hence the first differences for a quadratic function are not constant. In calculus, the rate of change of a function will be referred to as the derivative of a function.

In calculus, students will also study the "rate of change" of the "rate of change," which is referred to as the second derivative of a function. For a quadratic function, the rate of change of the rate of change is constant. Hence, the second differences for a quadratic function are constant.

Support Student Learning

Use the **Algebra I Companion** to engage and support students during instruction. See Lesson Resources at the end of this lesson for details.

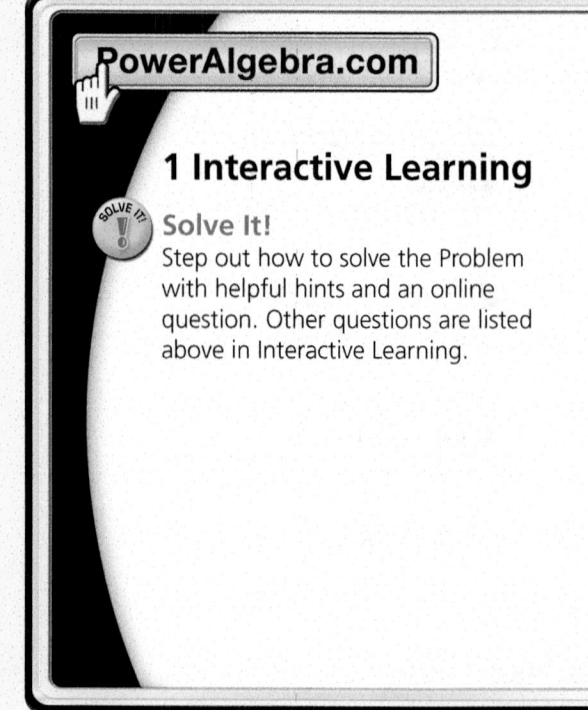

PowerAlgebra.com

1 Interactive Learning

Solve It!
Step out how to solve the Problem with helpful hints and an online question. Other questions are listed above in Interactive Learning.

Got It? **1.** Graph each set of points. Which model is most appropriate for each set?
  a. (0, 0), (1, 1), (−1, −0.5), (2, 3)   **b.** (−2, 11), (−1, 5), (0, 3), (1, 5)

When the *x*-values in a set of data pairs have a common difference, you can analyze data numerically to find the best model. You can use a linear function to model data pairs with *y*-values that have a common difference. You can use an exponential function to model data pairs with *y*-values that have a common ratio.

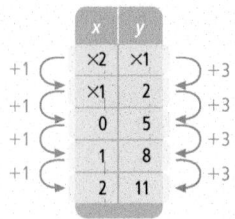

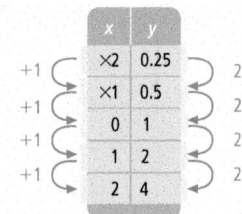

The *y*-values have a common difference of 3. A linear model fits the data.

The *y*-values have a common ratio of 2. An exponential model fits the data.

For quadratic functions, the second differences are constant.

In the table at the right, the second differences of the *y*-values are all 4, so a quadratic model fits the data.

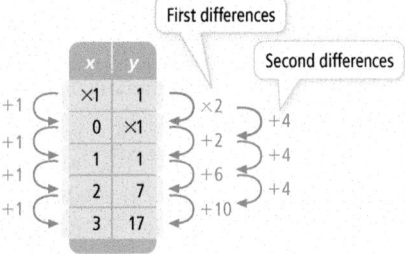

Problem 2 **Choosing a Model Using Differences or Ratios**

Which type of function best models the data? Use differences or ratios.

Plan

How can you get started?
Begin by checking the first differences of the *y*-values. Then check the second differences and ratios, if necessary.

A 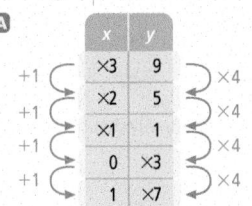   **B**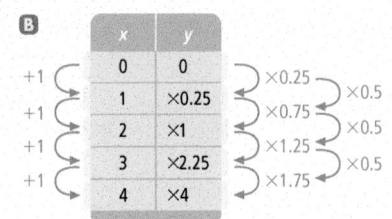

The first differences are constant, so a linear function models the data.

The second differences are constant, so a quadratic function models the data.

Got It?

Q The points in 1b are in order from least to greatest based on the *x*-coordinate. How can you determine the correct model by visually inspecting the *y*-coordinates? **[The *y*-coordinates decrease and then increase, so it is a quadratic model.]**

Students can examine the tables of values and generalize the format for the differences of the *y*-values. When they study the table of the quadratic function, they will notice that an additional stage of finding differences is necessary.

Refer students back to the data that they generated when working on the Solve It for this lesson. Students can note that the second differences in the table of values that they generated is 2.

Problem 2

Q How do you determine the first differences in a table of values? **[You subtract each pair of consecutive *y*-values in the table.]**

Q How do you determine the second differences in a table of values? **[You subtract each pair of consecutive first differences in the table.]**

Q How do you determine the ratios in a table of values? **[You divide each pair of consecutive *y*-values in the table.]**

---

2 Guided Instruction

Each Problem is worked out and supported online.

Problem 1
Choosing a Model by Graphing

Problem 2
Choosing a Model Using Differences or Ratios
Animated

Problem 3
Modeling Data
Animated

Problem 4
Modeling Real-World Data
Animated

Support in Algebra 1 Companion
• Vocabulary
• Key Concepts
• Got It?

Answers

Solve It!
81; explanations may vary.

Got It?

1. a.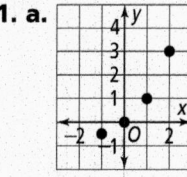

exponential

b.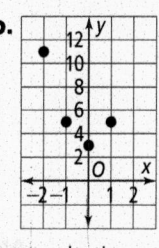

quadratic

Got It? **ERROR PREVENTION**

If students are having trouble determining the best function to model the given data, then remind them to order the pairs so that the *x*-values in the set of data pairs have a constant difference.

Problem 3

Q What model, other than quadratic, does the graph of the data resemble? **[It resembles an exponential function.]**

Q How can you confirm whether the data is quadratic or exponential? **[You can check second differences to see if it is quadratic and ratios to see if it is exponential.]**

Q If a point other than (2, 2) had been used to determine *a*, would the result be the same? Explain. **[Yes; each point is on the parabola. They all give the same value of *a*.]**

Q According to the data model, what is the value of *y* when *x* = 8? **[$y = 0.5 \cdot 8^2 = 32$]**

Got It? **ERROR PREVENTION**

Q What kind of function appears to fit a graph of the data? Explain. **[Exponential, because the graph decreases sharply and then slowly continues towards zero.]**

Q If an exponential function decreases from left to right, what do you know about the value of *b* in the model $y = a \cdot b^x$? **[The value of *b* is between 0 and 1.]**

 Got It? 2. Which type of function best models the ordered pairs (−1, 0.5), (0, 1), (1, 2), (2, 4), and (3, 8)? Use differences or ratios.

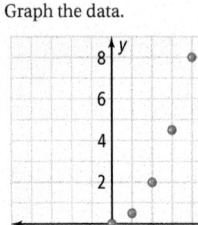 **Problem 3** Modeling Data

Which type of function best models the data in the table at the right? Write an equation to model the data.

x	y
0	0
1	0.5
2	2
3	4.5
4	8

Plan

How can a graph help you get started?
A graph may suggest the type of function that models the data. You can then use differences or ratios to confirm the type of function.

Step 1
Graph the data.

Step 2
The data appear to be quadratic. Test for a common second difference.

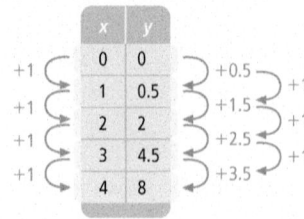

There is a common second difference, 1.

Step 3
The graph appears to be a parabola with vertex at (0, 0), so use $y = ax^2$.

$$y = ax^2$$
$$2 = a(2)^2 \quad \text{Use a point other than (0, 0) to find } a.$$
$$2 = 4a \quad \text{Simplify.}$$
$$0.5 = a \quad \text{Divide each side by 4.}$$
$$y = 0.5x^2 \quad \text{Write a quadratic function.}$$

Step 4
Test two points in the data set other than (2, 2) and (0, 0).

Test (3, 4.5):   Test (4, 8):
$$y = 0.5x^2 \quad\quad y = 0.5x^2$$
$$y = 0.5(3)^2 \quad y = 0.5(4)^2$$
$$y = 4.5 ✔ \quad\quad y = 8 ✔$$

The points (3, 4.5) and (4, 8) both satisfy $y = 0.5x^2$. The equation $y = 0.5x^2$ models the data.

 Got It? 3. a. Which type of function best models the data in the table at the right? Write an equation to model the data.

x	×1	0	1	2	3
y	30	6	1.2	0.24	0.048

b. Reasoning In Step 4 of Problem 3, why should you not test the points (2, 2) and (0, 0)?

Real-world data seldom fall exactly into linear, exponential, or quadratic patterns. However, you can determine which type of function represents the best possible model for the data.

Additional Problems

1. Which model is most appropriate for graphing each set of points?

   a. (0, 1), (1, 2), (2, 4), (3, 8)

   b. (−2, 5), (−1, 7), (0, 9), (1, 11)

   c. (−1, 2), (0, 0), (1, 2), (2, 8)

ANSWER a. exponential model   **b.** linear model
c. quadratic model

2. Which kind of function best models the data? Use differences or ratios.

a.

x	y
0	0
1	0.25
2	1
3	2.25
4	4

b.

x	y
−2	−6
−1	−2
0	2
1	6
2	10

ANSWER a. quadratic function; **b.** linear function

3. What kind of function best models the data? Write an equation to model the data.

x	y
0	0
1	2
2	8
3	18
4	32

ANSWER quadratic model;
$y = 2x^2$

4. The data in the table give the value of a painting over time. Which kind of function best models the data? Write an equation to model the data.

Value of a Painting

Years	Value ($)
0	3200
1	3360
2	3528
3	3704
4	3890
5	4084

ANSWER exponential model;
$y = 3200 \cdot 1.05^x$

 **Problem 4** Modeling Real-World Data

Transportation The data at the right give the value of a used car over time. Which type of function best models the data? Write an equation to model the data.

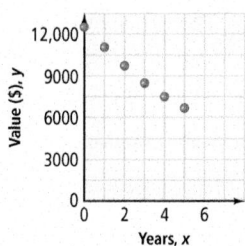

Know

The value of a used car over time

Need

The most appropriate model for the data

Plan

Graph the data and then use differences or ratios to find a model for the situation.

Value of Used Car

Years	Value ($)
0	12,575
1	11,065
2	9750
3	8520
4	7540
5	6710

Step 1
Graph the data.

The graph curves and does not look quadratic. It may be exponential.

Step 3
Write an exponential model.

Relate $y = a \cdot b^x$

Define Let a = the initial value, 12,575.
Let b = the decay factor, 0.88.

Write $y = 12,575 \cdot 0.88^x$

Step 2
Test for a common ratio.

	Years	Value ($)	
+1	0	12,575	$\frac{11,065}{12,575} \approx 0.88$
+1	1	11,065	$\frac{9750}{11,065} \approx 0.88$
+1	2	9750	$\frac{8520}{9750} \approx 0.87$
+1	3	8520	$\frac{7540}{8520} \approx 0.88$
+1	4	7540	$\frac{6710}{7540} \approx 0.89$
	5	6710	

The value of the car is roughly 0.88 times its value the previous year.

Step 4
Test two points other than (0, 12,575).

Test (2, 9750):
$y = 12,575 \cdot 0.88^2$
$y \approx 9738$

Test (4, 7540):
$y = 12,575 \cdot 0.88^4$
$y \approx 7541$

The point (2, 9738) is close to the data point (2, 9750). The point (4, 7541) is close to the data point (4, 7540). The equation $y = 12,575 \cdot 0.88^x$ models the data.

Got It? 4. The table shows the annual income of a small theater company. Which type of function best models the data? Write an equation to model the data.

Theater Company Annual Income

Year	0	1	2	3	4
Income ($)	18,254	18,730	19,215	19,695	20,175

Problem 4

Q What model, other than exponential, does the graph of the data resemble? **[It resembles a quadratic function.]**

Q How can you confirm whether the data is quadratic or exponential? **[You can check second differences to see if it is quadratic and ratios to see if it is exponential.]**

Q What does the value of a represent in the exponential model $y = a \cdot b^x$? **[It represents the initial value at time zero.]**

Q What does the value of b stand for in the exponential model $y = a \cdot b^x$? **[It represents the growth or decay factor.]**

Q Will the value of b in this exponential model be greater than 1 or between 0 and 1? Explain. **[The value of b will be between 0 and 1 because the graph is decreasing.]**

Q According to the data model, what is the approximate value of the car eight years after it is bought? Explain. **[$12,575 \cdot 0.88^8 \approx \$4,522$]**

Got It?

Q What model does a graph of the data points most resemble? **[Straight line]**

Q How can you determine if the function is linear? **[Test for a common difference of y-values.]**

Q Because the function is not linear, you can write a trend line that closely matches the path of the data. How can you write the equation of a trend line for the data? **[You can use two points to find the slope of the line. The y-intercept of the line is given in the table. Use the slope-intercept form to write the equation of a trend line for the function.]**

Answers

Got It? (continued)

2. exponential

3. a. exponential; $y = 6(0.2)^x$

   b. You have already used them to write the equation.

4. Answers will vary. Sample: linear;
   $y = 480.7x + 18,252.4$

3 Lesson Check

Do you know HOW?
- If students have difficulty with Exercise 3, then remind them to make sure that the *x*-values have a constant difference before analyzing the data numerically to find the best model.

Do you UNDERSTAND?
- If students have difficulty with Exercise 5, then have them review the characteristics of the three kinds of functions.

Close

> **Q** How do you determine if a function is linear, quadratic, or exponential? **[Examine a table of values to find constant differences in the *y*-values, a common second difference in *y*-values, or a common ratio of *y*-values.]**
>
> **Q** How can you write an equation to model data? **[After determining which model to use, you must use data to determine the values of the constants in the equations.]**

 Lesson Check

Do you know HOW?
Which type of function best models each set of data points?

1. $(0, 11), (1, 5), (2, 3), (3, 5), (4, 11)$
2. $(-4, -10), (-2, -7), (0, -4), (2, -1), (4, 2)$
3. $(-1, 8), (0, 4), (2, 1), (3, 0.5)$

Do you UNDERSTAND?
4. **Reasoning** Can the *y*-values in a set of data pairs have both a common ratio and a common difference? Explain why or why not.

5. **Writing** Explain how to decide whether a linear, exponential, or quadratic function is the most appropriate model for a set of data.

Practice and Problem-Solving Exercises

A Practice   Graph each set of points. Which model is most appropriate for each set?   *See Problem 1.*

6. $(-2, -3), (-1, 0), (0, 1), (1, 0), (2, -3)$
7. $(-2, -8), (0, -4), (3, 2), (5, 6)$
8. $(-3, 6), (-1, 0), (0, -1), (1, -1.5)$
9. $(-2, 5), (-1, -1), (0, -3), (1, -1), (2, 5)$
10. $(-1, -5\frac{2}{3}), (0, -5), (2, 3), (3, 27)$
11. $(-3, 8), (-1, 6), (0, 5), (2, 3), (3, 2)$

Which type of function best models the data in each table? Use differences or ratios.   *See Problem 2.*

12.

x	y
0	0
1	1.5
2	6
3	13.5
4	24

13.

x	y
0	×5
1	×3
2	×1
3	1
4	3

14.

x	y
0	1
1	1.2
2	1.44
3	1.728
4	2.0736

Which type of function best models the data in each table? Write an equation to model the data.   *See Problem 3.*

15.

x	y
0	0
1	2.8
2	11.2
3	25.2
4	44.8

16.

x	y
0	5
1	2
2	0.8
3	0.32
4	0.128

17.

x	y
0	2
1	1.5
2	1
3	0.5
4	0

Answers

Lesson Check
1. quadratic   2. linear
3. exponential
4. No, a function cannot be both linear and exponential.
5. Graph the points, or test ordered data for a common difference (linear function), a common ratio (exponential function), or a common second difference (quadratic function).

Practice and Problem-Solving Exercises
6.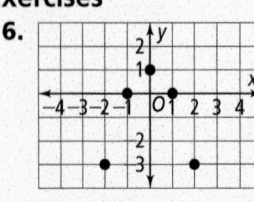

quadratic

7.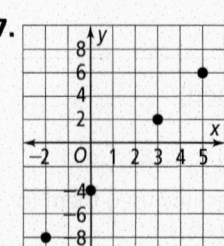

linear

8.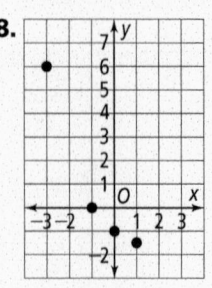

exponential

18. Sports The number of people attending a school's first five football games is shown in the table below. Which type of function best models the data? Write an equation to model the data.

Game	1	2	3	4	5
Attendance	248	307	366	425	484

19. Banking The average monthly balance of a savings account is shown in the table at the right. Which type of function best models the data? Write an equation to model the data.

Month	Balance ($)
0	540
1	556.20
2	572.89
3	590.07
4	607.77

 Apply

20. Error Analysis Tom claims that, because the data pairs (1, 4), (2, 6), (3, 9), and (4, 13.5) have y-value with a common ratio, they are best modeled by a quadratic function. What is his error?

21. a. Make a table of five ordered pairs for each function using consecutive x-values. Find the common second difference.
   i. $f(x) = x^2 - 3$ **ii.** $f(x) = 3x^2$ **iii.** $f(x) = 4x^2 - 5x$
  b. What is the relationship between the common second difference and the coefficient of the x^2-term?
  c. Reasoning Explain how you could use this relationship to model data.

22. Think About a Plan The number of visitors at a Web site over several days is shown in the table at the right. What is an equation that models the data?
- Does the graph of the data suggest a type of function to use?
- Will your equation fit the data exactly? How do you know?

Day	Visitors
1	52
2	197
3	447
4	805
5	1270

23. Open-Ended Write a set of data pairs that you could model with a quadratic function.

24. Zoology A conservation organization collected the data on the number of frogs in a local wetland, shown in the table at the right. Which type of function best models the data? Write an equation to model the data.

Year	Number of Frogs
0	120
1	101
2	86
3	72
4	60

25. The table below shows the projected population of a small town. Let $t = 0$ correspond to the year 2020.
  a. Graph the data. Does the graph suggest a linear, exponential, or quadratic model?
  b. Find the rate of change in population with respect to time from one data pair to the next. How do the results support your answer to part (a)?
  c. Write a function that models the data shown in the table.
  d. Use the function from part (c) to predict the town's population in 2050.

Year, t	0	5	10	15
Population, p	5100	5700	6300	6900

PowerAlgebra.com   **Lesson 9-7** Linear, Quadratic, and Exponential Models   **579**

9.

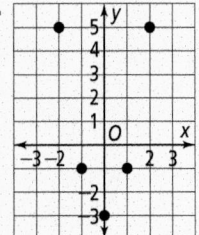

quadratic

10.

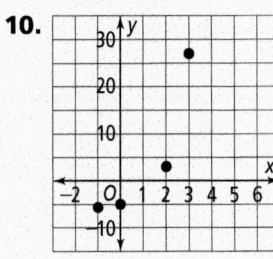

exponential

11.

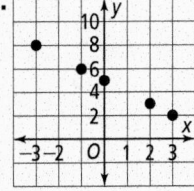

linear

12. quadratic

13. linear

14. exponential

15. quadratic; $y = 2.8x^2$

16. exponential; $y = 5(0.4)^x$

17. linear; $y = -0.5x + 2$

18. linear; $y = 59x + 189$

19. exponential; $y = 540(1.03)^x$

20. If ordered data have a common ratio, then they are best modeled by an exponential function.

---

4 Practice

ASSIGNMENT GUIDE

Basic: 6–19, 20, 22–24

Average: 7–19 odd, 20–25

Advanced: 7–19 odd, 20–27

Standardized Test Prep: 28–31

Mixed Review: 32–37

Reasoning exercises have blue headings.

Applications exercises have red headings.

EXERCISE 26: Use the Think About a Plan worksheet in the **Practice and Problem solving Workbook** (also available in the Teaching Resources in print and online) to further support students' development in becoming independent learners.

HOMEWORK QUICK CHECK

To check students' understanding of key skills and concepts, go over Exercises 9, 17, 20, 22, and 24.

21. a. Check students' work.
  b. The second common difference is twice the coefficient of the x^2-term.
  c. When second differences are the same, the data are quadratic. The coefficient of the x^2-term is one-half the second difference.

22. Answers will vary. Sample:
  $y = 53x^2 - 16x + 15$

23. Answers will vary. Sample: (0, 5), (2, 13), (4, 29), (6, 53)

24. exponential; $y = 120(0.84)^x$

25. See next page.

Lesson 9-7   **579**

Answers

Practice and Problem-Solving Exercises
(continued)

25. a.

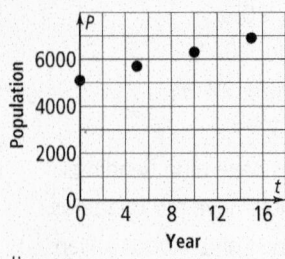

linear

b. The population changes by 600 every 5 years; the y-values have a common difference, so a linear model works best.

c. $p = 120t + 5100$

d. 8700

26. $y = 2x^2 - x + 7$

27. a. 6, 12, 18, 24; 6, 6, 6

b. 6

c. Yes, the first differences are constant for linear functions, the second differences are constant for quadratic functions, and the third differences are constant for cubic functions.

28. A　　　**29.** I　　　**30.** A

31. [2]　$(5x + 2)(2x - 1)$

　　　[1]　appropriate methods with minor calculation error

32. $-1.5, 0.5$　　**33.** $-3.83, 1.83$

34. $0.13, 2.54$　　**35.** $(6, 4)$

36. $(2, 7)$　　　　**37.** $(1, -2)$

 **Challenge**

26. Reasoning Write a quadratic function $y = ax^2 + bx + c$ whose graph passes through the points $(0, 7)$, $(2, 13)$, and $(4, 35)$.

27. Reasoning The diagram at the right shows the differences for the cubic function $f(x) = x^3 - 2x + 5$ for the x-values 0, 1, 2, 3, 4, and 5.

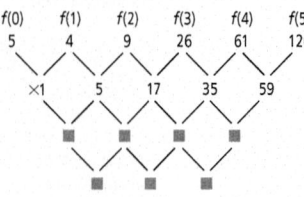

a. Write the second and third differences in the appropriate locations in the diagram.

b. What do you predict the third difference would be if $f(6)$ were added to the diagram?

c. Do you think that the third differences will be constant for other cubic functions? Explain why or why not.

Standardized Test Prep

SAT/ACT

28. The graph at the right shows the number y of visitors to a museum over x days. Which function models the number of visitors?

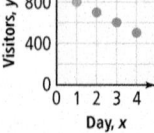

　ⓐ $y = -100x + 900$　　　ⓒ $y = -100x + 800$

　ⓑ $y = 900(0.875)^x$　　　ⓓ $y = -50x^2 - 400x + 1300$

29. Which expression is equivalent to $(4x^3 + 2x^2 + 1) + (3x^2 + 8x + 2)$?

　Ⓕ $7x^2 + 10x + 3$　　Ⓖ $7x^3 + 10x^2 + 3x$　　Ⓗ $4x^3 + 5x^2 + 3$　　Ⓘ $4x^3 + 5x^2 + 8x + 3$

30. Which line passes through the point $(1, 3)$ and is parallel to the line graphed at the right?

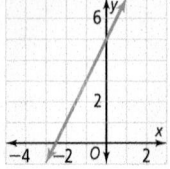

　ⓐ $y = 2x + 1$　　　ⓒ $y = 2x - 5$

　ⓑ $y = 2x + 3$　　　ⓓ $y = -5x + 8$

Short Response

31. What are the factors of $10x^2 - x - 2$? Show your work.

Mixed Review

Use the quadratic formula to solve each equation. If necessary, round to the nearest hundredth.　　◀ See Lesson 9-6.

32. $4x^2 + 4x - 3 = 0$　　**33.** $x^2 + 2x - 7 = 0$　　**34.** $3x^2 - 8x = -1$

Get Ready!　To prepare for Lesson 9-8, do Exercises 35–37.

Solve by elimination.　　◀ See Lesson 6-3.

35. $x + y = 10$　　**36.** $5x - 6y = -32$　　**37.** $-2x + 15y = -32$
　　$x - y = 2$　　　　$3x + 6y = 48$　　　　$7x - 5y = 17$

Additional Instructional Support

Algebra 1 Companion

Students can use the **Algebra 1 Companion** worktext (4 pages) as you teach the lesson. Use the Companion to support

- New Vocabulary
- Key Concepts
- Got It for each Problem
- Lesson Check

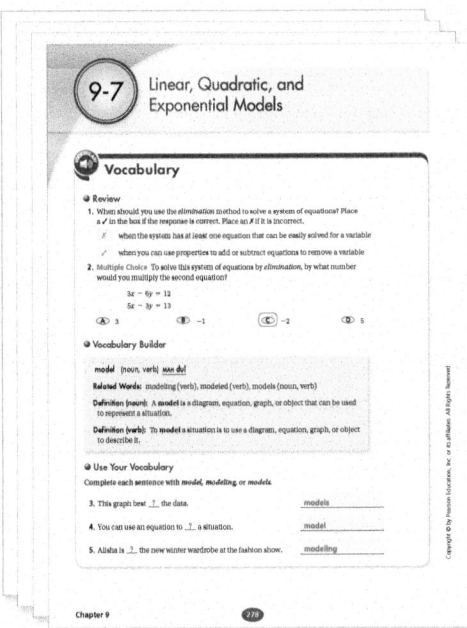

ELL Support

Focus on Communication Assign each student a model: linear, quadratic, or exponential. Have students form groups with the others assigned the same model. Assign a leader in each group. Students will discuss the meaning of their model, what the conditions of the data set will be, and how the graph will appear. Each group will make a data set appropriate for their model and take turns within their group teaching their examples to the others.

Arrange the students into heterogeneous groups of three, each student representing a different model. Students will take turns teaching the other students.

5 Assess & Remediate

Lesson Quiz

1. Graph the set of points $(-2, 7)$, $(-1, 4)$, $(0, 1)$, and $(1, -2)$. Which model is most appropriate for the set?

2. Which kind of function best models the data? Use differences or ratios.

x	y
0	0
1	−0.5
2	−2
3	−4.5
4	−8

3. Do you UNDERSTAND? The data in the table give the value of a certificate of deposit (CD) over time. Which kind of function best models the data? Write an equation to model the data.

Certificate of Deposit

Years	Value ($)
0	16,000
1	16,400
2	16,810
3	17,230
4	17,661
5	18,103

ANSWERS TO LESSON QUIZ

1. linear model

2. quadratic function

3. exponential model; $y = 16,000 \cdot 1.025^x$

PRESCRIPTION FOR REMEDIATION

Use the student work on the Lesson Quiz to prescribe a differentiated review assignment.

Points	Differentiated Remediation
0–1	Intervention
2	On-level
3	Extension

PowerAlgebra.com

5 Assess & Remediate

Assign the Lesson Quiz. Appropriate intervention, practice, or enrichment is automatically generated based on student performance.

Intervention

- **Reteaching** (2 pages) Provides reteaching and practice exercises for the key lesson concepts. Use with struggling students or absent students.

- **English Language Learner Support** Helps students develop and reinforce mathematical vocabulary and key concepts.

All-in-One Resources/Online
Reteaching

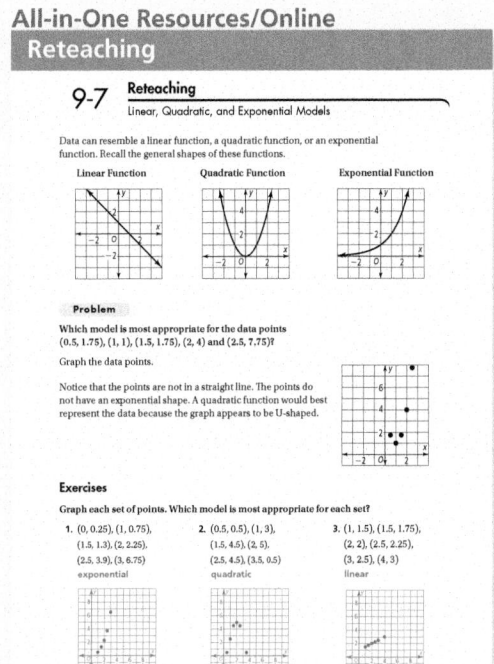

All-in-One Resources/Online
English Language Learner Support

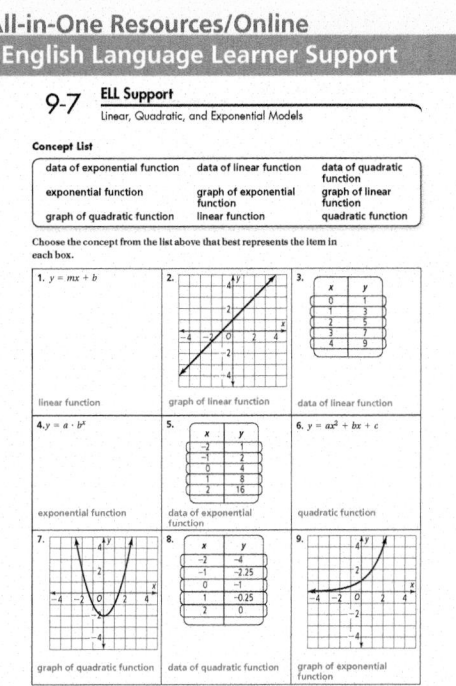

Differentiated Remediation *continued*

On-Level

- **Practice** (2 pages) Provides extra practice for each lesson. For simpler practice exercises, use the Form K Practice pages found in the All-in-One Teaching Resources and online.

- **Think About a Plan** Helps students develop specific problem-solving skills and strategies by providing scaffolded guiding questions.

- **Standardized Test Prep** Focuses on all major exercises, all major question types, and helps students prepare for the high-stakes assessments.

Extension

- **Enrichment** Provides students with interesting problems and activities that extend the concepts of the lesson.

- **Activities, Games, and Puzzles** Worksheets that can be used for concepts development, enrichment, and for fun!

Practice and Problem Solving WKBK/ All-in-One Resources/Online
Practice page 1

9-7 **Practice** *Form G*
Linear, Quadratic, and Exponential Models

Graph each set of points. Which model is most appropriate for each set?

1. (−3, −8), (−1, −2), (0, 1), (1, 4), (3, 10) linear;
2. (−2, 0.75), (−1, 1.5), (0, 3), (1, 6) exponential;

3. (−2, 1), (−1, 0), (0, 1), (1, 4), (2, 9) quadratic; check graphs
4. (−2, −11), (−1, −5), (0, −3), (1, −5), (2, −11) quadratic; check graphs

5. (−4, 0), (−2, −1), (0, −2), (2, −3), (4, −4) linear; check graphs
6. (−2, −0.67), (0, −2), (2, −6), (2, −18) exponential; check graphs

7. (−3, 10), (−1, 2), (0, 1), (1, 2), (3, 10) quadratic; check graphs
8. (−2, 4), (−1, 2), (0, 0), (1, −2), (2, −4) linear; check graphs

Which type of function best models the data in each table? Use differences or ratios.

9. quadratic

x	y
0	−12
1	−11
2	−8
3	−3
4	4

10. linear

x	y
0	3
1	−2
2	−7
3	−12
4	17

11. exponential

x	y
0	3
1	12
2	48
3	192
4	768

12. Which type of function best models the ordered pairs (−1, 6), (0, 1), (1, 2), and (2, 9)? Use differences or ratios. quadratic

13. Which type of function best models the ordered pairs (−1, −0.25), (0, −0.5), (1, −1), and (2, −2)? Use differences or ratios. exponential

---

Practice and Problem Solving WKBK/ All-in-One Resources/Online
Practice page 2

9-7 **Practice** *(continued)* *Form G*
Linear, Quadratic, and Exponential Models

Which type of function best models the data in each table? Write an equation to model the data.

14. linear; $y = -7 + 6x$

x	y
0	−7
1	−1
2	5
3	11
4	17

15. exponential; $y = 2 \cdot 0.5^x$

x	y
−4	32
−3	16
−2	8
−1	4
0	2

16. quadratic; $y = -4x^2 + 4$

x	y
0	4
1	0
2	−12
3	−32
4	−60

17. quadratic; $y = x^2 - 6x + 15$

x	y
−1	22
0	15
1	10
2	7
3	6

18. exponential; $y = -4 \cdot 2^x$

x	y
−2	−1
−1	−2
0	−4
1	−8
2	−16

19. linear; $y = -x - 1$

x	y
−1	0
0	−1
1	−2
2	−3
3	−4
4	−5

Which type of function best models the data in each ordered pair? Write an equation to model the data.

20. (−3, 33), (−1, 21), (0, 15), (1,9), (3, −3) linear; $y = -6x + 15$

21. (−2, −16), (−1, −8), (0, −4), (1, −2), (2, −1) exponential; $y = 4 \cdot 0.5^x$

22. (−2, $\frac{1}{27}$), (−1, $\frac{1}{9}$), (0, $\frac{1}{3}$), (1, 1), (2, 3) exponential; $y = \frac{1}{3} \cdot 3^x$

23. (−2, −2), (−1, −3.5), (0, −4), (1, −3.5), (2, −2) quadratic; $y = \frac{1}{2}x^2 - 4$

24. (−6, 5), (−3, 4.5), (0, 4), (3, 3.5), (6, 3) linear; $y = \frac{1}{6}x - 4$

25. (−1, 10), (0, 3), (1, 0), (2, 1) quadratic; $y = -2x^2 - 5x + 3$

26. The population of a city for years since 2000 is shown below. Which kind of function best models the data? Write an equation to model the data. exponential; $y = 1500 \cdot 4^x$

Years since 2000	0	2	4	6	8
Population	1500	6000	24,000	96,000	384,000

All-in-One Resources/Online
Enrichment

9-7 **Enrichment**
Linear, Quadratic, and Exponential Models

A regression curve is a mathematical curve that summarizes the general tendency of the relationship between the variables. The most typical type of regression is linear regression. However, there are other types of regression as well.

Match each type of regression described with its graph and equation.

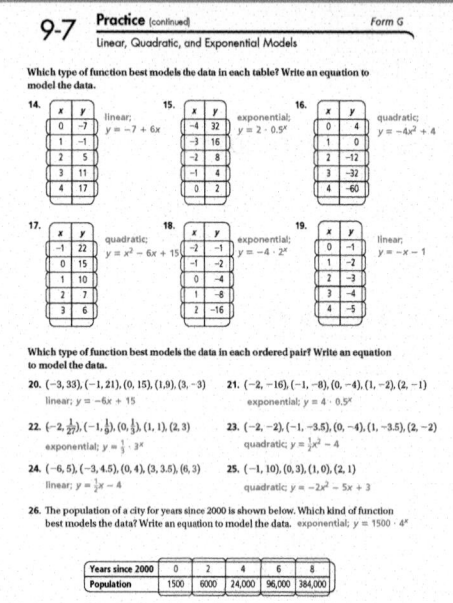

1. The ends of a cubic regression curve point in opposite directions. C

2. Exponential regression curves just decrease or just increase. E

3. Linear regression is a line. Lines increase or decrease. A

4. Quadratic regression is a parabola. Parabolas have U-shaped graphs. B

5. The ends of a quartic regression curve point in the same direction. These curves are M-shaped or W-shaped. D

A. $y = ax + b$
B. $y = ax^2 + bx + c$
C. $y = ax^3 + bx^2 + cx + d$
D. $y = ax^4 + bx^3 + cx^2 + dx + e$
E. $y = ab^x$

Practice and Problem Solving WKBK/ All-in-One Resources/Online
Think About a Plan

9-7 **Think About a Plan**
Linear, Quadratic, and Exponential Models

Zoology A conservation organization collected the data on the number of frogs in a local wetlands. Which kind of function best models the data? Write an equation to model the data.

Year	Number of Frogs
0	120
1	101
2	86
3	72
4	60

What do you know?

1. Let x = year and y = number of frogs. Graph the points in the table.

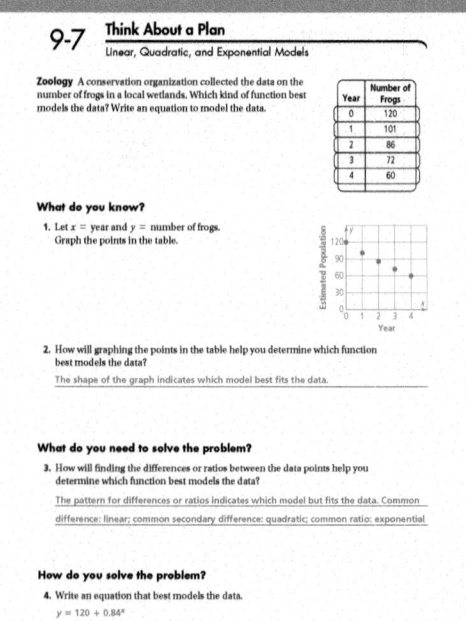

2. How will graphing the points in the table help you determine which function best models the data?
The shape of the graph indicates which model best fits the data.

What do you need to solve the problem?

3. How will finding the differences or ratios between the data points help you determine which function best models the data?
The pattern for differences or ratios indicates which model best fits the data. Common difference: linear; common secondary difference: quadratic; common ratio: exponential

How do you solve the problem?

4. Write an equation that best models the data.
$y = 120 \cdot 0.84^x$

Practice and Problem Solving WKBK/ All-in-One Resources/Online
Standardized Test Prep

9-7 **Standardized Test Prep**
Linear, Quadratic, and Exponential Models

Multiple Choice

For Exercises 1–4, choose the correct letter.

1. Which kind of function best models the set of data points (−1 ,22), (0, 6), (1, −10), (2, −26), (3, −42)? A
A. linear   B. quadratic   C. exponential   D. none of the above

2. Which kind of function best models the set of data points (−3, 18), (−2, 6), (−1, 2), (0, 11), (1, 27)? I
F. linear   G. quadratic   H. exponential   I. none of the above

3. What function can be used to model data pairs that have a common ratio? C
A. linear   B. quadratic   C. exponential   D. none of the above

4. The attendances at the high school basketball games seemed to be affected by the success of the team. The graph at the right models the attendance over the first half of the season. Which function would also represent the data shown in the graph where a represents the attendance and g represents the number of games the team has won? G
F. $a = 25(3)^g$
G. $a = 25g + 100$
H. $a = 25g^2 + 100$
I. $a = -25g^2 + 100$

Short Response

5. The data in the table show the population growth of a city since the year 2000. What kind of function models the data? How do you know? exponential, because the population is multiplied by a common ratio of 2 each year.

Year	Population
0	5275
1	10,550
2	21,100
3	42,200
4	84,400

[2] Both parts answered correctly.
[1] One part answered correctly.
[0] Neither part answered correctly.

Online Teacher Resource Center
Activities, Games, and Puzzles

9-7 **Game: Function Junction**
Choosing a Linear, Quadratic, or Exponential Model

This is a game for two players. You will need three markers to place on the game board.

You and your friends are returning home from a long trip. The diagram at the bottom of the page represents possible paths home. The numbers represent cities on your route.

Begin by placing the three markers at cities 6, 10, and 11. Take turns with your opponent. When it is your turn, choose a set of coordinates in the table and cross out the set. Then make a graph or a table to determine whether the set of coordinates can be best modeled by a *linear*, *quadratic*, or *exponential* model. If your opponent agrees with your answer, then move one of the markers along a path to a *lower*-numbered city. You may not pass through more than one city in a turn. Only one marker can occupy a city at any time. You do not move a marker if your opponent can show that you have chosen an incorrect model.

Remove any marker that reaches the home city. The player who moves the *last* marker to the home city is the winner! L = linear, Q = quadratic, E = exponential

(0, 1), (1, 1), (2, 3), (3, 7) Q	(2, 3), (3, 5), (4, 7), (5, 9) L	(0, 1), (1, 2), (4, 4), (6, 8) E
(2, 0), (3, 2), (4, 5), (5, 9) Q	(2, 2), (4, 4), (6, 8), (8, 16) E	(3, 9), (2, 6), (1, 3), (0, 0) L
(0, 1), (2, 3), (4, 9), (6, 27) E	(3, 3), (4, 5), (5, 7), (6, 9) L	(0, 0), (2, 1), (4, 4), (6, 9) Q
(0, 0), (1, 0), (2, 2), (3, 6) Q	(5, 0), (6, 1), (7, 2), (8, 3) L	(0, 1), (3, 2), (6, 4), (9, 8) E
(0, 3), (1, 4), (2, 6), (3, 9) Q	(0, 4), (2, 3), (8, 4), (12, 8) E	(2, −2), (4, 1), (6, 4), (8, 7) L
(0, 1), (1, 3), (6, 9), (9, 27) E	(0, 3), (1, 5), (2, 7), (3, 9) L	(0, 0), (2, 0), (4, 2), (6, 6) Q

Concept Byte
Use With Lesson 9-7

Performing Regressions

You can use a graphing calculator to perform quadratic regressions and exponential regressions.

Activity

Use a graphing calculator to find a model for the given data.

x	0	1	2	3	4	5
y	4	1	2	5	8	19

Step 1

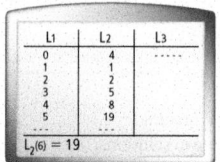

Enter the data into two lists. Enter the x-values in **L1** and the y-values in **L2**.

Step 2

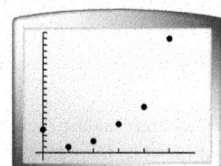

Make a scatter plot of the data. Press **zoom** 9 to graph. The graph appears to be quadratic.

Step 3

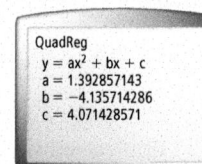

Perform the regression. Press **stat**. Select **CALC** and **QUADREG** to find the model.

The equation $y = 1.39x^2 - 4.14x + 4.07$ models the data. Check the equation by graphing it and the ordered pairs from the table in the same coordinate plane.

To perform an exponential regression, press **stat**. Select **CALC** and **EXPREG** to find the model.

Exercises

Use a graphing calculator to find a model for each set of data.

1.

x	y
−1	4.3
0	5.1
1	4.3
2	2.2
3	1.3

2.

x	y
−1	12.75
0	2.83
1	0.64
2	0.12
3	0.04

3.

x	y
−1	0.1
0	1.2
1	11.8
2	115.3
3	1129.4

Guided Instruction

PURPOSE To use graphing calculators to explore quadratic regressions and exponential regressions
PROCESS Students will
• display data in a scatter plot
• analyze the data and perform a regression

DISCUSS Review the general characteristics of linear, quadratic, and exponential functions. Students will need to be able to differentiate among them in the exercises.

ACTIVITY In this Activity students display data and perform a quadratic regression.

Q How do you know a quadratic regression is best? **[The data points form part of a parabola.]**
Q How can you be sure the data is not exponential? **[Find the exponential regression and check some of the data points.]**

Answers

Exercises

1. $y = -0.34x^2 - 0.22x + 4.67$

2. $y = 2.8(0.23)^x$

3. $y = 1.11(10.21)^x$

1 Interactive Learning

Solve It!

PURPOSE To find the common solution(s) of a linear equation and a quadratic equation

PROCESS Students may make a table of values, use trial and error, graph the equations, or write and solve an equation.

FACILITATE

Q At two seconds, how far has the blue scooter traveled? Explain. **[80 ft, since it travels at 40 ft/s]**

Q At two seconds, how far has the red scooter traveled? Explain. **[12.5 ft, since $2:5(2)^2 = 12.5$]**

Q How can you solve the system of two equations representing the distances of the scooters? **[Set $40t = 2.5t^2$ and solve for t.]**

ANSWER See Solve It in Answers on next page.

CONNECT THE MATH The Solve It poses a situation where a linear equation and a quadratic equation are used. In the lesson, students learn to find a solution to systems of equations that include a linear equation and a quadratic equation.

2 Guided Instruction

Problem 1

Q What steps should you follow to graph the equation $y = x^2 - x - 2$? **[Identify the vertex. Find the y-intercept and an additional point on one side of the axis of symmetry. Use symmetry to plot 2 additional points.]**

Objective To solve systems of linear and quadratic equations

Getting Ready!

Two scooters leave a stoplight at the same time. The blue scooter accelerates and then travels at a constant speed, and the red scooter accelerates at a constant rate. The distance d, in feet, each scooter travels after t seconds is shown. When does the red scooter catch up to the blue scooter? Explain.

Hey, look at that! Two equations with two unknowns—it looks like a system.

$d = 40t$

$d = 4.5t^2$

Essential Understanding You can solve systems of linear and quadratic equations graphically and algebraically. This type of system can have two solutions, one solution, or no solutions.

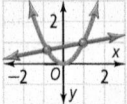
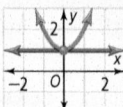
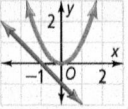

Two solutions   One solution   No solutions

Plan

How can you solve this system by graphing?
The points where the two graphs intersect are the solutions of the system.

Problem 1 Solving by Graphing

What are the solutions of the system? Solve by graphing.
$$y = x^2 - x - 2$$
$$y = -x + 2$$

Step 1 Graph both equations in the same coordinate plane.

Step 2 Identify the point(s) of intersection, if any. The points of intersection are $(-2, 4)$ and $(2, 0)$.

The solutions of the system are $(-2, 4)$ and $(2, 0)$.

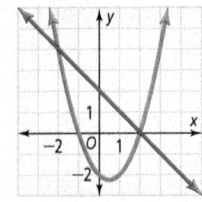

BIG ideas Solving Equations and Inequalities

Function

UbD

ESSENTIAL UNDERSTANDINGS

• Systems of linear and quadratic equations can be solved graphically and algebraically.

• Systems of linear and quadratic equations can have two solutions, one solution, or no solutions.

Math Background

Solving systems of equations that involve linear and nonlinear systems uses the same process students have used to solve systems of linear equations. Students may benefit from a review of how to solve a system of linear equations using the three methods previously learned: graphing, substitution, and elimination. Remind students that they should check solutions by substituting the ordered pairs into the original equations to verify that the ordered pair satisfies each equation.

Determining the solutions of nonlinear systems of equations is important in the field of engineering. Engineers must set up and solve systems of equations to determine equilibrium points in multiphase systems. Because of the complex nature of the nonlinear systems used in engineering and other applications, mathematicians have devised many complex methods for solving these systems accurately. Examples of these methods include Newton's method and the Runge-Kutta method.

Support Student Learning

Use the **Algebra 1 Companion** to engage and support students during instructions. See Lesson Resources at the end of this lesson for details.

PowerAlgebra.com

1 Interactive Learning

Solve It!

Step out how to solve the Problem with helpful hints and an online question. Other questions are listed above in Interactive Learning.

Got It? 1. What are the solutions of each system? Solve by graphing.

a. $y = 2x^2 + 1$
$y = -2x + 5$

b. $y = x^2 + x + 3$
$y = -x$

In Lesson 6-3, you solved linear systems using elimination. The same technique can be applied to systems of linear and quadratic equations.

 **Problem 2** Using Elimination

Recreation Since opening day, attendance at Pool A has increased steadily, while attendance at Pool B first rose and then fell. Equations modeling the daily attendance y at each pool are shown below, where x is the number of days since opening day. On what day(s) was the attendance the same at both pools? What was the attendance?

Pool A: $y = 20x + 124$
Pool B: $y = -x^2 + 39x + 64$

Know	Need	Plan
Equations giving the attendance at each pool	The day(s) when the attendance was the same	Use elimination to solve the system formed by the equations.

Step 1 Eliminate y.

$$y = -x^2 + 39x + 64$$
$$-(y = \qquad 20x + 124) \quad \text{Subtract the two equations.}$$
$$\overline{0 = -x^2 + 19x - 60} \quad \text{Subtraction Property of Equality}$$

Step 2 Factor and solve for x.

$$0 = -x^2 + 19x - 60$$
$$0 = -(x^2 - 19x + 60) \qquad \text{Factor out } -1.$$
$$0 = -(x - 4)(x - 15) \qquad \text{Factor.}$$
$$x - 4 = 0 \quad \text{or} \quad x - 15 = 0 \qquad \text{Zero-Product Property}$$
$$x = 4 \quad \text{or} \quad x = 15 \qquad \text{Solve for } x.$$

Step 3 Find the corresponding y-values. Use either equation.

$$y = 20x + 124 \qquad\qquad y = 20x + 124$$
$$y = 20(4) + 124 \qquad\qquad y = 20(15) + 124$$
$$y = 204 \qquad\qquad\qquad y = 424$$

The pools had the same attendance on days 4 and 15. On Day 4, each pool had 204 people. On Day 15, each pool had 424 people.

 Got It? 2. In Problem 2, suppose the daily attendance y at Pool A can be modeled by the equation $y = 32x + 74$. On what day(s) was the attendance the same at both pools? What was the attendance?

---

2 Guided Instruction

 Each Problem is worked out and supported online.

Problem 1
Solving by Graphing
Animated

Problem 2
Using Elimination
Animated

Problem 3
Using Substitution
Animated

Problem 4
Solving With a Graphing Calculator

Support in Algebra 1 Companion
• Vocabulary
• Key Concepts
• Got It?

Got It?

Graphing is invaluable in nonlinear systems because it helps students understand the number of solutions and the approximate solution(s).

Problem 2

Q How many points of intersection can the graphs of $y = 20x + 124$ and $y = -x^2 + 39x + 64$ have? **[0, 1, or 2]**

Q Why is y eliminated instead of x? **[The x^2 term makes eliminating x difficult.]**

Q What other methods could be used to solve the equation $-x^2 + 19x - 60 = 0$? **[graphing, completing the square, or the quadratic formula]**

Q Do both values of x make sense in the problem situation? Explain. **[Yes, both pools were open on day 4 and on day 15.]**

Got It?

It may be easier for some students to understand the elimination if the first equation is multiplied by -1 and written as $-y = x^2 - 39x - 64$. Then it can be added to the equation $y = 32x + 7$ to eliminate the y-terms.

Answers

Solve It!
About 8.9 s; explanations may vary.

Got It?
1. a. $(-2, 9)$, $(1, 3)$
   b. no solution
2. Days 2 and 5; 138 people and 234 people

Problem 3

> **Q** What form must a quadratic equation be in prior to solving by factoring or using the quadratic formula? **[It must be in standard form.]**
>
> **Q** A classmate wrote the point (2, 3) as the solution to the system of equations. What mistake might he or she have made? **[Answers will vary. Sample: The student wrote both x-values as an ordered pair. Instead, he or she needs to find the y-value that corresponds to each x-value.]**

Got It?

Encourage students to check their work by substituting each ordered pair into both original equations.

Problem 4

Introduce students to the TABLE features on the graphing calculator. They can analyze the tables generated by the calculator to find the common solutions for the system of equations. If necessary, students can modify the table start value and the table increment value.

> **Q** Why is using a graphing calculator better than graphing on graph paper? **[The intersection points might be hard to read from a hand-drawn graph. The CALC feature calculates them precisely.]**

Substitution is another method you have used to solve linear systems. This method also works with systems of linear and quadratic equations.

 **Problem 3** Using Substitution

What are the solutions of the system? $\qquad y = x^2 - 6x + 10$
$\qquad\qquad\qquad\qquad\qquad\qquad\qquad\qquad\qquad y = 4 - x$

Plan

Which variable should you substitute for?
Substitute for y since both equations are already solved for y.

Step 1 Write a single equation containing only one variable.

$$y = x^2 - 6x + 10$$
$$4 - x = x^2 - 6x + 10 \qquad \text{Substitute } 4 - x \text{ for } y.$$
$$4 - x - (4 - x) = x^2 - 6x + 10 - (4 - x) \qquad \text{Subtract } 4 - x \text{ from each side.}$$
$$0 = x^2 - 5x + 6 \qquad \text{Write in standard form.}$$

Step 2 Factor and solve for x.

$$0 = (x - 2)(x - 3) \qquad \text{Factor.}$$
$$x - 2 = 0 \quad \text{or} \quad x - 3 = 0 \qquad \text{Zero-Product Property}$$
$$x = 2 \quad \text{or} \qquad x = 3 \qquad \text{Solve for } x.$$

Step 3 Find corresponding y-values. Use either original equation.

$$y = 4 - x = 4 - 2 = 2 \qquad\qquad y = 4 - x = 4 - 3 = 1$$

The solutions of the system are (2, 2) and (3, 1).

Got It? 3. What are the solutions of the system? $\qquad y - 30 = 12x$
$\qquad\qquad\qquad\qquad\qquad\qquad\qquad\qquad\qquad\qquad\qquad y = x^2 + 11x - 12$

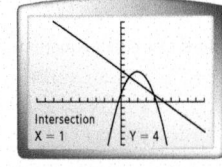 **Problem 4** Solving With a Graphing Calculator

What are the solutions of the system? $\qquad y = -x + 5$
Use a graphing calculator. $\qquad\qquad\qquad\qquad\qquad y = -x^2 + 4x + 1$

Step 1 Enter the equations on the **Y=** screen. Press $\boxed{\text{graph}}$ to display the system.

Step 2

Think

How can you check your solutions?
Substitute them into the original equations and simplify.

Intersection
X = 1 ⋮ Y = 4

Use the **CALC** feature. Select **INTERSECT**. Move the cursor close to a point of intersection. Press $\boxed{\text{enter}}$ three times to find the point of intersection.

Step 3

Intersection
X = 4 ⋮ Y = 1

Repeat Step 2 to find the second intersection point.

The solutions are (1, 4) and (4, 1).

Additional Problems

1. What are the solutions of the system? Solve by graphing.
$y = x^2 + x + 2$
$y = x + 6$
ANSWER $(-2, 4), (2, 8)$

2. The equations $y = 24x + 15$ and $y = -x^2 + 120x + 15$ model the daily sales of two types of computers, where x is the number of days since the computers were put on sale. On what day was the same number of each computer sold?
ANSWER day 96

3. What are the solutions of the system?
$y = x^2 - 4x + 2$
$y = -x$
ANSWER $(1, -1), (2, -2)$

4. What are the solutions of the system? Use a graphing calculator.
$y = x^2 - 3x + 1$
$y = -5x + 1$
ANSWER $(0, 1), (-2, 11)$

Answers

Got It? (continued)
3. $(-6, -42), (7, 114)$
4. a. $(-2, 2), (1, -1)$
  b. Substitution; substitute $-x$ for y in the first equation.

Got lt? **4. a.** What are the solutions of the system? $y = x^2 - 2$
Use a graphing calculator. $y = -x$
b. Reasoning How else can you solve the system in part (a)? Explain.

Lesson Check

Do you know HOW?

1. Use a graph to solve the system $y = x^2 + x - 2$ and $y = x + 2$.

2. Use elimination to solve the system $y = x^2 - 13x + 52$ and $y = -14x + 94$.

3. Use substitution to solve the system $y = x^2 - 6x + 9$ and $y + x = 5$.

4. Use a graphing calculator to solve the system $y = -x^2 + 4x + 1$ and $y = 2x + 2$.

Do you UNDERSTAND?

5. Use two different methods to solve the system $y = x$ and $y = 2x^2 + 10x + 9$. Which method do you prefer? Explain.

6. Open-Ended Write a system of linear and quadratic equations with the given number of solutions.
   a. two   **b.** exactly one   **c.** none

7. Compare and Contrast How are solving systems of linear equations and solving systems of linear and quadratic equations alike? How are they different?

Practice and Problem-Solving Exercises

Ⓐ Practice   Solve each system by graphing.   ◉ See Problem 1.

8. $y = x^2 + 1$
$y = x + 1$

9. $y = x^2 + 4$
$y = 4x$

10. $y = x^2 - 5x - 4$
$y = -2x$

11. $y = x^2 + 2x + 1$
$y = x + 1$

12. $y = x^2 + 2x + 5$
$y = -2x + 1$

13. $y = 3x + 4$
$y = -x^2 + 4$

Solve each system using elimination.   ◉ See Problem 2.

14. $y = -x + 3$
$y = x^2 + 1$

15. $y = x^2$
$y = x + 2$

16. $y = -x - 7$
$y = x^2 - 4x - 5$

17. Sales The equations at the right model the numbers y of two portable music players sold x days after both players were introduced. On what day(s) did the company sell the same number of each player? How many players of each type were sold?

Music Player A: $y = 48x + 20$
Music Player B: $y = -x^2 + 200x + 20$

Solve each system using substitution.   ◉ See Problem 3.

18. $y = x^2 - 2x - 6$
$y = 4x + 10$

19. $y = 3x - 20$
$y = -x^2 + 34$

20. $y = x^2 + 7x + 100$
$y + 10x = 30$

21. $-x^2 - x + 19 = y$
$x = y + 80$

22. $3x - y = -2$
$2x^2 = y$

23. $y = 3x^2 + 21x - 5$
$-10x + y = -1$

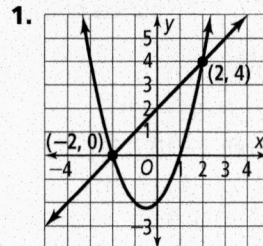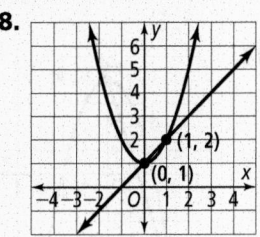
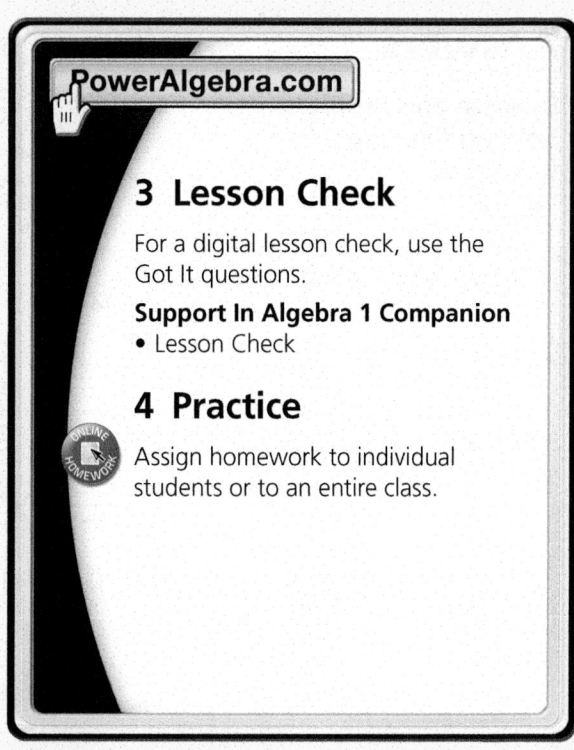

4 Practice

ASSIGNMENT GUIDE

Basic: 8–29, 31–33

Average: 9–29 odd, 30–34

Advanced: 9–29 odd, 30–36

Standardized Test Prep: 37–41

Mixed Review: 42–50

REASONING exercises have blue headings.

APPLICATIONS exercises have red headings.

EXERCISE 32: Use the Think About a Plan worksheet in the **Practice and Problem Solving Workbook** (also available in the Teaching Resources in print and online) to further support students' development in becoming independent learners.

HOMEWORK QUICK CHECK

To check students' understanding of key skills and concepts, go over Exercises 11, 19, 31, 32, and 33.

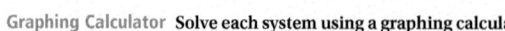 **Graphing Calculator** Solve each system using a graphing calculator. 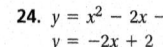 See Problem 4.

24. $y = x^2 - 2x - 2$
$y = -2x + 2$

25. $y = -x^2 + 2$
$y = 4 - 0.5x$

26. $y = x - 5$
$y = x^2 - 6x + 5$

27. $y = -0.5x^2 - 2x + 1$
$y + 3 = -x$

28. $y = 2x^2 - 24x + 76$
$y + 7 = 11$

29. $-x^2 - 8x - 15 = y$
$-x + y = 3$

B Apply

30. Reasoning The graph at the right shows a quadratic function and the linear function $y = d$.
  a. If the linear function were changed to $y = d + 3$, how many solutions would the system have?
  b. If the linear function were changed to $y = d - 5$, how many solutions would the system have?

31. Think About a Plan A company's logo consists of a parabola and a line. The parabola in the logo can be modeled by the function $y = 3x^2 - 4x + 2$. The line intersects the parabola when $x = 0$ and when $x = 2$. What is an equation of the line?
  • How can you find the coordinates of the points of intersection?
  • Can you write an equation of the line given the points of intersection?

32. Business The daily number of customers y at a coffee shop can be modeled by the function $y = 0.25x^2 - 5x + 80$, where x is the number of days since the beginning of the month. The daily number of customers at a second shop can be modeled by a linear function. Both shops have the same number of customers on days 10 and 20. What function models the number of customers at the second shop?

33. Error Analysis A classmate says that the system $y = x^2 + 2x + 4$ and $y = x + 1$ has one solution. Explain the classmate's error.

34. Writing Explain why a system of linear and quadratic equations cannot have an infinite number of solutions.

C Challenge

35. Geometry The figures below show rectangles that are centered on the y-axis with bases on the x-axis and upper vertices defined by the function $y = -0.3x^2 + 4$. Find the area of each rectangle.

a. 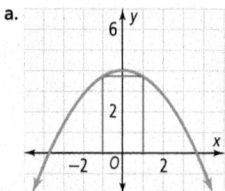   **b.**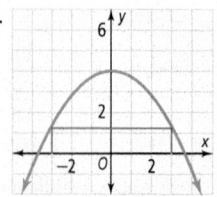

  c. Find the coordinates of the vertices of the square constructed in the same manner. Round to the nearest hundredth.
  d. Find the area of the square. Round to the nearest hundredth.

36. What are the solutions of the system $y = x^2 + x + 6$ and $y = 2x^2 - x + 3$? Explain how you solved the system.

Answers

Practice and Problem-Solving Exercises
(continued)

9.

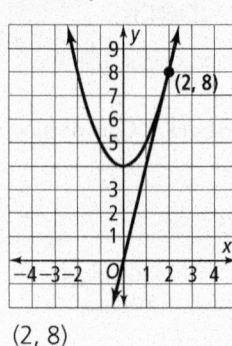

$(2, 8)$

10.

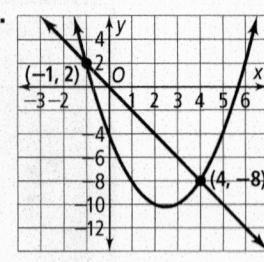

$(4, -8), (-1, 2)$

11.

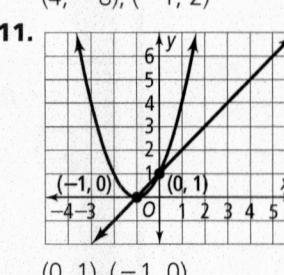

$(0, 1), (-1, 0)$

12.

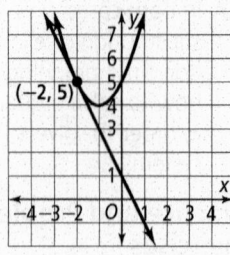

$(-2, 5)$

13.

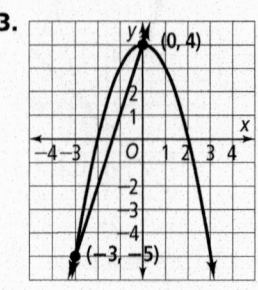

$(0, 4), (-3, -5)$

14. $(1, 2), (-2, 5)$

15. $(2, 4), (-1, 1)$

16. $(1, -8), (2, -9)$

17. Day 0, 20 players of each type; Day 152, 7316 players of each type

18. $(-2, 2), (8, 42)$

19. $(6, -2), (-9, -47)$

20. $(-7, 100), (-10, 130)$

21. $(9, -71), (-11, -91)$

22. $(2, 8), (-0.5, 0.5)$

23. $(-4, -41), \left(\frac{1}{3}, \frac{7}{3}\right)$

24. $(-2, 6), (2, -2)$

25. no solution

26. $(2, -3), (5, 0)$

27. $(2, -5), (-4, 1)$

28. $(6, 4)$

29. $(-3, 0), (-6, -3)$

30. a. 2
  b. 0

31. $y = 2x + 2$

32. $y = 2.5x + 30$

33. The system has no solution.

Standardized Test Prep

SAT/ACT

37. A designer sketches a design for a tabletop on graph paper. The table is bounded by a parabola and a line. The parabola can be modeled by the function $y = 2x^2 - 3x + 2$. The line intersects the parabola when $x = -1$ and when $x = 3$. What is an equation of the line?

  Ⓐ $y = -x + 8$ Ⓒ $y = 2x + 5$

  Ⓑ $y = x + 8$ Ⓓ $y = -2x + 5$

38. Which equation illustrates the Distributive Property?

  Ⓕ $4(x + 2) = 4x + 8$ Ⓗ $4(x + 2) = 4(2 + x)$

  Ⓖ $4(x + 2) = (x + 2)4$ Ⓘ $4(x + 2) = 4(x + 2)$

39. Which rate is equivalent to 30 m/s?

  Ⓐ 3 km/h   Ⓑ 108 km/h   Ⓒ 3000 km/h   Ⓓ 108,000 km/h

40. Which of the following is equivalent to 0.05%?

  Ⓕ 0.00005   Ⓖ 0.0005   Ⓗ 0.005   Ⓘ 0.05

Short Response

41. A box with 4 balls weighs 5 lb. The same box with 10 balls weighs 11 lb. Write an equation in slope-intercept form for the weight y of a box containing x balls. Then rewrite the equation in standard form using integer coefficients.

Mixed Review

Which type of function best models the data in each table? Write an equation to model the data.   ◀ See Lesson 9-7.

42.

x	y
−1	0.2
0	0
1	0.2
2	0.8
3	1.8
4	3.2

43.

x	y
−1	1.6
0	4
1	10
2	25
3	62.5
4	156.25

44.

x	y
−1	11.2
0	7
1	2.8
2	−1.4
3	−5.6
4	−9.8

Get Ready! To prepare for Lesson 10-1, do Exercises 45–50.

Simplify each expression.   ◀ See Lesson 1-3.

45. $\sqrt{196}$ **46.** $\sqrt{\frac{25}{49}}$ **47.** $\sqrt{1.44}$

48. $\sqrt{81}$ **49.** $\sqrt{0.36}$ **50.** $\sqrt{400}$

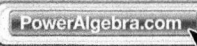

---

34. A line and a parabola intersect in at most 2 points, so a linear-quadratic system can have at most two solutions.

35. a. 7.4

  b. 7.8

  c. (1.61, 0), (1.61, 3.22), (−1.61, 3.22), (−1.61, 0)

  d. 10.38

36. (3, 18), (−1, 6); Check students' work

37. B

38. F

39. B

40. G

41. [2] Given (x, y), where x is the number of balls and y is the weight of the box, you have the points (4, 5) and (10, 11). The slope of the line that passes through these two points is $\frac{11 - 5}{10 - 4} = \frac{6}{6} = 1$. An equation of the line is $y - 5 = 1(x - 4)$, or $y = x + 1$. The equation of the line in standard form is $x - y = -1$.
[1] correct methods with minor calculation error

42. quadratic; $y = 0.2x^2$

43. exponential; $y = 4(2.5)^x$

44. linear; $y = -4.2x + 7$

45. 14

46. $\frac{5}{7}$

47. 1.2

48. 9

49. 0.6

50. 20

Additional Instructional Support

Algebra 1 Companion

Students can use the **Algebra 1 Companion** worktext (4 pages) as you teach the lesson. Use the Companion to support

- New Vocabulary
- Key Concepts
- Got It for each Problem
- Lesson Check

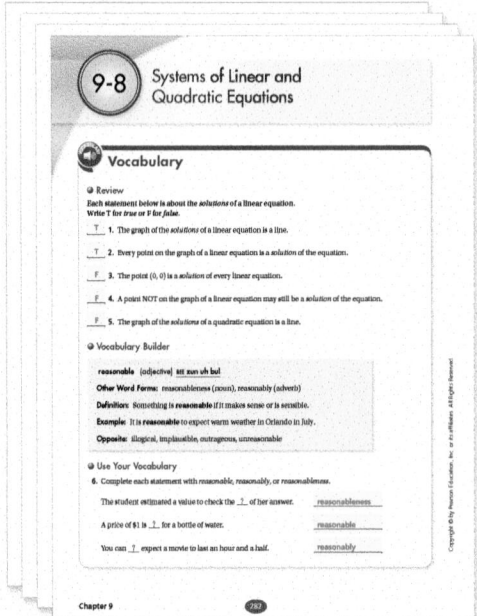

ELL Support

Focus on Communication Have students write the differences between solving equations by graphing, substitution, and elimination using their own words. Ask what the differences are between the three methods. When is it best to use substitution over elimination? Ask what method is preferred by students and why. Have students write a description of when a system of equation has one solution, two solutions, or no solutions. Ask them to provide an example graph of each.

Arrange students in pairs of mixed abilities. Ask them to share their writing by reading it aloud. Encourage students to question each other and ask for clarification.

5 Assess & Remediate

Lesson Quiz

1. What are the solutions of the system? Solve by graphing.
   $y = x^2 + 2x + 3$
   $y = 3x + 5$

2. The equations $y = 30x + 10$ and $y = -x^2 + 150x + 10$ model the daily sales of two car models, where x is the number of days since the cars went on sale. On what day was the same number of each car sold?

3. What are the solutions of the system?
   $y = 3x^2 + 5x + 4$
   $y = 2x + 10$

4. What are the solutions of the system? Use a graphing calculator.
   $y = -2x^2 + x + 5$
   $y = -x - 7$

5. **Do you UNDERSTAND?** A student graphed the following system using a graphing calculator. Based on the display, the student said there was no solution. What advice could you give him or her?
   $y = x^2 + 6$
   $y = -9x - 14$

ANSWERS TO LESSON QUIZ

1. $(-1, 2)$, $(2, 11)$
2. 120
3. $(-2, 6)$, $(1, 12)$
4. $(-2, -5)$, $(3, -10)$
5. Use a larger viewing window to see where the graphs intersect.

PRESCRIPTION FOR REMEDIATION

Use the student work on the Lesson Quiz to prescribe a differentiated review assignment.

Points	Differentiated Remediation
0–2	Intervention
3	On-level
4	Extension

PowerAlgebra.com

5 Assess & Remediate

Assign the Lesson Quiz. Appropriate intervention, practice, or enrichment is automatically generated based on student performance.

Intervention

- **Reteaching** (2 pages) Provides reteaching and practice exercises for the key lesson concepts. Use with struggling students or absent students.

- **English Language Learner Support** Helps students develop and reinforce mathematical vocabulary and key concepts.

All-in-One Resources/Online
Reteaching

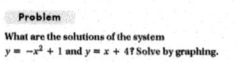
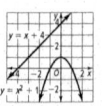

9-8 Reteaching
Systems of Linear and Quadratic Equations

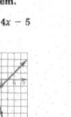
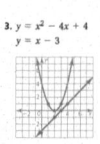

All-in-One Resources/Online
English Language Learner Support

9-8 ELL Support
Systems of Linear and Quadratic Equations

Differentiated Remediation *continued*

On-Level

- **Practice** (2 pages) Provides extra practice for each lesson. For simpler practice exercises, use the Form K Practice pages found in the All-in-One Teaching Resources and online.

- **Think About a Plan** Helps students develop specific problem-solving skills and strategies by providing scaffolded guiding questions.

- **Standardized Test Prep** Focuses on all major exercises, all major question types, and helps students prepare for the high-stakes assessments.

Extension

- **Enrichment** Provides students with interesting problems and activities that extend the concepts of the lesson.

- **Activities, Games, and Puzzles** Worksheets that can be used for concepts development, enrichment, and for fun!

Practice and Problem Solving Wkbk/ Resources/Online
Practice page 1

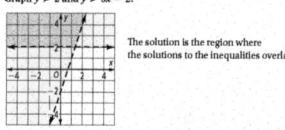

Practice and Problem Solving Wkbk/ All-in-One Resources/Online
Practice page 2

All-in-One Resources/Online
Enrichment

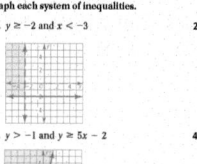
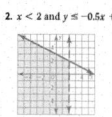

Practice and Problem Solving Wkbk/ All-in-One Resources/Online
Think About a Plan

Practice and Problem Solving Wkbk/ All-in-One Resources/Online
Standardized Test Prep

Online Teacher Resource Center
Activities, Games, and Puzzles

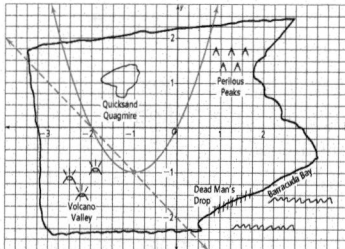

Performance Task UbD

Pull It All Together

The concepts and skills required to solve these problems are from several lessons within this chapter and from the previous chapter. As students solve these problems, they will demonstrate their reasoning strategies and their growth as independent problem solvers.

The following questions are designed to:
• Help support students as they do the Tasks.
• Gauge the amount of support students need as they become independent problem solvers.

Task 1
• What does the *a* term tell about the graph?
• What does the *b* term tell about the graph?
• What does the *c* term tell about the graph?
• Can you simplify the equation?

Task 2
• What is the formula for the area of a circle?
• How many circles must you calculate the area of?
• How do you use the length of the pipe?
• How can you solve the resulting quadratic equation?

Task 3
• What information are you given?
• What are you trying to find?
• Can you graph the data?
• The first few function values suggest an exponential model. Does that model hold up as you determine more values?

> To solve these problems you will pull together many concepts and skills that you have studied about quadratic functions and equations.

BIG idea Functions

The family of quadratic functions has equations of the form $y = ax^2 + bx + c$, where $a \neq 0$. The graph of a quadratic function is a parabola.

Task 1

Solve. Show your work and explain your steps.

Suppose you have a quadratic function $y = ax^2 + bx + c$, where $a < -1$, $b = 2a$, and $c = -b$. What do you know about the graph of this function? Justify each detail.

BIG idea Solving Equations and Inequalities

You can solve quadratic equations by several methods, including graphing, finding square roots, factoring, completing the square, and using the quadratic formula. Sometimes the characteristics of the equation make one method more efficient than the others.

Task 2

Solve. Show your work and explain your steps.

A manufacturer makes 50-cm lengths of steel pipe. A pipe uses 400 cm³ of steel and has an inner radius of 2 cm. What is the thickness *x* of the pipe?

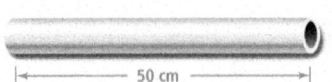
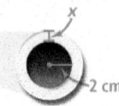

BIG idea Modeling

To model a data set, choose a function that most closely matches the pattern in the data or graph.

Task 3

Solve. Show your work and explain your steps.

Suppose you draw chords to divide a circle into as many regions as possible. The maximum number of regions *R* you can make is a quadratic function of the number of chords *x* you draw. The values of *R* for $x = 0$, $x = 1$, and $x = 2$ are shown. What function models this situation? How many regions can you make with 10 chords?

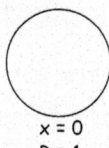
x = 0
R = 1

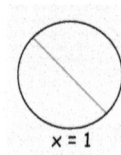
x = 1
R = 2

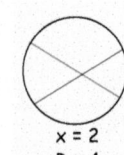
x = 2
R = 4

Assess Performance UbD

Pull It All Together

See p. 67 for a holistic scoring rubric to gauge a student's progress on Understanding the Problem, Planning a Solution, Getting an Answer, and Assesssing Autonomy.

SOLUTION OUTLINES

1. First step: Find the axis of symmetry.
$\frac{-b}{2a} = \frac{-2a}{2a} = -1$. $x = -1$ is the axis of symmetry.

Second step: Find the *y*-intercept.
$c = -b = -2a$.

Third step: Find the vertex.
Substitute -1 for *x* to find the *y*-coordinate. $a(-1)^2 + b(-1) + c = a(1) + (2a)(-1) + (-2a) = -3a$. The vertex is $(-1, -3a)$.

Fourth step: The parabola opens downward because $a < 0$.

2. First step: Find the volume of the empty space in the pipe. Use the formula, $V = \pi r^2 h$.
$\pi(2)^2 \, 50 = 200\pi \approx 628.31$

Second step: Represent the outer radius as $x + 2$. Find the volume of the entire pipe.
$\pi(x + 2)^2 \, (50)$ Volume of cylinder
$\pi(x^2 + 4x + 4)(50)$ Multiply.
$50\pi x^2 + 200\pi x + 200\pi$
$157.08x^2 + 628.31x + 628.31$
Substitute 3.14 for π.

Third step: The difference between the volume of the pipe and the empty space is 400 cm³. Solve for *x*, which is the thickness of the pipe.
$157.08x^2 + 628.31x + 628.31 - 628.31 = 400$
$157.08x^2 + 628.31x - 400 = 0$
$x \approx 0.56$ Solve. Reject the negative value.

3. First step: Let $y =$ the number of regions and let $x =$ the number of chords. $y = ax^2 + bx + c$

Second step: Solve for *c* by substituting the point (0, 1).
$1 = a(0) + b(0) = c, c = 1$

Third step: Substitute the points (1, 2) and (2, 4) in $y = ax^2 + bx + 1$.
$2 = a(1)^2 + b(1) + 1, a + b = 1$
$4 = a(2)^2 + b(2) + 1, 4a + 2b = 3$

Fourth step: Solve the system.
$a = 0.5, b = 0.5$

Fifth step: Substitute for *a* and *b*.
$y = 0.5x^2 + 0.5x + 1$. Use the equation to find the number of regions created by having 10 chords. (56 regions)

9 Chapter Review

Connecting **BIG** ideas and Answering the Essential Questions

1 Function
The family of quadratic functions has equations of the form $y = ax^2 + bx + c$, where $a \neq 0$. The graph of a quadratic function is a parabola.

Graphing Quadratic Functions (Lessons 9-1 and 9-2)

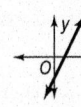
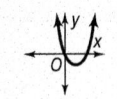
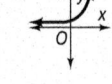
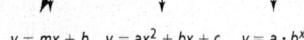

2 Solving Equations and Inequalities
You can solve quadratic equations using several methods.

Solving Quadratic Equations (Lessons 9-3, 9-4, 9-5, and 9-6)
$$ax^2 + bx + c = 0$$
$$x = \frac{-b \pm \sqrt{b^2 - 4ac}}{2a}$$

Systems of Linear and Quadratic Equations (Lesson 9-8)

Two solutions   One solution   No solution

3 Modeling
To model a data set, choose a function that most closely matches the pattern in the data or graph.

Choosing a Model (Lesson 9-7)

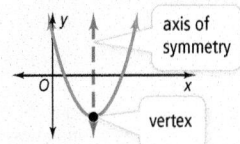

$y = mx + b$ $y = ax^2 + bx + c$ $y = a \cdot b^x$

Chapter Vocabulary

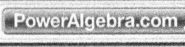

- axis of symmetry (p. 534)
- completing the square (p. 561)
- discriminant (p. 570)
- maximum (p. 535)
- minimum (p. 535)
- parabola (p. 534)
- quadratic equation (p. 548)
- quadratic formula (p. 567)
- quadratic function (p. 534)
- root of an equation (p. 548)
- vertex (p. 535)
- zero of a function (p. 548)

Choose the correct term to complete each sentence.

1. The U-shaped graph of a quadratic function is a(n) __?__.

2. The line that divides a parabola in half is the __?__.

3. The __?__ can be used to determine the number of real-number solutions of a quadratic equation.

4. The __?__ of a parabola is the point at which the parabola intersects the axis of symmetry.

Answers

Chapter Review

1. parabola   **2.** axis of symmetry
3. discriminant   **4.** vertex

Essential Questions

BIG idea **Function**
ESSENTIAL QUESTION What are the characteristics of quadratic functions?
ANSWER The family of quadratic functions has equations of the form $y = ax^2 + bx + c$, where $a \neq 0$. The graph of a quadratic function is a parabola.

BIG idea **Solving Equations and Inequalities**
ESSENTIAL QUESTION How can you solve a quadratic equation?
ANSWER You can solve quadratic equations using several methods, including graphing, square roots, factoring, completing the square, or using the quadratic formula.

BIG idea **Modeling**
ESSENTIAL QUESTION How can you use functions to model real-world situations?
ANSWER To model a data set, choose a function that most closely matches the pattern in the data or graph.

Summative Questions

Use the following prompts as you review this chapter with your students. The prompts are designed to help you assess your students' understanding of the BIG Ideas they have studied.

- How do you graph a quadratic equation?
- How can you solve a quadratic equation?
- What does the discriminant tell you about the solutions to a quadratic equation?

Answers

Chapter Review (continued)

5.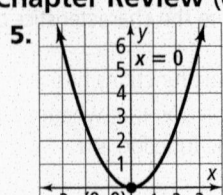

6.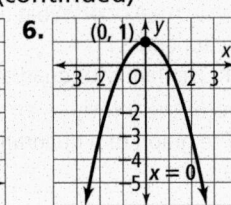

7.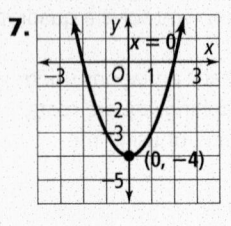

8.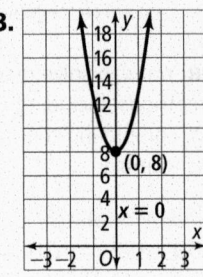

9.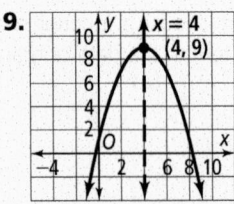

10.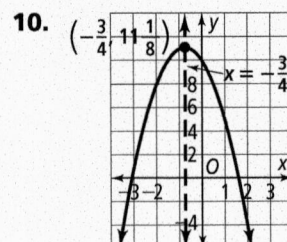

11.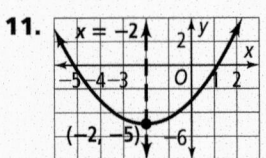

12.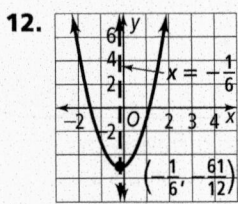

9-1 and 9-2 Graphing Quadratic Functions

Quick Review

A function of the form $y = ax^2 + bx + c$, where $a \neq 0$, is a **quadratic function**. Its graph is a **parabola**. The **axis of symmetry** of a parabola divides it into two matching halves. The **vertex** of a parabola is the point at which the parabola intersects the axis of symmetry.

Example

What is the vertex of the graph of $y = x^2 + 6x - 2$?

The x-coordinate of the vertex is given by $x = \frac{-b}{2a}$.

$$x = \frac{-b}{2a} = \frac{-6}{2(1)} = -3$$

Find the y-coordinate of the vertex.

$y = (-3)^2 + 6(-3) - 2$ Substitute -3 for x.

$y = -11$ Simplify.

The vertex is $(-3, -11)$.

Exercises

Graph each function. Label the axis of symmetry and the vertex.

5. $y = \frac{2}{3}x^2$ **6.** $y = -x^2 + 1$

7. $y = x^2 - 4$ **8.** $y = 5x^2 + 8$

9. $y = -\frac{1}{2}x^2 + 4x + 1$ **10.** $y = -2x^2 - 3x + 10$

11. $y = \frac{1}{2}x^2 + 2x - 3$ **12.** $y = 3x^2 + x - 5$

Open-Ended Give an example of a quadratic function that matches each description.

13. Its graph opens downward.

14. The vertex of its graph is at the origin.

15. Its graph opens upward.

16. Its graph is wider than the graph of $y = x^2$.

9-3 and 9-4 Solving Quadratic Equations

Quick Review

The **standard form of a quadratic equation** is $ax^2 + bx + c = 0$, where $a \neq 0$. Quadratic equations can have two, one, or no real-number solutions. You can solve a quadratic equation by graphing the related function and finding the x-intercepts. Some quadratic equations can also be solved using square roots. If the left side of $ax^2 + bx + c = 0$ can be factored, you can use the **Zero-Product Property** to solve the equation.

Example

What are the solutions of $2x^2 - 72 = 0$?

$2x^2 - 72 = 0$

$2x^2 = 72$ Add 72 to each side.

$x^2 = 36$ Divide each side by 2.

$x = \pm\sqrt{36}$ Find the square roots of each side.

$x = \pm 6$ Simplify.

Exercises

Solve each equation. If the equation has no real-number solution, write *no solution*.

17. $6(x^2 - 2) = 12$ **18.** $-5m^2 = -125$

19. $9(w^2 + 1) = 9$ **20.** $3r^2 + 27 = 0$

21. $4 = 9k^2$ **22.** $4n^2 = 64$

Solve by factoring.

23. $x^2 + 7x + 12 = 0$ **24.** $5x^2 - 10x = 0$

25. $2x^2 - 9x = x^2 - 20$ **26.** $2x^2 + 5x = 3$

27. $3x^2 - 5x = -3x^2 + 6$ **28.** $x^2 - 5x + 4 = 0$

29. Geometry The area of a circle A is given by the formula $A = \pi r^2$, where r is the radius of the circle. Find the radius of a circle with area 16 in.^{2}. Round to the nearest tenth of an inch.

---

13. Answers will vary. Sample: $y = -x^2$

14. Answers will vary. Sample: $y = x^2$

15. Answers will vary. Sample: $y = x^2$

16. Answers will vary. Sample: $y = 0.5x^2$

17. ± 2

18. ± 5

19. 0

20. no solution

21. $\pm\frac{2}{3}$

22. ± 4

23. $-3, -4$

24. $0, 2$

25. $4, 5$

26. $-3, \frac{1}{2}$

27. $-\frac{2}{3}, \frac{3}{2}$

28. $1, 4$

29. 2.3 in.

9-5 Completing the Square

Quick Review

You can solve any quadratic equation by writing it in the form $x^2 + bx = c$, **completing the square**, and finding the square roots of each side of the equation.

Example

What are the solutions of $x^2 + 8x = 513$?

$x^2 + 8x + 16 = 513 + 16$	Add $\left(\frac{8}{2}\right)^2$, or 16, to each side.
$(x + 4)^2 = 529$	Write $x^2 + 8x + 16$ as a square.
$x + 4 = \pm\sqrt{529}$	Find the square roots.
$x + 4 = \pm 23$	Simplify.
$x + 4 = 23$ or $x + 4 = -23$	Write as two equations.
$x = 19$ or $x = -27$	Solve for x.

Exercises

Solve each equation by completing the square. If necessary, round to the nearest hundredth.

30. $x^2 + 6x - 5 = 0$ **31.** $x^2 = 3x - 1$

32. $2x^2 + 7x = -6$ **33.** $x^2 + 10x = -8$

34. $4x^2 - 8x = 24$ **35.** $x^2 - 14x + 16 = 0$

36. Construction You are planning a rectangular patio with length that is 7 ft less than three times its width. The area of the patio is 120 ft². What are the dimensions of the patio?

37. Design You are designing a rectangular birthday card for a friend. You want the card's length to be 1 in. more than twice the card's width. The area of the card is 88 in.². What are the dimensions of the card?

9-6 The Quadratic Formula and the Discriminant

Quick Review

You can solve the quadratic equation $ax^2 + bx + c = 0$, where $a \neq 0$, by using the **quadratic formula** $x = \frac{-b \pm \sqrt{b^2 - 4ac}}{2a}$. The **discriminant** is $b^2 - 4ac$. The discriminant tells you how many real-number solutions the equation has.

Example

How many real-number solutions does the equation $x^2 + 3 = 2x$ have?

$x^2 - 2x + 3 = 0$	Write in standard form.
$b^2 - 4ac = (-2)^2 - 4(1)(3)$	Evaluate discriminant.
$= -8$	Simplify.

Because the discriminant is negative, the equation has no real-number solutions.

Exercises

Find the number of real-number solutions of each equation.

38. $x^2 + 7x - 10 = 3$ **39.** $3x^2 - 2 = 5x$

Solve each equation using the quadratic formula. Round to the nearest hundredth.

40. $4x^2 + 3x - 8 = 0$ **41.** $2x^2 - 3x = 20$

42. $-x^2 + 8x + 4 = 5$ **43.** $64x^2 + 12x - 1 = 0$

Solve each equation using any method. Explain why you chose the method you used.

44. $5x^2 - 10 = x^2 + 90$ **45.** $x^2 - 6x + 9 = 0$

46. Vertical Motion A ball is thrown into the air. The height h, in feet, of the ball can be modeled by the equation $h = -16t^2 + 20t + 6$, where t is the time, in seconds, the ball is in the air. When will the ball hit the ground?

30. −6.74, 0.74   **31.** 0.38, 2.62

32. −2, −1.5   **33.** −9.12, −0.88

34. −1.65, 3.65   **35.** 1.26, 12.74

36. 7.6 ft by 15.8 ft

37. 6.4 in. by 13.8 in.

38. two   **39.** two

40. −1.84, 1.09   **41.** −2.5, 4

42. 7.87, 0.13   **43.** −0.25, 0.06

44. ±5; square roots because there is no x-term

45. 3; factoring because it is easy to factor

46. 1.5 s

Answers

Chapter Review (continued)

47.

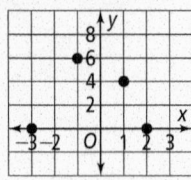

quadratic

48.

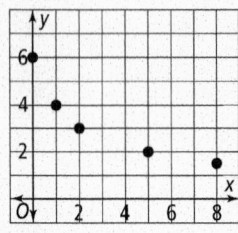

exponential

49. $y = 3x - 2$

50. $y = 5(2)^x$

51. $(-1, 8), (2, -1)$

52. $(0, -1), (1, -2)$

53. $(-1, -1), (1, 1)$

54. $(-2, -4), (3, 6)$

55. $(-8, 3), (12, 123)$

56. $(7, -2), (9, 6)$

57. $(-7, -45), (-4, -21)$

58. $(-13, 64), (3, -16)$

59. $(6, 69), (10, 145)$

60. $(-9, 33), (-12, 63)$

61. If you look at the graph and see how many times the graphs intersect, that is how many solutions the system will have.

9-7 Linear, Quadratic, and Exponential Models

Quick Review

Graphing data points or analyzing data numerically can help you find the best model. Linear data have a common first difference. Exponential data have a common ratio. Quadratic data have a common second difference.

Example

Graph the points $(1, 4), (4, 2), (2, 3), (5, 3.5),$ and $(6, 5)$. Which model is most appropriate?

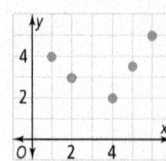

A quadratic model is most appropriate.

Exercises

Graph each set of points. Which model is most appropriate for each data set?

47. $(-3, 0), (1, 4), (-1, 6), (2, 0)$

48. $(0, 6), (5, 2), (1, 4), (8, 1.5), (2, 3)$

Write an equation to model the data.

49.

x	y
−1	−5
0	−2
1	1
2	4
3	7

50.

x	y
−1	2.5
0	5
1	10
2	20
3	40

9-8 Systems of Linear and Quadratic Equations

Quick Review

Systems of linear and quadratic equations can have two solutions, one solution, or no solution. These systems can be solved graphically or algebraically.

Example

What are the solutions of the system?
$$y = x^2 - 7x - 40$$
$$y = -3x + 37$$

$y = x^2 - 7x - 40$	Use elimination.
$-(y = -3x + 37)$	Subtract the equations.
$0 = x^2 - 4x - 77$	
$0 = (x - 11)(x + 7)$	Factor.
$x - 11 = 0$ or $x + 7 = 0$	Zero-Product Property
$x = 11$ or $x = -7$	Solve for x.

Find the corresponding y-values.

$$y = -3(11) + 37 = 4 \qquad y = -3(-7) + 37 = 58$$

The solutions are $(11, 4)$ and $(-7, 58)$.

Exercises

Solve each system by graphing.

51. $y = x^2 - 4x + 3$
$y = -3x + 5$

52. $y = x^2 - 2x - 1$
$y = -x - 1$

53. $y = -2x^2 + x + 2$
$y = x$

54. $y = x^2 + x - 6$
$y = 2x$

Solve each system algebraically.

55. $y = x^2 + 2x - 45$
$y = 6x + 51$

56. $y = x^2 - 12x + 33$
$y = 4x - 30$

57. $y = x^2 + 19x + 39$
$y - 11 = 8x$

58. $y = x^2 + 5x - 40$
$y + 1 = -5x$

59. $y = x^2 + 3x + 15$
$y + 45 = 19x$

60. $y = x^2 + 11x + 51$
$y = -10x - 57$

61. Writing Explain how you can use graphing to determine the number of solutions of a system of linear and quadratic equations.

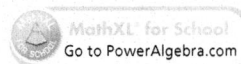

MathXL for School
Go to PowerAlgebra.com

Do you know HOW?

Graph each function.

1. $y = 3x^2 - 7$

2. $y = -x^2 - 2$

3. $y = -2x^2 + 10x - 1$

4. $y = x^2 - 3x + 2$

Solve each equation.

5. $x^2 + 11x - 26 = 0$

6. $x^2 - 25 = 0$

7. $x^2 - 19x + 80 = -8$

8. $x^2 - 5x = -4x$

9. $4x^2 - 100 = 0$

10. $5x^2 - 8x = 8 - 5x$

11. **Design** You are creating a rectangular banner for a school pep rally. You have 100 ft^2 of paper, and you want the length to be 15 ft longer than the width. What should be the dimensions of the banner?

Find the number of real-number solutions of each equation.

12. $x^2 + 4x = -4$

13. $x^2 + 8 = 0$

14. $3x^2 - 9x = -5$

Solve each equation. If necessary, round to the nearest hundredth.

15. $-3x^2 + 7x = -10$

16. $x^2 + 4x = 1$

17. $12x^2 + 16x - 28 = 0$

18. $x^2 + 6x + 9 = 25$

19. **Vertical Motion** You throw a ball upward. Its height h, in feet, after t seconds can be modeled by the function $h = -16t^2 + 30t + 6$. After how many seconds will it hit the ground?

20. Identify the graph at the right as *linear*, *quadratic*, or *exponential*. Write an equation that models the data points shown.

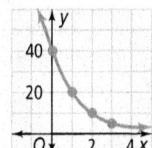

Solve each system.

21. $y = x^2 + 3x - 23$
    $y = 25 - 5x$

22. $y = x^2 + 2x - 2$
    $y = x + 10$

Do you UNDERSTAND?

23. **Writing** Explain what you can determine about the shape of a parabola from its equation alone.

24. **Open-Ended** Write an equation of a parabola that has two x-intercepts and a maximum value. Include a graph of your parabola.

25. Find a nonzero value of k such that $kx^2 - 10x + 25 = 0$ has one real-number solution.

26. **Reasoning** The graph of a quadratic function $y = ax^2 + bx + c$ is shown. What do you know about the values of a, b, and c just by looking at the graph?

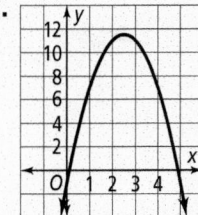

27. **Geometry** Suppose a rectangle has an area of 60 ft^2 and dimensions, in feet, of x and $x + 1$.
    a. Estimate each dimension of the rectangle to the nearest foot.
    b. Write a quadratic equation and use the quadratic formula to find each dimension to the nearest hundredth of a foot.

17. $1, -2\frac{1}{3}$

18. $-8, 2$

19. 2.06 s

20. exponential; $y = 40(0.5)^x$

21. $(-12, 85), (4, 5)$

22. $(-4, 6), (3, 13)$

23. Answers will vary. Sample: You can tell whether it opens upward or downward by looking at the sign of the x^2-coefficient. If $a > 0$, then it opens upward. If $a < 0$, then it opens downward. You can tell where the graph will intersect the y-axis by looking at the value of c. You also know whether the graph will be wider than or narrower than $y = x^2$ by looking at the value of a. If $|a| > 1$, it will be narrower. If $0 < |a| < 1$, it will be wider. You can also find the vertex by finding the value of $\frac{-b}{2a}$. The vertex is $\left(\frac{-b}{2a}, f\left(\frac{-b}{2a}\right)\right)$. The axis of symmetry is $x = \frac{-b}{2a}$. The x-intercepts are $\frac{-b \pm \sqrt{b^2 - 4ac}}{2a}$.

24. Check students' work.

25. 1

26. $a < 0, b = 0, c = 1$

27. a. 7 ft, 8 ft
    b. 7.26 ft, 8.26 ft

Answers

Chapter Test

1.
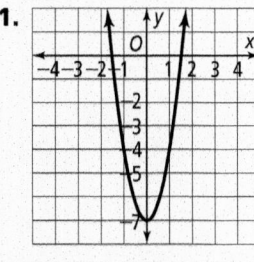

2.
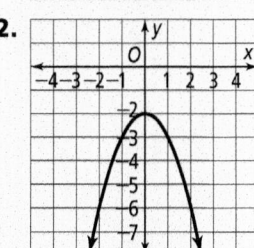

3.
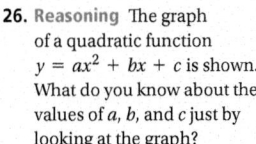

4.
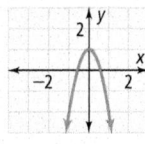

5. $2, -13$

6. ± 5

7. $8, 11$

8. $0, 1$

9. ± 5

10. $-1, 1.6$

11. 5 ft by 20 ft

12. 1

13. 0

14. 2

15. $-1, 3\frac{1}{3}$

16. $0.24, -4.24$

PowerAlgebra.com

MathXL for School
Prepare students for the Mid-Chapter Quiz and Chapter Test with online practice and review.

Item Number	Lesson
1	7-2
2	2-9
3	2-7
4	10-1
5	5-5
6	9-1
7	7-3
8	1-3
9	9-4
10	5-8
11	10-1
12	4-6
13	7-4
14	4-5
15	5-6
16	8-6
17	2-4
18	6-6
19	2-6
20	6-3
21	2-8
22	3-8
23	9-7
24	2-5
25	2-5
26	3-7
27	5-6
28	9-8

TIPS FOR SUCCESS

Some questions on standardized tests ask you to describe how changing an equation affects its graph. **Read the sample question at the right. Then follow the tips to answer it.**

TIP 1

You may want to sketch the graphs of both equations and compare the graphs.

How would the graph of $y = x^2 - 1$ change if the equation became $y = x^2 + 2$?

- Ⓐ The graph would shift 3 units down.
- Ⓑ The graph would shift 3 units up.
- Ⓒ The graph would shift 2 units down.
- Ⓓ The graph would shift 2 units up.

TIP 2

Think about what operation you would use to change $y = x^2 - 1$ to $y = x^2 + 2$.

Think It Through

To change the equation $y = x^2 - 1$ to $y = x^2 + 2$, you add 3 to the expression $x^2 - 1$:

$$y = x^2 - 1 + 3 = x^2 + 2$$

Adding 3 to the constant term of a quadratic function causes the graph to shift 3 units up.

The correct answer is B.

Vocabulary Builder

As you solve test items, you must understand the meanings of mathematical terms. Choose the correct term to complete each sentence.

A. The (*vertex*, *axis of symmetry*) is the highest or lowest point of a parabola.

B. Two distinct lines are (*parallel*, *perpendicular*) if they have the same slope.

C. The (*domain*, *range*) of a function is the set of all possible values for the input, or independent variable, of the function.

D. A (*proportion*, *rate*) is an equation that states that two ratios are equal.

E. A(n) (*quadratic*, *exponential*) function is a function of the form $y = ax^2 + bx + c$.

Multiple Choice

Read each question. Then write the letter of the correct answer on your paper.

1. The maximum distance from the sun to Mars is about 155 million miles. What is the round-trip distance in scientific notation?

- Ⓐ 3.1×10^{-8} mi
- Ⓒ 3.1×10^{8} mi
- Ⓑ 3.1×10^{7} mi
- Ⓓ 3.1×10^{9} mi

2. A copy center charges $.09 per copy for the first 100 copies and $.07 per copy for the next 100 copies. There is also a sales tax of 5% of the total order. How much will an order of 150 copies cost?

- Ⓕ $13.13
- Ⓗ $14.70
- Ⓖ $14.18
- Ⓘ $18.19

3. Manuela can type about 150 words in 4 minutes. At this rate, about how long will she take to type 2000 words?

- Ⓐ 10 minutes
- Ⓒ 75 minutes
- Ⓑ 50 minutes
- Ⓓ 750 minutes

Answers

Cumulative Test Prep

A. vertex

B. parallel

C. domain

D. proportion

E. quadratic

1. C

2. F

3. B

4. Which inequality represents the graph at the right?

    Ⓕ $2x - 3y < -4$

    Ⓖ $2x - 3y > -4$

    Ⓗ $3x - 2y < 4$

    Ⓘ $3x - 2y > 4$

5. What is an equation of the line at the right?

    Ⓐ $2x - y = 6$

    Ⓑ $x - 2y = 12$

    Ⓒ $2x + y = 3$

    Ⓓ $x + 2y = 6$

6. Which expression is equivalent to $(m^4n^{-1})(mp^2)(np^{-6})$?

    Ⓕ m^5p^{-4} Ⓗ m^3np^4

    Ⓖ m^5np^{-4} Ⓘ m^4np^{-12}

7. How would the graph of the function $y = x^2 - 5$ change if the function became $y = x^2 + 2$?

    Ⓐ The graph would shift 2 units down.

    Ⓑ The graph would shift 3 units up.

    Ⓒ The graph would shift 7 units up.

    Ⓓ The graph would shift 10 units down.

8. Let set A be the set containing 0 and all positive numbers. Let the universe U be the set of all real numbers. What is A'?

    Ⓕ {all real numbers}   Ⓗ {all positive numbers}

    Ⓖ {0}   Ⓘ {all negative numbers}

9. What are the solutions of $2x^2 - 11x + 5 = 0$?

    Ⓐ 2, 5   Ⓒ 0.5, 5

    Ⓑ −5, −0.5   Ⓓ −5, −2

10. What is the range of the function $y = |x|$?

    Ⓕ $y \geq 0$ Ⓗ all real numbers

    Ⓖ $y \leq 0$ Ⓘ $y = 0$

11. The area of a rectangle is $3n^2 + 10n + 3$. If the expression $n + 3$ represents the width, which expression represents the length?

    Ⓐ $3n + 1$ Ⓒ $3n^2 + 10$

    Ⓑ $3n + 10$ Ⓓ $3n^2 + 9$

12. Keisha's grandmother gave her a doll that she paid $6 for 60 years ago. The doll's current value is $96. Its value doubles every 15 years. What will the doll be worth in 60 years?

    Ⓕ $570   Ⓗ $1536

    Ⓖ $768   Ⓘ $3072

13. Rick's car holds 16 gal of gasoline. When he pulled into the gas station, he had less than half of a tank of gasoline. Gasoline costs $3.85 per gallon. Which is a reasonable amount that Rick paid to fill his tank?

    Ⓐ $19.25   Ⓒ $33.89

    Ⓑ $27.38   Ⓓ $69.30

14. Which expression is equivalent to $\left(\dfrac{x^4y^{-2}}{z^3}\right)^{-3}$?

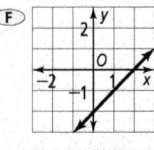   Ⓕ $\dfrac{y^6z^3}{x^{12}}$ 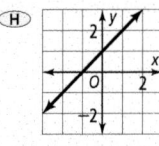 Ⓗ $\dfrac{y^6z^9}{x^{12}}$

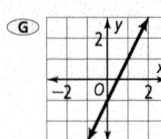   Ⓖ $\dfrac{y^6}{x^{12}z^9}$ 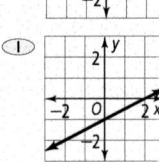 Ⓘ $\dfrac{y^6}{x^{12}z^3}$

15. The table shows the number of volunteers v needed based on the number of children c who will go on a field trip. Which equation best represents the relationship between the number of volunteers and the number of children?

c	v
20	6
25	7
30	8
35	9

    Ⓐ $v = 0.25c + 10$ Ⓒ $v = 0.2c + 2$

    Ⓑ $v = 5c - 10$ Ⓓ $v = 4c + 2$

16. Which graph shows a line that is parallel to the line with equation $4x - 8y = 10$?

    Ⓕ   Ⓗ

    Ⓖ   Ⓘ

4. F

5. A

6. F

7. C

8. I

9. C

10. F

11. A

12. H

13. C

14. H

15. C

16. I

Answers

Cumulative Test Prep (continued)

17. C

18. G

19. 432

20. 5

21. 3.6

22. 32

23. $\frac{3}{5}$

24. 0

25. 85

26. [2] Sometimes; $x^2 + 6x + 9 = 0$ has only one solution. $x^2 - 2x - 15 = 0$ has two solutions.

[1] Sometimes; student only gives one example.

27. [2] Slope must $= -\frac{1}{4}$. Using point-slope form, an equation is $y + 1 = -0.25(x - 8)$.

[1] appropriate methods but with one computational error

28. [4] **a.**

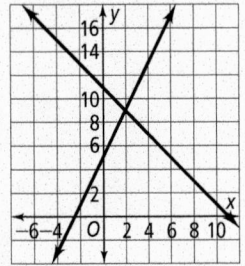

b. (2, 9)

[3] appropriate methods but with one computational error

[2] Either the graph or the point of intersection is given but not both.

[1] incomplete answer with computational errors

---

17. The difference of Ann's and Jay's heights is half of Jay's height. Which equation represents Ann's height a in terms of Jay's height j?

 Ⓐ $a = \frac{1}{2}j - j$ Ⓒ $a = \frac{1}{2}j + j$

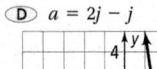 Ⓑ $a = j - \frac{1}{2}j$ Ⓓ $a = 2j - j$

18. The graphs of
$y = -7x + 12$ and
$y = -\frac{2}{3}x - \frac{2}{3}$ are shown.
Which region describes
the solutions of the
system of inequalities
$y \leq -7x + 12$ and
$y \leq -\frac{2}{3}x - \frac{2}{3}$?

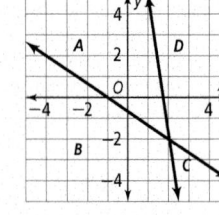

Ⓕ Region A   Ⓗ Region C
Ⓖ Region B   Ⓘ Region D

GRIDDED RESPONSE

Record your answers in a grid.

19. Alan is tiling a 6 ft-by-8 ft rectangular floor with square tiles that measure 4 in. on each side. How many tiles does Alan need to cover the floor?

20. A library is having a used book sale. All hardcover books have the same price and all softcover books have the same price. You buy 4 hardcover books and 2 softcover books for $24. Your friend buys 3 hardcover books and 3 softcover books for $21. What is the cost in dollars of a hardcover book?

21. The two triangles below are similar.

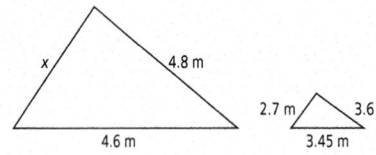

What is the length, in meters, of the side labeled x?

---

22. A soup company sells chicken broth in a container shaped like a rectangular prism. The container is 3.5 in. long, 2.5 in. wide, and 6.5 in. high. One cubic inch of broth weighs about 0.56 oz. To the nearest whole number, how many ounces does the container hold?

23. Anne surveyed 50 people at a movie theater to see whether they liked action or drama films. Her results are shown in the Venn diagram below.

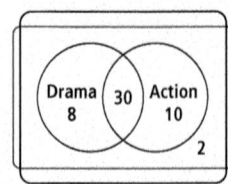

What fraction of the people surveyed liked both action and drama films? Write your answer in lowest terms.

24. How many real-number solutions does the quadratic equation $2x^2 + 7x + 9 = 0$ have?

25. A right circular cylinder has a diameter of 6 in. You pour water into the cylinder until the water level reaches 3 in. What is the volume, in cubic inches, of the water? Use 3.14 for π. Round your answer to the nearest cubic inch.

Short Response

26. Terry says that a quadratic equation has two real solutions. Is this statement *always*, *sometimes*, or *never* true? Give two examples to support your answer.

27. An equation of line p is $y = 4x - 3$. Line n is perpendicular to line p and contains the point $(8, -1)$. What is an equation of line n? Show your work.

Extended Response

28. A system of equations is shown below.
$$y = 2x + 5$$
$$y = -x + 11$$
a. Graph the equations in the same coordinate plane.
b. What is the point of intersection of the two graphs?

Get Ready!

  Solving Proportions

Solve each proportion.

1. $\frac{2}{3} = \frac{x}{15}$ **2.** $\frac{3}{a} = \frac{1}{6}$ **3.** $\frac{4}{3} = \frac{6}{m}$

  Estimating Square Roots

Estimate the square root. Round to the nearest integer.

4. $\sqrt{61}$ **5.** $\sqrt{94}$ **6.** $\sqrt{15}$ **7.** $\sqrt{148}$ **8.** $\sqrt{197}$

  Multiplying Binomials

Simplify each product.

9. $(2h + 3)(4 - h)$ **10.** $(3b^2 + 7)(3b^2 - 7)$ **11.** $(5x + 2)(-3x - 1)$

  Quadratic Graphs

Graph each function.

12. $y = 3x^2$ **13.** $y = x^2 + 4$ **14.** $y = 2x^2 + 3$

  The Quadratic Formula and the Discriminant

Find the number of real-number solutions of each equation.

15. $x^2 + 6x + 1 = 0$ **16.** $x^2 - 5x - 6 = 0$ **17.** $x^2 - 2x + 9 = 0$

18. $4x^2 - 4x = -1$ **19.** $6x^2 + 5x - 2 = -3$ **20.** $(2x - 5)^2 = 121$

Looking Ahead Vocabulary

21. Things are *alike* if part of them is the same. Why would $2\sqrt{3}$ and $6\sqrt{3}$ be *like radicals*?

22. The *conclusion* is the end of a book. Which part is the *conclusion* of the statement, "If I had a lot of money, I would be rich"?

Get Ready!

Assign this diagnostic assessment to determine if students have the prerequisite skills for Chapter 10.

Lesson	Skill
2-7	Solving Proportions
1-3	Estimating Square Roots
8-3	Multiplying Binomials
9-1	Quadratic Graphs
9-6	The Quadratic Formula and the Discriminant

To remediate students, select from these resources (available for every lesson).
- Online Problems (PowerAlgebra.com)
- Reteaching (All-in-One Teaching Resources)
- Practice (All-in-One Teaching Resources)

Why Students Need These Skills

SOLVING PROPORTIONS
Students will use proportions with trigonometry ratios to find missing measures in right triangles.

ESTIMATING SQUARE ROOTS
Students will estimate the value of a square root to find the length of the legs and hypotenuse of a right triangle.

MULTIPLYING BINOMIALS
Students will simplify radicals and perform operations with radical expressions.

QUADRATIC GRAPHS
Students will graph square root functions.

THE QUADRATIC FORMULA AND THE DISCRIMINANT
Students will simplify equations containing radicals.

Looking Ahead Vocabulary

LIKE RADICALS Ask students to give examples of items that are *alike*.

CONCLUSION Give students two statements. Have them draw a conclusion based on the statements.

Answers

Get Ready!

1. 10   **2.** 18   **3.** 4.5

4. 8   **5.** 10   **6.** 4

7. 12   **8.** 14

9. $-2h^2 + 5h + 12$

10. $9b^4 - 49$

11. $-15x^2 - 11x - 2$

12. 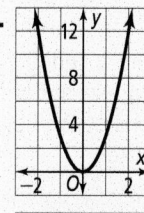   **13.**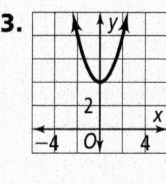

14.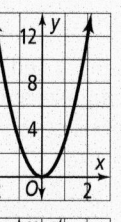

15. 2   **16.** 2   **17.** 0

18. 1   **19.** 2   **20.** 2

21. They both contain the same radical expression, $\sqrt{3}$.

22. I would be rich.

Chapter 10 Overview

UbD **Understanding by Design**

Chapter 10 introduces concepts related to the square root operation. In this chapter, students will develop the answers to the Essential Questions posed on the opposite page as they learn the concepts and skills listed below.

BIG idea **Equivalence**

ESSENTIAL QUESTION How are radical expressions represented?

- Students will add, subtract, multiply, and divide with radicals.
- Students will rationalize the denominators of radical expressions.

BIG idea **Functions**

ESSENTIAL QUESTION What are the characteristics of square root functions?

- Students will draw graphs to examine square root functions.
- Students will estimate values of square roots.

BIG idea **Solving Equations and Inequalities**

ESSENTIAL QUESTION How can you solve a radical equation?

- Students will use inverse operations, such as squaring both sides of an equation that has a square root.

CHAPTER 10

Radical Expressions and Equations

PowerAlgebra.com

Your place to get all things digital

VIDEO
Download videos connecting math to your world.

VOCABULARY
Math definitions in English and Spanish

SOLVE IT!
The online Solve It will get you in gear for each lesson.

DYNAMIC ACTIVITIES
Interactive! Vary numbers, graphs, and figures to explore math concepts.

ONLINE PROBLEMS
Download Step-by-Step Problems with Instant Replay.

ONLINE HOMEWORK
Get and view your assignments online.

MathXL FOR SCHOOL
Extra practice and review online

Chameleons like this one can curl their tails and use them to grab things. The spiral shape of their tails appears in other living things, too, like ferns and seashells. Many of these spirals are related to a shape called the golden rectangle. In this chapter, you'll learn about the golden rectangle and the radical expressions it involves.

Vocabulary

English/Spanish Vocabulary Audio Online:

English	Spanish
conditional, *p. 601*	condicional
conjugates, *p. 615*	valores conjugados
extraneous solution, *p. 622*	solución extraña
hypotenuse, *p. 600*	hipotenusa
like radicals, *p. 613*	radicales semejantes
Pythagorean Theorem, *p. 600*	Teorema de Pitágoras
radical expression, *p. 606*	expresión radical
square root function, *p. 626*	función de raíz cuadrada
trigonometric ratios, *p. 633*	razones trigonométricas

PowerAlgebra.com

Chapter 10 Overview

Use these online assets to engage your students. There is support for the Solve It and step-by-step solutions for Problems.

 Show the student-produced video demonstrating relevant and engaging applications of the new concepts in the chapter.

 Find online definitions for new terms in English and Spanish.

 Start each lesson with an attention-getting Problem. View the Problem online with helpful hints.

BIG ideas

1 **Equivalence**
Essential Question How are radical expressions represented?

2 **Functions**
Essential Question What are the characteristics of square root functions?

3 **Solving Equations and Inequalities**
Essential Question How can you solve a radical equation?

Chapter Preview

10-1 **The Pythagorean Theorem**
10-2 **Simplifying Radicals**
10-3 **Operations With Radical Expressions**
10-4 **Solving Radical Equations**
10-5 **Graphing Square Root Functions**
10-6 **Trigonometric Ratios**

 Increase students' depth of knowledge with interactive online activities.

 Show Problems from each lesson solved step by step. Instant replay allows students to go at their own pace when studying online.

 Assign homework to individual students or to an entire class.

 Prepare students for the Mid-Chapter Quiz and Chapter Test with online practice and review.

My Math Video

FACILITATE Use this photo to discuss the golden ratio and how it relates to spirals. The chameleon's tail forms a spiral where the ratio of the length of a spiral to its width is equal to the golden ratio or $\frac{1 + \sqrt{5}}{2}$.

Q What do you notice about the tail of the chameleon? **[It forms a spiral.]**

Q Where else in nature have you seen spirals like this? **[Answers may vary. Samples: shells, fern leaves, hurricanes]**

Q Do you think the spirals that occur naturally have anything in common? **[Answers may vary. Sample: Yes, the spirals seem to have similar shapes.]**

Q How can you confirm your conjecture? **[Measure and compare the ratios of lengths and widths in the spirals.]**

EXTENSION

The golden ratio, $\frac{1 + \sqrt{5}}{2}$, is often present in the human body. Have students take measurements of various parts of their body and compare them. Challenge students to find at least three proportions that are approximately equal to the golden ratio. Some examples are: total height to height to finger tips, forearm to hand length, navel to knee and knee to foot length, first two finger section to entire finger length, etc.

RADICAL EXPRESSIONS AND EQUATIONS
Math Background

UbD

Equivalence

BIG idea A single quantity may be represented by many different expressions. The facts about a quantity may be expressed by many different equations (or inequalities).

ESSENTIAL UNDERSTANDINGS

10-2 to 10-3 Operations can be performed with radical expressions and radical expressions can be simplified using the multiplication and division properties of square roots.

Functions

BIG idea A function is a relationship between variables in which each value of the input variable is associated with a unique value of the output variable. Functions can be represented in a variety of ways, such as graphs, tables, equations, or words. Each representation is particularly useful in certain situations. Some important families of functions are developed through transformations of the simplest form of the function.

ESSENTIAL UNDERSTANDINGS

10-5 Square root functions can be graphed by plotting points or using translations of the parent square root function.

10-6 Sine, cosine, and tangent ratios can be used to find the measurements of sides or angles of right triangles.

Solving Equations and Inequalities

BIG idea Solving an equation is the process of rewriting the equation to make what it says about its variable(s) as simple as possible. Properties of numbers and equality can be used to transform an equation (or inequality) into equivalent, simpler equations (or inequalities) in order to find solutions. Useful information about equations and inequalities (including solutions) can be found by analyzing graphs or tables. The numbers and types of solutions vary predictably, based on the type of equation.

ESSENTIAL UNDERSTANDING

10-4 Some radical equations can be solved by squaring both sides and testing the solutions.

Operations With Radicals

Consider the following two unlike radicals under the four basic operations: $\sqrt{2}, \sqrt{3}$.

Addition

$\sqrt{2} + \sqrt{3}$ These are not like radicals, so they cannot be added under radical signs.

Subtraction

$\sqrt{2} - \sqrt{3}$ Because these are not like radicals, they cannot be subtracted under radical signs.

Multiplication

$\sqrt{2} \cdot \sqrt{3}$ Unlike radicals can be multiplied under radical signs.

$$\sqrt{2} \cdot \sqrt{3} = \sqrt{2 \cdot 3} = \sqrt{6}$$

Division

$\dfrac{\sqrt{2}}{\sqrt{3}}$ Unlike radicals can be divided under radical signs. Manipulate the expression by multiplying it by an expression equivalent to 1 so that there is not a radical in the denominator.

$$\frac{\sqrt{2}}{\sqrt{3}} \cdot \frac{\sqrt{3}}{\sqrt{3}} = \frac{\sqrt{2} \cdot \sqrt{3}}{\sqrt{3} \cdot \sqrt{3}} = \frac{\sqrt{2 \cdot 3}}{\sqrt{3 \cdot 3}} = \frac{\sqrt{6}}{\sqrt{9}} = \frac{\sqrt{6}}{3}$$

Common Errors With Operations With Radicals

Students might try to add radicals in a similar manner as radicals can be multiplied.

Multiplication: $\sqrt{2} \cdot \sqrt{3} = \sqrt{2 \cdot 3} = \sqrt{6}$ Correct

Addition: $\sqrt{2} + \sqrt{3} = \sqrt{2 + 3} = \sqrt{5}$ Incorrect

Unlike radicals cannot be added under radical signs.

Radical Equations

A radical equation is an equation that has a radical expression with a variable in the radicand.

$4 + \sqrt{x} = 6$ Radical Equation

$\sqrt{4 + x} = 6$ Radical Equation

$\sqrt{4} + x = 6$ Not a Radical Equation

To solve a radical equation, the radical is isolated on one side of the equation. Then both sides are squared.

$$4 + \sqrt{x} = 6$$
$$4 + \sqrt{x} - 4 = 6 - 4 \quad \text{Subtract 4 from both sides.}$$
$$\sqrt{x} = 2$$
$$\left(\sqrt{x}\right)^2 = 2^2 \quad \text{Square both sides.}$$
$$x = 4$$

Common Errors With Radical Equations

Sometimes when solving radical equations, squaring both sides of an equation results in extraneous solutions.

$$x = \sqrt{10 - 3x}$$
$$x^2 = \left(\sqrt{10 - 3x}\right)^2$$
$$x^2 = 10 - 3x$$
$$x^2 + 3x - 10 = 0$$
$$(x + 5)(x - 2) = 0$$
$$x = -5 \text{ or } 2$$

In situations like this it is especially important to check the solutions in the original equation.

$-5 = \sqrt{10 - 3(-5)}$	$2 = \sqrt{10 - 3(2)}$
$-5 = \sqrt{25}$	$2 = \sqrt{4}$
$-5 = 5$	$2 = 2$
Incorrect	Correct

Students might incorrectly indicate that both -5 and 2 are solutions.

Trigonometric Ratios

The side lengths of a right triangle can be used to make ratios. The ratios $\frac{a}{c}$, $\frac{b}{c}$, and $\frac{a}{b}$ correspond to three trigonometric ratios with respect to $\angle A$.

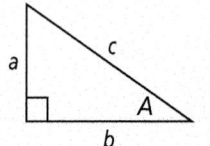

$$\sin A = \frac{a}{c} = \frac{\text{opposite}}{\text{hypotenuse}}$$
$$\cos A = \frac{b}{c} = \frac{\text{adjacent}}{\text{hypotenuse}}$$
$$\tan A = \frac{a}{b} = \frac{\text{opposite}}{\text{adjacent}}$$

Trigonometric ratios provide the tools needed to find missing right triangle measurements when certain combinations of side lengths and angle measures are known.

Case 1: $A = 27°$, $a = 9$

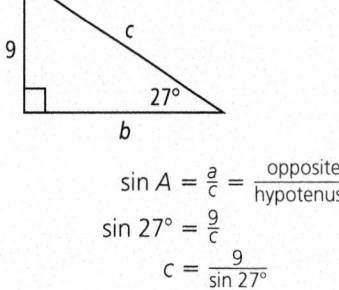

$$\sin A = \frac{a}{c} = \frac{\text{opposite}}{\text{hypotenuse}}$$
$$\sin 27° = \frac{9}{c}$$
$$c = \frac{9}{\sin 27°}$$
$$c \approx 19.8$$

Case 2: $b = 2$, $c = 6$

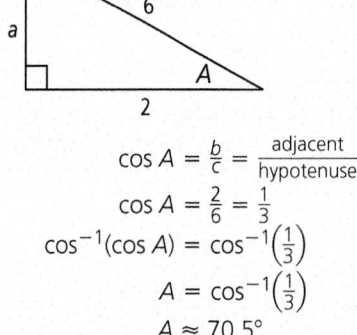

$$\cos A = \frac{b}{c} = \frac{\text{adjacent}}{\text{hypotenuse}}$$
$$\cos A = \frac{2}{6} = \frac{1}{3}$$
$$\cos^{-1}(\cos A) = \cos^{-1}\left(\frac{1}{3}\right)$$
$$A = \cos^{-1}\left(\frac{1}{3}\right)$$
$$A \approx 70.5°$$

Common Errors With Trigonometric Ratios

When working with trigonometric ratios it is important to know if the calculator is in degree or radian mode.

A calculator in degree mode computes $\sin 45° = 0.707$.

A calculator in radian mode computes $\sin 45° = 0.851$.

If students seem to be doing the problem correctly but getting the wrong answer, have them check that their calculator is in the right mode.

CHAPTER 10

RADICAL EXPRESSIONS AND EQUATIONS
Pacing and Assignment Guide

		TRADITIONAL			BLOCK
Lesson	**Teaching Day(s)**	**Basic**	**Average**	**Advanced**	**Block**
10-1	1	Problems 1-3 Exs. 6–28 all, 30–34 even, 36, 38, 43–54	Problems 1-3 Exs. 7–27 odd, 29–40, 43–54	Problems 1-3 Exs. 7–27 odd, 29–54	**Day 1** Problems 1-3 Exs. 7–27 odd, 29–40, 43–54
10-2	1	Problems 1-3 Exs. 10–33 all, 79–91	Problems 1-3 Exs. 11–47 odd, 79–91	Problems 1-3 Exs. 11–47 odd, 74–76, 79–91	Problems 1-3 Exs. 11–47 odd, 79–91
	2	Problems 4-6 Exs. 32–49 all, 50–68 even	Problems 4-6 Exs. 11–47 odd, 48–73	Problems 4-6 Exs. 11–47 odd, 48–73, 77–78	**Day 2** Problems 4-6 Exs. 11–47 odd, 48–73
10-3	1	Problems 1-3 Exs. 9–29 all, 64–81	Problems 1-3 Exs. 9–29 odd, 64–81	Problems 1-3 Exs. 9–37 odd, 64–81	Problems 1-3 Exs. 9–29 odd, 64–81
	2	Problems 4-5 Exs. 30–37 all, 38–58 even	Problems 4-5 Exs. 31–37 odd, 38–60	Problems 4-5 Exs. 9–37 odd, 38–63	**Day 3** Problems 4-5 Exs. 31–37 odd, 38–60
10-4	1	Problems 1-3 Exs. 7–24 all, 40, 53–65	Problems 1-3 Exs. 7–23 odd, 39–40, 53–65	Problems 1-3 Exs. 7–23 odd, 39–40, 51, 53–65	Problems 1-3 Exs. 7–23 odd, 39–40, 53–65
	2	Problems 4-5 Exs. 25–38 all, 44–48 even	Problems 4-5 Exs. 25–35 odd, 37–38, 41–50	Problems 4-5 Exs. 25–35 odd, 37–38, 41–50, 52	**Day 4** Problems 4-5 Exs. 25–35 odd, 37–38, 41–50
10-5	1	Problems 1-4 Exs. 7–38 all, 41–43 all, 44–54 even, 64–83	Problems 1-4 Exs. 7–37 odd, 39–60, 64–83	Problems 1-4 Exs. 7–37 odd, 39–83	Problems 1-4 Exs. 7–37 odd, 39–60, 64–83
10-6	1	Problems 1-4 Exs. 8–33 all, 37, 38–44 even	Problems 1-4 Exs. 9–33 odd	Problems 1-4 Exs. 9–33 odd	**Day 5** Problems 1-5 Exs. 9–35 odd, 36–44, 48–61
	2	Problem 5 Exs. 34–35, 37, 38–44 even, 48–61	Problem 5 Exs. 35–44, 48–61	Problem 5 Exs. 35–61	
Review	1	Chapter 10 Review	Chapter 10 Review	Chapter 10 Review	**Day 6** Chapter 10 Review
Assess	1	Chapter 10 Test	Chapter 10 Test	Chapter 10 Test	Chapter 10 Test
Total		**12 Days**	**12 Days**	**12 Days**	**6 Days**

Note: Pacing does not include Concept Bytes and other feature pages.

Resources

	For the Chapter	10-1	10-2	10-3	10-4	10-5	10-6
Planning							
Teacher Center Online Planner & Grade Book	I	I	I	I	I	I	I
Interactive Learning & Guided Instruction							
My Math Video	I						
Solve It!		I TM	I TM	I TM	I TM	I TM	I TM
Student Companion (SP)*		P M	P M	P M	P M	P M	
Vocabulary Support		I P M	I P M	I P M	I P M	I P M	I P M
Got It? Support		I P	I P	I P	I P	I P	I P
Dynamic Activity		I		I		I	
Online Problems		I	I	I	I	I	I
Additional Problems		M	M	M	M	M	M
English Language Learner Support (TR)		E P M	E P M	E P M	E P M	E P M	E P M
Activities, Games, and Puzzles		E M	E M	E M	E M	E M	E M
Teaching With TI Technology With CD-ROM					✓ P		
TI-Nspire™ Support CD-ROM		✓	✓	✓	✓	✓	✓
Lesson Check & Practice							
Student Companion (SP)*		P M	P M	P M	P M	P M	P M
Lesson Check Support		I P	I P	I P	I P	I P	I P
Practice and Problem Solving Workbook (SP)		P	P	P	P	P	P
Think About a Plan (TR)*		E P M	E P M	E P M	E P M	E P M	E P M
Practice Form G (TR)*		E P M	E P M	E P M	E P M	E P M	E P M
Standardized Test Prep (TR)*		P M	P M	P M	P M	P M	P M
Practice *Form K* (TR)*		E P M	E P M	E P M	E P M	E P M	E P M
Extra Practice	E M						
Find the Errors!	M						
Enrichment (TR)		E P M	E P M	E P M	E P M	E P M	E P M
Answers and Solutions CD-ROM	✓	✓	✓	✓	✓	✓	✓
Assess & Remediate							
ExamView CD-ROM	✓	✓	✓	✓	✓	✓	✓
Lesson Quiz		I TM	I TM	I TM	I TM	I TM	I TM
Quizzes and Tests *Form G* (TR)*	E P M				E P M		E P M
Quizzes and Tests *Form K* (TR)*	E P M				E P M		E P M
Reteaching (TR)*		E P M	E P M	E P M	E P M	E P M	E P M
Performance Tasks (TR)*	P M						
Cumulative Review (TR)*	P M						
Progress Monitoring Assessments	I P M						

(TR) Available in All-In-One Teaching Resources   *Spanish available

1 Interactive Learning

Solve It!

PURPOSE To determine the relationship among the squares of the sides of a right triangle

PROCESS Students may
- use the formula for the area of a square.
- use trial and error to write an equation.

FACILITATE

Q How do you determine the area of a square? **[You square the length of a side.]**

Q Which side length is opposite the right angle? **[Lot C (130 ft)]**

Q Which side lengths are adjacent to the right angle? **[Lot A (120 ft) and Lot B (50 ft)]**

Q What is the sum of the areas of Lot A and Lot B? **[16,900 ft²]**

ANSWER See Solve It in Answers on next page.

CONNECT THE MATH In the Solve It, students explore a special relationship among the side lengths of a right triangle. In the lesson, students learn that this relationship, the Pythagorean Theorem, is true for all right triangles.

2 Guided Instruction

Take Note

Q Use properties of real numbers to change the form of the Pythagorean Theorem so that it is solved for a^2 and then for b^2. What is the result?
$[b^2 = c^2 - a^2, a^2 = c^2 - b^2]$

10-1 The Pythagorean Theorem

Objectives To solve problems using the Pythagorean Theorem
To identify right triangles

Getting Ready!

The diagram shows three square house lots that border a pond shaped like a right triangle. What is the area of each house lot? Can you write an equation to relate all three areas? Explain.

This is almost like an optical illusion. What do you see, three squares or three sides of a triangle?

Lesson Vocabulary
- hypotenuse
- leg
- Pythagorean Theorem
- conditional
- hypothesis
- conclusion
- converse

There are special names for the sides of a right triangle like the one in the Solve It. The side opposite the right angle is the **hypotenuse.** It is the longest side. Each of the sides forming the right angle is a **leg.** The **Pythagorean Theorem,** named after the Greek mathematician Pythagoras, relates the lengths of the legs and the length of the hypotenuse.

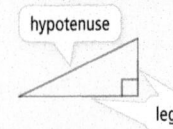

Essential Understanding The lengths of the sides of a right triangle have a special relationship. If you know the lengths of any two of the sides, you can find the length of the third side.

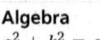

Theorem   The Pythagorean Theorem

Words
In any right triangle, the sum of the squares of the lengths of the legs is equal to the square of the length of the hypotenuse.

Diagram

Algebra
$a^2 + b^2 = c^2$

BIG idea Equivalence   **UbD**

ESSENTIAL UNDERSTANDINGS
- The lengths of the sides of a right triangle have a special relationship.
- If the lengths of any two sides of a right triangle are known, the length of the third side can be found.
- If the length of each side of a triangle is known, then whether the triangle is a right triangle can be determined.

Math Background

The Pythagorean Theorem was one of the first theorems used by mathematicians in ancient civilizations. Although named after and credited to the Greek mathematician Pythagoras, the theorem actually dates back to a millennium earlier, when it was first used by the Babylonians. The Pythagorean Theorem first introduced the conundrum of irrational numbers to Pythagoras and his followers. Up to this point in mathematical history, there

was a firm belief that all numbers were rational.

For most students the Pythagorean Theorem will be the first theorem that they memorize and the one they remember as they progress through the study of mathematics. Students should become comfortable with its versatility. The theorem is useful for finding:
- the length of the hypotenuse, given the length of the two legs.
- the length of a leg, given the length of one leg and the length of the hypotenuse.
- if three lengths can form a right triangle.

Support Student Learning

Use the **Algebra 1 Companion** to engage and support students during instructions. See Lesson Resources at the end of this lesson for details.

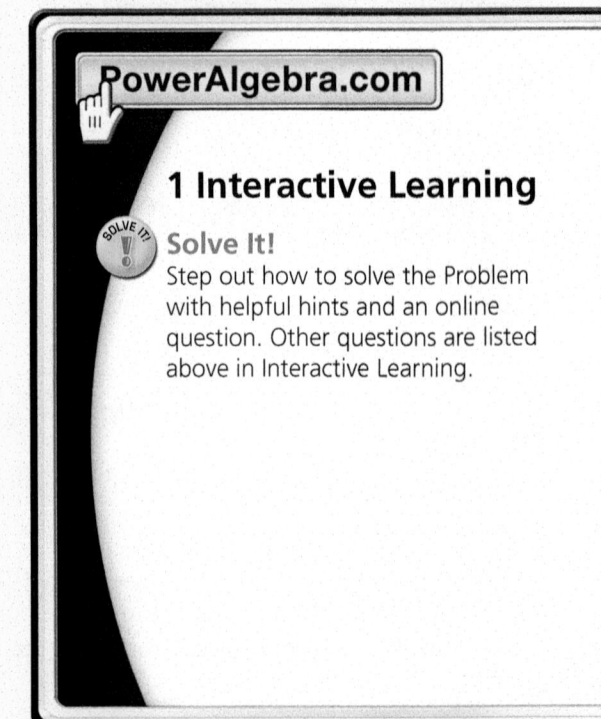

PowerAlgebra.com

1 Interactive Learning

Solve It!
Step out how to solve the Problem with helpful hints and an online question. Other questions are listed above in Interactive Learning.

You can use the Pythagorean Theorem to find the length of a right triangle's hypotenuse given the lengths of its legs. Using the Pythagorean Theorem to solve for a side length involves finding a principal square root, because side lengths are always positive.

 Problem 1 Finding the Length of a Hypotenuse

The tiles at the right are squares with 6-in. sides. What is the length of the hypotenuse of the right triangle shown?

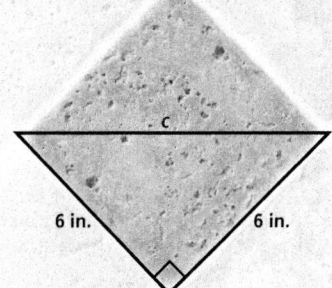

$$a^2 + b^2 = c^2 \quad \text{Pythagorean Theorem}$$
$$6^2 + 6^2 = c^2 \quad \text{Substitute 6 for } a \text{ and } b.$$
$$72 = c^2 \quad \text{Simplify.}$$
$$\sqrt{72} = c \quad \text{Find the principal square root.}$$
$$8.5 \approx c \quad \text{Use a calculator.}$$

The length of the hypotenuse is about 8.5 in.

6 in.   6 in.

Got It? 1. What is the length of the hypotenuse of a right triangle with legs of lengths 9 cm and 12 cm?

You can also use the Pythagorean Theorem to find the length of a leg of a right triangle.

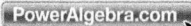 **Problem 2** Finding the Length of a Leg

What is the side length b in the triangle at the right?

$$a^2 + b^2 = c^2 \quad \text{Pythagorean Theorem}$$
$$5^2 + b^2 = 13^2 \quad \text{Substitute 5 for } a \text{ and 13 for } c.$$
$$25 + b^2 = 169 \quad \text{Simplify.}$$
$$b^2 = 144 \quad \text{Subtract 25 from each side.}$$
$$b = 12 \quad \text{Find the principal square root of each side.}$$

The side length b is 12 cm.

13 cm
5 cm
b

15   12
a

Got It? 2. What is the side length a in the triangle at the right?

An *if-then* statement such as "If an animal is a horse, then it has four legs" is called a **conditional.** Conditionals have two parts. The part following *if* is the **hypothesis.** The part following *then* is the **conclusion.**

Problem 1

Q What other special name can be given to the triangle in the diagram? Explain. **[It is an isosceles triangle; the lengths of the legs are equal.]**

Q Why is only the principal square root found when solving the equation $c^2 = 72$? **[$-\sqrt{72}$ does not make sense in the problem.]**

Q If you square 8.5, would the answer be 72? Explain. **[No; 8.5 is an approximation of $\sqrt{72}$.]**

Got It?

Q To find the length of the hypotenuse, what two perfect squares must you add together? **[81 and 144]**

Q Is the length you find for the hypotenuse an exact answer or an approximation? Explain. **[Exact; 225 is a perfect square.]**

Problem 2

Q What are the lengths of the legs of the right triangle? **[5 cm, b cm]**

Q What is the length of the hypotenuse? **[13 cm]**

Q If you substitute 5 for b and b for a into the Pythagorean Theorem, would you arrive at a different answer? Explain. **[No; the operation of addition is commutative.]**

Got It?

Q What is the length of the hypotenuse? **[15 units.]**

Q What are the three equations that can be written for this diagram? **[$15^2 = 12^2 + a^2$, $a^2 = 15^2 - 12^2$, $12^2 = 15^2 - a^2$]**

---

2 Guided Instruction

 Each Problem is worked out and supported online.

Problem 1
Finding the Length of a Hypotenuse
Animated

Problem 2
Finding the Length of a Leg
Animated

Problem 3
Identifying Right Triangles
Animated

Support in Algebra 1 Companion
• Vocabulary
• Key Concepts
• Got It?

Answers

Solve It!
Lot A: 14,400 ft², Lot B: 2500 ft², Lot C: 16,900 ft²; $A^2 + B^2 = C^2$. Explanations may vary.

Got It?
1. 15 cm
2. 9

Problem 3

> **Q** Is the hypotenuse of a right triangle always the longest side? Explain. **[Yes; by definition it must be longer than both of the legs.]**
>
> **Q** What should the hypotenuse be in Choice D (legs are 8 and 15) in order for the triangle to be a right triangle? Explain. **[17 ft, the lengths would satisfy the Converse of the Pythagorean Theorem.]**

Got It?

When answering 3b, students may benefit from using numerical examples to explore whether 2a, 2b, and 2c are also possible side lengths of a right triangle.

3 Lesson Check

Do you know HOW?

• If students have difficulty with Exercises 1-2, then have them explain the differences in the diagrams.

Do you UNDERSTAND?

• If students have difficulty with Exercise 4, then have them identify the hypothesis and conclusion of the original statement.

Close

> **Q** What is the difference between how the Pythagorean Theorem and its converse are used? **[The Pythagorean Theorem is used to determine the length of the third side of a right triangle given two of the sides. The converse is used to determine if three given side lengths form a right triangle.]**

The **converse** of a conditional switches the hypothesis and the conclusion. Sometimes the converse of a true conditional is not true.

You can write the Pythagorean Theorem as a conditional: "If a triangle is a right triangle with legs of lengths a and b and hypotenuse of length c, then $a^2 + b^2 = c^2$." The converse of the Pythagorean Theorem is always true.

 take note

Property   The Converse of the Pythagorean Theorem

If a triangle has sides of lengths a, b, and c, and $a^2 + b^2 = c^2$, then the triangle is a right triangle with hypotenuse of length c.

You can use the Pythagorean Theorem and its converse to determine whether a triangle is a right triangle. If the side lengths satisfy the equation $a^2 + b^2 = c^2$, then the triangle is a right triangle. If they do not, then it is not a right triangle.

Problem 3   Identifying Right Triangles

Multiple Choice Which set of lengths could be the side lengths of a right triangle?

Ⓐ 6 in., 24 in., 25 in.   Ⓑ 4 m, 8 m, 10 m   Ⓒ 10 in., 24 in., 26 in.   Ⓓ 8 ft, 15 ft, 16 ft

Determine whether the lengths satisfy $a^2 + b^2 = c^2$. The greatest length is c.

$6^2 + 24^2 \stackrel{?}{=} 25^2$	$4^2 + 8^2 \stackrel{?}{=} 10^2$	$10^2 + 24^2 \stackrel{?}{=} 26^2$	$8^2 + 15^2 \stackrel{?}{=} 16^2$
$36 + 576 \stackrel{?}{=} 625$	$16 + 64 \stackrel{?}{=} 100$	$100 + 576 \stackrel{?}{=} 676$	$64 + 225 \stackrel{?}{=} 256$
$612 \neq 625$	$80 \neq 100$	$676 = 676$ ✔	$289 \neq 256$

By the Converse of the Pythagorean Theorem, the lengths 10 in., 24 in., and 26 in. could be the side lengths of a right triangle. The correct answer is C.

Plan

Why should you check each answer choice?
If you find two answer choices that appear to be correct, then you know you have made a mistake.

Got It? **3. a.** Could the lengths 20 mm, 47 mm, and 52 mm be the side lengths of a right triangle? Explain.

  b. Reasoning If a, b, and c satisfy the equation $a^2 + b^2 = c^2$, are $2a$, $2b$, and $2c$ also possible side lengths of a right triangle? How do you know?

Lesson Check

Do you know HOW?

Find each missing side length.

1.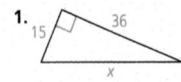

2.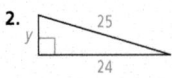

3. Could the lengths 12 cm, 35 cm, and 37 cm be the side lengths of a right triangle? Explain.

Do you UNDERSTAND?

4. Vocabulary What is the converse of the conditional, "If you study math, then you are a student"?

5. Error Analysis A student found the length x in the triangle at the right by solving the equation $12^2 + 13^2 = x^2$. Describe and correct the error.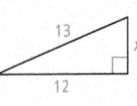

Additional Problems

1. Anita is tiling the backsplash in her kitchen with pieces of tile in the shape of a right triangle. If the sides of the triangle are 3 in. and 7 in., how long is the triangle's hypotenuse?

  ANSWER about 7.6 in.

2. What is the side length b in the triangle below?

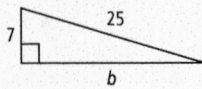

  ANSWER 24

3. Which set of lengths could be the side lengths of a right triangle?

  A. 5 in., 8 in., 10 in.

  B. 9 m, 40 m, 41 m

  C. 5 cm, 12 cm, 17 cm

  D. 8 ft, 14 ft, 17 ft

  ANSWER B

Answers

Got It? (continued)

3. a. no; $20^2 + 47^2 \neq 52^2$

  b. yes; $(2a)^2 + (2b)^2 = 4a^2 + 4b^2 = 4(a^2 + b^2) = 4c^2 = (2c)^2$

Lesson Check

1. 39

2. 7

3. yes; $12^2 + 35^2 = 37^2$

4. If you are a student, then you study math.

5. The value of 13 should be substituted for c since it is the hypotenuse. The correct equation is $12^2 + x^2 = 13^2$; $x = 5$.

Practice and Problem-Solving Exercises

 Practice

Use the triangle at the right. Find the missing side length. If necessary, round to the nearest tenth.

See Problems 1 and 2.

6. $a = 3, b = 4$ **7.** $a = 6, c = 10$ **8.** $b = 1, c = \frac{5}{4}$

9. $a = 5, c = 13$ **10.** $a = 0.3, b = 0.4$ **11.** $a = 8, b = 15$

12. $a = 1, c = \frac{5}{3}$ **13.** $b = 6, c = 7.5$ **14.** $b = 3.5, c = 3.7$

15. $a = 1.1, b = 6$ **16.** $a = 8, c = 17$ **17.** $a = 9, b = 40$

18. $b = 2.4, c = 7.4$ **19.** $a = 4, b = 7.5$ **20.** $a = 0.9, c = 4.1$

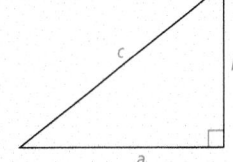

21. **Fitness** A jogger goes half a mile north and then turns west. If the jogger finishes 1.3 mi from the starting point, how far west did the jogger go?

22. **Construction** A construction worker is cutting along the diagonal of a rectangular board 15 ft long and 8 ft wide. What will be the length of the cut?

Determine whether the given lengths can be side lengths of a right triangle.

See Problem 3.

23. 15 ft, 36 ft, 39 ft   **24.** 12 m, 60 m, 61 m   **25.** 13 in., 35 in., 38 in.

26. 16 cm, 63 cm, 65 cm   **27.** 14 in., 48 in., 50 in.   **28.** 16 yd, 30 yd, 34 yd

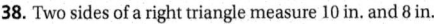 **Apply**

29. **Swimming** A swimmer asks a question to a lifeguard sitting on a tall chair, as shown in the diagram. The swimmer needs to be close to the lifeguard to hear the answer. What is the distance between the swimmer's head and the lifeguard's head?

Any set of three positive integers that satisfies the equation $a^2 + b^2 = c^2$ is a *Pythagorean triple*. Determine whether each set of numbers is a Pythagorean triple.

30. 11, 60, 61   **31.** 13, 84, 85   **32.** 40, 41, 58

33. 50, 120, 130   **34.** 32, 126, 130   **35.** 28, 45, 53

36. **Think About a Plan** A banner shaped like a right triangle has a hypotenuse of length 26 ft and a leg of length 10 ft. What is the area of the banner?
- What information do you need to find the area of a triangle?
- How can you find the length of the other leg?

37. **History** Originally, each face of the Great Pyramid of Giza was a triangle with the dimensions shown. How far was a corner of the base from the pyramid's top? Round to the nearest foot.

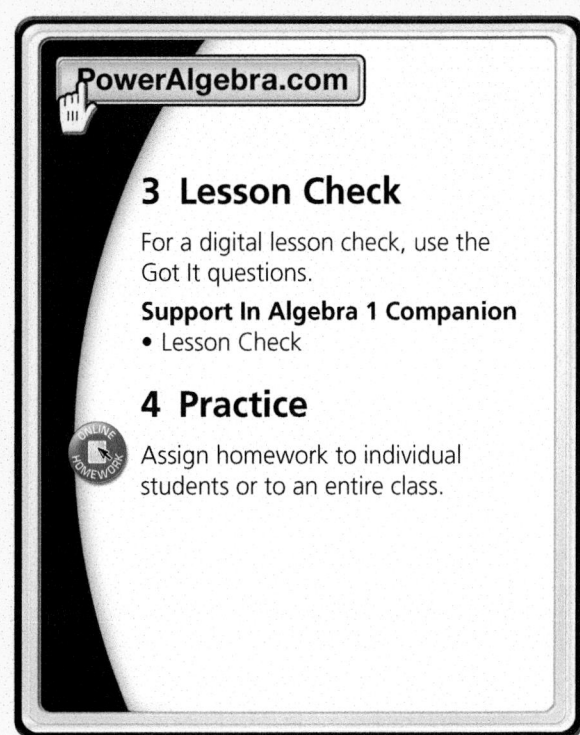

38. Two sides of a right triangle measure 10 in. and 8 in.
- **a.** **Writing** Explain why this is not enough information to be sure of the length of the third side.
- **b.** Give two possible values for the length of the third side.

Practice and Problem-Solving Exercises

6. 5   **7.** 8   **8.** $\frac{3}{4}$

9. 12   **10.** 0.5   **11.** 17

12. $\frac{4}{3}$ **13.** 4.5   **14.** 1.2

15. 6.1   **16.** 15   **17.** 41

18. 7   **19.** 8.5   **20.** 4

21. 1.2 mi   **22.** 17 ft   **23.** yes

24. no   **25.** no   **26.** yes

27. yes   **28.** yes   **29.** 10 ft

30. yes   **31.** yes   **32.** no

33. yes   **34.** yes   **35.** yes

36. 120 ft^2 **37.** 719 ft

38. a. These lengths could be the lengths of two legs or the lengths of one leg and the hypotenuse.

    b. about 12.8 in. or 6 in.

---

4 Practice

ASSIGNMENT GUIDE

Basic: 6–28 all, 30–34 even, 36, 38

Average: 7–27 odd, 29–40

Advanced: 7–27 odd, 29–42

Standardized Test Prep: 43–47

Mixed Review: 48–54

Reasoning exercises have blue headings.

Applications exercises have red headings.

EXERCISE 22: Use the Think About a Plan worksheet in the **Practice and Problem Solving Workbook** (also available in the Teaching Resources in print and online) to further support students' development in becoming independent learners.

HOMEWORK QUICK CHECK

To check students' understanding of key skills and concepts, go over Exercises 7, 22, 24, 26, and 38.

PowerAlgebra.com

3 Lesson Check

For a digital lesson check, use the Got It questions.

Support In Algebra 1 Companion
- Lesson Check

4 Practice

Assign homework to individual students or to an entire class.

Answers

Practice and Problem-Solving Exercises
(continued)

39. Yes; $50^2 + 120^2 = 130^2$, so the triangle formed by the forces is a right triangle.

40. 5.7 cm

41. a. $a^2 + 2ab + b^2$

    b. c^2

    c. $\frac{1}{2}ab$

    d. $a^2 + 2ab + b^2 = 4\left(\frac{1}{2}ab\right) + c^2$; $a^2 + b^2 = c^2$; it is the Pythagorean Theorem.

42. $n^2 + (n + 1)^2 = (n + 2)^2$; 3, 4, 5

43. 300   **44.** 20   **45.** $\frac{1}{2}$

46. 5.4   **47.** 0.275

48. 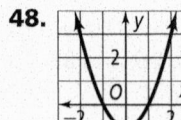   **49.**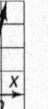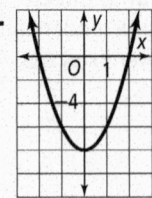

50.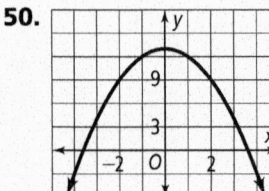

51. $45a^2 - 27a$

52. $12x^3 - 24x^2$ **53.** $16d^3 + 28d^4$

54. $-12m^2 - 6m^4$

---

39. Physics If two forces pull at right angles to each other, the resultant force can be represented by the diagonal of a rectangle, as shown at the right. This diagonal is a hypotenuse of a right triangle. A 50-lb force and a 120-lb force combine for a resultant force of 130 lb. Are the forces pulling at right angles to each other? Explain.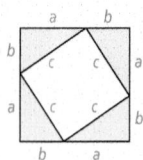

40. A rectangular box is 4 cm wide, 4 cm tall, and 10 cm long. What is the diameter of the smallest circular opening through which the box will fit? Round to the nearest tenth of a centimeter.

 **Challenge**

41. Reasoning Use the diagram at the right.
    a. Find the area of the larger square. Write your answer as a trinomial.
    b. Find the area of the smaller square.
    c. Find the area of each triangle in terms of a and b.
    d. The area of the larger square equals the sum of the area of the smaller square and the areas of the four triangles. Write this equation and simplify. What do you notice?

42. Geometry The lengths of the sides of a right triangle are three consecutive integers. Write and solve an equation to find the three integers.

Standardized Test Prep

GRIDDED RESPONSE

SAT/ACT

43. A park has two walking paths shaped like right triangles. The first path has legs 75 yd and 100 yd long. The second path has legs 50 yd and 240 yd long. What is the total length of the shorter path, in yards?

44. Joe plants a rectangular garden in the corner of his field, as shown. The area of the garden is 60% of the area of the field. What is the longest side length of Joe's field, in feet?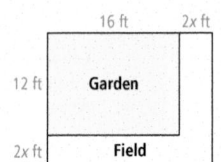

45. What is the slope of the graph of the equation $y = \frac{1}{2}x + 7$?

46. What is the positive solution of the equation $-3.2|t| = -17.28$?

47. A candidate in an election received 72.5% of the vote. What decimal represents the portion of the voters who did NOT vote for the candidate?

Mixed Review

Graph each function.   **See Lesson 9-1.**

48. $y = x^2 - 1$ **49.** $y = 2x^2 - 8$ **50.** $y = -x^2 + 13$

Get Ready! To prepare for Lesson 10-2, do Exercises 51–54.

Simplify each product.   **See Lesson 8-2.**

51. $9a(5a - 3)$ **52.** $4x(3x^2 - 6x)$ **53.** $4d(4d^2 + 7d^3)$ **54.** $(6m + 3m^3)(-2m)$

Additional Instructional Support

Algebra 1 Companion

Students can use the **Algebra 1 Companion** worktext (4 pages) as you teach the lesson. Use the Companion to support

- New Vocabulary
- Key Concepts
- Got It for each Problem
- Lesson Check

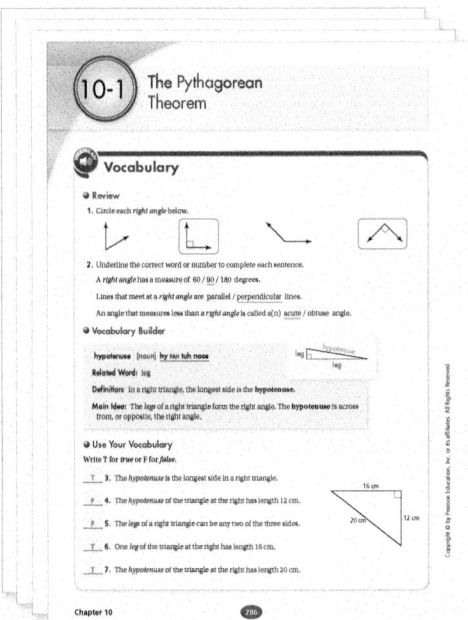

ELL Support

Use Graphic Organizers Have students create a single page organizer to organize the lesson concepts. At the top, have them draw a model of a right triangle. Do the same on the board, tracing the legs and hypotenuse as you say the name and define each part. Write the Pythagorean Theorem under the triangle.

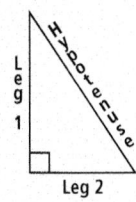

Ask: What is the sum of the angle measures in a triangle? Then draw two lines to two examples: one that asks how to find the hypotenuse and one that asks how to find a missing leg measure. Complete the organizer after the lesson.

5 Assess & Remediate

Lesson Quiz

1. Do you UNDERSTAND? Glen is planting square flower gardens surrounding a triangular fish pond as shown. If the sides of the triangular fish pond are 5 ft and 9 ft, how long is the triangle's hypotenuse?

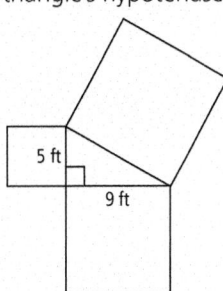

2. What is the side length a in the triangle below?

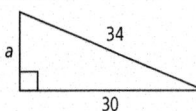

3. Which set of lengths could be the side lengths of a right triangle?
   A. 7 in., 7 in., 10 in.
   B. 10 m, 11 m, 15 m
   C. 8 cm, 10 cm, 13 cm
   D. 4.5 ft, 6 ft, 7.5 ft

ANSWERS TO LESSON QUIZ
   1. about 10.3 ft
   2. 16
   3. D

PRESCRIPTION FOR REMEDIATION
Use the student work on the Lesson Quiz to prescribe a differentiated review assignment.

Points	Differentiated Remediation
0–1	Intervention
2	On-level
3	Extension

PowerAlgebra.com

5 Assess & Remediate
Assign the Lesson Quiz. Appropriate intervention, practice, or enrichment is automatically generated based on student performance.

Intervention

- **Reteaching** (2 pages) Provides reteaching and practice exercises for the key lesson concepts. Use with struggling students or absent students.

- **English Language Learner Support** Helps students develop and reinforce mathematical vocabulary and key concepts.

All-in-One Resources/Online
Reteaching

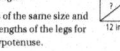

All-in-One Resources/Online
English Language Learner Support

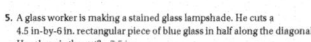

Differentiated Remediation *continued*

On-Level

- **Practice** (2 pages) Provides extra practice for each lesson. For simpler practice exercises, use the Form K Practice pages found in the All-in-One Teaching Resources and online.

- **Think About a Plan** Helps students develop specific problem-solving skills and strategies by providing scaffolded guiding questions.

- **Standardized Test Prep** Focuses on all major exercises, all major question types, and helps students prepare for the high-stakes assessments.

Extension

- **Enrichment** Provides students with interesting problems and activities that extend the concepts of the lesson.

- **Activities, Games, and Puzzles** Worksheets that can be used for concepts development, enrichment, and for fun!

Practice and Problem Solving WKBK/ All-in-One Resources/Online
Practice page 1

Practice and Problem Solving WKBK/ All-in-One Resources/Online
Practice page 2

All-in-One Resources/Online
Enrichment

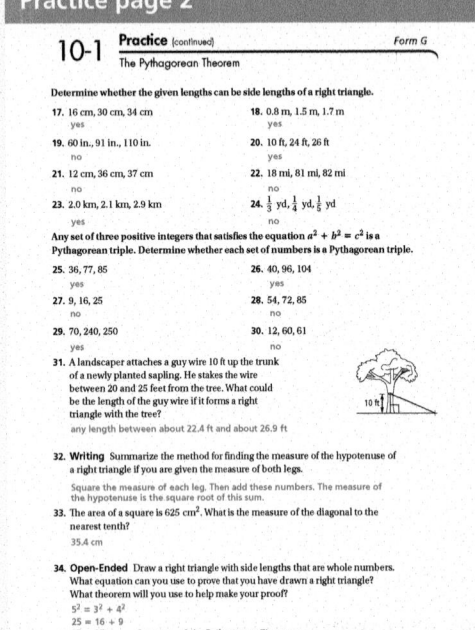

Practice and Problem Solving Wkbk/ All-in-One Resources/Online
Think About a Plan

Practice and Problem Solving Wkbk/ All-in-One Resources/Online
Standardized Test Prep

Online Teacher Resource Center
Activities, Games, and Puzzles

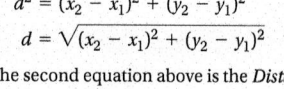

Concept Byte

Use With Lesson 10-1

Distance and Midpoint Formulas

The diagram at the right shows that you can use the Pythagorean Theorem to find the distance d between two points, (x_1, y_1) and (x_2, y_2).

$$d^2 = (x_2 - x_1)^2 + (y_2 - y_1)^2$$
$$d = \sqrt{(x_2 - x_1)^2 + (y_2 - y_1)^2}$$

The second equation above is the *Distance Formula*.

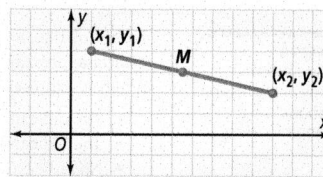

Example 1

What is the distance between points $(1, 1)$ and $(7, 9)$?

Let $(x_1, y_1) = (1, 1)$ and $(x_2, y_2) = (7, 9)$.

$$d = \sqrt{(x_2 - x_1)^2 + (y_2 - y_1)^2} \quad \text{Use the Distance Formula.}$$
$$= \sqrt{(7 - 1)^2 + (9 - 1)^2} \quad \text{Substitute for } (x_1, y_1) \text{ and } (x_2, y_2).$$
$$= \sqrt{(6)^2 + (8)^2} = 10 \quad \text{Simplify.}$$

The *midpoint* of a line segment is the point M on the segment that is the same distance from each endpoint, (x_1, y_1) and (x_2, y_2). The coordinates of M are given by the *midpoint formula*:

$$M\left(\frac{x_1 + x_2}{2}, \frac{y_1 + y_2}{2}\right)$$

Example 2

What is the midpoint of the line segment with endpoints $(3, 6)$ and $(-5, 1)$?

Let $(x_1, y_1) = (3, 6)$ and $(x_2, y_2) = (-5, 1)$.

$$\left(\frac{x_1 + x_2}{2}, \frac{y_1 + y_2}{2}\right) = \left(\frac{3 + (-5)}{2}, \frac{6 + 1}{2}\right) \quad \text{Substitute for } (x_1, y_1) \text{ and } (x_2, y_2).$$
$$= \left(-1, 3\tfrac{1}{2}\right) \quad \text{Simplify.}$$

Exercises

Find the distance between the two points. Then find the midpoint of the line segment joining the two points.

1. $(-1, 3), (11, -2)$

2. $(2, 1), (6, 4)$

3. $(-4, 1), (11, 9)$

4. $(-4, -3), (2, 5)$

5. $\left(\frac{1}{2}, 5\right), (3, -1)$

6. $(-6, 3), \left(6, -\frac{1}{2}\right)$

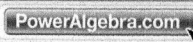

Guided Instruction

PURPOSE To explore the Distance Formula and the Midpoint Formula

PROCESS Students will

- use the Distance Formula to find the distance between two given points in a plane.
- use the Midpoint Formula to find the midpoint of a segment when given its endpoints.

DISCUSS Suggest students label the given points in the exercises as (x_1, y_1) and (x_2, y_2) to avoid incorrect placement of one or more of the coordinates.

Example 1

In this Example students use the Distance Formula.

Q What side of the right triangle shown in the diagram is used to represent the distance between the two points? **[hypotenuse]**

Q When the Distance Formula is derived from the Pythagorean Theorem, why is the negative root of d^2 ignored? **[because distance is a measure and cannot be negative]**

Example 2

In this Example students use the Midpoint Formula.

Q What measure of central tendency is used in the Midpoint Formula? Explain. **[Mean; to find the midpoint, you find the average of the coordinates of the endpoints.]**

Answers

Exercises

1. $13; \left(5, \frac{1}{2}\right)$

2. $5; \left(4, 2\frac{1}{2}\right)$

3. $17; \left(3\frac{1}{2}, 5\right)$

4. $10; (-1, 1)$

5. $6\frac{1}{2}; \left(1\frac{3}{4}, 2\right)$

6. $12\frac{1}{2}; \left(0, 1\frac{1}{4}\right)$

1 Interactive Learning

Solve It!

PURPOSE To create and simplify a radical expression associated with using the Pythagorean Theorem
PROCESS Students may use the Pythagorean Theorem, properties of real numbers, or mathematical and geometric reasoning.

FACILITATE

Q What is the maximum height of a mirror if the mirror is carried through the door in a vertical position? in a horizontal position? **[2w; w]**

Q Other than horizontal and vertical, what other positions might be used to carry the mirror through the door? **[The mirror might be held at an angle.]**

Q Which position would allow for the largest mirror possible to be carried through? **[passing the mirror through the plane that contains the diagonal of the door]**

ANSWER See Solve It in Answers on next page.
CONNECT THE MATH In the Solve It, students generate a radical expression associated with the situation. In the lesson, students learn to simplify radical expressions using properties of multiplication and division.

2 Guided Instruction

Take Note

Ask students to use the Multiplication Property of Square Roots to simplify $\sqrt{100}$ and $\sqrt{400}$. Students can use their knowledge that these two numbers are perfect squares to check if they correctly applied the property.

10-2 Simplifying Radicals

Objective To simplify radicals involving products and quotients

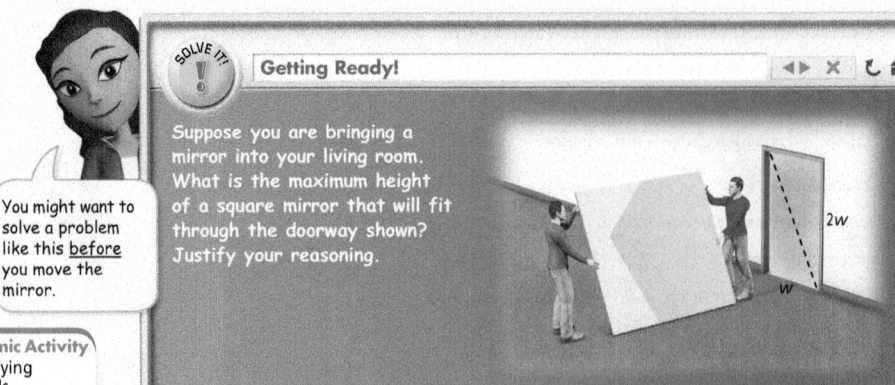

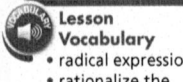

Dynamic Activity
Simplifying Radicals

Lesson Vocabulary
• radical expression
• rationalize the denominator

In the Solve It, the maximum height of the mirror is a *radical expression*. A **radical expression**, such as $2\sqrt{3}$ or $\sqrt{x+3}$, is an expression that contains a radical. A radical expression is simplified if the following statements are true.

• The radicand has no perfect-square factors other than 1.
• The radicand contains no fractions.
• No radicals appear in the denominator of a fraction.

Simplified

$3\sqrt{5}$ $9\sqrt{x}$ $\dfrac{\sqrt{2}}{4}$

Not Simplified

$3\sqrt{12}$ $\sqrt{\dfrac{x}{2}}$ $\dfrac{5}{\sqrt{7}}$

Essential Understanding You can simplify radical expressions using multiplication and division properties of square roots.

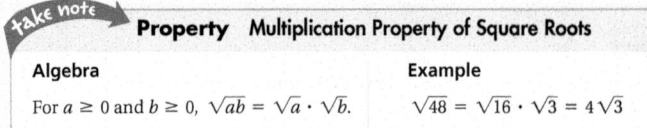

Property	Multiplication Property of Square Roots	
Algebra		**Example**
For $a \geq 0$ and $b \geq 0$, $\sqrt{ab} = \sqrt{a} \cdot \sqrt{b}$.		$\sqrt{48} = \sqrt{16} \cdot \sqrt{3} = 4\sqrt{3}$

You can use the Multiplication Property of Square Roots to simplify radicals by removing perfect-square factors from the radicand.

606 Chapter 10 Radical Expressions and Equations

10-2 Preparing to Teach

BIG idea Equivalence   UbD

ESSENTIAL UNDERSTANDINGS

• Radical expressions can be simplified using the multiplication and division properties of square roots.
• Rationalizing the denominator of a radical expression removes the radical from the denominator of the expression.

Math Background

Remind students that a radical includes a radical sign, or the symbol $\sqrt{}$, and the expression underneath the symbol is called the radicand.

Simplifying a radical involves removing any perfect-square factors (except 1), removing fractions in the radicand, and rationalizing the denominator (Lesson 10-3). Students will have greater success simplifying radicals if they are familiar with the perfect squares less than 100 and have a firm grasp on the process of prime factorization.

The Multiplication and Division Properties of Square Roots are extensions of the Properties of Exponents learned in Chapter 7. Students will learn in subsequent courses that all radical expressions can be written as expressions containing rational exponents and hence simplified using the Properties of Exponents.

Support Student Learning

Use the **Algebra 1 Companion** to engage and support students during instructions. See Lesson Resources at the end of this lesson for details.

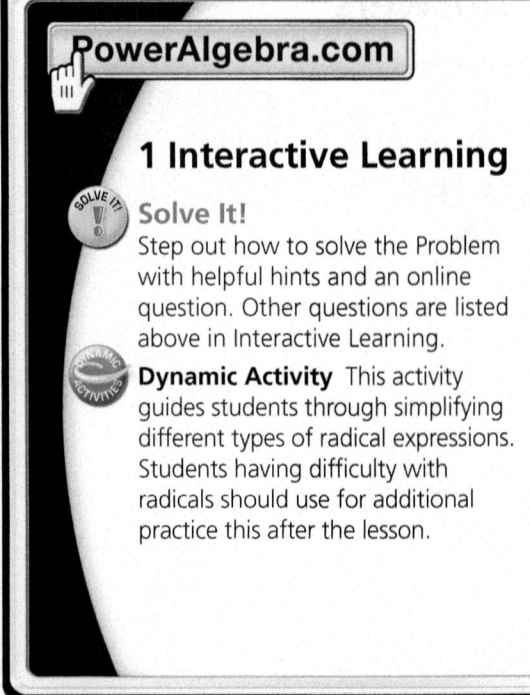

PowerAlgebra.com

1 Interactive Learning

Solve It!
Step out how to solve the Problem with helpful hints and an online question. Other questions are listed above in Interactive Learning.

Dynamic Activity This activity guides students through simplifying different types of radical expressions. Students having difficulty with radicals should use for additional practice this after the lesson.

What strategy can you use to find the factor to remove?
You can *solve a simpler problem* by first just listing the factors of the radicand. Then choose the greatest perfect square on the list.

 **Problem 1** **Removing Perfect-Square Factors**

What is the simplified form of $\sqrt{160}$?

$$\sqrt{160} = \sqrt{16 \cdot 10} \qquad \text{16 is the greatest perfect-square factor of 160.}$$
$$= \sqrt{16} \cdot \sqrt{10} \qquad \text{Use the Multiplication Property of Square Roots.}$$
$$= 4\sqrt{10} \qquad \text{Simplify } \sqrt{16}.$$

Got It? **1.** What is the simplified form of $\sqrt{72}$?

Sometimes you can simplify radical expressions that contain variables. A variable with an even exponent is a perfect square. A variable with an odd exponent is the product of a perfect square and the variable. For example, $n^3 = n^2 \cdot n$, so $\sqrt{n^3} = \sqrt{n^2 \cdot n}$. In this lesson, assume that all variables in radicands represent nonnegative numbers.

How is this problem similar to Problem 1?
In both problems, you need to remove a perfect-square factor from the radicand. In this problem, however, the factor you remove contains a variable.

 Problem 2 **Removing Variable Factors**

Multiple Choice What is the simplified form of $\sqrt{54n^7}$?

Ⓐ $n^3\sqrt{54n}$ Ⓑ $9n^6\sqrt{6n}$ Ⓒ $3n^3\sqrt{6n}$ Ⓓ $3n\sqrt{27n}$

$$\sqrt{54n^7} = \sqrt{9n^6 \cdot 6n} \qquad 9n^6 \text{, or } (3n^3)^2 \text{, is a perfect-square factor of } 54n^7.$$
$$= \sqrt{9n^6} \cdot \sqrt{6n} \qquad \text{Use the Multiplication Property of Square Roots.}$$
$$= 3n^3\sqrt{6n} \qquad \text{Simplify } \sqrt{9n^6}.$$

The correct answer is C.

Got It? **2.** What is the simplified form of $-m\sqrt{80m^9}$?

You can use the Multiplication Property of Square Roots to write $\sqrt{a} \cdot \sqrt{b} = \sqrt{ab}$.

What property allows you to multiply the whole numbers first?
The Commutative Property of Multiplication allows you to change the order of the factors.

 Problem 3 **Multiplying Two Radical Expressions**

What is the simplified form of $2\sqrt{7t} \cdot 3\sqrt{14t^2}$?

$$2\sqrt{7t} \cdot 3\sqrt{14t^2} = 6\sqrt{7t \cdot 14t^2} \qquad \text{Multiply the whole numbers and use the Multiplication Property of Square Roots.}$$
$$= 6\sqrt{98t^3} \qquad \text{Simplify under the radical symbol.}$$
$$= 6\sqrt{49t^2 \cdot 2t} \qquad 49t^2 \text{, or } (7t)^2 \text{, is a perfect-square factor of } 98t^3.$$
$$= 6\sqrt{49t^2} \cdot \sqrt{2t} \qquad \text{Use the Multiplication Property of Square Roots.}$$
$$= 6 \cdot 7t\sqrt{2t} \qquad \text{Simplify } \sqrt{49t^2}.$$
$$= 42t\sqrt{2t} \qquad \text{Simplify.}$$

PowerAlgebra.com   Lesson 10-2   Simplifying Radicals   607

Problem 1

Q Is it possible to simplify $\sqrt{160}$ if you mistakenly think that 4 is the largest perfect square that is a factor of 160? Explain. **[Yes, you will have to simplify twice.]**

Q How can you use a calculator to check that your simplification is correct? **[Calculate $\sqrt{160}$ and $4\sqrt{10}$.]**

Got It?
Many students benefit from writing a list of whole numbers and their perfect squares on their papers to use as a reference when simplifying radicals.

Problem 2
Show students that $\sqrt{54n^7}$ could also be rewritten as $\sqrt{9 \cdot 6 \cdot n^2 \cdot n^2 \cdot n^2 \cdot n}$, but that writing it as $\sqrt{9 \cdot 6 \cdot n^6 \cdot n}$ is more efficient.

Got It?

Q What is the largest perfect square that is a factor of $80m^9$? **[$16m^8$]**

Q How do you know when a term is in simplified form? **[There is one radicand and it does not have a factor that is a perfect square.]**

Problem 3

Q What four factors are being multiplied? Which grouping is most efficient for multiplying the factors? **[2, $\sqrt{7t}$, 3, and $\sqrt{14t^2}$; 2 · 3 and $\sqrt{7t} \cdot \sqrt{14t^2}$]**

Q What is the largest perfect square that is a factor of $98t^3$? **[$49t^2$]**

Answers

Solve It!
$w\sqrt{5}$; explanations may vary.

Got It?
1. $6\sqrt{2}$
2. $-4m^5\sqrt{5m}$

---

2 Guided Instruction

 Each Problem is worked out and supported online.

Problem 1
Removing Perfect-Square Factors

Problem 2
Removing Variable Factors
Animated

Problem 3
Multiplying Two Radical Expressions

Problem 4
Writing a Radical Expression
Animated

Problem 5
Simplifying Fractions Within Radicals

Problem 6
Rationalizing Denominators
Animated

Support in Algebra 1 Companion
- Vocabulary
- Key Concepts
- Got It?

Got It?

Q For 3a, before you even multiply, how do you know that the radicand will have a perfect square factor? [**The two radicands, $\sqrt{6}$ and $\sqrt{18}$ have a common factor of 6, which means that 36 is a factor of their product.**]

Q For 3c, how can you tell if the simplified answer will have a radical? [**If the radicand is a perfect square, the simplified answer will not have a radical. If the radicand is not a perfect square, the simplified answer will have a radical.**]

Problem 4

Q If the width of the door is w units, what is an expression for the height of the door? Explain. [**Because the height is 3 times the width, the expression $3w$ represents the height.**]

Q The diagonal of the doorway forms two right triangles. Which of the sides are the hypotenuses of the triangles? [**The diagonals of the doorway are the hypotenuses.**]

Q Can w^2 and $9w^2$ be added? Explain. [**Yes, they are like terms.**]

Q What is the largest perfect square that is a factor of $10w^2$? [**w^2**]

Got It?

Point out to students that this problem is identical to the problem in the Solve It.

Take Note

Remind students that they were familiarized with this property when they derived the Quadratic Formula in Chapter 9.

 Got It? 3. What is the simplified form of each expression in parts (a)–(c)?

  a. $3\sqrt{6} \cdot \sqrt{18}$ **b.** $\sqrt{2a} \cdot \sqrt{9a^3}$ **c.** $7\sqrt{5x} \cdot 3\sqrt{20x^5}$

  d. Reasoning In Problem 3, can you simplify the given product by first simplifying $\sqrt{14t^2}$? Explain.

 **Problem 4** Writing a Radical Expression

Art A rectangular door in a museum is three times as tall as it is wide. What is a simplified expression for the maximum length of a painting that fits through the door?

Know	Need
The door is w units wide and $3w$ units high.	The diagonal length d of the doorway

Plan

Use the Pythagorean Theorem.

Think

How is this like problems you have done before?
The width and height of the door are two legs of a right triangle. This is like finding the hypotenuse of a right triangle using the Pythagorean Theorem.

$d^2 = w^2 + (3w)^2$ Pythagorean Theorem

$d^2 = w^2 + 9w^2$ Simplify $(3w)^2$.

$d^2 = 10w^2$ Combine like terms.

$d = \sqrt{10w^2}$ Find the principal square root of each side.

$d = \sqrt{w^2} \cdot \sqrt{10}$ Multiplication Property of Square Roots

$d = w\sqrt{10}$ Simplify $\sqrt{w^2}$.

An expression for the maximum length of the painting is $w\sqrt{10}$, or about $3.16w$.

 Got It? 4. A door's height is four times its width w. What is the maximum length of a painting that fits through the door?

You can simplify some radical expressions using the following property.

 **take note** **Property** **Division Property of Square Roots**

Algebra

For $a \geq 0$ and $b > 0$, $\sqrt{\dfrac{a}{b}} = \dfrac{\sqrt{a}}{\sqrt{b}}$.

Example

$\sqrt{\dfrac{36}{49}} = \dfrac{\sqrt{36}}{\sqrt{49}} = \dfrac{6}{7}$

When a radicand has a denominator that is a perfect square, it is easier to apply the Division Property of Square Roots first and then simplify the numerator and denominator of the result. When the denominator of a radicand is not a perfect square, it may be easier to simplify the fraction first.

Additional Problems

1. What is the simplified form of $\sqrt{125}$?

   ANSWER $5\sqrt{5}$

2. What is the simplified form of $\sqrt{243x^5}$?

   A. $3x^2\sqrt{3x}$ B. $9x^2\sqrt{3x}$
   C. $3x^2\sqrt{3x^3}$ D. $9x^2\sqrt{3x^3}$

   ANSWER B

3. What is the simplified form of $3\sqrt{12z^2} \cdot 5\sqrt{4z}$?

   ANSWER $60z\sqrt{3z}$

4. Travel A boat traveled 4 times as far due east as it did due south. What is an expression for the distance the boat would have traveled in a straight line from its starting point to its destination?

   ANSWER $x\sqrt{17}$

5. What is the simplified form of each radical expression?

   a. $\sqrt{\dfrac{121}{81}}$

   b. $\sqrt{\dfrac{27x^5}{48x}}$

   ANSWER $\dfrac{11}{9}$, $\dfrac{3x^2}{4}$

6. What is the simplified form of each expression?

   a. $\dfrac{\sqrt{5}}{\sqrt{8}}$

   b. $\dfrac{\sqrt{3}}{\sqrt{20n}}$

   ANSWER $\dfrac{\sqrt{10}}{4}$, $\dfrac{\sqrt{15n}}{10n}$

Answers

Got It? (continued)

3. a. $18\sqrt{3}$

   b. $3a^2\sqrt{2}$

   c. $210x^3$

   d. yes; $\sqrt{14t^2} = t\sqrt{14}$

4. $w\sqrt{17}$

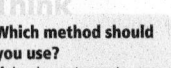 **Problem 5** Simplifying Fractions Within Radicals

Think

Which method should you use?
If the denominator is a perfect square, apply the Division Property of Square Roots first. If not, simplify the fraction first.

What is the simplified form of each radical expression?

Ⓐ $\sqrt{\dfrac{64}{49}}$

$\sqrt{\dfrac{64}{49}} = \dfrac{\sqrt{64}}{\sqrt{49}}$ Use the Division Property of Square Roots.

$= \dfrac{8}{7}$ Simplify $\sqrt{64}$ and $\sqrt{49}$.

Ⓑ $\sqrt{\dfrac{8x^3}{50x}}$

$\sqrt{\dfrac{8x^3}{50x}} = \sqrt{\dfrac{4x^2}{25}}$ Divide the numerator and denominator by $2x$.

$= \dfrac{\sqrt{4x^2}}{\sqrt{25}}$ Use the Division Property of Square Roots.

$= \dfrac{\sqrt{4} \cdot \sqrt{x^2}}{\sqrt{25}}$ Use the Multiplication Property of Square Roots.

$= \dfrac{2x}{5}$ Simplify $\sqrt{4}$, $\sqrt{x^2}$, and $\sqrt{25}$.

Got It? 5. What is the simplified form of each radical expression?

a. $\sqrt{\dfrac{144}{9}}$ **b.** $\sqrt{\dfrac{36a}{4a^3}}$ **c.** $\sqrt{\dfrac{25y^3}{z^2}}$

When a radicand in a denominator is not a perfect square, you may need to **rationalize the denominator** to remove the radical. To do this, multiply the numerator and denominator by the same radical expression. Choose an expression that makes the radicand in the denominator a perfect square. It may be helpful to start by simplifying the original radical in the denominator.

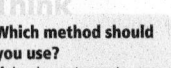 **Problem 6** Rationalizing Denominators

Think

Does multiplying an expression by $\dfrac{\sqrt{7}}{\sqrt{7}}$ change its value?
No. The fraction $\dfrac{\sqrt{7}}{\sqrt{7}}$ is equal to 1. Multiplying an expression by 1 won't change its value.

What is the simplified form of each expression?

Ⓐ $\dfrac{\sqrt{3}}{\sqrt{7}}$ **Ⓑ** $\dfrac{\sqrt{7}}{\sqrt{8n}}$

$\dfrac{\sqrt{3}}{\sqrt{7}} = \dfrac{\sqrt{3}}{\sqrt{7}} \cdot \dfrac{\sqrt{7}}{\sqrt{7}}$ [Multiply by $\dfrac{\sqrt{7}}{\sqrt{7}}$.] $\dfrac{\sqrt{7}}{\sqrt{8n}} = \dfrac{\sqrt{7}}{2\sqrt{2n}}$

$= \dfrac{\sqrt{21}}{\sqrt{49}}$ $= \dfrac{\sqrt{7}}{2\sqrt{2n}} \cdot \dfrac{\sqrt{2n}}{\sqrt{2n}}$

$= \dfrac{\sqrt{21}}{7}$ [Multiply by $\dfrac{\sqrt{2n}}{\sqrt{2n}}$.] $= \dfrac{\sqrt{14n}}{2\sqrt{4n^2}}$

                                      $= \dfrac{\sqrt{14n}}{4n}$

Got It? 6. What is the simplified form of each radical expression?

a. $\dfrac{\sqrt{2}}{\sqrt{3}}$ **b.** $\dfrac{\sqrt{5}}{\sqrt{18m}}$ **c.** $\sqrt{\dfrac{7s}{3}}$

Problem 5

Q Is the denominator of the radicand a perfect square in 5A? Explain. **[Yes, $49 = 7^2$.]**

Q Before simplifying, is the denominator of the radicand a perfect square in 5B? Explain. **[No, neither 50 nor x is a perfect square.]**

Q How do you simplify the expression $\dfrac{x^3}{x}$? **[You use the quotient rule and subtract the exponents.]**

Got It?

Q In which of the expression(s) will dividing, or simplifying the radicands, not produce smaller numbers in which to work? Explain. **[5c; there are no common factors in the numerator and denominator. In 5a, dividing produces a radicand of 16. In 5b, dividing produces a radicand of $\dfrac{9}{a^2}$.]**

Problem 6

Q In 6B, if you do not simplify the radical first, what would you multiply by to rationalize the denominator? **[$\sqrt{8n}$]**

Q How does this impact how you get to the simplified answer? **[You will need to simplify the radicand in the numerator, $\sqrt{56n}$, and then cancel common factors with the denominator.]**

Got It?

When you rationalize a denominator by multiplying it by itself, why is the product a rational number? **[Any number times itself produces a perfect square. The square root of a perfect square equals one of its equal factors.]**

---

5. a. 4

   b. $\dfrac{3}{a}$

   c. $\dfrac{5y\sqrt{y}}{z}$

6. a. $\dfrac{\sqrt{6}}{3}$

   b. $\dfrac{\sqrt{10m}}{6m}$

   c. $\dfrac{\sqrt{21s}}{3}$

3 Lesson Check

Do you know HOW?
- If students have difficulty with Exercise 3, then have them review Problem 3 to see how they can group the factors.

Do you UNDERSTAND?
- If students have difficulty with Exercise 9, then have them review the three bullets on the first page of the lesson and make a checklist for checking a radical expression.

Close

> **Q** What properties are used to simplify radical expressions? Explain. **[The Multiplication Property of Square Roots is used to simplify perfect squares in a radicand. The Division Property of Square Roots is used to rewrite a radicand that is a fraction.]**

 Lesson Check

Do you know HOW?

Simplify each radical expression.

1. $\sqrt{98}$ 2. $\sqrt{16b^5}$

3. $3\sqrt{5m} \cdot 4\sqrt{\frac{1}{5}m^3}$ 4. $\sqrt{\frac{15x}{x^3}}$

5. $\frac{\sqrt{5}}{\sqrt{3}}$ 6. $\frac{\sqrt{6}}{\sqrt{2n}}$

Do you UNDERSTAND?

7. **Vocabulary** Is the radical expression in simplified form? Explain.
   a. $\frac{\sqrt{31}}{3}$ b. $7\sqrt{\frac{6}{11}}$ c. $-5\sqrt{175}$

8. **Compare and Contrast** Simplify $\frac{3}{\sqrt{12}}$ two different ways. Which way do you prefer? Explain.

9. **Writing** Explain how you can tell whether a radical expression is in simplified form.

 Practice and Problem-Solving Exercises

 **Practice**

Simplify each radical expression.   **See Problems 1 and 2.**

10. $\sqrt{225}$ 11. $\sqrt{99}$ 12. $\sqrt{128}$ 13. $-\sqrt{60}$

14. $-4\sqrt{117}$ 15. $5\sqrt{700}$ 16. $\sqrt{192s^2}$ 17. $\sqrt{50t^5}$

18. $3\sqrt{18a^2}$ 19. $-21\sqrt{27x^9}$ 20. $3\sqrt{150b^8}$ 21. $-2\sqrt{243y^3}$

Simplify each product.   **See Problem 3.**

22. $\sqrt{8} \cdot \sqrt{32}$ 23. $\frac{1}{3}\sqrt{6} \cdot \sqrt{24}$ 24. $4\sqrt{10} \cdot 2\sqrt{90}$

25. $5\sqrt{6} \cdot \frac{1}{6}\sqrt{216}$ 26. $-5\sqrt{21} \cdot (-3\sqrt{42})$ 27. $\sqrt{18n} \cdot \sqrt{98n^3}$

28. $3\sqrt{5c} \cdot 7\sqrt{15c^2}$ 29. $\sqrt{2y} \cdot \sqrt{128y^5}$ 30. $-6\sqrt{15s^3} \cdot 2\sqrt{75}$

31. $-9\sqrt{28a^2} \cdot \frac{1}{3}\sqrt{63a}$ 32. $10\sqrt{12x^3} \cdot 2\sqrt{6x^3}$ 33. $-\frac{1}{3}\sqrt{18c^5} \cdot \left(-6\sqrt{8c^9}\right)$

34. **Construction** Students are building rectangular wooden frames for the set of a school play. The height of a frame is 6 times the width w. Each frame has a brace that connects two opposite corners of the frame. What is a simplified expression for the length of a brace?   **See Problem 4.**

35. **Park** A park is shaped like a rectangle with a length 5 times its width w. What is a simplified expression for the distance between opposite corners of the park?

Simplify each radical expression.   **See Problems 5 and 6.**

36. $\sqrt{\frac{16}{25}}$ 37. $7\sqrt{\frac{6}{32}}$ 38. $-4\sqrt{\frac{100}{729}}$ 39. $\sqrt{\frac{3x^3}{64x^2}}$

40. $-5\sqrt{\frac{162t^3}{2t}}$ 41. $11\sqrt{\frac{49a^5}{4a^3}}$ 42. $\frac{1}{\sqrt{11}}$ 43. $\frac{\sqrt{5}}{\sqrt{8x}}$

44. $\frac{3\sqrt{6}}{\sqrt{15}}$ 45. $\frac{22}{\sqrt{11}}$ 46. $\frac{2\sqrt{24}}{\sqrt{48t^4}}$ 47. $\frac{8\sqrt{7s}}{\sqrt{28s^3}}$

---

3 Lesson Check

For a digital lesson check, use the Got It questions.

Support In Algebra 1 Companion
- Lesson Check

4 Practice

Assign homework to individual students or to an entire class.

Answers

Lesson Check

1. $7\sqrt{2}$ 2. $4b^2\sqrt{b}$ 3. $12m^2$
4. $\frac{\sqrt{15}}{x}$ 5. $\frac{\sqrt{15}}{3}$ 6. $\frac{\sqrt{3n}}{n}$

7. a. Yes; there are no perfect-square factors in 31, there are no fractions in the radicand, and there are no radicals in the denominator.
   b. No; there is a fraction in the radicand.
   c. No; 25 is a perfect-square factor of 175.

8. Answer may vary. Sample:
$$\frac{3}{\sqrt{12}} = \frac{3}{2\sqrt{3}} \cdot \frac{\sqrt{3}}{\sqrt{3}} = \frac{3\sqrt{3}}{6} = \frac{\sqrt{3}}{2};$$
$$\frac{3}{\sqrt{12}} = \frac{3}{\sqrt{12}} \cdot \frac{\sqrt{12}}{\sqrt{12}} = \frac{3\sqrt{12}}{12} =$$
$$\frac{\sqrt{12}}{4} = \frac{2\sqrt{3}}{4} = \frac{\sqrt{3}}{2}$$

9. A radical expression is in simplified form if the radicand has no perfect-square factors other than 1, the radicand contains no fractions, and no radicals appear in the denominator of a fraction.

Practice and Problem-Solving Exercises

10. 15   11. $3\sqrt{11}$
12. $8\sqrt{2}$ 13. $-2\sqrt{15}$
14. $-12\sqrt{13}$ 15. $50\sqrt{7}$
16. $8s\sqrt{3}$ 17. $5t^2\sqrt{2t}$
18. $9a\sqrt{2}$ 19. $-63x^4\sqrt{3x}$
20. $15b^4\sqrt{6}$ 21. $-18y\sqrt{3y}$
22. 16   23. 4
24. 240   25. 30
26. $315\sqrt{2}$ 27. $42n^2$
28. $105c\sqrt{3c}$ 29. $16y^3$
30. $-180s\sqrt{5s}$ 31. $-126a\sqrt{a}$
32. $120x^3\sqrt{2}$ 33. $24c^7$
34. $w\sqrt{37}$ 35. $w\sqrt{26}$

Apply

48. Look for a Pattern From a viewing height of h feet, the approximate distance d to the horizon, in miles, is given by the equation $d = \sqrt{\frac{3h}{2}}$.

  a. To the nearest mile, what is the distance to the horizon from a height of 150 ft? 225 ft? 300 ft?
  b. How does the distance to the horizon increase as the height increases?

49. Think About a Plan A square picture on the front page of a newspaper occupies an area of 24 in.^{2}. What is the length of each side of the picture? Write your answer as a radical in simplified form.
  • How can you find the side length of a square if you know the area?
  • What property can you use to write your answer in simplified form?

Explain why each radical expression is or is not in simplified form.

50. $\frac{13x}{\sqrt{4}}$ **51.** $\frac{3}{\sqrt{3}}$ **52.** $-4\sqrt{5}$ **53.** $5\sqrt{30}$

54. Error Analysis A student simplified the radical expression at the right. What mistake did the student make? What is the correct answer?

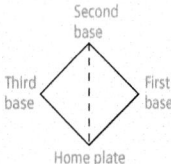

55. Reasoning You can simplify radical expressions with negative exponents by first rewriting the expressions using positive exponents. What are the simplified forms of the following radical expressions?

  a. $\frac{\sqrt{3}}{\sqrt{f^{-3}}}$ **b.** $\frac{\sqrt{x^{-3}}}{\sqrt{x}}$ **c.** $\frac{\sqrt{5a^{-2}}}{\sqrt{10a^{-1}}}$ **d.** $\frac{\sqrt{(2m)^{-3}}}{m^{-1}}$

56. Sports The bases in a softball diamond are located at the corners of a 3600-ft^2 square. How far is a throw from second base to home plate?

57. Suppose a and b are positive integers.
  a. Verify that if $a = 18$ and $b = 10$, then $\sqrt{a} \cdot \sqrt{b} = 6\sqrt{5}$.
  b. Open-Ended Find two other pairs of positive integers a and b such that $\sqrt{a} \cdot \sqrt{b} = 6\sqrt{5}$.

Second base / Third base / First base / Home plate

Simplify each radical expression.

58. $\sqrt{12} \cdot \sqrt{75}$ **59.** $\sqrt{26 \cdot 2}$ **60.** $\frac{\sqrt{72}}{\sqrt{64}}$ **61.** $\frac{-2}{\sqrt{a^3}}$

62. $\frac{\sqrt{180}}{\sqrt{3}}$ **63.** $\frac{\sqrt{x^2}}{\sqrt{y^3}}$ **64.** $\frac{-3\sqrt{2}}{\sqrt{6}}$ **65.** $\sqrt{8} \cdot \sqrt{10}$

66. $\sqrt{20a^2b^3}$ **67.** $\sqrt{a^3b^5c^3}$ **68.** $\sqrt{\frac{3m}{16m^2}}$ **69.** $\frac{16a}{\sqrt{6a^3}}$

Solve each equation. Leave your answer in simplified radical form.

70. $x^2 + 6x - 9 = 0$ **71.** $n^2 - 2n + 1 = 5$ **72.** $3y^2 - 4y - 2 = 0$

73. Open-Ended What are three numbers whose square roots can be written in the form $a\sqrt{3}$ for some integer value of a?

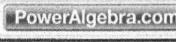 PowerAlgebra.com   Lesson 10-2   Simplifying Radicals   **611**

4 Practice

ASSIGNMENT GUIDE

Basic: 10–49 all, 50–68 even

Average: 11–47 odd, 48–73

Advanced: 11–47 odd, 48–78

Standardized Test Prep: 79–82

Mixed Review: 83–91

Reasoning exercises have blue headings.

Applications exercises have red headings.

EXERCISE 56: Use the Think About a Plan worksheet in the **Practice and Problem Solving Workbook** (also available in the Teaching Resources in print and online) to further support students' development in becoming independent learners.

HOMEWORK QUICK CHECK

To check students' understanding of key skills and concepts, go over Exercises 15, 23, 49, 54, and 56.

36. $\frac{4}{5}$ **37.** $\frac{7\sqrt{3}}{4}$ **38.** $-\frac{40}{27}$
39. $\frac{\sqrt{3x}}{8}$ **40.** $-45t$ **41.** $\frac{77a}{2}$
42. $\frac{\sqrt{11}}{11}$ **43.** $\frac{\sqrt{10x}}{4x}$ **44.** $\frac{3\sqrt{10}}{5}$
45. $2\sqrt{11}$ **46.** $\frac{\sqrt{2}}{t^2}$ **47.** $\frac{4}{5}$

48. a. 15 mi; 18 mi; 21 mi
  b. The distance increases rapidly at first as h increases, but then the distance does not increase as fast. A good way to see this is to look at the graph of $d = \sqrt{\frac{3h}{2}}$.

49. $2\sqrt{6}$ in.

50. not simplest form; radical in the denominator of a fraction

51. not simplest form; radical in the denominator of a fraction

52. Simplest form; radicand has no perfect-square factors other than 1.

53. Simplest form; radicand has no perfect-square factors other than 1.

54. The student should not have removed x from the radical; $\sqrt{\frac{5x}{25}} = \frac{\sqrt{5x}}{5}$.

55. a. $f\sqrt{3f}$
  b. $\frac{1}{x^2}$
  c. $\frac{\sqrt{2a}}{2a}$
  d. $\frac{\sqrt{2m}}{4m}$

56. $60\sqrt{2}$ ft, or about 85 ft

57. a. $\sqrt{18 \cdot 10} = \sqrt{180} = \sqrt{36} \cdot \sqrt{5} = 6\sqrt{5}$
  b. Answers may vary. Sample: 4 and 45

58. 30   **59.** $2\sqrt{13}$
60. $\frac{3\sqrt{2}}{4}$ **61.** $\frac{-2\sqrt{a}}{a^2}$
62. $2\sqrt{15}$ **63.** $\frac{x\sqrt{y}}{y^2}$
64. $-\sqrt{3}$ **65.** $4\sqrt{5}$
66. $2ab\sqrt{5b}$ **67.** $ab^2c\sqrt{abc}$
68. $\frac{\sqrt{3m}}{4m}$ **69.** $\frac{8\sqrt{6a}}{3a}$

70. $-3 \pm 3\sqrt{2}$ **71.** $1 \pm \sqrt{5}$
72. $\frac{2 \pm \sqrt{10}}{3}$
73. Answers may vary. Sample: 12, 27, 48

Lesson 10-2   611

Answers

Practice and Problem-Solving Exercises
(continued)

74. $12x$ **75.** $10b^2$ **76.** $30a^4$

77. a. $\frac{5\sqrt{2\pi}}{\pi}$ ft, 3.99 ft

  b. $\frac{4\sqrt{2\pi}}{\pi}$ in., 3.19 in.

  c. $\frac{\sqrt{10\pi}}{\pi}$ m, 1.78 m

78. $\frac{5}{6}$ **79.** C **80.** H

81. B

82. [2] $(-2, 0)$ and $(0, 3)$ are the given points.
This means that the slope of the line is
$\frac{3 - 0}{0 - (-2)} = \frac{3}{2}$. Since the y-intercept is 3,
the equation of the line is $y = \frac{3}{2}x + 3$ or
$3x - 2y = -6$.
[1] correct methods used with a minor
computational error

83. yes **84.** yes **85.** no

86. $(8y + 3)(8y - 3)$

87. $(a + 9)(a - 9)$

88. $(5 + 4b)(5 - 4b)$

89. $6a^2 - 5a - 4$

90. $-4m^2 + 14mn - 12n^2$

91. $4x^2 + 16x + 15$

 **Challenge** **Simplify each radical expression.**

74. $\sqrt{24} \cdot \sqrt{2x} \cdot \sqrt{3x}$ **75.** $2b(\sqrt{5b})^2$ **76.** $\sqrt{45a^7} \cdot \sqrt{20a}$

77. Geometry The equation $r = \sqrt{\frac{A}{\pi}}$ gives the radius r of a circle with area A. What is the radius of a circle with the given area? Write your answer as a simplified radical and as a decimal rounded to the nearest hundredth.

  a. 50 ft² **b.** 32 in.² **c.** 10 m²

78. For a linear equation in standard form $Ax + By = C$, where $A \neq 0$ and $B \neq 0$, the distance d between the x- and y-intercepts is given by $d = \sqrt{\left(\frac{C}{A}\right)^2 + \left(\frac{C}{B}\right)^2}$. What is the distance between the x- and y-intercepts of the graph of $4x - 3y = 2$?

Standardized Test Prep

SAT/ACT

79. What is the simplified form of $\sqrt{12y^5}$?
  Ⓐ $2\sqrt{3y^5}$ Ⓑ $4y^4\sqrt{3y}$ Ⓒ $2y^2\sqrt{3y}$ Ⓓ $3y^3$

80. In the proportion $\frac{3}{b} = \frac{7}{8-b}$, what is the value of b?
  Ⓕ 6 Ⓖ $\frac{21}{8}$ Ⓗ $\frac{12}{5}$ Ⓘ $\frac{5}{12}$

81. The area of the triangle at the right is 24 in.². What is the height of the triangle?
  Ⓐ 1.8 in. Ⓒ 7 in.
  Ⓑ 3 in. Ⓓ 16 in.

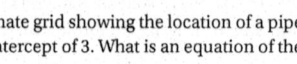

Short Response

82. An architect is sketching a line on a coordinate grid showing the location of a pipe. The line has an x-intercept of -2 and a y-intercept of 3. What is an equation of the architect's line?

Mixed Review

Determine whether the given lengths can be side lengths of a right triangle. ◆ See Lesson 10-1.

83. 7, 24, 25 **84.** $1, \frac{4}{3}, \frac{5}{3}$ **85.** 5, 13, 14

Factor each expression. ◆ See Lesson 8-7.

86. $64y^2 - 9$ **87.** $a^2 - 81$ **88.** $25 - 16b^2$

Get Ready! **To prepare for Lesson 10-3, do Exercises 89–91.**

Simplify each product. ◆ See Lesson 8-3.

89. $(3a - 4)(2a + 1)$ **90.** $(2m - 3n)(4n - 2m)$ **91.** $(5 + 2x)(2x + 3)$

Additional Instructional Support

Algebra 1 Companion

Students can use the **Algebra 1 Companion** worktext (4 pages) as you teach the lesson. Use the Companion to support

- New Vocabulary
- Key Concepts
- Got It for each Problem
- Lesson Check

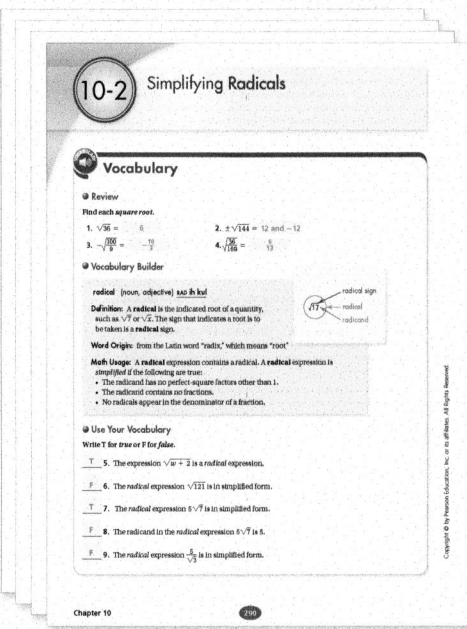

ELL Support

Assess Understanding Write the radical $\sqrt{125}$ on the board. Ask for the square root of 125. Ask: What are the factors of $\sqrt{125}$? Use the Multiplication Property of Square Roots and write $125 = 25 \times 5$ so $\sqrt{125} = \sqrt{25 \times 5} = \sqrt{25} \times \sqrt{5}$. Invite a student to simplify the expression. If needed, ask if either radicand is a perfect square or ask for the factors of each radicand. Now write $\sqrt{5^2} \times \sqrt{5} = 5\sqrt{5}$ on the board. Scaffold to an expression such as $\sqrt{\frac{20}{81}}$ and repeat the steps above to show how to use the Quotient Property of Square Roots.

5 Assess & Remediate

Lesson Quiz

1. What is the simplified form of $\sqrt{162}$?

2. What is the simplified form of $\sqrt{48t^9}$?

3. What is the simplified form of $2\sqrt{5s} \cdot 4\sqrt{15s^3}$?

4. **Do you UNDERSTAND?** Arlene is cutting square tiles along the diagonal to make pieces for a mosaic. What is an expression for the maximum length of the diagonal of the tile?

5. What is the simplified form of each radical expression?

   a. $\sqrt{\dfrac{169}{100}}$

   b. $\sqrt{\dfrac{20x^3}{36x}}$

6. What is the simplified form of each radical expression?

   a. $\dfrac{\sqrt{7}}{\sqrt{11}}$

   b. $\dfrac{\sqrt{3}}{\sqrt{18x}}$

ANSWERS TO LESSON QUIZ

1. $9\sqrt{2}$

2. $4t^4\sqrt{3t}$

3. $40s^2\sqrt{3}$

4. $x\sqrt{2}$

5. a. $\dfrac{13}{10}$ b. $\dfrac{x\sqrt{5}}{3}$

6. a. $\dfrac{\sqrt{77}}{11}$ b. $\dfrac{\sqrt{6x}}{6x}$

PRESCRIPTION FOR REMEDIATION

Use the student work on the Lesson Quiz to prescribe a differentiated review assignment.

Points	Differentiated Remediation
0–3	Intervention
4–5	On-level
6	Extension

PowerAlgebra.com

5 Assess & Remediate

Assign the Lesson Quiz. Appropriate intervention, practice, or enrichment is automatically generated based on student performance.

Intervention

- **Reteaching** (2 pages) Provides reteaching and practice exercises for the key lesson concepts. Use with struggling students or absent students.

- **English Language Learner Support** Helps students develop and reinforce mathematical vocabulary and key concepts.

All-in-One Resources/Online
Reteaching

All-in-One Resources/Online
English Language Learner Support

Differentiated Remediation *continued*

On-Level

- **Practice** (2 pages) Provides extra practice for each lesson. For simpler practice exercises, use the Form K Practice pages found in the All-in-One Teaching Resources and online.

- **Think About a Plan** Helps students develop specific problem-solving skills and strategies by providing scaffolded guiding questions.

- **Standardized Test Prep** Focuses on all major exercises, all major question types, and helps students prepare for the high-stakes assessments.

Extension

- **Enrichment** Provides students with interesting problems and activities that extend the concepts of the lesson.

- **Activities, Games, and Puzzles** Worksheets that can be used for concepts development, enrichment, and for fun!

Practice and Problem Solving WKBK/ All-in-One Resources/Online
Practice page 1

10-2 Practice — Form G
Simplifying Radicals

Simplify each radical expression.

1. $\sqrt{169}$ 13
2. $\sqrt{200}$ $10\sqrt{2}$
3. $\sqrt{125}$ $5\sqrt{5}$
4. $-5\sqrt{112}$ $-20\sqrt{7}$
5. $\sqrt{68}$ $2\sqrt{17}$
6. $3\sqrt{121}$ 33
7. $\sqrt{63t^4}$ $3t^2\sqrt{7}$
8. $\sqrt{48n^3}$ $4n\sqrt{3n}$
9. $-\sqrt{60m^7}$ $-2m^3\sqrt{15m}$
10. $x\sqrt{150x^2}$ $5x^3\sqrt{6x}$
11. $-3\sqrt{45y^3}$ $-9y\sqrt{5y}$
12. $-2b\sqrt{136b^2}$ $-4b^2\sqrt{34}$

Simplify each product.

13. $\sqrt{6} \cdot \sqrt{30}$ $6\sqrt{5}$
14. $\sqrt{5} \cdot \sqrt{70}$ $5\sqrt{14}$
15. $2\sqrt{3} \cdot \sqrt{96}$ $24\sqrt{2}$
16. $-4\sqrt{7} \cdot \sqrt{42}$ $-28\sqrt{6}$
17. $\sqrt{4a} \cdot \sqrt{12a^3}$ $4a^2\sqrt{3}$
18. $\sqrt{2n^2} \cdot \sqrt{30n}$ $2n\sqrt{15n}$
19. $-3\sqrt{40x} \cdot 2\sqrt{56x^5}$ $-48x^3\sqrt{35}$
20. $\frac{2}{3}\sqrt{12t^3} \cdot \sqrt{20t^3}$ $3t^3\sqrt{15}$
21. $4\sqrt{14d^2} \cdot \frac{1}{2}\sqrt{28d^3}$ $28d^2\sqrt{2d}$

22. A pool is shaped like a rectangle with a length 4 times its width w. What is an expression for the distance between opposite corners of the pool? $w\sqrt{17}$

23. Evelyn rode her horse along a triangular path. The distance she traveled south was five times the distance she traveled east. Then she rode directly back to her starting point. What is an expression for the total distance she rode? $6x + \sqrt{26}x$

Practice and Problem Solving WKBK/ All-in-One Resources/Online
Practice page 2

10-2 Practice (continued) — Form G
Simplifying Radicals

Simplify each radical expression.

24. $\sqrt{\frac{36}{49}}$ $\frac{6}{7}$
25. $\sqrt{\frac{81}{16}}$ $\frac{9}{4}$
26. $\sqrt{\frac{100}{225}}$ $\frac{2}{3}$
27. $\sqrt{\frac{18y}{36y^3}}$ $\frac{\sqrt{2}}{2y}$
28. $\sqrt{\frac{49x^4}{25x}}$ $\frac{7x^2}{5}$
29. $\sqrt{\frac{16a^2}{4b^4}}$ $\frac{2a}{b^2}$
30. $\frac{\sqrt{5}}{\sqrt{2}}$ $\frac{\sqrt{10}}{2}$
31. $\frac{\sqrt{12}}{\sqrt{15}}$ $\frac{2\sqrt{5}}{5}$
32. $\frac{\sqrt{72}}{\sqrt{40}}$ $\frac{3\sqrt{5}}{5}$
33. $\frac{\sqrt{25b}}{\sqrt{5b^3}}$ $\frac{\sqrt{5}}{b}$
34. $\frac{\sqrt{24}}{\sqrt{3n}}$ $\frac{2\sqrt{2n}}{n}$
35. $\frac{\sqrt{8}}{\sqrt{30m^2}}$ $\frac{2\sqrt{15}}{15m}$

36. You are making a mosaic design on a square table top. You have already covered half of the table top with 150 1-inch square tile pieces.
   a. What are the dimensions of the table top? $10\sqrt{3}$ in.
   b. What is the measure of the diagonal from one corner to the opposite corner of the table top? $10\sqrt{6}$ in.

37. The equation $r = \sqrt{\frac{SA}{4\pi}}$ gives the radius r of a sphere with surface area SA. What is the radius of a sphere with the given surface area? Write your answer as a simplified radical and as a decimal rounded to the nearest hundredth. Use 3.14 for π.
   a. 1256 in² 10 in.
   b. 200.96 cm² 4 cm
   c. 379.94 ft² 5.5 ft

38. **Open-Ended** What are three radical expressions that simplify to $2x\sqrt{3}$?
   Answers may vary. Samples: $2\sqrt{3x^2}$, $x\sqrt{12}$, $\sqrt{12x^2}$

All-in-One Resources/Online
Enrichment

10-2 Enrichment
Simplifying Radicals

Journey to Planet Radical

Imagine that you are among the first Americans to journey to Planet Radical, located in a distant solar system. As you disembark from your spaceship and begin to explore the nearest space colony, you discover that all the money on Planet Radical is computed in irrational numbers. A sign posted outside the Planetary National Bank explains the system of Radical currency and the value of U.S. money. Note that the Radicals value certain pieces of U.S. currency more than others, based on the currency's appearance, not on the U.S. value.

Radical Currency	Radical Rates of Exchange
1 chip = $3\sqrt{2}$	1 U.S. penny = $\sqrt{2}$
1 nugget = $4\sqrt{3}$	1 U.S. nickel = $\sqrt{3}$
1 bite = $3\sqrt{5}$	1 U.S. dime = $\sqrt{8}$
1 zip = $\sqrt{40}$	1 U.S. quarter = $2\sqrt{5}$
	1 U.S. dollar = $\sqrt{10}$

1. You count the change in your pocket and discover that you have 3 quarters, 2 dimes, and 3 pennies. How much is your change worth in Radical currency? $6\sqrt{5} + 9\sqrt{2}$
2. On Planet Radical, a good meal can be purchased for 6 zips. You go to the best restaurant in the space colony and charge the bill on your Galaxy Express Card. When you receive your monthly statement, what will you owe in U.S. dollars? $12
3. Since your trip to Planet Radical took 2.5 years, your spacesuit is a little threadbare. You decide to purchase a new one at the Asteroid Department Store, the leading department store on the planet. You give the clerk $75 in U.S. money and receive 4 bites and 1 nugget in change. How much did the spacesuit cost? $73.30
4. Juice and the morning newspaper cost 1 chip on Planet Radical. Which U.S. coin will pay for these items? a dime
5. You decide to open a savings account at the Planetary National Bank. You deposit 10 dollars, 6 quarters, 5 dimes, and 8 nickels. How much money in Radical currency have you deposited? 5 chips, 2 nuggets, 4 bites, and 5 zips

---

Practice and Problem Solving WKBK/ All-in-One Resources/Online
Think About a Plan

10-2 Think About a Plan
Simplifying Radicals

Sports The bases in a softball diamond are located at the corners of a 3600 ft² square. How far is a throw from second base to home plate?

Understanding the Problem

1. What is the area of the softball diamond? _____ 3600 ft²

2. Where are second base and home plate located? the ends of a diagonal of the square

3. What is the problem asking you to determine? the distance between second base and home plate

Planning the Solution

4. What equation can be used to determine the side length of the softball diamond? $3600 = s^2$

5. What equation can be used to determine the length of the throw from second base to home plate? $c^2 = 60^2 + 60^2$

6. How many steps will it take to solve this problem? two steps

Getting an Answer

7. What is the first step in finding the solution? What is the solution of the first step? What is the second step in finding the solution? What is the solution?
   Solve the equation $3600 = s^2$ to find the length of a side of the square; 60 ft; Use the Pythagorean Theorem to find the distance between second base and home plate; about 84.9 ft

---

Practice and Problem Solving WKBK/ All-in-One Resources/Online
Standardized Test Prep

10-2 Standardized Test Prep
Simplifying Radicals

Multiple Choice

For Exercises 1–5, choose the correct letter.

1. What is the simplified form of $\sqrt{140}$? D
   A. $4\sqrt{35}$
   B. $10\sqrt{14}$
   C. $2\sqrt{70}$
   D. $2\sqrt{35}$

2. What is the simplified form of $\sqrt{48n^8}$? G
   F. $4n^2\sqrt{3}$
   G. $4n^4\sqrt{3n}$
   H. $3n\sqrt{4n^8}$
   I. $4\sqrt{3n^9}$

3. What is the simplified form of $3\sqrt{5c} \cdot \sqrt{15c^3}$? A
   A. $15c^2\sqrt{3}$
   B. $6c^2\sqrt{5}$
   C. $5c^2\sqrt{3}$
   D. $12c^4\sqrt{5}$

4. Which radical expression is in simplified form? G
   F. $\frac{11y}{\sqrt{3}}$
   G. $\sqrt{\frac{8}{9y}}$
   H. $\frac{\sqrt{17}}{\sqrt{4}}$
   I. $\sqrt{\frac{25}{81}}$

5. A gardener is mowing a 20 yd-by-40 yd rectangular pasture using a diagonal pattern. He mows from one corner of the pasture to the corner diagonally opposite. What is the length of this pass with the mower? Give your answer in simplified form. D
   A. $10\sqrt{20}$
   B. $20\sqrt{5}$
   C. $400\sqrt{5}$
   D. $20\sqrt{5}$

Short Response

6. Suppose the height of the freight elevator in your building is half its width w when the doors are all the way open.
   a. What is an expression for the maximum side length of a sheet of metal that will fit through the elevator doors?
   $w\sqrt{5}$
   b. If the height of the elevator is 3 meters, what is the maximum length that will fit through the doors?
   $3\sqrt{5}$ m

[2] Both parts answered correctly
[1] One of the parts answered correctly
[0] Neither part answered correctly

Online Teacher Resource Center
Activities, Games, and Puzzles

10-2 Game: Classifying Numbers
Simplifying Radicals

This is a game for three students. Decide on a host and two players.

The host receives a sheet with the questions and answers. The contestants take turns answering questions starting from the top of the table and working down, and the host checks the answers.

Contestants are *not* allowed to work ahead. During the game, each contestant's sheet must be turned over to the blank side. When the host poses a question, the contestant turns the sheet over and answers. After answering, the contestant must turn the sheet to the blank side. Each correct answer is worth 3 points.
See Teacher Instructions Page.

Perfect square or not?	Player 1	Player 2
1	1000		
2	4900		
3	10,000		
4	250		
5	40,000		
6	2000		

Rational or irrational?	Player 1	Player 2
1	$\sqrt{360}$		
2	$\sqrt{2500}$		
3	$2\sqrt{6}$		
4	$-3\sqrt{49}$		
5	$\sqrt{10,000}$		
6	$\sqrt{600}$		

Which comparison is correct? Circle the correct one.	Player 1	Player 2
1	$\sqrt{49} > 3\sqrt{9}$ or $3\sqrt{9} > 4\sqrt{6}$		
2	$-\sqrt{64} < 2\sqrt{8}$ or $3\sqrt{9} < 4\sqrt{4}$		
3	$10\sqrt{9} < 24$ or $-\sqrt{25} < -3\sqrt{25}$		
4	$12 > 3\sqrt{144}$ or $-3\sqrt{4} > -\sqrt{64}$		
5	$-\sqrt{81} < -\sqrt{525}$ or $3\sqrt{100} < -\sqrt{36}$		
6	$\sqrt{481} < -3\sqrt{169}$ or $\sqrt{149} < 15\sqrt{121}$		

10-3 Operations With Radical Expressions

Objectives To simplify sums and differences of radical expressions
To simplify products and quotients of radical expressions

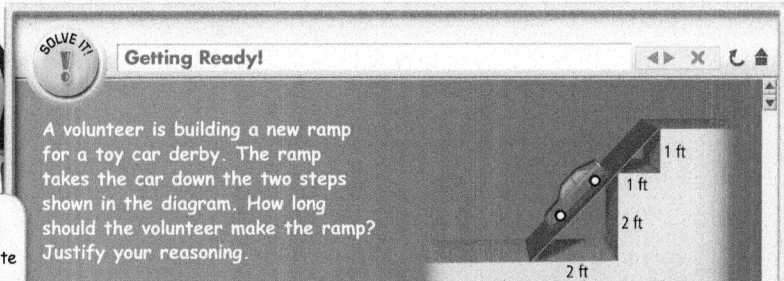

SOLVE IT!

Getting Ready!

A volunteer is building a new ramp for a toy car derby. The ramp takes the car down the two steps shown in the diagram. How long should the volunteer make the ramp? Justify your reasoning.

1 ft
1 ft
2 ft
2 ft

Dynamic Activity
Operations With Radical Expressions

Lesson Vocabulary
• like radicals
• unlike radicals
• conjugates

Essential Understanding You can use properties of real numbers to perform operations with radical expressions.

For example, you can use the Distributive Property to simplify sums or differences of radical expressions by combining *like radicals*. **Like radicals,** such as $3\sqrt{5}$ and $7\sqrt{5}$, have the same radicand. **Unlike radicals,** such as $4\sqrt{3}$ and $-2\sqrt{2}$, have different radicands.

Think

Have you seen a problem like this before?
Yes. Combining like radicals is similar to combining like terms. For example, simplifying the expression in part (A) is similar to simplifying $6x + 9x$.

Problem 1 Combining Like Radicals

What is the simplified form of each expression?

A $6\sqrt{11} + 9\sqrt{11}$

$6\sqrt{11} + 9\sqrt{11} = (6 + 9)\sqrt{11}$ Use the Distributive Property to combine like radicals.

$= 15\sqrt{11}$ Simplify.

B $\sqrt{3} - 5\sqrt{3}$

$\sqrt{3} - 5\sqrt{3} = 1\sqrt{3} - 5\sqrt{3}$ Write $\sqrt{3}$ as $1\sqrt{3}$.

$= (1 - 5)\sqrt{3}$ Use the Distributive Property to combine like radicals.

$= -4\sqrt{3}$ Simplify.

Got It? **1.** What is the simplified form of each expression?
a. $7\sqrt{2} - 8\sqrt{2}$
b. $5\sqrt{5} + 2\sqrt{5}$

---

1 Interactive Learning

Solve It!
PURPOSE To consider the simplified form of the sum of radical expressions
PROCESS Students may use the Pythagorean Theorem, geometric reasoning, or mathematical reasoning.

FACILITATE
Q What is the hypotenuse of the triangle formed by the ramp and the larger step? Explain.
$[\sqrt{8}; 2^2 + 2^2 = 8]$
Q What is the hypotenuse of the triangle formed by the ramp and the smaller step? Explain.
$[\sqrt{2}; 1^2 + 1^2 = 2]$
Q What is the simplified form of the expression representing the total length of the ramp? $[3\sqrt{2}]$

ANSWER See Solve It in Answers on next page.
CONNECT THE MATH You can use the properties of real numbers when performing basic operations involving radical expressions. In the lesson, students learn how to handle sums and differences when the radicands do not match.

2 Guided Instruction

Problem 1

Q In 1B, what are the factors of the first term? $[1 \text{ and } \sqrt{3}]$

Got It?

Q Which expression has a negative simplified form and why? $[1a; 7 - 8 = -1]$

10-3 Preparing to Teach

BIG idea Equivalence   **UbD**
ESSENTIAL UNDERSTANDINGS
• The properties of real numbers can be used to perform operations with radical expressions.
• The denominators of some radical expressions can be rationalized by multiplying by conjugates.

Math Background
Learning to use properties of real numbers to perform operations with radical expressions is a prerequisite skill for learning to solve radical equations. Just as a student cannot solve a linear equation such as $3x + 4(x - 7) = 12$ without first knowing how to use the Distributive Property and combine like terms, a student cannot solve a radical equation such as $\sqrt{x} + \sqrt{x + 3} = 3$ without first knowing how to multiply and combine radical expressions.

Rationalizing the denominator is a convention that was accepted because it makes calculations easier when a calculator is not used. Although the use of calculators is commonplace today, removing irrational numbers from a denominator is still considered a standard part of simplifying a radical. The process of rationalizing the denominator only changes the appearance of a radical expression; it does not change its value. The process uses the basic known fact that any number multiplied by 1 is unchanged. The number 1 is written as a fraction that will produce a rational number in the denominator.

Support Student Learning
Use the **Algebra I Companion** to engage and support students during instruction. See Lesson Resources at the end of this lesson for details.

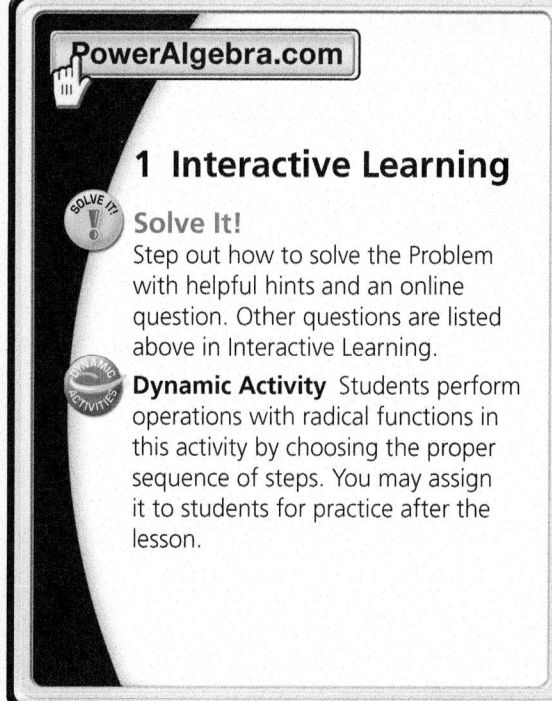

PowerAlgebra.com

1 Interactive Learning

Solve It!
Step out how to solve the Problem with helpful hints and an online question. Other questions are listed above in Interactive Learning.

Dynamic Activity Students perform operations with radical functions in this activity by choosing the proper sequence of steps. You may assign it to students for practice after the lesson.

Problem 2

> **Q** Can the expressions $5\sqrt{3}$ and $\sqrt{12}$ be combined using the Distributive Property? Explain. **[Yes, if $\sqrt{12}$ is first written as $\sqrt{4} \cdot \sqrt{3}$.]**
>
> **Q** How is this problem similar to Problem 1? How is it different? **[The terms cannot be combined immediately as in Problem 1, but after the second radical is simplified, you use the same steps as in Problem 1 to combine the two radical expressions.]**

Got It?

For 2c, use a numeric example such as $\sqrt{9} + \sqrt{16} \neq \sqrt{25}$ to emphasize that only like radicals can be combined.

Problem 3

> **Q** What factors of 60 do you use when you simplify the expression $\sqrt{60}$? **[4 and 15]**
>
> **Q** Can the expressions $2\sqrt{15}$ and $3\sqrt{10}$ be combined using the Distributive Property? Explain. **[No, both terms are already simplified and there is no common factor.]**
>
> **Q** Prior to simplification, how many terms will result when the two binomials are multiplied? Explain. **[4; each term in the first binomial is multiplied by each term in the second binomial.]**

Got It?   ERROR PREVENTION

If students provide an answer of 7 for 3b, then they likely incorrectly distributed the exponent across the difference expression.

You may need to simplify radical expressions first to determine if they can be added or subtracted by combining like radicals.

Problem 2 Simplifying to Combine Like Radicals

What is the simplified form of $5\sqrt{3} - \sqrt{12}$?

Think

How do you know if radical expressions can be combined?
Simplify all radicals. Although $\sqrt{3}$ and $\sqrt{12}$ are unlike radicals, they can be combined after $\sqrt{12}$ is simplified.

$$
\begin{aligned}
5\sqrt{3} - \sqrt{12} &= 5\sqrt{3} - \sqrt{4 \cdot 3} && \text{4 is a perfect-square factor of 12.}\\
&= 5\sqrt{3} - \sqrt{4} \cdot \sqrt{3} && \text{Multiplication Property of Square Roots}\\
&= 5\sqrt{3} - 2\sqrt{3} && \text{Simplify } \sqrt{4}.\\
&= (5 - 2)\sqrt{3} && \text{Use the Distributive Property to combine like radicals.}\\
&= 3\sqrt{3} && \text{Simplify.}
\end{aligned}
$$

Got It? 2. What is the simplified form of each expression in parts (a) and (b)?
  a. $4\sqrt{7} + 2\sqrt{28}$ **b.** $5\sqrt{32} - 4\sqrt{18}$
  c. Reasoning Can you combine two unlike radicals when the radicands have no common factors other than 1? Explain.

When simplifying a product like $\sqrt{10}(\sqrt{6} + 3)$, you can use the Distributive Property to multiply $\sqrt{10}$ times $\sqrt{6}$ and $\sqrt{10}$ times 3. If both factors in the product have two terms, as in $(\sqrt{6} - 2\sqrt{3})(\sqrt{6} + \sqrt{3})$, you can use FOIL to multiply just as you do when multiplying binomials.

Problem 3 Multiplying Radical Expressions

What is the simplified form of each expression?

Think

Have you seen a problem like this before?
Yes. Parts (A) and (B) are similar to simplifying products like $3(x + 2)$ and $(2x + 1)(x - 5)$.

Ⓐ $\sqrt{10}(\sqrt{6} + 3)$
$$
\begin{aligned}
\sqrt{10}(\sqrt{6} + 3) &= (\sqrt{10} \cdot \sqrt{6}) + (\sqrt{10} \cdot 3) && \text{Distributive Property}\\
&= \sqrt{60} + 3\sqrt{10} && \text{Multiplication Property of Square Roots}\\
&= \sqrt{4} \cdot \sqrt{15} + 3\sqrt{10} && \text{4 is a perfect-square factor of 60.}\\
&= 2\sqrt{15} + 3\sqrt{10} && \text{Simplify } \sqrt{4}.
\end{aligned}
$$

Ⓑ $(\sqrt{6} - 2\sqrt{3})(\sqrt{6} + \sqrt{3})$
$$
\begin{aligned}
(\sqrt{6} - 2\sqrt{3})(\sqrt{6} + \sqrt{3}) &= \sqrt{36} + \sqrt{18} - 2\sqrt{18} - 2\sqrt{9} && \text{Use FOIL.}\\
&= 6 - \sqrt{18} - 2(3) && \text{Combine like radicals and simplify.}\\
&= 6 - \sqrt{9} \cdot \sqrt{2} - 6 && \text{9 is a perfect-square factor of 18.}\\
&= -3\sqrt{2} && \text{Simplify.}
\end{aligned}
$$

Got It? 3. What is the simplified form of each expression?
  a. $\sqrt{2}(\sqrt{6} + 5)$ **b.** $(\sqrt{11} - 2)^2$ **c.** $(\sqrt{6} - 2\sqrt{3})(4\sqrt{3} + 3\sqrt{6})$

Answers

Solve It!
$3\sqrt{2}$ ft or about 4.24 ft; explanations may vary.

Got It?
  1. a. $-\sqrt{2}$
   b. $7\sqrt{5}$
  2. a. $8\sqrt{7}$
   b. $8\sqrt{2}$
   c. No; if they are unlike and have no common factors other than 1, even if they can be simplified, they still will not be like.
  3. a. $2\sqrt{3} + 5\sqrt{2}$
   b. $15 - 4\sqrt{11}$
   c. $-6\sqrt{2} - 6$

PowerAlgebra.com

2 Guided Instruction

Each Problem is worked out and supported online.

Problem 1
Combining Like Radicals

Problem 2
Simplifying to Combine Like Radicals

Problem 3
Multiplying Radical Expressions
Animated

Problem 4
Rationalizing a Denominator Using Conjugates
Animated

Problem 5
Solving a Proportion Involving Radicals
Animated

Support in Algebra 1 Companion
• Vocabulary
• Key Concepts
• Got It?

Conjugates are the sum and difference of the same two terms. For example, $\sqrt{7} + \sqrt{3}$ and $\sqrt{7} - \sqrt{3}$ are conjugates. The product of conjugates is a difference of squares.

$$(\sqrt{7} + \sqrt{3})(\sqrt{7} - \sqrt{3}) = (\sqrt{7})^2 - (\sqrt{3})^2$$
$$= 7 - 3 = 4 \quad \boxed{\text{The product of the conjugates has no radicals.}}$$

You can use conjugates to simplify a quotient whose denominator is a sum or difference of radicals.

 Problem 4 Rationalizing a Denominator Using Conjugates

What is the simplified form of $\frac{10}{\sqrt{7} - \sqrt{2}}$?

$$\frac{10}{\sqrt{7} - \sqrt{2}} = \frac{10}{\sqrt{7} - \sqrt{2}} \cdot \frac{\sqrt{7} + \sqrt{2}}{\sqrt{7} + \sqrt{2}} \quad \text{Multiply the numerator and denominator by the conjugate of the denominator.}$$

$$= \frac{10(\sqrt{7} + \sqrt{2})}{7 - 2} \quad \text{Multiply in the denominator.}$$

$$= \frac{10(\sqrt{7} + \sqrt{2})}{5} \quad \text{Simplify the denominator.}$$

$$= 2(\sqrt{7} + \sqrt{2}) \quad \text{Divide 10 and 5 by the common factor 5.}$$

$$= 2\sqrt{7} + 2\sqrt{2} \quad \text{Simplify the expression.}$$

Got It? 4. What is the simplified form of $\frac{-3}{\sqrt{10} + \sqrt{5}}$?

Plan
How do you rationalize the denominator?
Multiply by the conjugate of the denominator. If the denominator has the form $a - b$, the conjugate is $a + b$.

Golden rectangles appear frequently in nature and art. The ratio of the length to the width of a golden rectangle is $(1 + \sqrt{5}):2$.

 **Problem 5** Solving a Proportion Involving Radicals

Biology Fiddlehead ferns naturally grow in spirals that fit into golden rectangles. What is the width w of the fern shown?

$$\frac{1 + \sqrt{5}}{2} = \frac{4}{w} \quad \text{Write a proportion.}$$

$$w(1 + \sqrt{5}) = 8 \quad \text{Cross Products Property}$$

$$w = \frac{8}{1 + \sqrt{5}} \quad \text{Divide each side by } 1 + \sqrt{5}.$$

$$w = \frac{8}{1 + \sqrt{5}} \cdot \frac{1 - \sqrt{5}}{1 - \sqrt{5}} \quad \text{Multiply the numerator and denominator by the conjugate of the denominator.}$$

$$w = \frac{8 - 8\sqrt{5}}{1 - 5} \quad \text{Multiply.}$$

$$w = \frac{8 - 8\sqrt{5}}{-4} \quad \text{Simplify the denominator.}$$

$$w = -2 + 2\sqrt{5} \approx 2.5 \quad \text{Simplify. Use a calculator.}$$

The width of the fern is about 2.5 cm.

Think
How do you begin this problem?
Since the rectangle is a golden rectangle, the length divided by the width has to equal $\frac{1 + \sqrt{5}}{2}$.

w

4 cm

Problem 4

Q Does multiplying both the numerator and denominator by $\sqrt{7} + \sqrt{2}$ change the value of the expression? Explain. **[No, because you are multiplying by 1 written in the format $\frac{\sqrt{7} + \sqrt{2}}{\sqrt{7} + \sqrt{2}}$.]**

Q Is it necessary to use FOIL, or an alternative method when finding the product of the denominator and its conjugate? **[No, you can use the pattern for the difference of two squares.]**

Got It?

Q What is the product of $\sqrt{10} - \sqrt{5}$ and its conjugate? **[5]**

Problem 5

Q In the ratio $\frac{2}{\sqrt{5} + 1}$, is the ratio $\frac{w}{\ell}$ or $\frac{\ell}{w}$? Explain. **[$\sqrt{5} + 1 > 2$; the ratio is $\frac{w}{\ell}$.]**

Q Is the expression $\frac{8}{\sqrt{5} + 1}$ in simplified form? Explain. **[No, it has a radical expression in the denominator.]**

Q Is it necessary to simplify the value of w prior to approximating its value using a calculator? Explain. **[No, but the evaluation process is simpler once the expression is simplified.]**

Additional Problems

1. What is the simplified form of each expression?

a. $3\sqrt{7} + 11\sqrt{7}$

b. $9\sqrt{10} - 5\sqrt{10}$

ANSWER $14\sqrt{7}, 4\sqrt{10}$

2. What is the simplified form of $7\sqrt{6} - 2\sqrt{54}$?

ANSWER $\sqrt{6}$

3. What is the simplified form of each expression?

a. $\sqrt{5}(\sqrt{8} + 7)$

b. $(7\sqrt{8} + 2\sqrt{11})(3\sqrt{8} - \sqrt{11})$

ANSWER $2\sqrt{10} + 7\sqrt{5}$, $146 - 2\sqrt{22}$

4. What is the simplified form of $\frac{8}{\sqrt{3} + \sqrt{11}}$?

ANSWER $\sqrt{11} - \sqrt{3}$

5. The painting below fits into a golden rectangle. What is the width of the painting? Round to the nearest inch.

105 in.

ANSWER 65 in.

Answers

Got It? (continued)

4. $\frac{-3\sqrt{10} + 3\sqrt{5}}{5}$

Got It?

Q What equation can be written to represent this problem? [$\frac{w}{12} = \frac{2}{\sqrt{5}+1}$]

3 Lesson Check

Do you know HOW?

- If students have difficulty with Exercise 4, then remind them to rewrite it as the product of two binomials prior to simplifying or to use the pattern studied in Lesson 8-4 for the square of a binomial.

Do you UNDERSTAND?

- If students have difficulty with Exercise 7a, then tell them to determine the product of $\sqrt{13} - 2$ and $\sqrt{13} + 2$ to verify that their product will yield an expression without a radical.

Close

Q What are the steps for simplifying sums and/or differences of radical expressions? [**First, simplify each term containing a radical. Second, combine like radical terms.**]

 Got It? 5. A golden rectangle is 12 in. long. What is the width of the rectangle? Write your answer in simplified radical form. Round to the nearest tenth of an inch.

 ### Lesson Check

Do you know HOW?

Simplify each radical expression.

1. $4\sqrt{3} + \sqrt{3}$　　　2. $3\sqrt{6} - \sqrt{24}$

3. $\sqrt{7}(\sqrt{3} - 2)$　　4. $(\sqrt{5} - 6)^2$

5. $\frac{7\sqrt{5}}{3 + \sqrt{2}}$　　6. $\frac{6}{\sqrt{7} + 2}$

Do you UNDERSTAND?

7. **Vocabulary** What is the conjugate of each expression?
   a. $\sqrt{13} - 2$　b. $\sqrt{6} + \sqrt{3}$　c. $\sqrt{5} - \sqrt{10}$

8. **Error Analysis** A student simplified an expression, as shown below. Describe and correct the error.

   $$\frac{1}{\sqrt{3}-1} = \frac{1}{\sqrt{3}-1} \cdot \frac{\sqrt{3}+1}{\sqrt{3}+1} = \frac{\sqrt{3}+1}{9-1} = \frac{\sqrt{3}+1}{8}$$

 ### Practice and Problem-Solving Exercises

Ⓐ Practice — Simplify each sum or difference.　　See Problems 1 and 2.

9. $\sqrt{5} + 6\sqrt{5}$　10. $12\sqrt{5} - 3\sqrt{5}$　11. $7\sqrt{3} + \sqrt{3}$　12. $4\sqrt{2} - 7\sqrt{2}$

13. $3\sqrt{7} - \sqrt{63}$　14. $4\sqrt{128} + 5\sqrt{18}$　15. $3\sqrt{45} - 8\sqrt{20}$　16. $\sqrt{28} - 5\sqrt{7}$

17. $-6\sqrt{10} + 5\sqrt{90}$　18. $3\sqrt{3} - 2\sqrt{12}$　19. $-\frac{1}{2}\sqrt{5} + 2\sqrt{125}$　20. $5\sqrt{8} + 2\sqrt{72}$

Simplify each product.　　See Problem 3.

21. $\sqrt{6}(\sqrt{2} + \sqrt{3})$　22. $\sqrt{5}(\sqrt{15} - 3)$　23. $3\sqrt{7}(1 - \sqrt{7})$

24. $-\sqrt{12}(4 - 2\sqrt{3})$　25. $5\sqrt{11}(\sqrt{3} - 3\sqrt{2})$　26. $(3\sqrt{11} + \sqrt{7})^2$

27. $(2 + \sqrt{10})(2 - \sqrt{10})$　28. $(\sqrt{6} + \sqrt{3})(\sqrt{2} - 2)$　29. $(5\sqrt{2} - 2\sqrt{3})^2$

Simplify each quotient.　　See Problem 4.

30. $\frac{5}{\sqrt{2}-1}$　31. $\frac{3}{\sqrt{7}-\sqrt{3}}$　32. $\frac{-2}{\sqrt{6}+\sqrt{11}}$

33. $\frac{\sqrt{5}}{2-\sqrt{5}}$　34. $\frac{-1}{2-2\sqrt{3}}$　35. $\frac{7}{\sqrt{5}+\sqrt{13}}$

36. **Biology** A shell fits into a golden rectangle with a length of 8 in. What is the shell's width? Write your answer in simplified radical form and rounded to the nearest tenth of an inch.　　See Problem 5.

37. **Architecture** A room is approximately shaped like a golden rectangle. Its length is 23 ft. What is the room's width? Write your answer in simplified radical form and rounded to the nearest tenth of a foot.

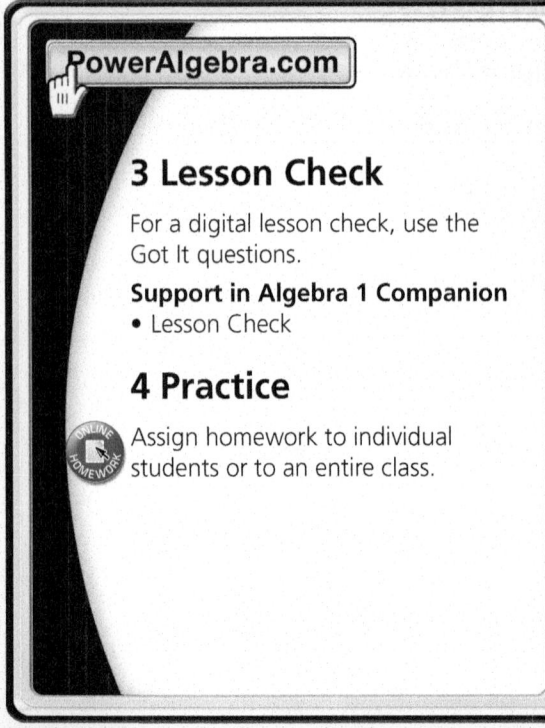

3 Lesson Check

For a digital lesson check, use the Got It questions.

Support in Algebra 1 Companion
- Lesson Check

4 Practice

Assign homework to individual students or to an entire class.

Answers

Got It? (continued)

5. $(6\sqrt{5} - 6)$ in., or about 7.4 in.

Lesson Check

1. $5\sqrt{3}$

2. $\sqrt{6}$

3. $\sqrt{21} - 2\sqrt{7}$

4. $41 - 12\sqrt{5}$

5. $3\sqrt{5} - \sqrt{10}$

6. $2\sqrt{7} - 4$

7. a. $\sqrt{13} + 2$
   b. $\sqrt{6} - \sqrt{3}$
   c. $\sqrt{5} + \sqrt{10}$

8. $\sqrt{3} \cdot \sqrt{3} \neq 9$; $\frac{\sqrt{3}+1}{3-1} = \frac{\sqrt{3}+1}{2}$

Practice and Problem-Solving Exercises

9. $7\sqrt{5}$　　10. $9\sqrt{5}$

11. $8\sqrt{3}$　　12. $-3\sqrt{2}$

13. 0　　14. $47\sqrt{2}$

15. $-7\sqrt{5}$　　16. $-3\sqrt{7}$

17. $9\sqrt{10}$　　18. $-\sqrt{3}$

19. $\frac{19\sqrt{5}}{2}$　　20. $22\sqrt{2}$

21. $2\sqrt{3} + 3\sqrt{2}$　22. $5\sqrt{3} - 3\sqrt{5}$

23. $3\sqrt{7} - 21$　24. $-8\sqrt{3} + 12$

25. $5\sqrt{33} - 15\sqrt{22}$

26. $106 + 6\sqrt{77}$　27. -6

28. $-\sqrt{6}$　　29. $62 - 20\sqrt{6}$

30. $5\sqrt{2} + 5$　31. $\frac{3\sqrt{7}+3\sqrt{3}}{4}$

32. $\frac{2\sqrt{6}-2\sqrt{11}}{5}$　33. $-2\sqrt{5} - 5$

34. $\frac{1+\sqrt{3}}{4}$　　35. $\frac{7\sqrt{13}-7\sqrt{5}}{8}$

36. $-4 + 4\sqrt{5}$ in., or about 4.9 in.

37. $\frac{23\sqrt{5}-23}{2}$ ft, or about 14.2 ft

Find the exact solution for each equation. Find the approximate solution to the nearest tenth.

38. $\dfrac{5\sqrt{2}}{\sqrt{2}-1} = \dfrac{x}{\sqrt{2}}$

39. $\dfrac{3}{1+\sqrt{5}} = \dfrac{1-\sqrt{5}}{x}$

40. $\dfrac{\sqrt{2}-1}{\sqrt{2}+1} = \dfrac{x}{2}$

41. $\dfrac{x}{2+\sqrt{7}} = \dfrac{3-\sqrt{7}}{4}$

42. $\dfrac{4\sqrt{15}}{1+\sqrt{3}} = \dfrac{1+\sqrt{3}}{x}$

43. $\dfrac{2+\sqrt{2}}{2-\sqrt{2}} = \dfrac{x}{3+\sqrt{10}}$

44. History The floor plan of the Parthenon in Athens, Greece, is shown below. The marked room approximates a golden rectangle. What is the width of the room? Write your answer in simplified radical form. Round to the nearest tenth of a meter.

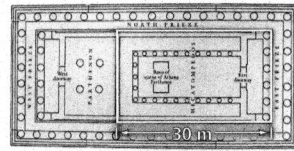

45. Writing Are $\sqrt{3}$ and $\sqrt{12}$ like radicals? Can their sum be simplified? Explain.

46. Error Analysis A student added two radical expressions as shown at the right. Describe and correct the student's mistake.

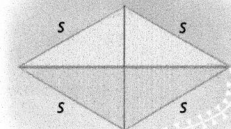

$$\sqrt{6} + \sqrt{24} = \sqrt{6} + 4\sqrt{6}$$
$$= 5\sqrt{6}$$

Simplify each expression.

47. $\sqrt{40} + \sqrt{90}$

48. $3\sqrt{2}(2+\sqrt{6})$

49. $\sqrt{12} + 4\sqrt{75} - \sqrt{36}$

50. $(\sqrt{3}+\sqrt{5})^2$

51. $\dfrac{\sqrt{13}+\sqrt{10}}{\sqrt{13}-\sqrt{5}}$

52. $(\sqrt{7}+\sqrt{8})(\sqrt{7}+\sqrt{8})$

53. $2\sqrt{2}(-2\sqrt{32}+\sqrt{8})$

54. $4\sqrt{50} - 7\sqrt{18}$

55. $\dfrac{2\sqrt{12}+3\sqrt{6}}{\sqrt{9}-\sqrt{6}}$

56. Chemistry The ratio of the diffusion rates of two gases is given by the formula $\dfrac{r_1}{r_2} = \dfrac{\sqrt{m_2}}{\sqrt{m_1}}$, where m_1 and m_2 are the masses of the molecules of the gases. Find $\dfrac{r_1}{r_2}$ if $m_1 = 12$ units and $m_2 = 30$ units. Write your answer in simplified radical form.

57. Reasoning The diagram at the right shows the dimensions of a kite. The length of the vertical blue crosspiece is s. What is the length of the horizontal red crosspiece in terms of s?

58. Think About a Plan The formula $r = \sqrt{\dfrac{A}{P}} - 1$ gives the interest rate r, expressed as a decimal, that will allow principal P to grow into amount A in 2 yr, if the interest is compounded annually. If you invest $10,000 and want to make $2000 in interest over 2 yr, what interest rate do you need?
• What amount do you want in the account after 2 yr?
• What radical expression gives the interest rate you need?

59. a. Suppose n is an even number. Simplify $\sqrt{x^n}$.
b. Suppose n is an odd number greater than 1. Simplify $\sqrt{x^n}$.

60. Reasoning Simplify $\dfrac{a\sqrt{b}}{b\sqrt{a}}$.

ASSIGNMENT GUIDE

Basic: 9–37 all, 38–56 even, 58

Average: 9–37 odd, 38–60

Advanced: 9–37 odd, 38–63

Standardized Test Prep: 64–67

Mixed Review: 68–81

Reasoning exercises have blue headings.

Applications exercises have red headings.

EXERCISE 56: Use the Think About a Plan worksheet in the **Practice and Problem Solving Workbook** (also available in the Teaching Resources in print and online) to further support students' development in becoming independent learners.

HOMEWORK QUICK CHECK

To check students' understanding of key skills and concepts, go over Exercises 11, 23, 46, 56, and 58.

---

38. $10(\sqrt{2}+1)$; 24.1

39. $-\dfrac{4}{3}$; −1.3

40. $6 - 4\sqrt{2}$; 0.3

41. $\dfrac{-1+\sqrt{7}}{4}$; −0.4

42. $\dfrac{2\sqrt{15}+3\sqrt{5}}{30}$; 0.5

43. $9 + 6\sqrt{2} + 4\sqrt{5} + 3\sqrt{10}$; 35.9

44. 18.5 m

45. No; yes; you can simplify $\sqrt{12}$ to $2\sqrt{3}$ and then combine the like radicals.

46. $\sqrt{24} = 2\sqrt{6} \neq 4\sqrt{6}$; $3\sqrt{6}$

47. $5\sqrt{10}$

48. $6\sqrt{2} + 6\sqrt{3}$

49. $22\sqrt{3} - 6$

50. $8 + 2\sqrt{15}$

51. $\dfrac{13 + \sqrt{65} + \sqrt{130} + 5\sqrt{2}}{8}$

52. $15 + 4\sqrt{14}$

53. −24

54. $-\sqrt{2}$

55. $4\sqrt{3} + 4\sqrt{2} + 3\sqrt{6} + 6$

56. $\dfrac{\sqrt{10}}{2}$

57. $s\sqrt{3}$

58. about 0.095, or about 9.5%

59. a. $x^{\frac{n}{2}}$
b. $x^{\frac{n-1}{2}}\sqrt{x}$

60. $\dfrac{\sqrt{ab}}{b}$

Answers

Practice and Problem-Solving Exercises
(continued)

61. $\frac{n\sqrt{5} - n}{2}$

62. Answers may vary. Sample: $\frac{\sqrt{2} - 3}{\sqrt{2} - 3}, \frac{2(\sqrt{2} - 3)}{2(\sqrt{2} - 3)},$
$\frac{3(\sqrt{2} - 3)}{3(\sqrt{2} - 3)};$ yes; you are always multiplying
by 1.

63. a. $3\sqrt{2}$
   b. $2\sqrt{7}$
   c. $\sqrt{2(p + q)}$

64. B   **65.** H   **66.** B

67. [2] The graph of this function, $y = |x|$, is
V-shaped with the vertex at the origin. The
domain is all real numbers and the range is
$\{y \mid y \geq 0\}$, because no matter what value
of x you input, the output will always be
nonnegative.

   [1] correct answer with no explanation given

68. $6\sqrt{3}$ **69.** $15\sqrt{6}$ **70.** $\frac{2\sqrt{2}}{3c}$

71. 15   **72.** 8^{16} **73.** 2^{11}

74. 5^{27} **75.** 3^3 **76.** -1

77. $-4, 3$ **78.** $-5, 3$ **79.** $-3, \frac{2}{3}$

80. $-2, \frac{1}{2}$ **81.** -7

61. Geometry A square has sides with length n. How much must be added to the
length of one side to transform the square into a golden rectangle?

62. Reasoning What are three fractions that you can multiply $\frac{1}{\sqrt{2} + 3}$ by to rationalize
the denominator? Will the resulting products be the same? Explain.

63. Geometry Find the length of each hypotenuse. Write your answer in simplified
radical form.

  a. 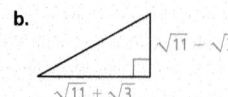   **b.**   **c.**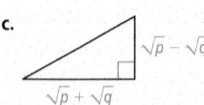

Standardized Test Prep

64. What is the simplified form of $2\sqrt{18} - \sqrt{32} + 4\sqrt{8}$?

  Ⓐ $8\sqrt{3}$ Ⓑ $10\sqrt{2}$ Ⓒ $18\sqrt{2}$ Ⓓ $10\sqrt{18}$

65. A surveyor is calculating the areas of lots that are going to be sold.
The dimensions of one lot are shown at the right. What is the area of
the lot shown?

  Ⓕ $8.82 \times 10^6 \text{ m}^2$ Ⓗ $4.41 \times 10^5 \text{ m}^2$

  Ⓖ $8.82 \times 10^5 \text{ m}^2$ Ⓘ $4.41 \times 10^6 \text{ m}^2$

66. What are the approximate solutions of the equation $\frac{5}{2}x^2 + \frac{3}{4}x - 5 = 0$?
Use a graphing calculator.

  Ⓐ $-5, 0$ Ⓑ $-1.57, 1.27$ Ⓒ $-1.36, 0.71$ Ⓓ $-0.96, 0.84$

67. What are the domain and range of the function $y = |x|$? Show how you find your
answer.

Mixed Review

Simplify each radical expression.   ◀ **See Lesson 10-2.**

68. $\sqrt{108}$ **69.** $3\sqrt{150}$ **70.** $\frac{4}{\sqrt{18c^2}}$ **71.** $\sqrt{5} \cdot \sqrt{45}$

Rewrite each expression using each base only once.   ◀ **See Lesson 7-3.**

72. $8^5 \cdot 8^{11}$ **73.** $2^{24} \cdot 2^{-13}$ **74.** $5^{11} \cdot 5^{16}$ **75.** $3^7 \cdot 3^{-4}$

Get Ready! To prepare for Lesson 10-4, do Exercises 76–81.

Solve by factoring.   ◀ **See Lesson 9-4.**

76. $x^2 + 2x + 1 = 0$ **77.** $x^2 + x - 12 = 0$ **78.** $x^2 + 2x - 15 = 0$

79. $3x^2 + 7x - 6 = 0$ **80.** $2x^2 + 3x - 2 = 0$ **81.** $x^2 + 14x + 49 = 0$

Lesson Resources

Additional Instructional Support

Algebra 1 Companion

Students can use the **Algebra 1 Companion** worktext (4 pages) as you teach the lesson. Use the Companion to support

- New Vocabulary
- Key Concepts
- Got It for each Problem
- Lesson Check

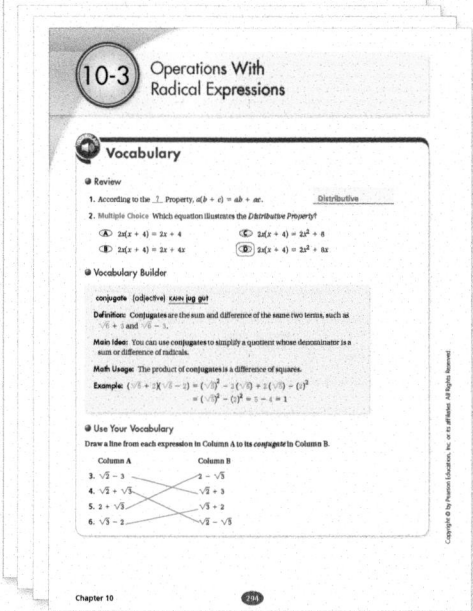

ELL Support

Focus on Communication Have students describe, using their own words, the differences between combining like and unlike radicals. Share answers. Ask, what does a compound inequality with *or* mean? How is the process of combining like and unlike radicals different?

Use Role Playing Place students in pairs either academically or by language levels so there is a more proficient student with a less proficient student. Have students read their paragraphs on combining like and unlike radicals to each other. Encourage students to role play a teacher/student situation to question one another and to explain their written words.

5 Assess & Remediate

Lesson Quiz

1. What is the simplified form of each expression?
   a. $8\sqrt{6} + 3\sqrt{6}$
   b. $7\sqrt{13} - 10\sqrt{13}$
2. What is the simplified form of $3\sqrt{2} + 4\sqrt{50}$?
3. What is the simplified form of each expression?
   a. $\sqrt{3}(\sqrt{7} - 4)$
   b. $(4\sqrt{13} + 3\sqrt{5})(6\sqrt{13} - 7\sqrt{5})$
4. What is the simplified form of $\frac{6}{\sqrt{5} - \sqrt{2}}$?
5. **Do you UNDERSTAND?** The Great Pyramids of Giza fit into golden rectangles. A picture shows one of the Great Pyramids with a base length of 230 m. What is the height of the pyramid? Round to the nearest meter.

ANSWERS TO LESSON QUIZ

1. a. $11\sqrt{6}$
   b. $-3\sqrt{13}$
2. $23\sqrt{2}$
3. a. $\sqrt{21} - 4\sqrt{3}$
   b. $207 - 10\sqrt{65}$
4. $2\sqrt{5} + 2\sqrt{2}$
5. 142 m

PRESCRIPTION FOR REMEDIATION

Use the student work on the Lesson Quiz to prescribe a differentiated review assignment.

Points	Differentiated Remediation
0–2	Intervention
3–4	On-level
5	Extension

PowerAlgebra.com

5 Assess & Remediate

Assign the Lesson Quiz. Appropriate intervention, practice, or enrichment is automatically generated based on student performance.

Intervention

- **Reteaching** (2 pages) Provides reteaching and practice exercises for the key lesson concepts. Use with struggling students or absent students.

- **English Language Learner Support** Helps students develop and reinforce mathematical vocabulary and key concepts.

All-in-One Resources/Online
Reteaching

10-3 **Reteaching**
Operations with Radical Expressions

You can use the Distributive Property with radical expressions.

Problem

What is the simplified form of $4\sqrt{2} - \sqrt{18}$?

You need to simplify the radical expressions before you know if there are any like radicals that can be subtracted.

All-in-One Resources/Online
English Language Learner Support

10-3 **ELL Support**
Operations With Radical Expressions

| conjugates | golden rectangle | like radicals | unlike radicals |

Differentiated Remediation *continued*

On-Level

- **Practice** (2 pages) Provides extra practice for each lesson. For simpler practice exercises, use the Form K Practice pages found in the All-in-One Teaching Resources and online.

- **Think About a Plan** Helps students develop specific problem-solving skills and strategies by providing scaffolded guiding questions.

- **Standardized Test Prep** Focuses on all major exercises, all major question types, and helps students prepare for the high-stakes assessments.

Extension

- **Enrichment** Provides students with interesting problems and activities that extend the concepts of the lesson.

- **Activities, Games, and Puzzles** Worksheets that can be used for concepts development, enrichment, and for fun!

Practice and Problem Solving WKBK/All-in-One Resources/Online
Practice page 1

10-3 Practice Form G
Operations with Radical Expressions

Simplify each sum or difference.

1. $3\sqrt{7} + 5\sqrt{7}$ $8\sqrt{7}$
2. $8\sqrt{3} + \sqrt{3}$ $9\sqrt{3}$
3. $11\sqrt{5} - 4\sqrt{5}$ $7\sqrt{5}$
4. $2\sqrt{11} - 6\sqrt{11}$ $-4\sqrt{11}$
5. $4\sqrt{13} + 4\sqrt{13}$ $8\sqrt{13}$
6. $\sqrt{7} - 4\sqrt{7}$ $-3\sqrt{7}$
7. $4\sqrt{7} - \sqrt{63}$ $\sqrt{7}$
8. $8\sqrt{3} + 2\sqrt{48}$ $16\sqrt{3}$
9. $6\sqrt{8} - 2\sqrt{50}$ $2\sqrt{2}$
10. $3\sqrt{20} - 2\sqrt{45}$ 0
11. $5\sqrt{18} + 4\sqrt{32}$ $31\sqrt{2}$
12. $\sqrt{12} - 7\sqrt{75}$ $-33\sqrt{3}$

Simplify each product.

13. $\sqrt{3}(\sqrt{12} + 4)$ $6 + 4\sqrt{3}$
14. $\sqrt{8}(\sqrt{3} + 3)$ $2\sqrt{6} + 6\sqrt{2}$
15. $\sqrt{7}(\sqrt{7} - 2)$ $7 - 2\sqrt{7}$
16. $(\sqrt{3} - 4)^2$ $19 - 8\sqrt{3}$
17. $(2\sqrt{3} + \sqrt{5})(6\sqrt{5} - 4\sqrt{3})$ $8\sqrt{15} + 6$
18. $(7 + 3\sqrt{5})(7 - 3\sqrt{5})$ 4

Simplify each quotient.

19. $\dfrac{12}{\sqrt{11} - \sqrt{7}}$ $3\sqrt{11} + 3\sqrt{7}$
20. $\dfrac{8}{\sqrt{3} + 1}$ $4\sqrt{3} - 4$
21. $\dfrac{32}{\sqrt{7} - \sqrt{3}}$ $8\sqrt{7} + 8\sqrt{3}$
22. $\dfrac{-2}{\sqrt{15} - \sqrt{7}}$ $\dfrac{-\sqrt{15} - \sqrt{7}}{4}$
23. $\dfrac{30}{\sqrt{5} + \sqrt{2}}$ $10\sqrt{5} - 10\sqrt{2}$
24. $\dfrac{128}{\sqrt{37} + \sqrt{5}}$ $4\sqrt{37} - 4\sqrt{5}$

Practice and Problem Solving WKBK/All-in-One Resources/Online
Practice page 2

10-3 Practice (continued) Form G
Operations with Radical Expressions

25. A painting is shaped like a golden rectangle. It's length is 24 cm. What is the painting's width to the nearest tenth of a cm? **14.8 cm**

26. A tomato fits into a 10-in.-long golden rectangle. What is the tomato's width to the nearest tenth of an inch? **6.2 in.**

27. The length of a golden rectangle is $4 + 4\sqrt{5}$. Use the ratio of length to width $(1 + \sqrt{5}):2$ to find the width of the golden rectangle. **8**

28. **Error Analysis** A student multiplied the radical expressions shown at the right. What mistake did the student make? What is the simplified form of the radical?
$\sqrt{3} \cdot (\sqrt{3} + \sqrt{6})$
$= \sqrt{9} + \sqrt{18}$
$= 6\sqrt{2}$
The student added 3 + 3√2 and got 6√2 but only terms with the same radical can be added, so the correct answer is 3 + 3√2.

29. **Writing** What is the conjugate of $8\sqrt{3} - \sqrt{7}$? What is the product of the conjugates? Show your work to explain your answer.
8√3 + √7; 185

30. Find the length of the hypotenuse of the right triangle to the right. Write your answer in simplified radical form.
√14
legs: $\sqrt{5-\sqrt{2}}$, $\sqrt{5+\sqrt{2}}$

31. **Open-Ended** Make up three differences that are greater than or equal to 10. Use the square roots of 2, 3, 5, or 7 and whole numbers less than or equal to 10. For example, $10\sqrt{3} - 2\sqrt{7} \ge 10$.
Answers may vary. Sample: 9√7 − 4√2, 8√5 − 2√7, 6√7 − 3√2

32. A large park is designed as two 10-km squares connected at the corner and with diagonals aligned. If Riley jogs along the diagonal from one end of the park to the other end, how many total kilometers will he jog? Give your answer as a simplified radical and to the nearest tenth of a kilometer. **20√2; 28.3 km**

All-in-One Resources/Online
Enrichment

10-3 Enrichment
Operations with Radical Expressions

Transcendental Numbers

Around 500 B.C. a Pythagorean mathematician named Hippasus proved that some numbers cannot be expressed as a ratio of integers. Some of these *irrational numbers*, such as the constants π and e, were later proved to fall into a special category of numbers: *transcendental numbers*. Transcendental numbers cannot be expressed in any finite series of arithmetical or algebraic operations. They cannot be expressed as the root of any algebraic equation with rational coefficients.

Most real and complex numbers are transcendental but it is difficult to prove that a specific number is transcendental. All transcendental numbers are irrational but not all irrational numbers are transcendental. To prove that a number is algebraic, and therefore not transcendental, find a polynomial equation with rational coefficients where the number is a root.

In 1761, Johann Lambert proved that π was irrational: The digits of pi never end, nor has anyone ever detected a pattern in the arrangement of its digits. In 1881, Ferdinand von Lindemann proved that π was a transcendental number.

1. Tell why you know that $\pi\sqrt{9}$ is transcendental.
   Since π is a transcendental number, 3π is transcendental.

2. All transcendental numbers are irrational but not all irrational numbers are transcendental. Use $x^2 - 2 = 0$ to prove this point.
   The square root of 2 is irrational. However, since it is a root of $x^2 - 2 = 0$, it is not transcendental.

3. Is $\frac{\sqrt[3]{5}}{2}$ transcendental or algebraic? Explain how you know your answer is correct.
   Algebraic because it is a root of $8x^3 - 5 = 0$.

4. The golden ratio is defined as $\frac{1 + \sqrt{5}}{2}$. Is the golden ratio algebraic or transcendental? Explain your answer.
   Algebraic because it is a root of the polynomial equation $x^2 - x - 1 = 0$.

5. State whether each number is *rational* or *irrational* and *algebraic* or *transcendental*.
   a. $\sqrt{121}$ rational, algebraic
   b. $\frac{\sqrt{3}}{4}$ irrational, algebraic
   c. $\sqrt{16\pi}$ irrational, transcendental

Practice and Problem Solving WKBK/All-in-One Resources/Online
Think About a Plan

10-3 Think About a Plan
Operations with Radical Expressions

Chemistry The ratio of the diffusion rates of two gases is given by the formula $\frac{r_1}{r_2} = \frac{\sqrt{m_2}}{\sqrt{m_1}}$, where m_1 and m_2 are the masses of the molecules of the gases. Find $\frac{r_1}{r_2}$ if $m_1 = 12$ units and $m_2 = 30$ units. Write your answer in simplified radical form.

Understanding the Problem

1. How many gases are involved in the problem? _____ two

2. What variables represent the masses of the molecules of the two gases? _____ m_1 and m_2

3. What are the masses (in units) of the molecules of the two gases? _____ 12 and 30

Planning the Solution

4. What ratio can you simplify to find the ratio $\frac{r_1}{r_2}$? _____ $\frac{\sqrt{m_2}}{\sqrt{m_1}}$

5. What values can you substitute for m_1 and m_2? _____ 12 and 30

6. How can you simplify the radical expression that results when you substitute values for m_1 and m_2? _____ simplify $\frac{30}{12}$ and then find the square root

Getting an Answer

7. Simplify the radical expression. What is the ratio of diffusion rates between the two gases? _____ $\frac{\sqrt{10}}{2}$

8. Is diffusion faster or slower for the molecule with less mass? _____ faster

9. Is the solution reasonable? Explain. _____ yes; if the item has less mass, it will diffuse more quickly

---

Practice and Problem Solving WKBK/All-in-One Resources/Online
Standardized Test Prep

10-3 Standardized Test Prep
Operations with Radical Expressions

Multiple Choice

For Exercises 1–6, choose the correct letter.

1. What is the simplified form of $8\sqrt{5} + 5\sqrt{5}$? B
   A. $3\sqrt{5}$ B. $13\sqrt{5}$ C. $40\sqrt{5}$ D. 200

2. What is the simplified form of $\sqrt{2} - 11\sqrt{2}$? F
   F. $-10\sqrt{2}$ G. $-11\sqrt{2}$ H. $-12\sqrt{2}$ I. -22

3. What is the simplified form of $4\sqrt{3} - \sqrt{27}$? C
   A. $-5\sqrt{3}$ B. $-7\sqrt{3}$ C. $\sqrt{3}$ D. $-\sqrt{9}$

4. What is the simplified form of $\sqrt{8}(\sqrt{5} + 4)$? I
   F. $16\sqrt{10}$ G. $2\sqrt{10} + 4\sqrt{2}$ H. $4\sqrt{10} + 4\sqrt{2}$ I. $2\sqrt{10} + 8\sqrt{2}$

5. What is the simplified form of $\frac{40}{\sqrt{11} + \sqrt{7}}$? A
   A. $10\sqrt{11} - 10\sqrt{7}$ B. $\frac{20\sqrt{11} - 20\sqrt{7}}{9}$ C. $30\sqrt{2}$ D. $10\sqrt{11} + 10\sqrt{7}$

6. A golden rectangle is 32 cm long. The ratio of length to width is $(1 + \sqrt{5}):2$. What is the width of the rectangle in simplest radical form? H
   F. $16\sqrt{5} + 16$ G. $8\sqrt{5} - 8$ H. $16\sqrt{5} - 16$ I. $\frac{32\sqrt{5} - 32}{3}$

Short Response

7. The diagram to the right shows the design of the 12-in. quilt block that a quilter is sewing.
   a. What are the dimensions of each triangle in the quilt block? Give your answers as simplified radicals.
   12 in., 12 in., 12√2 in.; 6√2 in., 6√2 in., 12 in.
   b. What are the dimensions of each triangle to the nearest tenth of an inch?
   12 in., 12 in., 17 in.; 8.5 in., 8.5 in., 12 in.

   [2] Both parts answered correctly
   [1] Both parts answered correctly with only some calculation errors
   [0] Neither Part answered correctly

Online Teacher Resource Center
Activities, Games, and Puzzles

10-3 Puzzle: Find the Buried Treasure
Operations With Radical Expressions

A band of pirates wrote a list of clues to help them locate a buried treasure. They used radical expressions because they are confident that they are better in math than others who also may be searching! Follow the clues by plotting each point and marking your path as you move from one point to the next.

1. From the Start, travel north $\sqrt{(3)^2}$ blocks. 3
2. Then, travel due east $5\sqrt{80} - 2\sqrt{80}$ blocks. $12\sqrt{5}$
3. Then travel due south $4\sqrt{80} - 3\sqrt{45}$ blocks. $7\sqrt{5}$
4. Then, travel due west $30\sqrt{5} - 6\sqrt{20}$ blocks. $18\sqrt{5}$
5. Then travel due south $\sqrt{20} + 2\sqrt{20}$ blocks. $6\sqrt{5}$
6. Then, travel due west $2\sqrt{45}$ blocks. $6\sqrt{5}$
7. Then travel due north $12\sqrt{45} - 10\sqrt{20}$ blocks. $16\sqrt{5}$
8. Then, travel due east $\sqrt{9 \times 20}$ blocks. $6\sqrt{5}$
9. Then travel due north $\sqrt{245} - \sqrt{80}$ blocks. $3\sqrt{5}$
10. Then, travel due east $5\sqrt{20} - 7\sqrt{5}$ blocks. $3\sqrt{5}$
11. Then travel due south $3\sqrt{20} + \sqrt{45}$ blocks. $9\sqrt{5}$
12. Then, travel due east $\sqrt{845} - 5\sqrt{20}$ blocks. $3\sqrt{5}$

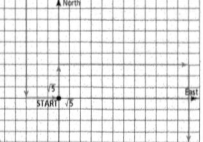

Where are you in relation to where you started? You are back at the starting point.

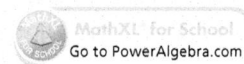
MathXL® for School
Go to PowerAlgebra.com

Do you know HOW?

Use the triangle at the right. Find the missing side length. If necessary, round to the nearest tenth.

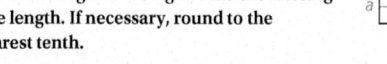

1. $a = 20, b = 25$ **2.** $a = 0.8, b = 1.5$

3. $a = 5, b = 12$ **4.** $a = 2.2, b = 12$

5. $a = 14, c = 50$ **6.** $a = 9, c = 41$

7. $b = 40, c = 41$ **8.** $b = 36, c = 39$

Determine whether the given lengths can be side lengths of a right triangle.

9. 8, 15, 17   **10.** 5, 24, 25   **11.** 60, 80, 100

Simplify each radical expression.

12. $\sqrt{80}$ **13.** $\sqrt{10} \cdot \sqrt{18}$

14. $\sqrt{6x} \cdot \sqrt{2x}$ **15.** $-2\sqrt{3b^2} \cdot \sqrt{12b}$

16. $\sqrt{\dfrac{64}{81}}$ **17.** $-\dfrac{\sqrt{5c}}{\sqrt{45c^3}}$

18. $\dfrac{-3\sqrt{14x^3}}{-\sqrt{21x}}$ **19.** $\dfrac{\sqrt{13f^3}}{\sqrt{5f^2}}$

20. **Sports** A rectangular soccer field is $6w$ yards wide and $10w$ yards long. What is an expression for the distance from one corner to the opposite corner?

Find the area of each figure.

21.

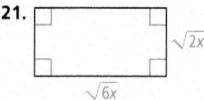

22.

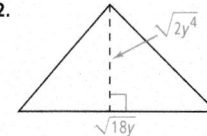

Simplify each radical expression.

23. $5\sqrt{5} + 3\sqrt{5}$

24. $2\sqrt{28} - 3\sqrt{7}$

25. $\sqrt{3}(\sqrt{6} - 4)$

26. $(2\sqrt{21} + 4\sqrt{3})(5\sqrt{21} - \sqrt{3})$

27. $\dfrac{1}{\sqrt{3} - 2}$

28. $\dfrac{3 + \sqrt{2}}{4\sqrt{2} + 2}$

Find the exact solution for each equation. Find the approximate solution to the nearest tenth.

29. $\dfrac{5}{\sqrt{8} - 2} = \dfrac{\sqrt{8} + 2}{x}$

30. $\dfrac{x}{\sqrt{10}} = \dfrac{3\sqrt{2}}{\sqrt{2} + 1}$

31. **Transportation** A bus leaves the bus station and drives 3.75 mi east. The bus then turns and drives 5 mi south. How far is the bus from the bus station?

Do you UNDERSTAND?

32. What type of angle is formed by the two legs of a right triangle?

33. **Writing** How do you use a conjugate to simplify a fraction with a radical expression in its denominator?

34. **Reasoning** Is the equation $\sqrt{a} + \sqrt{b} = \sqrt{a + b}$ *always*, *sometimes*, or *never* true? Justify your answer.

35. **Error Analysis** Describe and correct the error shown below in simplifying the radical expression.

$$\sqrt{45} = \sqrt{9 \cdot 5}$$
$$= 9\sqrt{5}$$

36. **Open-Ended** Give the side lengths of a triangle that is not a right triangle. Explain why these lengths cannot be the side lengths of a right triangle.

Answers

Mid-Chapter Quiz

1. 32.0   **2.** 1.7

3. 13   **4.** 12.2

5. 48   **6.** 40

7. 9   **8.** 15

9. yes   **10.** no

11. yes   **12.** $4\sqrt{5}$

13. $6\sqrt{5}$ **14.** $2x\sqrt{3}$

15. $-12b\sqrt{b}$ **16.** $\dfrac{8}{9}$

17. $-\dfrac{1}{3c}$ **18.** $x\sqrt{6}$

19. $\dfrac{\sqrt{65f}}{5}$ **20.** $2w\sqrt{34}$

21. $2x\sqrt{3}$ **22.** $3y^2\sqrt{y}$

23. $8\sqrt{5}$ **24.** $\sqrt{7}$

25. $3\sqrt{2} - 4\sqrt{3}$ **26.** $198 + 54\sqrt{7}$

27. $-\sqrt{3} - 2$ **28.** $\dfrac{5\sqrt{2} + 1}{14}$

29. $\dfrac{4}{5}$; 0.8

30. $6\sqrt{10} - 6\sqrt{5}$; 5.6

31. 6.25 mi   **32.** right angle

33. To simplify a fraction with a radical expression in its denominator, you multiply the numerator and the denominator by the conjugate of the denominator. The product of the conjugates in the denominator is a difference of squares, so the radicals are removed from the denominator.

34. Sometimes; explanations may vary. Sample:
$\sqrt{1} + \sqrt{0} = \sqrt{1}$, but
$\sqrt{1} + \sqrt{4} \neq \sqrt{5}$.

35. $\sqrt{9 \cdot 5} \neq 9\sqrt{5}$;
$\sqrt{9 \cdot 5} = \sqrt{9} \cdot \sqrt{5} = 3\sqrt{5}$

36. Answers may vary. Sample: 3, 4, 6; the side lengths do not satisfy $a^2 + b^2 = c^2$.

PowerAlgebra.com

MathXL for School
Prepare students for the Mid-Chapter Quiz and Chapter Test with online practice and review.

1 Interactive Learning

Solve It!

PURPOSE To write a solution to the problem in the form of a radical equation

PROCESS Students may use the Pythagorean Theorem, the properties of real numbers, or algebraic reasoning.

FACILITATE

Q If h represents the height of the pole still standing, what algebraic expression represents the length of the pole that has broken off? **[16 − h]**

Q Let d be the distance between the base of the pole still standing and the tip of the broken pole. How can the Pythagorean Theorem relate the three lengths? **[$h^2 + d^2 = (16 - h)^2$]**

ANSWER See Solve It in Answers on next page.
CONNECT THE MATH The Solve It can be solved for d, but part of the equation has a variable in the radicand. In the lesson, students learn to solve equations that contain radical expressions.

2 Guided Instruction

Problem 1

Q If you squared both sides before isolating the radical, how many terms would be in the product on the left side of the equation? **[3; you would be squaring a binomial.]**

Q Why does squaring both sides before isolating the radical not aid in the solution process? **[Instead of clearing the radical, it generates a new radical term.]**

Got It?   **ERROR PREVENTION**
If students report that $x = 3$, then they likely forgot to square the right side of the equation.

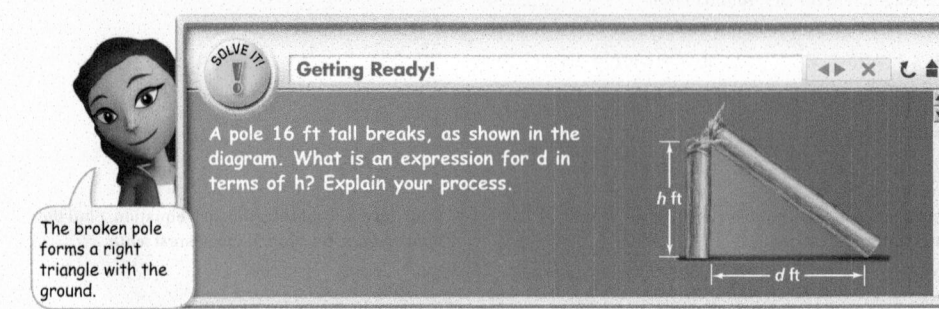

10-4 Solving Radical Equations

Objectives To solve equations containing radicals
To identify extraneous solutions

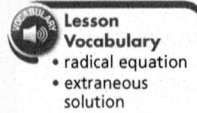

Getting Ready!

A pole 16 ft tall breaks, as shown in the diagram. What is an expression for d in terms of h? Explain your process.

The broken pole forms a right triangle with the ground.

h ft

d ft

Lesson Vocabulary
• radical equation
• extraneous solution

The expression for d in the Solve It has a variable in a radicand. A **radical equation** is an equation that has a variable in a radicand. Examples include $\sqrt{x} - 5 = 3$ and $\sqrt{x - 2} = 1$. To solve a radical equation, get the radical by itself on one side of the equation. Then square both sides. The expression under the radical must be nonnegative.

Essential Understanding You can solve some radical equations by squaring each side of the equation and testing the solutions.

Plan

How do you start when solving a radical equation?
Use the properties of equality to get the radical by itself on one side of the equation.

Problem 1 Solving by Isolating the Radical

What is the solution of $\sqrt{x} + 7 = 16$?

$$\sqrt{x} + 7 = 16$$
$$\sqrt{x} = 9 \quad \text{Get the radical by itself on one side of the equation.}$$
$$(\sqrt{x})^2 = 9^2 \quad \text{Square each side.}$$
$$x = 81 \quad \text{Simplify.}$$

Check $\sqrt{x} + 7 = 16$
$$\sqrt{81} + 7 \overset{?}{=} 16 \quad \text{Substitute 81 for } x.$$
$$9 + 7 = 16 \checkmark$$

Got It? **1.** What is the solution of $\sqrt{x} - 5 = -2$?

10-4 Preparing to Teach

BIG idea Solving Equations and Inequalities   **UbD**

ESSENTIAL UNDERSTANDINGS
• Some radical equations can be solved by squaring both sides and testing the solutions.
• When extraneous solutions are tested, they do not solve the original equation.

Math Background

A radical equation is an equation that has a variable in the radicand. You solve radical equations involving square roots by isolating the radical term and then squaring both sides of the equation.

Because x must be nonnegative for $\sqrt{x^2} = x$ to be true, solving a radical equation by squaring both sides can lead to an extraneous solution. An extraneous solution is one that does not satisfy the original equation. Students must understand that it is critical to check all solutions in the original

equation to eliminate extraneous solutions. Radical equations can have one solution, two solutions, or no solutions.

The algebraic techniques learned for solving radical equations in this lesson have been limited to those equations which require squaring only once and in which the index of the root is 2. In the future, students will apply these same techniques to equations in which it is necessary to square both sides of the equation more than one time, as well as to equations involving roots with indexes other than 2.

Support Student Learning

Use the **Algebra 1 Companion** to engage and support students during instructions. See Lesson Resources at the end of this lesson for details.

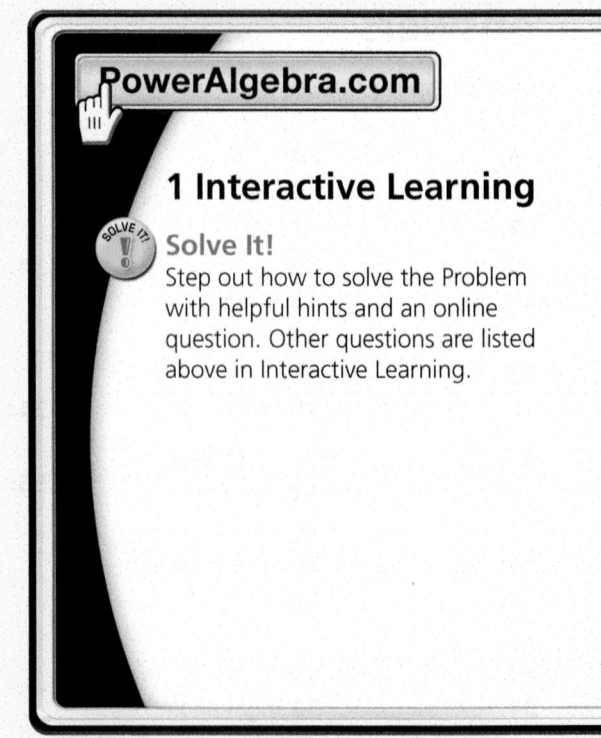

PowerAlgebra.com

1 Interactive Learning

Solve It!
Step out how to solve the Problem with helpful hints and an online question. Other questions are listed above in Interactive Learning.

Problem 2 Using a Radical Equation

Clocks The time t in seconds it takes for a pendulum of a clock to complete a full swing is approximated by the equation $t = 2\sqrt{\frac{\ell}{3.3}}$, where ℓ is the length of the pendulum, in feet. If the pendulum of a clock completes a full swing in 3 s, what is the length of the pendulum? Round to the nearest tenth of a foot.

Know	Need	Plan
• A function relating t and ℓ • The value of t	The value for ℓ, the length of the pendulum	Substitute for t in the function and solve for ℓ.

Think

Have you solved problems like this before?
Yes. You have substituted a value for one variable in a function and then solved for the other variable.

$$t = 2\sqrt{\frac{\ell}{3.3}}$$

$3 = 2\sqrt{\frac{\ell}{3.3}}$ Substitute 3 for t.

$1.5 = \sqrt{\frac{\ell}{3.3}}$ Divide each side by 2 to isolate the radical.

$(1.5)^2 = \left(\sqrt{\frac{\ell}{3.3}}\right)^2$ Square each side.

$2.25 = \frac{\ell}{3.3}$ Simplify.

$7.425 = \ell$ Multiply each side by 3.3.

Check $3 \stackrel{?}{=} 2\sqrt{\frac{7.425}{3.3}}$ Substitute 7.425 for ℓ.

$3 \stackrel{?}{=} 2\sqrt{2.25}$

$3 = 3$ ✔

The pendulum is about 7.4 ft long.

 Got It? 2. How long is a pendulum if each swing takes 1 s?

 **Problem 3** Solving With Radical Expressions on Both Sides

Think

How can you make the equation simpler to solve?
You can *solve a simpler problem* by squaring each side of the equation. You know how to solve equations like $5t - 11 = t + 5$.

What is the solution of $\sqrt{5t - 11} = \sqrt{t + 5}$?

$\sqrt{5t - 11} = \sqrt{t + 5}$

$(\sqrt{5t - 11})^2 = (\sqrt{t + 5})^2$ Square each side.

$5t - 11 = t + 5$ Simplify.

$4t - 11 = 5$ Subtract t from each side.

$4t = 16$ Add 11 to each side.

$t = 4$ Divide each side by 4.

Check $\sqrt{5(4) - 11} \stackrel{?}{=} \sqrt{4 + 5}$ Substitute 4 for t.

$\sqrt{9} = \sqrt{9}$ ✔

 Got It? 3. What is the solution of $\sqrt{7x - 4} = \sqrt{5x + 10}$?

Problem 2

Q If a pendulum is 13.2 ft long, how long does each swing take? Explain. **[4 s; $2\sqrt{(13.2 \div 3.3)} = 4$]**

Q Is 3 substituted for the value of ℓ or the value of t? Explain. **[Because 3 is the number of seconds per swing, it is substituted for t.]**

Q How is solving this equation similar to solving Problem 1? How is it different? **[In order to isolate the radical you must divide both sides rather than subtract from both sides. Both solutions require that you square each side of the equation.]**

Got It?

Q If you isolate the radical and then square both sides of the equation, what constant is on the left side of the equation? **[$\frac{1}{4}$]**

Q If you do not isolate the radical first and square both sides of the equation, what equation will you have to solve? **[$1 = 4\left(\frac{\sqrt{\ell}}{33}\right)^2$]**

Q Will both methods result in the same answer for ℓ? Explain. **[Yes; either way, you get $\frac{1}{4}$ on the left side of the equation and the radicand on the right side.]**

Problem 3

Q What kind of equation results when both sides of the radical equation are squared? How many solutions does it have? **[a linear equation; one solution]**

Got It?   **ERROR PREVENTION**

Students should check their answers in the original radical equation.

Answers

Solve It!
$4\sqrt{16 - 2h}$; explanations may vary.

Got It?

1. 9

2. 0.825 ft

3. 7

---

2 Guided Instruction

Each Problem is worked out and supported online.

Problem 1
Solving by Isolating the Radical

Problem 2
Using a Radical Equation
     Animated

Problem 3
Solving With Radical Expressions on Both Sides
     Animated

Problem 4
Identifying Extraneous Solutions
     Animated

Problem 5
Identifying Equations with No Solution

Support in Algebra 1 Companion
• Vocabulary
• Key Concepts
• Got It?

Problem 4

Q What is the first step for solving a quadratic equation that is not missing its "x" term? **[Set the equation equal to zero.]**

Q Could the quadratic equation be solved using any other methods? Explain. **[Yes, it could be solved using graphing, completing the square, or the Quadratic Formula.]**

Q Why should you check your work by substituting the possible solutions into the original equation rather than the quadratic equation formed when both sides are squared? **[The solutions might satisfy the quadratic equation but not the original equation.]**

Got It?

Remind students that $(-y)^2 = (-y) \cdot (-y) = y^2$.

Problem 5

Q Why is the first step for solving the equation to subtract 8 from each side? **[Because you need to isolate the radical before squaring both sides.]**

Q How can you use mathematical reasoning to determine that the equation $\sqrt{3y} + 8 = 2$ does not have a solution? **[The value that must be added to 8 to get a sum of 2 is −6, and the principal root of $\sqrt{3y}$ must be a nonnegative number.]**

When you solve an equation by squaring each side, you create a new equation. The new equation may have solutions that do not satisfy the original equation.

Original Equation	Square each side.	New Equation	Apparent Solutions
$x = 3$	$x^2 = 3^2$	$x^2 = 9$	3, −3

In the example above, −3 does not satisfy the original equation. It is an *extraneous* solution. An **extraneous solution** is an apparent solution that does not satisfy the original equation. Always substitute each apparent solution into the original equation to check for extraneous solutions.

 Problem 4 **Identifying Extraneous Solutions**

What is the solution of $n = \sqrt{n + 12}$?

$$n = \sqrt{n + 12}$$
$$n^2 = (\sqrt{n + 12})^2 \qquad \text{Square each side.}$$
$$n^2 = n + 12 \qquad \text{Simplify.}$$
$$n^2 - n - 12 = 0 \qquad \text{Subtract } n + 12 \text{ from each side.}$$
$$(n - 4)(n + 3) = 0 \qquad \text{Factor the quadratic equation.}$$
$$n - 4 = 0 \quad \text{or} \quad n + 3 = 0 \qquad \text{Use the Zero-Product Property.}$$
$$n = 4 \quad \text{or} \quad n = -3 \qquad \text{Solve for } n.$$

Check $\quad 4 \overset{?}{=} \sqrt{4 + 12} \quad$ Substitute 4 and −3 for n. $\quad -3 \overset{?}{=} \sqrt{-3 + 12}$

$\qquad\qquad 4 = 4$ ✔ $\qquad\qquad\qquad\qquad\qquad\qquad\qquad -3 \neq 3$

The solution of the original equation is 4. The value −3 is an extraneous solution.

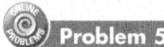 **Got It? 4.** What is the solution of $-y = \sqrt{y + 6}$?

Think

Does an extraneous solution solve the problem?
No. An extraneous solution solves only the new equation formed after squaring both sides. It is not a solution to the problem.

Sometimes you get only extraneous solutions after squaring each side of an equation. In that case, the original equation has no solution.

 Problem 5 **Identifying Equations With No Solution**

What is the solution of $\sqrt{3y} + 8 = 2$?

$$\sqrt{3y} + 8 = 2$$
$$\sqrt{3y} = -6 \qquad \text{Subtract 8 from each side.}$$
$$3y = 36 \qquad \text{Square each side.}$$
$$y = 12 \qquad \text{Divide each side by 3.}$$

Check $\quad \sqrt{3(12)} + 8 \overset{?}{=} 2 \quad$ Substitute 12 for y.

$\qquad\qquad\qquad 14 \neq 2 \quad y = 12$ does not satisfy the original equation.

The apparent solution 12 is extraneous. The original equation has no solution.

Think

Have you seen other equations with no solutions?
Yes. You learned that equations such as $x + 1 = x$ have no solution.

Additional Problems

1. What is the solution to the radical equation $\sqrt{x} + 11 = 21$?

ANSWER $x = 100$

2. The velocity of a projectile is determined by the function $v = \sqrt{\frac{S}{0.03}}$ where S is the horizontal distance in meters traveled by the projectile. If the velocity of a projectile is measured at 150 m/s, what is the distance the projectile travels?

ANSWER 675 m

3. What is the solution to $\sqrt{3m - 6} = \sqrt{m + 23}$?

ANSWER 14.5

4. What is the solution to $x = \sqrt{-x + 6}$?

ANSWER 2 is a solution, −3 is an extraneous solution.

5. Which is the solution to $\sqrt{4r} + 7 = 3$?

A. −4

B. 2

C. 4

D. no solution

ANSWER D

Answers

Got It? (continued)

4. −2

Got It? **5. a.** What is the solution of $6 - \sqrt{2x} = 10$?

b. **Reasoning** How can you determine that the equation $\sqrt{x} = -5$ does not have a solution without going through all the steps of solving the equation?

Lesson Check

Do you know HOW?

Solve each radical equation. Check your solution. If there is no solution, write *no solution*.

1. $\sqrt{3x} + 10 = 16$

2. $\sqrt{r + 5} = 2\sqrt{r - 1}$

3. $\sqrt{2x - 1} = x$

4. $\sqrt{x - 3} = \sqrt{x + 5}$

Do you UNDERSTAND?

5. **Vocabulary** Which is an extraneous solution of $s = \sqrt{s + 2}$?

Ⓐ 2 Ⓒ −1

Ⓑ 0 Ⓓ −2

6. **Reasoning** What is the converse of the conditional statement "If $x = y$, then $x^2 = y^2$"? Is the converse of this statement always true? Explain.

Practice and Problem-Solving Exercises

Ⓐ **Practice** Solve each radical equation. Check your solution.

See Problem 1.

7. $\sqrt{x} + 3 = 5$

8. $\sqrt{t} + 2 = 9$

9. $\sqrt{z} - 1 = 5$

10. $\sqrt{n} - 3 = 6$

11. $\sqrt{2b} + 4 = 8$

12. $3 - \sqrt{t} = -2$

13. $\sqrt{3a + 1} = 7$

14. $\sqrt{10b + 6} = 6$

15. $1 = \sqrt{-2v - 3}$

16. $\sqrt{x - 3} = 4$

17. **Recreation** You are making a tire swing for a playground. The time t in seconds for the tire to make one swing is given by $t = 2\sqrt{\frac{\ell}{3.3}}$, where ℓ is the length of the swing in feet. You want one swing to take 2.5 s. How many feet long should the swing be?

See Problem 2.

18. **Geometry** The length s of one edge of a cube is given by $s = \sqrt{\frac{A}{6}}$, where A represents the cube's surface area. Suppose a cube has an edge length of 9 cm. What is its surface area? Round to the nearest hundredth.

Solve each radical equation. Check your solution.

See Problem 3.

19. $\sqrt{3x + 1} = \sqrt{5x - 8}$

20. $\sqrt{2y} = \sqrt{9 - y}$

21. $\sqrt{7v - 4} = \sqrt{5v + 10}$

22. $\sqrt{s + 10} = \sqrt{6 - s}$

23. $\sqrt{n + 5} = \sqrt{5n - 11}$

24. $\sqrt{3m + 1} = \sqrt{7m - 9}$

Got It?

Be sure students understand why an equation such as $x^2 = 25$ has two solutions, 5 and −5, while the equation $\sqrt{x} = -5$ has no solutions.

3 Lesson Check

Do you know HOW?

- If students have difficulty with Exercise 2, then remind them to square both 2 and $\sqrt{r - 1}$.

Do you UNDERSTAND?

- If students have difficulty with Exercise 5, then remind them to make a distinction between a radical equation with extraneous solutions and one with no solutions.

Close

Q What is a radical equation? What is the major strategy for solving radical equations? **[Radical equations have variables in the radicand. The major strategy for solving is to isolate the radical and then square both sides of the equation to eliminate the radical expression from the equation.]**

Got It? (continued)

5. a. no solution

b. The principal root of a number is never negative.

Lesson Check

1. 12

2. 3

3. 1

4. no solution

5. C

6. If $x^2 = y^2$, then $x = y$; no, if $x = -1$ and $y = 1$, then $x^2 = y^2$, but $x \neq y$.

Practice and Problem-Solving Exercises

7. 4

8. 49

9. 36

10. 81

11. 8

12. 25

13. 16

14. 3

15. −2

16. 19

17. about 5.2 ft

18. 486 cm^2

19. 4.5

20. 3

21. 7

22. −2

23. 4

24. 2.5

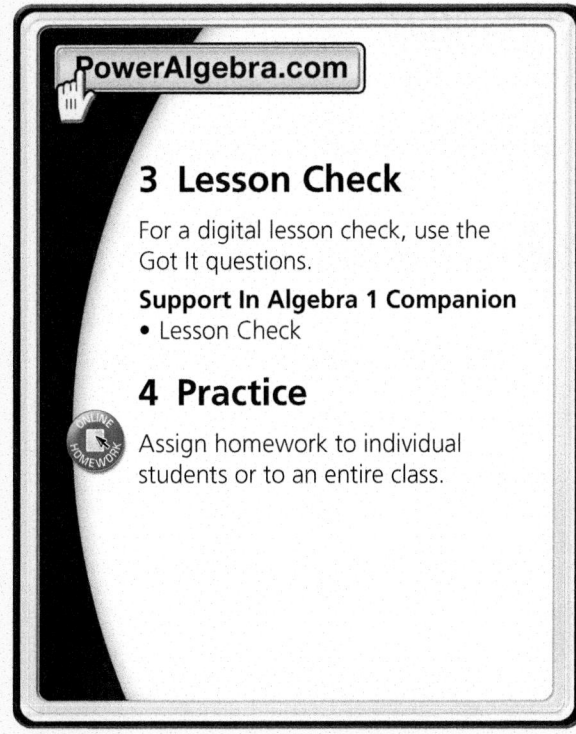

PowerAlgebra.com

3 Lesson Check

For a digital lesson check, use the Got It questions.

Support In Algebra 1 Companion
- Lesson Check

4 Practice

Assign homework to individual students or to an entire class.

4 Practice

ASSIGNMENT GUIDE

Basic: 7–38 all, 40, 44–48 even

Average: 7–35 odd, 37–50

Advanced: 7–35 odd, 37–52

Standardized Test Prep: 53–56

Mixed Review: 57–65

Reasoning exercises have blue headings.

Applications exercises have red headings.

EXERCISE 40: Use the Think About a Plan worksheet in the **Practice and Problem Solving Workbook** (also available in the Teaching Resources in print and online) to further support students' development in becoming independent learners.

HOMEWORK QUICK CHECK

To check students' understanding of key skills and concepts, go over Exercises 11, 25, 37, 38, and 40.

Tell which solutions, if any, are extraneous for each equation.   See Problems 4 and 5.

25. $-z = \sqrt{-z + 6}; z = -3, z = 2$

26. $\sqrt{12 - n} = n; n = -4, n = 3$

27. $y = \sqrt{2y}; y = 0, y = 2$

28. $2a = \sqrt{4a + 3}; a = \frac{3}{2}, a = -\frac{1}{2}$

29. $x = \sqrt{28 - 3x}; x = 4, x = -7$

30. $-t = \sqrt{-6t - 5}; t = -5, t = -1$

Solve each radical equation. Check your solution. If there is no solution, write *no solution*.

31. $x = \sqrt{2x + 3}$

32. $n = \sqrt{4n + 5}$

33. $\sqrt{3b} = -3$

34. $2y = \sqrt{5y + 6}$

35. $-2\sqrt{2r + 5} = 6$

36. $\sqrt{d + 12} = d$

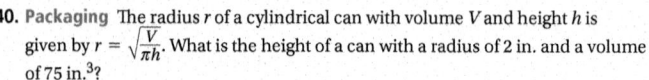

37. Error Analysis A student solved the equation $r = \sqrt{-6r - 5}$ and found the solutions -1 and -5. Describe and correct the student's error.

38. Think About a Plan The total surface area A of Earth, in square kilometers, is related to Earth's radius r, in kilometers, by $r = \sqrt{\frac{A}{4\pi}}$. Earth's radius is about 6378 km. What is its surface area? Round to the nearest square kilometer.
- What equation in one variable can you solve to find Earth's surface area?
- How can you check the reasonableness of your solution?

39. Geometry In the right triangle $\triangle ABC$, the altitude $\overline{CD}$ is at a right angle to the hypotenuse. You can use $CD = \sqrt{(AD)(DB)}$ to find missing lengths.
- **a.** Find AD if $CD = 10$ and $DB = 4$.
- **b.** Find DB if $AD = 20$ and $CD = 15$.

40. Packaging The radius r of a cylindrical can with volume V and height h is given by $r = \sqrt{\frac{V}{\pi h}}$. What is the height of a can with a radius of 2 in. and a volume of 75 in.³?

41. Writing Explain how you would solve the equation $\sqrt{2y} - \sqrt{y + 2} = 0$.

42. Open-Ended Write two radical equations that have 3 for a solution.

Solve each radical equation. Check your solution. If there is no solution, write *no solution*.

43. $\sqrt{5x + 10} = 5$

44. $-6 - \sqrt{3y} = -3$

45. $\sqrt{7p + 5} = \sqrt{p - 3}$

46. $a = \sqrt{7a - 6}$

47. $\sqrt{y + 12} = 3\sqrt{y}$

48. $3 - \sqrt{4a + 1} = 12$

49. Physics The formula $t = \sqrt{\frac{n}{16}}$ gives the time t in seconds for an object that is initially at rest to fall n feet. What is the distance an object falls in the first 10 s?

Answers

Practice and Problem-Solving Exercises
(continued)

25. 2   **26.** -4 **27.** none

28. $-\frac{1}{2}$ **29.** -7 **30.** none

31. 3   **32.** 5   **33.** no solution

34. 2   **35.** no solution

36. 4

37. The student did not check the solutions in the original equations. Both of those solutions are extraneous, so the equation has no solution.

38. 511,185,933 km²

39. a. 25
   b. 11.25

40. about 6 in.

41. Add $\sqrt{y + 2}$ to each side of the equation. Square each side of the equation. Solve for y. Check each apparent solution in the original equation.

42. Answers may vary. Sample: $x - 2 = \sqrt{7 - 2x}$, $\sqrt{3x} = 3$

43. 3   **44.** no solution

45. no solution   **46.** 1, 6

47. 1.5   **48.** no solution

49. 1600 ft

50. Packaging The diagram at the right shows a piece of cardboard that makes a box when sections of it are folded and taped. The ends of the box are x inches by x inches, and the body of the box is 10 in. long.
  a. Write an equation for the volume V of the box.
  b. Solve the equation in part (a) for x.
  c. Find the integer values of x that would give the box a volume between 40 in.^{3} and 490 in.^{3}, inclusive.

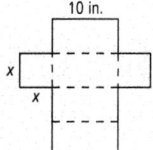

10 in.

Ⓒ **Challenge** **51. Reasoning** Explain the difference between squaring $\sqrt{x-1}$ and $\sqrt{x}-1$.

52. a. Reasoning What is the solution of $\sqrt{7y+18}=y$? What is the extraneous solution?
  b. Multiply one side of $\sqrt{7y+18}=y$ by -1. What is the solution of the new equation? What is an extraneous solution of the new equation?
  c. What do you think will happen to the solutions and extraneous solutions of $\sqrt{y+2}=y$ if you multiply one side by -1? Explain.

Standardized Test Prep

SAT/ACT **53.** What are the solutions of $\sqrt{c^2-17}=8$?
  Ⓐ 6, 9 Ⓑ 8, −8 Ⓒ 8, 0 Ⓓ 9, −9

54. Sam is building a fence around a triangular flower garden. What is the perimeter of the garden? Round your answer to the nearest tenth of a meter.
  Ⓕ 14.1 m Ⓗ 24.1 m
  Ⓖ 20.0 m Ⓘ 50.0 m

$5\sqrt{2}$ m $5\sqrt{2}$ m

10 m

55. What is the slope-intercept form of the equation $2x+5y=40$?
  Ⓐ $y=-2x+8$ Ⓑ $y=-\frac{2}{5}x+8$ Ⓒ $y=\frac{2}{5}x+8$ Ⓓ $y=2x+8$

Short Response **56.** Write the equation of the line passing through $(1,-1)$ with a slope of $\frac{1}{2}$ in three different forms. When would each of the forms be useful?

Mixed Review

Simplify each expression. ◀ See Lesson 10-3.

57. $\sqrt{8}+3\sqrt{2}$ **58.** $(2\sqrt{5}-6)(9+3\sqrt{5})$ **59.** $\dfrac{2}{\sqrt{3}+\sqrt{8}}$

Use the quadratic formula to solve each equation. ◀ See Lesson 9-6.

60. $3a^2+4a+3=0$ **61.** $2f^2-8=0$ **62.** $6m^2+13m+6=0$

Get Ready! To prepare for Lesson 10-5, do Exercises 63–65.

Graph each function by translating $y=|x|$. ◀ See Lesson 5-8.

63. $y=|x+2|$ **64.** $y=|x|-3$ **65.** $y=|x-4|$

---

57. $5\sqrt{2}$ **58.** −24

59. $-\dfrac{2\sqrt{3}-4\sqrt{2}}{5}$ **60.** no solution

61. −2, 2 **62.** $-\frac{3}{2}, -\frac{2}{3}$

63.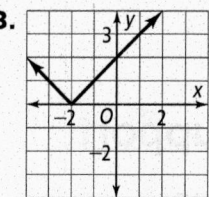

64.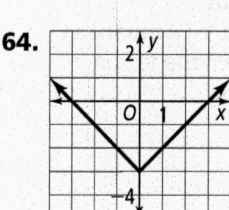

65.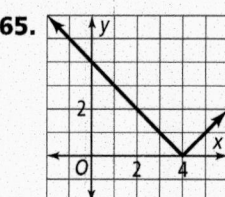

---

50. a. $V=10x^2$
  b. $x=\dfrac{\sqrt{10V}}{10}$
  c. 2, 3, 4, 5, 6, 7 in.

51. The square of $\sqrt{x-1}$ will have only 2 terms, while the square of $\sqrt{x}-1$ will have three terms.

52. a. 9; −2
  b. $\sqrt{7y+18}=-y$; 9
  c. They will switch. $\sqrt{y+2}=y$ has a solution of 2 and an extraneous solution of −1. $\sqrt{y+2}=-y$ has a solution of −1 and an extraneous solution of 2.

53. D **54.** H **55.** B

56. [4] Answers may vary. Sample:
  $y+1=\frac{1}{2}(x-1)$, useful for graphing the line using a point and the slope;
  $y=\frac{1}{2}x-\frac{3}{2}$, useful for finding the y-intercept; $x-2y=3$, useful for finding the x- and y-intercepts.
  [3] one minor error
  [2] two errors OR no explanations given
  [1] equations correct with no work or explanations shown

Additional Instructional Support

Algebra 1 Companion
Students can use the **Algebra 1 Companion** worktext (4 pages) as you teach the lesson. Use the Companion to support

- New Vocabulary
- Key Concepts
- Got It for each Problem
- Lesson Check

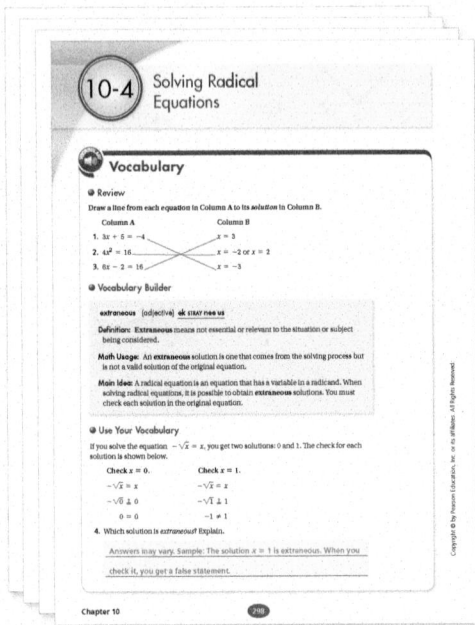

ELL Support
Focus on Language Investigate the word *extraneous*. Analyze the word for its root and suffix. "Extra-" means "outside or not belonging" and the suffix "-eous" means "composed of or resembling." The suffix –an (extr**an**eous) is used to form an adjective from a noun base. Discuss with students the meaning of *extraneous* (something that is outside or not belonging) and examples of things that do not belong.

Assess Understanding The period of a mechanical swing is $t = 2\sqrt{\ell}$, where t is the time of each swing in seconds and ℓ is the length of the swing in inches. Ask students to draw a picture to show the length of the swing after solving the problem when each swing takes 6 s.

5 Assess & Remediate

Lesson Quiz
1. What is the solution to the radical equation $\sqrt{x - 8} = 6$?
2. **Do you UNDERSTAND?** The average speed of an object (in feet per second) is determined by the equation $S = 4\sqrt{d}$, where d is the distance in feet the object is dropped. If a rock dropped from the top of a bridge reaches an average speed of 60 ft/sec, how high is the bridge?
3. What is the solution to $\sqrt{9r - 4} = \sqrt{6r + 2}$?
4. What is the solution to $x = \sqrt{-2x + 35}$?
5. Which is the solution to $5 - \sqrt{3x} = 11$?
   - **A.** −12
   - **B.** 6
   - **C.** 12
   - **D.** no solution

ANSWERS TO LESSON QUIZ
1. $x = 44$
2. 225 ft
3. $r = 22$
4. 5 is a solution, −7 is an extraneous solution.
5. D

PRESCRIPTION FOR REMEDIATION
Use the student work on the Lesson Quiz to prescribe a differentiated review assignment.

Points	Differentiated Remediation
0–2	Intervention
3–4	On-level
5	Extension

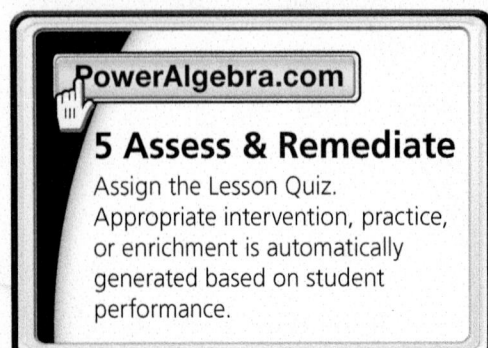

PowerAlgebra.com

5 Assess & Remediate
Assign the Lesson Quiz. Appropriate intervention, practice, or enrichment is automatically generated based on student performance.

Intervention
- **Reteaching** (2 pages) Provides reteaching and practice exercises for the key lesson concepts. Use with struggling students or absent students.
- **English Language Learner Support** Helps students develop and reinforce mathematical vocabulary and key concepts.

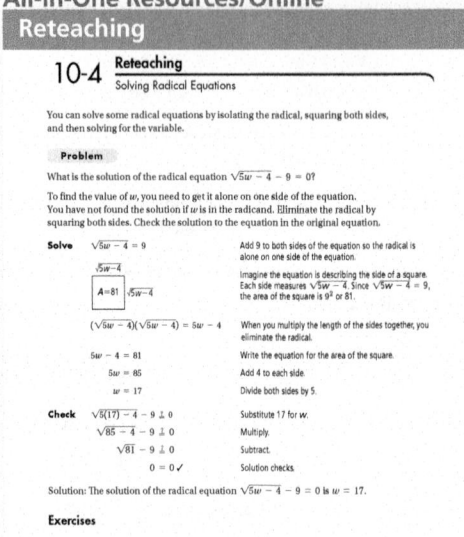

Differentiated Remediation *continued*

On-Level

- **Practice** (2 pages) Provides extra practice for each lesson. For simpler practice exercises, use the Form K Practice pages found in the All-in-One Teaching Resources and online.

- **Think About a Plan** Helps students develop specific problem-solving skills and strategies by providing scaffolded guiding questions.

- **Standardized Test Prep** Focuses on all major exercises, all major question types, and helps students prepare for the high-stakes assessments.

Extension

- **Enrichment** Provides students with interesting problems and activities that extend the concepts of the lesson.

- **Activities, Games, and Puzzles** Worksheets that can be used for concepts development, enrichment, and for fun!

Practice and Problem Solving WKBK/All-in-One Resources/Online
Practice page 1

10-4 Practice   Form G
Solving Radical Equations

Solve each radical equation. Check your solution.

1. $\sqrt{x} + 4 = 7$ 9
2. $\sqrt{2t} - 3 = 11$ 98
3. $4 - \sqrt{2x} = -6$ 50
4. $\sqrt{6c + 4} = 8$ 10
5. $\sqrt{3t - 2} = 5$ 9
6. $2 = \sqrt{-3y - 5}$ −3
7. $\sqrt{5n - 4} = 6$ 8
8. $\sqrt{\frac{k}{16}} = 16$ ±8
9. $\sqrt{\frac{q}{8}} - 3 = -32$ no solution

10. You decide to install a rope swing at the bend in the river. The time t in seconds for the rope swing to make one swing is given by $2\sqrt{\frac{l}{3.3}}$, where l is the length of the rope swing in feet. If one swing takes 3.5 seconds, how long is the rope swing? Round your answer to the nearest tenth of a foot. 10.1 ft

11. The radius r of a sphere is given by $r = \sqrt{\frac{SA}{4\pi}}$, where SA represents the sphere's surface area. If a sphere has a surface area of 531 in.², what is the length of its radius? Use $\pi = 3.14$. Round to the nearest hundredth of an inch. about 6.56 in.

12. The speed V in feet per second that an acorn falls from a tree is given by $V = \sqrt{64d}$, where d is the distance in feet that the acorn has fallen. An acorn hits the ground at a speed of 28 feet per second. How far did the acorn fall? 12.25 ft

13. Harrison bought a 10-foot ramp to load his dirt bike into the back of his truck. The ramp hooks to the 3-foot-high tailgate. How far away from the tailgate does the ramp sit on the ground? Round your answer to the nearest tenth of a foot. 9.5 ft

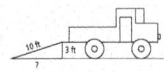

Practice and Problem Solving WKBK/All-in-One Resources/Online
Practice page 2

10-4 Practice *(continued)*   Form G
Solving Radical Equations

Solve each radical equation. Check your solution.

14. $\sqrt{4d + 3} = \sqrt{7d - 3}$ 2
15. $\sqrt{x + 7} = \sqrt{15 - x}$ 4
16. $\sqrt{48 - 3y} = \sqrt{3y - 6}$ 9
17. $\sqrt{a^2 + 20} = \sqrt{9a}$ 5; 4
18. $\sqrt{2x^2 + 17} = \sqrt{(x + 3)^2}$ 4; 2
19. $\sqrt{d + 7} = 3\sqrt{4d}$ $\frac{1}{5}$
20. $11 = \sqrt{12b - 59}$ 15
21. $\frac{t}{3} = \sqrt{f - 2}$ 6; 3
22. $\frac{t}{4} = \sqrt{\frac{7t - 10}{16}}$ 2; 5

Solve each radical equation. Check your solution. If there is no solution, write **no solution**.

23. $x = \sqrt{2x + 8}$ 4
24. $m = \sqrt{-6m + 7}$ 1
25. $-n = \sqrt{4n + 12}$ −2
26. $x = \sqrt{3x + 28}$ 7
27. $\frac{-y}{2} = \sqrt{\frac{-5y + 24}{4}}$ −8
28. $-f = \sqrt{-f + 56}$ −8

29. **Error Analysis** A student solved the equation $-t = \sqrt{5t + 14}$ and found the solutions 7 and −2. Describe and correct the error.
The student did not check the answers to find that 7 is an extraneous solution.

30. The distance d in feet that it takes an automobile to stop if it is traveling S miles per hour is given by $S = \sqrt{21d}$. Find the distance it would take an automobile traveling 60 miles per hour to stop. Round your answer to the nearest tenth of a foot. 171.4 ft

31. **Open-Ended** Write two radical equations that have no solutions. Explain why all the solutions are extraneous.
Answers may vary. Sample: $-4 = \sqrt{x} + 1$, $-9 = \sqrt{3y}$; Any value under a radical sign must be positive.

All-in-One Resources/Online
Enrichment

10-4 Enrichment
Solving Radical Equations

The Radical and the Pendulum

Before the invention of electric and digital clocks, people often used pendulum clocks to keep time. A simple pendulum is shown in the diagram at the right.

The time it takes for a pendulum to swing back and forth and return to its starting position is called the period (T) of the pendulum. The period can be calculated by using a radical equation, where l is the length of the pendulum and g is the acceleration due to gravity:

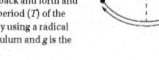

$$T = 2\pi\sqrt{\frac{l}{g}}$$

Solve. Calculate answers to the nearest tenth. Use 3.14 for π.

1. The pendulum of a large clock in the museum lobby has a period of 3 s. How long is the pendulum, in centimeters? (Assume that on Earth, acceleration due to gravity is 960 cm/s².)
219.1 cm

2. The pendulum of an antique wall clock makes one complete swing every 1 s. What is the length of the pendulum?
24.3 cm

3. The pendulum of a cuckoo clock is 4 cm long. How many full swings does the pendulum make in 3 s?
7 full swings

4. Acceleration due to gravity is only 160 cm/s² on the moon. If the museum clock in Exercise 1 is taken to the moon, how will the period of its pendulum change?
the period will be longer

5. Suppose the same museum clock is taken to a planet where acceleration due to gravity is three times that of the value on Earth. What will happen to the period of the pendulum?
the period will be shorter

6. Suppose the cuckoo clock in Exercise 3 is taken to the moon. How many full swings would the pendulum make in 5 s?
5 full swings

Practice and Problem Solving WKBK/All-in-One Resources/Online
Think About a Plan

10-4 Think About a Plan
Solving Radical Equations

Packaging The radius r of a cylindrical can with volume V and height h is given by $r = \sqrt{\frac{V}{\pi h}}$. What is the height of a can with a radius of 2 in. and a volume of 75 in.²?

KNOW

1. What equation can you use to find the height of a cylindrical can? $r = \sqrt{\frac{V}{\pi h}}$

2. What known values will you substitute into the equation?   radius; volume

3. What is the meaning of the symbol π?   3.14

NEED

4. Which variable represents the height of the can? h

PLAN

5. What equation do you get after substituting the known values? $2 = \sqrt{\frac{75}{\pi h}}$

6. Can you solve this equation by squaring both sides?   yes

7. How can you isolate the remaining variable?   multiply both sides by h and divide both sides by 4

8. Are there any extraneous solutions? If so, what are they?   no

9. What is the height of the can?   5.97 in.

10. Is the solution reasonable? Explain.   yes; the radius is 2 in., so it makes sense that the height is about 6 in.

Practice and Problem Solving WKBK/All-in-One Resources/Online
Standardized Test Prep

10-4 Standardized Test Prep
Solving Radical Equations

Multiple Choice

For Exercises 1–6, choose the correct letter.

1. What is the solution of the radical equation $\sqrt{t} + 9 = 16$?   D
A. 5   B. 7   C. 25   D. 49

2. What is the solution of $\sqrt{6g - 23} = \sqrt{12 - g}$?   F
F. 5   G. 7   H. 11   I. 35

3. What are the solutions of $\sqrt{d^2 - 11} = 5$?   D
A. 4, −4   B. 5, −5   C. 5, 6   D. 6, −6

4. Which is the extraneous solution of $-x = \sqrt{2x + 15}$?   I
F. −5   G. −3   H. 3   I. 5

5. The pendulum of a cuckoo clock completes one full swing every t seconds. The variable t is determined by the function $t = 2\sqrt{\frac{l}{3.3}}$ where l is the length in meters of the pendulum. Each swing takes 0.5 seconds. How many centimeters long is the pendulum?   A
A. 20.625 cm   B. 41.25 cm   C. 82.5 cm   D. 330 cm

6. A company invests $15,000 in an account that compounds interest annually. After two years, the account is worth $16,099.44. Use the function $A = P(1 + r)^2$, where r is the annual interest rate, P is the principal, and A is the amount of money after t years. What is the interest rate of the account?   G
F. 1.04%   G. 3.6%   H. 5.4%   I. 7.3%

Extended Response

7. The radius of Earth is about 6378 kilometers. The escape velocity V_e is determined by the function $V_e = \sqrt{2gR}$ where g is acceleration due to gravity in m/s² and R is the radius of Earth in meters. If g for Earth is 9.8 m/s², what is the escape velocity of Earth? Show your work. 11,180.7 m/s

[4] Correct solution with all work shown completely.
[3] All work shown with only a minor calculation error.
[2] Some parts of solution done correctly but major errors prevent correct completion.
[1] Correct solution with no work shown.
[0] No attempt made or no work done correctly.

Online Teacher Resource Center
Activities, Games, and Puzzles

10-4 Activity: Calculator Explorations
Solving Radical Equations

You have seen linear equations such as $y = x$ and nonlinear equations such as $y = x^2$. Now you will explore radical equations involving $\sqrt{x}$. You will discover that some equations have exact integer solutions, while others do not. Work with a partner to complete this activity.

Consider $\sqrt{x} + 10 = 15$. Which value of x makes this equation true? Use mental math and record your answer here.

Check your answer by evaluating $\sqrt{x} + 10$ for the values of x in the table below. Round your answers to the nearest hundredth if necessary.

x	20	21	22	23	24	25	26
$\sqrt{x} + 10$	14.47	14.58	14.69	14.80	14.90	15.00	15.10

1. Was your initial answer correct? Does the equation have an exact integer solution?
Answers may vary. Sample: yes; yes

2. Explain why you would not evaluate $\sqrt{x} + 10$ for any negative values of x.
If $x < 0$, then the square root is not defined.

3. Consider $\sqrt{x} - 1 = 5.8$. What can you tell about the value of x from the information in the table below? (Answers are rounded to two decimal places.)
It looks like there is some value of x between 40 and 50 for which $\sqrt{x} - 1 = 5.8$, but it is not possible to tell anything beyond this value.

x	30	40	50	60	70	80	90
$\sqrt{x} - 1$	4.48	5.32	6.07	6.75	7.37	7.94	8.49

Choose four values of x between 40 and 50 that should give you a better idea about the solution to the function $\sqrt{x} - 1 = 5.8$. Complete the table to get a better approximation of the solution. Answers may vary. Sample:

x	46	47	48	49
$\sqrt{x} - 1$	5.78	5.86	5.93	6.00

4. Between which two whole numbers would you find the solution to $\sqrt{x} - 1 = 5.8$?
Answers may vary. Sample: between 46 and 47

1 Interactive Learning

Solve It!

PURPOSE To graph data and write an equation for a square root function

PROCESS Students may write and graph an equation using a table of values or create a table of values to write an equation.

FACILITATE

Q What are five ordered pairs, of the format (area, length of wall), that will lie on the graph? **[Answers may vary. Sample: (16, 4), (9, 3), (4, 2), (1, 1), (0, 0)]**

Q After plotting the points, should you connect the points with a smooth curve? Explain. **[Yes, because area and length can both be measured using non-whole numbers.]**

Q Why is the curve only in the first quadrant? **[Area and length must be positive.]**

ANSWER See Solve It in Answers on next page.

CONNECT THE MATH In the Solve It, students relate the points on a curve to its equation. In the lesson, students learn to graph square root functions, including functions with horizontal and vertical translations from the origin.

2 Guided Instruction

Take Note

The square root function includes only the principal root of the independent variable, x. Discuss with students how the graph of $y = \pm\sqrt{x}$ looks different from the graph shown in the Take Note.

Objectives To graph square root functions
To translate graphs of square root functions

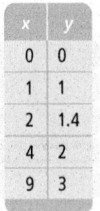

Getting Ready!

> This graph isn't a line or a complete parabola. It must be part of another family.

A landscaper is planning to build a square yard with a wall on one side. The size of the yard will determine the project's cost. Graph the length of the wall as a function of the area of the yard. What is an equation of this graph? Explain your reasoning.

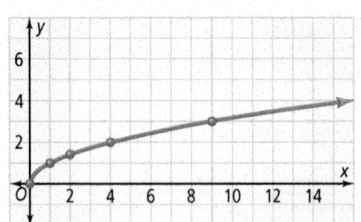

Dynamic Activity Square Root Functions

Lesson Vocabulary
• square root function

The Solve It involves a *square root function*. Square root functions are examples of radical functions.

Key Concept Square Root Functions

A **square root function** is a function containing a square root with the independent variable in the radicand. The parent square root function is $y = \sqrt{x}$.

The table and graph below show the parent square root function.

x	y
0	0
1	1
2	1.4
4	2
9	3

Essential Understanding You can graph a square root function by plotting points or using a translation of the parent square root function.

10-5 Preparing to Teach

BIG idea Functions

ESSENTIAL UNDERSTANDINGS

• The parent function for the family of square root functions is $y = \sqrt{x}$.

• Square root functions can be graphed by plotting points or using translations of the parent square root function.

Math Background

Square root functions can be graphed by creating a table of values and plotting points or by using translations of the function $y = \sqrt{x}$. The translations to a square root function have the following formats:

When a constant is added to the variable in the radicand, the translation is right or left. If the constant is positive, the translation is to the left. If the constant is negative, the translation is to the right. When a constant is added to the radical term, the translation is up or down. If the constant is positive, the translation up. If the constant is negative, the translation is down. When a constant is added or subtracted to the radicand and also added or subtracted to the radical term, then the translation is a horizontal shift and a vertical shift.

In addition to these methods, square root functions can be graphed by recognizing their inverse relationships to quadratic functions in which the domain has been restricted. Pointing out the physical relationship between the graphs and the algebraic relationship between the equations of the parent quadratic and square root functions will help students understand inverse functions in subsequent math courses.

Support Student Learning

Use the **Algebra 1 Companion** to engage and support students during instructions. See Lesson Resources at the end of this lesson for details.

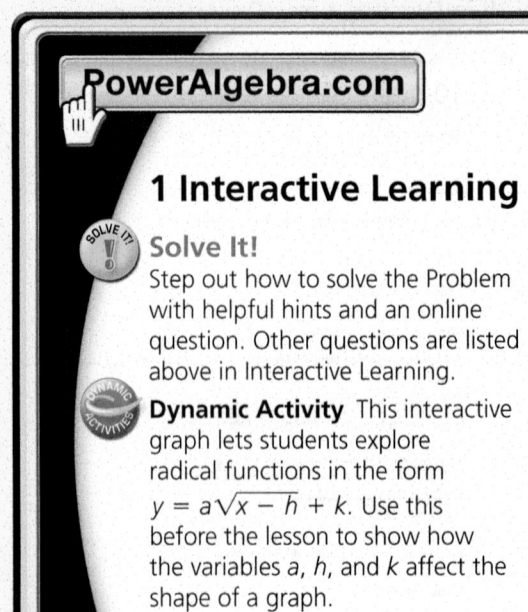

PowerAlgebra.com

1 Interactive Learning

Solve It!
Step out how to solve the Problem with helpful hints and an online question. Other questions are listed above in Interactive Learning.

Dynamic Activity This interactive graph lets students explore radical functions in the form $y = a\sqrt{x - h} + k$. Use this before the lesson to show how the variables a, h, and k affect the shape of a graph.

For real numbers, the value of the radicand cannot be negative. So the domain of a square root function is limited to values of x for which the radicand is greater than or equal to 0.

 Problem 1 Finding the Domain of a Square Root Function

What is the domain of the function $y = 2\sqrt{3x - 9}$?

Think	Write
The radicand cannot be negative.	$3x - 9 \geq 0$
Solve for x.	$3x \geq 9$
	$x \geq 3$
	The domain of the function is the set of real numbers greater than or equal to 3.

 **Got It? 1.** What is the domain of $y = \sqrt{-2x + 5}$?

 Problem 2 Graphing a Square Root Function

Engineering Graph the function $I = \frac{1}{5}\sqrt{P}$, which gives the current I in amperes for a certain circuit with P watts of power. When will the current exceed 2 amperes?

Plan
How can you solve this problem?
Make a chart of ordered pairs that satisfy the equation. Then plot the ordered pairs on a graph.

Step 1 Make a table.

Current in Circuit

Power (watts)	Current (amperes)
0	0
10	0.6
50	1.4
100	2

Step 2 Plot the points on a graph.

Current in Circuit

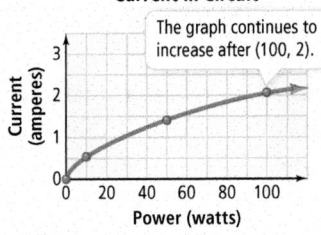

The graph continues to increase after (100, 2).

The current will exceed 2 amperes when the power is more than 100 watts.

 **Got It? 2. a.** When will the current in Problem 2 exceed 1.5 amperes?
  b. Reasoning By how many times must you increase the power to double the current?

Q What happens if you substitute 0 for x in the equation? [**The radicand is −9, and the square root of −9 is not a real number.**]

Q What other numbers can you substitute for x that also produce a negative radicand? [**Any numbers less than 3.**]

Q What value of x makes the radicand equal 0? [**3**]

Q What inequality names the restrictions for the domain of this function? [**$x \geq 3$**]

Q Given the domain for the function, what is the range of the function? [**All real numbers greater than or equal to 0.**]

Got It?   ERROR PREVENTION

If students report that the domain is $x \geq \frac{5}{2}$, then they likely forgot to reverse the direction of the inequality symbol when they divided by $−2$.

Problem 2

Q What equation could you use to determine the value of P for which I will be 2 amperes? [**$2 = \frac{1}{5}\sqrt{P}$**]

Q How does the graph of this function compare with the parent square root function? [**It has the same shape, but rises more slowly.**]

Got It?
Students can add more values to their tables to accurately determine when the current will be more than 1.5 amperes.

2 Guided Instruction

 Each Problem is worked out and supported online.

Problem 1
Finding the Domain of a Square Root Function
Animated

Problem 2
Graphing a Square Root Function
Animated

Problem 3
Graphing a Vertical Translation

Problem 4
Graphing a Horizontal Translation
Animated

Support in Algebra 1 Companion
• Vocabulary
• Key Concepts
• Got It?

Answers

Solve It!

Yard Size

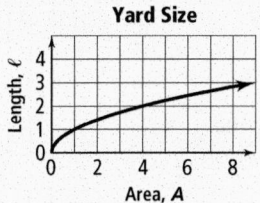

$\ell = \sqrt{A}$; explanations may vary.

Got It?

1. $x \leq 2.5$

2. a. when the power is more than 56.25 watts
  b. 4

Problem 3

> **Q** How can you use the graph of $y = \sqrt{x}$ to graph $y = \sqrt{x} + 2$? [For each point on $y = \sqrt{x}$ count up 2 units to plot a point.]

Got It?

Be sure students know that vertical translations affect only the range of a square root function.

Problem 4

> **Q** What is the domain for this function? [$x \geq -3$]
>
> **Q** What is the range for this function? [$y \geq 0$]

Got It?

Have students compare the function with the function in Problem 4. The difference should give them a clue about how the graph is different from the parent function.

3 Lesson Check

Do you know HOW?

- If students have difficulty with Exercise 2, then have them make a table of values or add values to the table they have.

Do you UNDERSTAND?

- If students have difficulty with Exercise 6, then remind them of the difference between having negative domain values and having negative radicand values.

Close

> **Q** Why are the domains of square root functions not all real numbers? [The domains of square root functions must be restricted to those values of x that give a radicand that is greater than or equal to 0.]

For any positive number k, graphing $y = \sqrt{x} + k$ translates the graph of $y = \sqrt{x}$ up k units. Graphing $y = \sqrt{x} - k$ translates the graph of $y = \sqrt{x}$ down k units.

Think

Is this similar to a problem you've seen before?
Yes. You have graphed functions of the form $y = |x| + k$ by translating the graph of $y = |x|$.

Problem 3 Graphing a Vertical Translation

What is the graph of $y = \sqrt{x} + 2$?

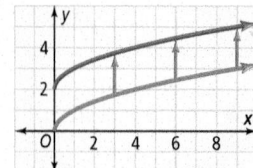

For the graph of $y = \sqrt{x} + 2$, the graph of $y = \sqrt{x}$ is shifted 2 units up.

Got It? 3. What is the graph of $y = \sqrt{x} - 3$?

For any positive number h, graphing $y = \sqrt{x + h}$ translates the graph of $y = \sqrt{x}$ to the left h units. Graphing $y = \sqrt{x - h}$ translates the graph of $y = \sqrt{x}$ to the right h units.

Think

Is there another way to solve this problem?
Yes. You could make a table of ordered pairs that satisfy the equation and then plot them.

Problem 4 Graphing a Horizontal Translation

What is the graph of $y = \sqrt{x + 3}$?

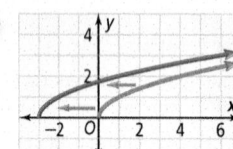

For the graph of $y = \sqrt{x + 3}$, the graph of $y = \sqrt{x}$ is shifted 3 units to the left.

Got It? 4. What is the graph of $y = \sqrt{x - 3}$?

Lesson Check

Do you know HOW?

1. What is the domain of the function $y = \sqrt{x + 3}$?

Graph each function.

2. $y = 2\sqrt{x}$

3. $y = \sqrt{x} - 6$

Do you UNDERSTAND?

4. **Vocabulary** Is $y = x\sqrt{5}$ a square root function? Explain.

5. **Writing** Explain how the graph of $y = \sqrt{x - 1}$ is related to the graph of $y = \sqrt{x}$.

6. **Reasoning** Can the domain of a square root function include negative numbers? Explain.

Additional Problems

1. What is the domain of the function $y = \sqrt{2x + 1}$?

   ANSWER $x \geq -0.5$

2. Graph the function $d = \sqrt{1.5h}$ which gives the distance in miles to a horizon when h is the height of the viewer's eyes above the ground in feet. When will the distance the viewer can see be greater than 10 mi?

   ANSWER The distance a viewer can see will exceed 10 mi when the height is approximately 67 ft or greater.

3. What is the graph of $y = \sqrt{x} + 4$?

   ANSWER

   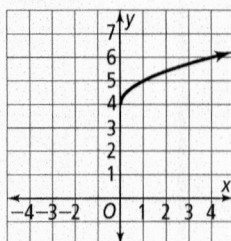

4. What is the graph of $y = \sqrt{x} + 2$?

   ANSWER

   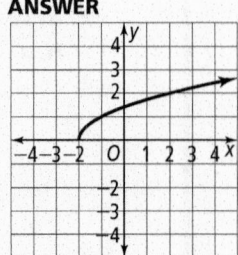

Answers

Got It? (continued)

3.

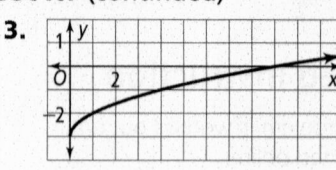

4.

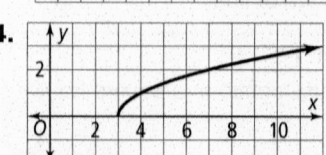

Lesson Check

1. $x \geq -3$

2–6. See back of book.

Practice and Problem-Solving Exercises

 See Problem 1.

Find the domain of each function.

7. $y = \frac{1}{2}\sqrt{x}$

8. $y = \sqrt{x} + 2$

9. $y = \sqrt{x - 7}$

10. $y = 3\sqrt{\frac{x}{3}}$

11. $y = 2.7\sqrt{x + 2} + 11$

12. $y = \sqrt{4x - 13}$

13. $y = \frac{4}{7}\sqrt{18 - x}$

14. $y = \sqrt{3x + 9} - 6$

15. $y = \sqrt{3(x - 4)}$

Make a table of values and graph each function.

 See Problem 2.

16. $y = \sqrt{2x}$

17. $f(x) = 4\sqrt{x}$

18. $y = \sqrt{4x - 8}$

19. $y = \sqrt{3x}$

20. $f(x) = 3\sqrt{x}$

21. $y = -3\sqrt{x}$

22. $f(x) = \frac{1}{3}\sqrt{x}$

23. $y = \sqrt{\frac{x}{2}}$

24. $y = 2\sqrt{x - 3}$

25. Physics The function $v = \sqrt{19.6h}$ models an object's velocity v in meters per second after it has fallen h meters, ignoring the effects of air resistance. Make a table and graph the function. For what values of h will the object's velocity be more than 10 m/s?

Match each function with its graph.

 See Problems 3 and 4.

26. $y = \sqrt{x + 4}$ **27.** $y = \sqrt{x - 2}$ **28.** $y = \sqrt{x} + 4$ **29.** $y = \sqrt{x} - 2$

A.
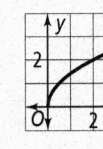

B.
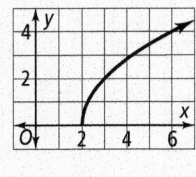

C.
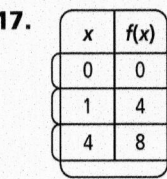

D.
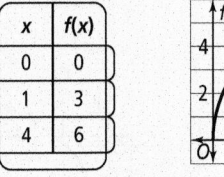

Graph each function by translating the graph of $y = \sqrt{x}$.

30. $y = \sqrt{x} + 5$

31. $y = \sqrt{x} - 5$

32. $y = \sqrt{x} - 1$

33. $y = \sqrt{x + 2}$

34. $f(x) = \sqrt{x - 5}$

35. $f(x) = \sqrt{x - 4}$

36. $y = \sqrt{x} + 1$

37. $y = \sqrt{x + 1}$

38. $y = \sqrt{x - 1}$

39. What are the domain and the range of the function $y = \sqrt{2x - 8}$?

40. What are the domain and the range of the function $y = \sqrt{8 - 2x}$?

Practice and Problem-Solving Exercises

7. $x \geq 0$ **8.** $x \geq 0$ **9.** $x \geq 7$

10. $x \geq 0$ **11.** $x \geq -2$ **12.** $x \geq \frac{13}{4}$

13. $x \leq 18$ **14.** $x \geq -3$ **15.** $x \geq 4$

16.

x	y
0	0
2	2
4.5	3

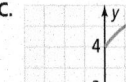

17.

x	f(x)
0	0
1	4
4	8

18.

x	y
2	0
3	2
6	4

19.

x	y
0	0
3	3
5.3	4

20.

x	f(x)
0	0
1	3
4	6

21–40. See back of book.

Answers

Practice and Problem-Solving Exercises
(continued)

41. a.

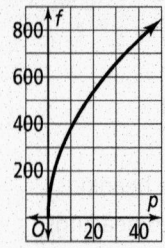

b. about 45 lb/in.²

42. The graph $y = \sqrt{x - 2}$ is the graph of $y = \sqrt{x}$ moved horizontally two units to the right. The student moved the graph two units down.

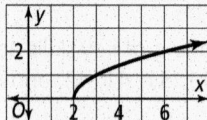

43. about 2800 m/s

44.

x	y
2.5	0
3.5	1
6.5	2

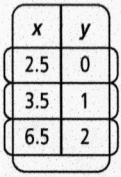

45.

x	f(x)
0	0
1	4
2	5.7
4	8

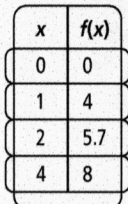

46.

x	y
−6	0
−5	1
−2	2
0	2.4

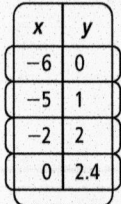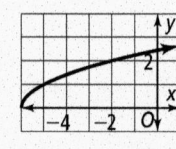

47.

x	y
0	0
2	1
4	1.4
8	2

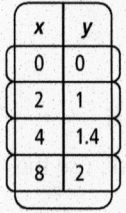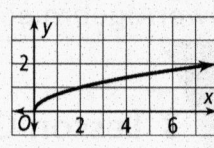

48.

x	y
2	3
3	4
6	5

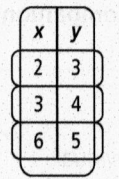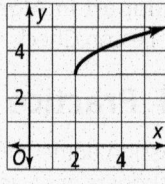

49.

x	f(x)
−2	−4
−1	−3
2	−2

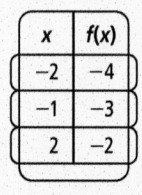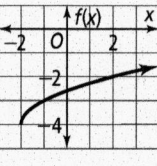

---

41. Firefighting When firefighters are trying to put out a fire, the rate at which they can spray water on the fire depends on the nozzle pressure. You can find the flow rate f in gallons per minute using the function $f = 120\sqrt{p}$, where p is the nozzle pressure in pounds per square inch.
   a. Graph the function.
   b. What nozzle pressure gives a flow rate of 800 gal/min?

42. Error Analysis A student graphed the function $y = \sqrt{x - 2}$ at the right. What mistake did the student make? Draw the correct graph.

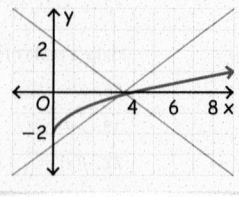

43. Think About a Plan The velocity v in meters per second of a 2,000,000-kg rocket is given by the function $v = \sqrt{E}$, where E is the rocket's kinetic energy in megajoules (MJ). When the rocket's kinetic energy is 8,000,000 MJ, what is its velocity?
   • How can you use a graph to solve the problem?
   • How can you check your answer?

Make a table of values and graph each function.

44. $y = \sqrt{x} - 2.5$ **45.** $f(x) = 4\sqrt{x}$ **46.** $y = \sqrt{x + 6}$

47. $y = \sqrt{0.5x}$ **48.** $y = \sqrt{x - 2} + 3$ **49.** $f(x) = \sqrt{x + 2} - 4$

50. $y = \sqrt{2x} + 3$ **51.** $y = \sqrt{2x + 6} + 1$ **52.** $y = \sqrt{3x - 3} - 2$

53. The graph of $x = y^2$ is shown at the right.
   a. Is this the graph of a function?
   b. How does $x = y^2$ relate to the square root function $y = \sqrt{x}$?
   c. Reasoning What is a function for the part of the graph that is shown in Quadrant IV? Explain.

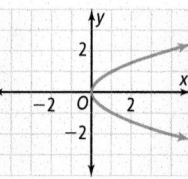

54. Reasoning Without graphing, determine which graph rises more steeply, $y = \sqrt{3x}$ or $y = 3\sqrt{x}$. Explain your answer.

Graph each function by translating the graph of $y = \sqrt{x}$.

55. $y = \sqrt{x + 4} - 1$ **56.** $y = \sqrt{x + 1} + 5$

57. $y = \sqrt{x - 3} - 2$ **58.** $y = \sqrt{x - 6} + 3$

59. $y = \sqrt{x + 2.5} - 1$ **60.** $y = \sqrt{x - 4.5} + 1.5$

Ⓒ **Challenge** **61. a.** Graph $y = \sqrt{x^2} + 5$.
   b. Write a function for the graph you drew that does not require a radical.

62. In parts (a)–(d), graph each function.
   a. $y = \sqrt{4x}$
   b. $y = \sqrt{5x}$
   c. $y = \sqrt{6x}$
   d. $y = \sqrt{-6x}$
   e. Reasoning Describe how the graph of $y = \sqrt{nx}$ changes as the value of n varies.

50.

x	y
0	3
1	4.4
2	5
3	5.4

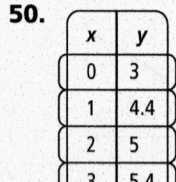

51.

x	y
−3	1
−2	2.4
−1	3
0	3.4

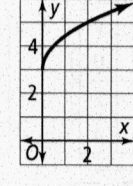

52.

x	y
1	−2
2	−0.3
3	0.4
4	1

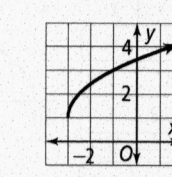

53. a. No; the graph does not pass the vertical-line test.

b. The graph of $y = \sqrt{x}$ is the first-quadrant portion of the graph of $x = y^2$.

c. $y = -\sqrt{x}$

54. $y = 3\sqrt{x}$ rises more steeply because $3 > \sqrt{3}$.

55.

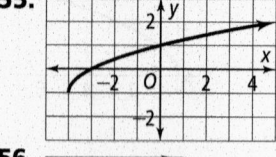

56.

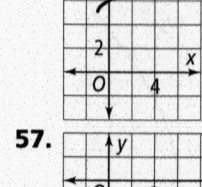

57.

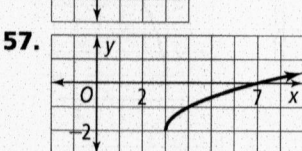

63. Data Collection Mark at least 6 places on a ramp that is at least 6 ft long. For each mark, measure the distance d from the mark to the bottom of the ramp. Measure the time t it takes a ball to roll from each mark to the bottom of the ramp.
  a. Graph the data points (d, t). Connect the points with a smooth curve.
  b. Describe your graph. What function does it resemble?
  c. Is the graph linear? Why or why not?

Standardized Test Prep

GRIDDED RESPONSE

SAT/ACT

64. What is the positive solution of the equation $5.2x^2 + 3.4x - 7.3 = 0$? Use a graphing calculator. Round your answer to the nearest thousandth.

65. What is the value of the expression $\sqrt{12} \cdot \frac{5}{\sqrt{2}}$? Round your answer to the nearest tenth.

66. A scientist graphs the results of a chemical reaction as a linear function that passes through the points $(4, 1)$ and $(-3, 0)$. What is the slope of the line?

67. The diagram at the right shows the distance between a new building and its nearest neighbor. The diagram has a scale of 1 in. : 100 ft. What is the actual distance between the buildings, in feet?

1.5 in.

68. What is the value of the expression $|-4^7| \div \left(\frac{3^3}{4^{-2}} + \frac{4^3}{\sqrt{16}} \right)$? Round your answer to the nearest tenth.

Mixed Review

Solve each radical equation. Check your solutions.   ◀ See Lesson 10-4.

69. $\sqrt{2s + 8} = s$ **70.** $\sqrt{f} = \sqrt{3f + 6}$ **71.** $\sqrt{2r - 3} = r$

72. $\sqrt{-3y} = 2$ **73.** $2x = \sqrt{x - 3}$ **74.** $2t = \sqrt{2t + 56}$

Simplify each expression.   ◀ See Lesson 8-1.

75. $3m + 5 + 2m + 7$ **76.** $(8h^3 + 3h) + (4h^3 + 5h)$

77. $(9b + 2) - (12b + 8)$ **78.** $(4a^2 + 3a + 1) - (3a^2 - 6a)$

79. $(24p + 13) + (9p^2 - 12)$ **80.** $(7c^5 + 5c^3 - 1) - (c^5 - 3c^3)$

Get Ready! **To prepare for Lesson 10-6, do Exercises 81–83.**

The figures in each pair are similar. Find the value of x.   ◀ See Lesson 2-8.

81.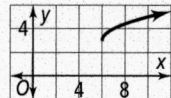
82.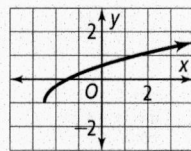
83.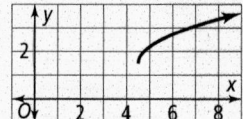

PowerAlgebra.com   **Lesson 10-5**   Graphing Square Root Functions   **631**

---

63. a–c. Check students' work.
64. 0.902   **65.** 12.2
66. $\frac{1}{7}$ **67.** 150
68. 36.6   **69.** 4
70. no solution   **71.** no solution
72. $-\frac{4}{3}$ **73.** no solution
74. 4   **75.** $5m + 12$
76. $12h^3 + 8h$ **77.** $-3b - 6$
78. $a^2 + 9a + 1$ **79.** $9p^2 + 24p + 1$
80. $6c^5 + 8c^3 - 1$ **81.** 9 ft
82. 13.5 ft   **83.** $\frac{4}{3}$ ft

58.

59.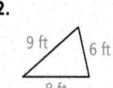

60.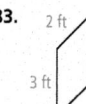

61. a.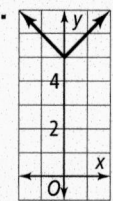

  b. $y = |x| + 5$

62. a.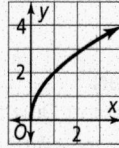

  b.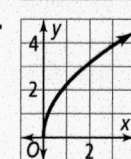

  c.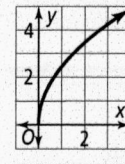

  d.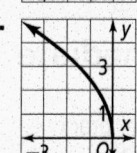

  e. The greater the absolute value of n, the steeper the graph is. If $n < 0$, then the graph lies in Quadrant II. If $n > 0$, then the graph lies in Quadrant I.

Differentiated Remediation

Additional Instructional Support

Algebra 1 Companion
Students can use the **Algebra 1 Companion** worktext (4 pages) as you teach the lesson. Use the Companion to support

- New Vocabulary
- Key Concepts
- Got It for each Problem
- Lesson Check

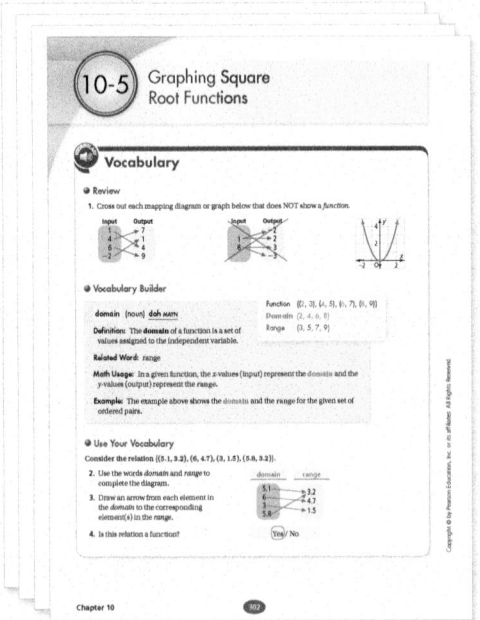

ELL Support
Connect to Previous Knowledge Students may have trouble grasping the notion that −5 is less in value than −3 and yet in a way −5 is a larger negative number than −3, as reflected in its greater absolute value. Discuss some real-world situations involving negative numbers: If your bank account has −$5000 in it, is that a large debt? If the temperature is −20°F, is that a big freeze? If you reach an elevation of −500 ft, is that a considerable depth?

Use Graphic Organizers Model for students how to use a Venn diagram to compare and contrast a simple concept, such as different polygons. Tell them to ask themselves, What is the same and what is different? Have students work in pairs of mixed abilities to make a Venn diagram for the graphs of absolute value and square root functions. Discuss their work and their graphs.

5 Assess & Remediate

Lesson Quiz
1. What is the domain of the function $y = 3\sqrt{4x - 8}$?
2. **Do you UNDERSTAND?** The function $f = 120\sqrt{p}$ gives the flow rate f in gallons per minute when p is the nozzle pressure in pounds per square inch. Estimate the nozzle pressure when the flow rate is 500 gal/min.
3. What is the graph of $y = \sqrt{x} - 1$?
4. What is the graph of $y = \sqrt{x - 4}$?

ANSWERS TO LESSON QUIZ
1. $x \geq 2$
2. The nozzle pressure is approximately 17.4 lb/in.^{2}.
3.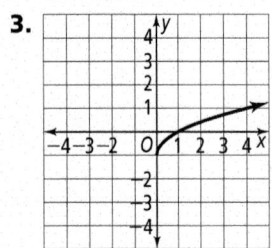
4.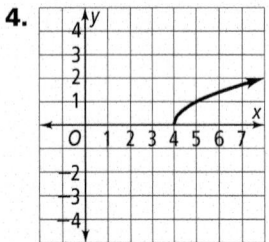

PRESCRIPTION FOR REMEDIATION
Use the student work on the Lesson Quiz to prescribe a differentiated review assignment.

Points	Differentiated Remediation
0–2	Intervention
3	On-level
4	Extension

PowerAlgebra.com

5 Assess & Remediate
Assign the Lesson Quiz. Appropriate intervention, practice, or enrichment is automatically generated based on student performance.

Intervention

- **Reteaching** (2 pages) Provides reteaching and practice exercises for the key lesson concepts. Use with struggling students or absent students.

- **English Language Learner Support** Helps students develop and reinforce mathematical vocabulary and key concepts.

All-in-One Resources/Online
Reteaching

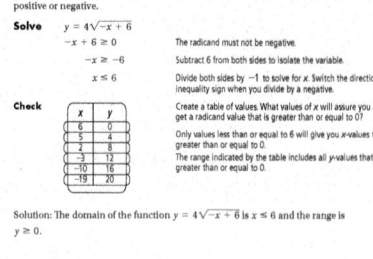

All-in-One Resources/Online
English Language Learner Support

Differentiated Remediation *continued*

On-Level

- **Practice** (2 pages) Provides extra practice for each lesson. For simpler practice exercises, use the Form K Practice pages found in the All-in-One Teaching Resources and online.

- **Think About a Plan** Helps students develop specific problem-solving skills and strategies by providing scaffolded guiding questions.

- **Standardized Test Prep** Focuses on all major exercises, all major question types, and helps students prepare for the high-stakes assessments.

Extension

- **Enrichment** Provides students with interesting problems and activities that extend the concepts of the lesson.

- **Activities, Games, and Puzzles** Worksheets that can be used for concepts development, enrichment, and for fun!

Practice and Problem Solving WKBK/All-in-One Resources/Online
Practice page 1

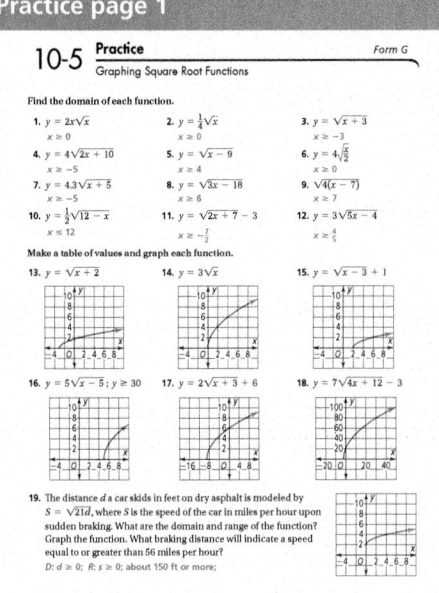

Practice and Problem Solving WKBK/All-in-One Resources/Online
Practice page 2

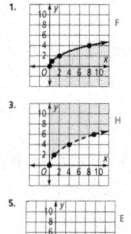 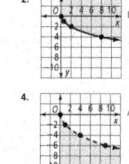
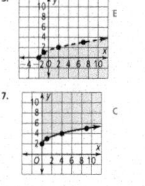 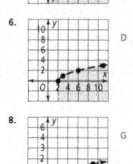

All-in-One Resources/Online
Enrichment

Practice and Problem Solving WKBK/All-in-One Resources/Online
Think About a Plan

Practice and Problem Solving WKBK/All-in-One Resources/Online
Standardized Test Prep

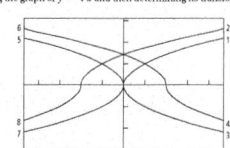

Online Teacher Resource Center
Activities, Games, and Puzzles

Guided Instruction

PURPOSE To explore the ratios of sides of similar right triangles

PROCESS Students will use rulers to make measurements of three given similar right triangles that will enable them to explore and make conjectures regarding the ratios that exist among their sides.

DISCUSS Have students use the smallest unit of measure possible (for example, millimeter) to help them get more precise ratios.

Activity 1

In this Activity students measure the sides of three similar right triangles and find the ratios between the lengths of their sides.

> **Q** How do you know all three triangles are similar? **[Each triangle has one right angle, and all right angles are congruent. Each triangle has an angle that measures 65°. So, all three triangles have three congruent angles, which makes them similar.]**

Activity 2

In this Activity students predict the lengths of the sides of a right triangle given an angle measure and the length of its shortest side.

> **Q** Which ratios from the columns in the table from Activity 1 can you use to find an answer in Exercise 4? $\left[\dfrac{\text{short leg}}{\text{hypotenuse}} \text{ or } \dfrac{\text{long leg}}{\text{short leg}}\right]$

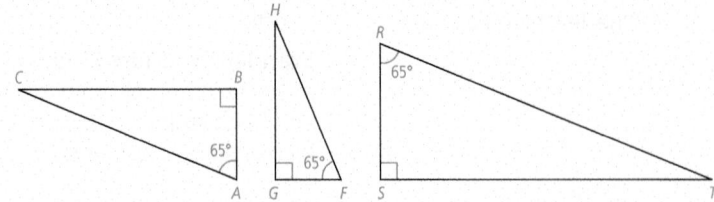

Concept Byte
Use With Lesson 10-6

Right Triangle Ratios

In this activity you will explore the ratios of side lengths of similar right triangles.

Activity 1

1. Measure the sides of the right triangles below to the nearest tenth of a centimeter.

2. Copy and complete the table using the side lengths you found in Exercise 1.

Triangle	Ratio of Side Lengths		
	length of longer leg / length of shorter leg	length of longer leg / length of hypotenuse	length of shorter leg / length of hypotenuse
△ABC	▪	▪	▪
△FGH	▪	▪	▪
△RST	▪	▪	▪

3. **Reasoning** How do the corresponding ratios in the three triangles compare? Will all right triangles with a 65° angle have the same ratios? Explain your reasoning.

Activity 2

4. A right triangle has a 65° angle, and its shortest side is 5 cm long. Predict the lengths of the other two sides.

5. Draw the triangle described in Exercise 4. Measure its sides.

6. How do your measurements compare to your predictions? Were there inaccuracies in your predictions, in the construction of the triangle, or in your measurements? Explain.

Answers

Activity 1

1–2. Check students' work.

3. The ratios in each column are the same; yes; explanations may vary. Sample: All right triangles with a 65° angle are similar.

Activity 2

4. about 10.7 cm and 11.8 cm

5–6. Check students' work.

10-6 Trigonometric Ratios

Objective To find and use trigonometric ratios

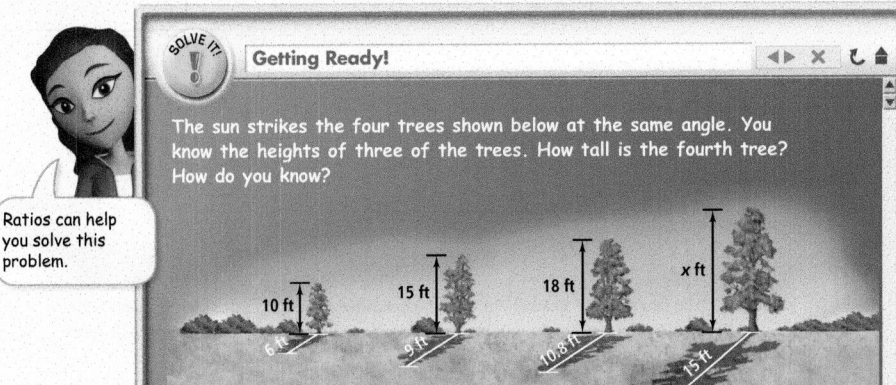

SOLVE IT!

Getting Ready!

The sun strikes the four trees shown below at the same angle. You know the heights of three of the trees. How tall is the fourth tree? How do you know?

Ratios can help you solve this problem.

10 ft   6 ft   15 ft   9 ft   18 ft   10.8 ft   x ft   15 ft

Lesson Vocabulary
• trigonometric ratios
• sine
• cosine
• tangent
• angle of elevation
• angle of depression

The Solve It involves ratios and right triangles. Ratios of the side lengths of a right triangle are called **trigonometric ratios.** Below are the definitions of three trigonometric ratios.

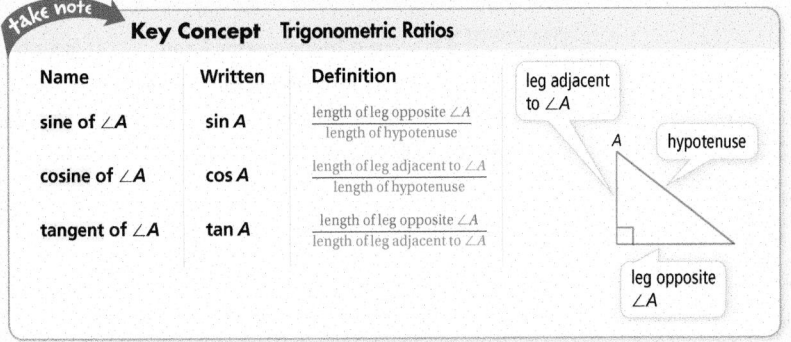

take note

Key Concept	**Trigonometric Ratios**	
Name	**Written**	**Definition**
sine of $\angle A$	$\sin A$	$\dfrac{\text{length of leg opposite } \angle A}{\text{length of hypotenuse}}$
cosine of $\angle A$	$\cos A$	$\dfrac{\text{length of leg adjacent to } \angle A}{\text{length of hypotenuse}}$
tangent of $\angle A$	$\tan A$	$\dfrac{\text{length of leg opposite } \angle A}{\text{length of leg adjacent to } \angle A}$

leg adjacent to $\angle A$

A hypotenuse

leg opposite $\angle A$

Essential Understanding You can use the sine, cosine, and tangent ratios to find the measurements of sides and angles of right triangles.

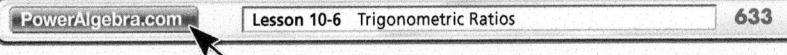

10-6 Preparing to Teach

BIG idea **Functions**   **UbD**

ESSENTIAL UNDERSTANDINGS

• Sine, cosine, and tangent ratios can be used to find the measurements of sides or angles of right triangles.
• Angles of elevation and depression can be used to solve real-world problems.

Math Background

Two similar right triangles have equal angle measures and proportional side lengths. Because a right triangle has three sides, there are six possible pairs or ratios of sides for each triangle. These six ratios are the trigonometric functions. The corresponding sides of similar triangles are proportional, so the trigonometric ratios for any two similar triangles are the same.

Review the terminology of right triangles. The longest side is the hypotenuse and is always opposite the right angle. The other two sides are called legs and their sum of their lengths must be greater than the length of the hypotenuse.

Make sure students set their calculators to the degree mode when calculating with the **sin**, **cos**, and **tan** functions and their inverses.

Support Student Learning

Use the **Algebra I Companion** to engage and support students during instruction. See Lesson Resources at the end of this lesson for details.

---

1 Interactive Learning

Solve It!

PURPOSE To use ratios to determine a missing value

PROCESS Students may determine the ratio of tree height to shadow length in order to write an equation to determine the missing height.

FACILITATE

Q What geometric shape does each tree and its shadow form? Explain. **[Each tree and its shadow are perpendicular, so a right triangle is formed if you connect the top of the tree to the tip of its shadow.]**

Q How are the four right triangles related? Explain. **[The sun strikes each tree at the same angle, so the triangles are similar.]**

Q What do you know about similar triangles? **[Corresponding sides are proportional and the measures of angles are congruent.]**

Q What is the ratio of tree height to shadow length for the first three triangles? **[1.67]**

ANSWER See Solve It in Answers on next page.

CONNECT THE MATH The ratios written in the Solve It are a typical real-world application of trigonometry for indirect measurement. In the lesson, students learn the trigonometric ratios and a variety of ways to solve problems involving these ratios.

2 Guided Instruction

Take Note

The classic mnemonic SOH-CAH-TOA can aid in the memory of the side relationships. Make sure students know the meaning of the mnemonic.

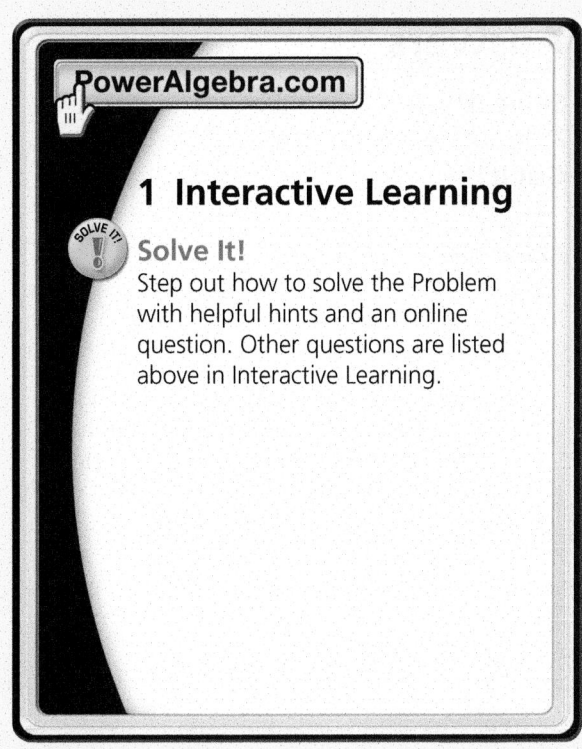

PowerAlgebra.com

1 Interactive Learning

SOLVE IT!

Solve It!

Step out how to solve the Problem with helpful hints and an online question. Other questions are listed above in Interactive Learning.

Problem 1

Q How can you identify the hypotenuse of a right triangle? **[The hypotenuse is the side opposite the right angle.]**

Q How is tan *A* related to tan *B*? **[They are reciprocals.]**

Q How is cos *A* related to sin *B*? **[They are the same.]**

Got It?   ERROR PREVENTION

Ask students to construct another triangle that has the same values for sin *E*, cos *E*, and tan *E*.

Problem 2

Have students use a calculator to explore the values of cos *A* for angle values from 0° to 90°. Have students explain the pattern in the values in terms of the corresponding right triangles.

Got It?

Discuss with students how they could determine the sine of 80° if their calculator did not have a **sin** function. Elicit that students could construct a triangle with angles of 10°, 80°, and 90°, measure the sides and then compute the correct ratio of opposite to hypotenuse for the 80° angle.

Often, students who know how to use their calculators for trigonometric ratios will still get incorrect answers. Rather than consider that the calculator might be set in the wrong mode, students will assume that they do not really understand trigonometric ratios. Tell students that it is good practice always to set the settings on their calculators by pressing **MODE**. Calculators should be set to degrees when solving trigonometric ratio problems.

Answers

Solve It!
25 ft; explanations may vary.

Got It?

1. $\frac{3}{5}, \frac{4}{5}, \frac{3}{4}$

2. **a.** 0.9848

   b. 1

   c. 0.9659

   d. 0.1564

   e. sin 45° = cos 45°; a 45°-45°-90° triangle is an isosceles right triangle, so the legs have the same length, and the sine and cosine are the same ratio.

3. 1.9

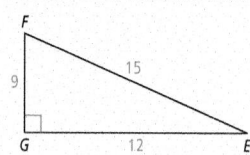
Problem 1 Finding Trigonometric Ratios

What are sin *A*, cos *A*, and tan *A* for the triangle shown?

Plan

How do you calculate trigonometric ratios?
Calculate a trigonometric ratio by substituting the lengths of the appropriate sides into the ratio.

$$\sin A = \frac{\text{opposite leg}}{\text{hypotenuse}} = \frac{15}{17}$$

$$\cos A = \frac{\text{adjacent leg}}{\text{hypotenuse}} = \frac{8}{17}$$

$$\tan A = \frac{\text{opposite leg}}{\text{adjacent leg}} = \frac{15}{8}$$

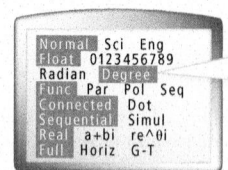

Got It? 1. What are sin *E*, cos *E*, and tan *E* for the triangle below?

You can also use a calculator to find trigonometric ratios. In this chapter, use Degree mode when finding trigonometric ratios. That allows you to enter angles in degrees.

Set your calculator to Degree mode.

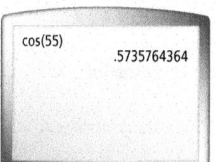
Problem 2 Finding a Trigonometric Ratio   GRIDDED RESPONSE

What is the value of cos 55° to the nearest ten-thousandth?

Think

What is an upper limit on the value of the cosine?
The cosine is the ratio $\frac{\text{adjacent leg}}{\text{hypotenuse}}$ in a right triangle. The hypotenuse is always the longest side. The cosine of an acute angle is always less than 1.

To find cos 55°, press **cos** 55 **)** **enter**.

The cosine of 55° is approximately 0.5736.

cos(55)
.5735764364

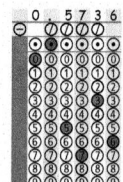

Got It? 2. What is the value of each expression in parts (a)–(d)?

   a. sin 80°   **b.** tan 45°   **c.** cos 15°   **d.** sin 9°

   e. Reasoning Describe the relationship between sin 45° and cos 45°. Explain why this is true.

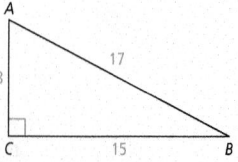

2 Guided Instruction

Each Problem is worked out and supported online.

Problem 1
Finding Trigonometric Ratios
Animated

Problem 2
Finding a Trigonometric Ratio

Problem 3
Finding a Missing Side Length
Animated

Problem 4
Finding the Measures of Angles
Animated

Problem 5
Using an Angle of Elevation or Depression

Support in Algebra 1 Companion
• Vocabulary
• Key Concepts
• Got It?

You can use trigonometry to find missing lengths in a right triangle when you know the length of one side and the measure of an acute angle.

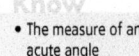 **Problem 3** Finding a Missing Side Length

To the nearest tenth, what is the value of *x* in the triangle at the right?

Know	Need	Plan
• The measure of an acute angle	The length of the opposite leg	Use the sine ratio.
• The length of the hypotenuse		

Write an equation and solve.

$\sin 48° = \dfrac{\text{opposite leg}}{\text{hypotenuse}}$ Use the definition of sine.

$\sin 48° = \dfrac{x}{14}$ Substitute *x* and 14 from the diagram.

$x = 14(\sin 48°)$ Solve for *x*.

$x \approx 10.40402756$ Use a calculator.

$x \approx 10.4$ Round to the nearest tenth.

The value of *x* is about 10.4.

 Got It? 3. To the nearest tenth, what is the value of *x* in the triangle at the right?

If you know the lengths of two sides of a right triangle, you can find a trigonometric ratio for each acute angle of the triangle. If you know a trigonometric ratio for an angle, you can use the inverse of the trigonometric ratio to find the measure of the angle. Use the $\sin^{-1}$, $\cos^{-1}$, or $\tan^{-1}$ feature on your calculator.

 **Problem 4** Finding the Measures of Angles

What is the measure of each angle in the triangle at the right?

Step 1 Since you know the length of the side adjacent to ∠A and the length of the hypotenuse, use the cosine ratio.

Step 2 Write an equation and solve.

$\cos A = \dfrac{12}{24}$ Use the definition of cosine.

$\cos A = 0.5$ Divide.

measure of $\angle A = \cos^{-1}(0.5)$ Use the inverse of cosine.

measure of $\angle A = 60°$ Use a calculator.

∠A measures 60°. The right angle *B* measures 90°. ∠C measures $180° - 90° - 60° = 30°$.

Think
How can you find the measure of the third angle of the triangle?
The sum of the measures of the angles of a triangle is 180°. You can subtract the measures of the two known angles from 180° to find the third angle's measure.

PowerAlgebra.com   Lesson 10-6   Trigonometric Ratios   635

Q What trigonometric ratio compares the opposite leg to the hypotenuse? **[sine]**

Q What are the measures of the other two angles in the triangle? Explain. **[90° and 42°, since it is a right triangle and the sum of the angles is 180°]**

Q How could you use the cosine ratio to find the value of *x*? **[Set up and solve the equation $\cos(42°) = \dfrac{x}{14}$.]**

Q How could you determine the length of the third side? **[Answers may vary. Sample: You could use the Pythagorean Theorem.]**

Got It?

Q Which side of the triangle has *x* as its length? **[hypotenuse]**

Q What trigonometric ratio do you use with 35°? **[cosine]**

Problem 4

Q How could you determine the length of the third side of the triangle? **[Answers may vary. Sample: You could use the Pythagorean Theorem.]**

Q Instead of first determining the measure of angle *A*, what trigonometric ratio can you use to determine the measure of angle *C*? **[sine]**

Additional Problems

1. What are sin *A*, cos *A*, and tan *A* for the triangle below?

ANSWER $\sin A = \dfrac{4}{5}$, $\cos A = \dfrac{3}{5}$, and $\tan A = \dfrac{4}{3}$

2. What is the sine of 39° to the nearest ten-thousandth?

ANSWER 0.6293

3. To the nearest tenth, how long is leg *x* in the triangle below?

ANSWER 18.9 cm

4. What is the measure of each angle in the triangle below?

ANSWER ∠A = 70.5°, ∠B = 19.5°, ∠C = 90°

5. Suppose a plane takes off at an angle of 42° with the ground. What horizontal distance has the plane traveled when it reaches an altitude of 30,000 ft? Round to the nearest foot.

ANSWER 33,318 ft

Got It?   VISUAL LEARNERS

Students should make a sketch and label the triangle prior to finding the measure of the angle.

To help students distinguish between angles of elevation and depression, they should sketch pictures showing an observer standing along the horizon looking at something above and something below. Have students associate the word *elevation* with up and the word *depression* with down.

Problem 5

> **Q** What trigonometric ratio compares the opposite side to the adjacent side for an angle? **[tangent]**
>
> **Q** What is the measure of the angle of elevation? Explain. **[20°; the angle of elevation is the angle formed by the line of sight above the ground.]**
>
> **Q** What is the measure of the angle of depression? Explain. **[The angle at the top of the triangle is 70°, so the angle of depression is 20°.]**
>
> **Q** What other equation could you write using the tangent ratio? Does it yield the same answer for *x*? **[$\tan(70°) = \frac{x}{150}$; yes]**

Got It?   VISUAL LEARNERS

Give students the following situation to help them visualize the problem more clearly: *The closer you are to a tall building, the more you have to "tilt" your head to be able to see the top of the object, which increases the angle of elevation.*

Got It? **4.** In a right triangle, the side opposite ∠A is 8 mm long and the hypotenuse is 12 mm long. What is the measure of ∠A?

You can use trigonometric ratios to measure some distances indirectly. To measure such distances, it is often convenient to use an *angle of elevation* or an *angle of depression*.

An **angle of elevation** is an angle from the horizontal up to a line of sight.

An **angle of depression** is an angle from the horizontal down to a line of sight.

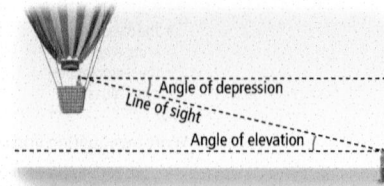

When you solve real-world problems using trigonometric ratios, you often need to round your answers. The problem may tell you how to round. Otherwise, round your answers to the precision of the measurements used in the problem. For instance, if the problem has measurements to the nearest 10 ft, round your answer to the nearest 10 ft.

Problem 5 Using an Angle of Elevation or Depression

Rides Suppose you are waiting in line for a ride. You see your friend at the top of the ride. How far are you from the base of the ride?

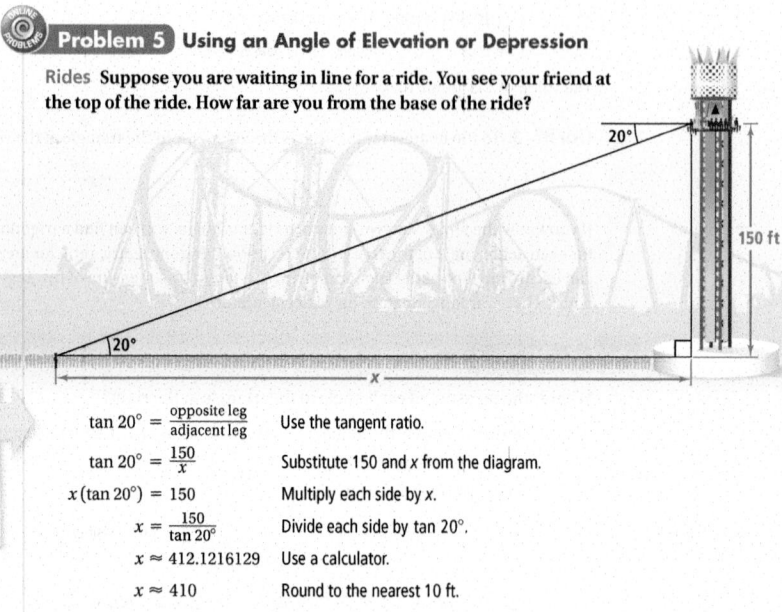

Think

Which ratio should you use?
You know the length of the opposite leg and want to find the length of the adjacent leg. Use the tangent ratio.

$\tan 20° = \dfrac{\text{opposite leg}}{\text{adjacent leg}}$	Use the tangent ratio.
$\tan 20° = \dfrac{150}{x}$	Substitute 150 and x from the diagram.
$x(\tan 20°) = 150$	Multiply each side by x.
$x = \dfrac{150}{\tan 20°}$	Divide each side by $\tan 20°$.
$x \approx 412.1216129$	Use a calculator.
$x \approx 410$	Round to the nearest 10 ft.

You are about 410 ft from the base of the ride.

Got It? **5.** After you move forward in the line, the angle of elevation to the top of the ride becomes 50°. How far are you from the base of the ride now?

Answers

Got It? (continued)
4. 41.8°

5. about 130 ft

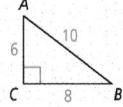

Lesson Check

Do you know HOW?

Find each trigonometric ratio for angle A in the triangle at the right.

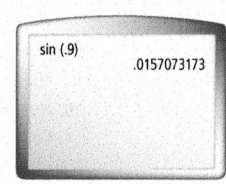

1. $\sin A$ **2.** $\cos A$ **3.** $\tan A$

Solve using trigonometric ratios.

4. A right triangle has a 40° angle. The hypotenuse is 10 cm long. What is the length of the side opposite the 40° angle?

5. A right triangle's legs are 7 in. and 24 in. long. What is the measure of the angle opposite the 24-in. leg?

Do you UNDERSTAND?

6. Vocabulary Describe the difference between finding the sine of an angle and the cosine of an angle.

7. Error Analysis In a right triangle, the hypotenuse is 5 in. long, and the side opposite $\angle A$ is 4.5 in. long. A student found the measure of $\angle A$ as shown on the calculator screen at the right. Describe and correct the student's error.

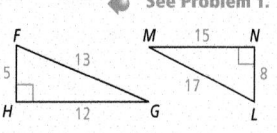

sin (.9)
.0157073173

Practice and Problem-Solving Exercises

A Practice

For $\triangle FGH$ and $\triangle LMN$, find the value of each expression. ◀ See Problem 1.

8. $\sin F$ **9.** $\cos F$ **10.** $\tan G$

11. $\cos L$ **12.** $\tan M$ **13.** $\sin M$

14. $\tan F$ **15.** $\sin G$ **16.** $\tan L$

Find the value of each expression. Round to the nearest ten-thousandth. ◀ See Problem 2.

17. $\sin 10°$ **18.** $\tan 25°$

19. $\cos 85°$ **20.** $\tan 12°$

21. $\sin 70°$ **22.** $\cos 22°$

23. $\sin 71°$ **24.** $\tan 30°$

Find the value of x to the nearest tenth. ◀ See Problem 3.

25.
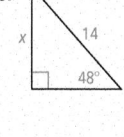

26.
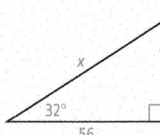

27.

28.
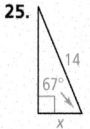

29.
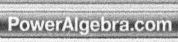

30.

Lesson Check

1. $\frac{4}{5}$ **2.** $\frac{3}{5}$ **3.** $\frac{4}{3}$

4. about 6.4 cm

5. 73.7°

6. To find the sine of an angle, you find the ratio of the length of the opposite leg to the length of the hypotenuse. To find the cosine of an angle, you find the ratio of the length of the adjacent leg to the length of the hypotenuse.

7. The student should use the $\sin^{-1}$ key; $\sin^{-1}(0.9) = 64.15806724$.

Practice and Problem-Solving Exercises

8. $\frac{12}{13}$ **9.** $\frac{5}{13}$ **10.** $\frac{5}{12}$

11. $\frac{8}{17}$ **12.** $\frac{8}{15}$ **13.** $\frac{8}{17}$

14. $\frac{12}{5}$ **15.** $\frac{5}{13}$ **16.** $\frac{15}{8}$

17. 0.1736 **18.** 0.4663 **19.** 0.0872

20. 0.2126 **21.** 0.9397 **22.** 0.9272

23. 0.9455 **24.** 0.5774 **25.** 5.5

26. 10.4 **27.** 19.2 **28.** 38.1

29. 66.0 **30.** 21.1

---

3 Lesson Check

Do you know HOW?

• If students have difficulty with Exercise 5, then have them make a sketch prior to finding the angle measure.

Do you UNDERSTAND?

• If students have difficulty with Exercise 6, then remind them that the data shown on the calculator screen reflects the sine of an angle that measures 0.9°.

Close

Q What do you know about the sides of a right triangle that has one acute angle of 40°? **[The ratio of the side opposite the 40° angle to the hypotenuse is 0.64. The ratio of the side adjacent to the 40° angle to the hypotenuse is 0.76. The ratio of the side opposite the 40° angle to the side adjacent to the 40° angle is 0.84.]**

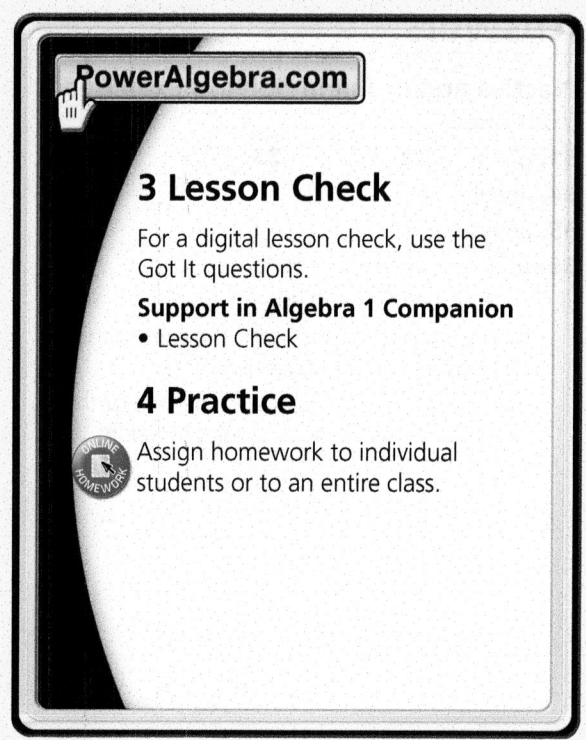

PowerAlgebra.com

3 Lesson Check

For a digital lesson check, use the Got It questions.

Support in Algebra 1 Companion
• Lesson Check

4 Practice

Assign homework to individual students or to an entire class.

4 Practice

ASSIGNMENT GUIDE

Basic: 8–35 all, 37, 38–44 even

Average: 9–35 odd, 36–44

Advanced: 9–35 odd, 36–47

Standardized Test Prep: 48–51

Mixed Review: 52–61

Reasoning exercises have blue headings.

Applications exercises have red headings.

EXERCISE 44: Use the Think About a Plan worksheet in the **Practice and Problem Solving Workbook** (also available in the Teaching Resources in print and online) to further support students' development in becoming independent learners.

HOMEWORK QUICK CHECK

To check students' understanding of key skills and concepts, go over Exercises 9, 27, 37, 38, and 44.

Find the value of x to the nearest degree.

See Problem 4.

31.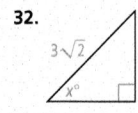

32.

33.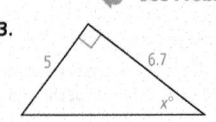

34. Geology From an observation point 20 ft from the base of a geyser, the angle of elevation to the top of the geyser is 50°. How tall is the geyser?

See Problem 5.

35. Architecture The wheelchair ramp shown is being planned for a new building. The ramp will rise a total of 2.5 ft and form a 3° angle with the ground. How far from the base of the building should the wheelchair ramp start?

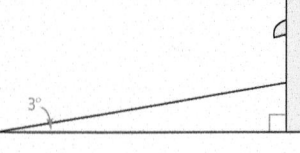

Ⓑ Apply

36. a. Find the values of each pair of expressions.
    i. sin 80°, cos 10°   **ii.** cos 25°, sin 65°
  b. What do you notice about your values and the angles in each pair?
  c. Reasoning Explain why your results make sense.

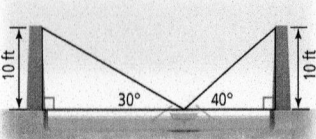

37. Writing Describe how you can find the length of the hypotenuse of a right triangle if you know the measure of one of the acute angles and the length of the leg adjacent to that angle.

38. Think About a Plan A boat is passing between two towers, as shown in the diagram. How far does the boat need to move to be in the middle of the channel?
• How far is the center of the boat from each tower?
• What is the distance from the base of a tower to the middle of the channel?

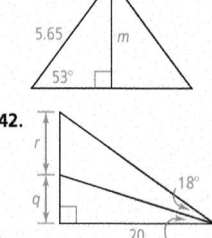

Find the value of each variable in each figure to the nearest tenth.

39.

40.

41.

42.

43. a. Aviation A pilot is flying a plane at an altitude of 30,000 ft. The angle of depression from the plane to the start of an airport runway is 1°. How far is the plane from the start of the runway, in horizontal distance along the ground?
  b. What is your answer to part (a) in miles?

Answers

Practice and Problem-Solving Exercises
(continued)

31. 60°   **32.** 45°   **33.** 37°

34. about 24 ft

35. about 47.7 ft

36. a. i. ≈ 0.9848; ≈ 0.9848
    ii. ≈ 0.9063; ≈ 0.9063
  b. The values are equal, and the sum of the measures of the angles is 90°.
  c. Answer may vary. Sample: The sum of the measures of the acute angles in a right triangle is 90°.

37. Divide the length of the adjacent side by the cosine of the acute angle.

38. 2.7 ft to the left

39. 514.3

40. 4.5

41. 78.4

42. $q = 6.1$; $r = 7.9$

43. a. about 1,720,000 ft
  b. about 326 mi

44. Hobbies Suppose you are flying a kite. The kite string is 60 m long, and the angle of elevation of the string is 65° from your hand. Your hand is 1 m above the ground. How high above the ground is the kite?

 **Challenge**

45. At a certain point in a large, level park, the angle of elevation to the top of an office building is 30°. If you move 400 ft closer to the building, the angle of elevation is 45°. To the nearest 10 ft, how tall is the building?

46. A line passes through the origin of a coordinate plane and forms a 14° angle with the positive x-axis. What is the slope of the line? Round to the nearest hundredth.

47. Reasoning Use the definitions of sine, cosine, and tangent to simplify each expression.

    a. $\cos A \cdot \tan A$ **b.** $\sin A \div \tan A$ **c.** $\sin A \div \cos A$

Standardized Test Prep

 SAT/ACT

48. What is the value of b in the proportion $\frac{3}{7} = \frac{2b}{4b+2}$?

    Ⓐ 3   Ⓒ 12

    Ⓑ 6   Ⓓ 28

49. The profits of a large corporation can be graphed as a line that passes through $(-3, 6)$ and $(4, -1)$. Which equation represents the line?

    Ⓕ $y = 3 - x$ Ⓗ $y = -3x + 1$

    Ⓖ $y = 3x + 1$ Ⓘ $y = x + 3$

50. Which expression is equivalent to $3\sqrt{12} + 2\sqrt{3}$?

    Ⓐ $5\sqrt{3}$ Ⓒ $5\sqrt{15}$

    Ⓑ $8\sqrt{3}$ Ⓓ $8\sqrt{12}$

Short Response

51. Graph the solutions of the inequality $-2x \geq 1$ on a number line.

Mixed Review

Graph each function.    See Lesson 10-5.

52. $y = \sqrt{x} + 8$ **53.** $y = \sqrt{x - 6}$ **54.** $y = 4\sqrt{x}$

Determine whether the given lengths can be side lengths of a right triangle.   See Lesson 10-1.

55. 15, 36, 39   **56.** $\frac{7}{9}, \frac{24}{9}, \frac{25}{9}$ **57.** 12, 35, 36

Get Ready!   To prepare for Lesson 11-1, do Exercises 58–61.

Factor each expression.   See Lesson 8-5.

58. $x^2 + x - 12$ **59.** $x^2 + 6x + 8$ **60.** $x^2 - 2x - 15$ **61.** $x^2 + 9x + 18$

---

44. about 55 m

45. 550 ft

46. 0.25

47. a. $\sin A$

    b. $\cos A$

    c. $\tan A$

48. A

49. F

50. B

51. [2] $-2x \geq 1$

        $x \leq -0.5$

[1] correct answer with no work shown or correct inequality graphed incorrectly

52.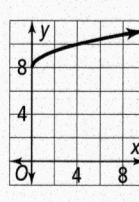

53.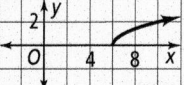

54.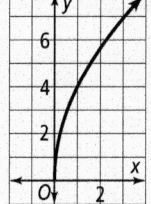

55. yes

56. yes

57. no

58. $(x - 3)(x + 4)$

59. $(x + 2)(x + 4)$

60. $(x + 3)(x - 5)$

61. $(x + 3)(x + 6)$

Additional Instructional Support

Algebra 1 Companion

Students can use the **Algebra 1 Companion** worktext (4 pages) as you teach the lesson. Use the Companion to support

- New Vocabulary
- Key Concepts
- Got It for each Problem
- Lesson Check

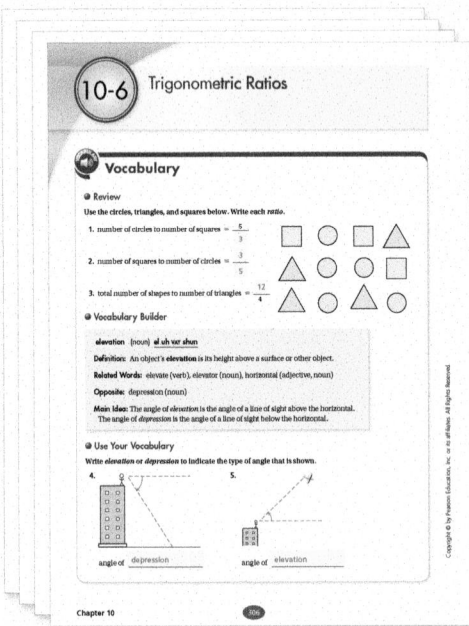

ELL Support

Focus on Language Project the lesson on an overhead projector and read the first page to students as you point to each word. Highlight key words and place question marks by words or ideas that are not clear. Discuss the highlighted text as well as the parts with question marks. Students can write down words and their definitions as you go along and use them later for review. After modeling the first page, have volunteers do the same with other pages of the lesson.

Use Manipulatives Arrange students into small groups of mixed abilities. Give each group a right triangle with the dimensions of two sides labeled. Tell students to find the length of the unknown side and the measure of the unknown angle. Vary which sides are labeled. Have students show and discuss their work. Use the discussion as instruction.

5 Assess & Remediate

Lesson Quiz

1. What are sin *F*, cos *F*, and tan *F* for the triangle below?

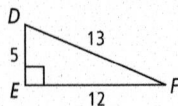

2. What is tan 82° to the nearest ten-thousandth?

3. To the nearest tenth, how long is the hypotenuse in the triangle below?

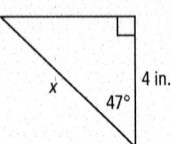

4. Do you UNDERSTAND? Suppose a scuba diver dives into the water at an angle of 25° for 300 yd. How deep is the diver submerged under water? Round to the nearest yard.

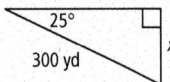

ANSWERS TO LESSON QUIZ

1. $\sin F = \frac{5}{13}$, $\cos F = \frac{12}{13}$, and $\tan F = \frac{5}{12}$

2. 7.1154

3. 5.9 in.

4. 127 yd

PRESCRIPTION FOR REMEDIATION

Use the student work on the Lesson Quiz to prescribe a differentiated review assignment.

Points	Differentiated Remediation
0–2	Intervention
3	On-level
4	Extension

PowerAlgebra.com

5 Assess & Remediate

Assign the Lesson Quiz. Appropriate intervention, practice, or enrichment is automatically generated based on student performance.

Intervention

- **Reteaching** (2 pages) Provides reteaching and practice exercises for the key lesson concepts. Use with struggling students or absent students.

- **English Language Learner Support** Helps students develop and reinforce mathematical vocabulary and key concepts.

All-in-One Resources/Online
Reteaching

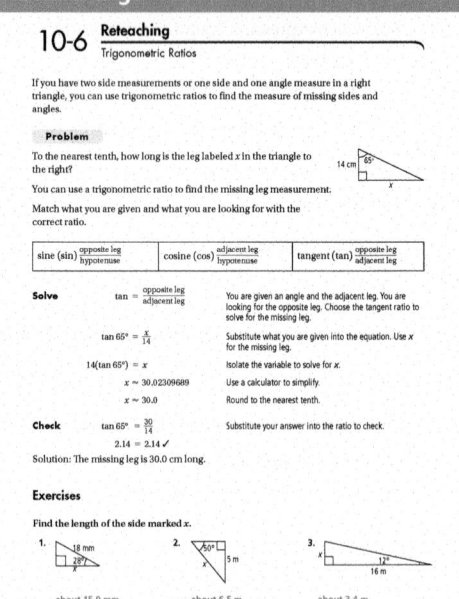

All-in-One Resources/Online
English Language Learner Support

Differentiated Remediation *continued*

On-Level

- **Practice** (2 pages) Provides extra practice for each lesson. For simpler practice exercises, use the Form K Practice pages found in the All-in-One Teaching Resources and online.

- **Think About a Plan** Helps students develop specific problem-solving skills and strategies by providing scaffolded guiding questions.

- **Standardized Test Prep** Focuses on all major exercises, all major question types, and helps students prepare for the high-stakes assessments.

Extension

- **Enrichment** Provides students with interesting problems and activities that extend the concepts of the lesson.

- **Activities, Games, and Puzzles** Worksheets that can be used for concepts development, enrichment, and for fun!

Practice and Problem Solving WKBK/All-in-One Resources/Online
Practice page 1

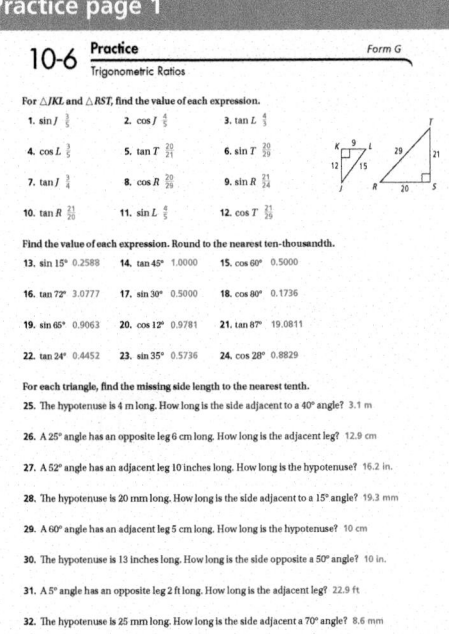

10-6 Practice Form G
Trigonometric Ratios

For △JKL and △RST, find the value of each expression.

1. sin J $\frac{3}{5}$ 2. cos J $\frac{4}{5}$ 3. tan L $\frac{4}{3}$

4. cos L $\frac{3}{5}$ 5. tan T $\frac{20}{21}$ 6. sin T $\frac{20}{29}$

7. tan J $\frac{3}{4}$ 8. cos R $\frac{20}{29}$ 9. sin R $\frac{21}{29}$

10. tan R $\frac{21}{20}$ 11. sin L $\frac{4}{5}$ 12. cos T $\frac{21}{29}$

Find the value of each expression. Round to the nearest ten-thousandth.

13. sin 15° 0.2588   14. tan 45° 1.0000   15. cos 60° 0.5000

16. tan 72° 3.0777   17. sin 30° 0.5000   18. cos 80° 0.1736

19. sin 65° 0.9063   20. cos 12° 0.9781   21. tan 87° 19.0811

22. tan 24° 0.4452   23. sin 35° 0.5736   24. cos 28° 0.8829

For each triangle, find the missing side length to the nearest tenth.

25. The hypotenuse is 4 m long. How long is the side adjacent to a 40° angle? 3.1 m

26. A 25° angle has an opposite leg 6 cm long. How long is the adjacent leg? 12.9 cm

27. A 52° angle has an adjacent leg 10 inches long. How long is the hypotenuse? 16.2 in.

28. The hypotenuse is 20 mm long. How long is the side adjacent to a 15° angle? 19.3 mm

29. A 60° angle has an adjacent leg 5 cm long. How long is the hypotenuse? 10 cm

30. The hypotenuse is 13 inches long. How long is the side opposite a 50° angle? 10 in.

31. A 5° angle has an opposite leg 2 ft long. How long is the adjacent leg? 22.9 ft

32. The hypotenuse is 25 mm long. How long is the side adjacent a 70° angle? 8.6 mm

---

Practice and Problem Solving WKBK/All-in-One Resources/Online
Practice page 2

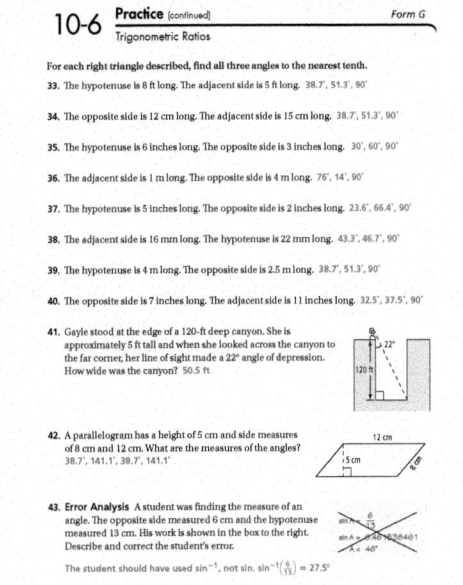

10-6 Practice (continued) Form G
Trigonometric Ratios

For each right triangle described, find all three angles to the nearest tenth.

33. The hypotenuse is 8 ft long. The adjacent side is 5 ft long. 38.7°, 51.3°, 90°

34. The opposite side is 12 cm long. The adjacent side is 15 cm long. 38.7°, 51.3°, 90°

35. The hypotenuse is 6 inches long. The opposite side is 3 inches long. 30°, 60°, 90°

36. The adjacent side is 1 m long. The opposite side is 4 m long. 76°, 14°, 90°

37. The hypotenuse is 5 inches long. The opposite side is 2 inches long. 23.6°, 66.4°, 90°

38. The adjacent side is 16 mm long. The hypotenuse is 22 mm long. 43.3°, 46.7°, 90°

39. The hypotenuse is 4 m long. The opposite side is 2.5 m long. 38.7°, 51.3°, 90°

40. The opposite side is 7 inches long. The adjacent side is 11 inches long. 32.5°, 57.5°, 90°

41. Gayle stood at the edge of a 120-ft deep canyon. She is approximately 5 ft tall and when she looked across the canyon to the far corner, her line of sight made a 22° angle of depression. How wide was the canyon? 50.5 ft

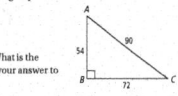

42. A parallelogram has a height of 5 cm and side measures of 8 cm and 12 cm. What are the measures of the angles? 38.7°, 141.1°, 38.7°, 141.1°

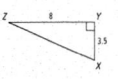

43. **Error Analysis** A student was finding the measure of an angle. The opposite side measured 6 cm and the hypotenuse measured 13 cm. His work is shown in the box to the right. Describe and correct the student's error.

The student should have used sin⁻¹, not sin. sin⁻¹($\frac{6}{13}$) ≈ 27.5°

All-in-One Resources/Online
Enrichment

10-6 Enrichment
Trigonometric Ratios

Indirect Measurement

Angles of depression or elevation can be used to determine speed.

A sailor wants to know how fast her sailboat is sailing. To do so she must determine how far she has moved in 15 minutes. The sailboat is moving toward a lighthouse that is 197 feet tall. From her first location, she knows that her angle of elevation to the top of the lighthouse is 1°. From her next location 15 minutes later, the angle of elevation to the top of the lighthouse is 5°.

1. How far away from the lighthouse is the sailor at her first location? 11,286.1 ft

2. How far away from the lighthouse is the sailor at her second location? 2251.7 ft

3. How far did the boat travel in 15 minutes? 9034.4 ft

4. What is the boat's speed? Round your answer to the nearest tenth of a mile per hour. 602.3 ft/min

5. How long will it take the boat to reach the lighthouse if the speed stays constant and the boat moves in the same direction? 3.7 min or 3 min 42 s

6. If the sailor discovers the lighthouse is actually 175 ft tall, how fast is the boat moving? 535.0 ft/s

---

Practice and Problem Solving WKBK/All-in-One Resources/Online
Think About a Plan

10-6 Think About a Plan
Trigonometric Ratios

Hobbies Suppose you are flying a kite. The kite string is 60 m long, and the angle of elevation of the string is 65° from your hand. Your hand is 1 m above the ground. How high above the ground is the kite?

KNOW

1. How high above the ground is the base of the triangle made by the kite string? 1 m

2. What is the length of the hypotenuse of the triangle made by the kite string? 60 m

3. What is the angle of elevation? 65°

NEED

4. What leg of the triangle do you need to find? opposite

PLAN

5. What diagram can you draw to help you solve the problem?

6. Which trigonometric ratio can you use to find the length of the missing leg? sine

7. Write and solve an equation to find the length of the missing leg. 54.4 m

8. Use the distance your hand is above the ground and the length of the missing leg to find how high the kite is above the ground. 55.4 m

9. Is the solution reasonable? Explain.
yes; The length of the leg of the triangle is close to, but less than, the length of the hypotenuse.

Practice and Problem Solving WKBK/All-in-One Resources/Online
Standardized Test Prep

10-6 Standardized Test Prep
Trigonometric Ratios

Gridded Response

Solve each exercise and enter your answer on the grid provided.

1. For △ABC, what is the value of cos C? 0.8

2. A right triangle's hypotenuse is 20 cm long. What is the length of the side opposite a 60° angle? Give your answer to the nearest tenth of an inch. 17.3

3. A right triangle's legs are 3 and 4 meters long. What is the measure of the angle adjacent to the 4-meter leg to the nearest tenth of a degree? 36.9

4. For △XYZ, what is the measure of the smallest angle to the nearest tenth of a degree? 23.6

5. Suppose that you are watching the tree warden trim branches from a large tree in your yard. He has climbed up 15 meters and his assistant is holding a rope that will be used to guide the branch when it falls. To the nearest meter, how long is the rope? 26

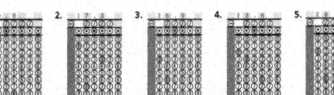

Online Teacher Resource Center
Activities, Games, and Puzzles

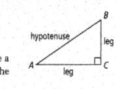

10-6 Game: Name That Ratio!
Trigonometric Ratios

This is a game the entire class can play in teams of two or three students. Your teacher or a student can serve as the host.

The host will assign each question in order and review the answers afterward. Your teacher and/or the host will determine a reasonable time limit to answer each question. The team with the highest score wins.

- Each team is allowed to use a calculator.
- For Round 1, write the ratio you used and the length you found (to the nearest tenth) in the table.
- Each correct ratio is worth 1 point. Each correct measure is worth 2 points.

1. ∠A = 60° and AC = 10; Find BC.   2. ∠B = 60° and AC = 10; Find BC.

3. ∠B = 23° and BC = 8; Find AB.   4. ∠B = 70° and AB = 12; Find AC.

5. ∠A = 30° and BC = 20; Find AC.   6. ∠A = 55° and BC = 45; Find AB.
See Teacher Instructions Page.

	Round 1					
	1	2	3	4	5	6
Ratio						
Length						

The rules are the same for Round 2, except this time you find a missing angle measure (to the nearest degree).

7. AC = 10 and BC = 20; Find ∠A.   8. AC = 7 and AB = 15; Find ∠B.

9. AB = 18 and BC = 12; Find ∠B.   10. BC = 30 and AC = 10; Find ∠A.

11. AC = 100 and AB = 200; Find ∠B.   12. AB = 36 and BC = 12; Find ∠A.

	Round 2					
	7	8	9	10	11	12
Ratio						
Angle Measure						

Here is a bonus question worth 6 points.

In a right triangle, one leg is four times as long as the other leg. To the nearest degree, what is the measure of the angle opposite the longer leg? 76°

Performance Task UbD

Pull It All Together

The concepts and skills required to solve these problems are from several lessons within this chapter and from the previous chapter. As students solve these problems, they will demonstrate their reasoning strategies and their growth as independent problem solvers.

The following questions are designed to:
- Help support students as they do the Tasks.
- Gauge the amount of support students need as they become independent problem solvers.

Task 1
- What kind of triangle is shown?
- How do you isolate c?
- Are there any excluded solutions?

Task 2
- How can you graph the function?
- What do you know about the value under the radical?
- What types of values can be the result of a square root function?

Task 3
- How does the left side of the equation change?
- How do you isolate A?
- How do you compare the areas?
- Is your answer realistic?

To solve these problems you will pull together many concepts and skills that you have studied about radical expressions and equations.

BIG idea Equivalence

Radical expressions can be represented many ways. To simplify a square root, factor out perfect squares from the radicand.

Task 1

Use the isosceles right triangle shown to answer the following questions.
- **a.** What is an expression for c in terms of x? Write your answer as a radical in simplified form.
- **b.** How can you use your result from part (a) to find the length of the hypotenuse of an isosceles right triangle if you know the length of each leg?

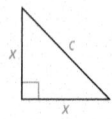

BIG idea Functions

Square root functions contain a variable in the radicand. The parent square root function is $y = \sqrt{x}$.

Task 2

Solve. Show your work.
- **a.** Graph the function $y = \sqrt{|x|}$.
- **b.** How does the graph of the function in part (a) differ from the graph of the parent square root function $y = \sqrt{x}$?
- **c.** What are the domain and range of the function in part (a)?

BIG idea Solving Equations and Inequalities

To isolate the variable in a radical equation, first isolate the radical, and then square both sides.

Task 3

Solve. Show all your work and explain your steps.

The distance d in feet of a certain projector from a screen is given by $d = 1.2\sqrt{A}$, where A is the area of the projector's image in square feet. Suppose you move the projector from its current position 8 ft from the screen to a new position 12 ft from the screen. By how much does the area of the image increase?

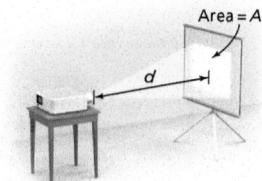
Area = A

Assess Performance UbD

Pull It All Together

See p. 67 for a holistic scoring rubric to gauge a student's progress on Understanding the Problem, Planning a Solution, Getting an Answer, and Assesssing Autonomy.

SOLUTION OUTLINES

Task 1
- **a.** Use the Pythagorean Theorem: $x^2 + x^2 = c^2$.
  (Answer: $x\sqrt{2}$)
- **b.** Use the expression you found in part (a). Multiply the length of a leg by $\sqrt{2}$.

Task 2
- **a.** Possible plan: Make a table of values and plot the points.

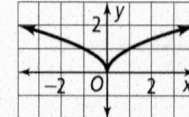

- **b.** Answers may vary. Sample: It is the parent square root function plus the reflection of the parent square root function over the y-axis.
- **c.** Possible plan: To find the domain, find the values for which the radicand is nonnegative. $|x|$ is nonnegative for all real numbers. To find the range, use the graph and the fact that the domain of the parent square root function is all nonnegative real numbers. (Answer: domain: all real numbers, range: all nonnegative real numbers)

Task 3
Possible plan: Substitute the values 8 and 12 for d in the equation. Solve each resulting equation for A. Find the difference of the two values of A. (Answer: about 56 ft²)

10 Chapter Review

Connecting BIG ideas and Answering the Essential Questions

1 Equivalence
Radical expressions can be represented in many ways. To simplify a square root, factor out perfect squares from the radicand.

Simplifying Radicals (Lesson 10-2)
$$\sqrt{12} = \sqrt{4} \cdot \sqrt{3} = 2\sqrt{3}$$

Operations With Radical Expressions (Lesson 10-3)
$$\sqrt{5} \cdot \sqrt{10} = \sqrt{50} = 5\sqrt{2}$$

2 Functions
Square root functions contain a variable in the radicand. The parent square root function is $y = \sqrt{x}$.

Graphing Square Root Functions (Lesson 10-5)
Graph of the parent square root function

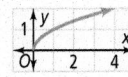

3 Solving Equations and Inequalities
To isolate the variable in a radical equation, first isolate the radical and then square both sides.

Solving Radical Equations (Lesson 10-4)
$$2x = \sqrt{4x + 3}$$

Chapter Vocabulary

- angle of depression (p. 636)
- angle of elevation (p. 636)
- conclusion (p. 601)
- conditional (p. 601)
- conjugates (p. 615)
- converse (p. 602)
- cosine (p. 633)
- extraneous solution (p. 622)
- hypotenuse (p. 600)
- hypothesis (p. 601)
- leg (p. 600)
- like radicals (p. 613)
- Pythagorean Theorem (p. 600)
- radical equation (p. 620)
- radical expression (p. 606)
- rationalize the denominator (p. 609)
- sine (p. 633)
- square root function (p. 626)
- tangent (p. 633)
- trigonometric ratios (p. 633)
- unlike radicals (p. 613)

Choose the correct term to complete each sentence.

1. Sine, cosine, and tangent are ___?___.

2. A(n) ___?___ is an apparent solution that does not make the original equation true.

3. The radical expressions $2\sqrt{3}$ and $3\sqrt{2}$ contain ___?___.

4. You ___?___ of a radical expression by rewriting it without radicals in the denominator.

5. The radical expressions $5 + \sqrt{5}$ and $5 - \sqrt{5}$ are ___?___.

Answers

Chapter Review

1. trigonometric ratios

2. extraneous solution

3. unlike radicals

4. rationalize the denominator

5. conjugates

Essential Questions

BIG idea Equivalence
ESSENTIAL QUESTION How are radical expressions represented?
ANSWER Radical expressions can be represented in many ways. To simplify a square root, factor out perfect squares from the radicand.

BIG idea Functions
ESSENTIAL QUESTION What are the characteristics of square root functions?
ANSWER Square root functions contain a variable in the radicand. The parent square root function is $y = \sqrt{x}$.

BIG idea Solving Equations and Inequalities
ESSENTIAL QUESTION How can you solve a radical equation?
ANSWER To isolate the variable in a radical equation, first isolate the radical, and then square both sides.

Summative Questions UbD

Use the following prompts as you review this chapter with your students. The prompts are designed to help you assess your students' understanding of the Big Ideas they have studied.

- How do you simplify radical expressions?
- How do you graph radical functions?
- How do you solve radical equations?

Answers

Chapter Review (continued)

6. 6.5   **7.** 12.5   **8.** 6.1

9. 84   **10.** 17.5   **11.** 0.7

12. 6.6   **13.** 2.4   **14.** yes

15. yes   **16.** no   **17.** yes

18. no   **19.** yes   **20.** no

21. no   **22.** yes   **23.** $-42\sqrt{6}$

24. $\sqrt{3}$ **25.** $\frac{5}{2}a$ **26.** $\frac{2}{3s}$

27. $-\frac{28}{3}x^2\sqrt{x}$

28. $30t^4\sqrt{3}$

29. Answers may vary. Sample: $\sqrt{32s}$, $\frac{8s}{\sqrt{2s}}$, $8\sqrt{\frac{s}{2}}$; they all have the s and the factor 2 under the radical.

30. $s\sqrt{10}$

10-1 The Pythagorean Theorem

Quick Review

Given the lengths of two sides of a right triangle, you can use the **Pythagorean Theorem** to find the length of the third side. Given the lengths of all three sides of a triangle, you can determine whether it is a right triangle.

Example

What is the side length x in the triangle at the right?

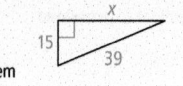

$$a^2 + b^2 = c^2 \qquad \text{Pythagorean Theorem}$$
$$15^2 + x^2 = 39^2 \qquad \text{Substitute 15 for } a, x \text{ for } b, \text{ and 39 for } c.$$
$$225 + x^2 = 1521 \qquad \text{Simplify.}$$
$$x^2 = 1296 \qquad \text{Subtract 225 from each side.}$$
$$x = 36 \qquad \text{Find the principal square root of each side.}$$

Exercises

Use the triangle at the right. Find the missing side length. If necessary, round to the nearest tenth.

6. $a = 2.5, b = 6$ **7.** $a = 3.5, b = 12$

8. $a = 1.1, b = 6$ **9.** $a = 13, c = 85$

10. $a = 6, c = 18.5$ **11.** $b = 2.4, c = 2.5$

12. $b = 8.8, c = 11$ **13.** $a = 1, c = 2.6$

Determine whether the given lengths can be side lengths of a right triangle.

14. 4, 7.5, 8.5   **15.** 22, 120, 122   **16.** 8, 40, 41

17. 1.6, 3, 3.4   **18.** 6, 24, 25   **19.** 18, 52.5, 55.5

20. 1.2, 6, 6.1   **21.** 0.7, 2.3, 2.5   **22.** 1.3, 8.4, 8.5

10-2 Simplifying Radicals

Quick Review

A **radical expression** is simplified if the following statements are true.
- The radicand has no perfect-square factors other than 1.
- The radicand contains no fractions.
- No radicals appear in the denominator of a fraction.

Example

What is the simplified form of $\frac{\sqrt{3x}}{\sqrt{2}}$?

$$\frac{\sqrt{3x}}{\sqrt{2}} = \frac{\sqrt{3x}}{\sqrt{2}} \cdot \frac{\sqrt{2}}{\sqrt{2}} \qquad \text{Multiply by } \frac{\sqrt{2}}{\sqrt{2}}.$$
$$= \frac{\sqrt{6x}}{\sqrt{4}} \qquad \text{Multiply numerators and denominators.}$$
$$= \frac{\sqrt{6x}}{2} \qquad \text{Simplify.}$$

Exercises

Simplify each radical expression.

23. $3\sqrt{14} \cdot (-2\sqrt{21})$ **24.** $\sqrt{8} \cdot \frac{1}{4}\sqrt{6}$

25. $\sqrt{\frac{25a^3}{4a}}$ **26.** $\frac{\sqrt{8s}}{\sqrt{18s^3}}$

27. $-2\sqrt{7x^2} \cdot \frac{1}{3}\sqrt{28x^3}$ **28.** $6\sqrt{5t^3} \cdot \sqrt{15t^5}$

29. Open-Ended Write three radical expressions that have $4\sqrt{2s}$ as their simplified form. What do the three expressions have in common? Explain.

30. Geometry The width of a rectangle is s. Its length is $3s$. How long is a diagonal of the rectangle? Express your answer in simplified radical form.

10-3 Operations With Radical Expressions

Quick Review

You can use the properties of real numbers to combine radical expressions. To simplify radical expressions such as $\frac{2}{\sqrt{5}+3}$, multiply the numerator and denominator by the **conjugate** of the denominator, $\sqrt{5}-3$.

Example

What is the simplified form of $\frac{2\sqrt{5}}{\sqrt{5}+2}$?

$$\frac{2\sqrt{5}}{\sqrt{5}+2} = \frac{2\sqrt{5}}{\sqrt{5}+2} \cdot \frac{\sqrt{5}-2}{\sqrt{5}-2} \qquad \text{Multiply by } \frac{\sqrt{5}-2}{\sqrt{5}-2}.$$

$$= \frac{2\sqrt{5}(\sqrt{5}-2)}{(\sqrt{5}+2)(\sqrt{5}-2)} \qquad \text{Multiply fractions.}$$

$$= \frac{10-4\sqrt{5}}{1} \qquad \text{Simplify the numerator and denominator.}$$

$$= 10 - 4\sqrt{5} \qquad \text{Simplify the fraction.}$$

Exercises

Simplify each radical expression.

31. $5\sqrt{6} - 3\sqrt{6}$

32. $\sqrt{2}(\sqrt{8} + \sqrt{6})$

33. $(3\sqrt{2} - 2\sqrt{5})(4\sqrt{2} + 2\sqrt{5})$

34. $\frac{3}{\sqrt{2}-3}$

35. $\frac{\sqrt{3}-3}{\sqrt{3}+3}$

36. Geometry A golden rectangle is 3 in. long. The ratio of its length to its width is $(1 + \sqrt{5}) : 2$. What is the width of the rectangle? Write your answer in simplified radical form.

10-4 Solving Radical Equations

Quick Review

You can solve some **radical equations** by isolating the radicals, squaring both sides of the equation, and then testing the solutions.

Some solutions may be extraneous. Some equations may have no solution.

Example

What is the solution of $\sqrt{x+16} = \sqrt{9x}$?

$$\sqrt{x+16} = \sqrt{9x}$$

$$(\sqrt{x+16})^2 = (\sqrt{9x})^2 \qquad \text{Square each side.}$$

$$x + 16 = 9x \qquad \text{Simplify.}$$

$$16 = 8x \qquad \text{Subtract } x \text{ from each side.}$$

$$2 = x \qquad \text{Divide each side by 8.}$$

Check $\quad \sqrt{2+16} \stackrel{?}{=} \sqrt{9(2)} \qquad \text{Substitute 2 for } x.$

$$\sqrt{18} = \sqrt{18} \;\checkmark$$

The solution is 2.

Exercises

Solve each radical equation. Check your solution. If there is no solution, write *no solution*.

37. $\sqrt{x} - 5 = 8$ **38.** $4 + \sqrt{y} = 7$

39. $\sqrt{w-2} = 4$ **40.** $\sqrt{f+4} = 5$

41. $\sqrt{2+d} = d$ **42.** $2\sqrt{r} = \sqrt{3r+1}$

43. $n\sqrt{2} = \sqrt{9-3n}$ **44.** $2x = \sqrt{2-2x}$

45. Geometry The radius r of a cylinder is given by the equation $r = \sqrt{\frac{V}{\pi h}}$, where V is the volume and h is the height. If the radius of a cylinder is 3 cm and the height is 2 cm, what is the volume of the cylinder? Round to the nearest tenth of a cubic centimeter.

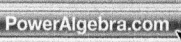
31. $2\sqrt{6}$ **32.** $4 + 2\sqrt{3}$

33. $4 - 2\sqrt{10}$ **34.** $\frac{-3\sqrt{2}+9}{7}$

35. $-2 + \sqrt{3}$ **36.** $\frac{-3+3\sqrt{5}}{2}$ in.

37. 169   **38.** 9

39. 18   **40.** 21

41. 2   **42.** 1

43. 1.5   **44.** $\frac{1}{2}$

45. 56.5 cm^3

Answers

Chapter Review (continued)

46. $x \geq 0$

47. $x \geq -4$

48.

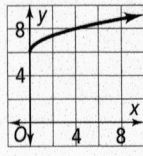

49.

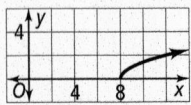

50.

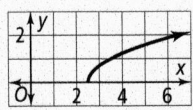

51.

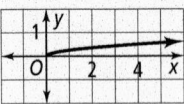

52.

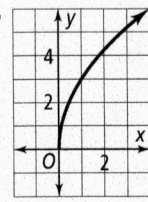

53. $\sin A = \frac{8}{17}$, $\cos A = \frac{15}{17}$, $\tan A = \frac{8}{15}$

54. $\sin A = \frac{\sqrt{5}}{5}$, $\cos A = \frac{2\sqrt{5}}{5}$, $\tan A = \frac{1}{2}$

55. $\sin A = \frac{\sqrt{7}}{4}$, $\cos A = \frac{3}{4}$, $\tan A = \frac{\sqrt{7}}{3}$

56. length of $\overline{AC} \approx 9.9$, length of $\overline{BC} \approx 6.7$

57. length of $\overline{AB} \approx 10.2$, length of $\overline{BC} \approx 6.3$

58. length of $\overline{AB} \approx 26.9$, length of $\overline{AC} \approx 20.0$

59. length of $\overline{AC} \approx 24.5$, length of $\overline{BC} \approx 5.2$

10-5 Graphing Square Root Functions

Quick Review

Graph a **square root function** by plotting points or translating the parent square root function $y = \sqrt{x}$.

The graphs of $y = \sqrt{x} + k$ and $y = \sqrt{x} - k$ are vertical translations of $y = \sqrt{x}$. The graphs of $y = \sqrt{x - h}$ and $y = \sqrt{x + h}$ are horizontal translations of $y = \sqrt{x}$.

Example

What is the graph of the square root function $y = \sqrt{x - 2}$?

The graph of $y = \sqrt{x - 2}$ is the graph of $y = \sqrt{x}$ shifted 2 units right.

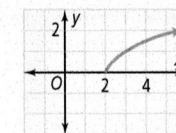

Exercises

Find the domain of each function.

46. $y = \sqrt{x} - 5$

47. $y = \sqrt{x + 4}$

Graph each function.

48. $y = \sqrt{x} + 6$

49. $y = \sqrt{x - 8}$

50. $y = \sqrt{x - 2.5}$

51. $y = \frac{1}{4}\sqrt{x}$

52. $y = 3\sqrt{x}$

10-6 Trigonometric Ratios

Quick Review

You can use the **sine**, **cosine**, and **tangent** ratios to find the measurements of sides or angles of right triangles.

$$\sin A = \frac{\text{opposite leg}}{\text{hypotenuse}}$$

$$\cos A = \frac{\text{adjacent leg}}{\text{hypotenuse}}$$

$$\tan A = \frac{\text{opposite leg}}{\text{adjacent leg}}$$

Example

What are the trigonometric ratios of angle A?

$$\sin A = \frac{3}{\sqrt{13}} = \frac{3\sqrt{13}}{13}$$

$$\cos A = \frac{2}{\sqrt{13}} = \frac{2\sqrt{13}}{13}$$

$$\tan A = \frac{3}{2}$$

Exercises

Find the trigonometric ratios for $\angle A$.

53.

54.

55.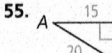

Suppose a right triangle ABC has right angle C. Find the measures of the other sides to the nearest tenth.

56. length of $\overline{AB} = 12$, measure of $\angle A = 34°$

57. length of $\overline{AC} = 8$, measure of $\angle B = 52°$

58. length of $\overline{BC} = 18$, measure of $\angle A = 42°$

59. length of $\overline{AB} = 25$, measure of $\angle A = 12°$

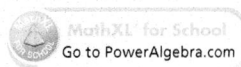

MathXL for School
Go to PowerAlgebra.com

Do you know **HOW?**

Use the triangle below. Find the missing side length. If necessary, round to the nearest tenth.

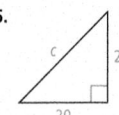

1. $a = 28, b = 35$

2. $a = 12, b = 35$

3. $b = 4.0, c = 4.1$

4. $a = 10, c = 26$

State whether segments of the given lengths can be sides of a right triangle.

5. 7, 24, 25

6. 0.9, 1.2, 1.5

7. 8, 16, 17

Simplify each radical expression.

8. $\sqrt{3} + \sqrt{12}$

9. $\sqrt{300}$

10. $4\sqrt{10} - \sqrt{10}$

11. $\dfrac{-\sqrt{18}}{\sqrt{12}}$

12. $\dfrac{1}{\sqrt{3} + 4}$

13. $\dfrac{\sqrt{6}}{4 - \sqrt{6}}$

14. $\dfrac{\sqrt{2}}{\sqrt{2} + 3}$

15. $-3\sqrt{5x^3} \cdot \sqrt{10x^3}$

Solve the following radical equations. Check your solutions.

16. $\sqrt{2x} + 4 = 7$

17. $\sqrt{k} - 8 = 28$

18. $\dfrac{\sqrt{3m + 2}}{3} = 1$

19. $\sqrt{2x + 4} = \sqrt{3x}$

20. $\sqrt{2 - x} = x$

21. $\sqrt{-5a + 6} = -a$

Graph each function.

22. $y = \sqrt{x} + 2$

23. $y = \sqrt{x} - 3$

24. $y = \sqrt{x} + 5$

For each triangle, find the missing side length.

25.

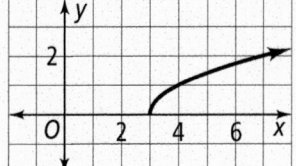

26.

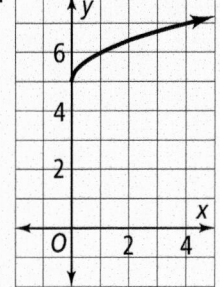

27. A right triangle has a 50° angle. The hypotenuse is 10 cm long. To the nearest tenth, what is the length of the side opposite the 50° angle?

Do you **UNDERSTAND?**

28. Reasoning Draw right △*ABC* with ∠*B* as the right angle. What is the relationship between sin *A* and cos *C*? Explain.

29. Open-Ended Give an example of a radical equation for which all solutions are extraneous. What is the solution to the equation? How do you know?

30. Reasoning Is the following conditional statement always true? "If a right triangle has a leg that is 3 in. long and a leg that is 4 in. long, then the hypotenuse is 5 in. long." Is its converse always true? Explain.

31. Writing Explain how you would simplify the radical expression $\dfrac{2}{\sqrt{5} + 2}$.

32. Geometry Find the length of a diagonal of a square with a side length of 3 in. Is the length of the diagonal a rational number? Explain.

30. Yes, by the Pythagorean Theorem, $3^2 + 4^2 = 5^2$; no, explanations may vary. Sample: A triangle with side lengths 1 in., $2\sqrt{6}$ in., and 5 in. is a right triangle with a hypotenuse that is 5 in. long.

31. Multiply the fraction by the conjugate of the denominator.

32. $3\sqrt{2}$ in.; no, 2 is not a perfect square, so $\sqrt{2}$ is an irrational number.

Answers

Chapter Test

1. 44.8   **2.** 37

3. 0.9   **4.** 24

5. yes   **6.** yes

7. no   **8.** $3\sqrt{3}$

9. $10\sqrt{3}$ **10.** $3\sqrt{10}$

11. $-\dfrac{\sqrt{6}}{2}$ **12.** $\dfrac{4 - \sqrt{3}}{13}$

13. $\dfrac{2\sqrt{6} + 3}{5}$ **14.** $\dfrac{3\sqrt{2} - 2}{7}$

15. $-15x^3\sqrt{2}$ **16.** 4.5

17. 1296   **18.** $\dfrac{7}{3}$

19. 4   **20.** 1

21. −6

22.

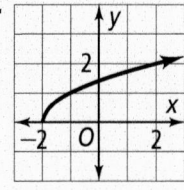

23.

24.

25. 29   **26.** 15   **27.** 7.7

28. sin A = cos C; sin A = $\dfrac{CB}{CA}$, cos C = $\dfrac{CB}{CA}$

29. Check students' work.

PowerAlgebra.com

MathXL for School

Prepare students for the Mid-Chapter Quiz and Chapter Test with online practice and review.

Item Number	Lesson
1	9-1
2	6-5
3	2-5
4	1-6
5	5-3
6	10-3
7	3-8
8	10-2
9	5-3
10	5-3
11	8-6
12	2-5
13	9-7
14	6-3
15	5-6
16	2-8
17	2-5
18	2-6
19	4-7
20	4-1
21	2-5
22	2-9
23	1-2
24	10-4
25	9-3
26	2-5

10 Cumulative Test Prep

TIPS FOR SUCCESS

Some questions on tests ask you to perform operations on radicals. Read the sample question at the right. Then follow the tips to answer it.

Which expression is equivalent to $\sqrt{180} - \sqrt{80}$?

Ⓐ 10   Ⓒ $10\sqrt{5}$

Ⓑ $2\sqrt{5}$ Ⓓ $5\sqrt{10}$

TIP 2

For any number $a \geq 0$, $\sqrt{a^2} = a$. So look for perfect-square factors when trying to simplify a radical.

TIP 1

Simplify each radical expression to see if you can obtain like radicals.

Think It Through

Simplify the expression.

$\sqrt{180} - \sqrt{80}$

$= \sqrt{36 \cdot 5} - \sqrt{16 \cdot 5}$

$= \sqrt{36} \cdot \sqrt{5} - \sqrt{16} \cdot \sqrt{5}$

$= 6\sqrt{5} - 4\sqrt{5}$

$= 2\sqrt{5}$

The correct answer is B.

Vocabulary Builder

As you solve test items, you must understand the meanings of mathematical terms. Match each term with its mathematical meaning.

A. square root

B. arithmetic sequence

C. function

D. literal equation

I. a number pattern formed by adding a fixed number to each previous term

II. a relation that pairs each input value with exactly one output value

III. an equation involving two or more variables

IV. a number a such that $a^2 = b$

Multiple Choice

Read each question. Then write the letter of the correct answer on your paper.

1. If the graph of the function $y = x^2 - 6$ were shifted 3 units down, which equation could represent the shifted graph?

Ⓐ $y = 3x^2 - 6$ Ⓒ $y = x^2 - 9$

Ⓑ $y = x^2 - 3$ Ⓓ $y = 3x^2 - 3$

2. Which ordered pair is a solution of $3x - y < 20$?

Ⓕ $(7, 1)$ Ⓗ $(8, 0)$

Ⓖ $(5, -6)$ Ⓘ $(-1, -4)$

3. Brianna has a cylindrical glass that is 15 cm tall. The diameter of the base is 5 cm. About how much water can the glass hold?

Ⓐ 75 cm^3 Ⓒ 295 cm^3

Ⓑ 118 cm^3 Ⓓ 1178 cm^3

Answers

Cumulative Test Prep

A. IV   **B.** I

C. I   **D.** III

1. C   **2.** I

3. C

4. Marco is laying a 15-ft² brick walkway. He used 18 bricks for the first 3 ft². Which is a reasonable number of bricks Marco should buy to finish the walkway?

 Ⓕ 50   Ⓗ 200
 Ⓖ 100   Ⓘ 300

5. Jeremiah made the graph at the right to show how much money he saved after working for a few months. Which of the following represents the amount of money Jeremiah had when he started working?

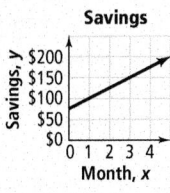

Savings

 Ⓐ x-intercept
 Ⓑ y-intercept
 Ⓒ slope
 Ⓓ domain

6. Which expression is equivalent to $\sqrt{18} + \sqrt{72}$?

 Ⓕ $30\sqrt{3}$ Ⓗ $3\sqrt{10}$
 Ⓖ $18\sqrt{2}$ Ⓘ $9\sqrt{2}$

7. Kieko took an inventory of the T-shirts she has in her store and displayed her data in the diagram below.

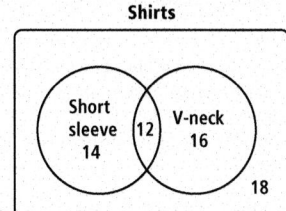

Shirts

How many short-sleeve shirts does she have?

 Ⓐ 12   Ⓒ 26
 Ⓑ 14   Ⓓ 42

8. What is the simplified form of $\sqrt{75x^3}$?

 Ⓕ $5x\sqrt{3x}$ Ⓗ $5\sqrt{3x}$
 Ⓖ $25x\sqrt{x}$ Ⓘ $25\sqrt{3x}$

9. Eduardo is drawing the graph of a function. Each time the x-value increases by 3, the y-value decreases by 4. The function includes the point $(1, 3)$. Which could be Eduardo's graph?

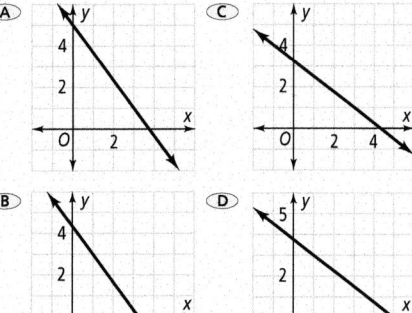

10. The data shown in the table at the right represent points on a line. What is the y-intercept of the line?

 Ⓕ -5
 Ⓖ -3
 Ⓗ 0
 Ⓘ 2.5

x	y
2	-1
3	1
4	3
5	5

11. What is the factored form of $3x^2 + 2xy - 8y^2$?

 Ⓐ $(x + y)(3x - 8y)$ Ⓒ $(x + 2y)(3x - 4y)$
 Ⓑ $(x + 4y)(3x - 2y)$ Ⓓ $(3x + 2y)(x - 4y)$

12. The formula for the area A of a circle is $A = \pi r^2$, where r is the radius of the circle. Which equation can be used to find the radius?

 Ⓕ $r = \dfrac{\sqrt{A\pi}}{\pi}$ Ⓗ $r = \dfrac{A^2}{\pi}$
 Ⓖ $r = \dfrac{A}{\pi}$ Ⓘ $r = \sqrt{A\pi}$

13. Which function has y-values that always increase when the corresponding x-values increase?

 Ⓐ $y = |x| + 2$ Ⓒ $y = x + 2$
 Ⓑ $y = x^2 + 2$ Ⓓ $y = -x - 1$

4. G   **5.** B
6. I   **7.** C
8. F   **9.** B
10. F   **11.** C
12. F

Answers

13. C   **14.** F

15. C   **16.** 4

17. 72   **18.** 2

19. 6.25   **20.** 2

21. 18   **22.** $\frac{2}{5}$

23. 41.69

24. [2]

$$x = \sqrt{x + 12}$$
$$x^2 = x + 12$$
$$x^2 - x - 12 = 0$$
$$(x - 4)(x + 3) = 0$$
$$(x - 4) = 0 \text{ or } (x + 3) = 0$$
$$x = 4 \text{ or } \qquad x = -3$$

The apparent solutions are 4 and -3. Check each solution. $4 = \sqrt{4 + 12}$, and $4 = 4$. $-3 = \sqrt{(-3) + 12}$, but $-3 \neq \sqrt{9}$. So -3 is an extraneous solution. The solution of the equation is 4.

[1] correct methods used with minor computation error

25. Methods may vary. Sample:

[2]
$$0 = -16t^2 + 40$$
$$16t^2 = 40$$
$$t^2 = \frac{40}{16}$$
$$t = \pm 1.58113$$

You can ignore the negative solution. The object will take about 1.6 s to reach the ground.

[1] correct method used with minor computational error

26. Methods may vary. Sample:

[4] Use the points $(-4, 2)$, $(-4, 5)$, $(4, 5)$ and $(4, -2)$ to make a rectangle. Find the area of the rectangle and then subtract the areas of triangles that are not

part of quadrilateral *MPQR*. The dimensions of the rectangle are $4 - (-4) = 8$ and $5 - (-2) = 7$, so the area is 56 square units. The area of one triangle is $\frac{1}{2}(5 - 2)(2 - (-4)) = 9$. The area of the other triangle is

$\frac{1}{2}(4 - 2)(5 - (-2)) = 7$. So the area of the quadrilateral

MPQR is $56 - (9 + 7) = 40$.

[3] correct methods used with minor computational error

[2] correct methods used with error in coordinates, but correct answer based on coordinates used

[1] correct answer with no work shown

---

14. What is the solution of this system of equations?

$$x + 2y = 23$$
$$4x - y = -7$$

   Ⓕ (1, 11)   Ⓗ (−1, −11)

   Ⓖ (−11, 1)   Ⓘ (11, 1)

15. If the graph of $y = 5x - 4$ is translated up 3 units, which of the following is true?

   Ⓐ The resulting line will have a slope that is greater than the slope of the graph of $y = 5x - 4$.

   Ⓑ The resulting line will have the same *x*-intercept as the graph of $y = 5x - 4$.

   Ⓒ The resulting line will be parallel to the graph of $y = 5x - 4$.

   Ⓓ The resulting line will have a slope of -1.

GRIDDED RESPONSE

Record your answers in a grid.

16. What is the solution of the following proportion?
$$\frac{-a}{4} = \frac{-3(a - 2)}{6}$$

17. Mariah made a model of a square pyramid. The height h of the pyramid is 6 in. The area of the base B is 36 in.^{2}. What is the volume V, in cubic inches, of the pyramid? Use the formula $V = \frac{1}{3}Bh$.

18. The list below shows the heights, in inches, of the students in Corey's class.

60, 64, 58, 57, 60, 65, 51, 53, 57, 56

How many students are more than 5 ft tall?

19. What is the fifth term in the sequence below?

3.25, 4, 4.75, 5.5, . . .

20. Mr. Wong drove to the grocery store. The graph at the right shows his distance from home during the drive. How many times did Mr. Wong stop the car before reaching the grocery store?

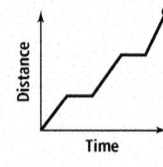

21. The volume of a rectangular prism is 720 in.^{3}. The height of the prism is 10 in. The width is 4 in. What is the length, in inches?

22. The freshman reading list contains 90 books, categorized as shown in the table below.

Freshman Reading List

Author	Mystery	Biography	Classic
Male	14	14	16
Female	10	16	20

What fraction of the books are classics?

23. Your cell phone plan costs $39.99 per month plus $.10 for every text message that you receive or send. This month, you receive 7 text messages and send 10 text messages. What is your bill, in dollars, for this month?

Short Response

24. Rosita states that the solutions of the equation $x = \sqrt{x + 12}$ are -3 and 4. Is Rosita's statement correct? Explain your answer by solving the equation and checking the possible solutions.

25. The formula $h = -16t^2 + c$ can be used to find the height h, in feet, of a falling object t seconds after it is dropped from a height of c feet. Suppose an object falls from a height of 40 ft. How long will the object take to reach the ground? Round your answer to the nearest tenth of a second.

Extended Response

26. What is the area, in square units, of quadrilateral *MPQR* shown below? Show your work.

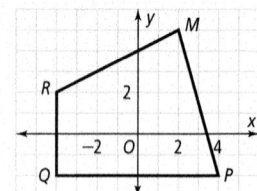

Get Ready!

Lesson 1-5 **Adding and Subtracting Fractions**

Find each sum or difference.

1. $\frac{6}{5} + \frac{5}{6}$ **2.** $\frac{5}{2} + \frac{3}{4}$ **3.** $\frac{7}{24} - \frac{9}{10}$ **4.** $\frac{3}{5} - \frac{2}{7}$

Lesson 7-5 **Simplifying Expressions**

Simplify each expression.

5. $\frac{m^2 p^{-3} q^4}{m^2 p^2 q^{-2}}$ **6.** $\frac{(3a^2)^3 (2b^{-1})^2}{(7a^3)^2 (3b^2)^{-1}}$ **7.** $\frac{\left(\frac{2}{3}\right)^4}{\left(\frac{3}{2}\right)^2}$ **8.** $\frac{8x^{-3} y^2 z^4}{5x^3 y z^{-2}}$

Lesson 9-4 **Factoring to Solve Quadratic Equations**

Solve each equation by factoring.

9. $x^2 - 2x - 63 = 0$ **10.** $12y^2 - y = 35$ **11.** $z^2 + 26z + 169 = 0$

12. $w^2 - 3w = 0$ **13.** $11p + 20 = 3p^2$ **14.** $6r^2 + 20 = -34r$

15. $3m^2 + 33m + 30 = 0$ **16.** $5d^2 - 20d = 105$ **17.** $6g^2 - 7g = 5$

Lesson 10-4 **Solving Radical Equations**

Solve each equation. If there is no solution, write *no solution*.

18. $\sqrt{x+1} = \sqrt{x-2}$ **19.** $2b = \sqrt{b+3}$ **20.** $\sqrt{x} + 2 = x$

 Looking Ahead Vocabulary

21. If tickets are required for admission to a show, anyone without a ticket will be *excluded*. What do you think it means when some input values of a function are allowed but other input values are *excluded*?

22. When people are *rational*, they make sense. When a number is *rational*, it can be written as the ratio of two integers. Do you think that the term *rational expression* refers to an expression that makes sense or to an expression that involves a ratio?

23. *Inverting* a cup or glass means changing its orientation to the opposite direction. If positive values *x* and *y* are related by an *inverse variation*, do you think they increase and decrease together? Or do you think they move in opposite directions, one decreasing as the other increases?

Get Ready!

Assign this diagnostic assessment to determine if students have the prerequisite skills for Chapter 11.

Lesson	Skill
1-5	Adding and Subtracting Fractions
7-5	Simplifying Expressions
9-4	Factoring to Solve Quadratic Equations
10-4	Solving Radical Equations

For remediation, select from these resources (available for every lesson).
• Online Problems (PowerAlgebra.com)
• Reteaching (All-in-One Teaching Resources)
• Practice (All-in-One Teaching Resources)

Why Students Need These Skills
ADDING AND SUBTRACTING FRACTIONS
Students will add and subtract rational expressions.
SIMPLIFYING EXPRESSIONS
Students will simplify algebraic rational expressions.
FACTORING TO SOLVE QUADRATIC EQUATIONS
Students will solve rational equations, including some of degree 2.
SOLVING RADICAL EQUATIONS
Students will solve rational equations, some of which have extraneous solutions, similar to radical equations.

Looking Ahead Vocabulary
EXCLUDED Ask students to give other real-world examples of situations where something is excluded.
RATIONAL EXPRESSION Show students the graph of a function that corresponds to a rational expression. Have them describe the graph.
INVERSE VARIATION Have students give examples of inverse operations.

Answers

Get Ready!

1. $2\frac{1}{30}$

2. $3\frac{1}{4}$

3. $-\frac{73}{120}$

4. $\frac{11}{35}$

5. $\frac{q^6}{p^5}$

6. $6\frac{30}{49}$

7. $\frac{64}{729}$

8. $\frac{8yz^6}{5x^6}$

9. $-7, 9$

10. $-\frac{5}{3}, \frac{7}{4}$

11. -13

12. $0, 3$

13. $-\frac{4}{3}, 5$

14. $-5, -\frac{2}{3}$

15. $-10, -1$

16. $-3, 7$

17. $-\frac{1}{2}, \frac{5}{3}$

18. no solution

19. 1

20. 4

21. The excluded values are not allowed.

22. A rational expression involves a ratio.

23. One is decreasing as the other increases.

Chapter 11 Overview

UbD **Understanding by Design**

Chapter 11 connects and extends the Big Ideas introduced in previous chapters to rational expressions and functions. In this chapter, students will develop the answers to the Essential Questions posed on the opposite page as they learn the concepts and skills listed below.

BIG idea **Equivalence**

ESSENTIAL QUESTION How are rational expressions represented?
• Students will graph rational expressions.
• Students will simplify rational expressions.

BIG ideas **Function**

ESSENTIAL QUESTION What are the characteristics of rational functions?
• Graphing will be used to show rational functions.
• Students will add, subtract, multiply, and divide rational expressions.
• The concept of inverse variation will be explored.

BIG ideas **Solving Equations and Inequalities**

ESSENTIAL QUESTION How can you solve a rational equation?
• Students will use inverse operations to solve a rational equation.
• Students will identify extraneous solutions.

CHAPTER 11

Rational Expressions and Functions

PowerAlgebra.com

Your place to get all things digital

VIDEO
Download videos connecting math to your world.

VOCABULARY
Math definitions in English and Spanish

SOLVE IT!
The online Solve It will get you in gear for each lesson.

DYNAMIC ACTIVITIES
Interactive! Vary numbers, graphs, and figures to explore math concepts.

ONLINE PROBLEMS
Download Step-by-Step Problems with Instant Replay.

ONLINE HOMEWORK
Get and view your assignments online.

MathXL FOR SCHOOL
Extra practice and review online

Wow, these robots are working together to cross a branch. I bet one robot would take a long time to cross the branch alone. Have you ever noticed that a job goes faster when you work with someone else? In this chapter, you'll learn how to use equations to model the work that people can complete when they work together.

Vocabulary

English/Spanish Vocabulary Audio Online:

English	Spanish
asymptote, *p. 694*	asíntota
constant of variation for an inverse variation, *p. 686*	constante de variación en variaciones inversas
excluded value, *p. 652*	valor excluido
inverse variation, *p. 686*	variación inversa
rational equation, *p. 679*	ecuación racional
rational expression, *p. 652*	expresión racional
rational function, *p. 693*	función racional

PowerAlgebra.com

Chapter 11 Overview

Use these online assets to engage your students. There is support for the Solve It and step-by-step solutions for Problems.

VIDEO Show the student-produced video demonstrating relevant and engaging applications of the new concepts in the chapter.

VOCABULARY Find online definitions for new terms in English and Spanish.

SOLVE IT! Start each lesson with an attention-getting Problem. View the Problem online with helpful hints.

My Math Video

 00:04:04

VIDEO ▶

BIGideas

1 Equivalence
Essential Question How are rational expressions represented?

2 Functions
Essential Question What are the characteristics of rational functions?

3 Solving Equations and Inequalities
Essential Question How can you solve a rational equation?

Chapter Preview

PowerAlgebra.com   Chapter 11   Rational Expressions and Functions   **651**

 Increase students' depth of knowledge with interactive online activities.

 Show Problems from each lesson solved step by step. Instant replay allows students to go at their own pace when studying online.

 Assign homework to individual students or to an entire class.

 Prepare students for the Mid-Chapter Quiz and Chapter Test with online practice and review.

My Math Video

FACILITATE Use this photo to discuss the concept of working together to complete a task. In this chapter, students will learn how to use rational expressions to model the work that can be done by multiple people.

Q In the photo, the robots are working together to cross an obstacle. How does working together help them get over the log? **[Answers may vary. Sample: By working together the robots can reach farther and help each other know where the obstacle is located.]**

Q What do the robots need in order to work together as shown? **[communication]**

Q In what other situations do people work together to accomplish a task? **[Answers may vary. Sample: painting a room, cleaning the house, building a large structure]**

Q How can working together help in the situations you named above? **[Answers may vary. Sample: It could shorten the amount of time it takes to complete the task.]**

ERROR PREVENTION

As students learn to write equations to represent work problems, remind them that each term represents the fraction of the job done by each person. The portions completed by each individual are then added and set equal to the portion of the job that gets completed in one unit of time.

RATIONAL EXPRESSIONS AND FUNCTIONS
Math Background

UbD

Equivalence

BIG idea A single quantity may be represented by many different expressions. The facts about a quantity may be expressed by many different equations (or inequalities).

ESSENTIAL UNDERSTANDINGS

11-1 The simplest form of a rational expression is like the simplest form of a numerical fraction. The numerator and denominator have no common factor other than 1. To simplify a rational expression, divide out common factors from the numerator and denominator.

11-2 to 11-4 Rational expressions and polynomials can be added, subtracted, multiplied and divided using the same properties used to multiply and divide numerical fractions.

Functions

BIG idea A function is a relationship between variables in which each value of the input variable is associated with a unique value of the output variable. Functions can be represented in a variety of ways, such as graphs, tables, equations, or words. Each representation is particularly useful in certain situations. Some important families of functions are developed through transformations of the simplest form of the function.

ESSENTIAL UNDERSTANDINGS

11-6 If the product of two variables is a nonzero constant, then the variables form an inverse variation.

11-7 To graph a rational function $f(x)$, it is necessary to understand the graph's behavior near values of x where the function is undefined.

Solving Equations and Inequalities

BIG idea Solving an equation is the process of rewriting the equation to make what it says about its variable or variables as simple as possible. Properties of numbers and equality can be used to transform an equation (or inequality) into equivalent, simpler equations (or inequalities) in order to find solutions. Useful information about equations and inequalities (including solutions) can be found by analyzing graphs or tables. The numbers and types of solutions vary predictably, based on the type of equation (or inequality).

ESSENTIAL UNDERSTANDING

11-5 A rational equation can be solved by first multiplying each side of the equation by the LCD. When each side of a rational equation is a single rational expression, the equation can be solved using the Cross Products Property.

Simplifying Rational Expressions

Students are familiar with simplifying fractions. First factor the numerator and denominator, and then divide out common terms. To factor $\frac{12}{42}$, for example, first write $\frac{12}{42} = \frac{2 \cdot 2 \cdot 3}{2 \cdot 3 \cdot 7}$, then simplify to get $\frac{2}{7}$.

A rational expression is a fraction in the form $\frac{\text{polynomial}}{\text{polynomial}}$. Even though the numerator and denominator are now polynomials, a rational expression can be simplified in the same way as a numerical fraction. First, factor each polynomial, then divide out common terms.

Consider the rational expression $\frac{4 - x}{-x^2 + 2x + 8}$. The numerator cannot be simplified, but the denominator can be factored to obtain $\frac{4 - x}{(x + 2)(4 - x)}$. Dividing out common terms leaves $\frac{1}{(x + 2)}$.

Rational expressions are not defined for values of x for which the denominator is zero. Because -2 and 4 are zeros of $-x^2 + 2x + 8$, $\frac{4 - x}{-x^2 + 2x + 8}$ is not defined for these values. Note that this is true even though $4 - x$ divides out.

Common Errors With Simplifying Rational Expressions

When finding the domain of rational expressions, it is important to find the zeros of the *original* denominator. If the simplified form is used, then some excluded values of x may be overlooked.

Dividing Polynomials

Dividing a Polynomial by a Monomial

When dividing a polynomial by a monomial, you can multiply by the reciprocal, use the Distributive Property, and simplify. For example:

$(9x^3 + 15x^2 + 6x) \div 3x$

$(9x^3 + 15x^2 + 6x) \cdot \frac{1}{3x}$ Multiply by the reciprocal.

$3x^2 + 5x + 2$ Distribute and simplify.

Dividing a Polynomial by a Binomial

When dividing a polynomial by a binomial, you can use the long-division algorithm.

$(9x^3 + 15x^2 + 6x) \div (3x + 4)$

$$
\begin{array}{r}
3x^2 + x \\
3x + 4 \overline{)\,9x^3 + 15x^2 + 6x} \\
\underline{9x^3 + 12x^2} \\
3x^2 + 6x \\
\underline{3x^2 + 4x} \\
2x
\end{array}
$$

$3x^2 + x + \frac{2x}{3x + 4}$

Common Errors With Dividing Polynomials

When dividing a polynomial using the long division algorithm, the dividend must be in standard form and missing terms must be included using coefficients of zero.

When missing terms are not included, the problem can become confusing and errors will likely be made.

Inverse Variation

Direct and inverse variation problems can be solved in a similar stepwise manner:

Suppose that y varies directly as x. If $y = 24$ when $x = 8$, find y when $x = 5$.

Step 1: $y = kx$ Write the formula.

Step 2: $24 = k \cdot 8$ Substitute values.

Step 3: $k = 3$ Solve for k.

Step 4: $y = 3x$ Write the formula with $k = 3$.

Step 5: $y = 3 \cdot 5$ Substitute known quantity.

When $x = 5$, $y = 15$.

Suppose that y varies inversely as x. If $y = 24$ when $x = 8$, find y when $x = 5$.

Step 1: $y = \frac{k}{x}$ Write the formula.

Step 2: $24 = \frac{k}{8}$ Substitute values.

Step 3: $k = 192$ Solve for k.

Step 4: $y = \frac{192}{x}$ Write the formula with $k = 192$.

Step 5: $y = \frac{192}{5}$ Substitute known quantity.

When $x = 5$, $y = 38.4$.

Common Errors With Inverse Variation

Suppose that y varies inversely as x. It is true that when y increases x decreases and when x increases y decreases. However, this is not what defines the relationship between the variables as an inverse variation. When one variable increases the other decreases can be true of data sets that are not inverse variations. For two variables to be inversely proportional, the product xy must be constant.

RATIONAL EXPRESSIONS AND FUNCTIONS
Pacing and Assignment Guide

		TRADITIONAL			BLOCK
Lesson	**Teaching Day(s)**	**Basic**	**Average**	**Advanced**	**Block**
11-1	1	Problems 1-3 Exs. 8–28 all, 54–72	Problems 1-3 Exs. 9-27 odd, 54–72	Problems 1-2 Exs. 9–27 odd, 54–72	**Day 1** Problems 1-4 Exs. 9–29 odd, 31–47, 54–72
	2	Problem 4 Exs. 29–30 all, 32–42 even, 43	Problem 4 Exs. 29, 31–47	Problems 1-2 Exs. 29, 31–53	
11-2	1	Problems 1-3 Exs. 11–28, 70–79	Problems 1-3 Exs. 11–27 odd, 70–79	Problems 1-3 Exs. 11–27 odd, 70–79	**Day 2** Problems 1-6 Exs. 11–49 odd, 51–65, 70–79
	2	Problems 4-6 Exs. 29–50, 59–61	Problems 4-6 Exs. 29–49 odd, 51–65	Problems 4-6 Exs. 29–49 odd, 51–69	
11-3	1	Problems 1-2 Exs. 8–19, 60–71	Problems 1-2 Exs. 9–19 odd, 60–71	Problems 1-2 Exs. 9–35 odd, 60–71	**Day 3** Problems 1-4 Exs. 9–35 odd, 36–54, 60–71
	2	Problems 3-4 Exs. 20–35, 37, 48–51	Problems 3-4 Exs. 21–35 odd, 36–54	Problems 3-4 Exs. 9–35 odd, 36–59	
11-4	1	Problems 1-2 Exs. 8–16 all, 55–67	Problems 1-2 Exs. 9–15 odd, 55–67	Problems 1-2 Exs. 9–15 odd, 55–67	**Day 4** Problems 1-5 Exs. 9–33 odd, 34–48, 55–67
	2	Problems 3-5 Exs. 17–33 all, 34–42 even, 43–44	Problems 3-5 Exs. 17–33 odd, 34–48	Problems 3-5 Exs. 17–33 odd, 34–54	
11-5	1	Problems 1-2 Exs. 8–22, 52–66	Problems 1-2 Exs. 9–21 odd, 52–66	Problems 1-2 Exs. 9–21 odd, 52–66	**Day 5** Problems 1-5 Exs. 9–29 odd, 31–44, 52–66
	2	Problems 3-5 Exs. 23–31, 39–40	Problems 3-5 Exs. 23–29 odd, 31–44	Problems 3-5 Exs. 23–29 odd, 31–51	
11-6	1	Problems 1-3 Exs. 9–24, 50–59	Problems 1-3 Exs. 9–23 odd, 50–59	Problems 1-3 Exs. 9–23 odd, 31–36, 50–59	**Day 6** Problems 1-5 Exs. 9–29 odd, 31–47, 50–59
	2	Problems 4-5 Exs. 25–30, 40–42	Problems 4-5 Exs. 25–29 odd, 31–47	Problems 4-5 Exs. 25–29 odd, 37–49	
11-7	1	Problems 1-3 Exs. 8–22 all, 50–66	Problems 1-3 Exs. 9–21 odd, 50–66	Problems 1-3 Exs. 9–21 odd, 50–66	**Day 7** Problems 1-4 Exs. 9–23 odd, 25–44, 50–66
	2	Problem 4 Exs. 23–24 all, 26–30 even, 31, 43–44	Problem 4 Exs. 23, 25–44	Problem 4 Exs. 23, 25–49	
Review	1	Chapter 11 Review	Chapter 11 Review	Chapter 11 Review	**Day 8** Chapter 11 Review
Assess	1	Chapter 11 Test	Chapter 11 Test	Chapter 11 Test	Chapter 11 Test
Total		**16 Days**	**16 Days**	**16 Days**	**8 Days**

Note: Pacing does not include Concept Bytes and other feature pages.

Resources

	For the Chapter	11-1	11-2	11-3	11-4	11-5	11-6	11-7
Planning								
Teacher Center Online Planner & Grade Book	I	I	I	I	I	I	I	I
Interactive Learning & Guided Instruction								
My Math Video	I							
Solve It!		I TM	I TM	I TM	I TM	I TM	I TM	I TM
Student Companion (SP)*		P M	P M	P M	P M	P M	P M	
Vocabulary Support		I P M	I P M	I P M	I P M	I P M	I P M	I P M
Got It? Support		I P	I P	I P	I P	I P	I P	I P
Dynamic Activity							I	
Online Problems		I	I	I	I	I	I	I
Additional Problems		M	M	M	M	M	M	M
English Language Learner Support (TR)		E P M	E P M	E P M	E P M	E P M	E P M	E P M
Activities, Games, and Puzzles		E M	E M	E M	E M	E M	E M	E M
Teaching With TI Technology With CD-ROM			✓ P					
TI-Nspire™ Support CD-ROM		✓	✓	✓	✓	✓	✓	✓
Lesson Check & Practice								
Student Companion (SP)*		P M	P M	P M	P M	P M	P M	P M
Lesson Check Support		I P	I P	I P	I P	I P	I P	I P
Practice and Problem Solving Workbook (SP)		P	P	P	P	P	P	P
Think About a Plan (TR)*		E P M	E P M	E P M	E P M	E P M	E P M	E P M
Practice Form G (TR)*		E P M	E P M	E P M	E P M	E P M	E P M	E P M
Standardized Test Prep (TR)*		P M	P M	P M	P M	P M	P M	P M
Practice _Form K_ (TR)*		E P M	E P M	E P M	E P M	E P M	E P M	E P M
Extra Practice	E M							
Find the Errors!	M							
Enrichment (TR)		E P M	E P M	E P M	E P M	E P M	E P M	E P M
Answers and Solutions CD-ROM	✓	✓	✓	✓	✓	✓	✓	✓
Assess & Remediate								
ExamView CD-ROM	✓	✓	✓	✓	✓	✓	✓	✓
Lesson Quiz		I TM	I TM	I TM	I TM	I TM	I TM	I TM
Quizzes and Tests _Form G_ (TR)*	E P M				E P			E P
Quizzes and Tests _Form K_ (TR)*	E P M				E P			E P
Reteaching (TR)*		E P M	E P M	E P M	E P M	E P M	E P M	E P M
Performance Tasks (TR)*	P M							
Cumulative Review (TR)*	P M							
Progress Monitoring Assessments	I P M							

(TR) Available in All-In-One Teaching Resources   *Spanish available

1 Interactive Learning

Solve It!

PURPOSE To create and use rational expressions as a means of comparison

PROCESS Students may compare surface area using visual judgment or the formulas for the surface area and volume of a rectangular prism.

FACILITATE

Q How can you determine the amount of cardboard used for each box? **[Calculate the surface areas.]**

Q How can you determine the amount of space that each box encloses? **[Calculate the volumes.]**

Q How can you determine the number of square inches of cardboard needed to enclose one cubic inch of space? **[Divide the surface area by the volume.]**

ANSWER See Solve It in Answers on next page.

CONNECT THE MATH In the Solve It, students write a ratio to find an answer. In the lesson, students learn about ratios where the numerator and denominator are polynomials.

2 Guided Instruction

Problem 1

Remind students that one method for simplifying a fraction requires writing each number in factored form and then dividing out common factors.

Got It?   ERROR PREVENTION

If students give an answer of $\frac{1}{2}$ for 1c, stress that they must factor the denominator first.

Objective To simplify rational expressions

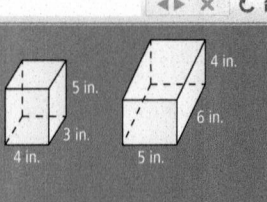

Getting Ready!

Which box uses less cardboard per cubic inch of space inside it? Justify your answer. (Hint: How would comparing a box's surface area to its volume help you answer this question?)

5 in. / 3 in. / 4 in.

4 in. / 6 in. / 5 in.

Get more volume for your surface area. That's efficient packaging.

Lesson Vocabulary
• rational expression
• excluded value

An expression of the form $\frac{\text{polynomial}}{\text{polynomial}}$ is a **rational expression.**

Essential Understanding The simplified form of a rational expression is like the simplified form of a numerical fraction. The numerator and denominator have no common factor other than 1. To simplify a rational expression, divide out common factors from the numerator and denominator.

Like a numerical fraction, a rational expression is undefined when the denominator is 0. A value of a variable for which a rational expression is undefined is an **excluded value.**

Problem 1 Simplifying a Rational Expression

What is the simplified form of $\frac{x-1}{5x-5}$? State any excluded values.

$$\frac{x-1}{5x-5} = \frac{x-1}{5(x-1)} \quad \text{Factor the denominator. The numerator cannot be factored.}$$

$$= \frac{x-1}{5(x-1)} \quad \text{Divide out the common factor } x-1.$$

$$= \frac{1}{5} \quad \text{Simplify.}$$

Think
Should you use the simplified form to find excluded values?
No. You must check the original expression to see which values of x make the denominator 0.

The denominator of the original expression is 0 when $x = 1$. The simplified form is $\frac{1}{5}$, where $x \neq 1$.

 Got It? 1. What is the simplified form of the expression? State any excluded values.

a. $\frac{21a^2}{7a^3}$ **b.** $\frac{18d^2}{4d+8}$ **c.** $\frac{2n-3}{6n-9}$ **d.** $\frac{26c^3+91c}{2c^2+7}$

11-1 Preparing to Teach

BIG idea Equivalence   **UbD**

ESSENTIAL UNDERSTANDINGS

• The simplest form of a rational expression is like the simplest form of a numerical fraction. The numerator and denominator have no common factor other than 1.

• To simplify a rational expression, divide out common factors from the numerator and denominator.

Math Background

When rational expressions are simplified, common factors from the numerator and denominator are divided out and are not part of the final simplified expression. However, any value of the independent variable that results in the expression being undefined must be excluded from the domain of the expression.

Excluded values from factors that remain in the denominator of the simplified form result in vertical asymptotes in the graph of the original function.

Excluded values from factors that divide out during the simplification process result in holes in the graph of the original function.

Support Student Learning

Use the **Algebra 1 Companion** to engage and support students during instruction. See Lesson Resources at the end of this lesson for details.

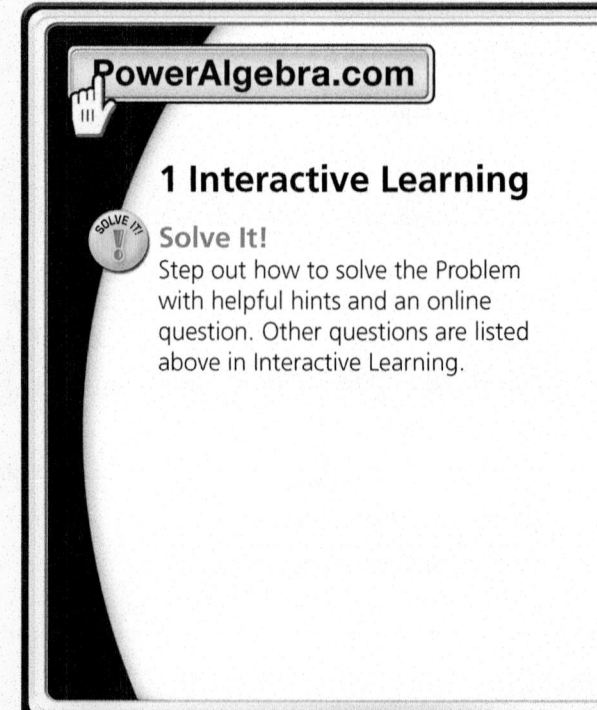

PowerAlgebra.com

1 Interactive Learning

Solve It!

Step out how to solve the Problem with helpful hints and an online question. Other questions are listed above in Interactive Learning.

 **Problem 2** Simplifying a Rational Expression Containing a Trinomial

What is the simplified form of $\frac{3x - 6}{x^2 + x - 6}$? State any excluded values.

Think	Write
To see if there are any common factors, factor the numerator and the denominator.	$\frac{3x - 6}{x^2 + x - 6} = \frac{3(x - 2)}{(x + 3)(x - 2)}$
Divide out the common factor $x - 2$. Simplify.	$= \frac{3(x - 2)^1}{(x + 3)_1(x - 2)}$ $= \frac{3}{(x + 3)}$
State the simplified form with any restrictions on the variable.	The denominator of the original expression is 0 when $x = -3$ or $x = 2$. So the simplified form is $\frac{3}{x + 3}$, where $x \neq -3$ and $x \neq 2$.

Think

Could you also find the restricted values *before* simplifying?
Yes. You use the original expression to find the restrictions on x, so you don't need to simplify first.

Got It? 2. What is the simplified form of the expression? State any excluded values.

a. $\frac{2x - 8}{x^2 - 2x - 8}$ b. $\frac{a^2 - 3a + 2}{3a - 3}$ c. $\frac{6z + 12}{2z^2 + 7z + 6}$ d. $\frac{c^2 - c - 6}{c^2 + 5c + 6}$

The numerator and denominator of $\frac{x - 3}{3 - x}$ are opposites. To simplify the expression, you can factor -1 from $3 - x$ to get $-1(-3 + x)$, which you can rewrite as $-1(x - 3)$. Then simplify $\frac{x - 3}{-1(x - 3)}$.

 Problem 3 Recognizing Opposite Factors

What is the simplified form of $\frac{4 - x^2}{7x - 14}$? State any excluded values.

Plan

When should you factor -1 from an expression?
You should factor -1 from $a - x$ when factoring -1 results in a common factor.

$\frac{4 - x^2}{7x - 14} = \frac{(2 - x)(2 + x)}{7(x - 2)}$ Factor the numerator and the denominator.

$= \frac{-1(x - 2)(2 + x)}{7(x - 2)}$ Factor -1 from $2 - x$.

$= \frac{-1(x - 2)^1(2 + x)}{7_1(x - 2)}$ Divide out the common factor $x - 2$.

$= -\frac{x + 2}{7}$ Simplify.

The denominator of the original expression is 0 when $x = 2$. The simplified form is $-\frac{x + 2}{7}$, where $x \neq 2$.

Problem 2

Q Is the original expression equal to zero when $x = 2$? Explain. **[No; when $x = 2$, both the numerator and denominator are equal to zero and the expression is undefined.]**

Got It? SYNTHESIZING

Q How can you find whether there are excluded values if the denominator is quadratic but does not factor? **[Set the quadratic polynomial equal to zero and solve the equation.]**

Problem 3

Q What kind of special product is the numerator? **[a difference of two squares]**

Q What factoring technique can be used to factor the denominator? **[greatest common factor]**

Q If a student answers that there are no excluded values, what mistake did he or she likely make? **[He or she likely only looked at the simplified expression, not at the original expression, when determining the values of x that make the denominator equal to 0.]**

---

2 Guided Instruction

 Each Problem is worked out and supported online.

Problem 1
Simplifying a Rational Expression

Problem 2
Simplifying a Rational Expression Containing a Trinomial

Problem 3
Recognizing Opposite Factors
Animated

Alternative Problem 3
Recognizing Opposite Factors

Problem 4
Using a Rational Expression
Animated

Support in Algebra 1 Companion
• Vocabulary
• Key Concepts
• Got It?

Answers

Solve It!
The box with dimensions 4 in. by 6 in. by 5 in.; explanations may vary.

Got It?
1. a. $\frac{3}{a}$, $a \neq 0$

b. $\frac{9d^2}{2d + 4}$, $d \neq -2$

c. $\frac{1}{3}$, $n \neq \frac{3}{2}$

d. $13c$, none

2. a. $\frac{2}{x + 2}$, $x \neq -2$, $x \neq 4$

b. $\frac{a - 2}{3}$, $a \neq 1$

c. $\frac{6}{2z + 3}$, $z \neq -2$, $z \neq -\frac{3}{2}$

d. $\frac{c - 3}{c + 3}$, $c \neq -3$, $c \neq -2$

Got It?

Some students may be more successful with these problems if they begin, whenever possible, by rewriting each of the polynomials in standard form with a positive lead coefficient.

Problem 4

Some students may understand the solution process for this problem more clearly if you first state the formula for the volume of a prism, and then substitute in values that you know to produce the equation: $\pi a^2(2a + 8) = 4a^2 h$.

Students can then be guided to divide both sides by $4a^2$ in order to solve the equation for h.

Got It?

VISUAL LEARNER

Q What is the area of the square? Explain.
[$36x^2 + 24x + 4$; the area of a square is the side length squared.]

Q If ℓ is the length of the rectangle, what expression represents the area of the rectangle? [$(3x + 1)\ell$]

 Got It? **3.** What is the simplified form of the expression? State any excluded values.

a. $\dfrac{2x - 5}{5 - 2x}$ **b.** $\dfrac{y^2 - 16}{4 - y}$ **c.** $\dfrac{3 - 9d}{6d^2 + d - 1}$ **d.** $\dfrac{3 - 3z}{2z^2 - 2}$

You can use rational expressions to model some real-world situations.

 Problem 4 **Using a Rational Expression**

Shopping You are choosing between the two wastebaskets that have the shape of the figures at the right. They both have the same volume. What is the height h of the rectangular wastebasket? Give your answer in terms of a.

Step 1 Find the volume of the cylinder.

$V = \pi r^2 h$ Formula for volume of a cylinder

$ = \pi a^2(2a + 8)$ Substitute a for r and $2a + 8$ for h.

Step 2 Find the height of a rectangular prism with volume $\pi a^2(2a + 8)$ and base area $B = (2a)^2 = 4a^2$.

$V = Bh$ Formula for volume of a prism

$h = \dfrac{V}{B}$ Solve for h.

$ = \dfrac{\pi a^2(2a + 8)}{4a^2}$ Substitute the volume of the cylinder for the volume of the rectangular prism and $4a^2$ for B.

$ = \dfrac{\pi a^2(2)(a + 4)}{4a^2}$ Factor.

$ = \dfrac{\pi a^2 (2)^1 (a + 4)}{{}_2 4_1 a^2}$ Divide out common factors 2 and a^2.

$ = \dfrac{\pi(a + 4)}{2}$ Simplify.

The height of the rectangular prism is $\dfrac{\pi(a + 4)}{2}$.

Got It? **4. a.** A square has side length $6x + 2$. A rectangle with width $3x + 1$ has the same area as the square. What is the length of the rectangle?

b. Reasoning Suppose the dimensions of the wastebaskets in Problem 4 are measured in feet. Is it possible for the height of the rectangular wastebasket to be 1 ft? What are the possible heights? Explain.

Plan

Is there another way to solve the problem?
Yes. You can set the volumes equal to each other and then solve for h.

Additional Problems

1. What is the simplified form of $\dfrac{x + 3}{2x + 6}$? State any excluded values.

ANSWER $\dfrac{1}{2}, x \neq -3$

2. What is the simplified form of $\dfrac{5x + 10}{x^2 - x - 6}$? State any excluded values.

ANSWER $\dfrac{5}{x - 3}, x \neq -2, x \neq 3$

3. What is the simplified form of $\dfrac{x^2 - 9}{-x^2 + 2x + 3}$? State any excluded values.

ANSWER $\dfrac{x + 3}{-1(x + 1)}, x \neq 3, x \neq -1$

4. The length of a rectangular prism is 5 units more than the width, w. The volume of the prism is $w^3 + 7w^2 + 10w$. What is a simplified expression for the height of the prism?

ANSWER $w + 2$

Answers

Got It? (continued)

3. a. $-1, x \neq 2.5$

b. $-y - 4, y \neq 4$

c. $-\dfrac{3}{2d + 1}, d \neq -\dfrac{1}{2}, d \neq \dfrac{1}{3}$

d. $-\dfrac{3}{2z + 2}, z \neq \pm 1$

4. a. $12x + 4$

b. No, h must be greater than 2π in order for the value of a to be greater than 0. If h is less than or equal to 2π, then a will be negative, and length cannot be negative.

Lesson Check

Do you know HOW?

Simplify each expression. State any excluded values.

1. $\frac{3x + 9}{x + 3}$

2. $\frac{5 - x}{x^2 - 2x - 15}$

3. The two rectangles below have the same area. What is a simplified expression for the length ℓ of the rectangle on the right?

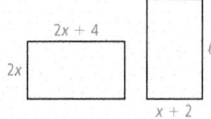

Do you UNDERSTAND?

4. **Vocabulary** Is each expression a rational expression? Explain your reasoning.

   a. $\frac{\sqrt{x} + 2}{x^2 + 4}$ b. $\frac{y}{y - 1}$

5. **Writing** When simplifying a rational expression, why may it be necessary to exclude values? Explain.

6. **Reasoning** Suppose neither the numerator nor the denominator of a rational expression can be factored. Is the expression necessarily in simplified form? Explain.

7. Are the given factors opposites? Explain.

   a. $3 - x; x - 3$ b. $2 - y; -y + 2$

Practice and Problem-Solving Exercises

Ⓐ Practice   Simplify each expression. State any excluded values.   ◀ See Problems 1, 2, and 3.

8. $\frac{6a + 9}{12}$

9. $\frac{4x^3}{28x^4}$

10. $\frac{2m - 5}{6m - 15}$

11. $\frac{2p - 24}{4p - 48}$

12. $\frac{3x^2 - 9x}{x - 3}$

13. $\frac{3x + 6}{3x^2}$

14. $\frac{2x^2 + 2x}{3x^2 + 3x}$

15. $\frac{2b - 8}{b^2 - 16}$

16. $\frac{m + 6}{m^2 - m - 42}$

17. $\frac{w^2 + 7w}{w^2 - 49}$

18. $\frac{a^2 + 2a + 1}{5a + 5}$

19. $\frac{m^2 + 7m + 12}{m^2 + 6m + 8}$

20. $\frac{c^2 - 6c + 8}{c^2 + c - 6}$

21. $\frac{b^2 + 8b + 15}{b + 5}$

22. $\frac{m + 4}{m^2 + 2m - 8}$

23. $\frac{5 - 4n}{4n - 5}$

24. $\frac{12 - 4t}{t^2 - 2t - 3}$

25. $\frac{4m - 8}{4 - 2m}$

26. $\frac{m - 2}{4 - 2m}$

27. $\frac{v - 5}{25 - v^2}$

28. $\frac{4 - w}{w^2 - 8w + 16}$

29. **Geometry** The length of a rectangular prism is 5 more than twice the width w.   ◀ See Problem 4.
The volume of the prism is $2w^3 + 7w^2 + 5w$. What is a simplified expression for the height of the prism?

30. **Geometry** Rectangle A has length $2x + 6$ and width $3x$. Rectangle B has length $x + 2$ and an area 12 square units greater than Rectangle A's area. What is a simplified expression for the width of Rectangle B?

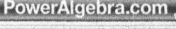

---

3 Lesson Check

Do you know HOW?

• If students have difficulty with Exercises 1-2, then make sure that they determine restrictions on the variable by considering the original expression rather than the simplified expression.

Do you UNDERSTAND?

• If students have difficulty with Exercise 5, remind them that division by zero is prohibited.

Close

Q How is simplifying a rational expression the same as simplifying a rational number? **[In both cases, you must write the numerator and the denominator in factored form, and then divide out common factors.]**

Lesson Check

1. $3; x \neq -3$

2. $-\frac{1}{x + 3}; x \neq -3, x \neq 5$

3. $4x$

4. **a.** No, the expression is not the ratio of two polynomials.

   b. Yes, the expression is the ratio of two polynomials.

5. If the denominator contains a polynomial, there may be values of the variable that make the denominator equal to zero, and division by zero is undefined.

6. The only way the rational expression is not in simplest form is if the numerator and the denominator are equal.

7. **a.** yes, $3 - x = -(x - 3)$

   b. no, $2 - y = -(y - 2)$

Practice and Problem-Solving Exercises

8. $\frac{2a + 3}{4}$

9. $\frac{1}{7x}, x \neq 0$

10. $\frac{1}{3}, m \neq 2.5$

11. $\frac{1}{2}, p \neq 12$

12. $3x, x \neq 3$

13. $\frac{x + 2}{x^2}, x \neq 0$

14. $\frac{2}{3}, x \neq -1, x \neq 0$

15. $\frac{2}{b + 4}, b \neq \pm 4$

16. $\frac{1}{m - 7}, m \neq -6, m \neq 7$

17. $\frac{w}{w - 7}, w \neq \pm 7$

18. $\frac{a + 1}{5}, a \neq -1$

19. $\frac{m + 3}{m + 2}, m \neq -4, m \neq -2$

20. $\frac{c - 4}{c + 3}, c \neq -3, c \neq 2$

21. $b + 3, b \neq -5$

22. $\frac{1}{m - 2}, m \neq -4, m \neq 2$

23. $-1, n \neq \frac{5}{4}$

24. $\frac{-4}{t + 1}, t \neq -1, t \neq 3$

25. $-2, m \neq 2$ 26. $-\frac{1}{2}, m \neq 2$

27. $\frac{-1}{v + 5}, v \neq \pm 5$ 28. $\frac{-1}{w - 4}, w \neq 4$

29. $w + 1$ 30. $6x + 6$

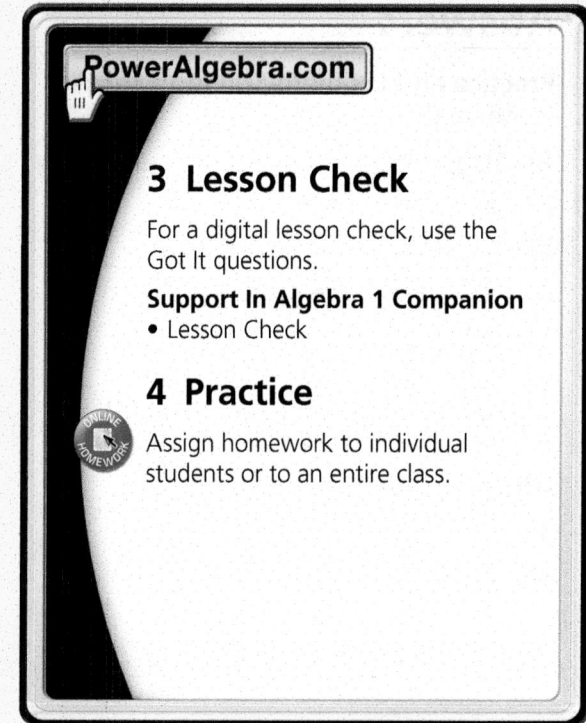

3 Lesson Check

For a digital lesson check, use the Got It questions.

Support In Algebra 1 Companion
• Lesson Check

4 Practice

Assign homework to individual students or to an entire class.

4 Practice

ASSIGNMENT GUIDE

Basic: 8–30 all, 32–42 even, 43

Average: 9–29 odd, 31–47

Advanced: 9–29 odd, 31–53

Standardized Test Prep: 54–57

Mixed Review: 58–72

Reasoning exercises have blue headings.

Applications exercises have red headings.

EXERCISE 42: Use the Think About a Plan worksheet in the **Practice and Problem Solving Workbook** (also available in the Teaching Resources in print and online) to further support students' development in becoming independent learners.

HOMEWORK QUICK CHECK

To check students' understanding of key skills and concepts, go over Exercises 15, 29, 40, 42, and 43.

 Apply

Simplify each expression. State any excluded values.

31. $\frac{2r^2 + 9r - 5}{r^2 + 10r + 25}$

32. $\frac{7z^2 + 23z + 6}{z^2 + 2z - 3}$

33. $\frac{5t^2 + 6t - 8}{3t^2 + 5t - 2}$

34. $\frac{32a^3}{16a^2 - 8a}$

35. $\frac{3z^2 + 12z}{z^4}$

36. $\frac{2s^2 + s}{s^3}$

37. $\frac{4a^2 - 8a - 5}{15 - a - 2a^2}$

38. $\frac{16 + 16m + 3m^2}{m^2 - 3m - 28}$

39. $\frac{10c + c^2 - 3c^3}{5c^2 - 6c - 8}$

40. Think About a Plan In the figure at the right, what is the ratio of the area of the shaded triangle to the area of the rectangle? Write your answer in simplified form.
- What is an expression for the length of the rectangle?
- How do you find the area of a triangle?

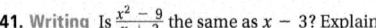

41. Writing Is $\frac{x^2 - 9}{x + 3}$ the same as $x - 3$? Explain.

42. a. Construction To keep heating costs down for a building, architects want the ratio of surface area to volume to be as small as possible. What is an expression for the ratio of surface area to volume for each figure?

   i. square prism 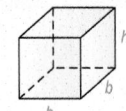   **ii.** cylinder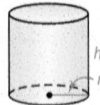

   b. For each figure, what is the ratio of surface area to volume when $b = 12$ ft, $h = 18$ ft, and $r = 6$ ft?

43. Error Analysis A student simplified a rational expression as shown at the right. Describe and correct the error.

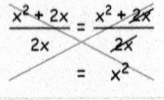

44. Banking A bank account with principal P earns interest at rate r (expressed as a decimal), compounded annually. What is the ratio of the balance after 3 yr to the balance after 1 yr? Write r as a decimal.

45. Open-Ended Write a rational expression that has 4 and -3 as excluded values.

Write a ratio in simplified form of the area of the shaded figure to the area of the figure that encloses it.

46.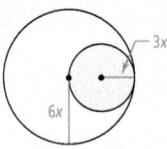

47.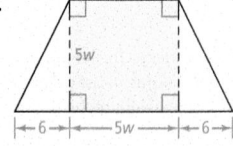

 Challenge   **Simplify each expression. State any excluded values.**

48. $\frac{m^2 - n^2}{m^2 + 11mn + 10n^2}$

49. $\frac{a^2 - 5ab + 6b^2}{a^2 + 2ab - 8b^2}$

50. $\frac{36v^2 - 49w^2}{18v^2 + 9vw - 14w^2}$

Answers

Practice and Problem-Solving Exercises
(continued)

31. $\frac{2r - 1}{r + 5}$, $r \neq -5$

32. $\frac{7z + 2}{z - 1}$, $z \neq -3$, $z \neq 1$

33. $\frac{5t - 4}{3t - 1}$, $t \neq -2$, $t \neq \frac{1}{3}$

34. $\frac{4a^2}{2a - 1}$, $a \neq 0$, $a \neq \frac{1}{2}$

35. $\frac{3(z + 4)}{z^3}$, $z \neq 0$

36. $\frac{2s + 1}{s^2}$, $s \neq 0$

37. $-\frac{2a + 1}{a + 3}$, $a \neq -3$, $a \neq \frac{5}{2}$

38. $\frac{3m + 4}{m - 7}$, $m \neq -4$, $m \neq 7$

39. $-\frac{c(3c + 5)}{5c + 4}$, $c \neq -\frac{4}{5}$, $c \neq 2$

40. $\frac{x}{2x + 16}$

41. No, $y = \frac{x^2 - 9}{x + 3}$ is not defined for $x = -3$, but $x - 3$ is.

42. a. i. $\frac{2b + 4h}{bh}$

   ii. $\frac{2r + 2h}{rh}$

  b. i. $\frac{4}{9}$

   ii. $\frac{4}{9}$

43. The student canceled terms instead of factors; $\frac{x^2 + 2x}{2x} = \frac{x(x + 2)}{2x} = \frac{x + 2}{2}$.

44. $(1 + r)^2$

45. Answers will vary. Sample: $\frac{1}{(x - 4)(x + 3)}$

46. $\frac{1}{4}$

47. $\frac{5w}{5w + 6}$

48. $\frac{m - n}{m + 10n}$, $m \neq -10n$, $m \neq -n$

49. $\frac{a - 3b}{a + 4b}$, $a \neq -4b$, $a \neq 2b$

50. $\frac{6v - 7w}{3v - 2w}$, $v \neq \frac{2}{3}w$, $v \neq -\frac{7}{6}w$

Reasoning Determine whether each statement is *always, sometimes,* or *never* true for real numbers a and b. Explain.

51. $\frac{2b}{b} = 2$

52. $\frac{ab^3}{b^4} = ab$

53. $\frac{a^2 + 6a + 5}{2a + 2} = \frac{a + 5}{2}$

Standardized Test Prep

 SAT/ACT

54. Which expression simplifies to -1?

  Ⓐ $\frac{x + 1}{x - 1}, x \neq 1$ Ⓑ $\frac{r + 3}{3 - r}, r \neq 3$ Ⓒ $\frac{n - 2}{2 - n}, n \neq 2$ Ⓓ $\frac{4 - p}{4 + p}, p \neq -4$

55. Which inequality represents the graph at the right?

  Ⓕ $y > \frac{1}{3}x + 1$ Ⓗ $y \geq \frac{1}{3}x + 1$

  Ⓖ $y < \frac{1}{3}x + 1$ Ⓘ $y \leq \frac{1}{3}x + 1$

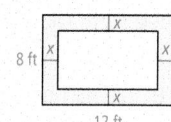

56. What is $\frac{\sqrt{6}}{\sqrt{96}}$ in simplified form?

  Ⓐ 16 Ⓒ $\frac{1}{4}$

  Ⓑ 4 Ⓓ $\frac{1}{16}$

Short Response

57. You are painting a wall for a display. You want to have a blue border of uniform width around a white rectangle, as shown. The areas of the blue border and the white rectangle should be the same. What should be the approximate width x of the blue border? Show your work.

Mixed Review

Use $\triangle ABC$ at the right. Find the value of each expression.

◀ *See Lesson 10-6.*

58. $\cos B$

59. $\sin A$

60. $\tan B$

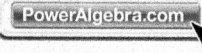

Simplify each radical expression.

◀ *See Lesson 10-2.*

61. $\sqrt{20} \cdot \sqrt{10}$

62. $\sqrt{a^4 b^7 c^8}$

63. $\sqrt{9x} \cdot \sqrt{11x}$

64. $\sqrt{\frac{2m}{25m^5}}$

65. $\frac{\sqrt{80}}{\sqrt{10}}$

66. $\sqrt{\frac{28y^5}{7y^2}}$

Get Ready! To prepare for Lesson 11-2, do Exercises 67–72.

Factor each expression.

◀ *See Lesson 8-6.*

67. $2c^2 + 15c + 7$

68. $15t^2 - 26t + 11$

69. $9q^2 + 12q + 4$

70. $4c^2 - 12c + 5$

71. $24t^2 - 14t - 3$

72. $3q^2 - q - 14$

---

51. Sometimes; it is true for all values of b except 0.

52. Sometimes; it is true only if $a = 0$ and $b \neq 0$ or if $b = \pm 1$.

53. Sometimes; it is true for all values of a except -1.

54. C

55. G

56. C

57. [2] Area of white rectangle
$= (12 - 2x)(8 - 2x)$, area of blue border $= 8(12) - (12 - 2x)(8 - 2x)$. Setting these two quantities equal, you get $2(12 - 2x)(8 - 2x) = 96$, or $2(2)(2)(6 - x)(4 - x) = 96$, which simplifies to $(6 - x)(4 - x) = 12$. $24 - 10x + x^2 = 12$, or $x^2 - 10x + 12 = 0$. Using the quadratic formula, you get $x = \frac{10 \pm \sqrt{100 - 48}}{2} \approx 8.6$ or 1.4. Reject the first solution as not possible. The width should be about 1.4 ft.

[1] a minor computational error

58. $\frac{15}{17}$

59. $\frac{15}{17}$

60. $\frac{8}{15}$

61. $10\sqrt{2}$

62. $a^2 b^3 c^4 \sqrt{b}$

63. $3x\sqrt{11}$

64. $\frac{\sqrt{2}}{5m^2}$

65. $2\sqrt{2}$

66. $2y\sqrt{y}$

67. $(2c + 1)(c + 7)$

68. $(15t - 11)(t - 1)$

69. $(3q + 2)^2$

70. $(2c - 1)(2c - 5)$

71. $(6t + 1)(4t - 3)$

72. $(3q - 7)(q + 2)$

Additional Instructional Support

Algebra 1 Companion

Students can use the **Algebra 1 Companion** worktext (4 pages) as you teach the lesson. Use the Companion to support

- New Vocabulary
- Key Concepts
- Got It for each Problem
- Lesson Check

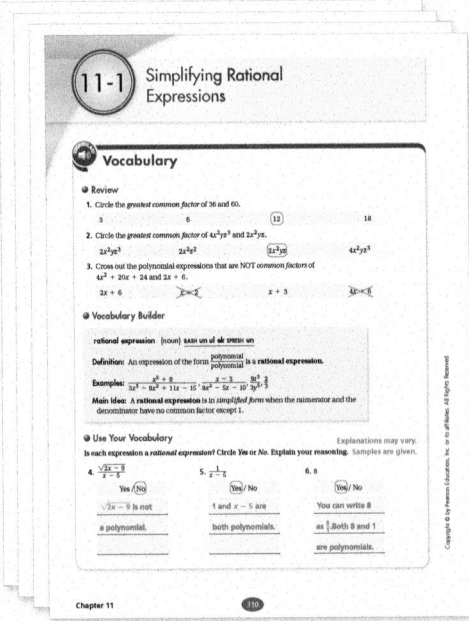

ELL Support

Focus on Language Group students into pairs. Have students analyze the term *rational expression*. What two words make up the term? What does each individual word mean? Encourage students to predict the meaning before reading the definition. Have them compare their predictions with the definition given in the text.

Assess Understanding Project the first Problem on an overhead projector and read aloud as you point to each word. Then model a similar example, or Problem 2, restating the steps from the text so they are repetitive. Invite volunteers to explain how they can simplify a rational expression. Provide an example for students to work independently. Monitor and assist as needed.

5 Assess & Remediate

Lesson Quiz

1. What is the simplified form of $\frac{x-1}{3x-3}$? State any excluded values.

2. What is the simplified form of $\frac{2x-8}{x^2-16}$? State any excluded values.

3. What is the simplified form of $\frac{25-x^2}{x^2-x-20}$? State any excluded values.

4. The length of a rectangle can be represented by the expression $x+6$. If the area of the rectangle is $2x^2+8x-24$, what is the expression for the width of the rectangle?

5. **Do you UNDERSTAND?** What is an expression that simplifies to $\frac{2}{5}$, with excluded values $x \neq 3$ and $x \neq -3$?

ANSWERS TO LESSON QUIZ

1. $\frac{1}{3}$, $x \neq 1$

2. $\frac{2}{x+4}$, $x \neq 4$, $x \neq -4$

3. $\frac{-x-5}{x+4}$, $x \neq 5$, $x \neq -4$

4. $2x-4$

5. Answers may vary. Sample: $\frac{2x^2-18}{5x^2-45}$

PRESCRIPTION FOR REMEDIATION
Use the student work on the Lesson Quiz to prescribe a differentiated review assignment.

Points	Differentiated Remediation
0–2	Intervention
3–4	On-level
5	Extension

PowerAlgebra.com

5 Assess & Remediate

Assign the Lesson Quiz. Appropriate intervention, practice, or enrichment is automatically generated based on student performance.

Intervention

- **Reteaching** (2 pages) Provides reteaching and practice exercises for the key lesson concepts. Use with struggling students or absent students.

- **English Language Learner Support** Helps students develop and reinforce mathematical vocabulary and key concepts.

All-in-One Resources/Online
Reteaching

All-in-One Resources/Online
English Language Learner Support

Differentiated Remediation *continued*

On-Level

- **Practice** (2 pages) Provides extra practice for each lesson. For simpler practice exercises, use the Form K Practice pages found in the All-in-One Teaching Resources and online.

- **Think About a Plan** Helps students develop specific problem-solving skills and strategies by providing scaffolded guiding questions.

- **Standardized Test Prep** Focuses on all major exercises, all major question types, and helps students prepare for the high-stakes assessments.

Extension

- **Enrichment** Provides students with interesting problems and activities that extend the concepts of the lesson.

- **Activities, Games, and Puzzles** Worksheets that can be used for concept development, enrichment, and for fun!

Practice and Problem Solving WKBK/All-in-One Resources/Online
Practice page 1

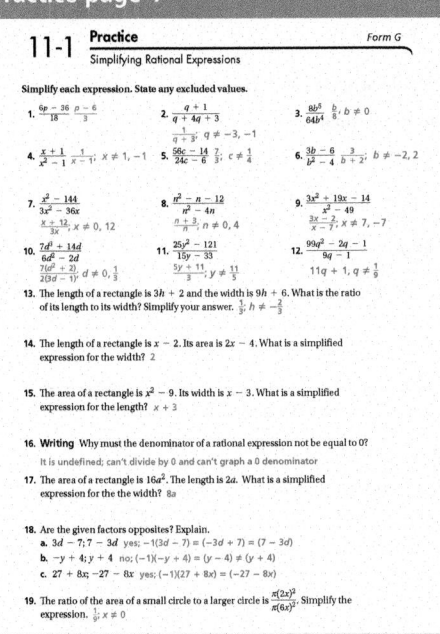

Practice and Problem Solving WKBK/All-in-One Resources/Online
Practice page 2

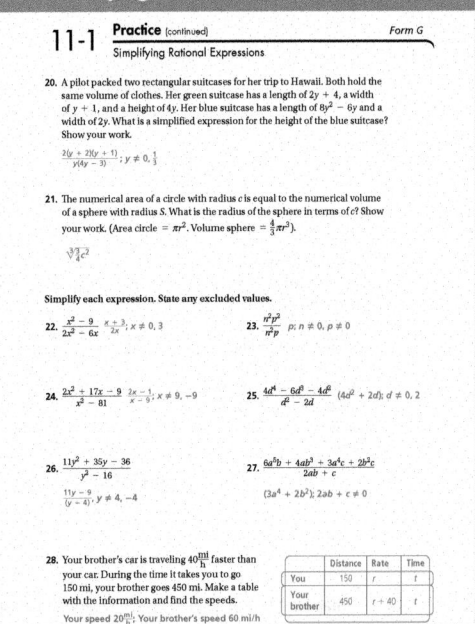

All-in-One Resources/Online
Enrichment

Practice and Problem Solving WKBK/All-in-One Resources/Online
Think About a Plan

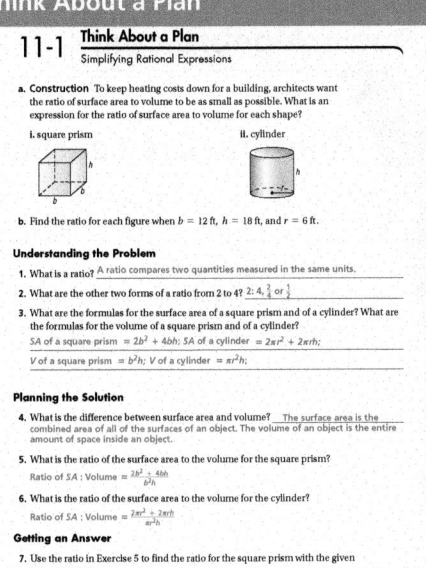

Practice and Problem Solving WKBK/All-in-One Resources/Online
Standardized Test Prep

Online Teacher Resource Center
Activities, Games, and Puzzles

1 Interactive Learning

Solve It!

PURPOSE To divide a rational expression by a polynomial

PROCESS Students may create expressions for the volume of each object using the volume formulas and calculate the percentages by dividing the appropriate volumes.

FACILITATE

Q What expression represents the volume of the cube? [**The volume of a cube with side length** x **is** x^3**.**]

Q What expression represents the radius cubed? volume of the sphere? [$\frac{x^3}{8}$, $\frac{\pi x^3}{6}$]

ANSWER See Solve It in Answers on next page.
CONNECT THE MATH In Solve It, students solve the problem by finding a quotient. Multiplying and dividing rational expressions follows the same procedures as multiplying and dividing numerical fractions.

2 Guided Instruction

Problem 1

Q Can the factored form in 1B be simplified? Explain. [**No; the numerator and denominator have no common factors.**]

Q How do you determine the excluded values for the products of the rational expressions? [**You determine the values of the variables which result in denominators of zero.**]

Got It?

Use substitution to check that the product is equivalent to the original expression.

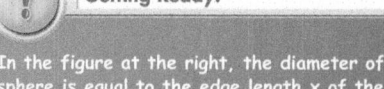

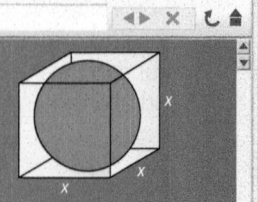

11-2 Multiplying and Dividing Rational Expressions

Objectives To multiply and divide rational expressions
To simplify complex fractions

Getting Ready!

In the figure at the right, the diameter of the sphere is equal to the edge length x of the cube. What percent of the cube's volume is taken up by the sphere? Justify your reasoning.

Sometimes you need to divide things that are already divided.

Lesson Vocabulary
• complex fraction

Many problems require finding products and quotients of rational expressions.

Essential Understanding You can multiply and divide rational expressions using the same properties you use to multiply and divide numerical fractions.

If a, b, c, and d represent polynomials (where $b \neq 0$ and $d \neq 0$), then $\frac{a}{b} \cdot \frac{c}{d} = \frac{ac}{bd}$.

Problem 1 Multiplying Rational Expressions

What is the product? State any excluded values.

A $\frac{6}{a^2} \cdot \frac{-2}{a^3}$

$\frac{6}{a^2} \cdot \frac{-2}{a^3} = \frac{6(-2)}{a^2(a^3)}$ Multiply numerators and multiply denominators.

$= \frac{-12}{a^5}$ Simplify.

The product is $\frac{-12}{a^5}$, where $a \neq 0$.

Think

Are products of rational expressions defined for all real numbers?
No. The products may have excluded values. In part (A), the excluded value is 0. In part (B), the excluded values are 0 and −3.

B $\frac{x-7}{x} \cdot \frac{x-5}{x+3}$

$\frac{x-7}{x} \cdot \frac{x-5}{x+3} = \frac{(x-7)(x-5)}{x(x+3)}$ Multiply numerators and multiply denominators. Leave the product in factored form.

The product is $\frac{(x-7)(x-5)}{x(x+3)}$, where $x \neq 0$ and $x \neq -3$.

Got It? **1.** What is the product? State any excluded values.

a. $\frac{5}{y} \cdot \frac{3}{y^3}$ **b.** $\frac{x}{x-2} \cdot \frac{x+1}{x-3}$

11-2 Preparing to Teach

BIG idea Equivalence **UbD**

ESSENTIAL UNDERSTANDINGS

• Rational expressions can be multiplied and divided using the same properties used to multiply and divide numerical fractions.

• Complex fractions contain one or more fractions in their numerator, in their denominator, or in both.

Math Background

The multiplication and division of rational expressions requires students to combine their skills of simplifying rational expressions together with their knowledge of multiplying and dividing numeric fractions. Each multiplication, division, and complex fraction problem in this lesson can be seen as a simplification problem once the rules for multiplying and/or dividing fractions are applied to the rational expressions.

For most students a complex fraction is a daunting sight. Train students to rewrite these problems using division symbols before beginning any simplification or factoring. Complex fractions provide an excellent way to reinforce that a fraction is another way to write a division problem.

Support Student Learning

Use the **Algebra 1 Companion** to engage and support students during instructions. See Lesson Resources at the end of this lesson for details.

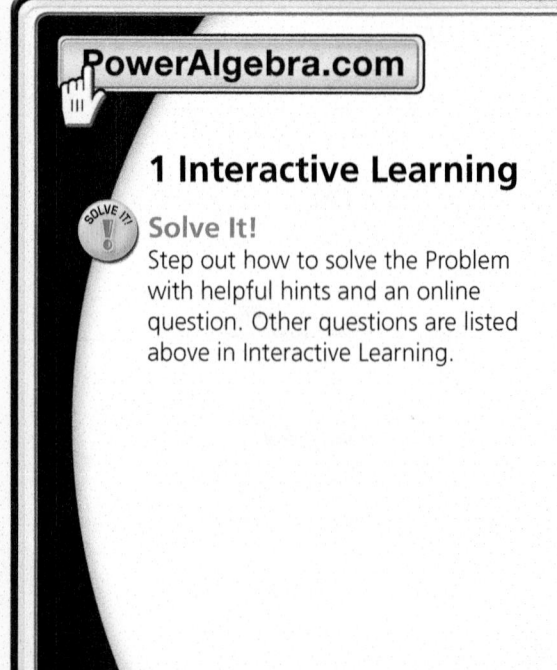

PowerAlgebra.com

1 Interactive Learning

Solve It!
Step out how to solve the Problem with helpful hints and an online question. Other questions are listed above in Interactive Learning.

As Problem 1 indicates, products of rational expressions may have excluded values. For the rest of this chapter, it is not necessary to state excluded values unless you are asked.

Sometimes the product $\frac{ac}{bd}$ of two rational expressions may not be in simplified form. You may need to divide out common factors.

 Problem 2 Using Factoring

Plan

What is a reasonable first step?
When you multiply rational expressions, a reasonable first step is to factor. Look for GCFs to factor out. Then look for quadratic expressions that you can factor.

What is the product $\frac{x+5}{7x-21} \cdot \frac{14x}{x^2+3x-10}$**?**

$$\frac{x+5}{7x-21} \cdot \frac{14x}{x^2+3x-10} = \frac{x+5}{7(x-3)} \cdot \frac{14x}{(x+5)(x-2)} \qquad \text{Factor denominators.}$$

$$= \frac{x+5^1}{_17(x-3)} \cdot \frac{14^2x}{_1(x+5)(x-2)} \qquad \begin{array}{l}\text{Divide out the common factors} \\ \text{7 and } x+5.\end{array}$$

$$= \frac{1}{x-3} \cdot \frac{2x}{x-2} \qquad \text{Simplify.}$$

$$= \frac{2x}{(x-3)(x-2)} \qquad \begin{array}{l}\text{Multiply numerators and} \\ \text{multiply denominators. Leave} \\ \text{the product in factored form.}\end{array}$$

 Got It? 2. a. What is the product $\frac{3x^2}{x+2} \cdot \frac{x^2+3x+2}{x}$?
    b. Reasoning In Problem 2, suppose you multiply the numerators and denominators *before* you factor. Will you still get the same product? Explain.

You can also multiply a rational expression by a polynomial. Leave the product in factored form.

 **Problem 3 Multiplying a Rational Expression by a Polynomial**

Plan

How do you get started?
Write the polynomial as a rational expression with denominator 1. Then multiply the two rational expressions.

What is the product $\frac{2m+5}{3m-6} \cdot (m^2+m-6)$**?**

$$\frac{2m+5}{3m-6} \cdot (m^2+m-6) = \frac{2m+5}{3(m-2)} \cdot \frac{(m-2)(m+3)}{1} \qquad \text{Factor.}$$

$$= \frac{(2m+5)}{3_1(m-2)} \cdot \frac{(m-2)^1(m+3)}{1} \qquad \begin{array}{l}\text{Divide out the common} \\ \text{factor } m-2.\end{array}$$

$$= \frac{(2m+5)(m+3)}{3} \qquad \begin{array}{l}\text{Multiply. Leave the product in} \\ \text{factored form.}\end{array}$$

 Got It? 3. What is the product?
    a. $\frac{2x-14}{4x-6} \cdot (6x^2-13x+6)$ **b.** $\frac{x^2+2x+1}{x^2-1} \cdot (x^2+2x-3)$

Recall that $\frac{a}{b} \div \frac{c}{d} = \frac{a}{b} \cdot \frac{d}{c}$, where $b \neq 0$, $c \neq 0$, and $d \neq 0$. When you divide rational expressions, first rewrite the quotient as a product using the reciprocal before dividing out common factors.

Problem 2

To help students recognize that factoring each expression is a reasonable first step, ask students to multiply the numeric fractions $\frac{25}{182}$ and $\frac{52}{375}$. Students should remember that dividing out common factors prior to multiplication is the most efficient way to find the simplified product.

Got It?   ERROR PREVENTION

Remind students that only identical expressions can be divided out. For example:

$$\frac{(3)(x)(x)}{(x+2)} \cdot \frac{(x+2)(x+1)}{(x)}$$

Problem 3

> **Q** How can you tell that $2m+5$ does not factor? **[It is not a trinomial or a difference of two squares and the GCF is 1.]**
>
> **Q** What value(s) of the variable are excluded? Explain. **[$x=2$; $3(2)-6=0$]**
>
> **Q** If the order of the expressions were reversed prior to determining the product, would you still arrive at the same answer? Explain. **[Yes; multiplication is commutative.]**

Got It?

Remind students of the FOIL method and other techniques for factoring polynomials of the form ax^2+bx+c.

---

2 Guided Instruction

 Each Problem is worked out and supported online.

Problem 1
Multiplying Rational Expressions

Problem 2
Using Factoring

Problem 3
Multiplying a Rational Expression by a Polynomial
                                   Animated

Problem 4
Dividing Rational Expressions

Problem 5
Dividing a Rational Expression by a Polynomial
                                   Animated

Problem 6
Simplifying a Complex Fraction
                                   Animated

Support in Algebra 1 Companion
• Vocabulary
• Key Concepts
• Got It?

Answers

Solve It!
About 52.4%; explanations may vary.

Got It?
1. a. $\frac{15}{y^4}$, $y \neq 0$
    b. $\frac{x(x+1)}{(x-2)(x-3)}$, $x \neq 3$, $x \neq 2$
2. a. $3x(x+1)$
    b. Yes, but you will have to simplify the resulting expression.
3. a. $(x-7)(3x-2)$
    b. $(x+1)(x+3)$

Problem 4

> **Q** What is the first step when dividing two numeric fractions? **[Rewrite the problem as multiplication by the reciprocal of the second fraction.]**
>
> **Q** What kind of special product is the polynomial $x^2 - 25$? **[difference of two squares]**
>
> **Q** If the order of the expressions were reversed prior to determining the quotient, would you still arrive at the same answer? Explain. **[No, because division is not commutative.]**

Got It?   ERROR PREVENTION

In 4a or 4b, if students claim that there are no common factors to divide, then they likely did not change the quotient to a product prior to factoring.

Problem 5

> **Q** What is the reciprocal of $x^2 - 3x - 4$? Explain. **[It can be written as $\frac{x^2 - 3x - 4}{1}$, so its reciprocal is $\frac{1}{x^2 - 3x - 4}$.]**

Got It?   ERROR PREVENTION

If students get the reciprocal of the actual answer, then they likely found the reciprocal of the rational expression and forgot to change division to multiplication.

 **Problem 4** Dividing Rational Expressions

What is the quotient $\dfrac{x^2 - 25}{4x + 28} \div \dfrac{x - 5}{x^2 + 9x + 14}$?

Think	Write
To divide by a rational expression, multiply by its reciprocal.	$\dfrac{x^2 - 25}{4x + 28} \div \dfrac{x - 5}{x^2 + 9x + 14}$
	$= \dfrac{x^2 - 25}{4x + 28} \cdot \dfrac{x^2 + 9x + 14}{x - 5}$
Before multiplying, factor.	$= \dfrac{(x + 5)(x - 5)}{4(x + 7)} \cdot \dfrac{(x + 7)(x + 2)}{x - 5}$
Divide out the common factors $x - 5$ and $x + 7$.	$= \dfrac{(x + 5)\cancel{(x - 5)}^1}{4_1\cancel{(x + 7)}} \cdot \dfrac{\cancel{(x + 7)}^1(x + 2)}{{}_1\cancel{x - 5}}$
Multiply numerators and multiply denominators. Leave the quotient in factored form.	$= \dfrac{(x + 5)(x + 2)}{4}$

 Got It? 4. What is the quotient?

    a. $\dfrac{x}{x + y} \div \dfrac{xy}{x + y}$ **b.** $\dfrac{4k + 8}{6k - 10} \div \dfrac{k^2 + 6k + 8}{9k - 15}$

The reciprocal of a polynomial such as $x^2 + 3x + 2$ is $\dfrac{1}{x^2 + 3x + 2}$.

 **Problem 5** Dividing a Rational Expression by a Polynomial

Multiple Choice What is the quotient $\dfrac{3x^2 - 12x}{5x} \div (x^2 - 3x - 4)$?

  Ⓐ $\dfrac{3x}{(x - 4)(x + 1)}$ Ⓑ $\dfrac{3x}{5x^2 + 5}$ Ⓒ $\dfrac{3(x - 4)^2(x + 1)}{5x}$ Ⓓ $\dfrac{3}{5(x + 1)}$

Plan

Why write the polynomial as a rational expression?
To divide a rational expression by a polynomial, you have to multiply by the reciprocal of the polynomial. Writing the polynomial over 1 may help you find its reciprocal.

$\dfrac{3x^2 - 12x}{5x} \div \dfrac{x^2 - 3x - 4}{1} = \dfrac{3x^2 - 12x}{5x} \cdot \dfrac{1}{x^2 - 3x - 4}$ Multiply by the reciprocal.

$= \dfrac{3x(x - 4)}{5x} \cdot \dfrac{1}{(x - 4)(x + 1)}$ Factor.

$= \dfrac{3\cancel{x}^1\cancel{(x - 4)}^1}{5_1\cancel{x}} \cdot \dfrac{1}{{}_1\cancel{(x - 4)}(x + 1)}$ Divide out the common factors x and $x - 4$.

$= \dfrac{3}{5(x + 1)}$ Simplify.

The correct answer is D.

 Got It? 5. What is the quotient $\dfrac{z^2 - 2z + 1}{z^2 + 2} \div (z - 1)$?

Additional Problems

1. What is the product?

  a. $\dfrac{3}{x} \cdot \dfrac{-2}{x^2}$

  b. $\dfrac{x}{x + 3} \cdot \dfrac{x - 2}{x + 5}$

  ANSWER a. $\dfrac{-6}{x^3}$

  b. $\dfrac{x(x - 2)}{(x + 3)(x + 5)}$

2. What is the product $\dfrac{x + 1}{4x - 8} \cdot \dfrac{x - 2}{x^2 + 4x + 3}$?

  ANSWER $\dfrac{1}{4(x + 3)}$

3. What is the product $\dfrac{3x + 4}{3x - 9} \cdot (x^2 + 5x - 24)$?

  ANSWER $\dfrac{(3x + 4)(x + 8)}{3}$

4. What is the quotient $\dfrac{x^2 - 36}{9x - 18} \div \dfrac{x + 6}{x^2 + 5x - 14}$?

  ANSWER $\dfrac{(x - 6)(x + 7)}{9}$

5. What is the quotient $\dfrac{8x^3 - 8x}{4x} \div (x^2 + 5x + 4)$?

  A. $\dfrac{8x(x + 1)^2(x - 1)(x + 4)}{4x}$

  B. $\dfrac{(x - 1)^2(x + 4)}{4x}$

  C. $\dfrac{2(x - 1)}{x + 4}$

  D. $\dfrac{2}{x + 4}$

  ANSWER C

6. What is the simplified form of $\dfrac{\frac{1}{x + 4}}{\frac{x - 3}{x^2 - 16}}$?

  ANSWER $\dfrac{x - 4}{x - 3}$

Answers

Got It? (continued)

4. a. $\dfrac{1}{y}$

  b. $\dfrac{6}{k + 4}$

5. $\dfrac{z - 1}{z^2 + 2}$

A **complex fraction** is a fraction that contains one or more fractions in its numerator, in its denominator, or in both. You can simplify a complex fraction by dividing its numerator by its denominator.

Any complex fraction of the form $\dfrac{\frac{a}{b}}{\frac{c}{d}}$ (where $b \neq 0$, $c \neq 0$, and $d \neq 0$) can be expressed as $\dfrac{a}{b} \div \dfrac{c}{d}$.

 Problem 6 Simplifying a Complex Fraction

Think

Have you solved a similar problem before?
Yes. In Problem 4, you found the quotient of two rational expressions. You simplify this complex fraction in the same way, but first write it as a quotient.

What is the simplified form of $\dfrac{\frac{1}{x-2}}{\frac{x+3}{x^2-4}}$?

$\dfrac{\frac{1}{x-2}}{\frac{x+3}{x^2-4}} = \dfrac{1}{x-2} \div \dfrac{x+3}{x^2-4}$ Write as a quotient.

$= \dfrac{1}{x-2} \cdot \dfrac{x^2-4}{x+3}$ Multiply by the reciprocal.

$= \dfrac{1}{x-2} \cdot \dfrac{(x+2)(x-2)}{x+3}$ Factor.

$= \dfrac{1}{x-2} \cdot \dfrac{(x+2)(x-2)^1}{x+3}$ Divide out the common factor $x - 2$.

$= \dfrac{x+2}{x+3}$ Simplify.

Got It? **6.** What is the simplified form of $\dfrac{\frac{1}{q+4}}{\frac{2q^2}{2q+8}}$?

 **Lesson Check**

Do you know HOW?

Multiply.

1. $\dfrac{2}{5t} \cdot \dfrac{3}{t^5}$ **2.** $\dfrac{2x+5}{4x-12} \cdot (x^2 - 8x + 15)$

Divide.

3. $\dfrac{k^2+k}{5k} \div \dfrac{1}{15k^2}$ **4.** $\dfrac{8x^2-12x}{x+7} \div (4x^2 - 9)$

Simplify each complex fraction.

5. $\dfrac{\frac{a^2+2a-8}{3a}}{\frac{a+4}{a-2}}$

6. $\dfrac{\frac{x^2+6x}{x+6}}{x}$

Do you UNDERSTAND?

7. Reasoning Are the complex fractions $\dfrac{\frac{a}{b}}{c}$ and $\dfrac{a}{\frac{b}{c}}$ equivalent? Explain.

8. Compare and Contrast How are multiplying rational expressions and multiplying numerical fractions similar? How are they different?

9. Reasoning Consider that $\dfrac{a}{b} \div \dfrac{c}{d} = \dfrac{a}{b} \cdot \dfrac{d}{c}$. Why must it be true that $b \neq 0$, $c \neq 0$, and $d \neq 0$?

10. a. Writing Explain how to multiply a rational expression by a polynomial.
     b. Explain how to divide a rational expression by a polynomial.

Problem 6

Q After rewriting the expression using a division symbol ($\div$), does the problem look familiar? Explain. **[Yes, the problem looks like Problem 4.]**

Q After rewriting the expression using a multiplication symbol, does the problem look familiar? Explain. **[Yes, the problem looks like Problem 2.]**

Got It?   **ERROR PREVENTION**

Q How can the problem be rewritten using a division symbol ($\div$)? $[\dfrac{1}{q+4} \div \dfrac{2q^2}{2q+8}]$

3 Lesson Check

Do you know HOW?

- If students have difficulty with Exercise 3, then have them review Problem 4.

Do you UNDERSTAND?

- If students have difficulty with Exercise 7, have them identify the numerator and denominator in each complex fraction.

Close

Q If a classmate missed the part of class when division was taught, what advice would you give him or her? **[Rewrite a division problem as the product of the dividend and the reciprocal of the divisor.]**

Got It? (continued)

6. $\dfrac{1}{q^2}$

Lesson Check

1. $\dfrac{6}{5t^6}$

2. $\dfrac{(2x+5)(x-5)}{4}$

3. $3k^2(k+1)$

4. $\dfrac{4x}{(x+7)(2x+3)}$

5. $\dfrac{(a-2)^2}{3a}$

6. x^2

7. no; $\dfrac{\frac{a}{b}}{c} = \dfrac{a}{b} \div c = \dfrac{a}{b} \cdot \dfrac{1}{c} = \dfrac{a}{bc}$, where $\dfrac{a}{\frac{b}{c}} = a \div \dfrac{b}{c} = a \cdot \dfrac{c}{b} = \dfrac{ac}{b}$

8. The procedures are the same, but when you multiply rational expressions, there may be values of the variables for which the rational expressions are not defined.

9. The variables b, c, and d appear in the denominators, and division by 0 is not defined.

10. a. Write the product of the rational expression and the polynomial, factor, divide out common factors, and write the product in factored form.

     b. Rewrite the quotient of the rational expression and the polynomial as the product of the rational expression and the reciprocal of the polynomial. Factor the numerators and denominators, divide out common factors, and write the answer in factored form.

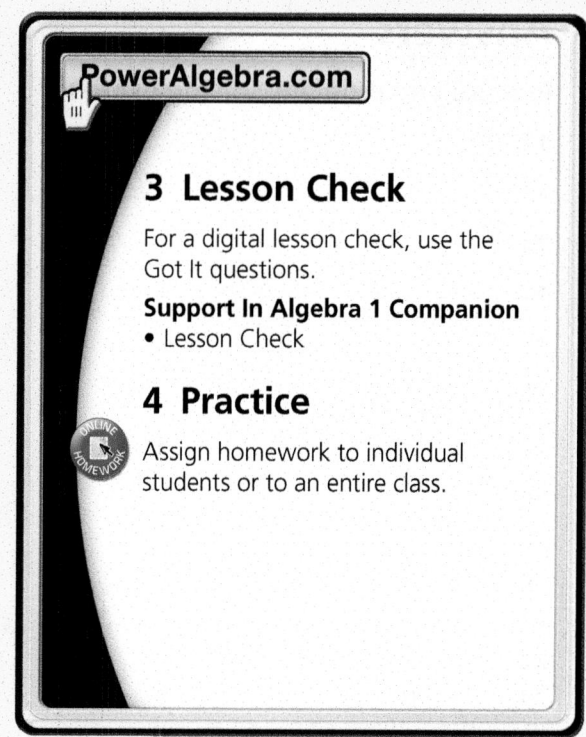

PowerAlgebra.com

3 Lesson Check

For a digital lesson check, use the Got It questions.

Support In Algebra 1 Companion
- Lesson Check

4 Practice

Assign homework to individual students or to an entire class.

4 Practice

ASSIGNMENT GUIDE

Basic: 11–50, 59–61

Average: 11–49 odd, 51–65

Advanced: 11–49 odd, 51–69

Standardized Test Prep: 70–73

Mixed Review: 74–79

Reasoning exercises have blue headings.

Applications exercises have red headings.

EXERCISE 60: Use the Think About a Plan worksheet in the **Practice and Problem Solving Workbook** (also available in the Teaching Resources in print and online) to further support students' development in becoming independent learners.

HOMEWORK QUICK CHECK

To check students' understanding of key skills and concepts, go over Exercises 17, 45, 59, 60, and 61.

Practice and Problem-Solving Exercises

A Practice

Multiply. ⬅ See Problems 1, 2, and 3.

11. $\frac{7}{3} \cdot \frac{5x}{12}$

12. $\frac{3}{t} \cdot \frac{4}{t}$

13. $\frac{5}{3a^2} \cdot \frac{8}{a^3}$

14. $\frac{m-2}{m+2} \cdot \frac{m}{m-1}$

15. $\frac{2x}{x+1} \cdot \frac{x-1}{3}$

16. $\frac{6x^2}{5} \cdot \frac{2}{x+1}$

17. $\frac{4c}{2c+2} \cdot \frac{c^2+3c+2}{c-1}$

18. $\frac{b^2+4b+4}{2b^2-8} \cdot \frac{3b-6}{4b}$

19. $\frac{r^2+5r+6}{2r} \cdot \frac{r-2}{r+3}$

20. $\frac{m-2}{3m+9} \cdot \frac{2m+6}{2m-4}$

21. $\frac{t^2-t-12}{t+1} \cdot \frac{t+1}{t+3}$

22. $\frac{4x+1}{5x+10} \cdot \frac{30x+60}{2x-2}$

23. $\frac{4t+4}{t-3} \cdot (t^2-t-6)$

24. $\frac{2m+1}{3m-6} \cdot (9m^2-36)$

25. $(x^2-1) \cdot \frac{x-2}{3x+3}$

26. $\frac{2y+9}{4y+12} \cdot (y^2+y-6)$

27. $\frac{h-1}{6h+3} \cdot (2h^2+9h+4)$

28. $(w^2-8w+15) \cdot \frac{w+3}{4w-20}$

Find the reciprocal of each expression. ⬅ See Problems 4 and 5.

29. $\frac{2}{x+1}$

30. $\frac{-6d^2}{2d-5}$

31. c^2-1

Divide.

32. $\frac{x-1}{x+4} \div \frac{x+3}{x+4}$

33. $\frac{3t+12}{5t} \div \frac{t+4}{10t}$

34. $\frac{x-3}{6} \div \frac{3-x}{2}$

35. $\frac{y-4}{10} \div \frac{4-y}{5}$

36. $\frac{x^2+6x+8}{x^2+x-2} \div \frac{x+4}{2x+4}$

37. $\frac{2n^2-5n-3}{4n^2-12n-7} \div \frac{4n+5}{2n-7}$

38. $\frac{3x+9}{x} \div (x+3)$

39. $\frac{11k+121}{7k-15} \div (k+11)$

40. $\frac{x^2+10x-11}{x^2+12x+11} \div (x-1)$

Simplify each complex fraction. ⬅ See Problem 6.

41. $\dfrac{\frac{4b-1}{b^2+2b+1}}{\frac{12b-3}{b^2-1}}$

42. $\dfrac{\frac{3x^2+2x+1}{8x}}{12x^2+8x+4}$

43. $\dfrac{\frac{6s+12}{s+2}}{3}$

44. $\dfrac{t^2-t-6}{\frac{t-3}{t+2}}$

45. $\dfrac{\frac{x^2-25}{x^2+6x+5}}{2x-10}$

46. $\dfrac{\frac{3}{3d^2+5d-2}}{\frac{3}{2d+4}}$

47. $\dfrac{\frac{g+2}{3g-1}}{\frac{g^2+2g}{6g+2}}$

48. $\dfrac{\frac{5f^2}{10f}}{f^2+1}$

49. $\dfrac{\frac{z-10}{z+10}}{3z^2-30z}$

50. $\dfrac{\frac{c+4}{c^2+5c+6}}{\frac{3c^2+12c}{2c^2+5c-3}}$

Answers

Practice and Problem-Solving Exercises

11. $\frac{35x}{36}$

12. $\frac{12}{t^2}$

13. $\frac{40}{3a^5}$

14. $\frac{m(m-2)}{(m+2)(m-1)}$

15. $\frac{2x(x-1)}{3(x+1)}$

16. $\frac{12x^2}{5(x+1)}$

17. $\frac{2c(c+2)}{c-1}$

18. $\frac{3(b+2)}{8b}$

19. $\frac{(r+2)(r-2)}{2r}$

20. $\frac{1}{3}$

21. $t-4$

22. $\frac{3(4x+1)}{x-1}$

23. $4(t+1)(t+2)$

24. $3(2m+1)(m+2)$

25. $\frac{(x-1)(x-2)}{3}$

26. $\frac{(2y+9)(y-2)}{4}$

27. $\frac{(h-1)(h+4)}{3}$

28. $\frac{(w-3)(w+3)}{4}$

29. $\frac{x+1}{2}$

30. $\frac{2d-5}{-6d^2}$

31. $\frac{1}{c^2-1}$

32. $\frac{x-1}{x+3}$

33. 6

34. $-\frac{1}{3}$

35. $-\frac{1}{2}$

36. $\frac{2(x+2)}{x-1}$

37. $\frac{n-3}{4n+5}$

38. $\frac{3}{x}$

39. $\frac{11}{7k-15}$

40. $\frac{1}{x+1}$

41. $\frac{b-1}{3(b+1)}$

42. $\frac{1}{32x}$

43. 18

44. $(t+2)^2$

45. $\frac{1}{2(x+1)}$

46. $\frac{2}{3d-1}$

47. $\frac{2(3g+1)}{g(3g-1)}$

48. $\frac{f(f^2+1)}{2}$

49. $\frac{1}{3z(z+10)}$

50. $\frac{2c-1}{3c(c+2)}$

Multiply or divide.

51. $\dfrac{t^2 + 5t + 6}{t - 3} \cdot \dfrac{t^2 - 2t - 3}{t^2 + 3t + 2}$

52. $\dfrac{c^2 + 3c + 2}{c^2 - 4c + 3} \div \dfrac{c + 2}{c - 3}$

53. $\dfrac{7t^2 - 28t}{2t^2 - 5t - 12} \cdot \dfrac{6t^2 - t - 15}{49t^3}$

54. $\dfrac{5x^2 + 10x - 15}{5 - 6x + x^2} \div \dfrac{2x^2 + 7x + 3}{4x^2 - 8x - 5}$

55. $\dfrac{x^2 + x - 6}{x^2 - x - 6} \div \dfrac{x^2 + 5x + 6}{x^2 + 4x + 4}$

56. $\left(\dfrac{x^2 - 25}{x^2 - 4x}\right)\left(\dfrac{x^2 + x - 20}{x^2 + 10x + 25}\right)$

Loan Payments The formula below gives the monthly payment m on a loan as a function of the amount borrowed A, the annual rate of interest r (expressed as a decimal), and the number of months n of the loan. Use this formula and a calculator for Exercises 57–60.

$$m = \dfrac{A\left(\frac{r}{12}\right)\left(1 + \frac{r}{12}\right)^n}{\left(1 + \frac{r}{12}\right)^n - 1}$$

57. What is the monthly payment on a loan of \$1500 at 8% annual interest paid over 18 months?

58. What is the monthly payment on a loan of \$3000 at 6% annual interest paid over 24 months?

59. **Think About a Plan** Suppose a family wants to buy the house advertised at the right. They have \$60,000 for a down payment. Their mortgage will have an annual interest rate of 6%. The loan is to be repaid over a 30-yr period. How much will it cost the family to repay this mortgage over the 30 yr?
   • What information can you obtain from the formula above?
   • How can you use the information given by the formula to solve the problem?

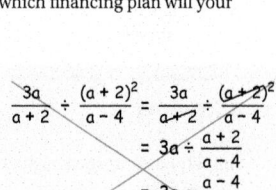

LilyRealty
Search Homes
\$300,000
518 Main St.
4 Bedroom
2 Bath

60. **Auto Loans** You want to purchase a car that costs \$18,000. The car dealership offers two different 48-month financing plans. The first plan offers 0% interest for 4 yr. The second plan offers a \$2000 discount, but you must finance the rest of the purchase price at an interest rate of 7.9% for 4 yr. For which financing plan will your total cost be less? How much less will it be?

61. **Error Analysis** In the work shown at the right, what error did the student make in dividing the rational expressions?

62. **Open-Ended** Write two rational expressions. Find their product.

63. **Reasoning** For what values of x is the expression $\dfrac{2x^2 - 5x - 12}{6x} \div \dfrac{-3x - 12}{x^2 - 16}$ undefined? Explain your reasoning.

$$\dfrac{3a}{a + 2} \div \dfrac{(a + 2)^2}{a - 4} = \dfrac{3a}{a + 2} \div \dfrac{(a + 2)^2}{a - 4}$$

$$= 3a \div \dfrac{a + 2}{a - 4}$$

$$= 3a \cdot \dfrac{a - 4}{a + 2}$$

$$= \dfrac{3a(a - 4)}{a + 2}$$

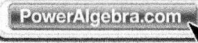
51. $t + 3$

52. $\dfrac{c + 1}{c - 1}$

53. $\dfrac{3t - 5}{7t^2}$

54. $\dfrac{5(2x - 5)}{x - 5}$

55. $\dfrac{x - 2}{x - 3}$

56. $\dfrac{x - 5}{x}$

57. \$88.71

58. \$132.96

59. \$518,011.65

60. You will save about \$713 with the first plan.

61. The student forgot to rewrite the divisor as its reciprocal before canceling.

$$\dfrac{3a}{a + 2} \div \dfrac{(a + 2)^2}{a - 4} = \dfrac{3a}{a + 2} \cdot \dfrac{a - 4}{(a + 2)^2}$$

$$= \dfrac{3a(a - 4)}{(a + 2)^3}$$

62. Check students' work.

63. 0, 4, and −4 make the denominators equal 0.

Answers

Practice and Problem-Solving Exercises
(continued)

64. $\frac{x + 2}{4(x + 7)}$

65. $\frac{2m^2(m + 2)}{(m - 1)(m + 4)}$

66. $\frac{9m^2(m + 1)}{2}$

67. 1

68. $\frac{x}{y + 5}$

69. $-\frac{(2a + 3b)(a + 2b)}{(5a + b)(2a - 3b)}$

70. B

71. G

72. A

73. [2] $0 = -16t^2 + 35t + 2.5$ or
$16t^2 - 35t - 2.5 = 0$; use the
quadratic formula to solve for t.

$t = \frac{35 \pm \sqrt{35^2 + 4 \cdot 16 \cdot 2.5}}{32} \approx \frac{35 \pm 37.2}{32}$,

$t \approx 2.26$ s

[1] minor computational error

74. $\frac{7}{3}$, $m \neq 2$

75. $\frac{1}{2a^2 - 3}$, $a \neq 0$, $a \neq \pm\frac{\sqrt{6}}{2}$

76. $\frac{2c - 9}{2c + 8}$, $c \neq -4$, $c \neq 4.5$

77. $2x^2 + 10x + 12$

78. $-3n^2 + 11n + 20$

79. $6a^3 - 21a^2 + 2a - 7$

Geometry Find the volume of each rectangular prism.

64.
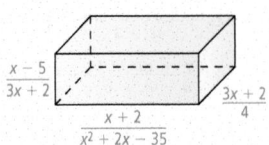

65.
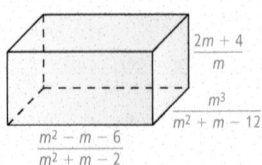

Challenge Multiply or divide.

66. $\frac{3m^3 - 3m}{4m^2 + 4m - 8} \cdot (6m^2 + 12m)$

67. $\frac{t^2 - r^2}{t^2 + tr - 2r^2} \cdot \frac{t^2 + 3tr + 2r^2}{t^2 + 2tr + r^2}$

68. $\frac{5x^2}{y^2 - 25} \div \frac{5xy - 25x}{y^2 - 10y + 25}$

69. $\frac{2a^2 - ab - 6b^2}{2b^2 + 9ab - 5a^2} \div \frac{2a^2 - 7ab + 6b^2}{a^2 - 4b^2}$

Standardized Test Prep

SAT/ACT

70. What is the simplified form of $(2x - 5) \cdot \frac{2x}{2x^2 - 9x + 10}$?

Ⓐ 1

Ⓑ $\frac{2x}{x - 2}$

Ⓒ $\frac{x - 5}{-4x + 5}$

Ⓓ $\frac{2x - 5}{-8x - 10}$

71. The volume of the rectangular prism is $4x^3 + 6x^2$.
What is the width w of the prism?

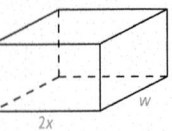

Ⓕ $4x^3 + 6x^2 - 2x$

Ⓗ $2x + 4$

Ⓖ $2x + 3$

Ⓘ $2x + 6$

72. What is the vertex of the parabola with the equation $y = 2x^2 + 3x - 1$?

Ⓐ $(-0.75, -2.125)$

Ⓒ $(-2.125, -0.75)$

Ⓑ $(0.75, 2.125)$

Ⓓ $(-0.75, 2.125)$

Short Response

73. A soccer ball is kicked with an initial upward velocity of 35 ft/s from a starting
height of 2.5 ft. If no one touches the ball, how long will it be in the air? Use the
formula $h = -16t^2 + vt + c$, where h is the ball's height at time t, v is the initial
upward velocity, and c is the starting height. Show your work.

Mixed Review

Simplify each expression. State any excluded values.
◀ See Lesson 11-1.

74. $\frac{7m - 14}{3m - 6}$

75. $\frac{5a^2}{10a^4 - 15a^2}$

76. $\frac{4c^2 - 36c + 81}{4c^2 - 2c - 72}$

Get Ready! **To prepare for Lesson 11-3, do Exercises 77–79.**

Find each product.
◀ See Lesson 8-3.

77. $(2x + 4)(x + 3)$

78. $(-3n - 4)(n - 5)$

79. $(3a^2 + 1)(2a - 7)$

Additional Instructional Support

Algebra 1 Companion

Students can use the **Algebra 1 Companion** worktext (4 pages) as you teach the lesson. Use the Companion to support

- New Vocabulary
- Key Concepts
- Got It for each Problem
- Lesson Check

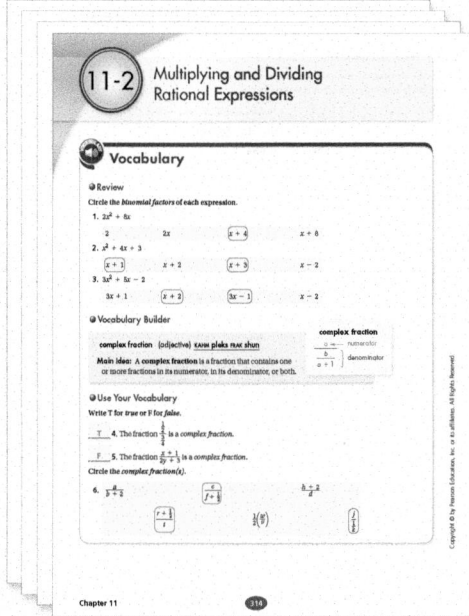

ELL Support

Assess Understanding Pair students.

Write rational expressions such as $\frac{-3}{x^2}$ and $\frac{8}{x^5}$ on index cards and give one to each student. Each pair of students will multiply the expressions, simplifying the product if needed. Discuss the results or invite volunteers to show their work on the board. Students will randomly trade cards with other students and repeat the process. When students proficiently improve, have them divide the expressions.

5 Assess & Remediate

Lesson Quiz

1. What is the product?

a. $\frac{4}{x^3} \cdot \frac{7}{2x^2}$

b. $\frac{x+1}{x-1} \cdot \frac{x+2}{x}$

2. What is the product

$\frac{x+2}{4x-12} \cdot \frac{x^2+2x-15}{7x+14}$?

3. What is the quotient

$\frac{2x-2}{2x+6} \div (3x^2 - 3x)$?

A. $\frac{1}{3x(x+3)}$

B. $\frac{2}{3x(x+3)}$

C. $\frac{x-1}{x+3}$

D. $\frac{x-1}{2(x+3)}$

4. What is the simplified form of $\dfrac{\frac{5}{x-1}}{\frac{10x}{x^2-1}}$?

5. Do you UNDERSTAND? Without simplifying the expression, can you identify the excluded values for the complex fraction $\dfrac{\frac{3x-9}{x-3}}{\frac{x+2}{-2x-4}}$? Explain.

ANSWERS TO LESSON QUIZ

1. a. $\frac{14}{x^5}$; **b.** $\frac{(x+1)(x+2)}{x(x-1)}$

2. $\frac{x+5}{28}$

3. A

4. $\frac{x+1}{2x}$

5. The excluded values are the numbers that would make any denominator of any fraction equal to 0.

PRESCRIPTION FOR REMEDIATION

Use the student work on the Lesson Quiz to prescribe a differentiated review assignment.

Points	Differentiated Remediation
0–2	Intervention
3–4	On-level
5	Extension

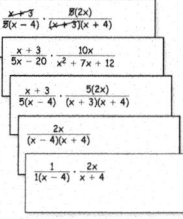

PowerAlgebra.com

5 Assess & Remediate

Assign the Lesson Quiz. Appropriate intervention, practice, or enrichment is automatically generated based on student performance.

Intervention

- **Reteaching** (2 pages) Provides reteaching and practice exercises for the key lesson concepts. Use with struggling students or absent students.

- **English Language Learner Support** Helps students develop and reinforce mathematical vocabulary and key concepts.

All-in-One Resources/Online
Reteaching

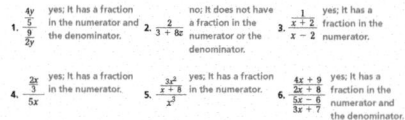

All-in-One Resources/Online
English Language Learner Support

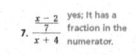
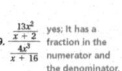

Differentiated Remediation *continued*

On-Level

- **Practice (2 pages)** Provides extra practice for each lesson. For simpler practice exercises, use the Form K Practice pages found in the All-in-One Teaching Resources and online.

- **Think About a Plan** Helps students develop specific problem-solving skills and strategies by providing scaffolded guiding questions.

- **Standardized Test Prep** Focuses on all major exercises, all major question types, and helps students prepare for the high-stakes assessments.

Extension

- **Enrichment** Provides students with interesting problems and activities that extend the concepts of the lesson.

- **Activities, Games, and Puzzles** Worksheets that can be used for concept development, enrichment, and for fun!

Practice and Problem Solving WKBK/ All-in-One Resources/Online
Practice page 1

11-2 Practice — Form G
Multiplying and Dividing Rational Expressions

Multiply.

1. $\frac{2}{4} \div \frac{z}{5z} \cdot \frac{3}{z}$

2. $\frac{x-9}{x+7} \cdot \frac{x}{x-6}$

$\frac{6-3z}{4z+5z^2}$

$\frac{x^2-9x}{x^2+x-42}$

3. $\frac{5w-25}{5w} \cdot \frac{w}{w^2-25}$

4. $\frac{16u-32}{2u} \cdot \frac{3u^3}{56u-24}$

$\frac{-w}{w^2+3w-10}$

$\frac{3u^3-6u^2}{7u-3}$

5. $\frac{j^2+11j-42}{26j-52} \cdot \frac{39j}{j-3}$

6. $\frac{15r}{18r^2+9r-27} \cdot \frac{3r-3}{r^2}$

$\frac{3(j^2+42j)}{2(j-4)}$

$\frac{5}{2r^2+3r}$

7. $\frac{45q^2-3q-6}{q^2} \cdot \frac{14q^2+10q}{35q^2+11q-10}$

8. $\frac{4y+17}{2y-3} \cdot (32y^2-22y-39)$

$\frac{18q+6}{q}$

$64y^2+324y+221$

9. $(12v^2+18v-84) \cdot \frac{v}{4v^3-49v}$

10. $(10x^2-7x+2) \cdot \frac{6x^2-13x-63}{3x+7}$

$\frac{6v-12}{2v-7}$

$20x^3-104x^2+67x-18$

11. Which of the following is the reciprocal of x^2-2x-8? B

A. $(x+2)(x-4)$ B. $\frac{1}{(x+2)(x-4)}$ C. $\frac{1}{x-8}$

Find the reciprocal of each expression.

12. $x^2-4x+18$

$\frac{1}{x^2-4x+18}$

13. $\frac{3q^2}{2q^2-13}$

$\frac{2q^2-13}{3q^2}$

Practice and Problem Solving WKBK/ All-in-One Resources/Online
Practice page 2

11-2 Practice *(continued)* — Form G
Multiplying and Dividing Rational Expressions

Divide.

14. $\frac{5y+7}{3y} \div \frac{5y+7}{y-6}$

15. $\frac{25l^2-36}{56l} \div \frac{5l-6}{8l}$

$\frac{y-6}{3y+19}$

$\frac{5l+6}{7}$

16. $\frac{12j-36}{2j+4} \div \frac{3j-9}{4j^2-16}$

17. $\frac{12x^2+x-13}{45x^2-20x-25} \div \frac{x-1}{9x+5}$

$8j-16$

$\frac{12x+13}{5x-5}$

18. $(72k^2+29k-21) \div \frac{9k^2-92k-77}{6k-1}$

$\frac{(8k-3)(6k-1)}{k-11}$

Simplify each complex fraction.

19. $\frac{1+\frac{1}{a}}{\frac{1}{a}}$

20. $\frac{\frac{a}{b}+1}{\frac{x}{b}+3}$

21. $\frac{\frac{1}{a}+\frac{b}{a}}{\frac{1}{b}}$

$\frac{1+a}{1}$

$\frac{x+a}{x+3b}$

$\frac{b+b^2}{a}$

22. A rectangular prism has a base area of $3x^2+21x-24$ and a height of $\frac{x}{33x-33}$. What is the volume of the prism?

$\frac{x(x+8)}{11}$ units³

23. Your friend runs for (x^2-225) seconds at a rate of $\frac{1}{2x-30}$ meters per second. How far does your friend run?

$\frac{x+15}{2}$ meters

24. **Writing** How do you simplify a complex fraction?

Multiply the numerator by the reciprocal of the denominator. Then factor out as many like terms as possible to simplify.

All-in-One Resources/Online
Enrichment

11-2 Enrichment
Multiplying and Dividing Rational Expressions

Sequences of Rational Expressions

Sometimes the terms of a sequence are numbers; sometimes the terms are algebraic expressions, including rational expressions.

Consider the sequence $\frac{x}{x+1}, \frac{x+1}{x+2}, \frac{x+2}{x+3}, \cdots$ where each successive term is determined by adding 1 to each of the numerator and denominator.

1. What are the fourth and fifth terms of this sequence?

$\frac{x+3}{x+4}; \frac{x+4}{x+5}$

2. Compute the ratio of the second term to the first, the ratio of the third term to the second, the ratio of the fourth term to the third, and the ratio of the fifth term to the fourth.

$\frac{(x+1)^2}{x(x+2)}; \frac{(x+2)^2}{(x+1)(x+3)}; \frac{(x+3)^2}{(x+2)(x+4)}; \frac{(x+4)^2}{(x+3)(x+5)}$

3. Evaluate each of the ratios you computed in Exercise 2 for $x=0$, 10, and 100.

0; undefined; 10: $\frac{4}{3}, \frac{9}{8}, \frac{16}{15}$; 10: $\frac{121}{120}, \frac{144}{143}, \frac{169}{168}, \frac{196}{195}$; 100: $\frac{10,201}{10,200}, \frac{10,404}{10,403}, \frac{10,609}{10,608}, \frac{10,816}{10,815}$

4. What seems to be happening to the ratios as the value of x increases? Explain.

The ratios are greater than 1 but are getting closer and closer to 1.

5. Form a new sequence with the first term $\frac{x}{x-1}$, but for which the successive terms are determined by subtracting 1 from each of the numerator and denominator.

$\frac{x}{x-1}, \frac{x-1}{x-2}, \frac{x-2}{x-3}, \frac{x-3}{x-4}$

6. Compute the ratios of successive terms of the new sequence.

$\frac{(x+1)(x-1)}{x^2}; \frac{x(x-2)}{(x-1)^2}; \frac{(x-1)(x-3)}{(x-2)^2}; \frac{(x-2)(x-4)}{(x-3)^2}$

7. Evaluate each of the ratios you computed in Exercise 6 for $x=0$, 10, and 100.

0: undefined, 0, $\frac{1}{3}, \frac{8}{9}$; 10: $\frac{99}{100}, \frac{80}{81}, \frac{63}{64}, \frac{48}{49}$; 100: $\frac{9999}{10,000}, \frac{9800}{9801}, \frac{9603}{9604}, \frac{9408}{9409}$

8. What seems to be happening to the ratios as the value of x increases? Explain.

The ratios are less than 1 but are getting closer and closer to 1.

Practice and Problem Solving WKBK/ All-in-One Resources/Online
Think About a Plan

11-2 Think About a Plan
Multiplying and Dividing Rational Expressions

Auto Loans You want to purchase a car that costs $18,000. The car dealership offers two different 48-month financing plans. The first plan offers 0% interest for 4 yr. The second plan offers a $2000 discount, but you must finance the rest of the purchase price at an interest rate of 7.9% for 4 yr. For which financing plan will your total cost be less? How much less will it be?

Know

1. The car costs $18,000 .

2. There are 2 different 48 -month plans.

3. The purchase price for Plan 1 is $18,000 .

4. The interest rate for Plan 1 is 0% .

5. The purchase price for Plan 2 is $16,000 .

6. The interest rate for Plan 2 is 7.9% .

Need

7. To solve the problems for the two plans, you need the equation/formula .

Plan

8. Write the formula to be used by the 2 plans. $y=a(1+r)^t$

9. Set up the 2 formulas, 1 for each plan. 18,000(1)⁴; 16,000(1.079)⁴

10. What is the total cost for Plan 1? What is the total cost for Plan 2? Plan 1 = $18,000; Plan 2 = $21,687.31

11. For which financing plan will the total cost be less and how much less? Plan 1 costs $3687.31 less.

Practice and Problem Solving WKBK/ All-in-One Resources/Online
Standardized Test Prep

11-2 Standardized Test Prep
Multiplying and Dividing Rational Expressions

Multiple Choice

For Exercises 1–3, choose the correct letter.

1. What is the quotient $\frac{x^2-16}{2x^2-9x+4} \div \frac{2x^2+14x+24}{4x+4}$? C

A. $\frac{1}{x+3}$ B. $\frac{2x+2}{x+3}$ C. $\frac{2x+2}{2x^2+5x-3}$ D. $\frac{2(x+1)}{2x^2-5x-3}$

2. What is the simplified form for the product $\frac{x+1}{x^2-25} \cdot \frac{x+5}{x^2+8x+7}$? H

F. $\frac{x+1}{(x+5)(x-7)}$ H. $\frac{1}{(x-5)(x+7)}$

G. $\frac{1}{(x+5)(x+7)}$ I. $\frac{1}{(x-5)(x-7)}$

3. What are the coordinates of the x-intercepts of the graph of $y=2x^2+6x-20$? A

A. $(-5,0),(2,0)$ B. $(5,0),(-2,0)$ C. $(-4,0),(10,0)$ D. $(4,0),(-10,0)$

Short Response

4. A football is kicked with an upward velocity of $25\frac{5}{8}$ from a starting height of 0.5 ft. How long does the ball stay in the air if no one catches it? Use the formula $h=-16t^2+vt+c$, where h is the ball's height at time t, v is the initial upward velocity, and c is the starting height. What is the height when the time is 1 second? How does the height change as the time increases? What happens at 5 seconds?

9.5 ft; as time increases, the height increases, reaches its maximum, and then starts to decrease; at 5 s the height is a negative value. This is not possible, so it means the ball has already landed on the ground.

[2] Questions answered correctly.

[1] Answer is incomplete.

[0] Answer is wrong.

Online Teacher Resource Center
Activities, Games, and Puzzles

11-2 Puzzle: The Last Word
Multiplying and Dividing Rational Expressions

Find the matching letter of the product or quotient of each rational expression. Write the matching letter in the table below. Note that you may have to write some letters more than once. The letters in the table should spell a word across each row and down each column.

1. $\frac{6}{x^3} \cdot \frac{-2}{x^3}$ S

2. $\frac{18}{x^2} \div \frac{3}{x}$ A

3. $\frac{x-2}{x} \cdot \frac{x}{x^2+x-6}$ N

4. $\frac{x-4}{x} \div \frac{x^2-3x-4}{x}$ R

5. $\frac{x+3}{8x-40} \cdot \frac{x-5}{3x^2+2x-3}$ O

6. $\frac{x-1}{6x+36} \cdot \frac{x^2+x+2}{x+6}$ U

7. $\frac{x^2-6x+8}{x^2+4x-12} \cdot \frac{x+6}{x^2-2x-8}$ P

8. $\frac{x^2-x-12}{x^2+2x-15} \div \frac{x+4}{3x+15}$ K

A. $\frac{6}{x}$

K. 3

N. $\frac{1}{x+3}$

O. $\frac{1}{8(x-1)}$

P. $\frac{1}{x+2}$

R. $\frac{1}{x+1}$

S. $\frac{-12}{x^6}$

U. $\frac{1}{6(x+2)}$

1. S	7. P	6. U	4. R
7. P	2. A	7. P	2. A
6. U	7. P	5. O	3. N
4. R	2. A	3. N	8. K

Concept Byte

Use With Lesson 11-3

Dividing Polynomials Using Algebra Tiles

You can use algebra tiles to model polynomial division.

Activity

What is $(x^2 + 4x + 3) \div (x + 3)$? Use algebra tiles.

Step 1 Use algebra tiles to model the dividend, $x^2 + 4x + 3$.

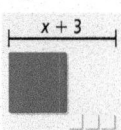

Step 2 Use the x^2-tile and the 1-tiles to form a figure with length $x + 3$, the divisor.

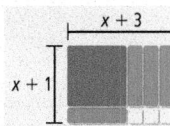

Step 3 Use the remaining tiles to fill in the rectangle.

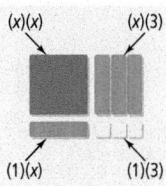

Since $(x + 1)(x + 3) = x^2 + 4x + 3$, you can write $(x^2 + 4x + 3) \div (x + 3) = x + 1$.

Check Check your result by multiplying $x + 1$ and $x + 3$. The product should be the dividend, $x^2 + 4x + 3$.

$$(x + 1)(x + 3) = (x)(x) + (x)(3) + (1)(x) + (1)(3)$$
$$= x^2 + 3x + x + 3$$
$$= x^2 + 4x + 3 \checkmark$$

Exercises

Use algebra tiles to find each quotient. Check your result.

1. $(x^2 + 6x + 8) \div (x + 4)$

2. $(x^2 + 5x + 6) \div (x + 2)$

3. $(x^2 + 8x + 12) \div (x + 6)$

4. $(x^2 + 8x + 7) \div (x + 1)$

5. Reasoning In Exercises 1–4, the divisor is a factor of the dividend. How do you know? Can you use algebra tiles to represent polynomial division when the divisor is *not* a factor of the dividend? Explain.

Guided Instruction

PURPOSE To use algebra tiles to divide polynomials
PROCESS Students
• use algebra tiles to model dividing polynomials.
• check their answers by multiplying the quotient by the divisor to verify that it yields the dividend as a product.

DISCUSS Students have used algebra tiles to perform other operations. They should start to see some connections between operations such as multiplying, factoring, and dividing.

Activity
In this Activity students use algebra tiles to divide polynomials.

Q What are some benefits for using algebra tiles as a method for dividing polynomials? **[Answers will vary. Sample: It allows you to visualize the process of dividing polynomials.]**

Q What part of the division problem do you place inside the frame? **[the dividend]**

Q Where do you place the divisor of your problem? **[along the outside of one of the sides of the area]**

Answers

Exercises
1. $x + 2$
2. $x + 3$
3. $x + 2$
4. $x + 7$
5. You can form a rectangle; you wouldn't be able to form a rectangle.

1 Interactive Learning

Solve It!

PURPOSE To divide one polynomial expression by another polynomial expression

PROCESS Students may create expressions for the surface area of each can and write an expression representing the ratio of the two expressions.

FACILITATE

Q What expression represents the surface area of the small can? large can? [$2\pi r^2 + 2\pi rh$; $8\pi r^2 + 8\pi rh$]

Q What operation must you use to determine the ratio of the surface areas? [division]

ANSWER See Solve It in Answers on next page.

CONNECT THE MATH Students solve another real-world situation involving rational expressions by finding a quotient. In this lesson, students continue to learn about dividing polynomials.

2 Guided Instruction

Problem 1

Q If you did not remember the quotient rule for exponents, how could you simplify the expression $\frac{9x^3}{3x^2}$? [You could write the numerator and denominator in factored form and divide out the common factors.]

Got It?

Explain to students that simplifying rational expressions is analogous to reducing numeric fractions, while dividing polynomial expressions is analogous to changing a numeric fraction to its decimal form.

11-3 Dividing Polynomials

Objective To divide polynomials

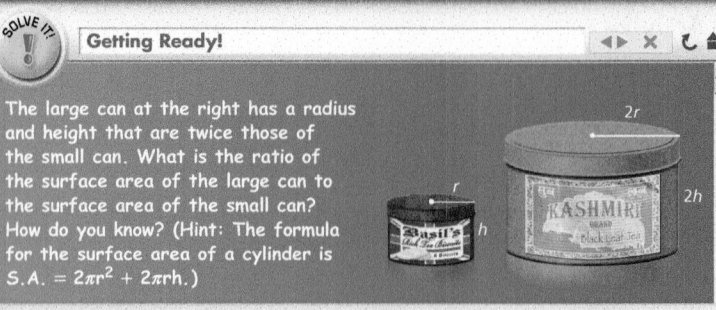

> **Getting Ready!**
>
> The large can at the right has a radius and height that are twice those of the small can. What is the ratio of the surface area of the large can to the surface area of the small can? How do you know? (Hint: The formula for the surface area of a cylinder is S.A. = $2\pi r^2 + 2\pi rh$.)
>
> *There are a lot of variables here! There must be an easier way to write the ratio.*

In the Solve It, finding the ratio of the cans' surface areas involves dividing one polynomial by another.

Essential Understanding You can divide polynomials using techniques similar to the techniques used for dividing real numbers, including long division.

 Problem 1 Dividing by a Monomial

Plan

How can you change this problem into one you know how to solve?
Change the division to multiplication so that you can use the Distributive Property.

What is $(9x^3 - 6x^2 + 15x) \div 3x^2$?

$(9x^3 - 6x^2 + 15x) \div 3x^2 = (9x^3 - 6x^2 + 15x) \cdot \frac{1}{3x^2}$ Multiply by $\frac{1}{3x^2}$, the reciprocal of $3x^2$.

$\quad = \frac{9x^3}{3x^2} - \frac{6x^2}{3x^2} + \frac{15x}{3x^2}$ Use the Distributive Property.

$\quad = 3x^1 - 2x^0 + 5x^{-1}$ Subtract exponents when dividing powers with the same base.

$\quad = 3x - 2 + \frac{5}{x}$ Simplify.

The answer is $3x - 2 + \frac{5}{x}$.

Got It? **1.** Divide.
  a. $(4a^3 + 10a^2 + 3a) \div 2a^2$
  b. $(5b^4 - 15b^2 + 1) \div 5b^3$
  c. $(12c^4 + 18c^2 + 9c) \div 6c$

BIG idea Equivalence   **UbD**

ESSENTIAL UNDERSTANDING

• Polynomials can be divided using techniques similar to the techniques used for dividing real numbers, including long division.

Math Background

Long division of polynomials is a necessary skill for working with polynomials with a degree higher than two. Because of its usefulness, mathematicians developed synthetic division as a means of dividing polynomials more efficiently. Division of polynomials can be used to find the roots of a polynomial equation as well as to evaluate a polynomial for a given value.

Some students have difficulty determining when the long division process is complete. After each term has been brought down, ask if the division process can continue. Emphasize that when the remainder is 0 or of a lower degree than the divisor, the process ends.

Support Student Learning

Use the **Algebra 1 Companion** to engage and support students during instruction. See Lesson Resources at the end of this lesson for details.

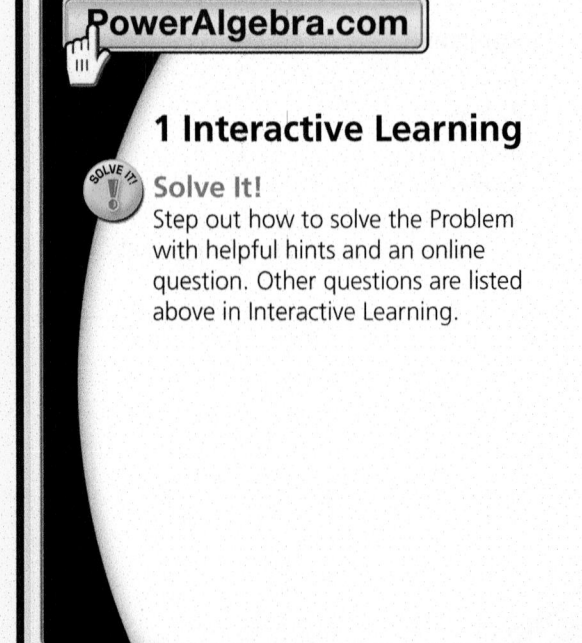

PowerAlgebra.com

1 Interactive Learning

Solve It!

Step out how to solve the Problem with helpful hints and an online question. Other questions are listed above in Interactive Learning.

The process of dividing a polynomial by a binomial is similar to long division of real numbers. You write the answer as quotient $+ \frac{\text{remainder}}{\text{divisor}}$.

 Problem 2 Dividing by a Binomial

What is $(3d^2 - 4d + 13) \div (d + 3)$?

Step 1 Begin the long division process.

> Align terms by their degrees. Put $3d$ above $-4d$ of the dividend.

$$
\begin{array}{r}
3d \\
d + 3\overline{)3d^2 - 4d + 13} \\
\underline{3d^2 + 9d} \\
-13d + 13
\end{array}
$$

Divide: $3d^2 \div d = 3d$.
Multiply: $3d(d + 3) = 3d^2 + 9d$. Then subtract.
Bring down 13.

Step 2 Repeat the process: divide, multiply, subtract, and bring down.

> Align terms by their degrees. Put -13 above 13 of the dividend.

$$
\begin{array}{r}
3d - 13 \\
d + 3\overline{)3d^2 - 4d + 13} \\
\underline{3d^2 + 9d} \\
-13d + 13 \\
\underline{-13d - 39} \\
52
\end{array}
$$

Divide: $-13d \div d = -13$.
Multiply: $-13(d + 3) = -13d - 39$. Then subtract.
The remainder is 52.

The answer is $3d - 13 + \frac{52}{d + 3}$.

Got It? 2. What is $(2m^2 - m - 3) \div (m + 1)$?

When the dividend has a missing term, add the missing term with a coefficient of zero.

 Problem 3 Dividing Polynomials With a Zero Coefficient

Geometry The width w of a rectangle is $3z - 1$. The area A of the rectangle is $18z^3 - 8z + 2$. What is an expression for the length of the rectangle?

Know	Need	Plan
Area: $18z^3 - 8z + 2$ Width: $3z - 1$	The length of the rectangle	Use the formula for the area of a rectangle, $A = \ell w$. Divide A by w to solve for ℓ.

$$
\begin{array}{r}
6z^2 + 2z - 2 \\
3z - 1\overline{)18z^3 + 0z^2 - 8z + 2} \\
\underline{18z^3 - 6z^2} \\
6z^2 - 8z \\
\underline{6z^2 - 2z} \\
-6z + 2 \\
\underline{-6z + 2} \\
0
\end{array}
$$

> The dividend has no z^2-term. So rewrite the dividend to include a z^2-term with coefficient 0.

An expression for the length of the rectangle is $6z^2 + 2z - 2$.

Lesson 11-3 Dividing Polynomials   **667**

Plan

How do you get started?
Divide the first term in the dividend by the first term in the divisor. Here, you divide $3d^2$ by d.

Think

Why add a term with a coefficient of 0?
If the dividend is missing a term when written in standard form, you must add the term with a coefficient of 0 to act as a placeholder.

Problem 2
Reminding students of the steps of numeric long division will aid them in their understanding of the steps of polynomial long division. Leave a numeric long division problem on the board as reference when completing this first problem. Highlight how the two processes parallel each other.

Also, remind students how they checked their final result when completing numeric long division and show them how they can do the same to check their final result in polynomial long division.

Got It?   ERROR PREVENTION
If students get an answer of $2m + 1 + \frac{-2}{m + 1}$, then they likely made the common error of adding rather than subtracting during the long division process.

Problem 3

Q What is the degree of the quotient when $18z^3 - 8z + 2$ is divided by $3z - 1$? Explain. **[2; a polynomial of degree 1 multiplied by a polynomial of degree 2 gives a polynomial of degree 3.]**

Q What monomial must be multiplied by $3z$ to give a product of $18z^3$? **[$6z^2$]**

Q What does a remainder of zero tell you about the polynomials $18z^3 - 8z + 2$ and $3z - 1$? **[$3z - 1$ is a factor of $18z^3 - 8z + 2$.]**

---

2 Guided Instruction

 Each Problem is worked out and supported online.

Problem 1
Dividing by a Monomial

Problem 2
Dividing by a Binomial
Animated

Problem 3
Dividing Polynomials With a Zero Coefficient
Animated

Problem 4
Reordering Terms and Dividing Polynomials
Animated

Support in Algebra 1 Companion
- Vocabulary
- Key Concepts
- Got It?

Answers

Solve It!
4 : 1; explanations may vary.

Got It?
1. a. $2a + 5 + \frac{3}{2a}$
   b. $b - \frac{3}{b} + \frac{1}{5b^3}$
   c. $2c^3 + 3c + \frac{3}{2}$
2. $2m - 3$

Lesson 11-3   667

Got It?

Show students what happens when the polynomials in 3a are divided without adding the term $0q^3$. Students will realize during the first subtraction step that $q^2 - (-q^3)$ cannot be simplified because the terms are not like terms.

Problem 4

Q Which answer choice implies that $(-3 + 2x)$ is a factor of $(-10x - 1 + 4x^2)$? Explain. **[Choice A; it has no remainder.]**

Q Why can you eliminate choice D? **[because the denominator of the remainder is not equal to the divisor]**

Q How do you write a polynomial in standard form? **[You write the terms in descending order of their exponents.]**

Got It?

ERROR PREVENTION

Q How should part 4a be written so that both polynomials are in standard form? **[(6y^2 − 11y − 7) ÷ (3y + 4)]**

Q How should part 4b be written so that both polynomials are in standard form? **[(18a^2 + 21a + 2) ÷ (6a + 5)]**

Take Note

Ask students to write steps to use as a checklist when using multiplication of polynomials to check that a quotient is correct.

 Got It? **3.** Divide.
  a. $(q^4 + q^2 + q - 3) \div (q - 1)$ **b.** $(h^3 - 4h + 12) \div (h + 3)$

To divide polynomials using long division, you must write the divisor and the dividend in standard form before you divide.

 Problem 4 Reordering Terms and Dividing Polynomials

Multiple Choice What is $(-10x - 1 + 4x^2) \div (-3 + 2x)$?

(A) $2x - 2$ (C) $2x - 2 + \dfrac{7}{2x - 3}$

(B) $2x - 2 - \dfrac{7}{2x - 3}$ (D) $2x - 2 + \dfrac{7}{2x + 2}$

$$2x - 3 \overline{)\,4x^2 - 10x - 1}$$
$$\underline{4x^2 - 6x}$$
$$-4x - 1$$
$$\underline{-4x + 6}$$
$$-7$$

You must rewrite $-10x - 1 + 4x^2$ and $-3 + 2x$ in standard form before you divide.

Think

How can you eliminate choices?
If the product of the divisor and choice A equals the dividend, then choice A is correct. Here, the product does not equal the dividend, so eliminate choice A.

The answer is $2x - 2 - \dfrac{7}{2x - 3}$. The correct answer is B.

 Got It? **4.** In parts (a) and (b), divide.
  a. $(-7 - 10y + 6y^2) \div (4 + 3y)$ **b.** $(21a + 2 + 18a^2) \div (5 + 6a)$
  c. Reasoning How can you check the answer to Problem 4? Show your work.

---

take note **Concept Summary** Dividing a Polynomial by a Polynomial

Step 1 Arrange the terms of the dividend and divisor in standard form. If a term is missing from the dividend, add the term with a coefficient of 0.

Step 2 Divide the first term of the dividend by the first term of the divisor. This is the first term of the quotient.

Step 3 Multiply the first term of the quotient by the whole divisor and place the product under the dividend.

Step 4 Subtract this product from the dividend.

Step 5 Bring down the next term.

Repeat Steps 2–5 as necessary until the degree of the remainder is less than the degree of the divisor.

Additional Problems

1. What is
$(5x^3 - 10x^2 + 20x) \div 5x^2$?

ANSWER $x - 2 + \dfrac{4}{x}$

2. What is
$(2x^2 - 19x + 24) \div (x - 8)$?

ANSWER $2x - 3$

3. The width and area of a rectangle are shown below. What is an expression for the length?

$A = x^2 + 3x - 18$ $x - 3$

ANSWER $x + 6$

4. What is
$(-21x - 20 + 9x^2) \div (-1 + x)$?

A. $-9x + 12 + \dfrac{8}{x - 1}$

B. $9x - 12 - \dfrac{32}{x - 1}$

C. $9x - 8 - \dfrac{24}{x - 1}$

D. $-9x + 6 + \dfrac{16}{x - 1}$

ANSWER B

Answers

Got It? (continued)

3. a. $q^3 + q^2 + 2q + 3$

  b. $h^2 - 3h + 5 - \dfrac{3}{h + 3}$

4. a. $2y - \dfrac{19}{3} + \dfrac{55}{3(3y + 4)}$

  b. $3a + 1 - \dfrac{3}{6a + 5}$

  c. Check whether
  $(2x - 3)(2x + 2) - 7$ equals
  $4x^2 - 10x - 1$.

Do you know HOW?

Divide.

1. $(20m^3 + 10m^2 - 5m - 3) \div 5m^2$

2. $(20c^2 + 23c - 7) \div (c - 1)$

3. $(25n^3 - 11n + 4) \div (5n + 4)$

4. $(-16a - 15 + 15a^2) \div (3 + 5a)$

Do you UNDERSTAND?

5. Vocabulary How is dividing polynomials like dividing real numbers? How is it different?

6. Writing What are the steps that you repeat when performing polynomial long division?

7. Reasoning How would you rewrite $1 - x^4$ before dividing it by $x - 1$?

Practice and Problem-Solving Exercises

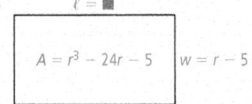 **Practice**

Divide.

See Problems 1, 2, and 3.

8. $(x^6 - x^5 + x^4) \div x^2$

9. $(12x^8 - 8x^3) \div 4x^4$

10. $(9c^4 + 6c^3 - c^2) \div 3c^2$

11. $(n^5 - 18n^4 + 3n^3) \div n^3$

12. $(8q^2 - 32q) \div 2q^2$

13. $(7t^5 + 14t^4 - 28t^3 + 35t^2) \div 7t^2$

14. $(6x^4 - 5x^3 + 6x^2) \div 2x^2$

15. $(21t^5 + 3t^4 - 11t^3) \div 7t^3$

16. $(n^2 - 5n + 4) \div (n - 4)$

17. $(y^2 - y + 2) \div (y + 2)$

18. $(3x^2 - 10x + 3) \div (x - 3)$

19. $(-4q^2 - 22q + 12) \div (2q + 1)$

20. $(5t^2 - 500) \div (t + 10)$

21. $(2w^3 + 3w - 15) \div (w - 1)$

22. $(3b^3 - 10b^2 + 4) \div (3b - 1)$

23. $(c^3 - c^2 - 1) \div (c - 1)$

Write an expression for the missing dimension in each figure.

24.
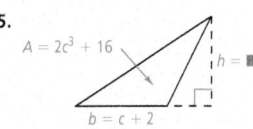
$\ell = \blacksquare$
$A = r^3 - 24r - 5$ $w = r - 5$

25.
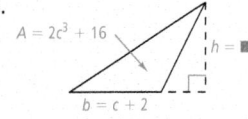
$A = 2c^3 + 16$
$h = \blacksquare$
$b = c + 2$

Divide.

See Problem 4.

26. $(49 + 16b + 2b^2) \div (2b + 4)$

27. $(4a^2 - 6 + 3a) \div (7 + 4a)$

28. $(39w + 14 + 3w^2) \div (9 + 3w)$

29. $(4t + 2t^2 - 9) \div (-6 + 2t)$

30. $(-13x + 6x^3 - 6 - x^2) \div (3x - 5)$

31. $(6 - q + 8q^3 - 4q^2) \div (2q - 2)$

32. $(6x^4 + 4x^3 - x^2) \div (6 + 2x)$

33. $(12c^3 + 11c^2 - 15c + 8) \div (-4 + 3c)$

34. $(7b + 16b^3) \div (-1 + 8b)$

35. $(4y + 9y^3 - 7) \div (-5 + 3y)$

---

3 Lesson Check

Do you know HOW?

- If students have difficulty with Exercise 4, then remind them to put the polynomials in standard form before dividing.

Do you UNDERSTAND?

- If students have difficulty with Exercise 7, then remind them that they need to write the dividend in standard form including any missing terms using zero coefficients, as necessary.

Close

> **Q** How is division of polynomials similar to long division? **[The division of polynomials is similar to long division in that both processes involve dividing, multiplying, subtracting, then "bringing down" and repeating as necessary.]**

Lesson Check

1. $4m + 2 - \frac{1}{m} - \frac{3}{5m^2}$

2. $20c + 43 + \frac{36}{c - 1}$

3. $5n^2 - 4n + 1$

4. $3a - 5$

5. Both processes involve dividing, multiplying, and subtracting, then "bringing down," and repeating as needed. When dividing polynomials you may need to insert a term with a coefficient of 0 as a placeholder.

6. Divide, multiply, subtract, bring down, and repeat as necessary.

7. $-x^4 + 0x^3 + 0x^2 + 0x + 1$

Practice and Problem-Solving Exercises

8. $x^4 - x^3 + x^2$ **9.** $3x^4 - \frac{2}{x}$

10. $3c^2 + 2c - \frac{1}{3}$ **11.** $n^2 - 18n + 3$

12. $4 - \frac{16}{q}$

13. $t^3 + 2t^2 - 4t + 5$

14. $3x^2 - 2.5x + 3$

15. $3t^2 + \frac{3t}{7} - \frac{11}{7}$

16. $n - 1$ **17.** $y - 3 + \frac{8}{y + 2}$

18. $3x - 1$

19. $-2q - 10 + \frac{22}{2q + 1}$

20. $5t - 50$

21. $2w^2 + 2w + 5 - \frac{10}{w - 1}$

22. $b^2 - 3b - 1 + \frac{3}{3b - 1}$

23. $c^2 - \frac{1}{c - 1}$ **24.** $r^2 + 5r + 1$

25. $4c^2 - 8c + 16$ **26.** $b + 6 + \frac{25}{2b + 4}$

27. $a - 1 + \frac{1}{4a + 7}$

28. $w + 10 - \frac{76}{3w + 9}$

29. $t + 5 + \frac{21}{2t - 6}$

30. $2x^2 + 3x + \frac{2}{3} + \frac{-8}{3(3x - 5)}$

31. $4q^2 + 2q + \frac{3}{2} + \frac{9}{2q - 2}$

32. $3x^3 - 7x^2 + \frac{41}{2}x - \frac{123}{2} + \frac{369}{2x + 6}$

33. $4c^2 + 9c + 7 + \frac{36}{3c - 4}$

34. $2b^2 + \frac{1}{4}b + \frac{29}{32} + \frac{29}{32(8b - 1)}$

35. $3y^2 + 5y + \frac{29}{3} + \frac{124}{3(3y - 5)}$

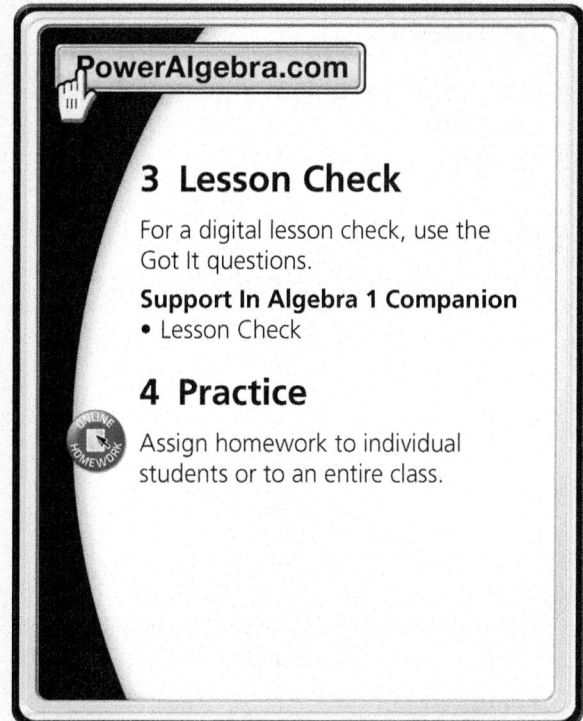

PowerAlgebra.com

3 Lesson Check

For a digital lesson check, use the Got It questions.

Support In Algebra 1 Companion
- Lesson Check

4 Practice

Assign homework to individual students or to an entire class.

4 Practice

ASSIGNMENT GUIDE

Basic: 8–35, 37, 48–51

Average: 9–35 odd, 36–54

Advanced: 9–35 odd, 36–59

Standardized Test Prep: 60–63

Mixed Review: 64–71

Reasoning exercises have blue headings.

Applications exercises have red headings.

EXERCISE 49: Use the Think About a Plan worksheet in the **Practice and Problem Solving Workbook** (also available in the Teaching Resources in print and online) to further support students' development in becoming independent learners.

HOMEWORK QUICK CHECK

To check students' understanding of key skills and concepts, go over Exercises 11, 29, 37, 48, and 49.

 Apply

36. Open-Ended Write a binomial and a trinomial using the same variable. Divide the trinomial by the binomial.

37. Think About a Plan The area A of a trapezoid is $x^3 + 2x^2 - 2x - 3$. The lengths of its two bases b_1 and b_2 are x and $x^2 - 3$, respectively. What is an expression for the height h of the trapezoid? Write your answer in the form quotient $+ \frac{\text{remainder}}{\text{divisor}}$.
- What formula can you use to find the area of a trapezoid?
- How can you use the formula to write an expression for h?

Divide.

38. $(56a^2 + 4a - 12) \div (2a + 1)$

39. $(5t^4 - 10t^2 + 6) \div (t + 5)$

40. $(3k^3 - 0.9k^2 - 1.2k) \div 3k$

41. $(-7s + 6s^2 + 5) \div (2s + 3)$

42. $(64c^3 - 125) \div (5 - 4c)$

43. $(21 - 5r^4 - 10r^2 + 2r^6) \div (r^2 - 3)$

44. $(2t^4 - 2t^3 + 3t - 1) \div (2t^3 + 1)$

45. $(z^4 + z^2 - 2) \div (z + 3)$

46. $(-2z^3 - z + z^2 + 1) \div (z + 1)$

47. $(6m^3 + 3m + 70) \div (m + 4)$

48. Writing Suppose you divide a polynomial by a binomial. How do you know if the binomial is a factor of the polynomial?

49. Geometry The volume of the rectangular prism shown at the right is $m^3 + 8m^2 + 19m + 12$. What is the area of the shaded base of the prism?

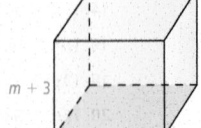

$m + 3$

50. Look for a Pattern Find a pattern by dividing the polynomials.
a. What is $(d^2 - d + 1) \div (d + 1)$?
b. What is $(d^3 - d^2 + d - 1) \div (d + 1)$?
c. What is $(d^4 - d^3 + d^2 - d + 1) \div (d + 1)$?
d. What do you think would be the result of dividing $d^5 - d^4 + d^3 - d^2 + d - 1$ by $d + 1$?
e. Verify your prediction by dividing the polynomials.

51. Business One way to measure a business's efficiency is by dividing the business's revenue by its expenses. The annual revenue, in millions of dollars, of a certain airline can be modeled by $200s^3 - s^2 + 400s + 1500$, where s is the number of passengers, in hundreds of thousands. The expenses, in millions of dollars, of the airline can be modeled by $200s + 300$. What is the airline's revenue divided by its expenses? Write your answer in the form quotient $+ \frac{\text{remainder}}{\text{divisor}}$.

52. Reasoning If $x + 3$ is a factor of $x^2 - x - k$, what is the value of k?

53. Physics Consider the formula for distance traveled, $d = rt$.
a. Solve the formula for t.
b. Use your answer from part (a). What is an expression for the time it takes to travel a distance of $t^3 - 6t^2 + 5t + 12$ miles at a rate of $t + 1$ miles per hour?

54. Packaging Three tennis balls with radius r are packed into a cylindrical can with radius r and height $6r + 1$. What fraction of the can is empty? Write your answer in the form quotient $+ \frac{\text{remainder}}{\text{divisor}}$.

Answers

Practice and Problem-Solving Exercises
(continued)

36. Check students' work.

37. $2x + 2$

38. $28a - 12$

39. $5t^3 - 25t^2 + 115t - 575 + \frac{2881}{t + 5}$

40. $k^2 - 0.3k - 0.4$

41. $3s - 8 + \frac{29}{2s + 3}$

42. $-16c^2 - 20c - 25$

43. $2r^4 + r^2 - 7$

44. $t - 1 + \frac{2t}{2t^3 + 1}$

45. $z^3 - 3z^2 + 10z - 30 + \frac{88}{z + 3}$

46. $-2z^2 + 3z - 4 + \frac{5}{z + 1}$

47. $6m^2 - 24m + 99 - \frac{326}{m + 4}$

48. If the remainder equals 0, the binomial is a factor of the polynomial.

49. $m^2 + 5m + 4$

50. a. $d - 2 + \frac{3}{d + 1}$

b. $d^2 - 2d + 3 - \frac{4}{d + 1}$

c. $d^3 - 2d^2 + 3d - 4 + \frac{5}{d + 1}$

d. $d^4 - 2d^3 + 3d^2 - 4d + 5 - \frac{6}{d + 1}$

e. $d^4 - 2d^3 + 3d^2 - 4d + 5 - \frac{6}{d + 1}$

51. $s^2 - \frac{301}{200}s + \frac{1703}{400} + \frac{891}{400(2s + 3)}$

52. 12

53. a. $t = \frac{d}{r}$

b. $(t^2 - 7t + 12)$ h

54. $\frac{1}{3} + \frac{2}{3(6r + 1)}$

55. Simplify $\frac{x^{16} - 1}{x - 1}$ by long division and by factoring. Which method do you prefer? Explain your answer.

Divide.

56. $(4a^3b^4 - 6a^2b^5 + 10a^2b^4) \div 2ab^2$

57. $(15x^2 + 7xy - 2y^2) \div (5x - y)$

58. $(90r^6 + 28r^5 + 45r^3 + 2r^4 + 5r^2) \div (9r + 1)$

59. $(2b^6 + 2b^5 - 4b^4 + b^3 + 8b^2 - 3) \div (b^3 + 2b^2 - 1)$

Standardized Test Prep

SAT/ACT

60. Which of the following is true for $(2x^2 + 4x + 2) \div 2x$?
  I. The remainder is negative.
  II. The dividend is in standard form.
  III. The quotient is greater than the divisor for positive values of x.
  Ⓐ I only Ⓑ II only Ⓒ I and II Ⓓ II and III

61. Which equation represents the line that passes through $(5, -8)$ and is parallel to the line at the right?

  Ⓕ $y = 2x + 2$ Ⓗ $y = -2x$
  Ⓖ $y + 2x = 2$ Ⓘ $y - 2x = 2$

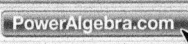

62. What are the factors of the expression $x^3 - 4x$?
  Ⓐ $x^3, -4x$ Ⓑ $x, x^2 - 4$ Ⓒ $x - 2, x + 2$ Ⓓ $x, x - 2, x + 2$

Short Response

63. A theater has 18 rows of seats. Each row has 28 seats. Tickets cost $4 for adults and $2.50 for children. The Friday night show was sold out and the revenue from ticket sales was $1935. Barbara says that 445 adults were at the show. Is her statement reasonable? Explain your answer.

Mixed Review

Multiply or divide.   ◀ See Lesson 11-2.

64. $\frac{n^2 + 7n - 8}{n - 1} \cdot \frac{n^2 - 4}{n^2 + 6n - 16}$

65. $\frac{6t^2 - 30t}{2t^2 - 53t - 55} \cdot \frac{6t^2 + 35t + 11}{18t^2}$

66. $\frac{3c^2 - 4c - 32}{2c^2 + 17c + 35} \div \frac{c - 4}{c + 5}$

67. $\frac{x^2 + 9x + 20}{x^2 + 5x - 24} \div \frac{x^2 + 15x + 56}{x^2 + x - 12}$

Get Ready!   To prepare for Lesson 11-4, do Exercises 68–71.

Simplify each expression.   ◀ See Lesson 1-5.

68. $\frac{4}{9} + \frac{2}{9}$ **69.** $\frac{1}{4} - \frac{1}{3}$ **70.** $\frac{7x}{8} + \frac{x}{8}$ **71.** $\frac{7}{12y} - \frac{1}{12y}$

---

55. $(x^8 + 1)(x^4 + 1)(x^2 + 1)(x + 1)$; factoring is much simpler and faster, since long division requires writing a polynomial with 17 terms.

56. $2a^2b^2 - 3ab^3 + 5ab^2$

57. $3x + 2y$

58. $10r^5 + 2r^4 + 5r^2$

59. $2b^3 - 2b^2 + 3$

60. B **61.** G **62.** D

63. [2] There are $18 \cdot 28 = 504$ seats in the theater. If 445 adults were at the theater, the revenue would be $445 \cdot 4 = 1780$. That means the revenue for the children's tickets is $1935 - 1780 = 155$. So the number of children's seats sold is $155 \div 2.5 = 62$. The total number of seats sold would be $62 + 445 = 507$. Since $507 > 504$, Barbara's answer is not reasonable.

[1] correct answer with no explanation given

64. $n + 2$

65. $\frac{(t - 5)(3t + 1)(2t + 11)}{3t(2t - 55)(t + 1)}$

66. $\frac{3c + 8}{2c + 7}$

67. $\frac{(x + 5)(x + 4)^2}{(x + 7)(x + 8)^2}$

68. $\frac{2}{3}$

69. $-\frac{1}{12}$

70. x

71. $\frac{1}{2y}$

Additional Instructional Support

Algebra 1 Companion

Students can use the **Algebra 1 Companion** worktext (4 pages) as you teach the lesson. Use the Companion to support

- New Vocabulary
- Key Concepts
- Got It for each Problem
- Lesson Check

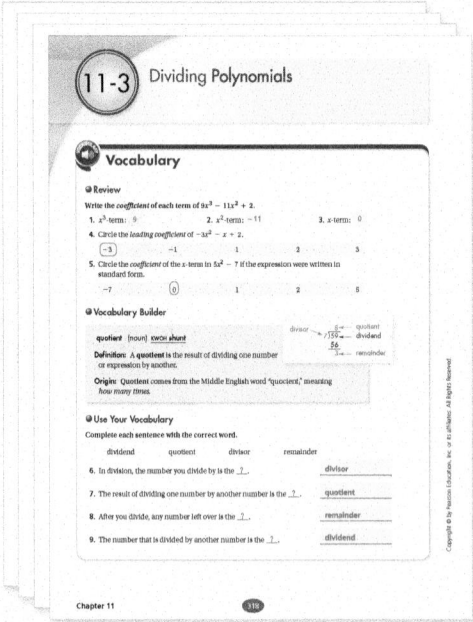

ELL Support

Use Graphic Organizers Arrange students into pairs. Have students make a "cycle" organizer like the one below on a sheet of paper.

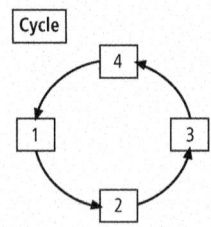

Have students fill in the four steps of dividing a polynomial by a binomial: divide first terms, multiply by the divisor, subtract by changing the signs and adding, and bring down the next term and start again. Students can use the organizer for guidance when solving problems.

5 Assess & Remediate

Lesson Quiz

1. What is $(3x^3 + 18x^2 - 9x) \div 3x$?

2. What is $(x^2 - 3x - 40) \div (x + 5)$?

3. The width and area of a rectangle are shown below. What is an expression for the length?

$$A = x^3 - 2x^2 - 5x + 6 \qquad x - 1$$

4. What is $(-x + 2 + x^3 + 3x^2) \div (-1 + x)$?

5. **Do you UNDERSTAND?** You are designing a rectangular garden with an area of $2x^2 - 3x - 35$. The width will be $x - 5$. If $x = 5$, what will the length be?

ANSWERS TO LESSON QUIZ

1. $x^2 + 6x - 3$

2. $x - 8$

3. $x^2 - x - 6$

4. $x^2 + 4x + 3 + \dfrac{5}{x - 1}$

5. If $x = 5$, then $x - 5 = 0$, so the division of the area by the width is undefined.

PRESCRIPTION FOR REMEDIATION
Use the student work on the Lesson Quiz to prescribe a differentiated review assignment.

Points	Differentiated Remediation
0–2	Intervention
3–4	On-level
5	Extension

PowerAlgebra.com

5 Assess & Remediate
Assign the Lesson Quiz. Appropriate intervention, practice, or enrichment is automatically generated based on student performance.

Intervention

- **Reteaching** (2 pages) Provides reteaching and practice exercises for the key lesson concepts. Use with struggling students or absent students.

- **English Language Learner Support** Helps students develop and reinforce mathematical vocabulary and key concepts.

All-in-One Resources/Online
Reteaching

11-3 Reteaching
Dividing Polynomials

A few important rules are needed for successful division of a polynomial. When dividing by a monomial, a single term, remember to divide each polynomial term by the monomial and reduce the fraction.

Problem

What is $(8x^3 - 3x^2 + 16x) \div 2x^2$?

Solve

$(8x^3 - 3x^2 + 16x) \div 2x^2$ Division equals multiplication by the reciprocal.

$= (8x^3 - 3x^2 + 16x) \cdot \dfrac{1}{2x^2}$ Multiply by $\frac{1}{2x^2}$, the reciprocal of $2x^2$.

$= \dfrac{8x^3}{2x^2} - \dfrac{3x^2}{2x^2} + \dfrac{16x}{2x^2}$ Use the Distributive Property.

$= 4x^1 - \dfrac{3}{2}x^0 + \dfrac{8}{x}$ Subtract exponents when dividing powers with the same base.

$= 4x - \dfrac{3}{2} + \dfrac{8}{x}$ Simplify.

Exercises

Divide.

1. $(2x^2 - 9x + 18) \div 2x$

2. $(16x^4 - 64) \div 4x^3$

3. $(x^5 - 3x^4 + 10x^3 - \frac{3}{4}x^2 - 6) \div 3x^2$

4. $(5x^3 - 25x^2 - 1) \div 5x$

When a polynomial (many terms) is divided by a binomial (2 terms), the polynomial terms should be in order from highest to lowest exponent.

To make the polynomial $-4 + 2x - 16x^2 + 3x^3$ division ready, put it in the correct order for division, from greatest exponent to lowest. The correct order for $-4 + 2x - 16x^2 + 3x^3$ to be division ready is $3x^3 - 16x^2 + 2x - 4$.

For any gaps or missing exponents, the place is held with 0. For example, $x^2 + 1$ becomes $x^2 + 0x + 1$, $0x$ being the placeholder for the x term.

All-in-One Resources/Online
English Language Learner Support

11-3 ELL Support
Dividing Polynomials

What is the solution to $(60x^{12} + 24x^{10} + 24x^3) \div 12x^2$? Justify your steps.

$(60x^{12} + 24x^{10} + 24x^3) \div 12x^2$ Copy the problem.

$(60x^{12} + 24x^{10} + 24x^3) \frac{1}{12x^2}$ Multiply by $\frac{1}{12x^2}$, the reciprocal of $12x^2$.

$\frac{60x^{12}}{12x^2} + \frac{24x^{10}}{12x^2} + \frac{24x^3}{12x^2}$ Use the Distributive Property.

$5x^{10} + 2x^8 + 2x$ Subtract exponents when dividing powers with the same base.

Exercises

What is the solution to $(44x^5 + 55x^6 + 22x^3) \div 11x^3$? Justify your steps.

$(44x^5 + 55x^6 + 22x^3) \div 11x^3$ Copy the problem.

$(44x^5 + 55x^6 + 22x^3)\frac{1}{11x^3}$ Multiply by $\frac{1}{11x^3}$, the reciprocal of $11x^3$.

$\frac{44x^5}{11x^3} + \frac{55x^6}{11x^3} + \frac{22x^3}{11x^3}$ Use the Distributive Property.

$4x^2 + 5x^3 + 2x^0$ Subtract exponents when dividing powers with the same base.

$4x^2 + 5x^3 + 2$ Simplify.

What is the solution to $(-36x^4 + 18x^7 + 30x^5) \div 6x^5$? Justify your steps.

$(-36x^4 + 18x^7 + 30x^5) \div 6x^5$ Copy the problem.

$(-36x^4 + 18x^7 + 30x^5)\frac{1}{6x^5}$ Multiply by $\frac{1}{6x^5}$, the reciprocal of $6x^5$.

$\frac{-36x^4}{6x^5} + \frac{18x^7}{6x^5} + \frac{30x^5}{6x^5}$ Use the Distributive Property.

$-6x^{-1} + 3x^2 + 5x^0$ Subtract exponents when dividing powers with the same base.

$\frac{-6}{x} + 3x^2 + 5$ Simplify.

Differentiated Remediation *continued*

On-Level

- **Practice** (2 pages) Provides extra practice for each lesson. For simpler practice exercises, use the Form K Practice pages found in the All-in-One Teaching Resources and online.

- **Think About a Plan** Helps students develop specific problem-solving skills and strategies by providing scaffolded guiding questions.

- **Standardized Test Prep** Focuses on all major exercises, all major question types, and helps students prepare for the high-stakes assessments.

Extension

- **Enrichment** Provides students with interesting problems and activities that extend the concepts of the lesson.

- **Activities, Games, and Puzzles** Worksheets that can be used for concept development, enrichment, and for fun!

Practice and Problem Solving WKBK/ All-in-One Resources/Online
Practice page 1

11-3 Practice — Form G
Dividing Polynomials

Divide.

1. $(c^3 - c - 1) \div c$
$c - 1 - \frac{1}{c}$

2. $(f^4 - 4f^3 - 8f^2) \div f^2$
$f^2 - 4f - 8$

3. $(3p^3 - 27p^2) \div 3p^2$
$p - 9$

4. $(2m^2 - 5m + 2) \div 2m$
$m - \frac{5}{2} + \frac{1}{m}$

5. $(3b^5 - 9b^4 + 3b^2) \div 6b^2$
$\frac{b^3}{2} - \frac{3b^2}{2} + \frac{1}{2}$

6. $(7x^4 - 28x^3) \div 4x^3$
$\frac{7x}{4} - 7$

7. $(6t^5 - 3t^4 + 18t^3 - 9t^2) \div 3t$
$2t^4 - t^3 + 6t^2 - 3t$

8. $(-104d^6 + 64d^7 - 86d^6 + 96d^5) \div 2d^4$
$-52d^4 + 32d^3 - 43d^2 + 48d$

9. $(-27q^4 + 51q^3 - 9q^2) \div 3q^2$
$-9q^2 + 17q - 3$

10. $(-1040r^{12} - 500r^{11} - 620r^{10} + 1600r^9 + r^8) \div 20r^7$
$-52r^5 - 25r^4 - 31r^3 + 80r^2 + \frac{r}{20}$

11. $(-3u^8 - 105u^5 + 147u^4) \div (-3u^3)$
$u^3 + 35u^2 - 49u$

12. $(11y^{26} - 132y^{25} + 121y^{24}) \div (-11y^{24})$
$-y^2 + 12y - 11$

13. $(p^2 + 3p + 2) \div (p + 1)$
$p + 2$

14. $(x^2 + 7x + 12) \div (x + 4)$
$x + 3$

15. $(p^2 - 5p - 36) \div (p + 4)$
$p - 9$

16. $(2q^2 - 4q - 240) \div (q - 12)$
$2q + 20$

17. $(6x^2 + x - 1) \div (3x - 1)$
$2x + 1$

18. $(20a^2 + 2a - 4) \div (2a + 1)$
$10a - 4$

19. $(4t^2 - 64) \div (t + 4)$
$4t - 16$

20. $(z^2 - 9) \div (z - 3)$
$z + 3$

21. $(3x^2 - x^3 + x - 3) \div (-x + 1)$
$x^2 - 2x - 3$

22. $(c^4 - 16) \div (c - 2)$
$c^3 + 2c^2 + 4c + 8$

23. The area of a rectangle is $x^2 - x - 2$ and the length of the rectangle is $x + 1$.
   a. Find the width of the rectangle. $x - 2$
   b. Find the area of the rectangle if the width is 4 m. 28 m^2

Practice and Problem Solving WKBK/ All-in-One Resources/Online
Practice page 2

11-3 Practice (continued) — Form G
Dividing Polynomials

Divide.

24. $(28n^2 - 17n - 3) \div (4n - 3)$
$7n + 1$

25. $(2t^2 - 8t + 6) \div (t - 3)$
$2t - 2$

26. $(3c^2 - 5c - 2) \div (6c + 2)$
$\frac{1}{2}c - 1$

27. $(3c^2 - 5c - 2) \div (3c + 1)$
$c - 2$

28. $(2j^2 - 3j - 9) \div (j - 3)$
$2j + 3$

29. $(4j^2 - 6j - 18) \div (j - 3)$
$4j + 6$

30. $(-3x^2 + x^3 - x + 3) \div (x - 1)$
$x^2 - 2x - 3$

31. $(3x^2 - x^3 + x - 3) \div (-x + 1)$
$x^2 - 2x - 3$

32. $9d^4 - 729 \div (-3 + d)$
$9d^3 + 27d^2 + 81d + 243$

33. $(-3x^2 + 6x^3 + x - 40) \div (-2 + x)$
$6x^2 + 9x + 19 + \frac{-2}{x - 2}$

34. Find the height of a trapezoid if the area of the trapezoid is $2x^2 + 11x + 5$, the length of one base is x, and the length of the other base is $x + 10$. The formula for the area A of a trapezoid with height h and bases b_1 and b_2 is $A = \frac{b_1 + b_2}{2} \cdot h$.
$2x + 1$

35. The area of the rectangle is $x^4 - 9x^3 - 7x^2 - 8x + 2$. The length is given. What is the width?
$x^2 - 10x + 2$

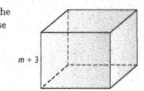
$x^2 + x + 1$

36. **Writing** If the area of a rectangle is a polynomial and the length of one of the sides is a polynomial, can the measurement of the width of the rectangle be a polynomial quotient with a remainder? Explain.
yes; the division of a polynomial by another polynomial can yield a polynomial with or without a remainder.

Practice and Problem Solving WKBK/ All-in-One Resources/Online
Think About a Plan

11-3 Think About a Plan
Dividing Polynomials

Geometry The volume of the rectangular prism shown at the right is $m^3 + 8m^2 + 19m + 12$. What is the area of the base of the prism?

$m + 3$

Understanding the Problem

1. What is a rectangular prism?
A rectangular prism is a solid (3-dimensional) object comprised of six faces that are rectangles.

2. What is the literal formula for the volume of a rectangular prism?
$V = l \times w \times h$

3. What is the formula for the volume of the rectangular prism shown?
$V = lw(m + 3) = m^3 + 8m^2 + 19m + 12$

Planning the Solution

4. Using the given information from Step 3, what is the area of the base of the rectangle equal to?
$B = lw = \frac{m^3 + 8m^2 + 19m + 12}{m + 3}$

Getting an Answer

5. Divide $(m^3 + 8m^2 + 19m + 12)$ by $(m + 3)$ to find the area of the base of the prism.
$m^2 + 5m + 4$

6. What does $m^2 + 5m + 4$ equal?
the area of the base of the prism (B)

Practice and Problem Solving WKBK/ All-in-One Resources/Online
Standardized Test Prep

11-3 Standardized Test Prep
Dividing Polynomials

Multiple Choice

For Exercises 1–4, choose the correct letter.

1. What is the remainder of $(x^3 - 6x^2 - 9x + 3) \div (x - 3)$? A
   A. -51 B. $\frac{-51}{x - 3}$ C. $\frac{-17}{x}$ D. $\frac{-17}{x - 3}$

2. If the area of a rectangle is $x^2 - 9$, can the length be $x - 1$? H
   F. Yes; it divides perfectly.
   G. No; the length would be larger.
   H. Yes; but the width will have a remainder.
   I. No; the measurements of the rectangle must multiply and divide evenly.

3. If a line passes through the points $(2, 0)$ and $(-2, -3)$, what is the y-intercept of the line? A
   A. $\frac{-3}{2}$ B. $\frac{3}{2}$ C. $\frac{3}{4}$ D. $\frac{-3}{4}$

4. What coordinates satisfy the equation of the line $y = -\frac{7}{8}x + 2$? G
   F. $(-8, 11)$ G. $\left(-4, \frac{11}{2}\right)$ H. both F and G   I. $\left(4, \frac{11}{2}\right)$

Short Response

5. What are the factors of the expression $x^2 + 12x - 64$? What numbers would you change to make it a perfect square? Explain.
$(x + 16), (x - 4)$; change -64 to 36, then the factors would be $(x + 6), (x + 6)$
[2] Questions answered correctly.
[1] Answer is incomplete.
[0] Answer is wrong.

All-in-One Resources/Online
Enrichment

11-3 Enrichment
Dividing Polynomials

Dividing $x^n - 1$ by $x - 1$
There is a pattern in the quotients when polynomials of the form $x^n - 1$ are divided by $x - 1$. Start by dividing $x^2 - 1$ by $x - 1$. Since there is no x term in $x^2 - 1$, rewrite $x^2 - 1$ as $x^2 + 0x - 1$ before performing long division.

$$
\begin{array}{r}
x + 1 \\
x - 1 \overline{)x^2 + 0x - 1} \\
\underline{x^2 - 1x} \\
x - 1 \\
\underline{x - 1} \\
0
\end{array}
$$

The quotient is $x + 1$.

1. Divide $x^3 - 1$ by $x - 1$.
$x^2 + x + 1$

2. Divide $x^4 - 1$ by $x - 1$.
$x^3 + x^2 + x + 1$

3. Based on the example and the first two exercises, predict the quotient when $x^5 - 1$ is divided by $x - 1$.
Answers may vary. Actual answer: $x^4 + x^3 + x^2 + x + 1$

4. Check your guess for Exercise 3 by performing long division for $x^5 - 1$ by $x - 1$.
$x^4 + x^3 + x^2 + x + 1$

5. If your guess was not correct, repeat Exercises 3 and 4 with higher exponents until you are able to predict the result of the division.
Check students' work.

6. State the pattern in words for the quotient when $x^n - 1$ is divided by $x - 1$.
The quotient is the sum of $x^{n-1} + x^{n-2} + \cdots + x + 1$.

Online Teacher Resource Center
Activities, Games, and Puzzles

11-3 Activity: Division Square-Off
Dividing Polynomials

You can make and use algebra tiles like those shown below to model dividing with polynomials.

$x^2 \quad -x^2 \quad x \quad -x \quad 1 \quad -1$

Example 1: $\frac{x^2 + 4x + 4}{x + 2} = x + 2$

Arrange the tiles in a rectangular shape so that one side represents the divisor and the whole shape represents the dividend. Then the other side will show the quotient.

Example 2: $\frac{x^2 - 9}{x + 3} = x - 3$

Tiles representing both positive and negative expressions must be used. To show the quotient, you will use a white block for x^2 and 9 shaded unit tiles for -9. To undo the adding of 3 white x-tiles for the divisor, you must add 3 shaded x-tiles when showing the dividend.

Example 3: $\frac{x^2 + 2x - 12}{x - 3} = x + 5 + \frac{3}{x - 3}$
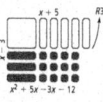
If there are too many or too few single tiles to form a rectangle, then write the quotient plus or minus the remainder over the divisor.

Use your tiles to model each of the following. Draw the models on a separate sheet of paper and write the quotient.

1. $\frac{x^2 + 5x + 6}{x + 2}$ $x + 3$

2. $\frac{x^2 + x - 6}{x + 3}$ $x - 2$

3. $\frac{x^2 - 6x + 9}{x - 3}$ $x - 3$

4. $\frac{x^2 - 25}{x + 5}$ $x - 5$

5. $\frac{x^2 + 2x - 9}{x - 2}$ $x + 4 + \frac{-1}{x - 2}$

6. $\frac{x^2 + 5x - 9}{x - 2}$ $x + 7 + \frac{5}{x - 2}$

1 Interactive Learning

Solve It!

PURPOSE To add numeric fractions that do not have common denominators

PROCESS Students may create a ratio for each dog's rate of consumption, add fractions, or multiply a fraction by a whole number.

FACILITATE

Q What addition expression represents the portion of a bag that all three dogs eat together in one day? $[\frac{1}{12} + \frac{1}{6} + \frac{1}{4}]$

Q What is the first step for simplifying the sum expression? **[Find a common denominator.]**

ANSWER See Solve It in Answers on next page.

CONNECT THE MATH In the Solve It students review adding numeric fractions. In the lesson, students learn how adding and subtracting rational expressions is similar to adding and subtracting numeric fractions.

2 Guided Instruction

Problem 1

Q Are both sums in simplest form? Explain. **[Yes, because neither sum contains a common factor that can be divided out.]**

Q What are the restrictions on the variable for 1A? for 1B? Explain. **[$y \neq 0$; $x \neq 2$; the variables cannot have a value that causes division by zero.]**

Got It?

ERROR PREVENTION

If students get an answer of $\frac{5a}{6a - 8}$, then they added the numerators and denominators.

Objective To add and subtract rational expressions

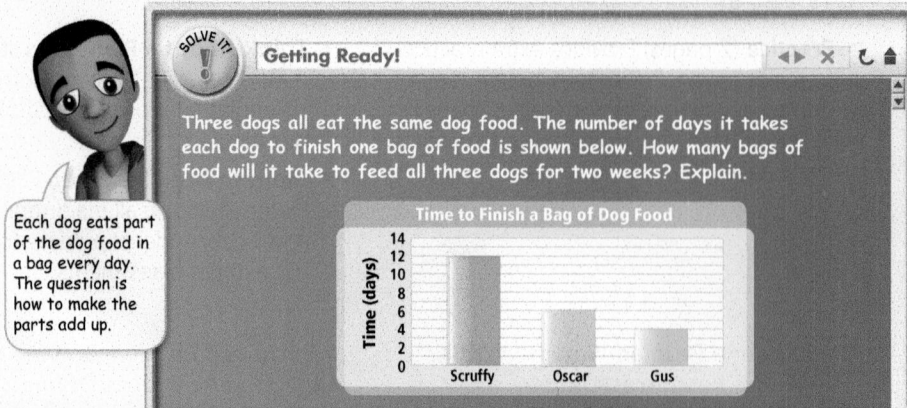

Getting Ready!

Three dogs all eat the same dog food. The number of days it takes each dog to finish one bag of food is shown below. How many bags of food will it take to feed all three dogs for two weeks? Explain.

Each dog eats part of the dog food in a bag every day. The question is how to make the parts add up.

Essential Understanding You can use the same rules to add and subtract rational expressions that you use to add and subtract numerical fractions.

You can add the numerators of rational expressions with like denominators. If a, b, and c represent polynomials (with $c \neq 0$), then $\frac{a}{c} + \frac{b}{c} = \frac{a + b}{c}$.

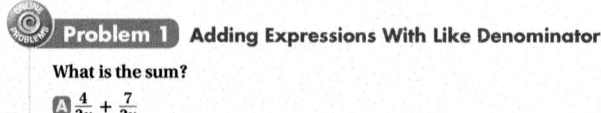

Problem 1 Adding Expressions With Like Denominators

What is the sum?

Think

Once you are comfortable adding rational expressions with like denominators, you can add the numerators and simplify all in one step.

A $\frac{4}{3y} + \frac{7}{3y}$

$\frac{4}{3y} + \frac{7}{3y} = \frac{4 + 7}{3y}$ Add the numerators.

$= \frac{11}{3y}$ Simplify the numerator.

B $\frac{3x}{x - 2} + \frac{x}{x - 2}$

$\frac{3x}{x - 2} + \frac{x}{x - 2} = \frac{3x + x}{x - 2}$ Add the numerators.

$= \frac{4x}{x - 2}$ Simplify the numerator.

Got It? 1. What is the sum $\frac{2a}{3a - 4} + \frac{3a}{3a - 4}$?

BIG idea Equivalence   **UbD**

ESSENTIAL UNDERSTANDINGS

- Rational expressions can be added and subtracted using the same rules used to add and subtract numerical fractions.
- The least common denominator of two rational expressions is the product of the factors of the denominators. Each factor is used the greatest number of times it appears in a denominator.

Math Background

The addition and subtraction of numeric fractions and rational expressions without common denominators relies on the use of the Multiplicative Identity and the concept that any number (except zero) divided by itself is one. When numeric fractions or rational expressions are rewritten so that they have common denominators, both the numerator and the denominator must be multiplied by the quantity that will change the original denominator to the new common denominator.

Many students identify a common denominator and multiply each rational expression accordingly; however, students may then incorrectly add the denominators as well as the numerators. When students make this mistake, take them back to simple fraction examples to review the process of rewriting denominators and then adding only the numerators. A problem as basic as $\frac{1}{2} + \frac{1}{2} = \frac{2}{2} = 1$ is often enough to remind students of the proper process.

Support Student Learning

Use the **Algebra 1 Companion** to engage and support students during instruction. See Lesson Resources at the end of this lesson for details.

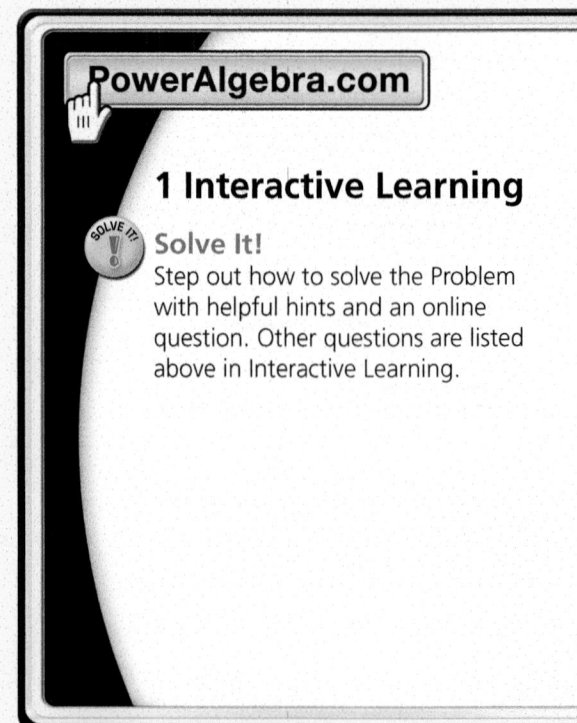

PowerAlgebra.com

1 Interactive Learning

Solve It!

Step out how to solve the Problem with helpful hints and an online question. Other questions are listed above in Interactive Learning.

Similarly, you can subtract rational expressions with like denominators.

 Problem 2 Subtracting Expressions With Like Denominators

Think

Why put parentheses around $4x + 3$?
You want to subtract the entire numerator $4x + 3$, and parentheses are needed to indicate that. Without the parentheses, you would only be subtracting $4x$.

What is the difference $\dfrac{7x + 5}{3x^2 - x - 2} - \dfrac{4x + 3}{3x^2 - x - 2}$?

$\dfrac{7x + 5}{3x^2 - x - 2} - \dfrac{4x + 3}{3x^2 - x - 2} = \dfrac{7x + 5 - (4x + 3)}{3x^2 - x - 2}$ Subtract the numerators.

$= \dfrac{7x + 5 - 4x - 3}{3x^2 - x - 2}$ Distributive Property

$= \dfrac{3x + 2}{3x^2 - x - 2}$ Simplify the numerator.

$= \dfrac{\cancel{3x + 2}}{\cancel{(3x + 2)}(x - 1)}$ Factor the denominator. Divide out the common factor $3x + 2$.

$= \dfrac{1}{x - 1}$ Simplify.

 Got It? 2. What is the difference?

a. $\dfrac{2}{z + 3} - \dfrac{7}{z + 3}$ **b.** $\dfrac{9n - 3}{10n - 4} - \dfrac{3n + 5}{10n - 4}$ **c.** $\dfrac{7q - 3}{q^2 - 4} - \dfrac{6q - 5}{q^2 - 4}$

To add or subtract rational expressions with different denominators, you can write the expressions with the least common denominator (LCD).

 Problem 3 Adding Expressions With Different Denominators

What is the sum $\dfrac{5}{6x} + \dfrac{3}{2x^2}$?

Step 1 Find the LCD of $\dfrac{5}{6x}$ and $\dfrac{3}{2x^2}$. First write the denominators $6x$ and $2x^2$ as products of prime factors. To form the LCD, list each factor the greatest number of times it appears in a denominator.

$6x = 2 \cdot 3 \cdot x$ Factor each denominator.

$2x^2 = 2 \cdot x \cdot x$

$\text{LCD} = 2 \cdot 3 \cdot x \cdot x = 6x^2$ The LCD is the LCM of $6x$ and $2x^2$.

Think

Why is the LCD $6x^2$ instead of $6x$?
One of the denominators has two factors of x. So the LCD must also have two factors of x.

Step 2 Rewrite each rational expression using the LCD and then add.

$\dfrac{5}{6x} + \dfrac{3}{2x^2} = \dfrac{5 \cdot x}{6x \cdot x} + \dfrac{3 \cdot 3}{2x^2 \cdot 3}$ Rewrite each fraction using the LCD.

$= \dfrac{5x}{6x^2} + \dfrac{9}{6x^2}$ Simplify numerators and denominators.

$= \dfrac{5x + 9}{6x^2}$ Add the numerators.

 Got It? 3. What is the sum $\dfrac{3}{7y^4} + \dfrac{2}{3y^2}$?

Problem 2

Q How can you use the Distributive Property to simplify the expression $7x + 5 - (4x - 3)$? **[Multiply each term in the parentheses by -1.]**

Q What is the quotient when $3x + 2$ is divided by $3x + 2$? Explain. **[1; anything divided by itself is 1.]**

Got It?   ERROR PREVENTION

If students do not give the correct difference in 2b and 2c, then they are most likely not subtracting each term of the second numerator.

Problem 3

Q Can the two rational expressions be added together as written? Explain. **[No, because they do not have a common denominator.]**

Q What must $6x$ be multiplied by to get the LCD of $6x^2$? **[x]**

Q What must $2x^2$ be multiplied by to get the LCD of $6x^2$? **[3]**

Q Is it possible to use a common denominator of $12x^2$? Explain. **[Yes, because $12x^2$ is a common denominator. But because it is not the least common denominator, the sum will require simplifying.]**

Got It?

Q What are the prime factors of $7y^4$? of $3y^2$? **[7 · y · y · y · y; 3 · y · y]**

Q What is the LCM of $7y^4$ and $3y^2$? **[21y^4]**

---

2 Guided Instruction

 Each Problem is worked out and supported online.

Problem 1
Adding Expressions With Like Denominators

Problem 2
Subtracting Expressions With Like Denominators

Problem 3
Adding Expressions With Different Denominators
     Animated

Problem 4
Subtracting Expressions With Different Denominators
     Animated

Problem 5
Using Rational Expressions

Support in Algebra 1 Companion
• Vocabulary
• Key Concepts
• Got It?

Answers

Solve It!
7 bags; explanations may vary.

Got It?

1. $\dfrac{5a}{3a - 4}$

2. a. $\dfrac{-5}{z + 3}$

   b. $\dfrac{3n - 4}{5n - 2}$

   c. $\dfrac{1}{q - 2}$

3. $\dfrac{9 + 14y^2}{21y^4}$

Problem 4

Students may understand this problem better if you show and reference the steps for how to subtract two numeric fractions such as $\frac{4}{7} - \frac{3}{5}$ which also have no common factors in their denominators.

Got It?   ERROR PREVENTION

> **Q** What is the LCD of the two denominators?
> [$(3c - 1)(c - 2)$]
>
> **Q** What do you multiply the first numerator by? the second numerator? [$c - 2$; $3c - 1$]
>
> **Q** When multiplying the second numerator, what do you distribute? [-4]

Problem 5

> **Q** If your truck gets 18 mi/gal and you travel 80 mi, how many gallons of gasoline do you use? Explain.
> [about 4.44; $80 \div 18 \approx 4.44$]
>
> **Q** If your truck gets m mi/gal and you travel 80 mi, how many gallons of gasoline do you use? [$\frac{80}{m}$]
>
> **Q** If the truck gets 18 mi/gal when fully loaded, how many miles per gallon does the truck get when it has no cargo? Explain.
> [22.5; $0.25 \cdot 18 + 18 = 22.5$]
>
> **Q** If the truck gets m miles per gallon when fully loaded, how many miles per gallon does the truck get when it has no cargo? Explain.
> [$1.25m$; $0.25m + m = 1.25m$]

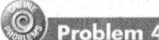 **Problem 4** Subtracting Expressions With Different Denominators

What is the difference $\frac{3}{d-1} - \frac{2}{d+2}$?

Step 1 Find the LCD of $\frac{3}{d-1}$ and $\frac{2}{d+2}$.

Since there are no common factors, the LCD is $(d-1)(d+2)$.

Step 2 Rewrite each rational expression using the LCD and then subtract.

$$\frac{3}{d-1} - \frac{2}{d+2} = \frac{3(d+2)}{(d-1)(d+2)} - \frac{2(d-1)}{(d-1)(d+2)}$$ Rewrite each fraction using the LCD.

$$= \frac{3d+6}{(d-1)(d+2)} - \frac{2d-2}{(d-1)(d+2)}$$ Simplify each numerator.

$$= \frac{3d+6-(2d-2)}{(d-1)(d+2)}$$ Subtract the numerators.

$$= \frac{d+8}{(d-1)(d+2)}$$ Simplify the numerator.

Think

Should you multiply the denominator or leave it in factored form?
There might be common factors to divide out later. So leave the denominator in factored form.

✓ **Got It? 4.** What is the difference $\frac{c}{3c-1} - \frac{4}{c-2}$?

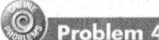 **Problem 5** Using Rational Expressions

Gas Mileage A certain truck gets 25% better gas mileage when it holds no cargo than when it is fully loaded. Let m be the number of miles per gallon of gasoline the truck gets when it is fully loaded. The truck drops off a full load and returns empty. What is an expression for the number of gallons of gasoline the truck uses?

Gas mileage = 1.25m

Gas mileage = m

Think

How can unit analysis help you?
You can use unit analysis to verify that gallons of gasoline used equals distance traveled divided by miles per gallon.
$$\frac{mi}{mi/gal} = mi \cdot \frac{gal}{mi} = gal$$

Step 1 Write expressions for the amount of gasoline used on the outward trip and on the return trip.

Outward trip: gasoline used $= \frac{\text{distance traveled}}{\text{miles per gallon}} = \frac{80}{m}$

Return trip: gasoline used $= \frac{\text{distance traveled}}{\text{miles per gallon}} = \frac{80}{1.25m}$

80-mi trip outward

80-mi return trip

Step 2 Add the expressions to find the total amount of gasoline the truck uses.

$$\text{total gasoline used} = \frac{80}{m} + \frac{80}{1.25m}$$

$$= \frac{80(1.25)}{1.25m} + \frac{80}{1.25m}$$ Rewrite using the LCD, $1.25m$.

$$= \frac{100}{1.25m} + \frac{80}{1.25m}$$ Simplify the first numerator.

$$= \frac{180}{1.25m}$$ Add the numerators.

$$= \frac{144}{m}$$ Simplify.

Additional Problems

1. What is the sum?

a. $\frac{2}{5a} + \frac{1}{5a}$

b. $\frac{7p}{x+4} + \frac{3p}{x+4}$

ANSWER a. $\frac{3}{5a}$ **b.** $\frac{10p}{x+4}$

2. What is the difference $\frac{3x}{5x^2 + 9x - 2} - \frac{-2x+1}{5x^2 + 9x - 2}$?

ANSWER $\frac{1}{x+2}$

3. What is the sum $\frac{2}{9x} + \frac{1}{3x^2}$?

ANSWER $\frac{2x+3}{9x^2}$

4. What is the difference $\frac{4}{x+2} - \frac{1}{x-3}$?

ANSWER $\frac{3x-14}{x^2-x-6}$

5. You paddle a canoe 3 mi downstream and then paddle back upstream to your starting point. On the return trip, your speed is reduced 40% due to the current of the stream. Let s be your speed in mi/hr downstream. What is an expression that represents your total time in hours riding downstream and upstream?

ANSWER $\frac{8}{s}$

Answers

Got It? (continued)

4. $\frac{c^2 - 14c + 4}{(3c-1)(c-2)}$

Got It? 5. a. A bicyclist rides 5 mi out and then rides back. His speed returning is reduced 20% because it is raining. Let r be his speed in miles per hour riding out. What is an expression that represents his total time in hours riding out and back?

b. Reasoning In Problem 5, suppose m represents the number of miles per gallon of gasoline the truck gets when it holds no cargo. What expression represents the number of miles per gallon of gasoline the truck gets when fully loaded? Explain.

Lesson Check

Do you know HOW?

Add or subtract.

1. $\dfrac{4}{x-7} + \dfrac{7}{x-7}$

2. $\dfrac{9}{2y+4} - \dfrac{5}{2y+4}$

3. $\dfrac{4}{6b^2} + \dfrac{5}{8b^3}$

4. A runner practices running 2 mi up a slope and 2 mi down. She runs down the slope 50% faster than she runs up it. Let r be the runner's speed, in miles per hour, when running up the slope. What expression represents the time she spends running?

Do you UNDERSTAND?

5. Writing Suppose your friend was absent today. How would you explain to your friend how to add and subtract rational expressions?

6. Compare and Contrast How is finding the LCD of two rational expressions similar to finding the LCD of two numerical fractions? How is it different?

7. Reasoning Your friend says she can always find a common denominator for two rational expressions by finding the product of the denominators.
a. Is your friend correct? Explain.
b. Will your friend's method always give you the LCD? Explain.

Practice and Problem-Solving Exercises

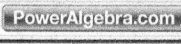 **Practice** Add or subtract. *See Problems 1 and 2.*

8. $\dfrac{5}{2m} + \dfrac{4}{2m}$

9. $\dfrac{5}{c-5} + \dfrac{9}{c-5}$

10. $\dfrac{3}{b-3} - \dfrac{b}{b-3}$

11. $\dfrac{5c}{2c+7} + \dfrac{c-28}{2c+7}$

12. $\dfrac{1}{2-b} - \dfrac{4}{2-b}$

13. $\dfrac{n}{n^2+4n+4} + \dfrac{2}{n^2+4n+4}$

14. $\dfrac{2y+1}{y-1} - \dfrac{y+2}{y-1}$

15. $\dfrac{3n+2}{n+4} - \dfrac{n-6}{n+4}$

16. $\dfrac{2t}{2t^2-t-3} - \dfrac{3}{2t^2-t-3}$

Find the LCD of each pair of expressions. *See Problems 3 and 4.*

17. $\dfrac{1}{2}; \dfrac{4}{x^2}$

18. $\dfrac{b}{6}; \dfrac{2b}{9}$

19. $\dfrac{1}{z}; \dfrac{3}{7z}$

20. $\dfrac{8}{5b}; \dfrac{12}{7b^3c}$

21. $\dfrac{3}{5}; \dfrac{x}{x+2}$

22. $\dfrac{2}{ab}; \dfrac{a-b}{b^2c}$

23. $\dfrac{3m}{m+n}; \dfrac{3n}{m-n}$

24. $\dfrac{1}{k}; \dfrac{3}{k^2-2}$

Q What formula relates distance, rate, and time? $[r \cdot t = d]$

Q What is the distance formula solved for the variable representing time? $[t = \dfrac{d}{r}]$

Q In 5a, what expression represents the travel time for the ride out? the ride back? $[\dfrac{5}{r}; \dfrac{5}{0.80r}]$

3 Lesson Check

Do you know HOW?

- If students have difficulty with Exercise 4, then have them use the Got It for Problem 5 as a template for setting up the expressions to represent the two running times.

Do you UNDERSTAND?

- If students have difficulty with Exercise 7, have them use a numeric example to explain.

Close

Q What are the steps for finding the sum or difference of two rational expressions? **[First, rewrite the expressions so that they have like denominators, if necessary. Second, add or subtract the numerators as indicated in the problem, and write the result over the common denominator. Finally, simplify the sum or difference, if possible.]**

Got It? (continued)

5. a. $\dfrac{45}{4r}$

b. $\dfrac{4m}{5}$; if n is the miles per gallon when the truck is full, then $m = 1.25n$ and therefore $n = \dfrac{m}{1.25}$ or $\dfrac{4m}{5}$.

Lesson Check

1. $\dfrac{11}{x-7}$

2. $\dfrac{2}{y+2}$

3. $\dfrac{16b+15}{24b^3}$

4. $\dfrac{10}{3r}$

5. If the expressions have like denominators, add or subtract numerators as indicated and place over the denominator. If they have unlike denominators, factor if needed, find the LCD, rewrite the expressions with the common denominator, add or subtract as indicated, and simplify.

6. The procedure is the same. The LCD is the LCM of the denominators.

7. a. yes

b. No, it will give you a common denominator, but not necessarily the least common denominator.

Practice and Problem-Solving Exercises

8. $\dfrac{9}{2m}$

9. $\dfrac{14}{c-5}$

10. -1

11. $\dfrac{6c-28}{2c+7}$

12. $-\dfrac{3}{2-b}$

13. $\dfrac{1}{n+2}$

14. 1

15. 2

16. $\dfrac{1}{t+1}$

17. $2x^2$

18. 18

19. $7z$

20. $35b^3c$

21. $5(x+2)$

22. ab^2c

23. $(m+n)(m-n)$

24. $k(k^2-2)$

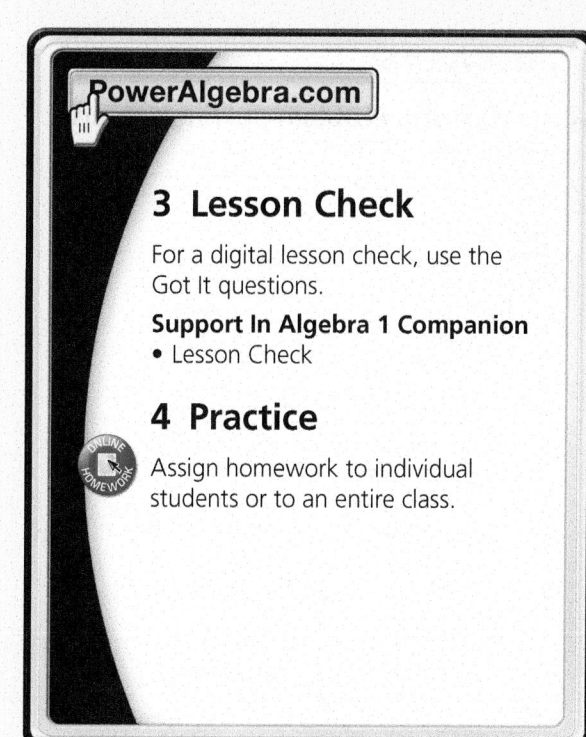

PowerAlgebra.com

3 Lesson Check

For a digital lesson check, use the Got It questions.

Support In Algebra 1 Companion
- Lesson Check

4 Practice

Assign homework to individual students or to an entire class.

4 Practice

ASSIGNMENT GUIDE

Basic: 8–33 all, 34–42 even, 43–44

Average: 9–33 odd, 34–48

Advanced: 9–33 odd, 34–54

Standardized Test Prep: 55–58

Mixed Review: 59–67

Reasoning exercises have blue headings.

Applications exercises have red headings.

EXERCISE 44: Use the Think About a Plan worksheet in the **Practice and Problem Solving Workbook** (also available in the Teaching Resources in print and online) to further support students' development in becoming independent learners.

HOMEWORK QUICK CHECK

To check students' understanding of key skills and concepts, go over Exercises 11, 27, 34, 43, and 44.

Add or subtract.

25. $\frac{7}{3a} + \frac{2}{5}$ **26.** $\frac{4}{x} - \frac{2}{3}$ **27.** $\frac{27}{n^3} - \frac{9}{7n^2}$ **28.** $\frac{6}{5x^8} + \frac{4}{3x^6}$

29. $\frac{a}{a+3} - \frac{4}{a+5}$ **30.** $\frac{9}{m+2} + \frac{8}{m-7}$ **31.** $\frac{a}{a+3} + \frac{a+5}{4}$ **32.** $\frac{5}{t^2} - \frac{4}{t+1}$

33. Exercise Jane walks one mile from her house to her grandparents' house. Then she returns home, walking with her grandfather. Her return rate is 70% of her rate walking alone. Let r represent her rate walking alone. **◀ See Problem 5.**
   a. Write an expression for the amount of time Jane spends walking.
   b. Simplify your expression.
   c. Suppose Jane's rate walking alone is 3 mi/h. About how much time does she spend walking?

Ⓑ Apply

34. Error Analysis A student added two rational expressions as shown. What error did the student make?

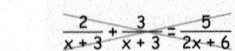

35. Writing When you use the LCD to add or subtract rational expressions, will the answer always be in simplest form if you use the LCD? Explain.

36. Open-Ended Write two rational expressions with different denominators. Find the LCD and add the two expressions.

Add or subtract.

37. $\frac{y^2 + 2y - 1}{3y + 1} - \frac{2y^2 - 3}{3y + 1}$ **38.** $\frac{h^2 + 1}{2t^2 - 7} + \frac{h}{2t^2 - 7}$

39. $\frac{r - 5}{9 + p^3} - \frac{2k + 1}{9 + p^3}$ **40.** $\frac{2 - x}{xy^2z} - \frac{5 + z}{xy^2z}$

41. $9 + \frac{x - 3}{x + 2}$ **42.** $\frac{t}{2t - 3} - 11$

43. Think About a Plan The groundspeed for jet traffic from Los Angeles to New York City can be about 100 mi/h faster than the groundspeed from New York City to Los Angeles. This difference is due to a strong westerly wind at high altitudes. If r is a jet's groundspeed from New York City to Los Angeles, write and simplify an expression for the round-trip air time. The two cities are about 2500 mi apart.
   • Can you write an expression for the air time from New York City to Los Angeles?
   • In terms of r, what is the jet's groundspeed from Los Angeles to New York City? Can you use this speed to write an expression for the air time from Los Angeles to New York City?

44. Rowing A rowing team practices rowing 2 mi upstream and 2 mi downstream. The team can row downstream 25% faster than they can row upstream.
   a. Let u represent the team's rate rowing upstream. Write and simplify an expression involving u for the total amount of time they spend rowing.
   b. Let d represent the team's rate rowing downstream. Write and simplify an expression involving d for the total amount of time they spend rowing.
   c. Reasoning Do the expressions you wrote in parts (a) and (b) represent the same time? Explain.

Answers

Practice and Problem-Solving Exercises
(continued)

25. $\frac{35 + 6a}{15a}$

26. $\frac{12 - 2x}{3x}$

27. $\frac{189 - 9n}{7n^3}$

28. $\frac{18 + 20x^2}{15x^8}$

29. $\frac{(a + 4)(a - 3)}{(a + 3)(a + 5)}$

30. $\frac{17m - 47}{(m + 2)(m - 7)}$

31. $\frac{a^2 + 12a + 15}{4(a + 3)}$

32. $\frac{5 + 5t - 4t^2}{t^2(t + 1)}$

33. a. $\frac{1}{r} + \frac{1}{0.7r} = \frac{1.7}{0.7r}$
   b. $\frac{17}{7r}$
   c. about 0.81 h or 48.6 min

34. The student added the denominators instead of finding the LCD.

35. Not always; the numerator may contain a factor of the LCD.

36. Check students' work.

37. $\frac{-y^2 + 2y + 2}{3y + 1}$

38. $\frac{h^2 + h + 1}{2t^2 - 7}$

39. $\frac{r - 2k - 6}{9 + p^3}$

40. $\frac{-3 + x + z}{xy^2z}$

41. $\frac{10x + 15}{x + 2}$

42. $\frac{-21t + 33}{2t - 3}$

43. $\frac{5000r + 250,000}{r(r + 100)}$

44. a. $\frac{18}{5u}$
   b. $\frac{9}{2d}$
   c. Yes; $\frac{18}{5u} = \frac{9}{2d}$ if and only if $d = 1.25u$.

For $f(x) = 8x$, $g(x) = \frac{1}{x}$, and $h(x) = \frac{4}{x-5}$, perform the indicated operation.

Example $f(x) \div g(x) = 8x \div \frac{1}{x} = 8x \cdot \frac{x}{1} = 8x^2$

45. $f(x) + g(x)$ **46.** $f(x) \cdot g(x)$ **47.** $g(x) - h(x)$ **48.** $h(x) \div f(x)$

Ⓒ Challenge   Simplify each complex fraction.

49. $\dfrac{3 + \frac{x}{2}}{2 + \frac{x}{3}}$ **50.** $\dfrac{x + y}{1 + \frac{x}{y}}$ **51.** $\dfrac{-4}{\frac{3}{x} + y}$

52. $\dfrac{\frac{1}{x} - \frac{4}{x}}{\frac{3}{y} + \frac{5}{y}}$ **53.** $\dfrac{\frac{3}{x} + \frac{4}{y}}{\frac{2}{x} - \frac{3}{y}}$ **54.** $\dfrac{\frac{7}{c+1} + 4}{3 - \frac{2}{c+1}}$

Standardized Test Prep

GRIDDED RESPONSE

SAT/ACT

55. What is the difference $\frac{3x}{3x-2} - \frac{2}{3x-2}$ when $x \neq \frac{2}{3}$?

56. The area of the figure shown at the right is 200 cm². What is the value of x to the nearest hundredth of a centimeter?

57. A band director can line up the band members in equal rows of 4, 5, or 8. What is the least number of band members?

58. The members of a bicycle club rode a 20-mi round-trip route. On the way back, they had a tailwind and averaged 3 mi/h faster than on the first half of the trip. Suppose the bicyclists averaged a rate of 12 mi/h for the first half of the trip. How many hours did the round trip take?

Mixed Review

Divide.   📘 See Lesson 11-3.

59. $(2x^4 + 8x^3 - 4x^2) \div 4x^2$ **60.** $(10b + 5b^2) \div (b + 2)$ **61.** $(y^4 - y^2) \div (y^2 - 2y - 3)$

Solve each radical equation. Check your answers. If there is no solution, write *no solution*.   📘 See Lesson 10-4.

62. $x = \sqrt{5x + 6}$ **63.** $n = \sqrt{24 - 5n}$ **64.** $\sqrt{16y} = -8$

Get Ready!   To prepare for Lesson 11-5, do Exercises 65–67.

Solve each proportion.   📘 See Lesson 2-7.

65. $\frac{1}{x} = \frac{3}{5}$ **66.** $\frac{3}{t} = \frac{5}{2}$ **67.** $\frac{m}{3} = \frac{17}{51}$

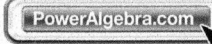
45. $\frac{8x^2 + 1}{x}$

46. 8

47. $\frac{-3x - 5}{x(x - 5)}$

48. $\frac{1}{2x(x - 5)}$

49. $\frac{3}{2}$

50. y

51. $\frac{-4x}{3 + xy}$

52. $-\frac{3y}{8x}$

53. $\frac{3y + 4x}{2y - 3x}$

54. $\frac{11 + 4c}{3c + 1}$

55. 1

56. 13.18

57. 40

58. 1.5 h

59. $\frac{1}{2}x^2 + 2x - 1$

60. $5b$

61. $\frac{y^2(y - 1)}{y - 3}$

62. 6

63. 3

64. no solution

65. $\frac{5}{3}$

66. $\frac{6}{5}$

67. 1

Additional Instructional Support

Algebra 1 Companion

Students can use the **Algebra 1 Companion** worktext (4 pages) as you teach the lesson. Use the Companion to support

- New Vocabulary
- Key Concepts
- Got It for each Problem
- Lesson Check

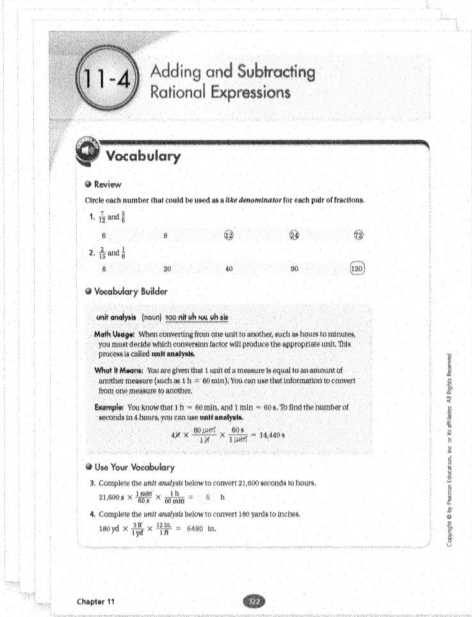

ELL Support

Connect to Prior Knowledge Write $\frac{2}{3} + \frac{1}{3}$ on the board. Ask: how do we find the sum? Think aloud and use gestures as you model how to add the numerators. Then introduce an addition problem with rational expressions. Model as you think aloud how to find the sum. Do the same with subtraction. Do the same with fractions and rational expressions with unlike denominators. Invite students to guide you through finding the LCD and the sum.

5 Assess & Remediate

Lesson Quiz

1. What is the sum?

   a. $\frac{7}{4b} + \frac{3}{4b}$

   b. $\frac{2h}{y-2} + \frac{7h}{y-2}$

2. What is the difference $\frac{-4x}{2x^2 + 13x + 6} - \frac{-6x - 1}{2x^2 + 13x + 6}$?

3. What is the difference $\frac{7}{x+1} - \frac{6}{x+5}$?

4. Curtis rides his bike 9 miles one way then turns around and rides back. On the return trip, his speed is increased 20% because the wind is at his back. Let s be his speed in miles per hour riding against the wind. What is an expression that represents his total time in hours riding down and back?

5. **Do you UNDERSTAND?** Rowing upstream for 5 mi against a strong current, your speed is 20% less than your normal rowing speed. On the return trip downstream, your speed is 20% greater than your normal rowing speed. Will you finish the whole trip in the same time as if you had rowed at normal speed throughout?

ANSWERS TO LESSON QUIZ

1. **a.** $\frac{5}{2b}$; **b.** $\frac{9h}{y-2}$

2. $\frac{1}{x+6}$

3. $\frac{x+29}{x^2 + 6x + 5}$

4. $\frac{16.5}{s}$

5. No; your total time will be about 4% longer than usual.

PRESCRIPTION FOR REMEDIATION

Use the student work on the Lesson Quiz to prescribe a differentiated review assignment.

Points	Differentiated Remediation
0–2	Intervention
3–4	On-level
5	Extension

PowerAlgebra.com

5 Assess & Remediate

Assign the Lesson Quiz. Appropriate intervention, practice, or enrichment is automatically generated based on student performance.

Intervention

- **Reteaching** (2 pages) Provides reteaching and practice exercises for the key lesson concepts. Use with struggling students or absent students.

- **English Language Learner Support** Helps students develop and reinforce mathematical vocabulary and key concepts.

All-in-One Resources/Online
Reteaching

All-in-One Resources/Online
English Language Learner Support

Differentiated Remediation *continued*

On-Level

- **Practice** (2 pages) Provides extra practice for each lesson. For simpler practice exercises, use the Form K Practice pages found in the All-in-One Teaching Resources and online.

- **Think About a Plan** Helps students develop specific problem-solving skills and strategies by providing scaffolded guiding questions.

- **Standardized Test Prep** Focuses on all major exercises, all major question types, and helps students prepare for the high-stakes assessments.

Extension

- **Enrichment** Provides students with interesting problems and activities that extend the concepts of the lesson.

- **Activities, Games, and Puzzles** Worksheets that can be used for concept development, enrichment, and for fun!

Practice and Problem Solving WKBK/ All-in-One Resources/Online
Practice page 1

11-4 **Practice** *Form G*
Adding and Subtracting Rational Expressions

Add or subtract.

1. $\frac{1}{y} + \frac{1}{y}$ 2. $\frac{11}{2y} + \frac{27}{2y}$ 3. $\frac{m}{m+4} + \frac{4}{m+4}$
 $\frac{2}{y}$ $\frac{19}{y}$ 1

4. $\frac{t-1}{t} - \frac{t+1}{t}$ 5. $\frac{n}{1-n} + \frac{1}{n-1}$ 6. $\frac{1-m}{m+4} - \frac{2m+1}{m+4}$
 $\frac{-2}{t}$ -1 $\frac{m^2-12m+8}{m^2-16}$

7. $\frac{2}{y} - \frac{3y}{8}$ 8. $\frac{4x}{3} - \frac{3}{4x}$ 9. $\frac{2a+1}{a} + \frac{2}{2}$
 $\frac{16-3y^2}{8y}$ $\frac{16x^2-9}{12x}$ $\frac{a^2+6a+2}{2a}$

Find the LCM of each pair of expressions.

10. $6x; \frac{1}{3}$ 11. $40x^3y^2; 8y^2$ 12. $3a-3; 3$
 $2x$ $40x^3y^2$ $3a-3$

13. $z^2-4; z+2$ 14. $4d^2-64; 4$ 15. $10a^2b^4c^4; 5ab^3c^2$
 z^2-4 $4d^2-64$ $10a^2b^4c^4$

16. Does it matter whether you use the LCD first or the GCF first when adding or subtracting a rational expression with different denominators and simplifying? Use an example to justify your claim.
You should get the same result no matter which technique you use first. Check students' work.

17. Is there ever a time when it is all right to add or subtract the denominators when adding or subtracting a rational expression? Explain.
No. The denominator must be the same to add or subtract the numerator.

Simplify. Add or subtract.

18. $\frac{x-3}{2(x+5)} + \frac{1}{2}$ 19. $\frac{3x}{2} - 2x$
 $\frac{x^2-x+10}{2x^2+10x}$ $\frac{3-4x}{2}$

Practice and Problem Solving WKBK/ All-in-One Resources/Online
Practice page 2

11-4 **Practice** *(continued)* *Form G*
Adding and Subtracting Rational Expressions

Add or subtract.

20. $\frac{2}{3} + \frac{4}{x}$ 21. $\frac{2}{x-1} + 10$ 22. $\frac{-x}{2} + 3$
 $\frac{3x+4x}{nx}$ $\frac{10x-8}{x-1}$ $\frac{-x+6}{2}$

23. $1 + \frac{a}{b}$ 24. $\frac{m}{x} + \frac{4}{m(x-1)}$ 25. $\frac{a}{x} + \frac{z}{y}$
 $\frac{b+a}{b}$ $\frac{m^2x-m^2+4x}{mx^2-mx}$ $\frac{ay+bx}{by}$

26. $\frac{21.5}{4x} - \frac{5.5}{3x}$ 27. $\frac{1}{x} + \frac{2}{2} - \frac{12}{5x}$ 28. $\frac{1}{x-1} + \frac{-x+1}{x^2}$
 $\frac{42.5x}{12x}$ $\frac{3}{5x}$ $\frac{2x-1}{x^2-x^3}$

29. Your friend bought $n+8$ outfits and her sister bought $\frac{n+2}{n+3}$ outfits. How many total outfits did they buy?
$\frac{n^2+12n+26}{n+3}$

30. What is the perimeter of a rectangular garden that is $\frac{6+x}{2}$ ft long and $\frac{2x}{3}$ ft wide?
$\frac{7x+13}{3}$

31. Your brother ran to school at a rate of 6 mi/h. He walked back home at a rate of 4 mi/h. How far is it to school if the round trip takes 1 hour?
$2\frac{2}{5}$ mi

32. Adding two rational expressions leads to a solution of $\frac{5x}{6}$. One expression is $\frac{x}{3}$. What is the other one? Show your work.
$\frac{5x}{6} - \frac{x}{3} = \frac{5x-2x}{6} = \frac{3x}{6} = \frac{x}{2}$

33. **Writing** Explain how to use opposites to find the sum $\frac{8}{1-2x} + \frac{x}{2x-1}$.
You can multiply $1 - 2x$ by -1 to get $-1(2x-1)$, so the common denominator is $-1(2x-1)$.

34. **Open-Ended** Write a problem that uses addition of rational expressions.
Answers may vary. Sample: A garden is $\frac{2+x}{x}$ ft long and $\frac{3}{x-1}$ ft wide. What is the perimeter of the garden?

All-in-One Resources/Online
Enrichment

11-4 **Enrichment**
Adding and Subtracting Rational Expressions

There are many real-world applications for rational expressions. Rational expressions are not simply theoretical problems in mathematics, but can be used daily to solve problems of speed, time, and distance just to name a few. For instance, for problems involving rate r (which in this case is equal to speed), distance d, and/or time t, the formula $r = \frac{d}{t}$ can be used. Depending upon which variable is being solved for, one can use this formula interchangeably to find rate, distance, and time.

1. A family spent their summer vacation driving across the United States on a road trip. They drove d miles before starting back home. Their car gets 62 miles per gallon. Because of the different roadways they used on the way back, they drove 140 miles less.
   a. If gas on the way up cost, on average, $3.65 per gallon and on the way back cost, on average, $3.05 per gallon, write an expression that shows how much the family spent on gas altogether. $3.65\left(\frac{d}{62}\right) + 3.05\left(\frac{d-140}{62}\right)$
   b. Simplify the expression in part (a). $\frac{6.7d - 427}{62}$
   c. The family drove 1364 miles before starting back home. How much money did they spend on gas? $140.51

2. A student on the cross-country team ran around the school course, 5 miles, at a rate of r mi/h, and ran straight back to the school, 3 miles, at a rate of $r-1$ mi/h.
   a. Write an expression to show the student's time for the first part of the run. $\frac{5}{r}$
   b. Write an expression to show the student's time for the second part of the run. $\frac{3}{r-1}$
   c. Write an expression that shows the student's time for the entire run. Then find the sum. $\frac{5}{r} + \frac{3}{r-1}; \frac{8r-5}{r^2-r}$
   d. The student ran the first part of the run at a rate of 6 mi/h. How long did it take the student to complete the entire run? $\frac{43}{30}$ h $= 1\frac{13}{30}$ h = 1 h 26 min

---

Practice and Problem Solving WKBK/ All-in-One Resources/Online
Think About a Plan

11-4 **Think About a Plan**
Adding and Subtracting Rational Expressions

Rowing A rowing team practices rowing 2 mi upstream and 2 mi downstream. The team can row downstream 25% faster than they can row upstream.
a. Let u represent the team's rate rowing upstream. Write and simplify an expression involving u for the total amount of time they spend rowing.
b. Let d represent the team's rate rowing downstream. Write and simplify an expression involving d for the total amount of time they spend rowing.
c. **Reasoning** Do the expressions you wrote in parts (a) and (b) represent the same time? Explain.

Know

1. What is the distance the team rows upstream? 2 mi
2. What is the distance the team rows downstream? 2 mi
3. How much faster does the team row downstream? 25% or 0.25 faster

Need

4. What is the formula for time written in terms of the distance d and the rate r? $t = \frac{d}{r}$
5. Write expressions for the time rowing upstream and the time rowing downstream by substituting values for the distance and variables for the rate in the formula in Exercise 4.
   a. Time rowing upstream $= \frac{2}{u}$
   b. Time rowing downstream $= \frac{2}{d}$

Plan

6. Write an equation that relates to u and d. $d = 1.25u$
7. Rewrite the expressions you wrote in Exercise 6 in terms of u.
   a. $\frac{2}{u}$
   b. $\frac{2}{1.25u}$
8. Do the expressions you wrote in Exercise 7 represent the same time? Why or why not?
no; distance is the same, but the trip downstream is at a faster rate, so it will take less time. So, $\frac{2}{1.25u} < \frac{2}{u}$.

Practice and Problem Solving WKBK/ All-in-One Resources/Online
Standardized Test Prep

11-4 **Standardized Test Prep**
Adding and Subtracting Rational Expressions

Multiple Choice

For Exercises 1–5, choose the correct letter.

1. What is the difference $\frac{5x-2}{4x} - \frac{x-2}{4x}$? A
   A. 1 B. $\frac{x-1}{x}$ C. 0 D. $\frac{3}{2}$

2. What is the sum $\frac{1}{2b} + \frac{b}{2}$? I
   F. $\frac{b+1}{2b+1}$ G. $2b$ H. $\frac{1}{4}$ I. $\frac{b^2+1}{2b}$

3. What is the sum $\frac{1}{g+2} + \frac{3}{g+1}$? C
   A. $\frac{3}{g+3}$ B. $\frac{g+3}{(g+1)(g+2)}$ C. $\frac{4g+7}{(g+1)(g+2)}$ D. $\frac{2g+3}{(g+1)(g+2)}$

4. What is the difference $\frac{r+2}{r+4} - \frac{3}{r+1}$? H
   F. $\frac{-1}{r+3}$ G. $\frac{r^2-1}{(r+1)(r+4)}$ H. $\frac{r^2-10}{(r+1)(r+4)}$ I. $\frac{r^2+14}{(r+1)(r+4)}$

5. What is the sum $\frac{a-1}{abc^2} + \frac{3-b}{abc^3}$? B
   A. $\frac{a-b-3}{abc^3}$ B. $\frac{a-4+b}{abc^3}$ C. $\frac{a-4+b}{abc^3}$ D. $\frac{-3}{c^3}$

Short Response

6. Elena went on a 6-mile walk. She completed the first half of the walk 1 mi/h faster than usual and the second half of the walk 2 mi/h slower than the first half.
   a. If it took her 7.2 h to complete the walk, what is her usual rate? 1.5 mi/h
   b. What is the formula necessary to solve this problem? $7.2 = \frac{3}{x+1} + \frac{3}{x-1}$
   [2] Both parts answered correctly.
   [1] One part answered correctly.
   [0] Neither part answered correctly.

Online Teacher Resource Center
Activities, Games, and Puzzles

11-4 **Game: That's a Rational Question**
Adding and Subtracting Rational Expressions

Divide the class into two teams. Your teacher or host will write the following grid of point values on the board.

10	20	30	40	50
10	20	30	40	50
10	20	30	40	50
10	20	30	40	50
10	20	30	40	50
10	20	30	40	50

The seating arrangement of each team determines the order of play.

During each turn, a team member selects a point value from the table. Your teacher will write a sum or difference of rational expressions that matches the point value on the board from a list of questions. The team member must simplify the expression.

For example, a team member selects 20 points, and your teacher or host writes a 20-point difference $\frac{7x+5}{3x^2-x-2} - \frac{4x+3}{3x^2-x-2}$ on the board. The team member finds and reads an answer $\frac{3x+2}{3x^2-x-2}$ ("3x plus 2 over 3x squared minus x minus 2").

A correct answer earns the corresponding point value for the team. Your teacher or host will then cross out that point value from the board.

An incorrect answer returns play to the next member of the other team, who can either answer the same question or select another question.

Any other student who shouts out an answer out-of-turn causes his or her team to lose the point value of the question.

The team that earns the most point wins!
See Teacher Instructions Page.

Answers

Mid-Chapter Quiz

1. $6(x - 2)$, $x \neq -2$

2. $\frac{c + 3}{c - 3}$, $c \neq 3$

3. $\frac{1}{k + 4}$, $k \neq -4$, and $k \neq 2$

4. $\frac{2x + 3}{2}$, $x \neq -5$

5. $\frac{-x - 3}{x + 4}$, $x \neq -4$, $x \neq 3$

6. $w + 2$

7. $\frac{-12}{5y^4}$

8. $\frac{(z - 3)(z + 8)}{3z(z + 2)}$

9. $(x + 2)(x + 4)$

10. $\frac{4}{3}$

11. $\frac{2a - 1}{(a - 3)^2(a + 2)}$

12. $\frac{1}{7(d + 1)}$

13. $\frac{3}{2}x - 1 + \frac{1}{2x}$

14. $\frac{x - 5}{3x}$

15. $3x^2 + 5x + 2$

16. $\frac{1}{x}$

17. $\frac{-2y}{y + 3}$

18. $\frac{6 + 25x}{10x^2}$

19. $\frac{3t - 5}{(t - 3)(t - 2)}$

20. $\frac{2x^2 + 17x - 45}{(x - 5)(x + 4)}$

21. $x^2 + 9x + 20$

22. **a.** It is not correct to call $x - 3$ and $3 - x$ common factors. Their quotient is not 1; it is -1.

   b. Answers will vary. Sample: Rewrite $3 - x$ as $-1(x - 3)$.

23. The student wanted the second term to be a fraction also. When you multiply fractions, you multiply the numerators and then the denominators.

24. Whether you use a reciprocal or long division, you will get equivalent answers. They are different because when you use the reciprocal your answer may be in factored form. When you use long division your answer may have a remainder. Check students' work.

25. When you divide monomials you subtract the exponents, so you would expect the degree to be less than five.

PowerAlgebra.com

MathXL for School

Prepare students for the Mid-Chapter Quiz and Chapter Test with online practice and review.

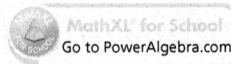 MathXL® for School
Go to PowerAlgebra.com

Do you know HOW?

Simplify each expression. State any excluded values.

1. $\frac{6x^2 - 24}{x + 2}$

2. $\frac{3c + 9}{3c - 9}$

3. $\frac{k - 2}{k^2 + 2k - 8}$

4. $\frac{2x^2 + 13x + 15}{2x + 10}$

5. $\frac{9 - x^2}{x^2 + x - 12}$

6. **Geometry** The height of a rectangular prism is 3 more than twice its width w. The volume of the prism is $2w^3 + 7w^2 + 6w$. Write a simplified expression for the length of the prism.

Multiply or divide.

7. $\frac{4}{y^3} \cdot \frac{-3}{5y}$

8. $\frac{z - 3}{3z} \cdot \frac{z + 8}{z + 2}$

9. $\frac{x^2 - 4}{x + 3} \cdot \frac{x^2 + 7x + 12}{x - 2}$

10. $\frac{z + 5}{z} \div \frac{3z + 15}{4z}$

11. $\frac{2a - 1}{a - 3} \div (a^2 - a - 6)$

12. $\frac{4d^2 - 3d}{7d} \div (4d^2 + d - 3)$

13. $(6x^3 - 4x^2 + 2x) \div 4x^2$

14. What is the simplified form of $\dfrac{\frac{1}{x + 5}}{\frac{3x}{x^2 - 25}}$?

15. The length of a rectangle is $4x + 1$ and the area is $12x^3 + 23x^2 + 13x + 2$. What is an expression for the width?

Add or subtract.

16. $\frac{3}{8x} + \frac{5}{8x}$

17. $\frac{5y}{y + 3} - \frac{7y}{y + 3}$

18. $\frac{3}{5x^2} + \frac{5}{2x}$

19. $\frac{4}{t - 3} - \frac{1}{t - 2}$

20. $\frac{2x}{x - 5} + \frac{9}{x + 4}$

Do you UNDERSTAND?

21. **Reasoning** The expression $\frac{p}{x^2 + x - 12}$ simplifies to $\frac{x + 5}{x - 3}$. Write the expression p represents.

22. **Error Analysis** Your friend says that the first step in simplifying $\frac{x - 3}{x + 4} \cdot \frac{x}{3 - x}$ is to divide out the common factors $x - 3$ and $3 - x$.

   a. Explain your friend's error.

   b. What is a possible correct first step?

23. **Writing** A student's first step in finding the product $\frac{7}{x} \cdot x^3$ was to rewrite the expression as $\frac{7}{x} \cdot \frac{x^3}{1}$. Why do you think the student did this?

24. **Compare and Contrast** When you are dividing a polynomial by a monomial, you can multiply by the reciprocal or use long division. How are these two methods the same? How are they different? Which method do you prefer? Explain your answer.

25. **Reasoning** You are dividing a polynomial in one variable with a degree of 5 by a monomial in the same variable with a degree of 2. Would you expect the quotient to have a degree greater than or less than 5? Explain your answer.

11-5 Solving Rational Equations

Objective To solve rational equations and proportions

 Getting Ready!

Geb can run the distance between his house and Katy's in 20 min. Katy can bicycle to Geb's house in 10 min. Geb runs toward Katy's house while Katy bicycles toward Geb's house. How long will it be before they meet on the road? Justify your reasoning.

I bet each of them only goes a fraction of the distance!

A **rational equation** is an equation that contains one or more rational expressions.

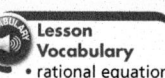

Lesson Vocabulary
• rational equation

Essential Understanding You can solve a rational equation by first multiplying each side of the equation by the LCD. When each side of a rational equation is a single rational expression, you can solve the equation using the Cross Products Property.

 Problem 1 Solving Equations With Rational Expressions

What is the solution of $\frac{5}{12} - \frac{1}{2x} = \frac{1}{3x}$? Check the solution.

$$\frac{5}{12} - \frac{1}{2x} = \frac{1}{3x} \qquad \text{The denominators are 12, } 2x, \text{ and } 3x. \text{ The LCD is } 12x.$$

$$12x\left(\frac{5}{12} - \frac{1}{2x}\right) = 12x\left(\frac{1}{3x}\right) \qquad \text{Multiply each side by } 12x.$$

$$12^1x\left(\frac{5}{12}\right) - 12x^6\left(\frac{1}{2x}\right) = 12x^4\left(\frac{1}{3x}\right) \qquad \text{Distributive Property}$$

$$5x - 6 = 4 \qquad \text{Simplify.}$$

$$5x = 10 \qquad \text{Add 6 to each side.}$$

$$x = 2 \qquad \text{Divide each side by 5.}$$

Check $\quad \frac{5}{12} - \frac{1}{2(2)} \overset{?}{=} \frac{1}{3(2)} \qquad$ See if $x = 2$ makes $\frac{5}{12} - \frac{1}{2x} = \frac{1}{3x}$ true.

$$\frac{1}{6} = \frac{1}{6} \checkmark$$

Plan

Have you seen an equation like this before?
Yes. In Lesson 2-3, you solved equations that contained fractions. As you did there, you can clear the fractions from the equation by multiplying by a common denominator.

PowerAlgebra.com | **Lesson 11-5** Solving Rational Equations | **679**

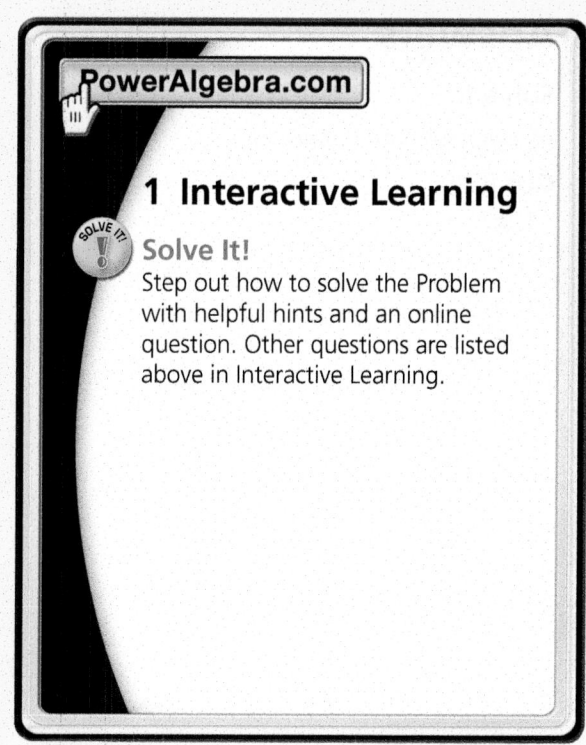

1 Interactive Learning

Solve It!

PURPOSE To solve a problem that can be represented using a rational equation
PROCESS Students may solve an equation, act out the problem, or use trial and error.

FACILITATE

Q In one minute, what fraction of the distance between the houses has Geb traveled? Explain. [$\frac{1}{20}$ **of the distance, because it takes 20 minutes to travel the entire distance.**]

Q In six minutes, what fraction of the total distance has been traveled by Geb and Katy? Explain. [$\frac{18}{20}$; $\frac{6}{20} + \frac{6}{10} = \frac{18}{20}$]

Q In seven minutes, what fraction of the total distance has been traveled by Geb and Katy? Explain. [**They passed each other**; $\frac{7}{20} + \frac{7}{10} = \frac{21}{20}$]

ANSWER See Solve It in Answers on next page.
CONNECT THE MATH The real-world situation in the Solve It can be modeled using rational equations. In the lesson, students learn to solve rational equations.

2 Guided Instruction

Problem 1

Q What are the prime factorizations of the three denominators? [$3 \cdot 2 \cdot 2$; $2 \cdot x$; $3 \cdot x$]

Q What property reminds you that you must multiply both sides of the equation by the LCD? [**Multiplicative Property of Equality**]

Q Is it possible to multiply by the correct LCD and have any fractions left in the equation? Explain. [**No, because if the LCD is correct, then each denominator will divide into the multiplier evenly.**]

11-5 Preparing to Teach

BIG idea Solving Equations and Inequalities **UbD**

ESSENTIAL UNDERSTANDINGS

• A rational equation can be solved by first multiplying each side of the equation by the LCD.
• When each side of a rational equation is a single rational expression, the equation can be solved using the Cross Products Property.
• The process of solving rational equations may produce extraneous solutions.

Math Background

Extraneous solutions are those solutions to an equation which arise due to the method of solution of an equation and are not actual solutions of the original equation. In the study of radical equations, extraneous

solutions arose at times due to the squaring of both sides of the equation. In the study of rational equations, extraneous solutions arise because of multiplying both sides of the equation by an expression that contains the variable. Students will next encounter extraneous solutions during the study of logarithmic equations.

Emphasize to students that they must check each solution in the original equation to ensure that it is true.

Support Student Learning

Use the **Algebra I Companion** to engage and support students during instruction. See Lesson Resources at the end of this lesson for details.

PowerAlgebra.com

1 Interactive Learning

Solve It!
Step out how to solve the Problem with helpful hints and an online question. Other questions are listed above in Interactive Learning.

Lesson 11-5 **679**

Got It?

SYNTHESIZING

These equations can be solved by first combining the terms on the left side of the equation and then using the Cross Products Property.

Problem 2

Q Why is each side of the equation multiplied by x^2? [x^2 **is the LCD. Each side of the equation must be multiplied by the LCD to create an equivalent equation with no fractions.**]

Q What method is the most efficient for solving this quadratic equation? [**factoring and using the Zero-Product Property**]

Q Why should you check your solutions in the original rational equation rather than in the quadratic equation? [**Answers may vary. Sample: Because you may have made a mistake when solving the quadratic equation. Also, checking in the original equation guards against producing extraneous solutions.**]

Got It?

Before students begin to solve 2b, remind them that in a rational expression, parentheses are implied around both the numerator and the denominator.

 Got It? 1. What is the solution of each equation? Check your solution.

a. $\frac{1}{3} + \frac{3}{x} = \frac{2}{x}$

b. $\frac{4}{7x} + \frac{1}{3} = \frac{7}{3x}$

To solve some rational equations, you need to factor a quadratic expression.

 Problem 2 Solving by Factoring

Multiple Choice What are the solutions of $1 - \frac{1}{x} = \frac{12}{x^2}$?

Ⓐ $-11, 12$ Ⓑ $-4, 3$ Ⓒ $-3, 4$ Ⓓ $12, 13$

$1 - \frac{1}{x} = \frac{12}{x^2}$	The denominators are x and x^2. The LCD is x^2.
$x^2\left(1 - \frac{1}{x}\right) = x^2\left(\frac{12}{x^2}\right)$	Multiply each side by x^2.
$x^2(1) - x^2\left(\frac{1}{x}\right) = x^2\left(\frac{12}{x^2}\right)$	Distributive Property
$x^2 - x = 12$	Simplify.
$x^2 - x - 12 = 0$	Collect terms on one side.
$(x - 4)(x + 3) = 0$	Factor the quadratic expression.
$x - 4 = 0 \text{ or } x + 3 = 0$	Zero-Product Property
$x = 4 \text{ or } \quad x = -3$	Solve for x.

Think

Is there a different way to solve this equation?
Yes. Because it's a quadratic equation, you can also solve it by using the quadratic formula, by completing the square, or by graphing.

Check Determine whether 4 and -3 both make $1 - \frac{1}{x} = \frac{12}{x^2}$ a true statement.

When $x = 4$:

$1 - \frac{1}{x} = \frac{12}{x^2}$

$1 - \frac{1}{4} \stackrel{?}{=} \frac{12}{(4)^2}$

$1 - \frac{1}{4} \stackrel{?}{=} \frac{12}{16}$

$\frac{3}{4} = \frac{3}{4}$ ✔

When $x = -3$:

$1 - \frac{1}{x} = \frac{12}{x^2}$

$1 - \frac{1}{(-3)} \stackrel{?}{=} \frac{12}{(-3)^2}$

$1 + \frac{1}{3} \stackrel{?}{=} \frac{12}{9}$

$\frac{4}{3} = \frac{4}{3}$ ✔

The solutions are 4 and -3. The correct answer is C.

 Got It? 2. What are the solutions of each equation in parts (a) and (b)? Check your solutions.

a. $\frac{5}{y} = \frac{6}{y^2} - 6$

b. $d + 6 = \frac{d + 11}{d + 3}$

c. **Reasoning** How can you tell that the rational equation $\frac{2}{x^2} = -1$ has no solutions just by looking at the equation?

Answers

Solve It!

$6\frac{2}{3}$ min; explanations may vary.

Got It?

1. a. -3

   b. $\frac{37}{7}$

2. a. $-\frac{3}{2}, \frac{2}{3}$

   b. $-7, -1$

   c. The expression $\frac{2}{x^2}$ cannot be negative.

PowerAlgebra.com

2 Guided Instruction

Each Problem is worked out and supported online.

Problem 1
Solving Equations With Rational Expressions
Animated

Alternative Problem 1
Solving Equations With Rational Expressions

Problem 2
Solving by Factoring
Animated

Problem 3
Solving a Work Problem

Problem 4
Solving a Rational Proportion

Problem 5
Checking to Find an Extraneous Solution
Animated

Support in Algebra 1 Companion
• Vocabulary
• Key Concepts
• Got It?

To solve a work problem, find the fraction of the job each person does in one unit of time (for example, in 1 h or 1 min). The sum of the fractions for everyone working is the fraction of the job completed in one unit of time.

 Problem 3 Solving a Work Problem

Painting Amy can paint a loft apartment in 7 h. Jeremy can paint a loft apartment of the same size in 9 h. If they work together, how long will it take them to paint a third loft apartment of the same size?

Know
- Amy's painting time is 7 h.
- Jeremy's painting time is 9 h.

Need
Amy and Jeremy's combined painting time

Plan
Find what fraction of a loft each person can paint in 1 h. Then write and solve a rational equation.

Relate   fraction of loft Amy can paint in 1 h   +   fraction of loft Jeremy can paint in 1 h   =   fraction of loft painted in 1 h

Define   Let t = the painting time, in hours, if Amy and Jeremy work together.

Think
Where have you seen a problem like this before?
In Problem 1 of this lesson, you solved a similar equation containing rational expressions.

Write $\frac{1}{7}$ + $\frac{1}{9}$ = $\frac{1}{t}$

$63t\left(\frac{1}{7}+\frac{1}{9}\right) = 63t\left(\frac{1}{t}\right)$ Multiply each side by the LCD, 63t.

$9t + 7t = 63$ Distributive Property

$16t = 63$ Simplify.

$t = \frac{63}{16}$, or $3\frac{15}{16}$ Divide each side by 16.

It will take Amy and Jeremy about 4 h to paint the loft apartment together.

 Got It? 3. One hose can fill a pool in 12 h. Another hose can fill the same pool in 8 h. How long will it take for both hoses to fill the pool together?

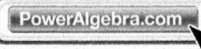

Problem 3

Some students may better understand this problem if the equation is written as: $\frac{t}{7} + \frac{t}{9} = 1$. Students can understand that the expression $\frac{t}{7} + \frac{t}{9}$ is the fraction of an apartment that both Amy and Jeremy can paint in t hours. The expression is set equal to 1 because the goal is to paint one apartment in its entirety.

Got It?

Instruct students to write the equation by using the equation for Problem 3 as a model.

Additional Problems

1. What is the solution of $\frac{2}{5x} - \frac{1}{2x} = -\frac{1}{2}$? Check the solution.

ANSWER $\frac{1}{5}$

2. What are the solutions of $1 - \frac{2}{x} = \frac{8}{x^2}$?

A. −2, 4

B. −4, 2

C. 2, 8

D. −6, 2

ANSWER A

3. You can mow the lawn in 1 h 15 min using a push mower. Your father can mow the lawn in 30 minutes on a riding mower. How long would it take you and your father to mow the lawn together?

ANSWER $21\frac{3}{7}$ min

4. What is the solution of $\frac{10}{6x + 7} = \frac{6}{2x + 9}$?

ANSWER 3

5. What is the solution of $\frac{x - 3}{x + 1} = \frac{1}{x + 1}$?

ANSWER 4

Answers

Got It? (continued)

3. 4.8 h

Problem 4

Q What is a proportion? **[A proportion is a statement that two ratios are equal.]**

Q What does the Cross Products Property state? **[The product of the first numerator and second denominator is equal to the product of the first denominator and the second numerator.]**

Q Why is it a good idea to put parentheses around the denominators prior to cross-multiplying? **[to ensure that you multiply the entire denominator, not just the first terms of the denominator, by the numerator]**

Got It?
ERROR PREVENTION

Illustrate why the Cross Products Property works by solving the equation in 4a using the method in Problems 1-3.

Problem 5

Q Can you use the Cross Products Property to solve this equation? Explain. **[Yes, because it is a proportion.]**

Q How can you tell that $6 = x + 3$ by looking at the original equation? **[Because the denominators of the two ratios in the proportion are the same, the numerators must be the same also.]**

Got It?

Remind students that they can solve rational equations either by multiplying both sides of the equation by the LCD of the denominators or using the Cross Products Property. In this case, since the denominators are $x^2 - 4$ and $x - 2$, it may be easier to multiply by the LCD.

Some rational equations are proportions. You can solve them by using the Cross Products Property.

 Problem 4 Solving a Rational Proportion

What is the solution of $\frac{4}{x+2} = \frac{3}{x+1}$?

Think

Can you use the LCD to solve this equation?
Yes, but when each side of a rational equation is a single rational expression, using cross products is often easier. Otherwise, you have to multiply each side of the equation by the LCD, $(x + 2)(x + 1)$.

$$\frac{4}{x+2} = \frac{3}{x+1}$$

$4(x + 1) = 3(x + 2)$ Cross Products Property

$4x + 4 = 3x + 6$ Distributive Property

$x = 2$ Solve for x.

Check $\frac{4}{2+2} \stackrel{?}{=} \frac{3}{2+1}$

$1 = 1$ ✔

Got It? **4.** Find the solution(s) of each equation. Check your solutions.

a. $\frac{3}{b+2} = \frac{5}{b-2}$ **b.** $\frac{c}{3} = \frac{7}{c-4}$

The process of solving a rational equation may give a solution that is extraneous because it makes a denominator in the original equation equal 0. An extraneous solution is a solution of an equation that is derived from the original equation, but is not a solution of the original equation itself. So you must check your solutions.

 Problem 5 Checking to Find an Extraneous Solution

What is the solution of $\frac{6}{x+5} = \frac{x+3}{x+5}$?

Think

What extraneous solutions are possible?
Since $\frac{6}{x+5}$ and $\frac{x+3}{x+5}$ are undefined when $x = -5$, a possible extraneous solution is -5.

$$\frac{6}{x+5} = \frac{x+3}{x+5}$$

$6(x + 5) = (x + 3)(x + 5)$ Cross Products Property

$6x + 30 = x^2 + 8x + 15$ Simplify each side of the equation.

$0 = x^2 + 2x - 15$ Collect terms on one side.

$0 = (x - 3)(x + 5)$ Factor.

$x - 3 = 0$ or $x + 5 = 0$ Zero-Product Property

$x = 3$ or $x = -5$ Solve for x.

Check $\frac{6}{3+5} \stackrel{?}{=} \frac{3+3}{3+5}$ $\frac{6}{-5+5} \stackrel{?}{=} \frac{-5+3}{-5+5}$

$\frac{6}{8} = \frac{6}{8}$ ✔ $\frac{6}{0} = \frac{-2}{0}$ ✗   Undefined!

The equation has one solution, 3.

Got It? **5.** What is the solution of $\frac{x-4}{x^2-4} = \frac{-2}{x-2}$? Check your solution.

Answers

Got It? (continued)

4. a. -8

    b. $-3, 7$

5. 0

Lesson Check

Do you know HOW?

Solve each equation. Check your solutions.

1. $\frac{1}{2x} + \frac{3}{10} = \frac{1}{5x}$

2. $\frac{5}{x^2} = \frac{6}{x} - 1$

3. $\frac{-2}{x+2} = \frac{x+4}{x^2-4}$

4. Sarah picks a bushel of apples in 45 min. Andy picks a bushel of apples in 75 min. How long will it take them to pick a bushel together?

Do you UNDERSTAND?

5. **Vocabulary** How is an extraneous solution of a rational equation similar to an excluded value of a rational expression? How is it different?

6. **Open-Ended** Write a rational equation that has one solution and one extraneous solution.

7. **Error Analysis** In the work shown at the right, what error did the student make in solving the rational equation?

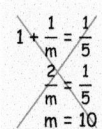
$$1 + \frac{1}{m} = \frac{1}{5}$$
$$\frac{2}{m} = \frac{1}{5}$$
$$m = 10$$

Practice and Problem-Solving Exercises

A Practice

Solve each equation. Check your solutions. *See Problems 1 and 2.*

8. $\frac{1}{2} + \frac{2}{x} = \frac{1}{x}$

9. $5 + \frac{2}{p} = \frac{17}{p}$

10. $\frac{3}{a} - \frac{5}{a} = 2$

11. $y - \frac{6}{y} = 5$

12. $\frac{5}{2s} + \frac{3}{4} = \frac{9}{4s}$

13. $7 + \frac{3}{x} = \frac{7}{x} + 9$

14. $\frac{2}{c-2} = 2 - \frac{4}{c}$

15. $\frac{5}{3p} + \frac{2}{3} = \frac{5+p}{2p}$

16. $\frac{8}{x+3} = \frac{1}{x} + 1$

17. $\frac{1}{t-2} = \frac{t}{8}$

18. $\frac{v+2}{v} + \frac{4}{3v} = 11$

19. $\frac{4}{3(c+4)} + 1 = \frac{2c}{c+4}$

20. $\frac{3+a}{2a} = \frac{1}{3} + \frac{5}{6a}$

21. $\frac{a}{a+3} = \frac{2a}{a-3} - 1$

22. $\frac{z}{z+2} - \frac{1}{z} = 1$

23. **Gardening** Marian can weed a garden in 3 h. Robin can weed the same garden in 4 h. If they work together, how long will the weeding take them? *See Problem 3.*

24. **Trucking** David can unload a delivery truck in 20 min. Allie can unload the same delivery truck in 35 min. If they work together, how long will the unloading take?

Solve each equation. Check your solutions. If there is no solution, write *no solution*. *See Problems 4 and 5.*

25. $\frac{5}{x+1} = \frac{x+2}{x+1}$

26. $\frac{4}{c+4} = \frac{c}{c+25}$

27. $\frac{3}{m-1} = \frac{2m}{m+4}$

28. $\frac{2x+4}{x-3} = \frac{3x}{x-3}$

29. $\frac{30}{x+3} = \frac{30}{x-3}$

30. $\frac{x+2}{x+4} = \frac{x-2}{x-1}$

B Apply

31. **Writing** How could you use cross products to solve $\frac{1}{x-2} = \frac{2x-6}{x+6} + 1$?

32. **Open-Ended** Write a rational equation that has 5 as a solution.

PowerAlgebra.com   **Lesson 11-5** Solving Rational Equations   **683**

---

3 Lesson Check

Do You Know HOW?

- If students have difficulty with Exercise 3, then ask them to solve the equation using both methods presented in the lesson.

Do You UNDERSTAND?

- If students have difficulty with Exercise 6, then have them review Problem 5 to know what makes a solution extraneous.

Close

Q What are the two methods of solving a rational equation? When is it appropriate to use each method? **[Multiplying through by the common denominator is a method that can be used on any rational equation. Using the Cross Products Property is a method that can only be used on rational equations that are proportions.]**

Lesson Check

1. -1

2. 1, 5

3. 0

4. about 28 min

5. An extraneous solution of a rational equation is an excluded value of the associated rational function.

6. Answers will vary. Sample:
$\frac{x^2}{x-1} = \frac{1}{x-1}$

7. The student forgot to first multiply both sides of the equation by the LCD, 5m.

Practice and Problem-Solving Exercises

8. -2

9. 3

10. -1

11. $-1, 6$

12. $-\frac{1}{3}$

13. -2

14. 1, 4

15. 5

16. 1, 3

17. $-2, 4$

18. $\frac{1}{3}$

19. $\frac{16}{3}$

20. -4

21. -1

22. $-\frac{2}{3}$

23. $1\frac{5}{7}$ h

24. about 12.7 min

25. 3

26. ± 10

27. $-\frac{3}{2}, 4$

28. 4

29. no solution

30. 6

31. You could rewrite the right side of the equation as $\frac{3x}{x+6}$ and then cross multiply.

32. Answers will vary. Sample:
$\frac{9}{x-2} = \frac{x+4}{3}$

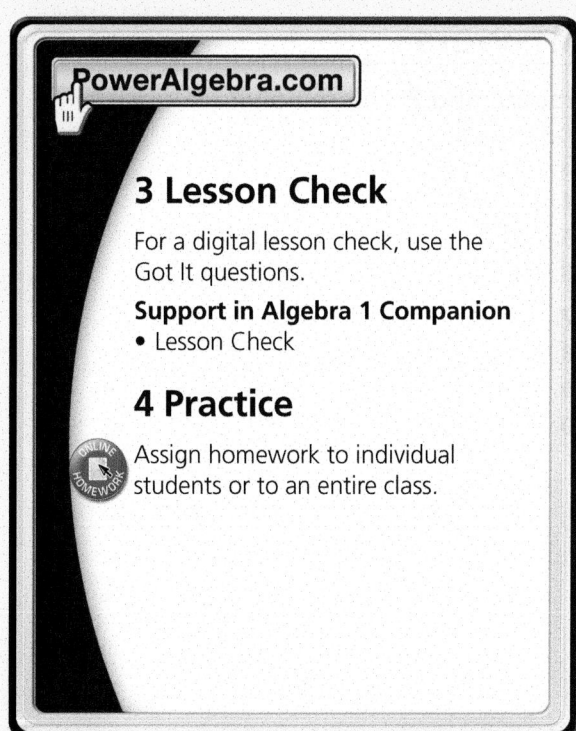

PowerAlgebra.com

3 Lesson Check

For a digital lesson check, use the Got It questions.

Support in Algebra 1 Companion
- Lesson Check

4 Practice

Assign homework to individual students or to an entire class.

Lesson 11-5 683

4 Practice

Solve each equation. Check your solutions.

33. $\dfrac{2r}{r-4} - 2 = \dfrac{4}{r+5}$

34. $\dfrac{r+1}{r-1} = \dfrac{r}{3} + \dfrac{2}{r-1}$

35. $\dfrac{3}{s-1} + 1 = \dfrac{12}{s^2-1}$

36. $\dfrac{d}{d+2} - \dfrac{2}{2-d} = \dfrac{d+6}{d^2-4}$

37. $\dfrac{s}{3s+2} + \dfrac{s+3}{2s-4} = \dfrac{-2s}{3s^2-4s-4}$

38. $\dfrac{u+1}{u+2} = \dfrac{-1}{u-3} + \dfrac{u-1}{u^2-u-6}$

39. **Think About a Plan** Two pipes fill a storage tank with water in 9 h. The smaller pipe takes three times as long to fill the tank as the larger pipe. How long would it take the larger pipe to fill the tank alone?
   • What variable should you define for this situation?
   • In terms of your variable, what fraction of the tank is filled in 1 h by the larger pipe alone? By the smaller pipe alone?

40. **Running** You take 94 min to complete a 10-mi race. Your average speed during the first half of the race is 2 mi/h greater than your average speed during the second half. What is your average speed during the first half of the race?

 41. **a. Graphing Calculator** Write two functions using the expressions on the two sides of the equation $\dfrac{6}{x^2} + 1 = \dfrac{(x+7)^2}{6}$. Graph the functions.
   b. What are the coordinates of the points of intersection?
   c. Reasoning Are the x-coordinates of the points of intersection solutions of the equation? Explain.

Electricity Two lamps can be connected to a battery in a circuit in series or in parallel. You can calculate the total resistance R_T in a circuit if you know the resistance in each lamp. Resistance is measured in ohms (Ω). For a circuit connected in series, $R_T = R_1 + R_2$. For a circuit connected in parallel, $\dfrac{1}{R_T} = \dfrac{1}{R_1} + \dfrac{1}{R_2}$.

42. The lamps are connected in series. $R_T = 20\ \Omega$. Find R_2.

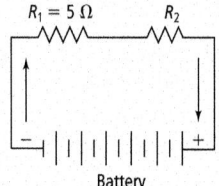

Battery

43. The lamps are connected in parallel. $R_T = 12\ \Omega$. Find R_2.

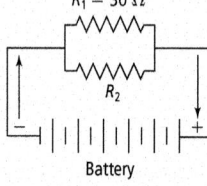

Battery

44. **Travel** A plane flies 450 mi/h. It can travel 980 mi with a tailwind in the same amount of time as it travels 820 mi against the wind. Solve the equation $\dfrac{980}{450+s} = \dfrac{820}{450-s}$ to find the speed s of the wind.

Challenge

45. **Chemistry** A chemist has one solution that is 80% acid and a second solution that is 30% acid. How many liters of each solution will the chemist need in order to make 50 L of a solution that is 62% acid?

Answers

Practice and Problem-Solving Exercises
(continued)

33. −14

34. 3

35. −5, 2

36. −1

37. $-\frac{6}{5}$, −1

38. 0, 2

39. 12 h

40. about 7.5 mi/h

41. a.

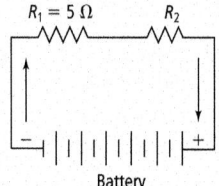

b. (−9.53, 1.07), (−4.16, 1.35), (−1.12, 5.76), (0.81, 10.16)

c. Yes; the x-values are solutions to the original equation since both sides are equal.

42. 15 Ω

43. 20 Ω

44. 40 mi/h

45. 32 L of 80% solution, 18 L of 30% solution

Solve each equation. Check your answers.

46. $\dfrac{x-6}{x+3} + \dfrac{2x}{x-3} = \dfrac{4x+3}{x+3}$

47. $\dfrac{n}{n-2} + \dfrac{n}{n+2} = \dfrac{n}{n^2-4}$

48. $\dfrac{2}{r} + \dfrac{1}{r^2} + \dfrac{r^2+r}{r^3} = \dfrac{1}{r}$

49. $\dfrac{3}{t} - \dfrac{t^2-2t}{t^3} = \dfrac{4}{t^2}$

50. Painting To paint a room, it takes Mike 75 min, Joan 60 min, and Kyle 80 min when each person works alone. If all three work together, how long will the painting take?

51. Window Washing Sumi can wash the windows of an office building in $\frac{3}{4}$ the time it takes her apprentice. One day they worked on a building together for 2 h 16 min, and then Sumi continued alone. It took her 4 h 32 min more to complete the job. How long would it take her apprentice to wash all the windows alone?

Standardized Test Prep

SAT/ACT

52. Which inequality contains both solutions of $x = \frac{1}{2} + \frac{3}{x}$?

Ⓐ $-1 < x < 3$ Ⓑ $-2 < x \le 2$ Ⓒ $-2 \le x < 0$ Ⓓ $-3 \le x \le -1$

53. Which expression is equivalent to $\dfrac{\frac{4}{x+3}}{\frac{2x-6}{x^2-9}}$?

Ⓕ 2 Ⓖ -2 Ⓗ $\dfrac{8}{x^2+6x+9}$ Ⓘ $\dfrac{2x+6}{x-3}$

54. Which is the least common denominator of $\frac{1}{x}, \frac{x}{3},$ and $\frac{3}{2x}$?

Ⓐ $2x$ Ⓑ $3x$ Ⓒ $6x$ Ⓓ $6x^2$

Short Response

55. A grizzly bear can run as fast as 30 mi/h. At that rate, how many feet would a grizzly bear travel in 1 s? Explain your answer.

Mixed Review

Add or subtract.   ◀ See Lesson 11-4.

56. $\dfrac{5}{x^2y^2z} - \dfrac{8}{x^2y^2z}$

57. $\dfrac{3h^2}{2t^2-8} + \dfrac{h}{t-2}$

58. $\dfrac{k-11}{k^2+6k-40} - \dfrac{5}{k-4}$

Graph each function, either by translating the graph of $y = \sqrt{x}$ or by making a table of values.   ◀ See Lesson 10-5.

59. $f(x) = -2\sqrt{x}$ **60.** $y = \sqrt{x+7}$ **61.** $f(x) = \sqrt{x-2} - 8$ **62.** $y = \sqrt{0.25x}$

Get Ready!   **To prepare for Lesson 11-6, do Exercises 63–66.**

Determine whether each equation represents a direct variation. If it does, find the constant of variation.   ◀ See Lesson 5-2.

63. $y - 3x = 0$ **64.** $y + 7 = x$ **65.** $x + 4y + 1 = 1$ **66.** $8x = 3y$

PowerAlgebra.com | **Lesson 11-5**   Solving Rational Equations   **685**

46. 9
47. $0, \frac{1}{2}$
48. -1
49. 1
50. about 23.5 min
51. $11\frac{1}{3}$ h
52. B
53. F
54. C
55. [2] $\dfrac{30\ mi}{1\ h} \cdot \dfrac{1\ h}{3600\ s} \cdot \dfrac{5280\ ft}{1\ mi} = 44$ ft/s
    [1]   minor computational error
56. $-\dfrac{3}{x^2y^2z}$
57. $\dfrac{3h^2+2ht+4h}{2(t-2)(t+2)}$
58. $\dfrac{-4k-61}{(k-4)(k+10)}$

59.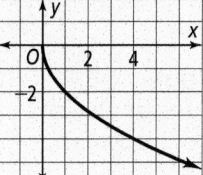

60.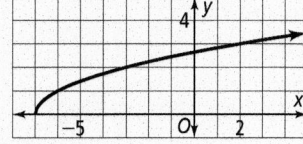

61.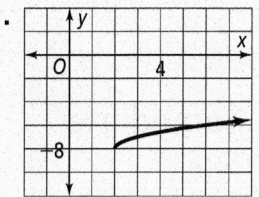

62.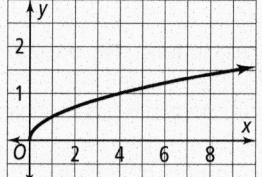

63. yes; 3
64. no
65. yes; $-\frac{1}{4}$
66. yes; $\frac{8}{3}$

Additional Instructional Support

Algebra 1 Companion

Students can use the **Algebra 1 Companion** worktext (4 pages) as you teach the lesson. Use the Companion to support

- New Vocabulary
- Key Concepts
- Got It for each Problem
- Lesson Check

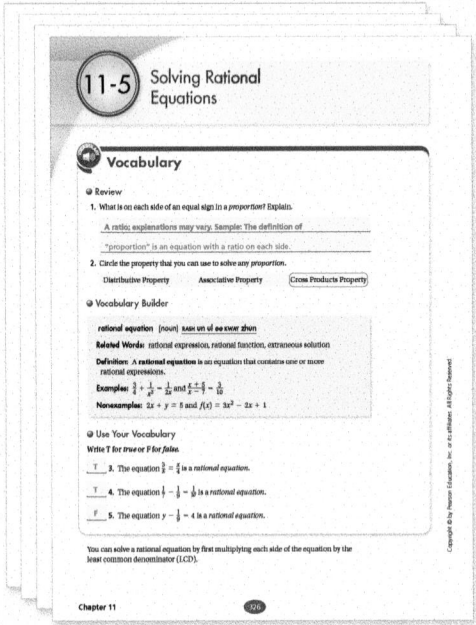

ELL Support

Focus on Language Pair students. Have them review the vocabulary for the chapter. Ask them to write a definition of each word in their own words. Tell them to discuss their ideas and then quiz each other on the definitions. Encourage them to question each other for specific details and clarity.

5 Assess & Remediate

Lesson Quiz

1. What is the solution of $\frac{1}{3} - \frac{3}{x-5} = -\frac{5}{12}$? Check the solution.

2. What are the solutions of $1 + \frac{35}{x^2} = \frac{12}{x}$?
   - **A.** $-7, 5$
   - **B.** $-3, 1$
   - **C.** $1, 5$
   - **D.** $5, 7$

3. You can paint a room in 2 h 30 min. Your brother can paint the same room in 2 h 15 min. How long would it take you and your brother to paint the room working together? Round to the nearest whole minute.

4. What is the solution of $\frac{4}{x-15} = \frac{2}{3x-5}$?

5. **Do you UNDERSTAND?** Two identical gardens are to be weeded, each by a two-person team. Team A includes one gardener who could weed the garden in 2 h and another who could weed the garden in 4 h. Team B includes two gardeners, either of whom could weed the garden in 3 h. Which team will finish first? Explain.

ANSWERS TO LESSON QUIZ

1. 9
2. D
3. about 71 min
4. -1
5. Team A can weed $\frac{3}{4}$ of the garden in an hour. Team B can weed $\frac{2}{3}$ of the garden in an hour. Team A will finish first.

PRESCRIPTION FOR REMEDIATION
Use the student work on the Lesson Quiz to prescribe a differentiated review assignment.

Points	Differentiated Remediation
0–2	Intervention
3–4	On-level
5	Extension

PowerAlgebra.com

5 Assess & Remediate

Assign the Lesson Quiz. Appropriate intervention, practice, or enrichment is automatically generated based on student performance.

Intervention

- **Reteaching** (2 pages) Provides reteaching and practice exercises for the key lesson concepts. Use with struggling students or absent students.
- **English Language Learner Support** Helps students develop and reinforce mathematical vocabulary and key concepts.

All-in-One Resources/Online
Reteaching

11-5 Reteaching
Solving Rational Equations

Solving rational equations uses the properties of simplifying rational expressions in an equation that solves for an unknown variable.

Problem
What is the solution of $\frac{2}{x} + \frac{3}{2x} = \frac{1}{4}$?

All-in-One Resources/Online
English Language Learner Support

11-5 ELL Support
Solving Rational Equations

Differentiated Remediation *continued*

On-Level

- **Practice** (2 pages) Provides extra practice for each lesson. For simpler practice exercises, use the Form K Practice pages found in the All-in-One Teaching Resources and online.

- **Think About a Plan** Helps students develop specific problem-solving skills and strategies by providing scaffolded guiding questions.

- **Standardized Test Prep** Focuses on all major exercises, all major question types, and helps students prepare for the high-stakes assessments.

Extension

- **Enrichment** Provides students with interesting problems and activities that extend the concepts of the lesson.

- **Activities, Games, and Puzzles** Worksheets that can be used for concept development, enrichment, and for fun!

Practice and Problem Solving WKBK/All-in-One Resources/Online
Practice page 1

11-5 Practice Form G
Solving Rational Equations

Solve each equation. Check your solutions.

1. $\frac{1}{2} - \frac{1}{j} + 2 = \frac{4}{2-j}$

2. $\frac{8}{c+2} - 6 = \frac{4}{c+2}$

3. $\frac{3}{2p-2} - 1 = \frac{4}{p-1} + 2$

4. $\frac{2}{x+4} + \frac{3}{4} = \frac{2}{x-2}$

5. $\frac{5}{d+2} + \frac{d}{5} = \frac{d+5}{5}$

6. $\frac{-3}{d} - \frac{3}{d-3} = \frac{3}{4}$

7. $\frac{4}{N} - 1 = \frac{2}{n+2} - 1$

8. $\frac{x}{x-3} + \frac{x}{x+3} = 1$

9. $\frac{p+7}{p+2} - 2 = \frac{2-p}{p+4}$

10. $\frac{2}{p+3} = \frac{7}{18p}$

11. $\frac{a}{a+6} = \frac{2}{a+6}$

12. $\frac{-6}{d-2} = \frac{2d}{d-2}$

13. It takes you about an hour to make one batch of cookie dough and your brother about 42 minutes to make one batch. How much time does it take you to make a batch of cookie dough together?

14. Your dad can clean the house in 2 hours and 10 minutes. Your mom can clean it in an hour and 45 minutes. How many hours does it take them to clean the house if they work together?

Solve each equation. Check your solutions. If there is no solution, write *no solution*.

15. $\frac{x-1}{x+2} + \frac{4x}{2x^2-2x-12} = 2$

16. $\frac{t-1}{3t^2-t-2} - \frac{2t-3}{3t+2} = \frac{4}{2t-2}$

17. $\frac{2-2p}{p^2-6p+8} + \frac{3p}{p-4} = \frac{p}{p-2}$

18. $\frac{d-4}{d+4} = \frac{4+d}{d-2} - \frac{d+8}{d^2+2d-8}$

Practice and Problem Solving WKBK/All-in-One Resources/Online
Practice page 2

11-5 Practice *(continued)* Form G
Solving Rational Equations

19. It takes you 12 hours to paint a house, your brother 14 hours, and your sister 10 hours. If all three of you work together, how long will it take you to paint the house?

20. Maria, LaShawn, and Mike are all students. It takes Maria 8 hours to write half of her paper for history class. It takes LaShawn 2x hours to write one third of her paper, and Mike takes $(x-2)$ hours to write half of his paper. If the teacher tells them they can work on the paper as a group, how long will it take them to complete it?

21. **Error Analysis** Edward solved the rational equation $\frac{3x(x-2)}{x} - x\left(\frac{96}{3x}\right) = 3x\left(\frac{1}{3}\right)$ and got an answer of $x = -19$. What was his mistake?

22. **Writing** Write a rational equation that has $n = 10$ for the answer. Include at least 3 terms in your equation, one of which should be a quadratic equation or a perfect square.

23. A pool has 2 pipes, one to fill it and one to empty it. Ms. Simon wants to fill the pool, but she mistakenly turns on both pipes at the same time. The pipe that fills the pool can fill it in 6 hours and the one that drains it can do that job in 10 hours. How long will it take to fill the pool now that both pipes are filling and emptying it at the same time?

24. What is the LCD of the equation $\frac{4(t-2)}{2t-3} - 4\left(\frac{1}{t}\right) = 5t - \frac{3(t+4)}{t+1}$?

Solve each equation. Check your solutions.

25. $\frac{c}{c+4} + \frac{3}{c-3} = \frac{16}{c^2+c-12}$

26. $\frac{12}{y+1} - \frac{(y+4)(y-4)}{y-2} = -1$

All-in-One Resources/Online
Enrichment

11-5 Enrichment
Solving Rational Equations

Going "green" is an expression that is used for products, techniques, and even buildings that are being presented into society or are being changed in order to be more environmentally friendly—to help save the environment and make the world a better and safer place for future generations. There are various ways to go "green" and the use of organic products is one of them.

1. The Environmental Club is planting an organic garden for their school. First, the members must build a fence surrounding the garden. Alone, it would take Maria, Julie, and Gerry x, $3x$, and $6x$ hours to finish the fence, respectively. Together, they finish the fence in 2 hours. How long would it take each member to build the fence if working alone?

2. The Environmental Club decides to plant carrots, tomatoes, and lettuce. Maria can plant a carrot patch in 3 hours, a tomato patch in 7 hours, and a lettuce patch in 2 hours. Julie can plant a carrot patch in 4 hours, a tomato patch in 5 hours, and a lettuce patch in 4 hours. Gerry can plant a carrot patch in 2 hours, a tomato patch in 14 hours, and a lettuce patch in 1 hour. Maria and Julie plant the carrots together and Maria and Gerry plant the tomatoes together. How long does it take to plant each vegetable?

3. All three members plant the lettuce patch together. How long will it take to plant the lettuce?

4. The Environmental Club is dismayed to find that flea beetles and aphids have infested their new tomato patch. Alone, the beetles could seriously damage the crops in two weeks and the aphids could seriously damage the crops in three days. With flea beetles and aphids simultaneously attacking their crops, how long before the garden is destroyed?

5. To rid the garden of the pests, the members of the Environmental Club make an organic insecticidal soap. The soap is 95% water, 4% cayenne pepper, and 1% organic dish soap.
   a. Write an equation for making the soap using those ingredients and proportions.
   b. How many liters of each ingredient will they need if they start with 15 liters of water?

Practice and Problem Solving WKBK/All-in-One Resources/Online
Think About a Plan

11-5 Think About a Plan
Solving Rational Equations

Running You take 94 min to complete a 10-mi race. Your average speed during the first half of the race is 2 mi/h greater than your average speed during the second half of the race. What is your average speed during the first half of the race?

Understanding the Problem

1. What is the distance of the first half of the race? _____ 5 mi

2. What is the distance of the second half of the race? _____ 5 mi

3. What is the total time it takes to complete the race? _____ 94 min

Planning the Solution

4. Rewrite the distance formula $d = rt$ for time t in terms of distance d and rate r. $t = \frac{d}{r}$

5. Use your answer to Exercise 4 to write an expression for the time it takes to run each part of the race.
   a. Time for first half of race = $\frac{5}{r+2}$
   b. Time for second half of race = $\frac{5}{r}$

6. Compare the units of the given time it takes to complete the race with the units of the description of the average speed. Write the time so that it matches the units in the rates.
   the average rates are in mi/h and the given time is in min; $\frac{94}{60}$ h

Getting an Answer

7. Write an equation for the total time it takes to complete the race. Solve the equation. What is the rate for the first half of the race?
   $\frac{5}{r+2} + \frac{5}{r} = \frac{94}{60}$; about 5.5 mi/h; about 7.5 mi/h

---

Practice and Problem Solving WKBK/All-in-One Resources/Online
Standardized Test Prep

11-5 Standardized Test Prep
Solving Rational Equations

Multiple Choice

For Exercises 1–4, choose the correct letter.

1. What is the excluded value of the equation $y = \frac{2}{x-1} + 1$? C
   A. –1   B. 0   C. 1   D. 2

2. A bus trip along the coast takes one route going, for a total of 1024 miles, and another route returning, for a total of 896 miles. If the bus travels at a constant speed of 65 mi/h, how far did the bus travel per second on the return trip?
   F. 0.07 mi/s   G. 13.8 mi/s   H. 896 mi/s   I. 0.0181 mi/s

3. What is the LCD for the equation $\frac{6-x}{2x^2y} - \frac{2x}{3xy^2} = \frac{x-3}{x^2y^3}$? A
   A. $6x^2y^3$ B. x^2y^3 C. $12x^2y^3$ D. $6xy$

4. What is the excluded value of the rational expression? Include all possible solutions. I
   $$y = \frac{1}{x^2+2x-24}$$
   F. 0, 24   G. 6, –4   H. 4, 6   I. 4, –6

Short Response

5. Every morning Diane runs 6 miles in about an hour. What is her rate in feet per second? What equations would you use to solve? Explain and show your work.
   Use the conversion factors $\frac{5280 \text{ ft}}{1 \text{ mi}}$ and $\frac{1 \text{ h}}{3600 \text{ s}}$. 8.8 ft/sec
   [2] Both parts answered correctly.
   [1] One part answered correctly.
   [0] Neither part answered correctly.

Online Teacher Resource Center
Activities, Games, and Puzzles

11-5 Activity: Together or Alone?
Solving Rational Equations

Work in small groups for this activity.

Each group is hiring two workers to mow a golf course. Roll a number cube to determine the number of hours h that one worker would take to mow the course. The expression $12 - h$ is the number of hours it takes the other worker to mow the course. The sum of h and $12 - h$ equals 12. Then compute how long it will take the two workers to mow the course together.

1. After each group has made its computations, complete the table below. Make a table of results for different h-values. If the time for any h from 1 to 6 has not been computed, the class should compute this.

h	$12 - h$	Time
1	11	$\frac{11}{12}$
2	10	$\frac{5}{3}$
3	9	$\frac{9}{4}$
4	8	$\frac{8}{3}$
5	7	$\frac{35}{12}$
6	6	3

2. Which value of h gives the two workers the fastest time?
   $h = 1$

3. Go back into small groups to find a formula for the time t using h. What expression do you get for t? What type of expression is it?
   $t = \frac{1}{12}(12h - h^2)$; quadratic expression

4. Use your graphing calculator to graph the formula you found in Exercise 3. In the graph, what occurs when the value of h equals 6?
   The vertex of the graph is located at $h = 6$.

5. Discuss your results to Exercises 1–4 as a class. What would happen if the sum of the two workers' times was a number other than 12?
   Answers will vary. Sample: The vertex of the parabola will not have an h-value

1 Interactive Learning

Solve It!

PURPOSE To solve a problem in which two variables form an inverse variation

PROCESS Students may write an equation, make a table of values or chart, or use trial and error.

FACILITATE

Q What is the product of the variables for each scenario shown in the diagram? **[168 worker days]**

Q If the number of people on the crew is 20, how many construction days will be needed? Explain. **[8.4 days, since 20 · 8.4 = 168.]**

Q Why is the combination of 12 crew members and 14 construction days not a solution? **[Although it meets the requirement for the number of crew members it does not meet the requirement for construction days.]**

ANSWER See Solve It in Answers on next page.
CONNECT THE MATH In the Solve It, students investigate how changes in the number of crew members affect the number of construction days. In the lesson, students will learn about inverse variations.

2 Guided Instruction

Problem 1

Q If two variables are inversely related, what quantity is constant? **[The product of the two variables is constant.]**

Q How can you use the equation to find other ordered pairs that satisfy the inverse variation? **[You can substitute a value for either variable and then solve the equation to find the corresponding value of the other variable.]**

11-6 Inverse Variation

Objectives To write and graph equations for inverse variations
To compare direct and inverse variations

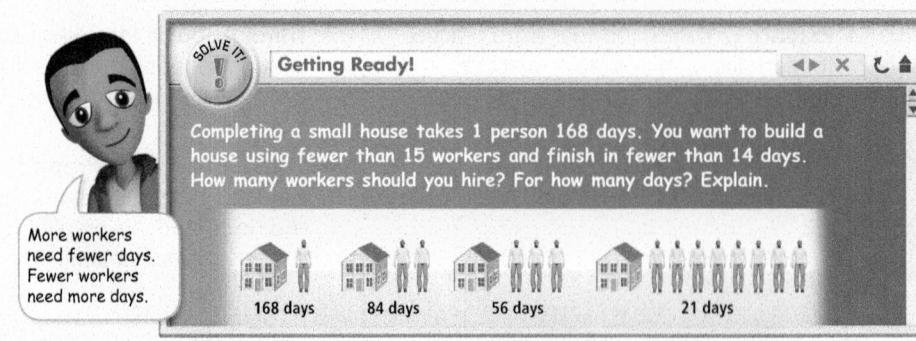

SOLVE IT! **Getting Ready!**

Completing a small house takes 1 person 168 days. You want to build a house using fewer than 15 workers and finish in fewer than 14 days. How many workers should you hire? For how many days? Explain.

More workers need fewer days. Fewer workers need more days.

168 days   84 days   56 days   21 days

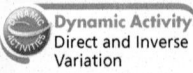
Dynamic Activity Direct and Inverse Variation

Lesson Vocabulary
• inverse variation
• constant of variation for an inverse variation

In the Solve It, the number of construction days decreases as the number of workers increases. The product of crew size and construction days is constant.

Essential Understanding If the product of two variables is a nonzero constant, then the variables form an inverse variation.

Key Concept Inverse Variation

An equation of the form $xy = k$ or $y = \frac{k}{x}$, where $k \neq 0$, is an **inverse variation**.

The **constant of variation for an inverse variation** is k, the product $x \cdot y$ for an ordered pair (x, y) that satisfies the inverse variation.

Problem 1 Writing an Equation Given a Point

Suppose y varies inversely with x, and $y = 8$ when $x = 3$. What is an equation for the inverse variation?

$xy = k$	Use the general form of an inverse variation.
$3(8) = k$	Substitute 3 for x and 8 for y.
$24 = k$	Simplify.
$xy = 24$	Write an equation. Substitute 24 for k in $xy = k$.

An equation for the inverse variation is $xy = 24$, or $y = \frac{24}{x}$.

Think
Make sure you don't stop at $24 = k$. To write the inverse variation equation, you have to substitute 24 for k in $xy = k$.

11-6 Preparing to Teach

BIG idea Function   **UbD**

ESSENTIAL UNDERSTANDINGS

• If the product of two variables is a nonzero constant, then the variables form an inverse variation.
• Inverse variations can be graphed by making a table of values and plotting points.

Math Background

Variation relates how one quantity changes to the way another quantity changes. A variation may be expressed as an equation that states a constant relationship between the values of two variables.

In an inverse variation with a positive constant of variation, the values of the two variables change

in an opposite manner. When one variable increases, the other decreases in proportion in order to maintain a constant product. The study of inverse variation provides for an introduction to the characteristics of rational functions. Rational functions often have restricted domains which lead to graphs that behave asymptotically.

Support Student Learning

Use the **Algebra 1 Companion** to engage and support students during instruction. See Lesson Resources at the end of this lesson for details.

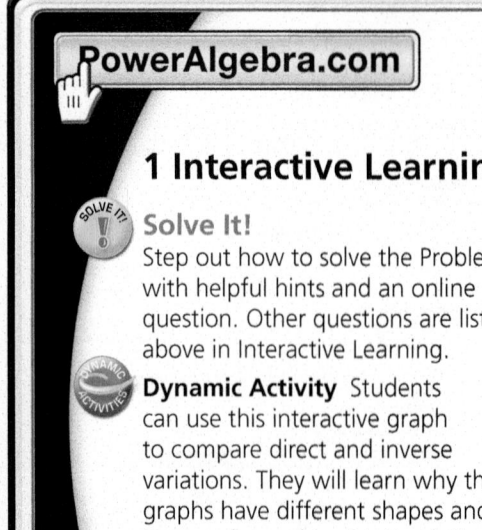

PowerAlgebra.com

1 Interactive Learning

Solve It!
Step out how to solve the Problem with helpful hints and an online question. Other questions are listed above in Interactive Learning.

Dynamic Activity Students can use this interactive graph to compare direct and inverse variations. They will learn why the graphs have different shapes and how each graph varies in relation to k.

Got It? **1.** Suppose y varies inversely with x, and $y = 9$ when $x = 6$. What is an equation for the inverse variation?

 **Problem 2** Using Inverse Variation   **GRIDDED RESPONSE**

Physics The weight needed to balance a lever varies inversely with the distance from the fulcrum to the weight. How far away from the fulcrum should the person sit to balance the lever?

160 lb   1000 lb

x 7 ft

Relate   The 1000-lb elephant is 7 ft from the fulcrum. The 160-lb person is x ft from the fulcrum. Weight and distance vary inversely.

Define   Let weight$_1$ = 1000 lb. Let distance$_1$ = 7 ft. Let weight$_2$ = 160 lb. Let distance$_2$ = x ft.

Write $\text{weight}_1 \cdot \text{distance}_1 = \text{weight}_2 \cdot \text{distance}_2$

$1000 \cdot 7 = 160 \cdot x$ Substitute.

$7000 = 160x$ Simplify.

$43.75 = x$ Divide each side by 160.

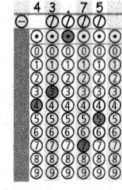

The person should sit 43.75 ft from the fulcrum to balance the lever.

Think

Is your answer reasonable?
The heavier object must be closer to the fulcrum to balance the lever. Since the elephant weighs more than the person, the person should sit more than 7 ft from the fulcrum.

 **Got It?** **2.** A 120-lb weight is placed on a lever, 5 ft from the fulcrum. How far from the fulcrum should an 80-lb weight be placed to balance the lever?

Several graphs of inverse variations $xy = k$ are shown at the right. Notice that each graph has two unconnected parts. When $k > 0$, the graph lies in the first and third quadrants. When $k < 0$, the graph lies in the second and fourth quadrants. Since k is a nonzero constant, $xy \neq 0$. So neither x nor y can equal 0.

As it moves away from the origin, the graph of an inverse variation equation approaches the x-axis and the y-axis without actually intersecting them.

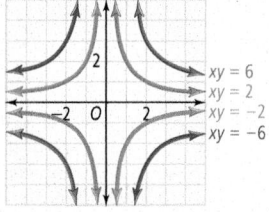

$xy = 6$
$xy = 2$
$xy = -2$
$xy = -6$

PowerAlgebra.com   **Lesson 11-6**   Inverse Variation   **687**

---

2 Guided Instruction

Each Problem is worked out and supported online.

Problem 1
Writing an Equation Given a Point

Problem 2
Using Inverse Variation
Animated

Problem 3
Graphing an Inverse Variation
Animated

Problem 4
Determining Direct or Inverse Variation
Animated

Problem 5
Identifying Direct or Inverse Variation

Support in Algebra 1 Companion
- Vocabulary
- Key Concepts
- Got It?

Got It?
Ask students to write the inverse variation equation in both forms: $xy = k$ and $y = \frac{k}{x}$.

Problem 2

Q What is the constant of variation for this situation? Explain. **[Because the weight and distance vary inversely, $1000 \cdot 7 = 7000$ is the constant of variation.]**

Q What is an equation for this inverse variation? Explain. **[The constant of variation is 7000, so the equation is $xy = 7000$.]**

Q If a person was seated 35 ft from the fulcrum, how much would he or she need to weigh in order to balance the lever in the diagram? **[200 lb]**

Got It?   **TACTILE LEARNERS**
Students can explore the inverse relationship between weight and distance by modeling a lever with a pencil as the fulcrum and a ruler. Students can use coins as weights to balance the ruler.

Answers

Solve It!
14 people and 12 days of construction; explanations may vary.

Got It?
1. $xy = 54$
2. 7.5 ft

Lesson 11-6   **687**

Problem 3

Q What is another form of the inverse variation equation? [$xy = 8$]

Q If you are unsure of how to connect the ordered pairs from the table of values using a curve, what strategy can you use? **[You can find more ordered pairs in the areas of the graph in which you are unsure.]**

Q How do you think the graph of $y = \frac{8}{x} + 3$ differs from the graph of $y = \frac{8}{x}$? **[Answers may vary. Sample: The graph of $y = \frac{8}{x} + 3$ is translated 3 units up from the graph of $y = \frac{8}{x}$.]**

Got It?

Q If the product of two numbers is negative, what do you know about the signs of the two numbers? **[The signs of the numbers must be opposite.]**

Q In which quadrants do ordered pairs have x- and y-values that are opposite in sign? **[quadrants II and IV]**

Take Note

Ask students to compare and contrast the constants of variation. Elicit that if y varies directly with x, then x varies directly with y and the two variations have constants of variation that are reciprocals. If y varies inversely with x, then x varies inversely with y and the two variations have equal constants of variation.

You can graph an inverse variation $xy = k$ or $y = \frac{k}{x}$ by making a table of values and plotting points.

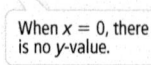 **Problem 3** Graphing an Inverse Variation

What is the graph of $y = \frac{8}{x}$?

Step 1   Make a table of values.

x	−8	−4	−2	−1	0	1	2	4	8
y	−1	−2	−4	−8	undefined	8	4	2	1

Plan

How do you know which x-values to choose?
Choose positive and negative values. Choose x-values that divide easily into 8 to get ordered pairs that are easy to graph.

When $x = 0$, there is no y-value.

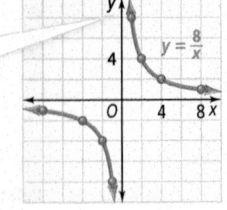

Step 2   Plot the points from the table. Connect the points in Quadrant I with a smooth curve. Do the same for the points in Quadrant III.

Got It? 3. a. What is the graph of $y = \frac{-8}{x}$?
b. Reasoning For $k > 0$, how are the graphs of $y = \frac{k}{x}$ and $y = \frac{-k}{x}$ alike? How are they different?

Recall that a direct variation is an equation of the form $y = kx$. The following summary will help you recognize and use direct and inverse variations.

take note

Concept Summary   Direct and Inverse Variations

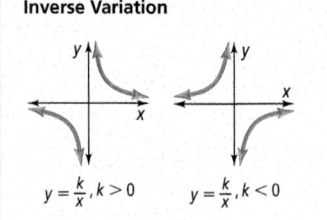

Direct Variation

$y = kx, k > 0$ $y = kx, k < 0$

y varies directly with x.
y is directly proportional to x.
The ratio $\frac{y}{x}$ is constant.

Inverse Variation

$y = \frac{k}{x}, k > 0$ $y = \frac{k}{x}, k < 0$

y varies inversely with x.
y is inversely proportional to x.
The product xy is constant.

Additional Problems

1. Suppose y varies inversely with x, and $y = 12$ when $x = 6$. What is an equation for the inverse variation?
ANSWER $xy = 72$

2. Suppose a 200-lb weight is placed on a lever, 8 ft from the fulcrum. How far from the fulcrum should a 160-lb weight be placed to balance the lever?
ANSWER 10 ft

3. What is the graph of $y = \frac{2}{x}$?
ANSWER

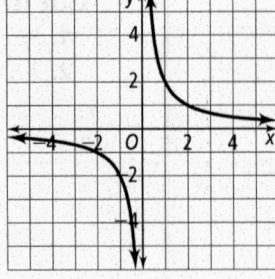

4. Do the data in each table represent a *direct variation* or an *inverse variation*? For each table, write an equation to model the data.

a.

x	y
2	20
5	8
10	4

b.

x	y
3	24
6	48
12	96

ANSWER a. inverse variation, $xy = 40$
b. direct variation, $y = 8x$

5. Does each situation represent a *direct variation* or an *inverse variation*? Explain your reasoning.

a. It costs $25 per day for a rental car.

b. Several runners compete in a 200-m run. Their times and speeds vary.

ANSWER a. Direct variation; the cost per day times the number of days equals the total cost
b. Inverse variation; the product of each runner's speed and time equals the same distance.

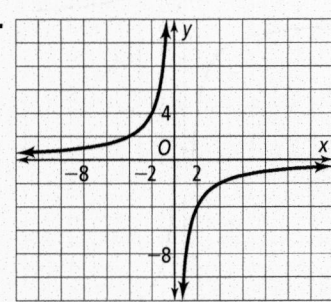 **Problem 4** Determining Direct or Inverse Variation

Do the data in each table represent a *direct variation* or an *inverse variation*? For each table, write an equation to model the data.

A

x	y
3	−15
4	−20
5	−25

The values of y seem to vary directly with the values of x. Check each ratio $\frac{y}{x}$.

$\frac{-15}{3} = -5$ $\frac{-20}{4} = -5$ $\frac{-25}{5} = -5$

The ratio $\frac{y}{x}$ is the same for all data pairs. So this is a direct variation, and $k = -5$.

An equation is $y = -5x$.

B

x	y
2	9
4	4.5
6	3

The values of y seem to vary inversely with the values of x. Check each product xy.

$2(9) = 18$ $4(4.5) = 18$ $6(3) = 18$

The product xy is the same for all data pairs. So this is an inverse variation, and $k = 18$.

An equation is $xy = 18$, or $y = \frac{18}{x}$.

Think

How can you check the reasonableness of your answers?
Substitute each x-value from the table into the equation and find the corresponding value of y. The y-values given by the equation should match the y-values in the table.

Got It? 4. Do the data in each table represent a *direct variation* or an *inverse variation*? For each table, write an equation to model the data.

a.

x	y
4	−12
6	−18
8	−24

b.

x	y
4	−12
6	−8
8	−6

Problem 5 Identifying Direct or Inverse Variation

Does each situation represent a *direct variation* or an *inverse variation*? Explain your reasoning.

Think

To answer these problems, you may find it helpful to first make a table of values. In part (A), for instance, let x be the number of friends and let y be the cost per person.

A Boating The cost of a $120 boat rental is split among several friends.

The cost per person times the number of friends equals the total cost of the boat rental. Since the total cost is a constant product of $120, the cost per person varies inversely with the number of friends. This is an inverse variation.

B Entertainment You download several movies for $14.99 each.

The cost per download times the number of movies downloaded equals the total cost of the downloads. Since the ratio $\frac{\text{total cost}}{\text{number of movies downloaded}}$ is constant at $14.99, the total cost varies directly with the number of movies downloaded. This is a direct variation.

Problem 4

Q If ordered pairs are directly related, what relationship exists between the *x*- and *y*-values? [The ratio is constant.]

Q If ordered pairs are inversely related, what relationship exists between the *x*- and *y*-values? [The product is constant.]

Q In 4A, is it acceptable to compute the ratio of $\frac{x}{y}$ instead of $\frac{y}{x}$? Explain. [Yes; if they are directly related, it is also a constant.]

Q In 4A, if you compute the ratio of $\frac{x}{y}$ instead of $\frac{y}{x}$, what is the variation equation? [$x = -\frac{1}{5}y$]

Got It?   **VISUAL LEARNERS**

Students may benefit from plotting the data points in order to discern whether the data in each table vary directly or inversely.

Problem 5

Q What is a simple question to ask to help determine if the variation is direct? [Does a change of the same size in *x* always produce a change of the same size in *y*?]

You can use this opportunity to enrich students' knowledge by letting them know that there is a type of variation called joint variation in which a variable depends on two (or more) other variables, and varies directly with some of them and inversely with others. An example of a joint variation is: The cost per person for several $120 boat rentals split among several friends.

Answers

Got It? (continued)

3. a.

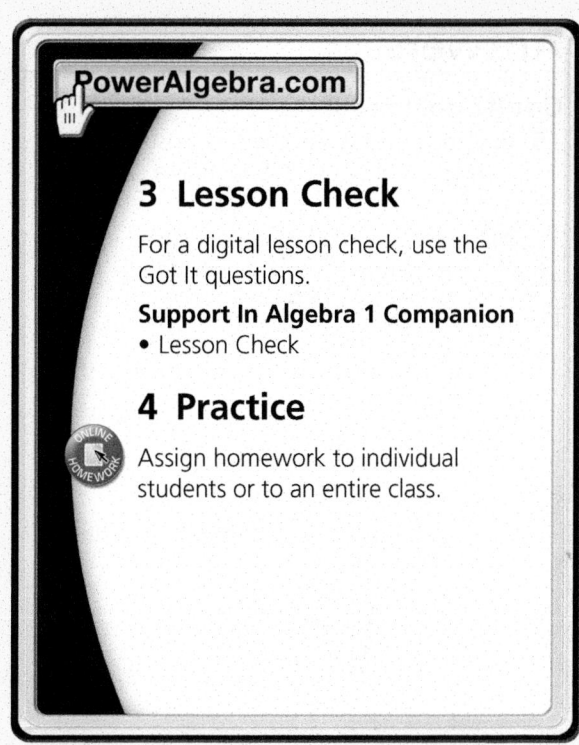

b. They are the same shape. They are reflections of each other over the *y*-axis.

4. a. direct; $y = -3x$

b. inverse; $xy = -48$

PowerAlgebra.com

3 Lesson Check

For a digital lesson check, use the Got It questions.

Support In Algebra 1 Companion
• Lesson Check

4 Practice

Assign homework to individual students or to an entire class.

Got It?

Q What equation can you use to represent 5a? 5b? $[y = 35x; xy = 5]$

3 Lesson Check

Do you know HOW?
- If students have difficulty with Exercise 3, then ask them to determine in which two quadrants the graph of $y = \frac{10}{x}$ is located.

Do you UNDERSTAND?
- If students have difficulty with Exercise 6, then have them graph several inverse variations.

Close

Q What is the relationship between the variables in an inverse variation, and how does a change in one variable affect the other variable? **[In an inverse variation, the product of the variables is a constant, so if the constant of variation is positive, as the value of one variable increases, the value of the other variable decreases, and vice versa.]**

 Got It? 5. Does each situation represent a *direct variation* or an *inverse variation*? Explain your reasoning.
  a. You buy sweaters in a clothing store for $35 each.
  b. You walk 5 mi each day. Your speed and time spent walking vary each day.

 Lesson Check

Do you know HOW?

1. Suppose y varies inversely with x, and $y = -3$ when $x = 17$. What is an equation for the inverse variation?

2. An 80-lb weight is placed on a lever, 9 ft from the fulcrum. What amount of weight should you put 6 ft from the fulcrum to balance the lever?

3. What is the graph of $y = \frac{10}{x}$?

4. Do the data in the table represent a *direct variation* or an *inverse variation*? Write an equation that models the data.

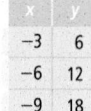

x	y
−3	6
−6	12
−9	18

Do you UNDERSTAND?

5. **Vocabulary** Is the equation $\frac{xy}{3} = 5$ an inverse variation? If so, what is the constant of variation?

6. Does the graph of an inverse variation *always*, *sometimes*, or *never* pass through the origin? Explain.

7. **Reasoning** Suppose you place two different weights on a lever. Which weight must be closer to the fulcrum in order for the lever to balance? Explain.

8. **Reasoning** Suppose the price per pencil at an office supply store decreases as the number of pencils you buy increases. Does the price per pencil necessarily vary inversely with the number of pencils bought? Explain.

 Practice and Problem-Solving Exercises

 **Practice** Suppose y varies inversely with x. Write an equation for the inverse variation.   **See Problem 1.**

9. $y = 6$ when $x = 3$
10. $y = 1$ when $x = -2$
11. $y = 7$ when $x = 8$
12. $y = 3$ when $x = 0.5$
13. $y = -10$ when $x = -2.4$
14. $y = 3.5$ when $x = 2.2$

15. **Travel** A family takes $2\frac{1}{2}$ h to drive from their house to a lake at 48 mi/h. The travel time varies inversely with the speed of the car. How long will the return trip take at 40 mi/h?   **See Problem 2.**

16. **Bicycling** A camper takes 2 h to ride a bike around a reservoir at 10 mi/h at the beginning of the summer. By the end of the summer, she can ride around the reservoir in $1\frac{1}{2}$ h. The time to travel around the reservoir varies inversely with the speed she pedals. What is her speed at the end of the summer?

Graph each inverse variation.   **See Problem 3.**

17. $y = \frac{9}{x}$
18. $xy = 12$
19. $y = \frac{-15}{x}$
20. $\frac{14}{x} = y$
21. $20 = xy$
22. $y = \frac{7.5}{x}$
23. $xy = -24$
24. $y = \frac{-1}{x}$

Answers

Got It? (continued)

5. a. Direct; the ratio of the total cost to the number of sweaters bought is a constant, 35.

  b. Inverse; the product of your speed and the time spent walking is a constant, 5.

Lesson Check

1. $xy = -51$
2. 120 lb
3.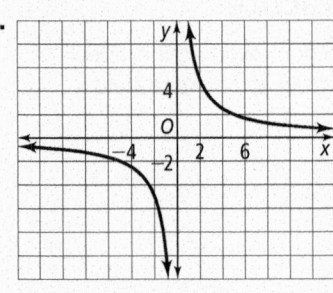

4. direct; $y = -2x$
5. yes; 15
6. Never; the equation is of the form $y = \frac{k}{x}$, and 0 is not in the domain of the function.
7. The heavier must be closer because the product of the weight and its distance from the fulcrum is a constant.
8. No; it will only vary inversely if the product of the number of pencils purchased times the price per pencil is a constant.

Practice and Problem-Solving Exercises

9. $xy = 18$
10. $xy = -2$
11. $xy = 56$
12. $xy = 1.5$
13. $xy = 24$
14. $xy = 7.7$
15. 3 h
16. $13\frac{1}{3}$ mi/h

17.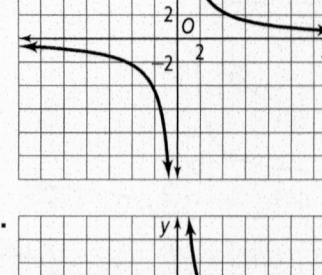

18.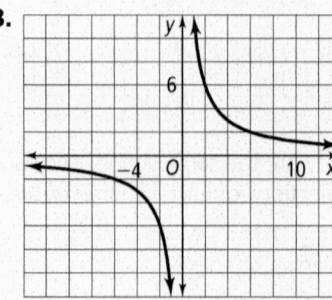

19–24. See next page.

Do the data in each table represent a *direct variation* or an *inverse variation*? Write an equation to model the data in each table.

See Problem 4.

25.

x	y
2	1
5	2.5
8	4

26.

x	y
4	15
6	10
10	6

27.

x	y
−3	−24
9	8
12	6

Tell whether each situation represents a *direct variation* or an *inverse variation*. Explain your reasoning.

See Problem 5.

28. You buy some chicken for $1.79/lb.

29. An 8-slice pizza is shared equally by a group of friends.

30. You find the length and width of several rectangles. Each has an area of 24 cm².

B Apply

Suppose *y* varies inversely with *x*. Find the constant of variation *k* for each inverse variation. Then write an equation for the inverse variation.

31. $y = -8$ when $x = -32$ **32.** $x = \frac{1}{2}$ when $y = 5$ **33.** $y = 25$ when $x = 0.04$

Each pair of points is on the graph of an inverse variation. Find the missing value.

34. $(3, 5)$ and $(1, y)$ **35.** $(2.5, 4)$ and $(x, 2)$ **36.** $\left(x, \frac{1}{2}\right)$ and $\left(\frac{1}{3}, \frac{1}{4}\right)$

Measurement Does each formula represent a *direct variation* or an *inverse variation*? Explain your reasoning.

37. the perimeter *P* of an equilateral triangle with side length *s*: $P = 3s$

38. the time *t* to travel 150 mi at a rate of *r* mi/h: $t = \frac{150}{r}$

39. the circumference *C* of a circle with radius *r*: $C = 2\pi r$

40. Think About a Plan Suppose 4 people can paint a house if they work 3 days each. How long would it take a crew of 5 people to paint the house?
 • Can you determine whether this situation represents a direct variation or an inverse variation?
 • How can you write an equation that will help you solve the problem?

41. Writing Explain how the variable *y* changes in each situation.
 a. *y* varies directly with *x*. The value of *x* is doubled.
 b. *y* varies inversely with *x*. The value of *x* is doubled.

42. Surveying Both of the two rectangular building lots shown at the right have the same area. Write an equation to find the length of the second lot.

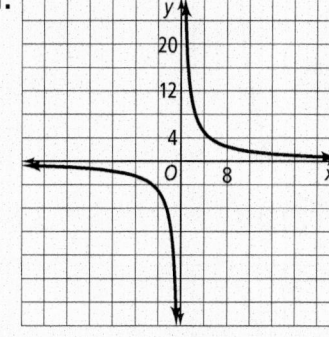
← 99 ft → ← 90 ft →
110 ft

4 Practice

ASSIGNMENT GUIDE

Basic: 9–30, 40–42

Average: 9–29 odd, 31–47

Advanced: 9–29 odd, 31–49

Standardized Test Prep: 50–52

Mixed Review: 53–59

Reasoning exercises have blue headings.

Applications exercises have red headings.

EXERCISE 41: Use the Think About a Plan worksheet in the **Practice and Problem Solving Workbook** (also available in the Teaching Resources in print and online) to further support students' development in becoming independent learners.

HOMEWORK QUICK CHECK

To check students' understanding of key skills and concepts, go over Exercises 11, 25, 40, 41, and 42.

Answers

Practice and Problem-Solving Exercises (continued)

19.

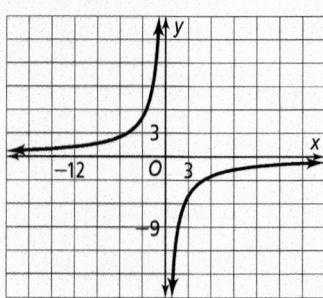

20.

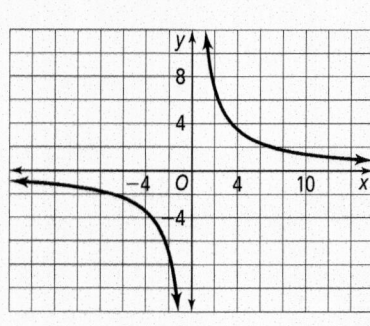

21.

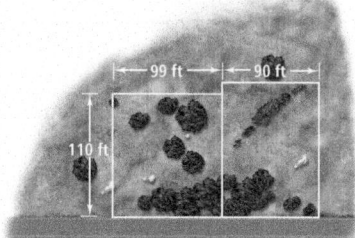

22.

23.

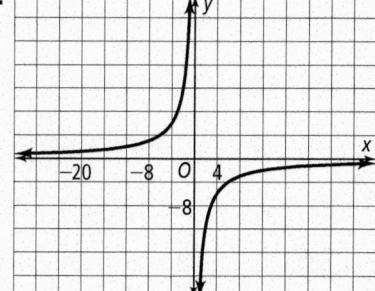

24.

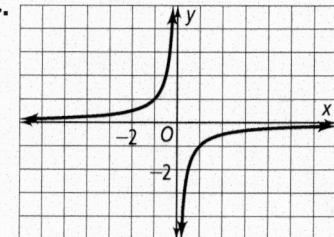

25–42. See next page.

Answers

Practice and Problem-Solving Exercises
(continued)

25. direct; $y = \frac{x}{2}$

26. inverse; $xy = 60$

27. inverse; $xy = 72$

28. Direct; the ratio of total slices to number of pounds bought is a constant, 1.79.

29. Inverse variation; the product of cost per person times the number of people is a constant.

30. Inverse; the product of length and width is a constant, 24.

31. 256; $xy = 256$

32. 2.5; $xy = 2.5$

33. 1; $xy = 1$

34. 15

35. 5

36. $\frac{1}{6}$

37. Direct; the ratio $\frac{P}{s}$ is a constant, 3.

38. Inverse; the product rt is a constant, 150.

39. Direct; the ratio $\frac{C}{r}$ is a constant, 2π.

40. 2.4 days

41. a. The value of y doubles.
b. The value of y is cut in half.

42. $99(110) = 90\ell$

43. direct; $y = 0.4x$; 8

44. direct; $y = 70x$; 0.9

45. inverse; $xy = 48$; 0.5

46. $PV = 612$

47. No; the equation of the graph is of the form $y = -2x + b$.

48. 4; $s\left(\frac{d}{2}\right)^2 = \frac{sd^2}{4} = k$, so $s = \frac{4k}{d^2}$.

49. a. $x^4 y = k$
b. $\frac{x^4 y}{z} = k$

50. 4

51. 8

52. 196

53. −25

54. no solution

55. $-\frac{5}{3}$

56.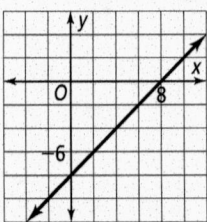

57.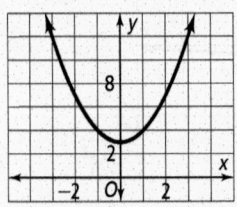

Tell whether each table represents a *direct variation* or an *inverse variation*. Write an equation to model the data. Then complete the table.

43.

x	y
10	4
20	■
8	3.2

44.

x	y
0.4	28
1.2	84
■	63

45.

x	y
1.6	30
4.8	10
■	96

46. Physics Boyle's Law states that volume *V* varies inversely with pressure *P* for any gas at a constant temperature in an enclosed space. Suppose a gas at constant temperature occupies 15.3 L at a pressure of 40 mm of mercury. What equation models this situation?

47. Error Analysis When graphing a certain function, Pedro sees that the value of *y* decreases by 2 whenever the value of *x* increases by 1. Pedro says that the graph represents an inverse variation. Is he correct? Explain.

Ⓒ Challenge **48. Physics** The intensity of a sound *s* varies inversely with the square of the distance *d* from the sound. This can be modeled by the equation $sd^2 = k$, where *k* is a constant. If you decrease your distance from the source of a sound by half, by what factor will the intensity of the sound increase? Explain your reasoning.

49. Write an equation to model each situation.
a. *y* varies inversely with the fourth power of *x*.
b. *y* varies inversely with the fourth power of *x* and directly with *z*.

Standardized Test Prep

GRIDDED RESPONSE

SAT/ACT **50.** What is the value of $\dfrac{1}{(64)^{-\frac{1}{3}}}$?

51. The diagram shows two squares. The area of the nonshaded region is $4x^2 + 16x + 16$. The area of the shaded region is $5x^2 + 14x + 9$. What is $|a + b|$?

52. What is the value of $\dfrac{7^3 \cdot 2^5}{7 \cdot 2^3}$?

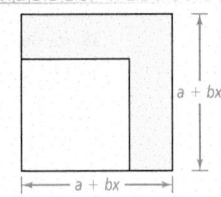

Mixed Review

Solve each equation. If there is no solution, write *no solution*. ◀ See Lesson 11-5.

53. $\dfrac{2}{d+5} = \dfrac{3}{d-5}$

54. $\dfrac{-1}{y} + \dfrac{1}{y} = 1$

55. $\dfrac{3}{m-4} + 2 = \dfrac{5m}{m-4}$

Get Ready! To prepare for Lesson 11-7, do Exercises 56–59.

Graph each function. ◀ See Lessons 4-4, 7-6, and 9-1.

56. $f(x) = x - 8$ **57.** $g(x) = x^2 + 3$ **58.** $y = 3^x$ **59.** $f(x) = 2x + 1$

58.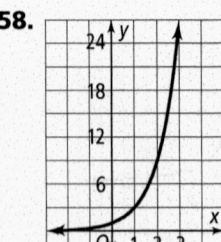

59.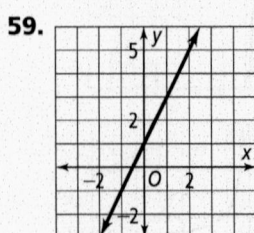

Additional Instructional Support

Algebra 1 Companion

Students can use the **Algebra 1 Companion** worktext (4 pages) as you teach the lesson. Use the Companion to support

- New Vocabulary
- Key Concepts
- Got It for each Problem
- Lesson Check

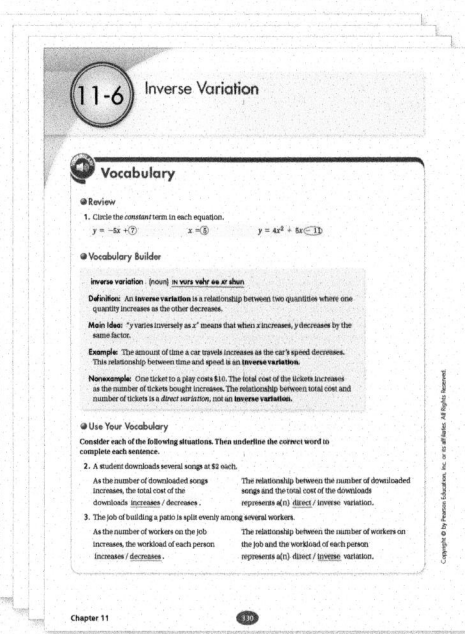

ELL Support

Connect to Prior Knowledge Write $y = kx$ on the board and ask students where they have seen it before. Encourage volunteers to help guide you in graphing the direct variation by making a table of values. Model another direct variation graph to remind students of their previous experience. Then model how to graph $xy = k$, making a table of values first. Have students compare the tables and graphs.

5 Assess & Remediate

Lesson Quiz

1. Suppose y varies inversely with x, and $y = 8$ when $x = 15$. What is an equation for the inverse variation?

2. What is the graph of $y = -\frac{4}{x}$?

3. Do the data in the table represent a *direct variation* or an *inverse variation*? Write an equation to model the data.

x	y
−3	6
2	−4
5	−10

4. Do you UNDERSTAND? If y decreases when x increases, does that mean that y varies inversely with x?

ANSWERS TO LESSON QUIZ

1. $xy = 120$

2.

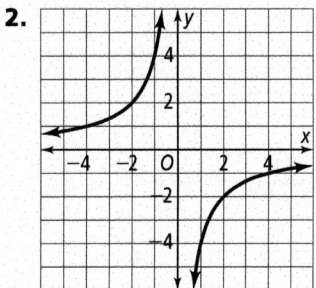

3. direct variation, $y = -2x$

4. Not necessarily; the relation could be a direct variation, $y = kx$, where $k < 0$.

PRESCRIPTION FOR REMEDIATION

Use the student work on the Lesson Quiz to prescribe a differentiated review assignment.

Points	Differentiated Remediation
0–2	Intervention
3	On-level
4	Extension

PowerAlgebra.com

5 Assess & Remediate

Assign the Lesson Quiz. Appropriate intervention, practice, or enrichment is automatically generated based on student performance.

Intervention

- **Reteaching** (2 pages) Provides reteaching and practice exercises for the key lesson concepts. Use with struggling students or absent students.
- **English Language Learner Support** Helps students develop and reinforce mathematical vocabulary and key concepts.

All-in-One Resources/Online
Reteaching

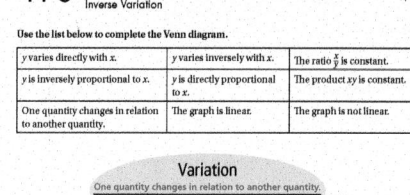

All-in-One Resources/Online
English Language Learner Support

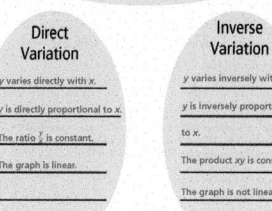

Differentiated Remediation *continued*

On-Level

- **Practice** (2 pages) Provides extra practice for each lesson. For simpler practice exercises, use the Form K Practice pages found in the All-in-One Teaching Resources and online.

- **Think About a Plan** Helps students develop specific problem-solving skills and strategies by providing scaffolded guiding questions.

- **Standardized Test Prep** Focuses on all major exercises, all major question types, and helps students prepare for the high-stakes assessments.

Extension

- **Enrichment** Provides students with interesting problems and activities that extend the concepts of the lesson.

- **Activities, Games, and Puzzles** Worksheets that can be used for concept development, enrichment, and for fun!

Practice and Problem Solving WKBK/ All-in-One Resources/Online
Practice page 1

Practice and Problem Solving WKBK/ All-in-One Resources/Online
Practice page 2

All-in-One Resources/Online
Enrichment

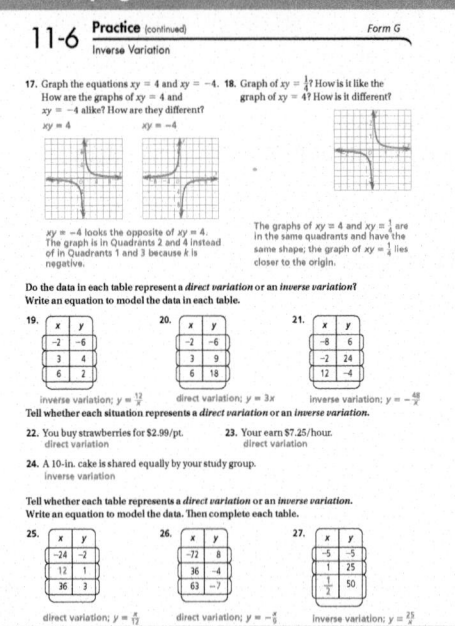

Practice and Problem Solving WKBK/ All-in-One Resources/Online
Think About a Plan

Practice and Problem Solving WKBK/ All-in-One Resources/Online
Standardized Test Prep

Online Teacher Resource Center
Activities, Games, and Puzzles

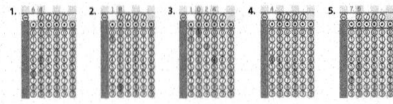

11-7 Graphing Rational Functions

Objective To graph rational functions

You can never make the trip in no time. Can you get close?

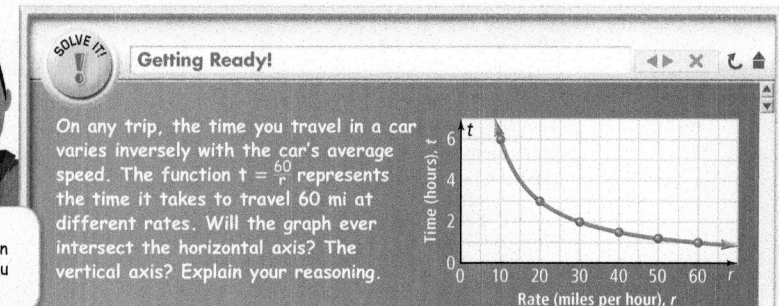

Getting Ready!

On any trip, the time you travel in a car varies inversely with the car's average speed. The function $t = \frac{60}{r}$ represents the time it takes to travel 60 mi at different rates. Will the graph ever intersect the horizontal axis? The vertical axis? Explain your reasoning.

Inverse variations are examples of *rational functions*. A **rational function** can be written in the form $f(x) = \frac{polynomial}{polynomial}$, where the denominator cannot be 0.

Essential Understanding To graph a rational function $f(x)$, you need to understand the graph's behavior near values of x where the function is undefined.

Lesson Vocabulary
• rational function
• asymptote

Any value of the variable that makes the denominator of a rational function equal to 0 is an excluded value.

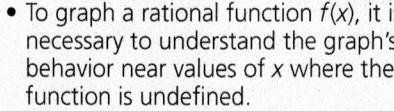 **Problem 1** Identifying Excluded Values

What is the excluded value for each function?

A $f(x) = \dfrac{5}{x-2}$

$x - 2 = 0$ ← Set the denominator equal to 0. →

$x = 2$ ← Solve for x. →

The excluded value is $x = 2$.

B $y = \dfrac{-3}{x+8}$

$x + 8 = 0$

$x = -8$

The excluded value is $x = -8$.

Think

Why are some values of x excluded?
Division by 0 is undefined. So any value of x that makes the denominator equal to 0 is excluded.

Got It? 1. What is the excluded value for $y = \frac{3}{x+7}$?

---

1 Interactive Learning

Solve It!
PURPOSE To analyze the asymptotic behavior of the graph of an inverse variation function
PROCESS Students may use visual judgment, additional ordered pairs (found using the function equation), or mathematical reasoning.

FACILITATE

Q If the rate is 25 mi/h, what is the corresponding time? Does this ordered pair fall on the graph of the function? **[2.4 h; yes]**

Q As the rate increases, what happens to the amount of time it takes to complete a 60-mi trip? **[The amount of time decreases.]**

Q As the rate decreases, what happens to the amount of time it takes to complete a 60-mi trip? **[The amount of time increases.]**

ANSWER See Solve It in Answers on next page.
CONNECT THE MATH In the Solve It, students study a graph that shows an inverse relationship between time traveled and speed. In the lesson, students study the behavior of numerous graphs of rational functions.

2 Guided Instruction

Problem 1

Q What is the domain of a function? **[the set of values for the independent variable]**

Q What is the domain of the function in 1A? 1B? **[all real numbers except 2; all real numbers except −8]**

Got It? SYNTHESIZING
Compare and contrast the excluded values of the given function with the excluded values of the function $y = \frac{x+7}{3}$.

11-7 Preparing to Teach

BIG idea Functions **UbD**

ESSENTIAL UNDERSTANDINGS

• To graph a rational function $f(x)$, it is necessary to understand the graph's behavior near values of x where the function is undefined.

• The graphs of rational functions have vertical and horizontal asymptotes.

Math Background

A vertical asymptote for a function $f(x)$ occurs at $x = c$ when the value of $f(c)$ is undefined. As the value of x approaches c from either the left or the right, $f(x)$ will either increase or decrease without bound. A rational function can be thought of as a ratio of two separate functions that will have

a vertical asymptote whenever the function in the denominator of the ratio is zero.

In future mathematics courses, students will study the vertical asymptotes of certain trigonometric functions. Some trigonometric functions can be thought of as ratios of two other trigonometric functions and will have a vertical asymptote whenever the function in the denominator of the ratio is zero.

Support Student Learning

Use the **Algebra I Companion** to engage and support students during instruction. See Lesson Resources at the end of this lesson for details.

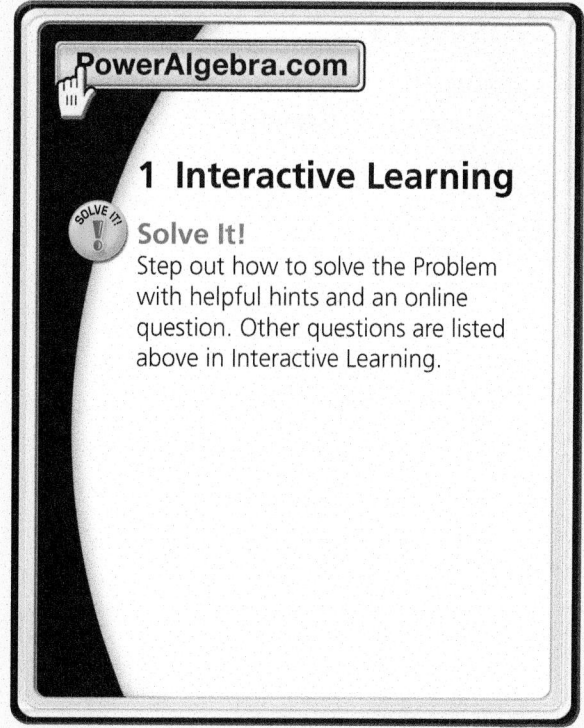

PowerAlgebra.com

1 Interactive Learning

Solve It!
Step out how to solve the Problem with helpful hints and an online question. Other questions are listed above in Interactive Learning.

Relate the horizontal translations of the graphs of rational functions to the horizontal translations of other parent functions studied in this text.

Problem 2

Q How is the graph of $y = \frac{5}{x+2}$ related to the graph of $y = \frac{5}{x}$? **[The graph of $y = \frac{5}{x+2}$ is a translation of 2 units to the left of $y = \frac{5}{x}$.]**

Q What is the horizontal asymptote of the function? Explain. **[$y = 0$; the graph gets close to but does not cross the x-axis.]**

Q Would it be possible for an equation to have two vertical asymptotes? Explain. **[Yes, if the polynomial on the bottom of the function were a quadratic polynomial with two different factors, then there would be two excluded values for x.]**

Got It?   VISUAL LEARNERS

Allow students to use a spreadsheet to make an extensive table of values for the rational function. Students can use tenths or hundredths as an increment value to get a strong sense of the behavior of the function as it approaches the asymptote lines.

The graphs of many rational functions are related to each other. Compare the graphs below of $y = \frac{1}{x}$ and $y = \frac{1}{x-3}$.

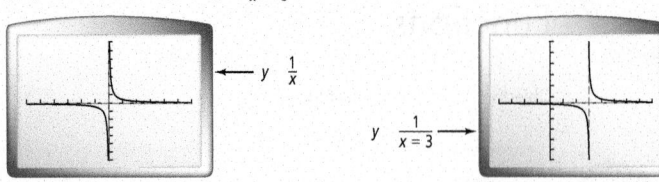

The graphs are identical in shape, but the second graph is translated 3 units right.

Notice that the graph of $y = \frac{1}{x}$ approaches both axes but does not cross either axis. The axes in this graph function as *asymptotes*. A line is an **asymptote** of a graph if the graph gets closer to the line as x or y gets larger in absolute value. In the graph of $y = \frac{1}{x-3}$ above, the x-axis and the line $x = 3$ are asymptotes.

When the numerator and denominator of a rational function have no common factors other than 1, there is a vertical asymptote at each excluded value.

Problem 2 Using a Vertical Asymptote

What is the vertical asymptote of the graph of $y = \frac{5}{x+2}$? Graph the function.

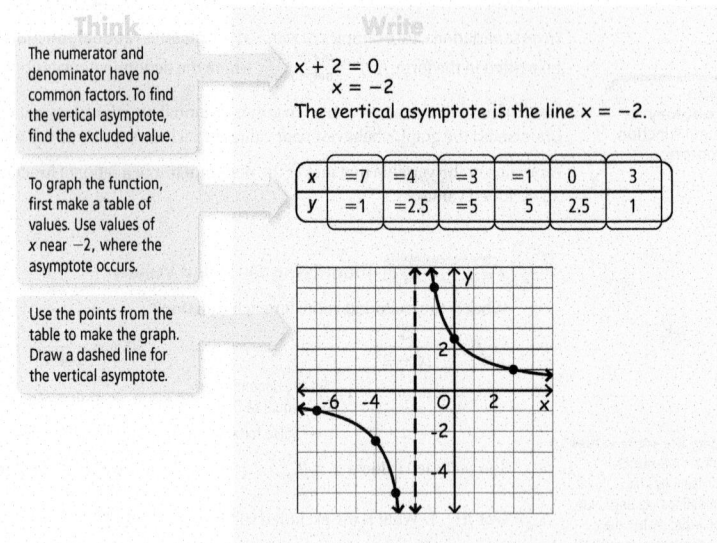

Think	Write
The numerator and denominator have no common factors. To find the vertical asymptote, find the excluded value.	$x + 2 = 0$ $x = -2$ The vertical asymptote is the line $x = -2$.

To graph the function, first make a table of values. Use values of x near -2, where the asymptote occurs.

x	-7	-4	-3	-1	0	3
y	-1	-2.5	-5	5	2.5	1

Use the points from the table to make the graph. Draw a dashed line for the vertical asymptote.

Got It? 2. What is the vertical asymptote of the graph of $h(x) = \frac{-3}{x-6}$? Graph the function.

Answers

Solve It!
No; no; explanations may vary.

Got It?
1. -7

2. $x = 6$;

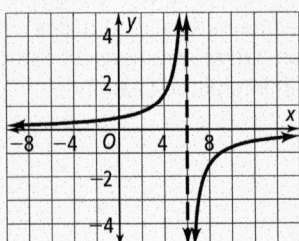

---

2 Guided Instruction

 Each Problem is worked out and supported online.

Problem 1
Identifying Excluded Values

Problem 2
Using a Vertical Asymptote
Animated

Problem 3
Using Vertical and Horizontal Asymptotes

Problem 4
Using a Rational Function
Animated

Support in Algebra 1 Companion
• Vocabulary
• Key Concepts
• Got It?

Compare the graphs and asymptotes below of $y = \frac{1}{x}$ and $y = \frac{1}{x} + 3$.

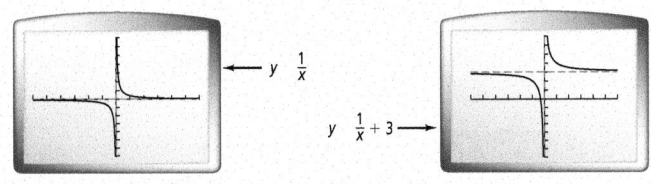

$\leftarrow y \;\; \frac{1}{x}$

$y \;\; \frac{1}{x} + 3 \rightarrow$

vertical asymptote at $x = 0$
horizontal asymptote at $y = 0$

vertical asymptote at $x = 0$
horizontal asymptote at $y = 3$

The graphs are identical in shape, but notice in the second graph that both the graph and the horizontal asymptote of $y = \frac{1}{x}$ have been translated 3 units up.

For a rational function of the form $y = \frac{a}{x - b} + c$, there is a horizontal asymptote at $y = c$.

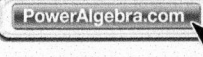

Concept Summary   Identifying Asymptotes

Words

The graph of a rational function of the form $y = \frac{a}{x - b} + c$ has a vertical asymptote at $x = b$ and a horizontal asymptote at $y = c$.

Example

$y = \frac{1}{x + 4} + 1$
$y = \frac{1}{x - (-4)} + 1$

vertical asymptote: $x = -4$
horizontal asymptote: $y = 1$

Problem 3   Using Vertical and Horizontal Asymptotes

What are the asymptotes of the graph of $f(x) = \frac{3}{x - 1} - 2$? Graph the function.

Step 1   From the form of the function, you can see that there is a vertical asymptote at $x = 1$ and a horizontal asymptote at $y = -2$.

Think

How do you choose x-values for the table?
The vertical asymptote is $x = 1$. So you should choose x-values on either side of 1. That way, your sketch will show both parts of the graph.

Step 2   Make a table of values using values of x near 1.

Step 3   Sketch the asymptotes. Graph the function.

x	=5	=2	=1	0	2	3	4
y	=2.5	=3	=3.5	=5	1	=0.5	=1

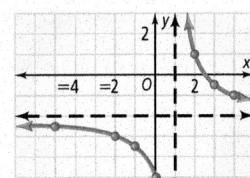

Take Note
Students should realize that not all rational functions are of the form $y = \frac{a}{x - b} + c$. Rules for determining the horizontal asymptotes of other forms of rational functions will be introduced in future math courses.

Problem 3

Q What value is excluded from the domain of the function $f(x)$? Explain. **[1; it would make the denominator of the fraction 0.]**

Q How can you use the asymptotes to connect the ordered pairs accurately? **[You should draw curves that get close to, but never cross the asymptotes.]**

Q How do you think the graph of $f(x) = \frac{-3}{x - 1} - 2$ differs from the graph of the given function? Explain. **[Answers may vary. Sample: Just as the graphs of inverse variations were in quadrants II and IV when the constant of variation was negative, this graph would have its branches in other quadrants.]**

Additional Problems

1. What is the excluded value for each function?

a. $f(x) = \frac{2}{x + 3}$

b. $y = \frac{-1}{x - 4}$

ANSWER a. $x \neq -3$
b. $x \neq 4$

2. What is the vertical asymptote of the graph of $y = \frac{3}{x + 1}$? Graph the function.

ANSWER $x = -1$

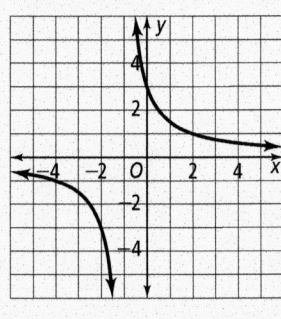

3. What are the asymptotes of the graph of $f(x) = \frac{1}{x - 2} + 3$? Graph the function.

ANSWER $x = 2$, $y = 3$

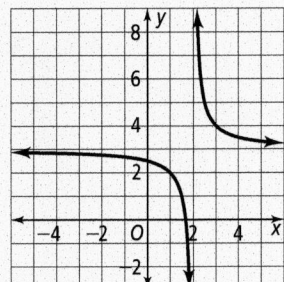

4. The zoo charges \$250 for a group field trip tour. The cost will be divided equally among the students and teachers on the field trip. In addition to this, each person will need \$5 for lunch.

a. What equation gives the total cost per person y of going on the field trip as a function of the number of people x who go on the field trip?

b. What is the graph of the function in part (a)? Use the graph to describe the change in the cost per person as the number of people who go on the field trip increases.

c. Approximately how many people must go on the field trip for the total cost per person to be about \$10?

ANSWER a. $y = \frac{250}{x} + 5$

b.

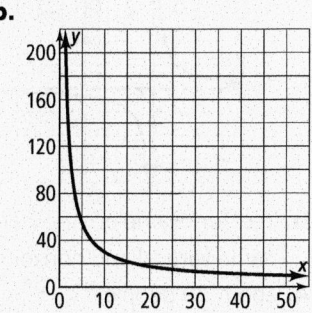

As the number of people attending the field trip increases, the cost per person decreases.

c. about 50 people

Got It?

Ask students to supply examples of two different rational functions which both have a vertical asymptote at $x = 5$ and a horizontal asymptote at $y = -3$.

Problem 4

> **Q** What is the cost per person if only seven people enter the contest? Explain. **[$80; 350 ÷ 7 + 30 = 80]**
>
> **Q** What are the vertical and horizontal asymptotes for the graph of $y = \frac{350}{x} + 30$? **[horizontal: $y = 30$, vertical: $x = 0$]**
>
> **Q** Is it possible for the cost per person to be less than $30? Explain. **[No; each person must always pay the $30 entrance fee.]**
>
> **Q** Is it possible for the cost per person to be exactly $30? Explain. **[No; no matter how many people enter the contest, each person will have to contribute some amount towards the $350.]**

Got It?   VISUAL LEARNERS

An alternate method for using the graphing calculator to determine the number of people necessary to achieve a cost of about $50 is to graph the equation $y = 50$ simultaneously with the rational function. Students can then use the **intersect** feature on the calculator.

Got It? 3. a. What are the asymptotes of the graph of $y = \frac{-1}{x+3} - 4$? Graph the function.

b. Reasoning Is it possible for two different rational functions to have the same vertical and horizontal asymptotes? Explain your reasoning.

Problem 4 Using a Rational Function

Dancing Your dance club sponsors a contest at a local reception hall. Reserving a private room costs $350, and the cost will be divided equally among the people who enter the contest. Each person also pays a $30 entry fee.

A What equation gives the total cost per person y of entering the contest as a function of the number of people x who enter the contest?

Relate total cost per person = $\dfrac{\text{cost of renting private room}}{\text{number of people entering contest}}$ + entry fee per person

Write y = $\dfrac{350}{x}$ + 30

The equation $y = \frac{350}{x} + 30$ models the situation.

B What is the graph of the function in part (A)? Use the graph to describe the change in the cost per person as the number of people who enter the contest increases.

Use a graphing calculator to graph $y = \frac{350}{x} + 30$.

Since both y and x must be nonnegative numbers, use only the part of the graph in the first quadrant.

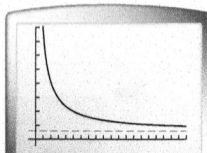

You can see from the graph that as the number of people who enter the contest increases, the cost per person decreases. Because the graph has a horizontal asymptote at $y = 30$, the cost per person will eventually approach $30.

C Approximately how many people must enter the contest in order for the total cost per person to be about $50?

Use the (trace) key or the TABLE feature. When $y \approx 50$, $x \approx 18$. So if 18 people enter the contest, the cost per person will be about $50.

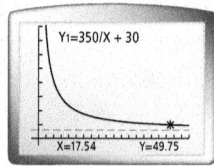

Think
How can you check the reasonableness of your answer?
Substitute 18 for x in the equation you found in part (A) and simplify. If y is approximately $50, your answer is reasonable.

Got It? 4. In Problem 4, suppose the cost to rent a private room increases to $400. Approximately how many people must then enter the contest in order for the total cost per person to be about $50?

Answers

Got It? (continued)

3. a. $x = -3$, $y = -4$;

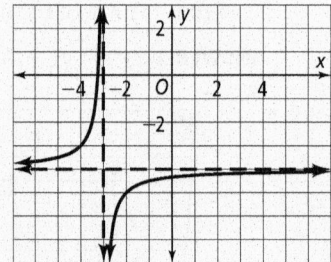

b. Yes; for example, $y = \frac{1}{x}$ and $y = -\frac{1}{x}$ have the same vertical and horizontal asymptotes.

4. about 20 people

You can think of functions whose graphs have similar features as families of functions. You have studied six families of functions in this book. Their properties and graphs are shown in the summary.

Concept Summary   Families of Functions

Linear function

$y = mx + b$

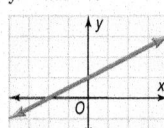

parent function: $f(x) = x$
slope = m
y-intercept = b
The greatest exponent is 1.

Absolute value function

$y = |x - a| + b$

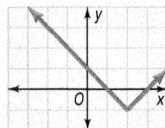

parent function: $f(x) = |x|$
Shift $y = |x|$ horizontally a units.
Shift $y = |x|$ vertically b units.
vertex at (a, b)
The greatest exponent is 1.

Square root function

$y = \sqrt{x - b} + c$

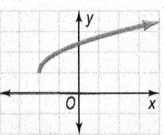

Shift $y = \sqrt{x}$ horizontally b units.
Shift $y = \sqrt{x}$ vertically c units.
The variable is under the radical.

Quadratic function

$y = ax^2 + bx + c$

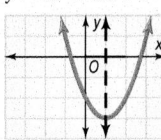

parent function: $f(x) = x^2$
parabola with axis of
symmetry at $x = \frac{-b}{2a}$
The greatest exponent is 2.

Exponential function

$y = ab^x$

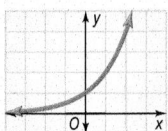

growth where $b > 1$
decay where $0 < b < 1$
The variable is the exponent.

Rational function

$y = \frac{a}{x - b} + c$

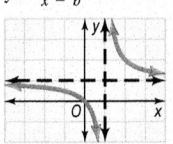

vertical asymptote at $x = b$
horizontal asymptote at $y = c$
The variable is in the denominator.

Take Note

Discuss with students that all functions can be graphed by creating a table of values, but that often more efficient techniques exist. Ask students to describe in detail the techniques that they would use to graph each type of function as efficiently as possible. For some functions, students may respond that a table of values is the only technique.

Q Which types of functions exhibit asymptotic behavior? **[exponential functions and rational functions]**

Q Which function(s) may not have a domain of all real numbers? **[rational functions and square root functions]**

Q Which function(s) do not have a range of all real numbers? **[all but linear functions]**

Q Which functions either always decrease or always increase? **[linear (nonconstant), exponential (of the form given), square root]**

Q Which functions have turning points on the graph at which the function changes from increasing to decreasing or from decreasing to increasing? **[quadratic and absolute value functions]**

3 Lesson Check

Do you know HOW?
- If students have difficulty with Exercise 3, then have them review Problem 4 as a guide to write a verbal model from which to begin their work.

Do you UNDERSTAND?
- If students have difficulty with Exercise 6, then have them follow the steps in Problem 3.

Close

> **Q** How can you identify a rational expression and produce its graph efficiently? **[A rational expression is an expression that can be written in the form $\frac{\text{polynomial}}{\text{polynomial}}$. You can graph it by identifying the asymptotes (if any) and then creating a table of values with points on both sides of any vertical asymptote.]**

 Lesson Check

Do you know HOW?

1. What is the excluded value for $y = \frac{4}{x+1}$?

2. What are the asymptotes of $f(x) = \frac{8}{x-2} + 3$? Graph the function.

3. The function $t = \frac{240}{r} + 0.5$ models the total time t, in hours, it will take you to travel 240 mi at r mi/h, assuming you stop for a half-hour break along the way. Graph this function. What must your average speed be in order for your travel time to be about 4 h?

Do you UNDERSTAND?

4. Vocabulary Find the excluded value and the vertical and horizontal asymptotes of the function $y = \frac{7}{x-5} + 1$.

5. Reasoning Write an example of a rational function with a vertical asymptote at $x = -2$ and a horizontal asymptote at $y = 4$.

6. Error Analysis Your friend says that the vertical asymptote of the graph of $f(x) = \frac{1}{x+5} + 2$ is $x = 5$. Describe and correct your friend's error.

7. Compare and Contrast How are an excluded value and a vertical asymptote of a rational function alike? How are they different?

 Practice and Problem-Solving Exercises

(A) Practice Identify the excluded value of each rational function. ◀ See Problem 1.

8. $f(x) = \frac{3}{x}$ **9.** $y = \frac{1}{x-2}$ **10.** $y = \frac{x}{x+2}$ **11.** $h(x) = \frac{-3}{2x-6}$

Identify the vertical and horizontal asymptotes of each graph. ◀ See Problems 2 and 3.

12. 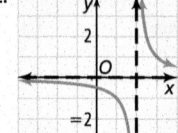   **13.** 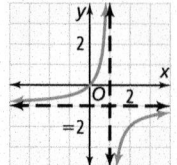   **14.**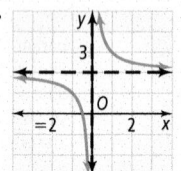

Identify the asymptotes of the graph of each function. Then graph the function.

15. $y = \frac{3}{x}$ **16.** $y = \frac{-10}{x}$ **17.** $f(x) = \frac{1}{x-5}$ **18.** $g(x) = \frac{4}{x+4}$

19. $y = \frac{1}{x} - 5$ **20.** $y = \frac{-3}{x} + 6$ **21.** $h(x) = \frac{2}{x+1} + 4$ **22.** $f(x) = \frac{-1}{x-3} - 5$

23. Nutrition For lunch, you bought two veggie pizzas for you and your friends to divide evenly. Each pizza contains 960 Calories. In addition, each person eats a banana, which contains 100 Calories. ◀ See Problem 4.
  a. Write and graph an equation that gives the number of Calories C consumed by each person as a function of the total number of people n.
  b. Approximately how many people must share the pizzas in order for each person to consume about 500 Calories?

Answers

Lesson Check
1. -1

2. $x = 2, y = 3$

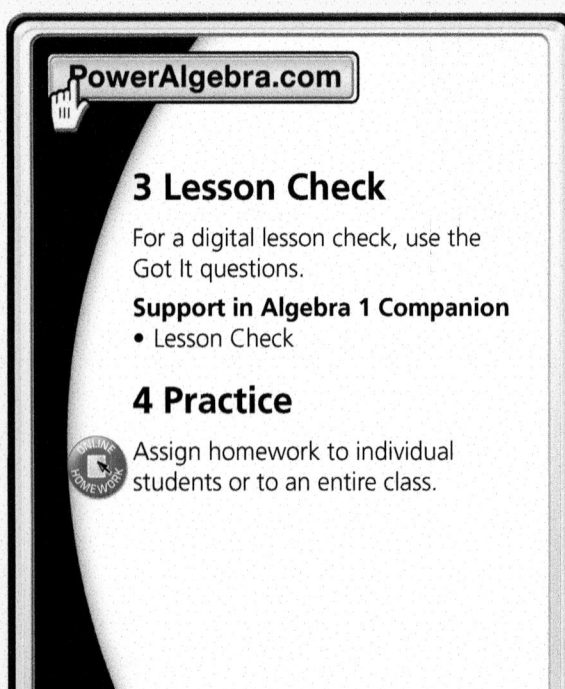

3.

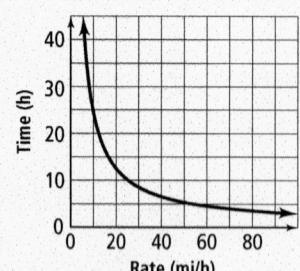

about 68.6 mi/h

4. 5; $x = 5, y = 1$

5. Answers may vary. Sample: $y = \frac{1}{x+2} + 4$

6. The vertical asymptote is $x + 5 = 0$, or $x = -5$.

7. If the excluded value is a, then the vertical asymptote is $x = a$.

Practice and Problem-Solving Exercises
8. 0   **9.** 2   **10.** -2 **11.** 3

12. $x = 2, y = 0$ **13.** $x = 1, y = -1$

14–23. See back of book.

24. Event Planning You have a budget of $1200 to pay the musicians who will play a charity benefit. Two musicians have agreed to perform without charge.
   a. Write and graph an equation that gives the cost c of hiring one paid musician as a function of the number of musicians m who play the benefit.
   b. Suppose you use your entire budget and get 18 musicians to play the benefit. What is the cost of hiring each paid musician?

 Apply

Describe how the graph of each function is a translation of the graph of $f(x) = \frac{7}{x}$.

25. $g(x) = \frac{7}{x+1}$ **26.** $y = \frac{7}{x} - 15$ **27.** $h(x) = \frac{7}{x} + 1$

28. $y = \frac{7}{x+3} - 2$ **29.** $g(x) = \frac{7}{x-3}$ **30.** $f(x) = \frac{7}{x+12}$

31. Think About a Plan In the formula $I = \frac{445}{x^2}$, I is the intensity of light, in lumens, at a distance of x feet from a light bulb of 445 watts. At about what distance is the intensity 25 lumens?
   • How can you use the graph of the function to determine the answer?
   • How can you check the reasonableness of your answer?

32. Open-Ended Write equations of two rational functions with graphs that are identical except that one is shifted vertically 3 units with respect to the other.

33. a. Graph $y = \frac{1}{x}$ and $y = \frac{1}{x^2}$.
   b. What are the vertical and horizontal asymptotes of the graph of each function?
   c. What is the range of $y = \frac{1}{x}$? Of $y = \frac{1}{x^2}$?

Describe the graph of each function.

34. $y = 4x + 1$ **35.** $h(x) = |x - 4|$ **36.** $y = 0.4^x$

37. $f(x) = \frac{x}{4}$ **38.** $y = \frac{4}{x} + 1$ **39.** $h(x) = \sqrt{x - 4} + 1$

40. $g(x) = x^2 - 4$ **41.** $f(x) = \frac{4}{x+4} - 1$ **42.** $g(x) = \frac{3}{x} - 12$

43. Writing Describe the similarities and differences in the graphs of $y = \frac{3}{x+2}$ and $y = \frac{-3}{x+2}$.

44. Physics As radio signals move away from a transmitter, they become weaker. The function $s = \frac{1600}{d^2}$ gives the strength s of a signal at a distance of d miles from a transmitter.
   a. Graphing Calculator Graph the function. For what distances is $s \leq 1$?
   b. Find the signal strength at 10 mi, 1 mi, and 0.1 mi.
   c. Reasoning Suppose you drive by the transmitter for one radio station while your car radio is tuned to a second station. The signal from the transmitter can interfere and come through your radio. Use your results from part (b) to explain why.

4 Practice

ASSIGNMENT GUIDE

Basic: 8–24 all, 26–30 even, 31, 43–44

Average: 9–23 odd, 25–44

Advanced: 9–23 odd, 25–49

Standardized Test Prep: 50–54

Mixed Review: 55–66

Reasoning exercises have blue headings.

Applications exercises have red headings.

EXERCISE 44: Use the Think About a Plan worksheet in the **Practice and Problem Solving Workbook** (also available in the Teaching Resources in print and online) to further support students' development in becoming independent learners.

HOMEWORK QUICK CHECK

To check students' understanding of key skills and concepts, go over Exercises 13, 23, 31, 43, and 44.

---

24. a. $c = \frac{1200}{m - 2}$;

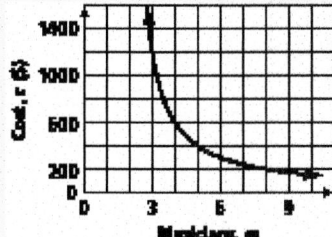

   b. $75

25. translates the graph 1 unit to the left

26. translates the graph 15 units down

27. translates the graph 1 unit up

28. translates the graph 3 units left and 2 units down

29. translates the graph 3 units to the right

30. translates the graph 12 units to the left

31. about 4.2 ft

32. Answers will vary. Sample: $y = \frac{2}{x}$ and $y = \frac{2}{x} + 3$

33. a.

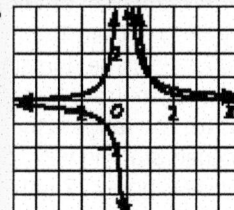

   b. $x = 0$, $y = 0$

   c. all real numbers except 0; all real numbers greater than 0

34. line with slope 4, y-intercept 1

35. absolute value function with vertex $(4, 0)$

36. exponential decay

37. line with slope $\frac{1}{4}$ through origin

38. rational function with asymptotes $x = 0$, $y = 1$

39. translation of radical function $y = \sqrt{x}$ shifted right 4 units and up 1 unit

40. parabola with axis of symmetry $x = 0$ and vertex $(0, -4)$

41. rational function with asymptotes $x = -4$ and $f(x) = -1$

42. rational function with asymptotes $x = 0$ and $g(x) = -12$

43. The graph of $y = \frac{3}{x+2}$ and $y = -\frac{3}{x+2}$ are both composed of two curves with asymptotes $x = -2$ and $y = 0$. The graph of $y = -\frac{3}{x+2}$ is a reflection of the graph of $y = \frac{3}{x+2}$ across the x-axis.

44. a. $d \geq 40$

   b. 16; 1600; 160,000

   c. The signal is extremely strong when you are very close to a transmitter, and it will interfere with the other station.

Answers

Practice and Problem-Solving Exercises
(continued)

45.

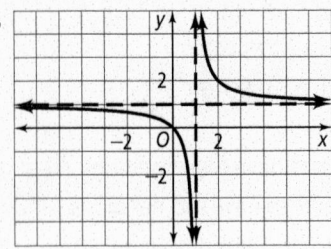

46.

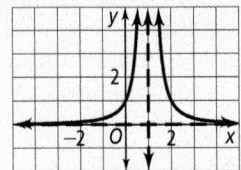

47.

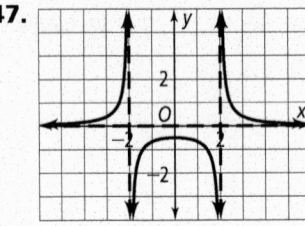

48.

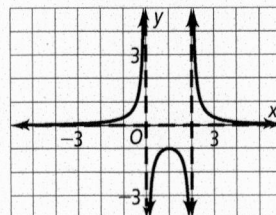

49.

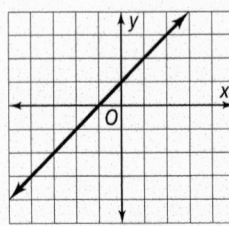

No; $f(x)$ is not defined when $x = -2$.

50. B

51. F

52. C

53. F

 Challenge Graph each function. Include a dashed line for each asymptote.

45. $g(x) = \frac{x}{x - 1}$

46. $y = \frac{1}{(x - 1)^2}$

47. $y = \frac{2}{(x - 2)(x + 2)}$

48. $y = \frac{1}{x^2 - 2x}$

49. Graph $f(x) = \frac{(x + 2)(x + 1)}{x + 2}$ and $g(x) = x + 1$. Are the graphs the same? Explain.

Standardized Test Prep

SAT/ACT

50. A caterer spends $75 on sliced cheese. As a bonus, he receives 1 lb of sliced cheese free with his order. What equation gives the caterer's cost y per pound of cheese as a function of the total number of pounds x of cheese the caterer receives?

Ⓐ $y = \frac{75}{x + 1}$ Ⓑ $y = \frac{75}{x - 1}$ Ⓒ $y = \frac{75}{x} + 1$ Ⓓ $y = \frac{75}{x} - 1$

51. Which is an equation of the line with the same y-intercept but half the slope of the line $y = 4 - 10x$?

Ⓕ $y = -5x + 4$ Ⓖ $y = 2 - 10x$ Ⓗ $y = 2 - 5x$ Ⓘ $y = -5x - 2$

52. How many x-intercepts does the graph of $y = x^2 + 7x + 11$ have?

Ⓐ 0 Ⓑ 1 Ⓒ 2 Ⓓ 3

53. Which expression is equivalent to $\frac{4x^2 + 24x + 36}{2x^2 + 4x - 6}$, where $x \neq 1$ and $x \neq -3$?

Ⓕ $\frac{2x + 6}{x - 1}$ Ⓖ $2x^2 + 6x + 6$ Ⓗ $\frac{x + 3}{x - 1}$ Ⓘ $2x + 4$

Extended Response

54. The drama club plans to attend a professional production. From 10 to 35 students will go. Each ticket costs $25 plus a $2 surcharge. There is a one-time handling fee of $3 for the entire order of tickets. Write a linear function that models this situation. What domain and range are reasonable for the function?

Mixed Review

Suppose y varies inversely with x. Write an equation for the inverse variation. ◀ See Lesson 11-6.

55. $y = 4$ when $x = 5$

56. $y = -1$ when $x = 8$

57. $y = \frac{1}{2}$ when $x = 24$

58. $y = 7$ when $x = -6$

Find the number of real-number solutions of each equation. ◀ See Lesson 9-6.

59. $x^2 + x + 1 = 0$

60. $-3x^2 + 4x = -5$

61. $2x^2 + 5 = 0$

62. $9x^2 + 144 = 7x$

Get Ready! To prepare for Lesson 12-1, do Exercises 63–66.

Find each sum or difference. ◀ See Lesson 1-5.

63. $-7.2 + 8.9$ **64.** $8.7 - (-4.4)$ **65.** $16.2 + 4.95$ **66.** $-10.25 - (-5.35)$

54. [4] Let x = number of attendees and y = total cost. Then $y = 27x + 3$. The domain is the set of integers from 10 to 35, inclusive. The range is the set of integers starting with 273 and increasing by 27 until you reach 948.

[3] correct methods used with one minor error

[2] The function is correct, but the domain and range are incorrect.

[1] correct answers with no work shown

55. $xy = 20$

56. $xy = -8$

57. $xy = 12$

58. $xy = -42$

59. 0

60. 2

61. 0

62. 0

63. 1.7

64. 13.1

65. 21.15

66. −4.9

Differentiated Remediation

Additional Instructional Support

Algebra 1 Companion

Students can use the **Algebra 1 Companion** worktext (4 pages) as you teach the lesson. Use the Companion to support

- New Vocabulary
- Key Concepts
- Got It for each Problem
- Lesson Check

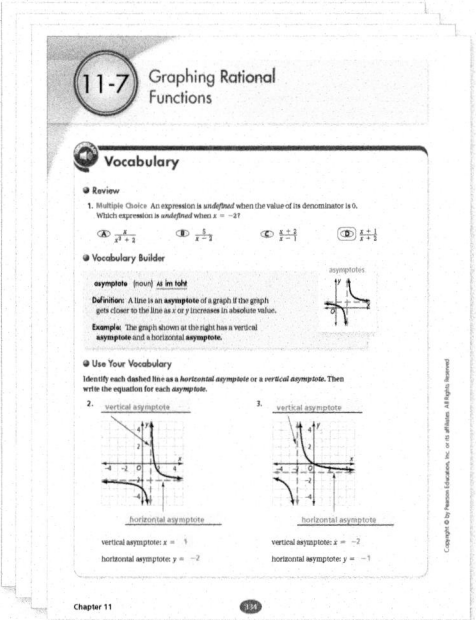

ELL Support

Focus on Communication Group students into six equal-sized heterogeneous groups. Assign a leader. Have a student from each group form a temporary group with one student from each of the other groups. Assign each group a function from the concept summary table in this lesson. Students in each temporary group will focus on the properties and graphs of their function and write a specific example of that function. Students should practice teaching each other about their functions before returning to their original groups. Then, those students will peer-teach their group's members about their functions.

5 Assess & Remediate

Lesson Quiz

1. What is the excluded value for each function?

a. $f(x) = \dfrac{-10}{x - 8}$

b. $y = \dfrac{5}{x + 3}$

2. What is the vertical asymptote of the graph of $y = \dfrac{2}{x - 4}$? Graph the function.

3. Do you UNDERSTAND? What are the asymptotes of the graph of $f(x) = \dfrac{2}{x - 3} - 2$? Graph the function.

ANSWERS TO LESSON QUIZ

1. a. $x = 8$; **b.** $x = -3$

2. $x = 4$

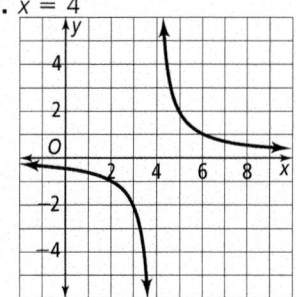

3. $x = 3, y = -2$

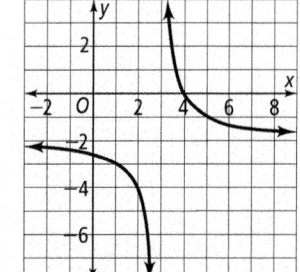

PRESCRIPTION FOR REMEDIATION

Use the student work on the Lesson Quiz to prescribe a differentiated review assignment.

Points	Differentiated Remediation
0–1	Intervention
2	On-level
3	Extension

PowerAlgebra.com

5 Assess & Remediate

Assign the Lesson Quiz. Appropriate intervention, practice, or enrichment is automatically generated based on student performance.

Intervention

- **Reteaching** (2 pages) Provides reteaching and practice exercises for the key lesson concepts. Use with struggling students or absent students.

- **English Language Learner Support** Helps students develop and reinforce mathematical vocabulary and key concepts.

All-in-One Resources/Online
Reteaching

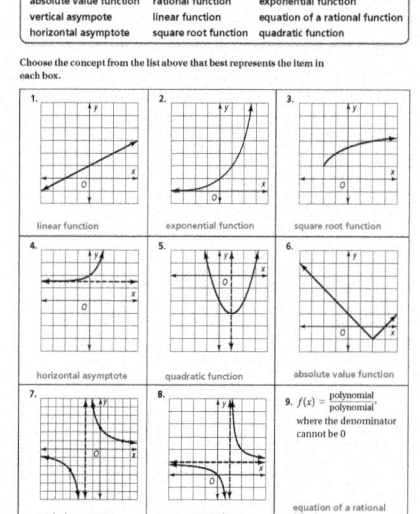

All-in-One Resources/Online
English Language Learner Support

Differentiated Remediation *continued*

On-Level

- **Practice** (2 pages) Provides extra practice for each lesson. For simpler practice exercises, use the Form K Practice pages found in the All-in-One Teaching Resources and online.

- **Think About a Plan** Helps students develop specific problem-solving skills and strategies by providing scaffolded guiding questions.

- **Standardized Test Prep** Focuses on all major exercises, all major question types, and helps students prepare for the high-stakes assessments.

Extension

- **Enrichment** Provides students with interesting problems and activities that extend the concepts of the lesson.

- **Activities, Games, and Puzzles** Worksheets that can be used for concept development, enrichment, and for fun!

Practice and Problem Solving WKBK/ All-in-One Resources/Online
Practice page 1

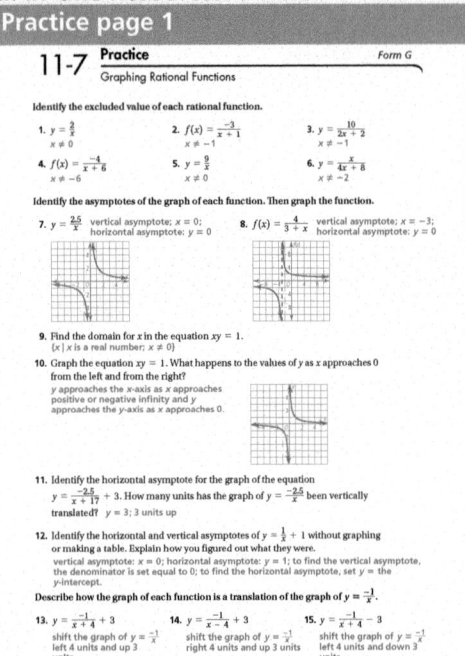

Practice and Problem Solving WKBK/ All-in-One Resources/Online
Practice page 2

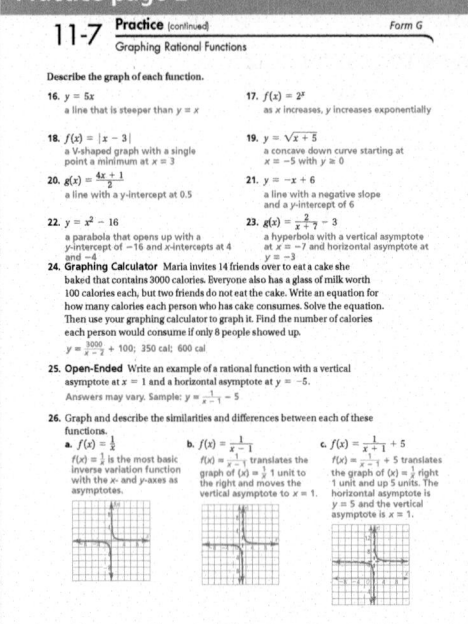

All-in-One Resources/Online
Enrichment

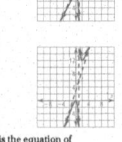

Practice and Problem Solving WKBK/ All-in-One Resources/Online
Think About a Plan

Practice and Problem Solving WKBK/ All-in-One Resources/Online
Standardized Test Prep

Online Teacher Resource Center
Activities, Games, and Puzzles

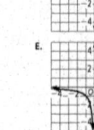
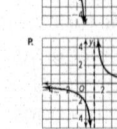
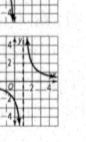
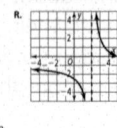
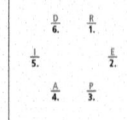

Concept Byte
Use With Lesson 11-7

Graphing Rational Functions

Functions such as $y = \frac{1}{x}$, $y = \frac{1}{x+2}$, and $y = \frac{1}{x} - 4$ are examples of rational functions. When you use a graphing calculator to graph a rational function, false connections may appear on the screen. When this happens, you need to make adjustments to see the true shape of the graph.

Graph the function $y = \frac{1}{x+2} - 4$. You can enter this as $y = 1 \div (x + 2) - 4$. The graph on your screen may look like the one at the right. The highest point and the lowest point on the graph that appear on the screen are not supposed to connect. If you use the (trace) key on the calculator, you can see that no point on the graph lies on this connecting line. So this is a false connection.

Here's how you can graph a rational function and avoid false connections.

Step 1 Press the (mode) key. Then scroll down and right to highlight the word **DOT**. Then press (enter).

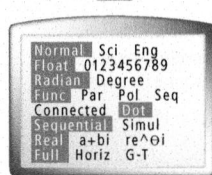

Step 2 Graph the function $y = \frac{1}{x+2} - 4$ again. Now the false connection is gone.

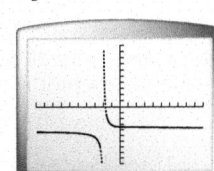

Step 3 Use the (trace) key or **TABLE** feature to find some points on the graph. Sketch the graph.

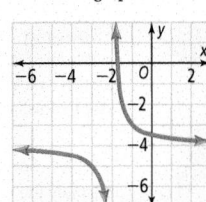

Exercises

Use a graphing calculator to graph each function. Then sketch the graph.

1. $y = \frac{3}{x}$ **2.** $y = -\frac{4}{x}$ **3.** $y = \frac{1}{x+2}$ **4.** $y = \frac{1}{x-4}$

5. $y = \frac{1}{x} + 2$ **6.** $y = \frac{1}{x} - 3$ **7.** $y = \frac{1}{x-1} + 2$ **8.** $y = \frac{3}{x-2} - 4$

9. a. Graph $y = \frac{1}{x}$, $y = \frac{1}{x-4}$, and $y = \frac{1}{x+3}$.
   b. Make a Conjecture How does adding or subtracting a positive number in the denominator of $y = \frac{1}{x}$ translate the graph?

10. a. Graph $y = \frac{1}{x}$, $y = \frac{1}{x} - 4$, and $y = \frac{1}{x} + 3$.
   b. Make a Conjecture How does adding or subtracting a positive number on the right side of $y = \frac{1}{x}$ translate the graph?

PowerAlgebra.com Concept Byte Graphing Rational Functions 701

Guided Instruction

PURPOSE To use a graphing calculator to graph and make conjectures about rational functions
PROCESS Students will graph a rational function and make conjectures about transformations of the graph.

DISCUSS It may be helpful for students to work in pairs for this Activity so that they can provide support to each other by comparing their calculator graphs, data, and sketches.

Activity

In this Activity students use a graphing calculator to graph rational functions and to make conjectures about the graph.

Q What are some of the significant points and lines that you might want to draw attention to and plot in the graphs that you sketch of rational functions? **[the *x-intercept(s)* and the *y-intercept* (if both are present), and the asymptotes]**

Answers

Exercises

1.
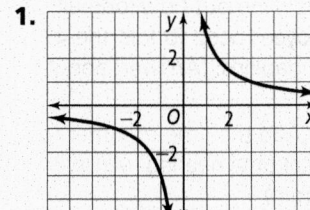

2.
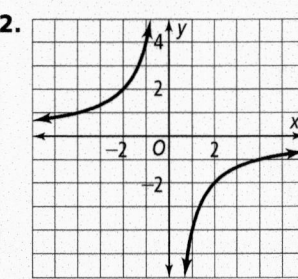

3.
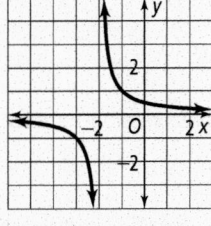

4.
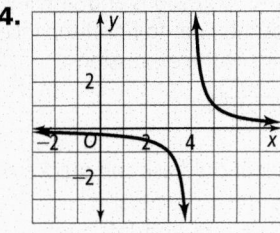

5-10. See back of book.

Performance Task UbD

Pull It All Together

The concepts and skills required to solve these problems are from several lessons within this chapter and from the previous chapters. As students solve these problems, they will demonstrate their reasoning strategies and their growth as independent problem solvers.

The following questions are designed to:
- Help support students as they do the Tasks.
- Gauge the amount of support students need as they become independent problem solvers.

Task 1
- What is the formula for the volume of a cylinder?
- What is the formula for the volume of a cube?
- What operation allows you to find the fraction of space taken up by the cube?

Task 2
- What information is known?
- What variable must be identified?
- What equation can you use to help solve the problem?

Task 3
- What rational expressions can be used?
- What percent of the total job does the manager want completed? What number represents this percentage?
- What equation can you use to help solve the problem?

> To solve these problems you will pull together many concepts and skills that you have studied about rational expressions and functions.

BIG idea Equivalence

Rational expressions can be represented in many ways. When a rational expression is simplified, the numerator and denominator have no common factors except 1.

Task 1

A cylinder with radius r and height $2r + 4$ contains a cube with edge length $r\sqrt{2}$, as shown. What fraction of the cylinder's volume is taken up by the cube? Write your answer in simplified form.

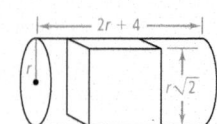

BIG idea Functions

Rational functions have equations of the form $f(x) = \frac{polynomial}{polynomial}$. The graph of a rational function may have vertical and horizontal asymptotes.

Task 2

In a bike race, a rider covers a 5-mi flat stretch of road at a speed of s mi/h. She then doubles her speed down a hill 1 mi long. Finally, she reduces her downhill speed by 12 mi/h as she rides the last 3 mi of the race. What function gives the time t it takes the rider to finish the race in terms of s?

BIG idea Solving Equations and Inequalities

To isolate the variable in a rational equation, multiply each side by the LCD and then solve the resulting equation. Check for extraneous solutions.

Task 3

A restaurant has 45 tables. Each table seats 4 people. The manager has 4 employees to prepare the tables. The chart shows how fast each employee works. Use this information to answer the following questions.

a. In order to get the tables ready in the least amount of time, which two employees should the manager ask to fold napkins? Which two employees should the manager ask to set the tables?

b. If everyone starts working at the same time, how quickly can the employees get the tables ready for dinner? The first pair of employees to finish their job should help the other pair to finish the tables. Explain your answer.

Employee	Time to Fold 4 Napkins (min)	Time to Set 4 Places (min)
Stacie	3	5
Jeff	4	3
Tiffany	5	2
Nick	3.5	4

Assess Performance UbD

Pull It All Together

See p. 67 for a holistic scoring rubric to gauge a student's progress on Understanding the Problem, Planning a Solution, Getting an Answer, and Assessing Autonomy.

SOLUTION OUTLINES

Task 1
First step: Find the volume of the cylinder.
(Answer: $\pi r^2(2r + 4)$)
Second step: Find the volume of the cube.
(Answer: $2r^3 \sqrt{2}$)
Third step: Write the ratio of the volume of the cube to the volume of the cylinder.
$\left(\text{Answer: } \frac{r\sqrt{2}}{\pi(r + 2)}\right)$

Task 2
First step: Solve $d = rt$ for t.
$\left(\text{Answer: } t = \frac{d}{r}\right)$
Second step: Write an expression for each part of the race.
$\left(\text{Answer: } \frac{5}{s}, \frac{1}{2s}, \frac{3}{2s - 12}\right)$
Third step: Add the expressions and simplify. The time t it takes the rider to finish the race is equal to the sum of the expressions.
$\left(\text{Answer: } t = \frac{7s - 33}{s(s - 6)}\right)$

Task 3
a. The manager should ask the quickest two for each task. Stacie and Nick should fold napkins and Jeff and Tiffany should set the places.

b. First step: Find out how long Stacie and Nick need to fold all the napkins. (Answer: about 73 min)

Second step: Find out how long Jeff and Tiffany need to set all the places. (Answer: 54 min)

Third step: Find the number of napkins needed after 54 min. (Answer: about 47 napkins)

Fourth step: Find out how long all four employees need to fold the 47 remaining napkins. (Answer: about 11 min)

Fifth step: Add the time together to get the total time needed. (Answer: about 65 min)

11 Chapter Review

Connecting BIG ideas and Answering the Essential Questions

1 Equivalence
Rational expressions can be represented many ways. When a rational expression is simplified, the numerator and denominator have no common factors except 1.

Simplifying Rational Expressions (Lesson 11-1)
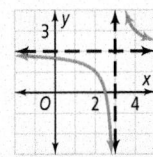
$$\frac{7y + 21}{y + 3} = \frac{7(y + 3)^1}{_1 y + 3}$$
$$= 7$$

Multiplying, Dividing, Adding, and Subtracting Rational Expressions (Lessons 11-2, 11-3, and 11-4)
$$\frac{7}{3x} - \frac{5}{3x} = \frac{7 - 5}{3x}$$
$$= \frac{2}{3x}$$

2 Functions
Rational functions have equations of the form $f(x) = \frac{polynomial}{polynomial}$. The graph of a rational function may have vertical and horizontal asymptotes.

Graphing Rational Functions (Lesson 11-7)
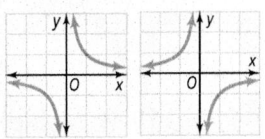

Inverse Variation (Lesson 11-6)

3 Solving Equations and Inequalities
To isolate the variable in a rational equation, multiply by the LCD and then solve the resulting equation. Check for extraneous solutions.

Solving Rational Equations (Lesson 11-5)
$$\frac{1}{2} + \frac{3}{t} = \frac{5}{8}$$
$$8t\left(\frac{1}{2} + \frac{3}{t}\right) = 8t\left(\frac{5}{8}\right)$$
$$4t + 24 = 5t$$
$$24 = t$$

Chapter Vocabulary

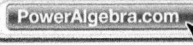

- asymptote (p. 694)
- constant of variation for an inverse variation (p. 686)
- excluded value (p. 652)
- inverse variation (p. 686)
- rational equation (p. 679)
- rational expression (p. 652)
- rational function (p. 693)

Choose the correct term to complete each sentence.

1. A value of x for which a rational function $f(x)$ is undefined is a(n) __?__ .

2. A line that the graph of a function gets closer to as x or y gets larger in absolute value is a(n) __?__ .

3. A(n) __?__ is a ratio of two polynomial expressions.

PowerAlgebra.com | Chapter 11 Chapter Review | 703

Essential Questions

BIG idea Equivalence
ESSENTIAL QUESTION How are rational expressions represented?
ANSWER Rational expressions can be represented many ways. When a rational expression is simplified, the numerator and denominator have no common factors except 1.

BIG idea Function
ESSENTIAL QUESTION What are the characteristics of rational functions?
ANSWER Rational functions have equations of the form $f(x) = \frac{polynomial}{polynomial}$. The graph of a rational function may have vertical and horizontal asymptotes.

BIG idea Solving Equations and Inequalities
ESSENTIAL QUESTION How can you solve a rational equation?
ANSWER To isolate the variable in a rational equation, multiply by the LCD and then solve the resulting equation. Check for extraneous solutions.

Answers

Chapter Review
1. excluded value
2. asymptote
3. rational expression

Summative Questions

Use the following prompts as you review this chapter with your students. The prompts are designed to help you assess your students' understanding of the BIG Ideas they have studied.
- How do you simplify rational expressions?
- How do you graph rational functions?
- How do you solve rational equations?

Chapter Review 703

Answers

Chapter Review (continued)

4. $\frac{x+3}{5x^2}$, $x \neq 0$

5. $\frac{1}{3}$, $m \neq 3$

6. $\frac{x+3}{5}$, $x \neq -3$

7. $\frac{2(a-1)}{3(a+1)}$, $a \neq -1$, $a \neq 1$

8. $\frac{2s+3}{2s-1}$, $x \neq \frac{1}{2}$, $x \neq 4$

9. $-\frac{1}{2}$, $c \neq 4$

10. $\frac{1}{x+2}$

11. $\frac{2}{3(x-2)}$

12. $\frac{(a+4)(a-2)}{a^2(a+2)}$

13. $(x+5)(x+7)$

14. $4x - 3 - \frac{7}{3x}$

15. $3d - 7 - \frac{8}{d+3}$

16. $2b^2 + b + 3$

11-1 Simplifying Rational Expressions

Quick Review

A **rational expression** is an expression that can be written in the form $\frac{\text{polynomial}}{\text{polynomial}}$. A rational expression is in simplified form when the numerator and denominator have no common factors other than 1.

Example

What is the simplified form of $\frac{x^2 - 9}{x^2 - 2x - 15}$?

$\frac{x^2 - 9}{x^2 - 2x - 15} = \frac{(x+3)(x-3)}{(x+3)(x-5)}$ Factor the numerator and denominator.

$= \frac{\overset{1}{\cancel{(x+3)}}(x-3)}{\underset{1}{\cancel{(x+3)}}(x-5)}$ Divide out the common factor.

$= \frac{x-3}{x-5}$ Simplify.

Exercises

Simplify each expression. State any excluded values.

4. $\frac{2x^2 + 6x}{10x^3}$

5. $\frac{m-3}{3m-9}$

6. $\frac{x^2 + 6x + 9}{5x + 15}$

7. $\frac{2a^2 - 4a + 2}{3a^2 - 3}$

8. $\frac{2s^2 - 5s - 12}{2s^2 - 9s + 4}$

9. $\frac{4-c}{2c-8}$

10. **Geometry** What fraction of the rectangle is shaded? Write your answer as a rational expression in simplified form.

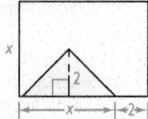

11-2 and 11-3 Multiplying and Dividing Rational Expressions and Dividing Polynomials

Quick Review

You can multiply and divide rational expressions using the same properties you use to multiply and divide numerical fractions.

$\frac{a}{b} \cdot \frac{c}{d} = \frac{ac}{bd}$, where $b \neq 0$ and $d \neq 0$.

$\frac{a}{b} \div \frac{c}{d} = \frac{a}{b} \cdot \frac{d}{c} = \frac{ad}{bc}$, where $b \neq 0$, $c \neq 0$, and $d \neq 0$.

To divide a polynomial by a monomial, divide each term of the polynomial by the monomial. To divide a polynomial by another polynomial, use long division. When dividing polynomials, write the answer as quotient $+ \frac{\text{remainder}}{\text{divisor}}$.

Example

What is the quotient $\frac{y}{y+3} \div \frac{y-3}{y-2}$?

$\frac{y}{y+3} \div \frac{y-3}{y-2} = \frac{y}{y+3} \cdot \frac{y-2}{y-3}$

$= \frac{y(y-2)}{(y+3)(y-3)}$

Exercises

Multiply or divide.

11. $\frac{4x + 12}{x^2 - 2x} \cdot \frac{x}{6x + 18}$

12. $\frac{a^2 + 5a + 4}{a^3} \div \frac{a^2 + 3a + 2}{a^2 - 2a}$

13. $\frac{x^2 + 13x + 40}{x - 7} \div \frac{x + 8}{x^2 - 49}$

14. $(12x^2 + 9x - 7) \div 3x$

15. $(3d^2 + 2d - 29) \div (d + 3)$

16. **Geometry** The width and area of a rectangle are shown in the figure at the right. What is the length of the rectangle?

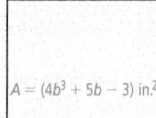

11-4 Adding and Subtracting Rational Expressions

Quick Review

You can add and subtract rational expressions. To add or subtract expressions with like denominators, add or subtract the numerators and write the result over the common denominator. To add or subtract expressions with different denominators, write the expressions with the LCD and then add or subtract the numerators.

Example

What is $\dfrac{1}{a+7} + \dfrac{a}{a-5}$?

$$\dfrac{1}{a+7} + \dfrac{a}{a-5} = \dfrac{1(a-5)}{(a+7)(a-5)} + \dfrac{a(a+7)}{(a+7)(a-5)}$$

$$= \dfrac{a-5}{(a+7)(a-5)} + \dfrac{a^2+7a}{(a+7)(a-5)}$$

$$= \dfrac{a-5+a^2+7a}{(a+7)(a-5)}$$

$$= \dfrac{a^2+8a-5}{(a+7)(a-5)}$$

Exercises

Add or subtract.

17. $\dfrac{8x}{x+1} - \dfrac{3}{x+1}$

18. $\dfrac{6}{7x} + \dfrac{1}{4}$

19. $\dfrac{5}{2+x} + \dfrac{x}{x-4}$

20. $\dfrac{9}{3x-1} - \dfrac{5x}{2x+3}$

21. Air Travel The distance between Atlanta, Georgia, and Albuquerque, New Mexico, is about 1270 mi. The groundspeed for jet traffic from Albuquerque to Atlanta can be about 18% faster than the groundspeed from Atlanta to Albuquerque. Let r be the speed from Atlanta to Albuquerque in miles per hour. What is a simplified expression for the round-trip flying time?

11-5 Solving Rational Equations

Quick Review

You can solve a **rational equation** by multiplying each side by the LCD. Check possible solutions to make sure each satisfies the original equation.

Example

What is the solution of $\dfrac{3}{8} + \dfrac{4}{x} = \dfrac{7}{x}$?

$$\dfrac{3}{8} + \dfrac{4}{x} = \dfrac{7}{x}$$

$$8x\left(\dfrac{3}{8} + \dfrac{4}{x}\right) = 8x\left(\dfrac{7}{x}\right)$$

$$8^1 x\left(\dfrac{3}{8}\right) + 8x^1\left(\dfrac{4}{x_1}\right) = 8x^1\left(\dfrac{7}{1^x}\right)$$

$$3x + 32 = 56$$

$$3x = 24$$

$$x = 8$$

Check $\dfrac{3}{8} + \dfrac{4}{8} \overset{?}{=} \dfrac{7}{8}$

$\dfrac{7}{8} = \dfrac{7}{8}$ ✔

Exercises

Solve each equation. Check your solutions.

22. $\dfrac{1}{2} + \dfrac{3}{t} = \dfrac{5}{8}$

23. $\dfrac{3}{m-4} + \dfrac{1}{3(m-4)} = \dfrac{6}{m}$

24. $\dfrac{2c}{c-4} - 2 = \dfrac{4}{c+5}$

25. $\dfrac{5}{2x-3} = \dfrac{7}{3x}$

26. Business A new photocopier can make 72 copies in 2 min. When an older photocopier is operational, the two photocopiers together can make 72 copies in 1.5 min. How long would it take the older photocopier to make 72 copies working alone?

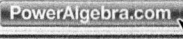
17. $\dfrac{8x-3}{x+1}$

18. $\dfrac{24+7x}{28x}$

19. $\dfrac{x^2+7x-20}{(x+2)(x-4)}$

20. $\dfrac{-15x^2+23x+27}{(3x-1)(2x+3)}$

21. $\dfrac{138,430}{59r}$

22. 24

23. 9

24. −14

25. −21

26. 6 min

Answers

Chapter Review (continued)

27. $xy = 21$

28. $xy = 10$

29. $xy = -18$

30. $xy = -25$

31.

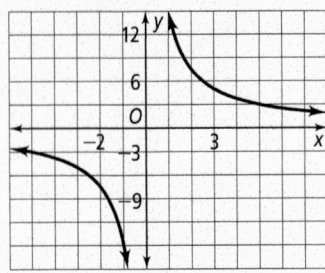

32.

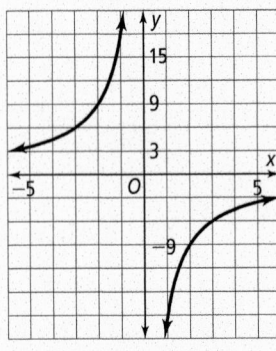

33. about 9.5 mi/h

34. $x \neq 0$

35. $x \neq -4$

36. $x = -2,\ y = 0$

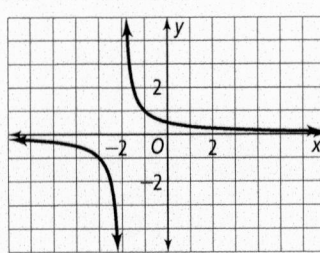

37. $x = -3,\ y = 0$

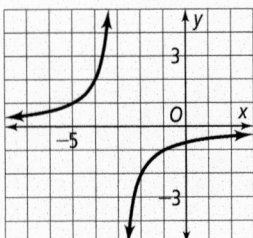

11-6 Inverse Variation

Quick Review

When the product of two variables is constant, the variables form an **inverse variation.** You can write an inverse variation in the form $xy = k$ or $y = \frac{k}{x}$, where k is the constant of variation.

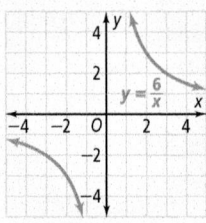

Example

Suppose y varies inversely with x, and $y = 8$ when $x = 6$. What is an equation for the inverse variation?

$xy = k$ General form of an inverse variation

$6(8) = k$ Substitute 6 for x and 8 for y.

$48 = k$ Simplify.

$xy = 48$ Write an equation.

Exercises

Suppose y varies inversely with x. Write an equation for the inverse variation.

27. $y = 7$ when $x = 3$ **28.** $y = 4$ when $x = 2.5$

29. $y = -9$ when $x = 2$ **30.** $y = 5$ when $x = -5$

Graph each inverse variation.

31. $xy = 15$ **32.** $y = \frac{-18}{x}$

33. Running Suppose a runner takes 45 min to run a route at 8 mi/h at the beginning of training season. By the end of training season, she can run the same route in 38 min. What is her speed at the end of training season?

11-7 Graphing Rational Functions

Quick Review

A **rational function** can be written in the form $f(x) = \frac{polynomial}{polynomial}$. The graph of a rational function in the form $y = \frac{a}{x - b} + c$ has a vertical asymptote at $x = b$ and a horizontal asymptote at $y = c$. A line is an **asymptote** of a graph if the graph gets closer to the line as x or y gets larger in absolute value.

Example

What is the graph of $f(x) = \frac{1}{x - 1} + 2$?

From the form of the function, you can see that there is a vertical asymptote at $x = 1$ and a horizontal asymptote at $y = 2$. Sketch the asymptotes.

Make a table of values. Then graph the function.

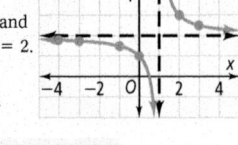

x	−4	−3	−1	0	2	3
y	1.8	1.75	1.5	1	3	2.5

Exercises

Identify the excluded value for each function.

34. $f(x) = \frac{5}{x}$ **35.** $y = \frac{3}{x + 4}$

Identify the asymptotes of the graph of each function. Then graph the function.

36. $y = \frac{1}{x + 2}$ **37.** $f(x) = \frac{-2}{x + 3}$

38. $y = \frac{5}{x - 4} + 1$ **39.** $f(x) = \frac{3}{x - 5} - 1$

40. Physics For a 225-watt bulb, the intensity I of light in lumens at a distance of x feet is $I = \frac{225}{x^2}$.
   a. What is the intensity of light 5 ft from the bulb?
   b. Suppose your distance from the bulb doubles. How does the intensity of the light change? Explain.

38. $x = 4,\ y = 1$ **39.** $x = 5,\ y = -1$

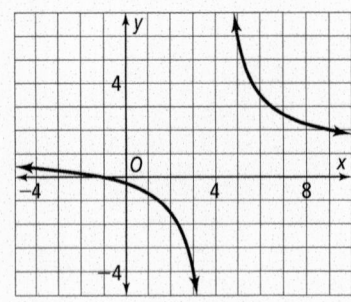

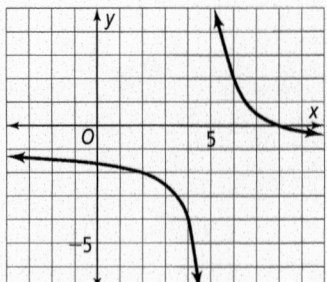

40. a. 9 lumens

   b. Intensity is inversely related to the square of the distance, so at twice the distance, the intensity is $\frac{1}{4}$ as great.

Chapter Test

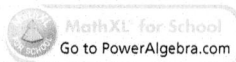
Do you know HOW?

Write an equation of the inverse variation that includes the given point.

1. $(2, 2)$

2. $(-8, -4)$

Identify the excluded value for each rational function.

3. $f(x) = \frac{19 + x}{x - 5}$

4. $y = \frac{2x}{8x - 12}$

Identify the asymptotes of each function. Then graph the function.

5. $y = \frac{6}{x}$

6. $y = \frac{1}{x} + 3$

7. $f(x) = \frac{4}{x - 2}$

Simplify each expression. State any excluded values.

8. $\frac{6p - 30}{3p - 15}$

9. $\frac{n^2 + 4n - 5}{n + 5}$

Multiply or divide.

10. $\frac{3}{x - 2} \cdot \frac{x^2 - 4}{12}$

11. $\frac{5x}{x^2 + 2x} \div \frac{30x^2}{x + 2}$

Divide.

12. $(12x^4 + 9x^3 - 10x^2) \div 3x^3$

13. $(4x^4 - 6x^3 - 2x^2 - 2x) \div (2x - 1)$

Find the LCD of each pair of expressions.

14. $\frac{5}{h}, \frac{6}{3h}$

15. $\frac{4}{a^2 b^3}, \frac{3}{9ab^4}$

Add or subtract.

16. $\frac{4b - 2}{3b} + \frac{b}{b + 2}$

17. $\frac{9}{n} - \frac{8}{n + 1}$

Solve each equation. Check your solutions.

18. $\frac{v}{3} + \frac{v}{v + 5} = \frac{-4}{v + 5}$

19. $\frac{16}{x + 10} = \frac{8}{2x - 1}$

20. **Cleaning** Mark can clean his father's office in 30 min. His younger sister Lynn can clean the office in 40 min. How long will it take the two of them together to clean the office?

Do you UNDERSTAND?

21. **Open-Ended** Write a rational expression for which 6 and 3 are excluded values.

22. **Geometry** The height of a square prism is $3n + 1$. The volume of the prism is $3n^3 + 13n^2 + 16n + 4$. What is the area of the square base of the prism?

23 **Reasoning** Rosa divided a polynomial $p(x)$ by $x - 4$ and obtained this result: $2x + 13 + \frac{59}{x - 4}$. What is $p(x)$?

24. **Error Analysis** Your friend says the solution of the rational equation $\frac{m}{m - 3} + \frac{1}{4} = \frac{3}{m - 3}$ is 3. Explain the error that your friend may have made.

25. **Reasoning** Consider the equation $\frac{3}{x - a} = \frac{x}{x - a}$. For what value(s) of a does the equation have exactly one solution? No solution? Explain.

8. $2, p \neq 5$

9. $(n - 1), n \neq -5$

10. $\frac{x + 2}{4}$

11. $\frac{1}{6x^2}$

12. $4x + 3 - \frac{10}{3x}$

13. $2x^3 - 2x^2 - 2x - 2 - \frac{2}{2x - 1}$

14. $3h$

15. $9a^2 b^4$

16. $\frac{7b^2 + 6b - 4}{3b(b + 2)}$

17. $\frac{n + 9}{n(n + 1)}$

18. $-6, -2$

19. 4

20. about 17 min

21. Answers will vary. Sample: $\frac{1}{(x - 6)(x - 3)}$

22. $n^2 + 4n + 4$

23. $2x^2 + 5x + 7$

24. Your friend forgot to the check the solution in the original equation.

25. Any real number other than 3; 3; if $a = 3$, then the denominator equals 0.

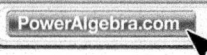

Answers

Chapter Test

1. $xy = 4$

2. $xy = 32$

3. 5

4. 1.5

5. $x = 0, y = 0$

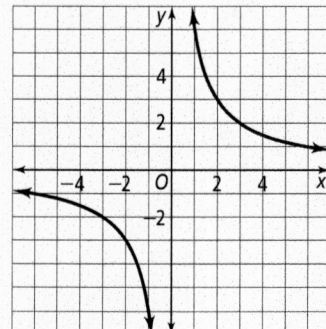

6. $x = 0, y = 3$

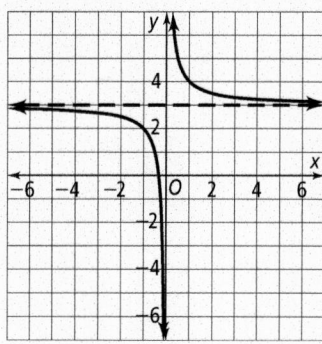

7. $x = 2, f(x) = 0$

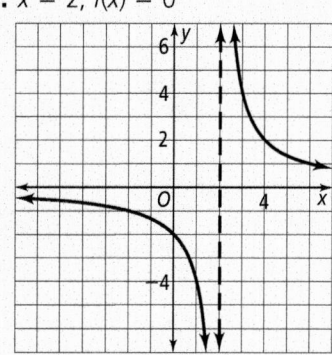

Item Number	Lesson
1	4-6
2	8-6
3	11-4
4	11–5
5	11-2
6	5-3
7	1-7
8	11-7
9	2-6
10	7-4
11	9-1
12	10-2
13	5-5
14	6-2
15	10-3
16	8-2
17	10-2
18	11-1
19	6-4
20	11-7
21	9-4
22	11-5
23	2-7
24	2-9
25	2-2
26	5-6
27	1-6
28	4-5
29	11-1
30	2-3

11 Cumulative Test Prep

TIPS FOR SUCCESS

Some questions on tests ask you to simplify an expression. Read the question at the right. Then follow the tips to answer it.

Which expression is equivalent to $\dfrac{20x^3y^5 - 30x^6y^4}{5x^3y^3}$?

A. $4x^6y^8 - 6x^9y^7$

B. $4y^2 - 6x^3y$

C. $-2x^6y^6$

D. $15y^2 - 25x^3y$

TIP 1

Use the fact that a fraction $\dfrac{a + b}{c}$ can be written in the form $\dfrac{a}{c} + \dfrac{b}{c}$.

TIP 2

When you divide powers that have the same base, you subtract the exponents.

Think It Through

Write the expression as a difference of two fractions. Then simplify each fraction using the laws of exponents.

$$\frac{20x^3y^5 - 30x^6y^4}{5x^3y^3}$$

$$= \frac{20x^3y^5}{5x^3y^5} - \frac{30x^6y^4}{5x^3y^3}$$

$$= 4x^{3-3}y^{5-3} - 6x^{6-3}y^{4-3}$$

$$= 4x^0y^2 - 6x^2y^1$$

$$= 4y^2 - 6x^3y$$

Vocabulary Builder

As you solve test items, you must understand the meanings of mathematical terms. Choose the correct term to complete each sentence.

A. The quantity $b^2 - 4ac$ is the (*vertex, discriminant*) of the equation $ax^2 + bx + c = 0$.

B. Two lines are (*parallel, perpendicular*) if their slopes are negative reciprocals of each other.

C. A (*linear, quadratic*) equation is an equation that can be written in the form $Ax + By = C$, where A, B, and C are real numbers, and A and B are not both 0.

D. A(n) (*rational, exponential*) expression is a ratio of two polynomials.

E. When you (*solve, evaluate*) an equation, you are finding the value or values that make the equation true.

Multiple Choice

Read each question. Then write the letter of the correct answer on your paper.

1. Which function describes the tables of values?

x	-2	-1	0	1
f(x)	-3	-1	1	3

A. $f(x) = x - 1$ C. $f(x) = x + 1$

B. $f(x) = 2x$ D. $f(x) = 2x + 1$

2. A rectangle has an area of $8x^2 + 16x + 6$. Which of the following could be the length and width of the rectangle?

F. $4x + 1, 2x + 6$ H. $4x + 6, 2x + 1$

G. $4x + 3, 2x + 2$ I. $8x + 1, x + 6$

Answers

Cumulative Test Prep

A. discriminant

B. perpendicular

C. linear

D. rational

E. solve

1. D

2. H

3. Which expression is equivalent to $\frac{x+2}{x+4} - \frac{x+1}{x-3}$?

(A) $\dfrac{-2(3x-5)}{(x+4)(x-3)}$

(B) $\dfrac{-2(3x+5)}{(x+4)(x-3)}$

(C) $\dfrac{-2(3x+5)}{(x-4)(x+3)}$

(D) $\dfrac{2(3x-5)}{(x+4)(x-3)}$

4. Which is equivalent to $\dfrac{18x^2y + 24x^3y^4 - 12x^7y^2}{6x^2y}$?

(F) $12 + 18xy^3 - 6x^5y$

(G) $4xy^3 - 2x^5y$

(H) $3 + 4xy^3 - 2x^5y$

(I) $3x^2y + 4x^3y^4 - 2x^7y^2$

5. Which expression is equivalent to $\dfrac{x-4}{\frac{x+3}{x-1}}$?

(A) $\dfrac{x^2 + 5x - 4}{x+3}$

(B) $\dfrac{x+4}{x^2 + 2x - 3}$

(C) $\dfrac{x^2 + 7x + 12}{x-1}$

(D) $\dfrac{x^2 - 5x + 4}{x+3}$

6. Which of the following points are on the graph of $y = -2x + 3$?

(F) $(0, -2)$ and $(1, 1)$

(G) $(0, 3)$ and $(1, -1)$

(H) $(1, 1)$ and $(0, 3)$

(I) $(-1, 1)$ and $(0, -2)$

7. Which real-number property is illustrated below?

$$2x^2 + 3x^2 = (2 + 3)x^2 = 5x^2$$

(A) Associative Property of Addition

(B) Commutative Property of Addition

(C) Distributive Property

(D) Identity Property of Addition

8. What is (are) the solution(s) of the equation $\dfrac{2x+1}{5x} = \dfrac{4x-5}{3x}$?

(F) 0

(G) 2

(H) 0 and 2

(I) no solution

9. About 8 babies are born in the United States each minute. Using this estimate, about how many babies are born each year?

(A) 70,000

(B) 200,000

(C) 4,000,000

(D) 300,000,000

10. Which expression is equivalent to $(3m^2n^4)^3$?

(F) $27m^6n^{12}$

(G) $27m^5n^7$

(H) $9m^6n^{12}$

(I) $9m^5n^7$

11. Which statement below about the function $y = 2x^2 - 3$ is correct?

(A) The value of y is never less than -3.

(B) The value of y is never greater than 2.

(C) The value of x is always greater than the value of y.

(D) The value of y is always greater than the value of x.

12. Each day Michael goes for a run through a rectangular park. The diagonal of the park is $\sqrt{80,000}$ m long. Which of the following is equivalent to $\sqrt{80,000}$?

(F) $100\sqrt{2}$

(G) $200\sqrt{2}$

(H) $800\sqrt{2}$

(I) $8000\sqrt{10}$

13. What is the x-intercept of the graph of $-5x + y = -20$?

(A) -20

(B) -4

(C) 4

(D) 20

14. Davis bought 2 candy bars and 3 bags of chips for $5.45. Reese bought 5 bags of chips for $6.25. How much did each candy bar cost?

(F) $.85

(G) $.95

(H) $1.25

(I) $1.70

3. B

4. H

5. D

6. H

7. C

8. G

9. B

10. F

11. A

12. G

13. C

14. F

Answers

Cumulative Test Prep (continued)

15. C
16. G
17. C
18. I
19. 20
20. 8
21. $-\frac{3}{2}$
22. 6
23. 8
24. 0.4
25. 30
26. $\frac{3}{11}$
27. 565.2
28. [2] $f(h) = 8.5h$
   [1] minor computational error
29. [2] $\frac{(x + 6)(x - 3)}{6(x + 6)} = \frac{x - 3}{6}$
   [1] factoring error
30. [4] **a.** $9C = 5F - 160$, $5F = 9C + 160$,
      $F = \frac{9}{5}C + 32$
   b. $F = \frac{9}{5}(35) + 32 = 95°C$
   [3] correct methods used with minor computational error
   [2] correct formula with wrong answer, or minor error in formula with correct answer based on that
   [1] correct answers with no work shown

---

15. What is the simplified form of $\sqrt{5}\,(2 + \sqrt{10})$?
   Ⓐ $2\sqrt{10}$
   Ⓑ $2\sqrt{5} + \sqrt{50}$
   Ⓒ $2\sqrt{5} + 5\sqrt{2}$
   Ⓓ $2\sqrt{5} + \sqrt{10}$

16. What is the factored form of $6w^4 + 15w^2$?
   Ⓕ $w^2(6w^2 + 15)$
   Ⓖ $3w^2(2w^2 + 5)$
   Ⓗ $3w(2w^3 + 5w)$
   Ⓘ $3w^2(2w^2 + 5w)$

17. Which of the following is equivalent to $(3\sqrt{2})^2$?
   Ⓐ 6   Ⓒ 18
   Ⓑ $9\sqrt{2}$ Ⓓ 36

18. What is the simplified form of $\frac{x^2 - 81}{2x^2 + 23x + 45}$?
   Ⓕ $\frac{x + 9}{2x + 5}$
   Ⓖ $\frac{x - 9}{x + 9}$
   Ⓗ $\frac{x - 9}{2x - 5}$
   Ⓘ $\frac{x - 9}{2x + 5}$

GRIDDED RESPONSE

Record your answers in a grid.

19. A dinner party at a restaurant had 37 people. Each person ordered one of two entrées. One entrée cost $15, and the other entrée cost $18. The total cost of all the entrées was $606. How many $15 entrées were ordered?

20. A chemistry student needs to make 20 liters of a solution that is 60% acid. She plans to make the solution by mixing a solution that is 70% acid with another solution that is 45% acid. How many liters of the 45% acid solution will she need?

21. What is the negative solution of $2x^2 + x = 3$?

22. Karen can mow the lawn in 15 min. Her friend Kim can mow the lawn in 10 min. If they work together, how many minutes will they take to mow the lawn?

23. Sandra takes 6 h to drive 300 mi. If she increases her speed by 5 mi/h, how many hours will she take to drive 440 mi?

24. Suzanne rolled a number cube 200 times and recorded her results in the table below. What percent of the time did she roll an even number? Write the percent in decimal form.

Numbers	1	2	3	4	5	6
Rolls	56	30	20	36	44	14

25. A roof on a house has a triangular cross section with at least two angles of equal measure. One angle of the triangle measures $120°$. What is the measure, in degrees, of one of the other two angles?

26. Line p passes through points $(5, -4)$ and $(2, 7)$. What is the slope of a line that is perpendicular to line p?

27. A cylinder has a height of 20 cm and a diameter of 6 cm. What is the volume, in cubic centimeters, of the cylinder? Use 3.14 for π.

Short Response

28. Phillip works at a grocery store after school and on weekends. He earns $8.50 per hour. What is a function rule for his total earnings $f(h)$ for working h hours?

29. What is the simplified form of $\frac{x^2 + 3x - 18}{6x + 36}$? Show your work.

Extended Response

30. The formula $C = \frac{5}{9}(F - 32)$ can be used to find the Celsius temperature C if you know the Fahrenheit temperature F.
   a. Transform the equation to find the Fahrenheit temperature F in terms of the Celsius temperature C.
   b. Use the formula in part (a) to find the Fahrenheit temperature equivalent to $35°C$.

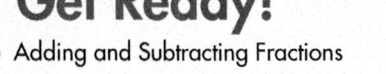

Get Ready!

Skills Handbook, p. 791

Adding and Subtracting Fractions

Add or subtract. Write each answer in simplest form.

1. $\frac{2}{3} + \frac{1}{2}$ **2.** $\frac{7}{12} - \frac{5}{8}$ **3.** $\frac{16}{25} + \frac{3}{10}$ **4.** $\frac{5}{9} - \frac{5}{36}$

Lesson 1-6

Multiplying and Dividing Real Numbers

Simplify each fraction.

5. $\frac{6 + 4 + 7 + 9}{4}$ **6.** $\frac{1.7 + 4.2 + 3.1}{3}$ **7.** $\frac{11 + 16 + 9 + 12 + 7}{5}$

Lesson 1-7

Distributive Property

Simplify each expression.

8. $6(x - 7)$ **9.** $\frac{1}{2}(4x + 6)$ **10.** $-2(5 - x)$ **11.** $0.5(5 + 4x)$

Lesson 3-8

Unions and Intersections of Sets

Let $X = \{x \mid x \text{ is an odd whole number less than 16}\}$, $Y = \{2, 6, 9, 10, 16\}$, and $Z = \{z \mid z \text{ is an even whole number less than 19}\}$. Find each union or intersection.

12. $X \cup Y$ **13.** $X \cap Y$ **14.** $Y \cap Z$ **15.** $X \cup Y \cup Z$

Lesson 5-7

Scatter Plots

For each table, make a scatter plot of the data. Describe the type of correlation that the scatter plot shows.

16.

Messenger Bag Sales				
Price ($)	30	45	60	75
Number Sold	150	123	85	50

17.

Driving Distances and Times				
Distance (mi)	5	38	15	8
Time (min)	15	56	28	22

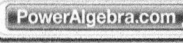

Looking Ahead Vocabulary

18. There are three *outcomes* for a hockey team during a game: win, lose, or tie. What are the possible *outcomes* for flipping a coin?

19. On a highway, the *median* is the strip of land that divides the two sides of opposing traffic. How would you expect a *median* to divide a data set?

20. The color purple is a *combination* of the colors red and blue. Does the order in which the colors are combined change the result of the *combination*?

PowerAlgebra.com   **Chapter 12** Data Analysis and Probability   **711**

Get Ready!

Assign this diagnostic assessment to determine if students have the prerequisite skills for Chapter 12.

Lesson	Skill
Skill Handbook, p. T791	Adding and Subtracting Fractions
1-6	Multiplying and Dividing Real Numbers
1-7	Distributive Property
3-8	Unions and Intersections of Sets
5-7	Scatter Plots

To remediate students, select from these resources (available for every lesson).
- Online Problems (PowerAlgebra.com)
- Reteaching (All-in-One Teaching Resources)
- Practice (All-in-One Teaching Resources)

Why Students Need These Skills

ADDING AND SUBTRACTING FRACTIONS
Concepts of fraction operations are essential to solving problems involving probability.

MULTIPLYING AND DIVIDING REAL NUMBERS
The problems given will serve as a prerequisite for finding the mean of a set of data.

DISTRIBUTIVE PROPERTY
Students will organize data in matrices. Multiplying a matrix by a scalar is similar to using the Distributive Property.

UNIONS AND INTERSECTIONS OF SETS
Students will find probabilities of compound events. Venn diagrams will help students find the overlap in these problems.

SCATTER PLOTS
Scatter plots provide the raw material for analysis of trends.

Looking Ahead Vocabulary

OUTCOMES Give students an event and have them name possible outcomes.

MEDIAN Have students draw a picture of a highway median.

COMBINATION Have students give examples of other real-world objects that are a result of a combination.

Answers

Get Ready!

1. $\frac{7}{6}$

2. $-\frac{1}{24}$

3. $\frac{47}{50}$

4. $\frac{5}{12}$

5. $\frac{13}{2}$

6. 3

7. 11

8. $6x - 42$

9. $2x + 3$

10. $-10 + 2x$

11. $2.5 + 2x$

12. $\{1, 2, 3, 5, 6, 7, 9, 10, 11, 13, 15, 16\}$

13. $\{9\}$

14. $\{2, 6, 10, 16\}$

15. $\{0, 1, 2, 3, 4, 5, 6, 7, 8, 9, 10, 11, 12, 13, 14, 15, 16, 18\}$

16.

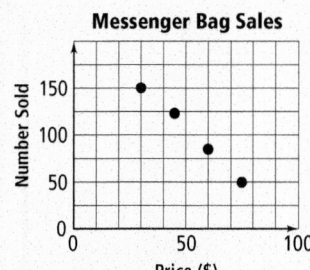

negative

17.

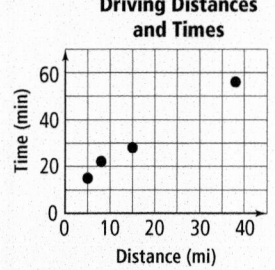

positive

18. heads or tails

19. into two parts with an equal number of data values

20. no

Chapter 12 Overview

UbD **Understanding by Design**

Chapter 12 introduces the topics of data analysis and probability. In this chapter, students will develop the answers to the Essential Questions posed on the opposite page as they learn the concepts and skills bulleted below.

BIG idea **Data Collection and Analysis**

ESSENTIAL QUESTION How can collecting and analyzing data help you make decisions or predictions?

- Students will find measures of central tendency.
- Students will examine samples and conduct surveys.
- Students will make predictions based on the data they collect and observe.

BIG idea **Data Representation**

ESSENTIAL QUESTION How can you make and interpret different representations of data?

- Students will organize data in displays such as matrices, frequency tables, histograms, and box-and-whisker plots.
- Students will describe a data set by using measures of central tendency.

BIG idea **Probability**

ESSENTIAL QUESTION How is probability related to real-world events?

- Theoretical and experimental probabilities will be compared.
- Students will find probabilities of simple events and compound events.

CHAPTER 12

Data Analysis and Probability

PowerAlgebra.com

Your place to get all things digital

VIDEO
Download videos connecting math to your world.

VOCABULARY
Math definitions in English and Spanish

SOLVE IT!
The online Solve It will get you in gear for each lesson.

DYNAMIC ACTIVITIES
Interactive! Vary numbers, graphs, and figures to explore math concepts.

ONLINE PROBLEMS
Download Step-by-Step Problems with Instant Replay.

ONLINE HOMEWORK
Get and view your assignments online.

MathXL FOR SCHOOL
Extra practice and review online

One of these ducks is different from the others! If I close my eyes and grab one, do you think I'll get a pink one or a yellow one? You'll learn how to use probability to decide whether an event is likely or not in this chapter.

Vocabulary

English/Spanish Vocabulary Audio Online:

English	Spanish
combination, p. 753	combinación
event, p. 757	suceso
matrix, p. 714	matriz
measure of central tendency, p. 726	medida de tendencia central
outcome, p. 757	resultado
outlier, p. 726	valor extremo
permutation, p. 751	permutación
probability, p. 757	probabilidad
quartile, p. 734	cuartiles
sample space, p. 757	espacio de muestra

PowerAlgebra.com

Chapter 12 Overview

Use these online assets to engage your students. There is support for the Solve It and step-by-step solutions for Problems.

 Show the student-produced video demonstrating relevant and engaging applications of the new concepts in the chapter.

 Find online definitions for new terms in English and Spanish.

 Start each lesson with an attention-getting Problem. View the Problem online with helpful hints.

My Math Video

My Math Video

FACILITATE Use this photo to discuss probability. There is one duck in the pool that is different from the others. In this chapter, students will learn to calculate the probability of selecting that particular duck.

Q Are all the ducks in the pool the same? **[No, there is one duck that is pink instead of yellow.]**

Q How many total ducks are in the pool? **[43]**

Q How can you represent the number of pink ducks compared to the number of yellow ducks? **[The ratio $\frac{1}{42}$ represents the number of pink ducks compared to yellow ducks.]**

Q How can you represent the number of yellow ducks compared to the total number of ducks? **[The ratio $\frac{42}{43}$ represents the number of yellow ducks compared to the total number of ducks.]**

Q If you were to select one duck at random, what would be the probability of selecting the pink duck? Explain. **[The ratio $\frac{1}{43}$ represents the number of pink ducks to the total number of ducks in the pool.]**

EXTENSION

Practice probability with the class. Ask students to tell you the probabilities of selecting particular students from the class. You can ask them to find the probability of selecting a male student, a student with glasses, a student wearing boots, etc.

BIG ideas

1 **Data Collection and Analysis**
Essential Question How can collecting and analyzing data help you make decisions or predictions?

2 **Data Representation**
Essential Question How can you make and interpret different representations of data?

3 **Probability**
Essential Question How is probability related to real-world events?

Chapter Preview

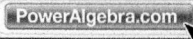

Chapter 12 Data Analysis and Probability   713

 Increase students' depth of knowledge with interactive online activities.

 Show Problems from each lesson solved step by step. Instant replay allows students to go at their own pace when studying online.

 Assign homework to individual students or to an entire class.

 Prepare students for the Mid-Chapter Quiz and Chapter Test with online practice and review.

UbD

Data Collection and Analysis

BIG idea Sampling techniques are used to gather data from real-world situations. If the data are representative of the larger population, inferences can be made about that population. Biased sampling techniques yield data unlikely to be representative of the larger population. Sets of numerical data are described using measures of central tendency and dispersion.

ESSENTIAL UNDERSTANDINGS

12-3 Different measures can be used to interpret and compare sets of data.

12-5 When collecting data, it is important for the results to accurately represent the situation.

Data Representation

BIG idea The most appropriate data representation depends on the type of data—quantitative or qualitative, and univariate or bivariate. Line plots, box plots, and histograms are different ways to show distribution of data over a possible range of values.

ESSENTIAL UNDERSTANDINGS

12-1 to 12-4 Data can be organized in matrices or in intervals. Different measures can be used to interpret and compare sets of data. Separating data into subsets is a useful way to summarize and compare data sets.

Probability

BIG idea Probability expresses the likelihood that a particular event will occur. Data can be used to calculate an experimental probability, and mathematical properties can be used to determine a theoretical probability. Either experimental or theoretical probability can be used to make predictions or decisions about future events. Various counting methods can be used to develop theoretical probabilities.

ESSENTIAL UNDERSTANDINGS

12-6 Counting methods can be used to find the number of possible ways to choose objects with and without regard to order.

12-7 to 12-8 The probability of an event, or P(event), tells how likely it is that the event will occur. Probabilities can be found by reasoning mathematically or by using experimental data. The probability of a compound event can sometimes be found from expressions of the probabilities of simpler events.

Measures of Central Tendency

When dealing with a set of values, it is often useful to find one value that best represents the set. Two values commonly used to represent a set are mean and median.

The mean, usually associated with the word *average*, is found by adding the values and dividing by the number of values.

$$\text{Mean: } \frac{a_1 + a_2 + \cdots + a_n}{n}$$

Consider the prices of homes in a certain neighborhood:

$122,900; $106,680; $143,660; $535,800; $91,530; $120,410

$$\frac{\begin{array}{c}122,900 + 106,680 + 143,660 + \\ 535,800 + 91,530 + 120,410\end{array}}{6} = 186,830$$

Notice that the number found to represent the set of values, $186,830, is larger than all but one of the values. In this case the mean is not a very good representation of the data because there is one value that is much greater than the other values. The number $535,800 is called an *outlier*. An outlier is any element in a set that is more than 1.5 times the interquartile range above the third quartile or below the first quartile. When a set has outliers, the median is often a better choice to represent the set.

The median is the middle value when the data is written in numerical order. When a set has an even number of values, find the sum of the middle two values and divide by two.

91,530; 106,680; (120,410; 122,900;) 143,660; 535,800

$$\frac{120,410 + 122,900}{2} = 121,655$$

This number, $121,655, seems to better represent the set of home values given above.

Common Errors With Measures of Central Tendency

Without criteria for defining outliers—and students often forget them or do not remember how to find the interquartiles—making a determination of any outliers might be subjective. Students might struggle to decide if a value is an outlier and therefore be unsure whether to use mean or median as the measure of central tendency.

Data Displays

Frequency tables and histograms are two related ways to display data. Once a frequency table has been created, a corresponding histogram can be readily made.

Consider the number of hours per year that students in a class spent doing volunteer work:

75, 86, 73, 98, 104, 50, 76, 95, 81, 92, 60, 118, 45, 66, 90, 71, 52, 104, 112, 99, 58, 87, 69, 100, 65, 88, 63, 119

Frequency Table

Number of Hours	Frequency
40–59	4
60–79	9
80–99	9
100–119	6

Histogram

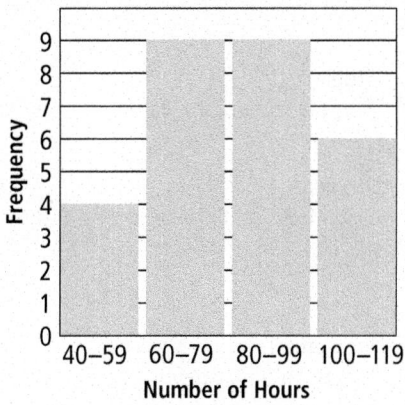

Yearly Volunteering

Common Errors With Data Displays

When choosing intervals to make a frequency table, the intervals should not overlap. If students choose overlapping intervals, the table will be incorrect. Compare the following incorrect table to the correct table above.

Yearly Volunteering

Number of Hours	Frequency
40–60	5
60–80	9
80–100	10
100–120	6

Probability

Lesson 12-8 introduces the following four methods for finding the probabilities of compound events.

   1. $P(A \text{ or } B) = P(A) + P(B)$

This method is used to find the probability that two mutually exclusive events will occur.

Mutually exclusive events are events that cannot happen at the same time in any given outcome. For example, if you roll a number cube, rolling a 1 and rolling a 2 are mutually exclusive. You cannot roll a 1 and a 2 at the same time.

   2. $P(A \text{ or } B) = P(A) + P(B) - P(A \text{ and } B)$

This method is used to find the probability that two overlapping events will occur.

Overlapping events are events that can happen at the same time in any given outcome. For example, if you roll a number cube, rolling an even number and a prime number can overlap because 2 is even and prime.

   3. $P(A \text{ and } B) = P(A) + P(B)$

This method is used to find the probability that two independent events will occur.

Independent events are events in which one outcome does not affect the outcome of the other. This is the case in experiments with replacement.

   4. $P(A \text{ then } B) = P(A) + P(B \text{ after } A)$

This method is used to find the probability that two dependent events will occur.

Dependent events are events in which one outcome does affect the outcome of the other. This is the case in experiments without replacement.

Common Errors With Probability

In experiments without replacement students may forget to reduce the number of possible outcomes in the second event.

DATA ANALYSIS AND PROBABILITY
Pacing and Assignment Guide

		TRADITIONAL			BLOCK
Lesson	Teaching Day(s)	Basic	Average	Advanced	Block
12-1	1	Problems 1-3 Exs. 8–24 all, 26–28 even, 29–30, 33–41	Problems 1-3 Exs. 9–23 odd, 25–30, 33–41	Problems 1-3 Exs. 9–23 odd, 25–41	**Day 1** Problems 1-3 Exs. 9–23 odd, 25–30, 33–41
12-2	1	Problems 1-4 Exs. 7–20 all, 22–30 even, 31, 34–41	Problems 1-4 Exs. 7–19 odd, 21–31, 34–41	Problems 1-4 Exs. 7–19 odd, 21–41	Problems 1-4 Exs. 7–19 odd, 21–31, 34–41
12-3	1	Problems 1-3 Exs. 7–19 all, 40–50	Problems 1-5 Exs. 7–29 odd, 30–37, 40–50	Problems 1-5 Exs. 7–29 odd, 30–50	**Day 2** Problems 1-5 Exs. 7–29 odd, 30–37, 40–50
	2	Problems 4-5 Exs. 20–29 all, 30, 32, 36			
12-4	1	Problems 1-4 Exs. 8–21 all, 24, 27–33	Problems 1-4 Exs. 9–17 odd, 19–24, 27–33	Problems 1-4 Exs. 9–17 odd, 19–33	Problems 1-4 Exs. 9–17 odd, 19–24, 27–33
12-5	1	Problems 1-3 Exs. 7–17 all, 41–52	Problems 1-5 Exs. 7–21 odd, 23–38, 41–52	Problems 1-5 Exs. 7–21 odd, 23–52	**Day 3** Problems 1-5 Exs. 7–21 odd, 23–38, 41–52
	2	Problems 4-5 Exs. 18–26 all, 28–34 even			
12-6	1	Problems 1-4 Exs. 11–39 all, 40–46 even, 53–55 all, 66–81	Problems 1-4 Exs. 11–39 odd, 40–61, 66–81	Problems 1-4 Exs. 11–39 odd, 40–81	Problems 1-4 Exs. 11–39 odd, 40–61, 66–81
12-7	1	Problems 1-3 Exs. 10–27 all, 47–59	Problems 1-3 Exs. 11–27 odd, 47–59	Problems 1-5 Exs. 11–33 odd, 34–59	**Day 4** Problems 1-5 Exs. 11–33 odd, 34–41, 47–59
	2	Problems 4-5 Exs. 28–36 all, 38	Problems 4-5 Exs. 29–33 odd, 34–41		
12-8	1	Problems 1-2 Exs. 8–20 all, 46–55	Problems 1-2 Exs. 9–19 odd, 46–55	Problems 1-5 Exs. 9–35 odd, 36–55	**Day 5** Problems 1-5 Exs. 9–35 odd, 36–43, 46–55
	2	Problems 3-5 Exs. 21–35 all, 36–40 even, 41–42	Problems 3-5 Exs. 21–35 odd, 36–43		
Review	1	Chapter 12 Review	Chapter 12 Review	Chapter 12 Review	**Day 6** Chapter 12 Review
Assess	1	Chapter 12 Test	Chapter 12 Test	Chapter 12 Test	Chapter 12 Test
Total		**14 Days**	**12 Days**	**10 Days**	**6 Days**

Note: Pacing does not include Concept Bytes and other feature pages.

Resources

KEY

I = Interactive asset at PowerAlgebra.com
E = Editable master at PowerAlgebra.com
P = Available in Print
T = Available as a Transparency
M = Master at PowerAlgebra.com
✓ = CD-ROM

	For the Chapter	12-1	12-2	12-3	12-4	12-5	12-6	12-7	12-8
Planning									
Teacher Center Online Planner & Grade Book	I	I	I	I	I	I	I	I	I
Interactive Learning & Guided Instruction									
My Math Video	I								
Solve It!		I TM	I TM	I TM	I TM	I TM	I TM	I TM	I TM
Student Companion (SP)*		P M	P M	P M	P M	P M	P M	P M	P M
Vocabulary Support		I P M	I P M	I P M	I P M	I P M	I P M	I P M	I P M
Got It? Support		I P	I P	I P	I P	I P	I P	I P	I P
Dynamic Activity					I			I	I
Online Problems		I	I	I	I	I	I	I	I
Additional Problems		M	M	M	M	M	M	M	M
English Language Learner Support (TR)		E P M	E P M	E P M	E P M	E P M	E P M	E P M	E P M
Activities, Games, and Puzzles		E M	E M	E M	E M	E M	E M	E M	E M
Teaching With TI Technology With CD-ROM									
TI-Nspire™ Support CD-ROM		✓	✓	✓	✓	✓	✓	✓	✓
Lesson Check & Practice									
Student Companion (SP)*		P M	P M	P M	P M	P M	P M	P M	P M
Lesson Check Support		I P	I P	I P	I P	I P	I P	I P	I P
Practice and Problem Solving Workbook (SP)		P	P	P	P	P	P	P	P
Think About a Plan (TR)*		E P M	E P M	E P M	E P M	E P M	E P M	E P M	E P M
Practice Form G (TR)*		E P M	E P M	E P M	E P M	E P M	E P M	E P M	E P M
Standardized Test Prep (TR)*		P M	P M	P M	P M	P M	P M	P M	P M
Practice Form K (TR)*		E P M	E P M	E P M	E P M	E P M	E P M	E P M	E P M
Extra Practice	E M								
Find the Errors!	M								
Enrichment (TR)		E P M	E P M	E P M	E P M	E P M	E P M	E P M	E P M
Answers and Solutions CD-ROM	✓	✓	✓	✓	✓	✓	✓	✓	✓
Assess & Remediate									
ExamView CD-ROM	✓	✓	✓	✓	✓	✓	✓	✓	✓
Lesson Quiz		I TM	I TM	I TM	I TM	I TM	I TM	I TM	I TM
Quizzes and Tests Form G (TR)*	E P M					E P			E P
Quizzes and Tests Form K (TR)*	E P M					E P			E P
Reteaching (TR)*		E P M	E P M	E P M	E P M	E P M	E P M	E P M	E P M
Performance Tasks (TR)*	P M								
Cumulative Review (TR)*	P M								
Progress Monitoring Assessments	I P M								

(TR) Available in All-In-One Teaching Resources   *Spanish available

1 Interactive Learning

Solve It!

PURPOSE To use matrices as a method of organizing data

PROCESS Students may
- make an organized list or chart.
- use the process of elimination.

ANSWER See Solve It in Answers on next page.

CONNECT THE MATH In the Solve It, students organize data. Matrices are a way to organize data that can make it easier to perform mathematical operations.

Organizing Data Using Matrices

Objectives To organize data in a matrix
To add and subtract matrices and multiply a matrix by a scalar

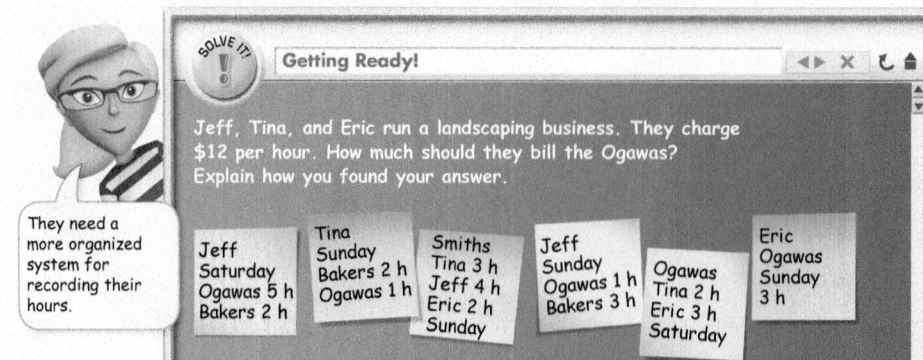

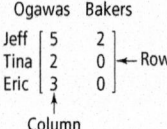

They need a more organized system for recording their hours.

Lesson Vocabulary
- matrix
- element
- scalar
- scalar multiplication

A **matrix** is a rectangular arrangement of numbers in rows and columns. The plural of *matrix* is *matrices* (pronounced MAY truh seez). The matrix below shows the hours Jeff, Tina, and Eric worked on Saturday.

$$\begin{array}{c} \\ \text{Jeff} \\ \text{Tina} \\ \text{Eric} \end{array} \begin{array}{cc} \text{Ogawas} & \text{Bakers} \\ \left[\begin{array}{cc} 5 & 2 \\ 2 & 0 \\ 3 & 0 \end{array}\right. \end{array} \leftarrow \text{Row}$$

Column

You identify the size of a matrix by the number of rows and the number of columns. The matrix above has 3 rows and 2 columns, so it is a 3 × 2 matrix.

Each number in a matrix is an **element.** Matrices are equal if they are the same size and the elements in corresponding positions are equal.

$$\begin{bmatrix} -1 & 2 \\ 4 & 0 \end{bmatrix} = \begin{bmatrix} -1 & \frac{4}{2} \\ (5-1) & 0 \end{bmatrix}$$

Essential Understanding You can use matrices to organize data. This may make it easier to perform calculations on the data.

12-1 Preparing to Teach

BIG idea **Data Representation** UbD

ESSENTIAL UNDERSTANDINGS
- Matrices can be used to organize data.
- Using matrices can make it easier to perform calculations on data.
- Matrices can be added or subtracted or multiplied by a scalar.

Math Background

Matrices in this lesson are used as a means for organizing and performing computations with data. Students often struggle to remember that the dimensions of a matrix are given as rows × columns, not vice versa.

Students are introduced to the matrix operations of addition and subtraction as well as to scalar multiplication. Matrices with the same dimensions can be added and subtracted; therefore, students simply think of these operations as extensions of the operations of adding and subtracting real numbers. Scalar multiplication can be related to the idea of the Distributive Property. The scalar factor is multiplied by each element of the matrix.

In a future mathematics course, students will be introduced to a new operation called matrix multiplication. Learning to create and perform operations with matrices will lead students to solving systems of equations using matrices.

Support Student Learning

Use the **Algebra 1 Companion** to engage and support students during instructions. See Lesson Resources at the end of this lesson for details.

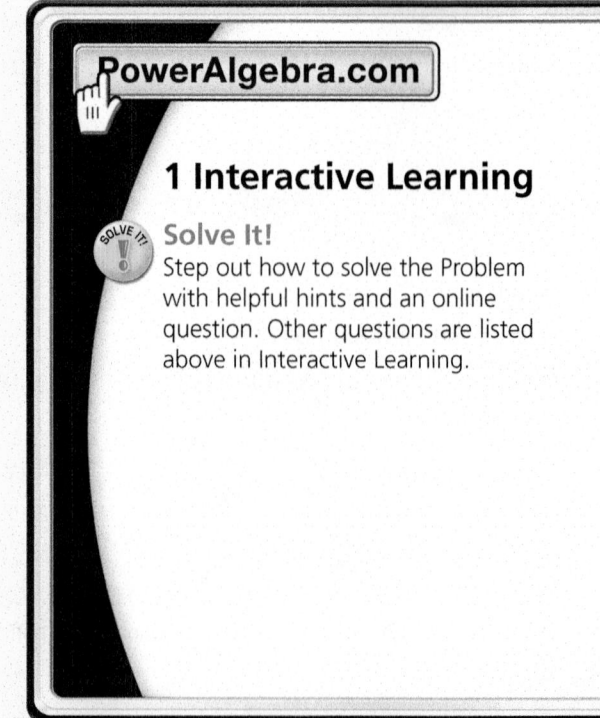

PowerAlgebra.com

1 Interactive Learning

Solve It!

Step out how to solve the Problem with helpful hints and an online question. Other questions are listed above in Interactive Learning.

You may need to add or subtract matrices in order to solve problems. You can only add or subtract matrices that are the same size. You add or subtract matrices by adding or subtracting the corresponding elements.

 Problem 1 Adding and Subtracting Matrices

What is each sum or difference?

A $\begin{bmatrix} -5 & 2.7 \\ 7 & -3 \end{bmatrix} + \begin{bmatrix} -3 & -3.9 \\ -4 & 2 \end{bmatrix} = \begin{bmatrix} -5 + (-3) & 2.7 + (-3.9) \\ 7 + (-4) & -3 + 2 \end{bmatrix}$ Add corresponding elements.

$= \begin{bmatrix} -8 & -1.2 \\ 3 & -1 \end{bmatrix}$ Simplify.

B $\begin{bmatrix} 2 & 11 \\ -4 & 3.2 \\ 1.5 & -5 \end{bmatrix} - \begin{bmatrix} -1 & 8 \\ -6.5 & 4 \\ 0 & -3 \end{bmatrix} = \begin{bmatrix} 2 - (-1) & 11 - 8 \\ -4 - (-6.5) & 3.2 - 4 \\ 1.5 - 0 & -5 - (-3) \end{bmatrix}$ Subtract corresponding elements.

$= \begin{bmatrix} 3 & 3 \\ 2.5 & -0.8 \\ 1.5 & -2 \end{bmatrix}$ Simplify.

Got It? 1. What is each sum or difference in parts (a) and (b)?

a. $\begin{bmatrix} 5 \\ 3.2 \\ -4.9 \end{bmatrix} + \begin{bmatrix} -9 \\ -1.7 \\ -11.1 \end{bmatrix}$
b. $\begin{bmatrix} -4 & 0 \\ 3 & 7 \end{bmatrix} - \begin{bmatrix} -5 & -1 \\ 0.5 & -3 \end{bmatrix}$

c. Reasoning Explain why you cannot add or subtract matrices that are not the same size.

You may also need to multiply a matrix by a real number in order to solve problems. The real-number factor is called a **scalar**. Multiplying a matrix by a scalar is called **scalar multiplication**. To use scalar multiplication, multiply each element in the matrix by the scalar.

 Problem 2 Multiplying a Matrix by a Scalar

What is the product $3\begin{bmatrix} 4 & -1.5 \\ 1 & -6 \end{bmatrix}$?

$3\begin{bmatrix} 4 & -1.5 \\ 1 & -6 \end{bmatrix} = \begin{bmatrix} 3(4) & 3(-1.5) \\ 3(1) & 3(-6) \end{bmatrix}$ Multiply each element by the scalar, 3.

$= \begin{bmatrix} 12 & -4.5 \\ 3 & -18 \end{bmatrix}$ Simplify.

Think

Can you add the matrices?
Yes, you can add the matrices because they are the same size. Each matrix has 2 rows and 2 columns.

Think

Which factor is the scalar?
The scalar is the real-number factor, 3.

---

2 Guided Instruction

 Each Problem is worked out and supported online.

Problem 1
Adding and Subtracting Matrices
Animated

Problem 2
Multiplying a Matrix by a Scalar
Animated

Problem 3
Using Matrices
Animated

Support in Algebra 1 Companion
• Vocabulary
• Key Concepts
• Got It?

---

2 Guided Instruction

Problem 1

Q How many rows and columns does each matrix in 1A contain? **[two rows and two columns]**

Q How many rows and columns does each matrix in 1B contain? **[three rows and two columns]**

Q How could you change the operation in 1B to addition? **[You could change the sign of each number in the second matrix and then add the matrices.]**

Got It?

Q Is matrix addition commutative? Explain. **[Yes; the order of addition does not matter.]**

Q Is matrix subtraction commutative? Explain. **[No; the order of the subtraction matters.]**

Problem 2

Q Will the product of a scalar and a matrix always have the same dimensions as the original matrix? Explain. **[Yes; each element in the original matrix is multiplied by the scalar and is placed in the same position in the product matrix.]**

Q How can your knowledge of the Distributive Property help you remember how to perform scalar multiplication? **[When you use the Distributive Property, all terms inside the parentheses get multiplied by the term on the outside of the parentheses. In scalar multiplication, all numbers on the inside of the brackets get multiplied by the scalar that is outside of the brackets.]**

Answers

Solve It!
$180; explanations may vary.

Got It?

1. a. $\begin{bmatrix} -4 \\ 1.5 \\ -16 \end{bmatrix}$

b. $\begin{bmatrix} 1 & 1 \\ 2.5 & 10 \end{bmatrix}$

c. You add or subtract matrices by adding or subtracting the corresponding elements. If matrices are not the same size they will not have corresponding elements in each case.

Got It?

SYNTHESIZING

Elicit from students that while the multiplicative identity would be multiplying by a scalar of 1, there is no scalar which would act as a multiplicative inverse unless all elements of the matrix were identical.

Problem 3

Q Why is it important to create both matrices with consistent labels? **[So that when you add the matrices, you will be adding data which corresponds.]**

Q What matrix operation is necessary to determine the highest average number of clear days in a full year? **[matrix addition]**

Q If you subtract the two matrices, what does the new matrix represent? **[the differences in the numbers of clear and cloudy days between the two recorded time periods]**

Got It?

Q How can you determine the approximate number of cloudy days in each city in four years time? **[You can multiply the sum of the two matrices by the scalar 4.]**

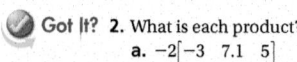 **Got It? 2.** What is each product?

   a. $-2[-3 \quad 7.1 \quad 5]$

   b. $1.5\begin{bmatrix} -11 & 3 \\ 0 & -1.5 \end{bmatrix}$

You can use matrices to organize real-world data.

Problem 3 Using Matrices

Weather Use the weather chart below. Which city has the greatest average number of clear days in a full year?

Average Number of Clear and Cloudy Days

September – February	March – August
Phoenix: 102 clear, 41 cloudy	Phoenix: 110 clear, 27 cloudy
Miami: 43 clear, 58 cloudy	Miami: 31 clear, 59 cloudy
Portland: 55 clear, 82 cloudy	Portland: 45 clear, 83 cloudy

Portland, ME

Phoenix, AZ

Miami, FL

Plan

What size matrices should you use?
There are three cities and two types of weather represented by the data. So you can use 3 × 2 matrices or 2 × 3 matrices.

Step 1 Use matrices to organize the information.

September–February

	Clear	Cloudy
Phoenix	102	41
Miami	43	58
Portland	55	82

March–August

	Clear	Cloudy
Phoenix	110	27
Miami	31	59
Portland	45	83

Step 2 Add the matrices to find the average numbers of clear and cloudy days in a full year for each city. The matrices are the same size, so you can add them.

$$\begin{bmatrix} 102 & 41 \\ 43 & 58 \\ 55 & 82 \end{bmatrix} + \begin{bmatrix} 110 & 27 \\ 31 & 59 \\ 45 & 83 \end{bmatrix} = \begin{bmatrix} 212 & 68 \\ 74 & 117 \\ 100 & 165 \end{bmatrix}$$ Add corresponding elements.

Step 3 Find the greatest average number of clear days in a full year. The first column of the matrix represents the average number of clear days in a full year for each city. The greatest number in that column is 212, which corresponds to Phoenix. So Phoenix has the greatest average number of clear days in a full year.

$$\begin{bmatrix} 212 & 68 \\ 74 & 117 \\ 100 & 165 \end{bmatrix}$$

Got It? 3. Which city in Problem 3 has the greatest average number of cloudy days in a full year?

716　Chapter 12　Data Analysis and Probability

Additional Problems

1. What is each sum or difference?

a. $\begin{bmatrix} 4.1 & 6 \\ -2 & 3 \\ 7.5 & -8 \end{bmatrix} + \begin{bmatrix} 2.9 & 5 \\ 7 & 4.2 \\ -9 & 11 \end{bmatrix}$

b. $\begin{bmatrix} 9 & 14 \\ -8 & 5 \end{bmatrix} - \begin{bmatrix} 15 & -6 \\ -12 & 4 \end{bmatrix}$

ANSWER a. $\begin{bmatrix} 7 & 11 \\ 5 & 7.2 \\ -1.5 & 3 \end{bmatrix}$;

b. $\begin{bmatrix} -6 & 20 \\ 4 & 1 \end{bmatrix}$

2. What is the product of $12\begin{bmatrix} -1.25 & 3 \\ 2 & -1.5 \end{bmatrix}$?

ANSWER $\begin{bmatrix} -15 & 36 \\ 24 & -18 \end{bmatrix}$

3. The tables show the votes for two candidates running for student council president. Which candidate won the election?

Student Council President

	Maria	Clarence
Freshmen	117	145
Sophomores	96	132

Student Council President

	Maria	Clarence
Juniors	151	108
Seniors	112	119

ANSWER Clarence

Answers

Got It? (continued)

2. a. $[6 \quad -14.2 \quad -10]$

  b. $\begin{bmatrix} -16.5 & 4.5 \\ 0 & -2.25 \end{bmatrix}$

3. Portland

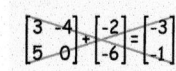

Lesson Check

Do you know HOW?

Find each sum or difference.

1. $\begin{bmatrix} 0 & 7 \\ -4 & 5 \end{bmatrix} + \begin{bmatrix} -3 & 2 \\ 4 & -1 \end{bmatrix}$ **2.** $\begin{bmatrix} 5 & 4 \\ -1 & 0 \end{bmatrix} - \begin{bmatrix} 3 & 1 \\ -3 & 3 \end{bmatrix}$

Find each product.

3. $2 \begin{bmatrix} 4 & 0 & 5 \\ -2 & 1 & 2 \end{bmatrix}$ **4.** $-6 \begin{bmatrix} 5 & 0 \\ 2 & -3 \end{bmatrix}$

Do you UNDERSTAND?

5. Vocabulary How many elements are there in a 3×3 matrix?

6. Error Analysis A student added two matrices as shown at the right. Describe and correct the mistake.

$\begin{bmatrix} 3 & -4 \\ 5 & 0 \end{bmatrix} + \begin{bmatrix} -2 \\ -6 \end{bmatrix} = \begin{bmatrix} -3 \\ -1 \end{bmatrix}$

7. Open-Ended Write two different 3×3 matrices. Then add your matrices.

Practice and Problem-Solving Exercises

Ⓐ Practice

Find each sum or difference. ◆ See Problem 1.

8. $\begin{bmatrix} 1 & -1 \\ 0 & 1 \end{bmatrix} + \begin{bmatrix} 0 & 1 \\ 1 & -1 \end{bmatrix}$ **9.** $\begin{bmatrix} -3 & 6 \\ 2 & 0 \end{bmatrix} - \begin{bmatrix} -2 & 5 \\ 2 & 0 \end{bmatrix}$ **10.** $\begin{bmatrix} 5 & 2 \\ -1 & 8 \end{bmatrix} - \begin{bmatrix} 7 & -4 \\ 0 & 2 \end{bmatrix}$

11. $\begin{bmatrix} 4 & -1 \\ 2 & 0 \\ 3 & 5 \end{bmatrix} + \begin{bmatrix} -2 & 0 \\ 3 & -1 \\ -3 & 5 \end{bmatrix}$ **12.** $\begin{bmatrix} 0 & 0.4 \\ -2 & 5.3 \\ 1.2 & 3.7 \end{bmatrix} + \begin{bmatrix} 1.8 & -5 \\ 7.1 & 0 \\ 0.3 & 2.3 \end{bmatrix}$ **13.** $\begin{bmatrix} 4.7 & -0.3 \\ 2.9 & 0.7 \\ -3.5 & 1.3 \end{bmatrix} - \begin{bmatrix} 2.3 & 7.3 \\ -5.1 & 0.4 \\ 4.2 & 0 \end{bmatrix}$

Find each product. ◆ See Problem 2.

14. $4 \begin{bmatrix} 6 & -3 \\ 0 & 5 \end{bmatrix}$ **15.** $-2 \begin{bmatrix} 3 & -1 \\ 7 & -2 \end{bmatrix}$ **16.** $0 \begin{bmatrix} 5.3 & -7.2 \\ -1.8 & 0.6 \end{bmatrix}$ **17.** $-5 \begin{bmatrix} 3.8 & 2.1 & 7 \\ 9.4 & -6 & 0 \end{bmatrix}$

18. $2.7 \begin{bmatrix} 3 & 4.7 \\ 0 & -3 \\ 5.7 & 2.7 \end{bmatrix}$ **19.** $-3.1 \begin{bmatrix} 4 & 7.5 \\ 9 & -5 \\ 1 & 4.6 \end{bmatrix}$ **20.** $8.3 \begin{bmatrix} -1 & 8.2 \\ 0.3 & -4.1 \\ 6.2 & 9.5 \end{bmatrix}$ **21.** $-0.2 \begin{bmatrix} 8.3 & -3 & 0 \\ 4.5 & 5.6 & 1 \\ -1 & 2.9 & 7 \end{bmatrix}$

22. Sports For a certain city, the tables below show the numbers of participants in various sports in 2005 and 2010. Which sport had the greatest numerical increase in student participation between 2005 and 2010? Find your answer using matrices. ◆ See Problem 3.

Sports Participation, 2005

Sport	Students	Adults
Baseball	739	215
Basketball	1023	437
Football	690	58
Soccer	1546	42

Sports Participation, 2010

Sport	Students	Adults
Baseball	892	351
Basketball	1114	483
Football	653	64
Soccer	1712	37

Answers

Lesson Check

1. $\begin{bmatrix} -3 & 9 \\ 0 & 4 \end{bmatrix}$ **2.** $\begin{bmatrix} 2 & 3 \\ 2 & -3 \end{bmatrix}$

3. $\begin{bmatrix} 8 & 0 & 10 \\ -4 & 2 & 4 \end{bmatrix}$ **4.** $\begin{bmatrix} -30 & 0 \\ -12 & 18 \end{bmatrix}$

5. 9

6. The student added entries across the rows, but the matrices are not the same size so they cannot be added.

7. Check students' work.

Practice and Problem-Solving Exercises

8. $\begin{bmatrix} 1 & 0 \\ 1 & 0 \end{bmatrix}$ **9.** $\begin{bmatrix} -1 & 1 \\ 0 & 0 \end{bmatrix}$

10. $\begin{bmatrix} -2 & 6 \\ -1 & 6 \end{bmatrix}$ **11.** $\begin{bmatrix} 2 & -1 \\ 5 & -1 \\ 0 & 10 \end{bmatrix}$

12. $\begin{bmatrix} 1.8 & -4.6 \\ 5.1 & 5.3 \\ 1.5 & 6 \end{bmatrix}$ **13.** $\begin{bmatrix} 2.4 & -7.6 \\ 8 & 0.3 \\ -7.7 & 1.3 \end{bmatrix}$

14. $\begin{bmatrix} 24 & -12 \\ 0 & 20 \end{bmatrix}$ **15.** $\begin{bmatrix} -6 & 2 \\ -14 & 4 \end{bmatrix}$

16. $\begin{bmatrix} 0 & 0 \\ 0 & 0 \end{bmatrix}$

17. $\begin{bmatrix} -19 & -10.5 & -35 \\ -47 & 30 & 0 \end{bmatrix}$

18. $\begin{bmatrix} 8.1 & 12.69 \\ 0 & -8.1 \\ 15.39 & 7.29 \end{bmatrix}$

19. $\begin{bmatrix} -12.4 & -23.25 \\ -27.9 & 15.5 \\ -3.1 & -14.26 \end{bmatrix}$

20. $\begin{bmatrix} -8.3 & 68.06 \\ 2.49 & -34.03 \\ 51.46 & 78.85 \end{bmatrix}$

21. $\begin{bmatrix} -1.66 & 0.6 & 0 \\ -0.9 & -1.12 & -0.2 \\ 0.2 & -0.58 & -1.4 \end{bmatrix}$

22. soccer

---

3 Lesson Check

Do you know HOW?

- If students have difficulty with Exercise 2, then have them review Problem 1 to see how to handle the subtraction sign between the two matrices.

Do you UNDERSTAND?

- If students have difficulty with Exercise 7, then make sure they are adding corresponding elements.

Close

Q What are the two purposes for using matrices to represent data? **[Matrices provide organization for data and simplify calculations with the data.]**

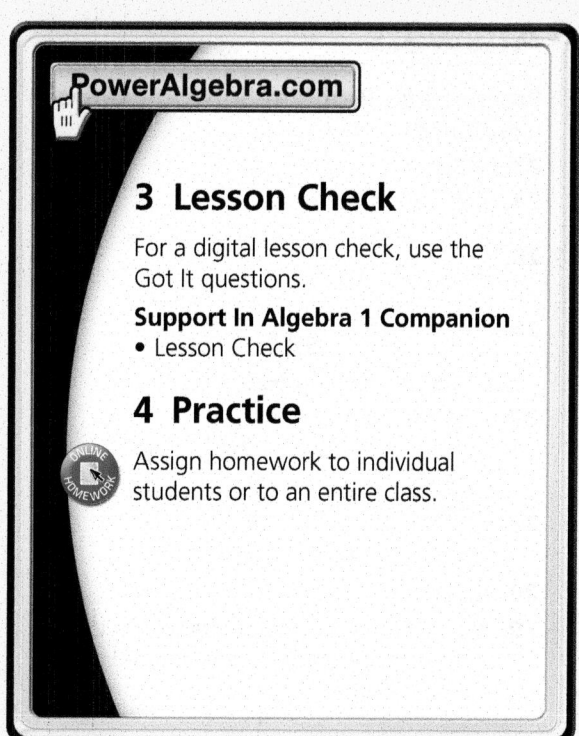

3 Lesson Check

For a digital lesson check, use the Got It questions.

Support In Algebra 1 Companion
- Lesson Check

4 Practice

Assign homework to individual students or to an entire class.

4 Practice

ASSIGNMENT GUIDE

Basic: 8–24 all, 26–28 even, 29–30

Average: 9–23 odd, 25–30

Advanced: 9–23 odd, 25–32

Standardized Test Prep: 33–36

Mixed Review: 37–41

Reasoning exercises have blue headings.

Applications exercises have red headings.

EXERCISE 30: Use the Think About a Plan worksheet in the Practice and Problem Solving Workbook (also available in the Teaching Resources in print and online) to further support students' development in becoming independent learners.

HOMEWORK QUICK CHECK

To check students' understanding of key skills and concepts, go over Exercises 11, 15, 23, 29, and 30.

---

23. **Manufacturing** A furniture company has two factories. During the first shift, Factory A made 250 chairs and 145 tables, and Factory B made 300 chairs and 75 tables. During the second shift, Factory A made 275 chairs and 90 tables, and Factory B made 240 chairs and 120 tables. Which factory made more chairs during the two shifts? Find your answer using matrices.

24. **Sales** The weekly sales records below show the numbers of different colors and models of shoes sold in two weeks. Which is the color and model shoe with the highest sales between February 2 and 15? Find your answer using matrices.

Shoe Sales, Feb. 2–8

Color	Model 73	Model 84
Black	153	79
White	241	116
Blue	58	32
Brown	95	47

Shoe Sales, Feb. 9–15

Color	Model 73	Model 84
Black	172	82
White	278	130
Blue	65	29
Brown	103	54

 Apply

Simplify each expression. (*Hint:* Multiply before adding or subtracting.)

25. $2\begin{bmatrix} 6 & 0 & -2 \\ -5 & 3 & 1 \end{bmatrix} - \begin{bmatrix} 3 & -1 & -6 \\ 0 & 4 & 2 \end{bmatrix}$

26. $\begin{bmatrix} 0 & 3.4 & 5 \\ 4.1 & -2 & 1 \end{bmatrix} + 0.5\begin{bmatrix} -8 & 6.4 & 0 \\ 0.2 & -2.8 & 4.2 \end{bmatrix}$

27. $-3\begin{bmatrix} 4.2 & -7.3 & 0.7 \\ 2.7 & -9.3 & 11.8 \\ 3.6 & 8.2 & -4.8 \end{bmatrix} - 2\begin{bmatrix} 7.8 & -4.1 & 9.4 \\ -8 & 0 & 0.8 \\ -1.4 & 5.9 & 3.3 \end{bmatrix}$

28. $\begin{bmatrix} -3.7 & 2.5 & -7.5 \\ 2.2 & -6.2 & 0.3 \\ 1.5 & -3.1 & 4.9 \end{bmatrix} + (-5)\begin{bmatrix} 8.7 & 1.5 & 4.5 \\ -4 & 0.1 & -7.3 \\ 5.8 & 4.1 & 7.3 \end{bmatrix}$

29. **Think About a Plan** Use the table at the right that shows nutrition information for 1 serving of each type of food. For which item(s) do 6 servings have less than 1000 Calories?
    - What matrix represents the nutrition information for 1 serving?
    - How can you find the nutrition information for 6 servings?

FOOD ITEM		Serving	Calories	Protein (g)	Fat (g)
Chicken		1	148	29	3.5
Fruit salad		1	221	1	0
Spaghetti & meatballs		1	273	11	13

Source: U.S. Department of Agriculture

30. **Politics** The results of an election for mayor are shown below. The town will hold a runoff election between the top two candidates if no one received more than 50% of the votes. Should the town hold a runoff? If so, which candidates should be in the runoff? Explain your reasoning.

Votes by Precinct

Candidate	Precinct			
	1	2	3	4
Greene	373	285	479	415
Jackson	941	871	114	97
Voigt	146	183	728	682

Answers

Practice and Problem-Solving Exercises
(continued)

23. Factory B

24. model 73 in white

25. $\begin{bmatrix} 9 & 1 & 2 \\ -10 & 2 & 0 \end{bmatrix}$

26. $\begin{bmatrix} -4 & 6.6 & 5 \\ 4.2 & -3.4 & 3.1 \end{bmatrix}$

27. $\begin{bmatrix} -28.2 & 30.1 & -20.9 \\ 7.9 & 27.9 & -37 \\ -8 & -36.4 & 7.8 \end{bmatrix}$

28. $\begin{bmatrix} -47.2 & -5 & -30 \\ 22.2 & -6.7 & 36.8 \\ -27.5 & -23.6 & -31.6 \end{bmatrix}$

29. chicken

30. Yes; Jackson and Voigt; there were a total of 5314 votes cast and no one received more than 2657 votes.

Find the values of x and y that make each equation true.

31. $\begin{bmatrix} 0 & x \\ 2x & -4 \end{bmatrix} + \begin{bmatrix} 3 & 4y \\ y & 8 \end{bmatrix} = \begin{bmatrix} 3 & 18 \\ 1 & 4 \end{bmatrix}$

32. $\begin{bmatrix} x & -1 \\ 4 & 3x \end{bmatrix} + \begin{bmatrix} -3y & 5 \\ -6 & 2y \end{bmatrix} = \begin{bmatrix} 7 & 4 \\ -2 & 10 \end{bmatrix}$

Standardized Test Prep

SAT/ACT

33. Which matrix is equal to $-3 \begin{bmatrix} 5.5 & -1 \\ -3 & 2 \end{bmatrix}$?

 Ⓐ $\begin{bmatrix} 8.5 & 2 \\ 0 & 5 \end{bmatrix}$ Ⓑ $\begin{bmatrix} 2.5 & -4 \\ -6 & -1 \end{bmatrix}$ Ⓒ $\begin{bmatrix} 16.5 & -3 \\ -9 & 6 \end{bmatrix}$ Ⓓ $\begin{bmatrix} -16.5 & 3 \\ 9 & -6 \end{bmatrix}$

34. Which equation represents a line parallel to the graph of $y = 3x + 6$?

 Ⓕ $x - \frac{1}{3}y = 0$ Ⓗ $y = \frac{1}{3}x + 2$
 Ⓖ $y = -3x + 2$ Ⓘ $y = 2x + 6$

35. What is the simplified form of $2\sqrt{108}$?

 Ⓐ $12\sqrt{3}$ Ⓑ $6\sqrt{12}$ Ⓒ $3\sqrt{26}$ Ⓓ $2\sqrt{6}$

Short Response

36. Carlos does his homework at a rate of 25 problems per hour. Cecelia does her homework at a rate of 30 problems per hour. Carlos started his homework 12 min before Cecelia. How many hours after Carlos started his homework will they have done the same number of problems? Show your work.

Mixed Review

See Lesson 11-7.

Identify the excluded value of each rational function.

37. $y = \frac{3}{x-5}$ **38.** $y = \frac{-1}{x}$ **39.** $f(x) = \frac{5x}{x-4}$

Get Ready! To prepare for Lesson 12-2, do Exercises 40 and 41.

For each table, make a scatter plot of the data. Tell whether a correlation exists. If so, tell whether the correlation reflects a causal relationship. Explain your reasoning.

See Lesson 5-7.

40. Shoe Sizes and Test Scores

Name	Shoe Size	Test Score
Baker	9	87
Johns	11	94
Rivera	8	96
Samuels	7	75

41. Sales Commissions

Employee	Products Sold	Commission Earned ($)
Andrews	38	310
Garcia	24	250
Jordan	47	448
Walker	53	495

---

31. $x = -2$, $y = 5$

32. $x = 4$, $y = -1$

33. D

34. F

35. A

36. [2] Let x represent the number of hours after Carlos started.

$25x = 30(x - 0.2)$

$25x = 30x - 6$

$-5x = -6$

$x = 1.2$

Carlos and Cecelia will have done the same number of problems 1.2 h after Carlos started his homework.

[1] correct methods used with minor computational error

37. 5

38. 0

39. 4

40.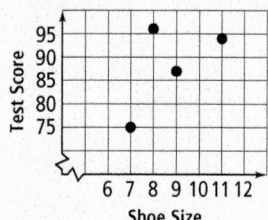

not likely

41.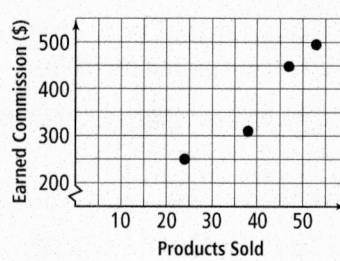

Causal; the amount of sales is related to earnings.

Additional Instructional Support

Algebra 1 Companion

Students can use the **Algebra 1 Companion** worktext (4 pages) as you teach the lesson. Use the Companion to support

- New Vocabulary
- Key Concepts
- Got It for each Problem
- Lesson Check

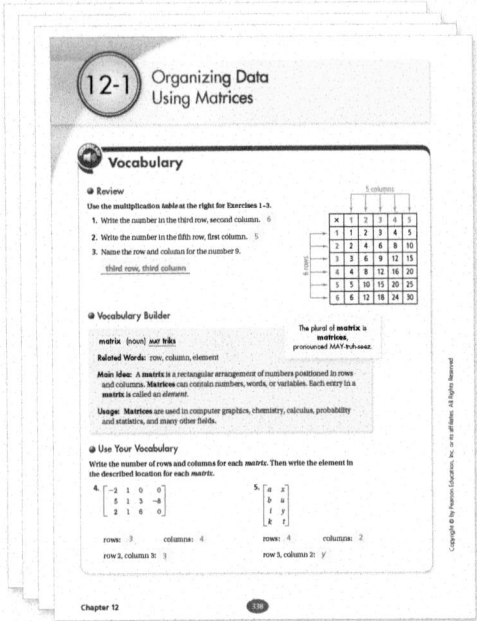

ELL Support

Connect to Prior Knowledge Begin the lesson by writing an addition problem with integers, such as: $-5 + 8 = ?$ on the board. Model finding the sum, using a number line if needed. Repeat with subtraction and then multiplication. Invite students to solve the problems.

Assess Understanding When introducing matrices, use letters instead of numbers. For example, to show how to add matrices, use a model such as this:

$$\begin{bmatrix} A & C \\ B & D \end{bmatrix} + \begin{bmatrix} W & Y \\ X & Z \end{bmatrix} = \begin{bmatrix} A+W & C+Y \\ B+X & D+Z \end{bmatrix}.$$

5 Assess & Remediate

Lesson Quiz

1. Find the sum.

$$\begin{bmatrix} 19.2 \\ 4.5 \\ 2 \\ -8 \end{bmatrix} + \begin{bmatrix} -13 \\ 1.5 \\ 6 \\ 3 \end{bmatrix}$$

2. What is the product of $-2.5 \begin{bmatrix} 4 & -8 \\ 10 & -6 \end{bmatrix}$?

3. Do you UNDERSTAND? The sales records for two skateboard models are shown below. Which is the color and model of a skateboard with the highest sales over the 2-week period?

Week 1 Sales

	Thrasher	Revolution
Blue	6	11
Red	9	6
Black	8	10

Week 2 Sales

	Thrasher	Revolution
Blue	9	7
Red	4	10
Black	8	6

ANSWERS TO LESSON QUIZ

1. $\begin{bmatrix} 6.2 \\ 6 \\ 8 \\ -5 \end{bmatrix}$ **2.** $\begin{bmatrix} -10 & 20 \\ -25 & 15 \end{bmatrix}$

3. Blue Revolution

PRESCRIPTION FOR REMEDIATION
Use the student work on the Lesson Quiz to prescribe a differentiated review assignment.

Points	Differentiated Remediation
0–1	Intervention
2	On-level
3	Extension

PowerAlgebra.com

5 Assess & Remediate

Assign the Lesson Quiz. Appropriate intervention, practice, or enrichment is automatically generated based on student performance.

Intervention

- **Reteaching** (2 pages) Provides reteaching and practice exercises for the key lesson concepts. Use with struggling students or absent students.

- **English Language Learner Support** Helps students develop and reinforce mathematical vocabulary and key concepts.

All-in-One Resources/Online
Reteaching

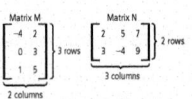

All-in-One Resources/Online
English Language Learner Support

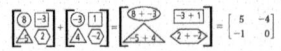

Differentiated Remediation *continued*

On-Level

- **Practice** (2 pages) Provides extra practice for each lesson. For simpler practice exercises, use the Form K Practice pages found in the All-in-One Teaching Resources and online.

- **Think About a Plan** Helps students develop specific problem-solving skills and strategies by providing scaffolded guiding questions.

- **Standardized Test Prep** Focuses on all major exercises, all major question types, and helps students prepare for the high-stakes assessments.

Extension

- **Enrichment** Provides students with interesting problems and activities that extend the concepts of the lesson.

- **Activities, Games, and Puzzles** Worksheets that can be used for concepts development, enrichment, and for fun!

Practice and Problem Solving Wkbk/All-in-One Resources/Online
Practice page 1

12-1 Practice — Form G
Organizing Data Using Matrices

Find each sum or difference.

(exercises 1–19, matrix addition, subtraction, and products)

Practice and Problem Solving Wkbk/All-in-One Resources/Online
Practice page 2

12-1 Practice (continued) — Form G
Organizing Data Using Matrices

20. Seasonal rainfall, in inches, for four cities is shown below. Which city had the greatest increase in summer rainfall between 2006 and 2010? Find the answer using matrices. **Lafayette**

Rainfall in 2006	Spring	Summer
Franklin	6.32	7.21
Eugene	4.19	6.97
Millerville	1.24	5.46
Lafayette	5.51	7.19

Rainfall in 2010	Spring	Summer
Franklin	6.41	7.52
Eugene	4.18	7.02
Millerville	1.67	4.24
Lafayette	6.01	7.94

21. Race times, in seconds, for four members of the track team are shown below. Which runner showed the greatest improvement, in seconds, from the preliminary race to the final race? Find the answer using matrices.

Preliminary race	200m	400m
Haddock	24.69	57.02
Romano	25.53	61.16
Chandra	25.56	59.67
Moore	24.81	58.11

Final race	200m	400m
Haddock	24.61	58.08
Romano	25.52	60.38
Chandra	25.63	57.72
Moore	24.72	58.52

200 m: Moore; 400 m: Chandra

Simplify each expression. (*Hint:* Multiply before adding or subtracting.)

(exercises 22–29)

Practice and Problem Solving Wkbk/All-in-One Resources/Online
Think About a Plan

12-1 Think About a Plan
Organizing Data Using Matrices

Politics The results of an election for mayor are shown below. The town will hold a runoff election between the top two candidates if no one receives more than 50% of the votes. Should the town hold a runoff? If so, which candidates should be in the runoff? Explain your reasoning.

	Votes by Precinct			
Candidate	1	2	3	4
Greene	373	285	479	415
Jackson	941	871	114	97
Voigt	146	183	728	682

Understanding the Problem

1. What does each column in the table represent? votes by precinct

2. What does each row in the table represent? votes for a candidate

Planning the Solution

3. How will you find how many total votes each candidate received? Add the numbers in the row for the candidate.

4. How will you find how many total votes were cast? Add the number of votes for each candidate.

5. How will you find the percentage of votes for each candidate? Divide the candidate's vote total by the total number of votes cast.

Getting an Answer

6. How many votes did each candidate receive? Greene: 1552, Jackson: 2023, Voigt: 1739

7. What percent of the votes did each candidate receive? Greene: 29%, Jackson: 38%, Voigt: 33%

8. Did any candidate receive more than 50% of the total votes? no

9. Who are the top two candidates? Jackson and Voigt

10. Should the town hold a runoff between the top two candidates? yes

---

Practice and Problem Solving Wkbk/All-in-One Resources/Online
Standardized Test Prep

12-1 Standardized Test Prep
Organizing Data Using Matrices

Multiple Choice

For Exercises 1–5, choose the correct letter.

1. What is the sum of $\begin{bmatrix} 3 & -2 \\ 4 & -3 \end{bmatrix} + \begin{bmatrix} -5 & -4 \\ 3 & -2 \end{bmatrix}$? D

A. $\begin{bmatrix} -8 & 2 \\ 1 & 6 \end{bmatrix}$ B. $\begin{bmatrix} -2 & 2 \\ 7 & -1 \end{bmatrix}$ C. $\begin{bmatrix} 2 & 6 \\ -7 & 5 \end{bmatrix}$ D. $\begin{bmatrix} -2 & -6 \\ 7 & -5 \end{bmatrix}$

2. What is the difference of $\begin{bmatrix} 3 & -2 \\ 4 & -3 \end{bmatrix} - \begin{bmatrix} 2 & -5 \\ 7 & 12 \end{bmatrix}$? G

F. $\begin{bmatrix} -3 & 3 \\ -1 & 7 \end{bmatrix}$ G. $\begin{bmatrix} 1 & 3 \\ -3 & 15 \end{bmatrix}$ H. $\begin{bmatrix} -3 & -3 \\ 3 & 15 \end{bmatrix}$ I. $\begin{bmatrix} -1 & 3 \\ 3 & -15 \end{bmatrix}$

3. Which matrix is equal to $-6 \begin{bmatrix} 2 & -7 \\ -3 & 4 \end{bmatrix}$? C

A. $\begin{bmatrix} -4 & -13 \\ -9 & -2 \end{bmatrix}$ B. $\begin{bmatrix} -8 & 1 \\ -3 & -10 \end{bmatrix}$ C. $\begin{bmatrix} -12 & 42 \\ 18 & -24 \end{bmatrix}$ D. $\begin{bmatrix} 12 & -42 \\ -18 & 24 \end{bmatrix}$

4. What is the value of x in the equation $2\begin{bmatrix} 6 & 9 \\ -3 & 1 \end{bmatrix} - \begin{bmatrix} 4 & -6 \\ -5 & 3 \end{bmatrix} = \begin{bmatrix} 8 & x \\ -1 & -1 \end{bmatrix}$? I
F. −24 G. −12 H. 12 I. 24

5. What is the value of x in the equation $-x\begin{bmatrix} 5 & 12 \\ -2 & -3 \end{bmatrix} = \begin{bmatrix} -35 & -84 \\ 14 & 21 \end{bmatrix}$? C
A. −40 B. −7 C. 7 D. 16

Short Response

6. The table at the right shows the sales of cell phones and televisions at an electronics store on Fridays, Saturdays, and Sundays of June and July. On which day did the store sell the most televisions during these two months? Find the answer using matrices.
[2] correct matrix and correct day
[1] incorrect matrix OR incorrect day
[0] incorrect matrix and incorrect day

June	Cell Phones	TVs
Fri	127	114
Sat	138	146
Sun	98	106

July	Cell Phones	TVs
Fri	112	117
Sat	122	152
Sun	101	92

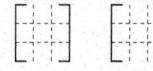
239 231
260 298 ; Saturday
199 198

All-in-One Resources/Online
Enrichment

12-1 Enrichment
Organizing Data Using Matrices

In this lesson, you learned about multiplying a matrix by a scalar. Matrices can also be multiplied by other matrices.

You can multiply two matrices if and only if the number of columns in the first matrix equals the number of rows in the second matrix. Otherwise, the product is undefined.

For example, a 3 × 2 matrix can be multiplied by a 2 × 4 matrix. Since the inner dimensions match, the matrices can be multiplied. The resulting matrix will have the same dimensions as the exterior dimensions, 3 × 4.

Example

To multiply two matrices, multiply the numbers in the first row of the first matrix by the numbers in the first column of the second matrix. Add the products and put the result in the first row, first column of the product matrix.

$\begin{bmatrix} 2 & -1 \\ 0 & 4 \\ -3 & 3 \end{bmatrix} \cdot \begin{bmatrix} 1 & 5 & 0 & -2 \\ -4 & 1 & 2 & 0 \end{bmatrix}$ The first term of the product matrix is $2 \cdot 1 + (-1) \cdot (-4)$.

Repeat this pattern for the remaining numbers in the matrix.

$= \begin{bmatrix} 2 \cdot 1 + (-1)\cdot(-4) & 2\cdot 5 + (-1)\cdot 1 & 2\cdot 0 + (-1)\cdot 2 & 2\cdot(-2)+(-1)\cdot 0 \\ 0\cdot 1 + 4\cdot(-4) & 0\cdot 5 + 4\cdot 1 & 0\cdot 0 + 4\cdot 2 & 0\cdot(-2)+4\cdot 0 \\ (-3)\cdot 1 + 3\cdot(-4) & (-3)\cdot 5 + 3\cdot 1 & (-3)\cdot 0 + 3\cdot 2 & (-3)\cdot(-2)+3\cdot 0 \end{bmatrix}$

$= \begin{bmatrix} 6 & 9 & -2 & -4 \\ -16 & 4 & 8 & 0 \\ -15 & -12 & 6 & 6 \end{bmatrix}$

Determine whether the product of the matrices is defined. If so, determine the dimensions of the resulting matrix.

1. $C_{5\times 6} \times D_{6\times 3}$ yes; 5 × 3
2. $X_{4\times 3} \times Y_{2\times 4}$ no
3. $F_{9\times 10} \times G_{10\times 6}$ yes; 9 × 6

Find each product, if possible.

4. $\begin{bmatrix} -1 \\ 4 \end{bmatrix} \cdot \begin{bmatrix} 2 & -3 \end{bmatrix}$ $\begin{bmatrix} -2 & 3 \\ 8 & -12 \end{bmatrix}$
5. $\begin{bmatrix} 1 & -3 \\ 2 & -4 \end{bmatrix} \cdot \begin{bmatrix} -2 & 6 \\ -4 & 8 \end{bmatrix}$ $\begin{bmatrix} 10 & -18 \\ 12 & -20 \end{bmatrix}$
6. $\begin{bmatrix} 5 & 2 & 3 \\ -3 & 1 & 4 \end{bmatrix} \cdot \begin{bmatrix} 2 & 10 \\ -5 & 9 \end{bmatrix}$ not possible
7. $\begin{bmatrix} -2 & -1 & 5 \\ -6 & 3 & -3 \end{bmatrix} \cdot \begin{bmatrix} 4 \\ 5 \\ 1 \end{bmatrix}$ $\begin{bmatrix} -8 \\ -12 \end{bmatrix}$

Online Teacher Resource Center
Activities, Games, and Puzzles

12-1 Activity: An Array of Math Problems
Organizing Data Using Matrices

In this activity you will work with a partner to understand addition of matrices. You will each build your own matrix and then add them together.

A. Building a Matrix

Color will be used to represent the rows of your matrix. That is, everything in the same row of your matrix must be the same color. The first row will be red, the second row green, and the third row blue. Similarly, shapes will be used to represent the columns of your matrix. So everything in the same column must have the same shape. For now we will build a matrix with only three columns.

On a separate piece of paper, draw a matrix by placing a square in each row of the first column, a circle in each row of the second, and a triangle in each row of the third (do not forget to change colors with rows).

1. In which row would you find a blue triangle? third

2. In which column would you find a blue triangle? third

3. Would a green circle be out of place in the second row, third column? yes

4. Where would you put a red square? first row, first column

Now draw a number of shapes in each matrix position using the color/row, shape/column convention. For instance, you might draw two green circles in the second row and second column. Your partner might draw two green circles in the same position.

B. Adding Matrices Check students' work.

5. In the space below, write the number of objects you put in each position. The position of the number you write down should correspond to the position of the objects in your matrix.

Your matrix   Partner's matrix

6. Write down your partner's numbers.

7. Add the objects in your partner's matrix to your own, being careful not to mix colors or shapes. Count the number of items in each position and write them to the right.

1 Interactive Learning

Solve It!

PURPOSE To analyze data that is summarized using a frequency table

PROCESS Students may interpret the data in the frequency table and use mathematical reasoning to make an estimate.

FACILITATE

Q How many trees are between 26 ft and 50 ft tall? **[44]**

Q Can you determine how many trees are between 30 ft and 50 ft tall? Explain. **[No; the exact heights are not given.]**

ANSWER See Solve It in Answers on next page.

CONNECT THE MATH Students use a data display that they cannot retrieve exact data from. In the lesson, students learn how and when frequency tables and histograms are useful.

2 Guided Instruction

Problem 1

Q How can you use the highest and lowest data values to approximate the interval size? **[You subtract the lowest data value from the highest data value and add one. Then divide by the number of intervals.]**

Q What percentage of the data falls into the 10–13 interval? Explain. $[\frac{3}{14} = 0.214 \approx 21\%]$

Got It?

Ask students to conjecture why a person constructing a histogram might choose to use a few intervals or a large number of intervals.

12-2 Frequency and Histograms

Objective To make and interpret frequency tables and histograms

SOLVE IT! **Getting Ready!**

As part of an environmental science project, you measure the trees in a park to the nearest foot. Your data are shown at the right. You want to estimate the number of trees between 30 ft and 60 ft tall. Choose a method for estimating and state any assumptions you make. What is your estimate? Explain your reasoning.

If you don't have the exact information you need, sometimes you have to estimate.

Tree Height

Height (ft)	Number of Trees
0–25	‖‖ ‖‖ ‖
26–50	‖‖ ‖‖ ‖
51–75	‖‖‖
76–100	‖‖ ‖

Lesson Vocabulary
- frequency
- frequency table
- histogram
- cumulative frequency table

Essential Understanding There are many ways to organize and visually display data. Sometimes it is helpful to organize numerical data into intervals.

The **frequency** of an interval is the number of data values in that interval. A **frequency table** groups a set of data values into intervals and shows the frequency for each interval. Intervals in frequency tables do not overlap, do not have any gaps, and are usually of equal size.

Plan

How do you choose intervals?
The data values range from 2 to 17, so there are a total of 16 possible values. You can divide these 16 values into 4 intervals of size 4.

Problem 1 Making a Frequency Table

Baseball The numbers of home runs by the batters in a local home run derby are listed below. What is a frequency table that represents the data?

7 17 14 2 7 9 5 12 3 10 4 12 7 15

The minimum data value is 2 and the maximum is 17. Intervals of 4 seem reasonable. In the first column of the table, list the intervals. Count the number of data values in each interval and list the number in the second column.

Home Run Results

Home Runs	Frequency
2–5	4
6–9	4
10–13	3
14–17	3

Got It? **1.** What is a frequency table for the data in Problem 1 that uses intervals of 5?

Preparing to Teach

BIG idea Data Representation **UbD**

ESSENTIAL UNDERSTANDINGS
- Sometimes it is helpful to organize numerical data into intervals.
- Frequency tables and histograms display numerical data organized into intervals.

Math Background

A histogram is a special type of bar graph. The histogram is a summary graph showing a count of data points that fall into intervals of the range of a set of data values. Histograms and frequency tables work hand in hand. Histograms summarize a set of data by providing a snapshot of the distribution of the data throughout the set. Histograms are frequently used by businesses and scientists to analyze the distribution of the data of specific

processes. If the distribution of the data is not as desired, then the histogram can be used to guide the modification of the process.

Support Student Learning

Use the **Algebra 1 Companion** to engage and support students during instructions. See Lesson Resources at the end of this lesson for details.

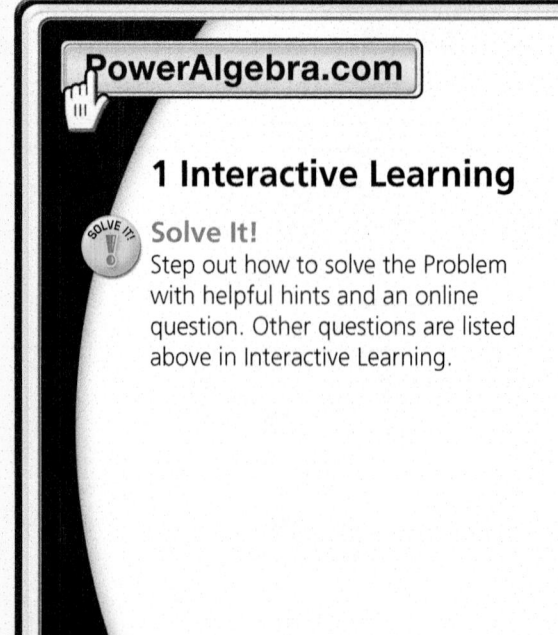

PowerAlgebra.com

1 Interactive Learning

SOLVE IT! **Solve It!**
Step out how to solve the Problem with helpful hints and an online question. Other questions are listed above in Interactive Learning.

A **histogram** is a graph that can display data from a frequency table. A histogram has one bar for each interval. The height of each bar shows the frequency of data in the interval it represents. There are no gaps between bars. The bars are usually of equal width.

 Problem 2 Making a Histogram

Television The data below are the numbers of hours per week a group of students spent watching television. What is a histogram that represents the data?

7 10 1 5 14 22 6 8 0 11 13 3 4 14 5

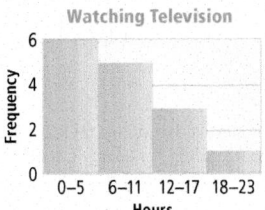

Know	Need	Plan
A set of data values	A histogram of the data values	Make a frequency table. This will help you construct the histogram.

Use the intervals from the frequency table for the histogram. Draw a bar for each interval. Make the height of each bar equal to the frequency of its interval. The bars should touch but not overlap. Label each axis.

Watching Television

Hours	Frequency
0–5	6
6–11	5
12–17	3
18–23	1

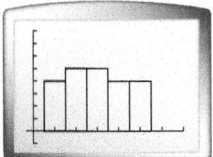

Watching Television

 Got It? 2. The finishing times, in seconds, for a race are shown below. What is a histogram that represents the data?

95 105 83 80 93 98 102 99 82 89 90 82 89

You can describe histograms in terms of their shape. Three types are shown below.

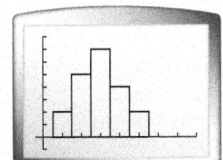 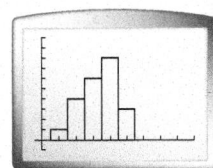 

If the bars are roughly the same height, the histogram is *uniform*.

If a vertical line can divide the histogram into two parts that are close to mirror images, then the histogram is *symmetric*.

If the histogram has one peak that is not in the center, the histogram is *skewed*.

---

2 Guided Instruction

 Each Problem is worked out and supported online.

Problem 1
Making a Frequency Table
Animated

Problem 2
Making a Histogram
Animated

Problem 3
Interpreting Histograms

Problem 4
Making a Cumulative Frequency Table
Animated

Support in Algebra 1 Companion
• Vocabulary
• Key Concepts
• Got It?

Problem 2

Q What is the difference between a histogram and a bar graph? **[The bars in a bar graph represent the frequency within categories; the bars in a histogram represent the frequency within numeric intervals.]**

Q Why should the bars in a histogram touch? **[to show that the bars represent an entire range of values without any gaps]**

Q What trend does the shape of the histogram suggest about the weekly television watching? **[As the number of hours of weekly viewing increases, the corresponding number of students decreases.]**

Got It?

Make sure that students first construct a frequency table prior to creating a histogram. Before making the frequency table, students must choose appropriate intervals.

You can help students associate the names given to the different types of histograms by reviewing the meanings of the words: (sample definitions are given)

uniform – having the same form as others; conforming with one rule

symmetric – having a balanced form; corresponding size and shape on opposite sides match

skewed – having a distorted view from a symmetrical form; more developed on one side than another

---

Answers

Solve It!

Assume tree heights are distrbiuted evenly and that "between 30 and 60" means "greater than 30 and less than 60." Of the 44 trees that are 26–50 ft tall, $\frac{4}{5}$ or about 35 will be greater than 30 ft tall. Of the trees 51–75 ft tall, $\frac{9}{25}$ or about 11 trees will be less than 60 ft tall. So about 46 trees will be between 30 and 60 ft in height.

Got It?

1. Answers may vary. Sample:

Home Runs	Frequency
2–6	4
7–11	5
12–16	4
17–21	1

2. See back of book.

Problem 3

Q What does the shape of the histogram in 3A imply about the data? **[Most of the data falls near the middle of the interval rather than at the extremes.]**

Q What does the shape of a histogram that has a uniform shape imply about the data? **[data is for the most part evenly distributed through the intervals]**

Got It?

Q What is a practical first step for organizing the data? **[Order the data from least to greatest.]**

Q Will the intervals used to make the histogram affect the shape of the graph? Explain. **[Yes; if the intervals are small, the graph is more spread out. If the intervals are large, the graph is more condensed.]**

Problem 4

Q How many students are represented in the table? **[21]**

Q How many students sent at most 29 text messages? Explain. **[17; the cumulative frequency is 17 for the interval that ends in 29.]**

Q How many students sent between 10 and 39 text messages, inclusive? Explain. **[8; 3 + 3 + 2]**

Got It?

Q If you were to make a histogram of a cumulative frequency table, what shape would always result? Explain. **[Skewed to the right; the cumulative frequency always increases as you move to the right.]**

Think

Where have you seen symmetry before?
The parabolas you graphed in Chapter 9 are symmetric with respect to their axis of symmetry.

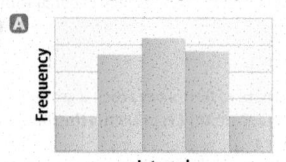 **Problem 3** Interpreting Histograms

Is each histogram *uniform*, *symmetric*, or *skewed*?

A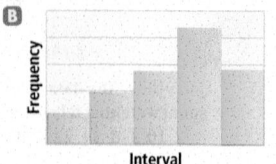

This histogram is symmetric because the halves are close to mirror images.

B

This histogram is skewed because the peak is not in the center.

Got It? **3. a.** The following set of data shows the numbers of dollars Jay spent on lunch over the last two weeks. Make a histogram of the data. Is the histogram *uniform*, *symmetric*, or *skewed*?

17 1 4 11 14 14 5 16 6 5 9 10 13 9

b. **Reasoning** How much money should Jay plan to bring for lunch next week? Explain your reasoning.

A **cumulative frequency table** shows the number of data values that lie in or below a given interval. For example, if the cumulative frequency for the interval 70–79 is 20, then there are 20 data values less than or equal to 79.

Problem 4 Making a Cumulative Frequency Table

Text Messaging The numbers of text messages sent on one day by different students are shown below. What is a cumulative frequency table that represents the data?

17 3 1 30 11 7 1 5 2 39 22 13 2 0 21 1 49 41 27 2 0

Think

What does a cumulative frequency table tell you?
A cumulative frequency table tells you the number of data values that are less than or equal to the upper limit of each interval.

Step 1 Divide the data into intervals. The minimum is 0 and the maximum is 49. You can divide the data into 5 intervals.

Step 2 Write the intervals in the first column. Record the frequency of each interval in the second column.

Daily Text Messaging

Number of Text Messages	Frequency	Cumulative Frequency	
0–9	11	11	
10–19	3	14	11 + 3 = 14
20–29	3	17	14 + 3 = 17
30–39	2	19	17 + 2 = 19
40–49	2	21	19 + 2 = 21

Step 3 For the third column, add the frequency of each interval to the frequencies of all the previous intervals.

Got It? **4.** What is a cumulative frequency table that represents the data below?

12 13 15 1 5 7 10 9 2 2 7 11 2 1 0 15

722 Chapter 12 Data Analysis and Probability

Additional Problems

1. The quiz scores earned by 20 students are listed below. What is a frequency table that represents the data?

9 8 5 8 10 3 6 7 6 7
8 10 8 5 7 9 7 8 4 9

ANSWER Sample answer:

Quiz Scores

Score	Frequency
1–2	0
3–4	2
5–6	4
7–8	9
9–10	5

2. The data below are the numbers of hours per week spent playing sports by a group of students. What is a histogram that represents the data?

2 7 17 9 6 13 8 4 6 5
12 3 11 1 8 15

ANSWER Sample answer:

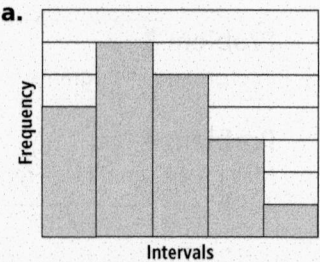

Playing Sports

(histogram with x-axis labeled Hours: 1–4, 5–8, 9–12, 13–16, 17–20; y-axis labeled Number of Students 0–7)

3. Is each histogram *uniform*, *symmetric*, or *skewed*?

a.

(histogram, y-axis Frequency, x-axis Intervals)

b.

(histogram, y-axis Frequency, x-axis Intervals)

ANSWER a. skewed;
b. symmetric

4. The ages of people at a family restaurant one evening are shown below. What is a cumulative frequency table that represents the data?

5 38 40 10 47 53 33 8
42 25 35 3 16 37 48 27
4 43 32 14 39 56

ANSWER Sample answer:

Restaurant Patrons

Age	Frequency	Cumulative Frequency
0–9	4	4
10–19	3	7
20–29	2	9
30–39	6	15
40–49	5	20
50–59	2	22

Lesson Check

Do you know HOW?

The data below show battery life, in hours, for different brands of batteries.

  12 9 10 14 10 11 10 18 21 10 14 22

1. Make a frequency table of the data.

2. Make a histogram of the data.

3. Make a cumulative frequency table of the data.

Do you UNDERSTAND?

4. **Vocabulary** How might a frequency table help a store owner determine the busiest business hours?

5. **Compare and Contrast** What is the difference between a symmetric histogram and a skewed histogram?

6. **Writing** How can you use a frequency table of a data set to construct a cumulative frequency table?

Practice and Problem-Solving Exercises

 Practice   **Use the data to make a frequency table.**   ◀ See Problem 1.

7. wing spans (cm): 150 126 139 144 125 149 133 140 142 149 150 127 130

8. marathon times (min): 135 211 220 180 175 161 246 201 192 167 235 208

9. top speeds (mi/h): 108 90 96 150 120 115 135 126 165 155 130 125 100

Use the data to make a histogram.   ◀ See Problem 2.

10. costs of items: $11 $30 $22 $8 $15 $28 $17 $17 $1 $19 $29 $21 $12 $25

11. ages of relatives: 18 5 27 34 56 54 9 14 35 22 78 94 47 52 2 16 17 10

12. restaurant waiting times (min): 20 35 15 25 5 10 40 30 10 50 20 60 10 8

13. points per game: 10 2 13 18 22 20 8 9 12 33 10 13 21 18 5 16 17 13

Tell whether each histogram is *uniform*, *symmetric*, or *skewed*.   ◀ See Problem 3.

14.
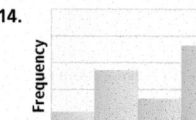

15.
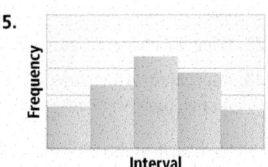

16.
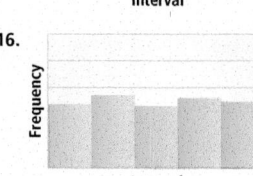

17.
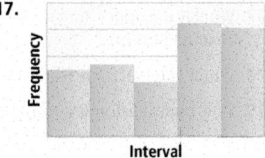

---

3 Lesson Check

Do you know HOW?
• If students have difficulty with Exercise 2, then have them review Problem 2 and follow the process to include the elements of a histogram.

Do you UNDERSTAND?
• If students have difficulty with Exercise 4, then tell them that because the data for a frequency table is univariate, the store owner would need to record the time of each transaction that occurred in the store.

Close

Q What does the shape of a histogram demonstrate about a data set? **[The shape of a histogram demonstrates how numeric data is distributed throughout the range of the data values.]**

Answers

Got It! (continued)

3. a.

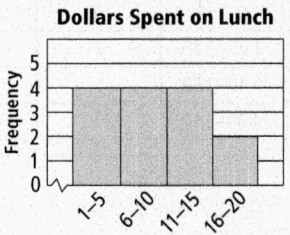

Dollars Spent on Lunch

uniform

b. Answers may vary. Sample: $70 for the week; the data is fairly uniform, so on average he spends about $10 per day.

4.

Interval	Frequency	Cumulative Frequency
0–4	6	6
5–9	4	10
10–14	4	14
15–19	2	16

Lesson Check

1. **Battery Life**

Hours	Frequency
9–12	7
13–16	2
17–20	1
21–24	2

2. **Battery Life**

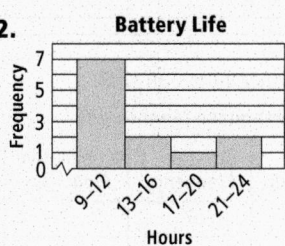

3–17. See back of book.

---

4 Practice

ASSIGNMENT GUIDE

Basic: 7–20 all, 22–30 even, 31

Average: 7–19 odd, 21–31

Advanced: 7–19 odd, 21–33

Standardized Test Prep: 34–37

Mixed Review: 38–41

Reasoning exercises have blue headings.

Applications exercises have red headings.

EXERCISE 31: Use the Think About a Plan worksheet in the **Practice and Problem Solving Workbook** (also available in the Teaching Resources in print and online) to further support students' development in becoming independent learners.

HOMEWORK QUICK CHECK

To check students' understanding of key skills and concepts, go over Exercises 11, 19, 22, 30, and 31.

Use the data to make a cumulative frequency table.   ◀ See Problem 4.

18. trail lengths (mi): 4 1 5 2 1 3 7 12 6 3 11 9 2 1 3 4 1 2 5 3 1 1

19. heights of buildings (ft): 105 245 300 234 225 156 180 308 250 114 150 285

20. earthquake magnitudes: 2.1 5.4 6.7 3.2 4.5 2.7 2.6 3.1 4.4 8.1 4.1 2.9 2.1

Ⓑ Apply

21. **Music** The Perpendicular Bisectors' new CD is shown at the right.
   a. Make a cumulative frequency table that represents the lengths of the songs in seconds.
   b. About what percent of the songs are under 4 min? How do you know?

22. **Think About a Plan** A travel agent conducted a survey to find out how many times people go to the beach each year. The results of the survey are shown in the histogram below. About how many people were surveyed?

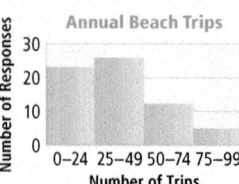

   • What does the height of each bar represent?
   • How can you use the bar heights to find the number of people surveyed?

Use the test scores below.

81 70 73 89 68 79 91 59 77 73 80 75 88 65 82 94 77 67 82

23. What is a histogram of the data that uses intervals of 5?

24. What is a histogram of the data that uses intervals of 10?

25. What is a histogram of the data that uses intervals of 20?

26. **Reasoning** Which interval size would you use—5, 10, or 20—to make it seem as though there were little variation in the test scores?

The histogram at the right shows the amounts of money that 50 customers spent in a supermarket.

27. What is the upper limit on the amount of money that any customer spent?

28. Which interval represents the greatest number of customers?

29. How many customers spent less than $20?

30. **Writing** Summarize the spending of the 50 customers represented in the histogram.

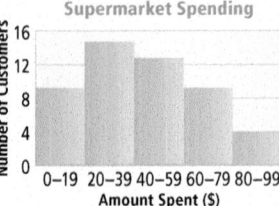

Answers

Practice and Problem-Solving Exercises
(continued)

18. Answers may vary. Sample:

Trail Lengths

Miles	Frequency	Cumulative Frequency
1–3	13	13
4–6	5	18
7–9	2	20
10–12	2	22

19. Answers may vary. Sample:

Heights of Buildings

Feet	Frequency	Cumulative Frequency
100–149	2	2
150–199	3	5
200–249	3	8
250–299	2	10
300–349	2	12

20. Answers may vary. Sample:

Earthquake Magnitudes

Magnitude	Frequency	Cumulative Frequency
2.0–3.9	7	7
4.0–5.9	4	11
6.0–7.9	1	12
8.0–9.9	1	13

21. a.   **The Perpendicular Bisectors**

Time/Song (min)	Frequency	Cumulative Frequency
0–1:19	0	0
1:20–2:39	2	2
2:40–3:59	5	7
4:00–5:19	3	10

b. 70%; 7 out of 10 songs are shorter than 4 min.

22. about 60

23. Answers may vary. Sample:

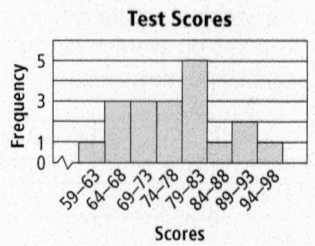

31. Error Analysis A student made the frequency table at the right using the data below. Describe and correct the error.

40 21 28 53 24 48 50 55 42 29 22 52 43 26 44

Interval	Frequency
20-29	6
40-49	5
50-59	4

Challenge

32. Make a histogram for a set of 200 data values. The histogram must have 40% of the values lie in the interval 20-29. The remaining values should be evenly divided among the intervals 0-9, 10-19, 30-39, and 40-49.

33. Copy and complete the cumulative frequency table at the right.

Interval	Frequency	Cumulative Frequency
0-9	■	6
10-19	■	17
20-29	■	26
30-39	■	35

SAT/ACT

34. What is the shape of the histogram at the right?

Ⓐ symmetric Ⓒ skewed
Ⓑ proportional Ⓓ uniform

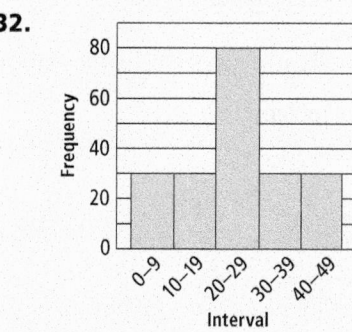

35. What is the solution of $(-4x - 6) + (6x + 1) = -13$?

Ⓕ −4 Ⓗ 6
Ⓖ 5 Ⓘ 9

36. What is the factored form of $x^2 - 6x - 16$?

Ⓐ $(x + 2)(x + 8)$ Ⓑ $(x - 2)(x + 8)$ Ⓒ $(x + 2)(x - 8)$ Ⓓ $(x - 2)(x - 8)$

Short Response

37. Between what two integer values of x do the graphs of $y = 20(0.5)^x$ and $y = 0.5 \cdot 4^x$ intersect? Show your work.

Mixed Review

Find each sum or difference. ◆ See Lesson 12-1.

38. $\begin{bmatrix} 4 & 6 \\ 5 & 7 \end{bmatrix} + \begin{bmatrix} 8 & 10 \\ 9 & 11 \end{bmatrix}$

39. $\begin{bmatrix} 0.2 & 0.6 \\ 0.8 & 0.5 \end{bmatrix} - \begin{bmatrix} 2.3 & 5.9 \\ 7.5 & 1.0 \end{bmatrix}$

Get Ready! To prepare for Lesson 12-3, do Exercises 40 and 41.

Order the numbers in each exercise from least to greatest. ◆ See Lesson 1-3.

40. $13, \frac{5}{4}, -4, -16, 0, 2, 16, \frac{1}{2}$

41. $0.9, -0.2, 1.2, 5, -1, 0, 0.1, 2$

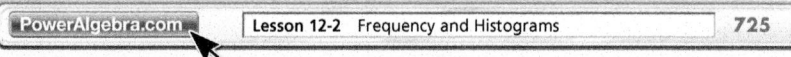

24. Answers may vary. Sample:

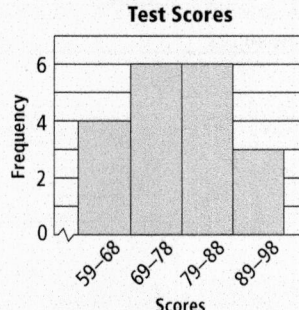

Test Scores

25. Answers may vary. Sample:

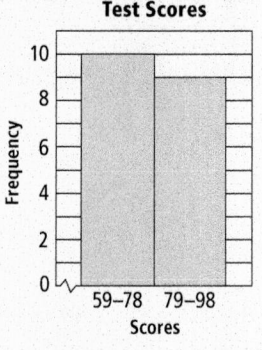

Test Scores

26. 20; fewer intervals show less variation in the data.

27. $99

28. 20–39

29. 9 customers

30. Nine customers spent less than $19, while 15 customers spent between $20 and $39. Thirteen customers spent between $40 and $59. Another nine customers spent between $60 and $79, and the least number of customers, four, spent between $80 and $99.

31. There were no numbers in the range of 30 to 39 so the student just left out this interval. The intervals in a frequency table should not have any gaps, so the student should have included the interval 30–39.

Interval	Frequency
20–29	6
30–39	0
40–49	5
50–59	4

32.

[histogram: Frequency vs Interval, bars at 0-9, 10-19, 20-29, 30-39, 40-49]

33.

Interval	Frequency	Cumulative Frequency
0–9	6	6
10–19	11	17
20–29	9	26
30–39	9	35

34. C

35. F

36. C

37. Methods may vary. Sample:

[2] Graph the two functions using your calculator. Use the trace and intersect features to find the intersection. Since $x \approx 1.77$, the x value where the two graphs intersect is between 1 and 2.

[1] correct methods used with minor error

38. $\begin{bmatrix} 12 & 16 \\ 14 & 18 \end{bmatrix}$

39. $\begin{bmatrix} -2.1 & -5.3 \\ -6.7 & -0.5 \end{bmatrix}$

40. $-16, -4, 0, \frac{1}{2}, \frac{5}{4}, 2, 13, 16$

41. $-1, -0.2, 0, 0.1, 0.9, 1.2, 2, 5$

Additional Instructional Support

Algebra 1 Companion

Students can use the **Algebra 1 Companion** worktext (4 pages) as you teach the lesson. Use the Companion to support

- New Vocabulary
- Key Concepts
- Got It for each Problem
- Lesson Check

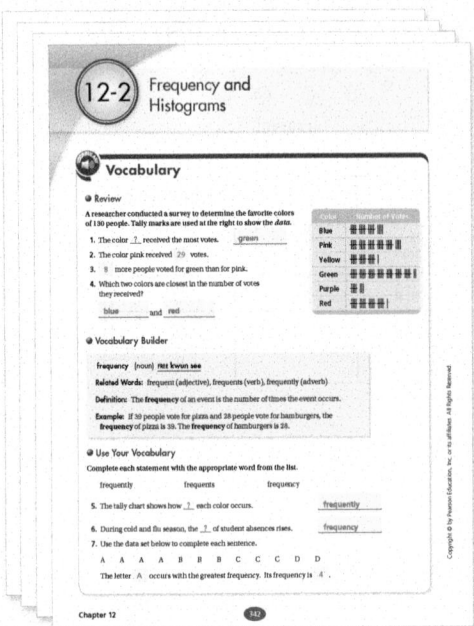

ELL Support

Use Multiple Representation Ask students for the number of pets they own, their ages, the number of siblings they have, or their heights in inches. Draw a frequency table on the board with appropriate intervals and have students guide you as to where to place their tally mark. After the table is complete, model how to make a histogram, thinking aloud as you work. Repeat with another set of data, inviting students to suggest appropriate intervals for the data. Discuss how different intervals could be used, as long as they are of equal size.

5 Assess & Remediate

Lesson Quiz

1. The car sales for the month by 15 salespeople are shown below. What is a frequency table that represents the data?

   3 14 6 7 5 12 8 4 9 17 8 4 9 10 19

2. **Do you UNDERSTAND?** The numbers of MP3 files downloaded each year by 25 different teenagers are shown below. What is a cumulative frequency table that represents the data?

   5 12 22 2 14 6 5 34 4 21 16 0 11 28
   4 4 10 33 12 9 20 19 7 16 22

ANSWERS TO LESSON QUIZ

1.

Car Sales

Number of Sales	Frequency
1–5	4
6–10	7
11–15	2
16–20	2

2.

Number of MP3 files	Frequency	Cumulative Frequency
0–6	8	8
7–13	6	14
14–20	5	19
21–27	3	22
28–34	3	25

PRESCRIPTION FOR REMEDIATION

Use the student work on the Lesson Quiz to prescribe a differentiated review assignment.

Points	Differentiated Remediation
0	Intervention
1	On-level
2	Extension

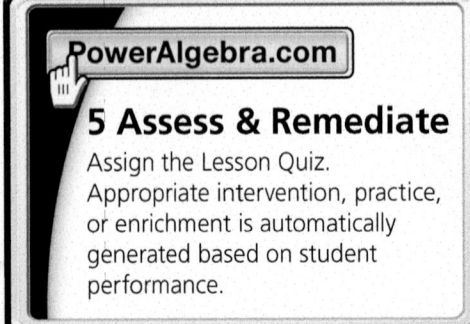

PowerAlgebra.com

5 Assess & Remediate

Assign the Lesson Quiz. Appropriate intervention, practice, or enrichment is automatically generated based on student performance.

Intervention

- **Reteaching** (2 pages) Provides reteaching and practice exercises for the key lesson concepts. Use with struggling students or absent students.

- **English Language Learner Support** Helps students develop and reinforce mathematical vocabulary and key concepts.

All-in-One Resources/Online
Reteaching

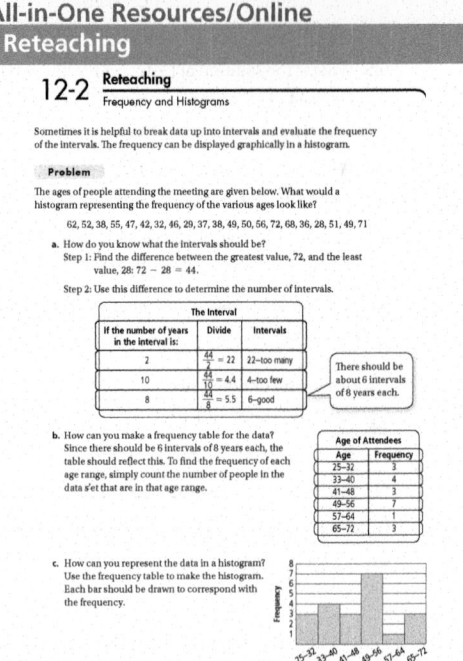

All-in-One Resources/Online
English Language Learner Support

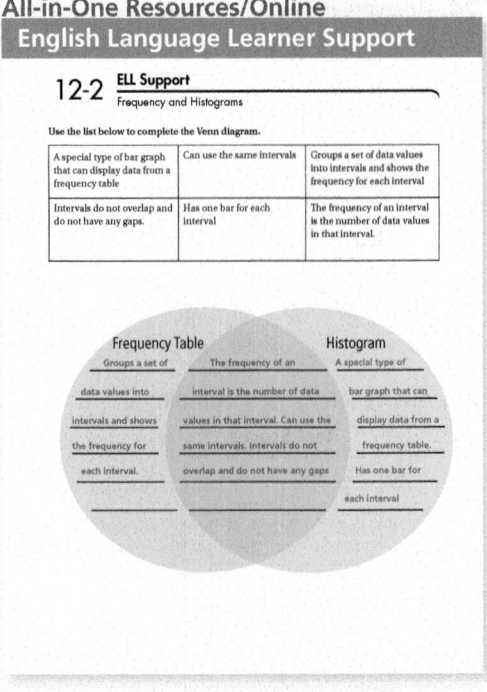

Differentiated Remediation continued

On-Level

- **Practice** (2 pages) Provides extra practice for each lesson. For simpler practice exercises, use the Form K Practice pages found in the All-in-One Teaching Resources and online.

- **Think About a Plan** Helps students develop specific problem-solving skills and strategies by providing scaffolded guiding questions.

- **Standardized Test Prep** Focuses on all major exercises, all major question types, and helps students prepare for the high-stakes assessments.

Extension

- **Enrichment** Provides students with interesting problems and activities that extend the concepts of the lesson.

- **Activities, Games, and Puzzles** Worksheets that can be used for concepts development, enrichment, and for fun!

Practice and Problem Solving Wkbk/ All-in-One Resources/Online
Practice page 1

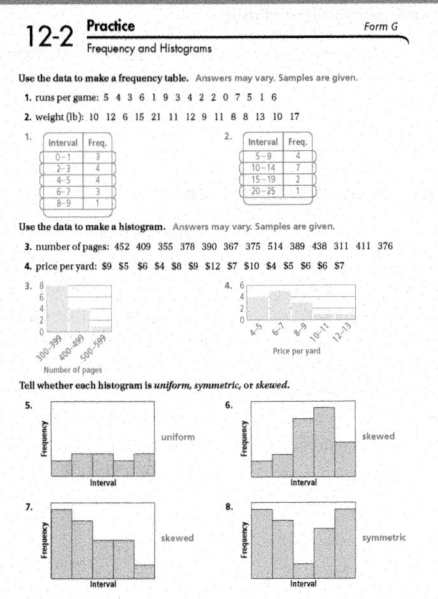

Practice and Problem Solving Wkbk/ All-in-One Resources/Online
Practice page 2

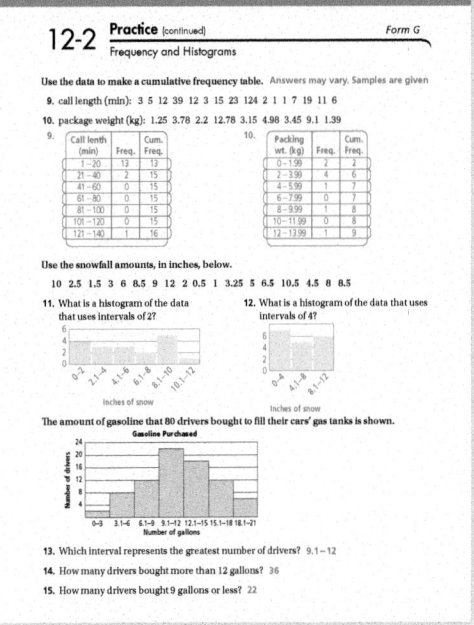

All-in-One Resources/Online
Enrichment

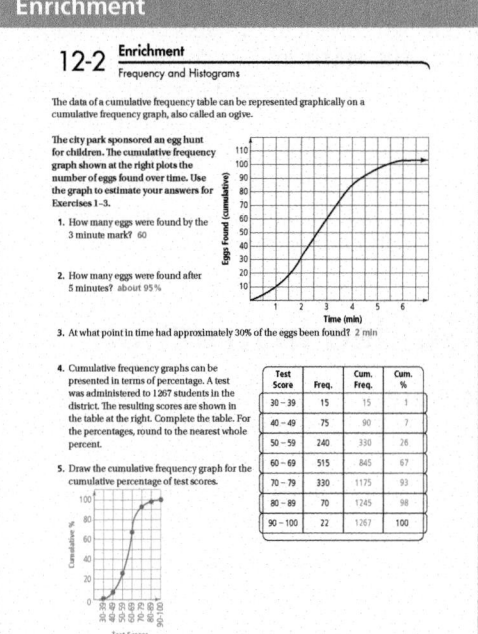

Practice and Problem Solving Wkbk/ All-in-One Resources/Online
Think About a Plan

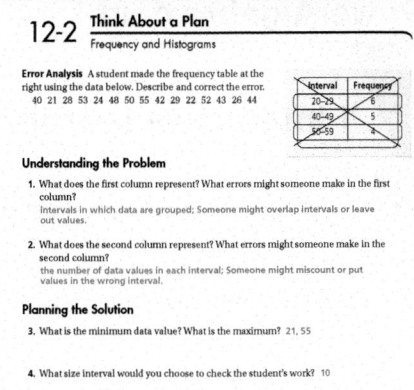

Practice and Problem Solving Wkbk/ All-in-One Resources/Online
Standardized Test Prep

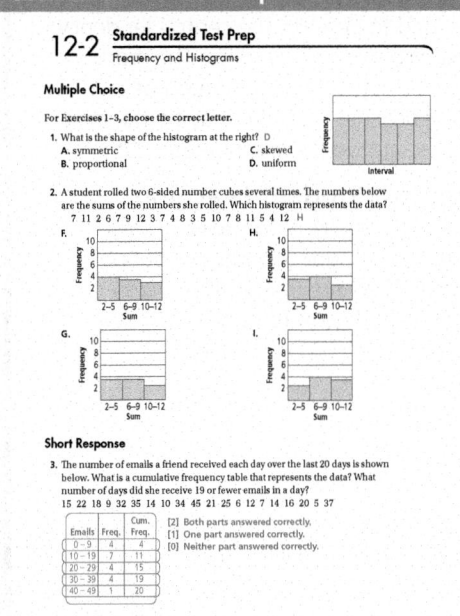

Online Teacher Resource Center
Activities, Games, and Puzzles

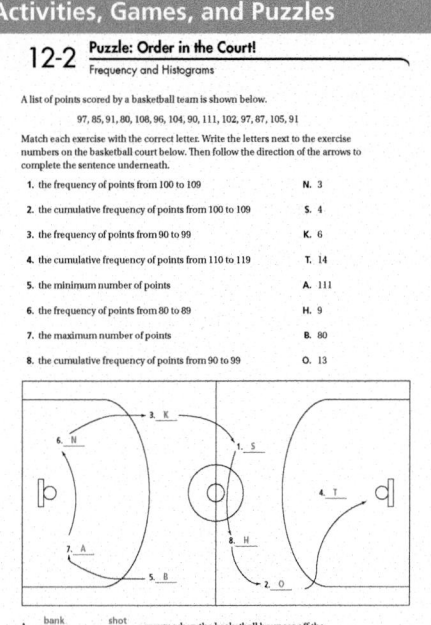

1 Interactive Learning

Solve It!

PURPOSE To analyze the central tendency and dispersion of a set of data

PROCESS Students may analyze the data by finding the totals and by visual inspection.

FACILITATE

Q How can you use the data to determine which player scores more points and which player makes more assists? **[You can find the total number of points scored and the total number of assists made for each player.]**

Q How can you use the data to determine which player is more consistent in his or her scoring and assists? **[You can analyze the data by visual inspection to check for either consistency or high variation.]**

ANSWER See Solve It in Answers on next page.

CONNECT THE MATH In the Solve It, students look at the number of points and number of assists for each player. In the lesson, students make predictions about future data based on the central tendency of the existing data. Students also consider the dispersion of the data to determine a level of confidence about their predictions.

2 Guided Instruction

Take Note

Discuss with students how an outlier does or does not affect each of the measures of central tendency. Use example sets of data, as necessary, to illustrate the effects.

Objective To find mean, median, mode, and range

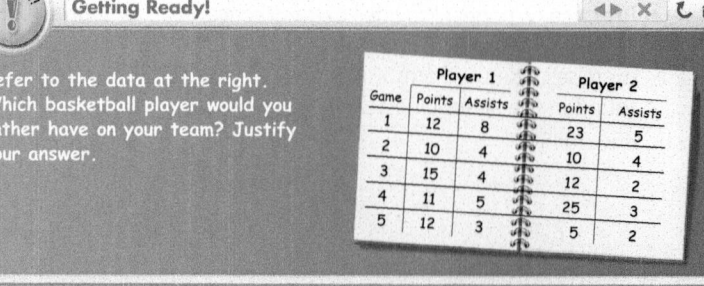

SOLVE IT!

Getting Ready!

Refer to the data at the right. Which basketball player would you rather have on your team? Justify your answer.

A good player scores a lot of points and makes a lot of assists.

Game	Player 1		Player 2	
	Points	Assists	Points	Assists
1	12	8	23	5
2	10	4	10	4
3	15	4	12	2
4	11	5	25	3
5	12	3	5	2

Lesson Vocabulary
• measure of central tendency
• outlier
• mean
• median
• mode
• measure of dispersion
• range of a set of data

Essential Understanding You can use different measures to interpret and compare sets of data.

One way to summarize a set of data is to use a *measure of central tendency*. Mean, median, and mode are all **measures of central tendency**.

The measure of central tendency that best describes a data set may depend on whether the data set has an *outlier*. An **outlier** is a data value that is much greater or less than the other values in the set. Below is a review of mean, median, and mode, and when to use each as the measure of central tendency.

take note

Key Concept — Mean, Median, and Mode

Measure	**When to Use**
The **mean** equals $\frac{\text{sum of the data values}}{\text{total number of data values}}$. The mean is often referred to as the *average*.	Use mean to describe the middle of a set of data that *does not* have an outlier.
The **median** is the middle value in a data set when the values are arranged in order. For a set containing an even number of data values, the median is the mean of the two middle data values.	Use median to describe the middle of a set of data that *does* have an outlier.
The **mode** is the data item that occurs the most times. A data set can have no mode, one mode, or more than one mode.	Use mode when the data are nonnumeric or when choosing the most popular item.

BIG idea Data Collection and Analysis UbD
ESSENTIAL UNDERSTANDINGS

• Different measures can be used to interpret and compare sets of data.
• Three measures of central tendency of a set of data are mean, median, and mode.

Math Background

Descriptive statistics are used to describe and summarize the characteristics of a set of numerical data. The three major characteristics of univariate data are the distribution, the central tendency, and the dispersion. The study of histograms in the last lesson provided an introduction to the distribution patterns that data can show. In this lesson, students are introduced to three measures of central tendency and one measure of dispersion. Each of these descriptive statistics is prone to distortions by certain data traits. For example, both the mean and the range of a set of data can be

distorted by an outlier. When this occurs, other measures such as the median can be used to describe the central tendency and dispersion of the data. The mode is rarely a good representation of a numerical data set, but may be the best representative for non-numeric data.

Support Student Learning

Use the **Algebra 1 Companion** to engage and support students during instructions. See Lesson Resources at the end of this lesson for details.

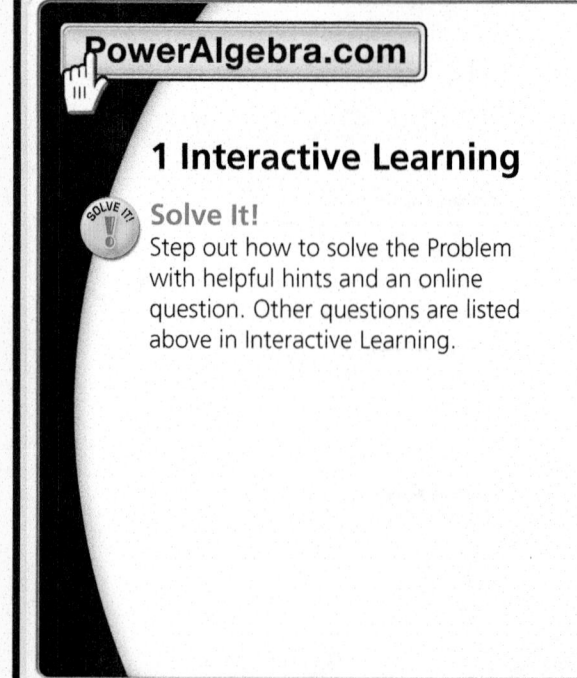

PowerAlgebra.com

1 Interactive Learning

SOLVE IT!

Solve It!

Step out how to solve the Problem with helpful hints and an online question. Other questions are listed above in Interactive Learning.

Problem 1 Finding Measures of Central Tendency

Bowling What are the mean, median, and mode of the bowling scores below? Which measure of central tendency best describes the scores?

Bowler 1: 104	Bowler 5: 189
Bowler 2: 117	Bowler 6: 109
Bowler 3: 104	Bowler 7: 113
Bowler 4: 136	Bowler 8: 104

Think

Is there an outlier in the data set?
Yes, the score 189 is much higher than the other scores.

Mean: $\dfrac{104 + 117 + 104 + 136 + 189 + 109 + 113 + 104}{8} = 122$

The mean is the sum of the scores divided by the number of scores.

Median: 104 104 104 109 113 117 136 189   List the data in order.

$\dfrac{109 + 113}{2} = 111$

The median of an even number of data values is the mean of the two middle data values.

Mode: 104

The mode is the data item that occurs the most times.

Because there is an outlier, 189, the median is the best measure to describe the scores. The mean, 122, is greater than most of the scores. The mode, 104, is the lowest score. Neither the mean nor the mode describes the data well. The median best describes the data.

 **Got It?** **1.** Consider the scores from Problem 1 that do not include the outlier, 189. What are the mean, median, and mode of the scores? Which measure of central tendency best describes the data?

You can use an equation to find a value needed to achieve a given average.

Problem 2 Finding a Data Value

Grades Your grades on three exams are 80, 93, and 91. What grade do you need on the next exam to have an average of 90 on the four exams?

Plan

What information is unknown?
The grade on the fourth exam is unknown. Use a variable to represent this grade.

$\dfrac{80 + 93 + 91 + x}{4} = 90$ Use the formula for the mean. Let x = the grade on the fourth exam.

$\dfrac{264 + x}{4} = 90$ Simplify the numerator.

$264 + x = 360$ Multiply each side by 4.

$x = 96$ Subtract 264 from each side.

Your grade on the next exam must be 96 for you to have an average of 90.

Problem 1

Q If the data set contains an outlier, which measure of central tendency will not reflect the data well? **[mean]**

Q Would an outlier impact the mean of a large set of data as much as it impacts the mean of a small set of data? Explain. **[No, the larger the data set, the less an outlier contributes to the total when you compute the mean.]**

Q If one of the bowlers bowls another game, what is your prediction for his score? Explain. **[I would predict a score of 111, because the median is the best description of the data.]**

Got It?

Q How can you use the work you did in Problem 1 to find the mean of the revised set of data? **[Use the total and subtract 189. Then divide the new total by 7.]**

Q Do you have to do anything differently with the revised set of data to find the median? the mode? Explain. **[Yes; no; when looking for the middle number, only look at the first 7 scores when they are listed in order from least to greatest. The median is the fourth score.]**

Problem 2

Q If the mean score for four exams is 90, what is the total of the four scores? Explain. **[360; the total of scores has to be 90 × 4, or 360.]**

Q What is the difference between the total of the three scores and the total needed to have a mean score of 90? **[360 − 264 = 96]**

---

2 Guided Instruction

Each Problem is worked out and supported online.

Problem 1
Finding Measures of Central Tendency

Problem 2
Finding a Data Value
Animated

Problem 3
Finding the Range

Problem 4
Adding a Constant to Data Values
Animated

Problem 5
Multiplying Data Values by a Constant
Animated

Support in Algebra 1 Companion
• Vocabulary
• Key Concepts
• Got It?

Answers

Solve It!
Answers may vary. Sample: both players are about the same. While Player 2 scored more points on average, Player 1 makes more assists leading to points.

Got It?
1. 112.4, 1 09, 104; mean

Got It?

Q For 2B, do you use the same steps as you used in 2A or is there a shorter method? Explain. **[Shorter; find the average of the first three scores and a score of 100 to see if the average is 92.]**

Problem 3

Q Does either data set appear to have an outlier? **[No; the price of 47 in the first data set is extreme but does not meet the definition of an outlier.]**

Q In general, how does an outlier affect the range of a data set? **[An outlier would increase the range of the data.]**

Q Based on the range value for each data set, which stock might be considered a safe investment and which stock might be considered a risky investment? **[The stock with the low range would be considered safer because it is more predictable than the stock with the high range.]**

Got It?

Encourage students either to put the data set into numeric order or to circle the greatest and least data values to ensure accuracy when computing the range.

With only one example given, many students will not be convinced that the mean, median, and mode increase by the number added to each element. Have students write a data set that contains six elements and find the mean, median, and mode for the set. Then have them add 10 to each element and recalculate the measures of central tendencies. Students can then trade their data sets with another student's data set and verify their calculations.

Got It? **2. a.** The grades in Problem 2 were 80, 93, and 91. What grade would you need on your next exam to have an average of 88 on the four exams?
  b. *Reasoning* If 100 is the highest possible score on the fourth exam, is it possible to raise your average to 92? Explain.

A **measure of dispersion** describes how *dispersed*, or spread out, the values in a data set are. One measure of dispersion is *range*. The **range of a set of data** is the difference between the greatest and least data values.

Problem 3 Finding the Range

Finance The closing prices, in dollars, of two stocks for the first five days in February are shown below. What are the range and mean of each set of data? Use the results to compare the data sets.

Stock A: 25 30 30 47 28

range: $47 - 25 = 22$

mean: $\dfrac{25 + 30 + 30 + 47 + 28}{5}$

$= \dfrac{160}{5} = 32$

Stock B: 34 28 31 36 31

range: $36 - 28 = 8$

mean: $\dfrac{34 + 28 + 31 + 36 + 31}{5}$

$= \dfrac{160}{5} = 32$

Both sets of stock prices have a mean of 32. The range of the prices for Stock A is 22, and the range of the prices for Stock B is 8. Both stocks had the same average price during the 5-day period, but the prices for Stock A were more spread out.

Think

How do the purposes of the range and the mean differ?
The range helps you find how spread out the data values are. The mean helps you find a typical data value.

Got It? **3.** For the same days, the closing prices, in dollars, of Stock C were 7, 4, 3, 6, and 1. The closing prices, in dollars, of Stock D were 24, 15, 2, 10, and 5. What are the range and mean of each set of data? Use your results to compare Stock C with Stock D.

Adding the same amount to each value in a set of data has special consequences for the mean, median, mode, and range.

Consider the data set 5, 16, 3, 5, 11.

mean: 8   median: 5   mode: 5   range: 13

If you add 5 to each data value, you get the data set 10, 21, 8, 10, 16.

mean: 13   median: 10   mode: 10   range: 13

Notice that the mean, median, and mode all increased by 5. The range did not change. For any data set, if you add the same amount k to each item, the mean, median, and mode of the new data set also increase by k. The range does not change.

Additional Problems

1. What are the mean, median, and mode of the test scores below? Which measure of central tendency best describes the scores?

Test Scores

72	88	95	91	87
85	77	82	90	77

ANSWER mean: 84.4, median: 86, mode: 77; Sample answer: The mean or median is a good measure of central tendency. The mode is too low.

2. Graham has sales of $1280, $1125, $965, and $1210 the first four days of the week. How much must he have in sales on the fifth day to average $1150 for the week?

ANSWER $1170

3. The points scored by Eduardo and Paul during the first 5 games of the season are shown below. What is the range of each set of data?
Eduardo: 8, 14, 16, 9, 12
Paul: 13, 15, 10, 11, 17

ANSWER Eduardo: 8 points, Paul: 7 points

4. The table shows the number of laps several swimmers swim during the first week of training. The swimmers add 10 laps to

their training regimens during the second week. What are the mean, median, mode, and range of the laps for the second week of training?

Swimming Training Week 1

Swimmer	Laps
Tonya	35
Eric	20
Michael	40
Suzie	45
Tien	40
Jamal	30
Chris	50

ANSWER mean: 47.1 laps; median: 50 laps; mode: 50 laps; range: 30 laps

5. Kenny is researching the prices of binoculars. He finds 6 different models at a sporting goods store with prices of $65, $88, $120, $25, $40, and $75. Kenny has a coupon good for 25% off the purchase of a single item at the store. What are the mean, median, mode, and range of the discounted prices?

ANSWER mean: $51.63; median: $52.50; mode: none; range: $71.25

Problem 4 **Adding a Constant to Data Values**

Athletics The table shows the times several athletes spend on a treadmill each day during the first week of training. The athletes add 5 min to their training times during the second week. What are the mean, median, mode, and range of the times for the second week?

Time on Treadmill	
Athlete	Time (min)
Bob	50
Carlota	20
Juan	41
Manuel	20
Rosita	30
Sonia	20
Xavier	50

Step 1 Find the mean, median, mode, and range for the first week.

$$\text{mean: } \frac{20 + 20 + 20 + 30 + 41 + 50 + 50}{7} = 33$$

median: 30   mode: 20   range: $50 - 20 = 30$

Step 2 Find the mean, median, mode, and range for the second week.

mean: $33 + 5 = 38$ ⎫
median: $30 + 5 = 35$ ⎬ Add 5 to each measure of central tendency.
mode: $20 + 5 = 25$ ⎭
range: 30   The range does not change.

Think

How can you check your results?
Add 5 to each time in the first week to find the times for the second week. Then calculate the mean, median, mode, and range of the new data set directly.

 Got It? **4.** In the third week of training, the athletes add 10 min to their training times from the second week. What are the mean, median, mode, and range of the athletes' training times for the third week?

Suppose you multiply each value in a data set by the same amount k. You can find the mean, median, mode, and range of the new data set by multiplying the mean, median, mode, and range of the original data set by k.

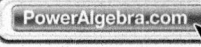 **Problem 5** **Multiplying Data Values by a Constant**

Shopping A store sells seven models of televisions. The regular prices are $144, $479, $379, $1299, $171, $479, and $269. This week the store offers a 30% discount on all televisions. What are the mean, median, mode, and range of the discounted prices?

Step 1 Find the mean, median, mode, and range of the regular prices.

$$\text{mean: } \frac{144 + 171 + 269 + 379 + 479 + 479 + 1299}{7} = 460$$

median: 379   mode: 479   range: $1299 - 144 = 1155$

Step 2 Multiply the mean, median, mode, and range in Step 1 by 0.7 to find the mean, median, mode, and range of the discounted prices.

mean: $460(0.7) = 322$ mode: $479(0.7) = 335.30$
median: $379(0.7) = 265.30$ range: $1155(0.7) = 808.50$

Think

How do you calculate a discounted price?
To calculate a price discounted by 30%, multiply the original amount by $(1 - 0.3)$, or 0.7.

Got It? **5.** The following week the store offers a 25% discount off the regular prices. What are the mean, median, mode, and range of the discounted prices?

Problem 4

Q How can putting the data into numeric order help to complete this problem? **[Putting the data into numeric order can help you identify the mode, find the median, and compute the range.]**

Q Which measure of central tendency best describes the data? Explain. **[The median or mean best describes the data because the mode of the data is also the least value.]**

Q What statement can you make about the dispersion of the data? **[Answers may vary. Sample: The range is relatively high, so the data are rather spread out.]**

Got It?

Q Do you have to actually add 10 to each athlete's time and recalculate to find each measure? Explain. **[No; I can add 10 to the mean, median, and mode to find the new measure. The range does not change.]**

Problem 5

Q What one number best describes the typical price of a television in the store? Explain. **[Answers may vary. Sample: Because $1299 is an outlier, the median of $379 best represents the typical price.]**

Q What statement can you make about the dispersion of the data? **[Answers may vary. Sample: The range is relatively high, so the data are rather spread out.]**

Got It?

Q What numbers can you multiply by 75% to find the new measures of central tendencies and the new range? **[$144, $171, $269, $379, $479, and $1299]**

Answers

Got It? (continued)

2. a. 88%

   b. No; you would need a grade of 104.

3. Stock C: 6, 4.2; Stock D: 22, 11.2; Stock C had a range of 6 and a mean of 4.2, while Stock D had a range of 22 and a mean of 10.8 for this 5-day period.

4. 48, 45, 35, 30

5. $345, $284.25, $359.25, $866.25

3 Lesson Check

Do you know HOW?
- If students have difficulty with Exercise 3, then have them review Problems 4 and 5 to determine how a change to all data affects the measures of central tendencies and the range.

Do you UNDERSTAND?
- If students have difficulty with Exercise 5, then have them review Problem 3 and write the set in order from least to greatest.

Close

> **Q** What is the difference between a measure of central tendency and a measure of dispersion? **[A measure of central tendency is used to describe a typical data value, while a measure of dispersion is used to describe how much variation is contained within a data set.]**

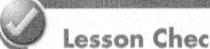 **Lesson Check**

Do you know HOW?
Find the mean, median, and mode of each data set. Explain which measure best describes the data.

1. 1 29 33 31 30 33   **2.** 8.2 9.3 8.5 8.8 9.0

3. If you multiply each value in the data set below by 3, what are the mean, median, mode, and range of the resulting data set?

8 2 5 7 0 6 5

Do you UNDERSTAND?
4. Vocabulary How do mean, median, and mode describe the central tendency of a data set? Why are three different measures needed?

5. Error Analysis One student said 10 was the range of the data set 2, 10, 8, and 3. Another student said the range was 8. Which student is correct? Explain.

6. Reasoning How is the range of a data set affected by an outlier?

 ## Practice and Problem-Solving Exercises

A Practice Find the mean, median, and mode of each data set. Tell which measure of central tendency best describes the data.

◀ See Problem 1

7. weights of books (oz): 12 10 9 15 16 10

8. golf scores: 98 96 98 134 99

9. time spent on Internet (min/day): 75 38 43 120 65 48 52

10. ages of students on math team: 14 14 15 15 16 15 15 16

Find the value of x such that the data set has the given mean.

◀ See Problem 2

11. 3.8, 4.2, 5.3, x; mean 4.8   **12.** 99, 86, 76, 95, x; mean 91

13. 100, 121, 105, 113, 108, x; mean 112   **14.** 31.7, 42.8, 26.4, x; mean 35

15. Sales The line plot at the right shows the numbers of weekly sales a salesperson made in the first nine weeks of a ten-week sales period. The salesperson's target is an average of 14 sales each week. How many sales does the salesperson need in the tenth week to meet the target average?

Number of Weekly Sales

		X	X
	X	X	X
X	X	X	X
12	13	14	15

Find the range and mean of each data set. Use your results to compare the two data sets.

◀ See Problem 3

16. Set A: 0 12 7 19 21
Set B: 13 16 15 17 12

17. Set C: 4.5 7.1 8.3 6.9
Set D: 2.1 29.5 1.2 3.3

18. Set E: 113 183 479 120 117
Set F: 145 129 153 135 142

19. Sports Over the past 6 seasons, one baseball player's batting averages were .265, .327, .294, .316, .281, and .318. A second player's batting averages were .304, .285, .312, .291, .303, and .314. What are the range and mean of each player's batting averages? Use your results to compare the players' batting skills.

PowerAlgebra.com

3 Lesson Check

For a digital lesson check, use the Got It questions.

Support In Algebra 1 Companion
- Lesson Check

4 Practice

Assign homework to individual students or to an entire class.

Answers

Lesson Check
1. 26.2, 30.5, 33; the median, since there is an outlier in this set
2. 8.76, 8.8, no mode; the mean, since there is no outlier
3. 14.1, 15, 15, 24
4. All are describing the data set by finding a representative measure of central tendency. The mean can be influenced by outliers, which can overstate or understate the measure. The median is the middle value of the ranked data, and the mode is the most commonly occurring piece of data.
5. The correct range is 8 because the range is defined as the difference between the highest and lowest values.
6. Since an outlier is either much larger or much smaller than most of the data, it causes the range to get larger.

Practice and Problem-Solving Exercises
7. 12, 11, 10; mean
8. 105, 98, 98; median
9. 63, 52, no mode; median
10. 15, 15, 15; any of the three
11. 5.9 **12.** 99 **13.** 125 **14.** 39.1
15. 15
16. Set A: 21, 11.8; Set B: 5, 14.6; the range of Set A is 21 with a mean of 11.8, while the range of Set B is 5 with a mean of 14.6.
17. Set C: 3.8, 6.7; Set D: 28.3, 9.0; the range of Set C is 3.8 with a mean of 6.7, while Set D has a range of 28.3 and a mean of 9.
18. Set E: 366, 202.4; Set F: 24, 140.8; the range of Set E is 366 with a mean of 202.4, while Set F has a range of 24 and a mean of 140.8.

Find the mean, median, mode, and range of each data set after you perform the given operation on each data value. ◀ See Problems 4 and 5.

20. 9, 7, 12, 13, 9, 3; add 5

21. 10.6, 9.5, 0, 9.4, 10.3, 10.6; add 15

22. 13.2, 12.4, 15.1, 14.7, 14.2; multiply by 3

23. 14, 7, 34, 29, 14, 6; multiply by 6

24. 23, 53, 37, 64, 53, 70, 20; multiply by 0.1

25. 13, 17, 15, 18, 21, 13, 20; add 3.7

26. 169, 54, 92, 107, 92; divide by 5

27. 5.8, 2.3, 6.4, 6.1, 6.4; subtract 2.1

28. Shopping The costs of 6 different belts available from an online store are $6.95, $15.99, $5.25, $7.45, $5.25, and $8.85. A shipping charge of $.50 is added to each price. Including the shipping charge, what are the mean, median, mode, and range of the prices of the belts?

29. Workshop The lengths of the electrical extension cords in a workshop are 6 ft, 8 ft, 25 ft, 8 ft, 12 ft, 50 ft, and 25 ft. What are the mean, median, mode, and range of the lengths of the cords *in inches*?

Ⓑ Apply

30. Reasoning The mean of a data set is 7.8, the mode is 6.6, and the median is 6.8. What is the least possible number of data values in the set? Explain.

31. Manufacturing Two manufacturing plants make sheets of steel for medical instruments. The back-to-back stem-and-leaf plot at the right shows data collected from the two plants.
 a. What is the mean, median, mode, and range of each data set?
 b. Which measure of central tendency best describes each data set? Explain.
 c. Which plant has better quality control? Explain.

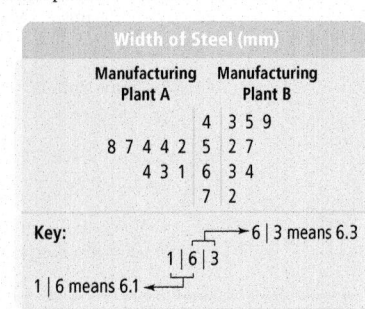

32. Think About a Plan The diameters of 5 circles are given below. What are the mean, median, mode, and range of the circumferences of the circles?
 6.5 in. 3.2 in. 7.4 in. 6.5 in. 5.8 in.
 • What are the mean, median, mode, and range of the diameters?
 • How do the mean, median, mode, and range change when the data change from diameters to circumferences?

33. Reasoning How does subtracting the same amount from each value in a data set affect the mean, median, mode, and range? Explain.

34. Reasoning How does dividing each value in a data set by the same nonzero amount affect the mean, median, mode, and range? Explain.

35. Test Scores The 22 students present for a recent test in Ms. Huang's class had an average score of 88. When students who were absent took the test, three scored 4 points higher than the average and two scored 1 point higher than the average. What is the new class average when the new scores are included?

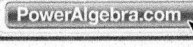

4 Practice

ASSIGNMENT GUIDE

Basic: 7–29 all, 30, 32, 36

Average: 7–29 odd, 30–37

Advanced: 7–29 odd, 30–39

Standardized Test Prep: 40–43

Mixed Review: 44–50

Reasoning exercises have blue headings.

Applications exercises have red headings.

EXERCISE 36: Use the Think About a Plan worksheet in the **Practice and Problem Solving Workbook** (also available in the Teaching Resources in print and online) to further support students' development in becoming independent learners.

HOMEWORK QUICK CHECK

To check students' understanding of key skills and concepts, go over Exercises 9, 21, 30, 32, and 36.

---

19. First player: .062, .300; Second player: .029, .302; the second player had a slightly higher mean over the six seasons and was more consistent as shown by the smaller range.

20. 13.8, 14, 14, 10

21. 23.4, 24.9, 25.6, 10.6

22. 41.8, 42.6, no mode; 8.1

23. 104, 84, 84, 168

24. 4.6, 5.3, 5.3, 5

25. 20.4, 20.7, 16.7, 8

26. 20.6, 18.4, 18.4, 23.0

27. 3.3, 4, 4.3, 4.1

28. $8.79, $7.70, $5.75, $10.74

29. 229.7, 144, 96 and 300, 528

30. 4; in order for 6.6 to be the mode, it has to occur at least twice. So then a value of 7 is needed to obtain a median of 6.8 and then a value of 11 is needed to obtain a mean of 7.8.

31. a. Plant A: 5.8, 5.8, 5.4, 1.2; Plant B: 5.6, 5.5, no mode; 2.9
 b. Plant A: mean as there is no outlier; Plant B: either mean or median, if you consider 7.2 to be an outlier
 c. Plant A; it has a smaller range.

32. 18.5, 20.4, 20.4, 13.2

33. The mean, median and mode will each decrease by that amount, while the range will stay the same. If you subtract the same number d from each set then the sum will decrease by nd where n is the number of data values. Therefore when you divide the total by n, the mean will decrease by d. $\frac{S - nd}{n} = \frac{S}{n} - d$.
For the median, the middle number will decrease by d. The mode will decrease by d. The range, on the other hand, will remain the same since (highest value $- d$) $-$ (lowest value $- d$) = highest $-$ lowest.

34. All the values will be divided by the value of that nonzero number. If each data value is divided by some nonzero number n, then the sum of the original data will be divided by n. Therefore, the value of the mean will also be divided by n. $\frac{x_1}{n} + \frac{x_2}{n} + \frac{x_3}{n} = \frac{S}{n}$
The median is the middle number so it will also be divided by n. The mode is the most commonly occurring value in the data set, so it too will be divided by n. The range will also be divided by n, as $\frac{\text{(highest value)}}{n} - \frac{\text{(lowest value)}}{n} = \frac{\text{highest} - \text{lowest}}{n}$.

35. 88.5

Answers

Practice and Problem-Solving Exercises
(continued)

36. 2.8 m, 2.8 m, 2.8 m and 2.9 m, 0.7 m

37. Yes; because one salesperson earned $150,000, the mean was $47,500, but a better indicator might be the median, which was only $39,500.

38. 46.4 mi/h

39. $\frac{20}{3}x$,6x, 4x, 7x

40. B

41. I

42. C

43. [2] $\frac{1 \text{ in.}}{100 \text{ m}} = \frac{2.5 \text{ in.}}{x \text{ m}}$

   $x = 250$

   Therefore, the locations are 250 m apart.

   [1] correct methods used with minor calculation error

44. Answers may vary. Sample:

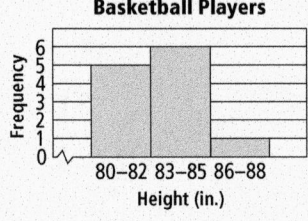

Heights of Basketball Players

45. Answers may vary. Sample:

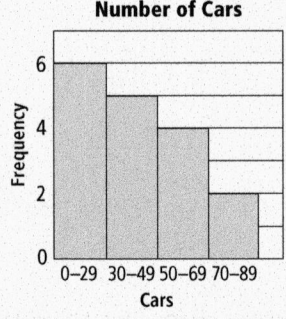

Number of Cars

46.

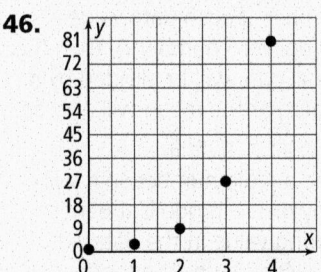

exponential

47.

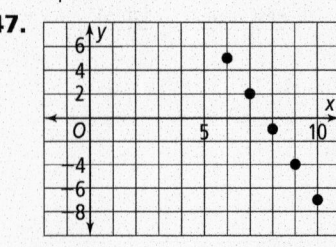

linear

48. 21, 0   **49.** 50, 22.5   **50.** 8.9, 2.1

---

36. Wildlife Management A wildlife manager measured and tagged twelve adult male crocodiles. The data he collected are at the right. He estimates the crocodiles will grow 0.1 m each year. What will be the mean, median, mode, and range of the crocodiles' lengths after 4 yr?

Crocodile Lengths (m)			
2.4	2.5	2.5	2.3
2.8	2.4	2.3	2.4
2.1	2.2	2.5	2.7

37. Reasoning A friend tells you to apply for a sales job at a certain company because the salespeople earned an average of $47,500 last year. Last year, 6 salespeople earned $33,000, 3 earned $46,000, 2 earned $42,000, and 1 earned $150,000. Would you apply for the job based on what your friend says? Explain.

Challenge

38. Travel During the first 6 h of a car trip, your average speed is 44 mi/h. During the last 4 h of your trip, your average speed is 50 mi/h. What is your average speed for the whole trip? (*Hint:* First find the total number of miles traveled.)

39. Find the mean, median, mode, and range of the following algebraic expressions: $9x, 4x, 11x, 7x, 5x, 4x$. Assume that $x > 0$.

Standardized Test Prep

SAT/ACT

40. What is the mean of the data set 9, 16, 13, 20, and 17?

   Ⓐ 13   Ⓑ 15   Ⓒ 16   Ⓓ 17

41. What is the slope of a line perpendicular to the graph of $y = -\frac{1}{2}x + 3$?

   Ⓕ −2   Ⓖ $-\frac{1}{2}$ Ⓗ $\frac{1}{2}$ Ⓘ 2

42. What are the solutions of the equation $x^2 + 4x = 5$?

   Ⓐ −5 and 0   Ⓑ −5 and −1   Ⓒ −5 and 1   Ⓓ 1 and 5

Short Response

43. Two points are 2.5 in. apart on a map with a scale of 1 in. : 100 m. How far apart are the actual locations represented by the points on the map? Show your work.

Mixed Review

Make a histogram of each data set.   *See Lesson 12-2.*

44. heights of professional basketball players:
   85 in. 82 in. 83 in. 84 in. 80 in. 82 in. 86 in. 85 in. 83 in. 84 in. 81 in. 82 in.

45. numbers of cars: 53 84 22 38 41 27 25 12 17 27 33 41 60 73 62 59 43

Graph each set of points. Is a *linear*, *quadratic*, or *exponential* model most appropriate for each set?   *See Lesson 9-7.*

46. (0, 1), (1, 3), (2, 9), (3, 27), (4, 81)   **47.** (6, 5), (7, 2), (8, −1), (9, −4), (10, −7)

Get Ready!   **To prepare for Lesson 12-4, do Exercises 48–50.**

Find the range and median of each data set.   *See Lesson 12-3.*

48. 0 2 7 10 −1 −4 −11   **49.** 64 16 23 57 14 22   **50.** 2.1 3.3 −5.4 0.8 3.5

Differentiated Remediation

Additional Instructional Support

Algebra 1 Companion
Students can use the **Algebra 1 Companion** worktext (4 pages) as you teach the lesson. Use the Companion to support

- New Vocabulary
- Key Concepts
- Got It for each Problem
- Lesson Check

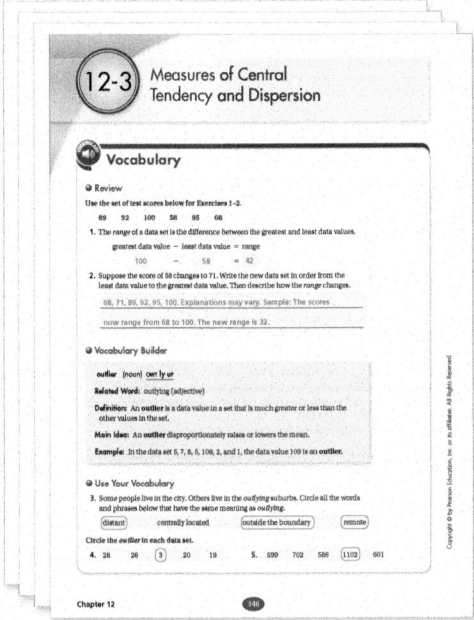

ELL Support
Use Graphic Organizers Draw a 5-point star on the board with the word "mean" in the center. Begin at the top point, and ask students for a definition. Then proceed around the star, inviting students to participate and supply the part of speech, synonyms, antonym, and examples. Repeat with median and mode. Students can copy the star in the notes for later review.

Focus on Language Some students may be confused by the word *mean*. Explain that a mean in mathematics has nothing to do with acting mean or behaving badly: the means we talk about in mathematics are a different word that comes from the French word for *middle*. So both means and medians, in their way, are supposed to show the midpoint of a set of values.

5 Assess & Remediate

Lesson Quiz
1. What are the mean, median, and mode of the number of cars washed at a car wash over the past 12 days? Which measure of central tendency best describes the data?

Number of Cars

42	71	55	21
67	86	36	45
44	50	52	67

2. **Do you UNDERSTAND?** Lucinda has quiz scores of 18, 15, 14, 16, and 15 this quarter. What score must she earn on her next quiz to have an average score of 16 for the quarter?

3. The table below shows the prices of 8 different treadmills at a sporting goods store. This week the store is having a 10% off sale on all treadmills. What are the mean, median, mode, and range of the discounted prices?

Treadmill Prices

$640	$810	$755	$810
$1175	$900	$1080	$530

ANSWERS TO LESSON QUIZ
1. mean: 53 cars; median: 51 cars: mode: 67 cars; Sample answer: The mean or median are the best measures of central tendency. The mode is too high.

2. 18

3. mean: $753.75; median: $729; mode: $729; range: $580.50

PRESCRIPTION FOR REMEDIATION
Use the student work on the Lesson Quiz to prescribe a differentiated review assignment.

Points	Differentiated Remediation
0–1	Intervention
2	On-level
3	Extension

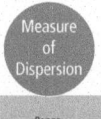

PowerAlgebra.com

5 Assess & Remediate
Assign the Lesson Quiz. Appropriate intervention, practice, or enrichment is automatically generated based on student performance.

Intervention

- **Reteaching** (2 pages) Provides reteaching and practice exercises for the key lesson concepts. Use with struggling students or absent students.

- **English Language Learner Support** Helps students develop and reinforce mathematical vocabulary and key concepts.

All-in-One Resources/Online
Reteaching

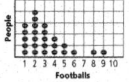

All-in-One Resources/Online
English Language Learner Support

Differentiated Remediation *continued*

On-Level

- **Practice (2 pages)** Provides extra practice for each lesson. For simpler practice exercises, use the Form K Practice pages found in the All-in-One Teaching Resources and online.

- **Think About a Plan** Helps students develop specific problem-solving skills and strategies by providing scaffolded guiding questions.

- **Standardized Test Prep** Focuses on all major exercises, all major question types, and helps students prepare for the high-stakes assessments.

Extension

- **Enrichment** Provides students with interesting problems and activities that extend the concepts of the lesson.

- **Activities, Games, and Puzzles** Worksheets that can be used for concepts development, enrichment, and for fun!

Practice and Problem Solving Wkbk/ All-in-One Resources/Online
Practice page 1

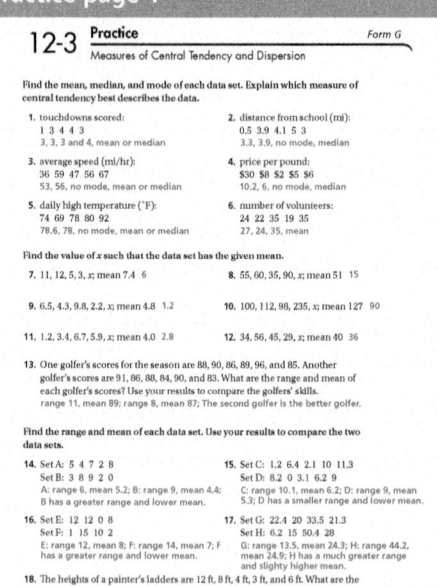

Practice and Problem Solving Wkbk/ All-in-One Resources/Online
Practice page 2

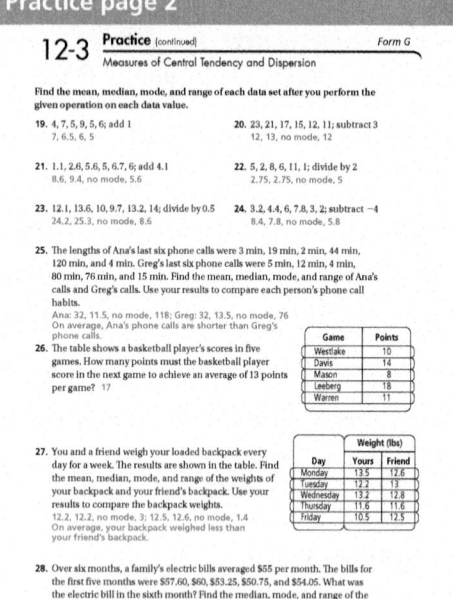

All-in-One Resources/Online
Enrichment

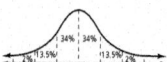

Practice and Problem Solving Wkbk/ All-in-One Resources/Online
Think About a Plan

Practice and Problem Solving Wkbk/ All-in-One Resources/Online
Standardized Test Prep

Online Teacher Resource Center
Activities, Games, and Puzzles

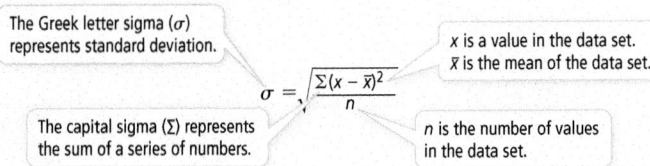

Concept Byte
Use With Lesson 12-3

Standard Deviation

You have learned about one measure of dispersion, range. Another measure of dispersion is *standard deviation*. **Standard deviation** is a measure of how the values in a data set vary, or deviate, from the mean.

Statisticians use several special symbols in the formula for standard deviation.

The Greek letter sigma (σ) represents standard deviation.

x is a value in the data set.
$\bar{x}$ is the mean of the data set.

$$\sigma = \sqrt{\dfrac{\Sigma (x - \bar{x})^2}{n}}$$

The capital sigma (Σ) represents the sum of a series of numbers.

n is the number of values in the data set.

Example

Find the mean and standard deviation of the data set 12.6, 15.1, 11.2, 17.9, and 18.2. Use a table to help organize your work.

Step 1 Find the mean: $\bar{x} = \dfrac{12.6 + 15.1 + 11.2 + 17.9 + 18.2}{5} = 15.$

Step 2 Find the difference between each data value and the mean: $x - \bar{x}$.

Step 3 Square each difference: $(x - \bar{x})^2$.

Step 4 Find the average (mean) of these squares: $\dfrac{\Sigma (x - \bar{x})^2}{n}$.

$\dfrac{5.76 + 0.01 + 14.44 + 8.41 + 10.24}{5} = 7.772$

Step 5 Take the square root to find the standard deviation:

$$\sqrt{\dfrac{\Sigma (x - \bar{x})^2}{n}} = \sqrt{7.772} \approx 2.79.$$

The mean is 15 and the standard deviation is about 2.79.

x	$\bar{x}$	$x - \bar{x}$	$(x - \bar{x})^2$
12.6	15	−2.4	5.76
15.1	15	0.1	0.01
11.2	15	−3.8	14.44
17.9	15	2.9	8.41
18.2	15	3.2	10.24

A small standard deviation (compared to the data values) means that the data are clustered tightly around the mean. As the data become more widely distributed, the standard deviation increases.

Exercises

Find the mean and standard deviation of each data set. Round to the nearest hundredth.

1. 4 8 5 12 3 9 5 2

2. 102 98 103 86 101 110

3. 8.2 11.6 8.7 10.6 9.4 10.1 9.3

Guided Instruction

PURPOSE To find the standard deviation of a data set

PROCESS Students
- find the mean of a given data set.
- use the mean to find the standard deviation of the data set.

DISCUSS Define the term *dispersion*. Tell students that dispersion is another way to identify the spread of a data set. Identify the parts of the standard deviation formula and discuss ways to find the values of each part.

Example

In this Example students find the standard deviation of a given data set.

Q Why is a table used to help find standard deviation? **[Answers will vary. Sample: The table provides a very effective way to organize the data. Each column of the table represents a different element of the formula.]**

Q If there is a relatively large standard deviation, would this indicate a small or large range in data values? **[a large, more spread-out range of values]**

Q If many of the data values are very close to the mean, then how would you describe the standard deviation? **[relatively small]**

Answers

Exercises
1. 6, 3.16
2. 100, 7.23
3. 9.7, 1.07

1 Interactive Learning

Solve It!

PURPOSE To sort a set of data into subsets based on various criteria

PROCESS Students may analyze the set of data as a whole to determine appropriate criteria, and then analyze each piece of data in order to sort it based on each chosen criterion.

FACILITATE

Q How many months was the average monthly temperature greater in Morrell? **[4 months]**

Q How can you confirm that Glenville has a warmer climate? **[Possible answer: find the median or mean temperature for each town.]**

Q How can you find the median temperature for each town? **[Arrange the temperatures in numerical order. The median is the average of the 6th and 7th lowest temperatures.]**

ANSWER See Solve It in Answers on next page.

CONNECT THE MATH In the Solve It, students sort numeric data and compare the sets based on the criterion of a warmer climate. In the lesson, students will use subsets to summarize and compare data sets according to the criteria for a box-and-whisker-plot.

2 Guided Instruction

Use the word *quartile* to get students to think of grouping the data into four equal parts. Be sure students realize they will be finding the median for each equal part and that they are already familiar with the median of the second quartile. Demonstrate the difference in process when the quartiles have an even number of data and when they have an odd number of data.

Objectives To make and interpret box-and-whisker plots
To find quartiles and percentiles

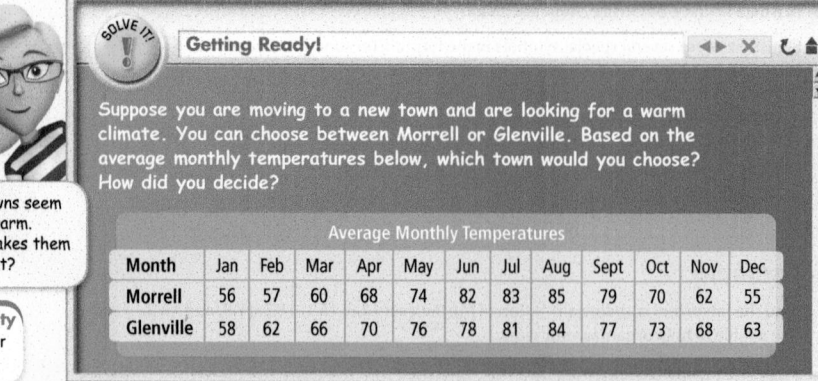

Getting Ready!

Suppose you are moving to a new town and are looking for a warm climate. You can choose between Morrell or Glenville. Based on the average monthly temperatures below, which town would you choose? How did you decide?

Both towns seem pretty warm. What makes them different?

Average Monthly Temperatures												
Month	Jan	Feb	Mar	Apr	May	Jun	Jul	Aug	Sept	Oct	Nov	Dec
Morrell	56	57	60	68	74	82	83	85	79	70	62	55
Glenville	58	62	66	70	76	78	81	84	77	73	68	63

Dynamic Activity
Box-and-Whisker Plots

Lesson Vocabulary
• quartile
• interquartile range
• box-and-whisker plot
• percentile
• percentile rank

In the Solve It, you may have looked at different parts of each data set in order to compare the two data sets.

Essential Understanding Separating data into subsets is a useful way to summarize and compare data sets.

Quartiles are values that divide a data set into four equal parts. The median (or second quartile, Q_2) separates the data into upper and lower halves. The first quartile (Q_1) is the median of the lower half of the data. The third quartile (Q_3) is the median of the upper half of the data. The **interquartile range** is the difference between the third and first quartiles.

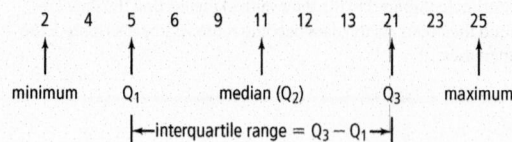

2   4   5   6   9   11   12   13   21   23   25

minimum Q_1 median (Q_2) Q_3 maximum

|←interquartile range = $Q_3 - Q_1$→|

For a set of data that has an odd number of values, you do not include the median in either half when finding the first and third quartiles.

BIG idea **Data Representation**   **UbD**

ESSENTIAL UNDERSTANDINGS

• Separating data into subsets is a useful way to summarize and compare data sets.

• A box-and-whisker plot displays the maximum, minimum, and quartiles of a data set.

Math Background

Visual displays are often used as part of the summary process of descriptive statistics because they are better suited than numerical methods for making patterns in the data quickly identifiable. Univariate numeric data is often displayed using histograms or box-and-whisker plots. Histograms are used to summarize the distribution of a data set. When a pictorial representation of the dispersion of a set of data is desired, a box-and-whisker plot is constructed.

In a box-and-whisker plot, the box shows the median two fourths of the data set, while the first and fourth fourths are shown by the whiskers.

Outliers are usually indicated with an asterisk or a similar type of symbol. They will be beyond either whisker. To determine if a data value is indeed an outlier, you must first find the interquartile range. An outlier is any data value that is more than 1.5 times the interquartile range above the fourth quartile or below the first quartile.

Support Student Learning

Use the **Algebra 1 Companion** to engage and support students during instructions. See Lesson Resources at the end of this lesson for details.

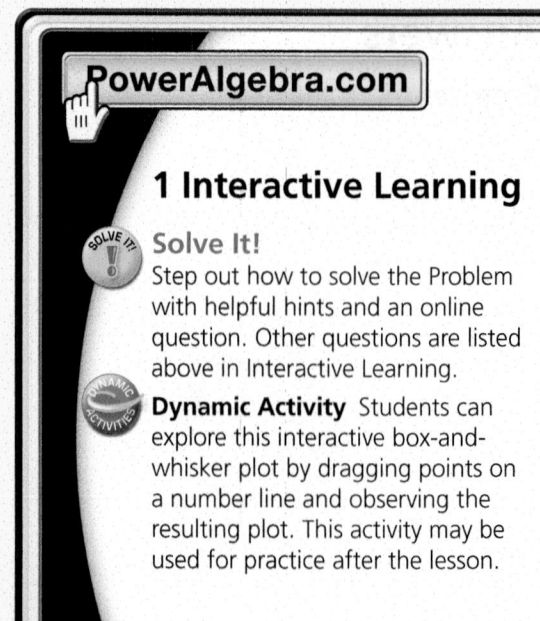

PowerAlgebra.com

1 Interactive Learning

Solve It!
Step out how to solve the Problem with helpful hints and an online question. Other questions are listed above in Interactive Learning.

Dynamic Activity Students can explore this interactive box-and-whisker plot by dragging points on a number line and observing the resulting plot. This activity may be used for practice after the lesson.

 **Problem 1** Summarizing a Data Set

What are the minimum, first quartile, median, third quartile, and maximum of the data set below?

125 80 140 135 126 140 350 75

Step 1 Arrange the data in order from least to greatest.

75 80 125 126 135 140 140 350

Step 2 Find the minimum, maximum, and median.

75 80 125 126 135 140 140 350

$$\text{median } (Q_2) = \frac{126 + 135}{2} = 130.5$$

The minimum is 75. The maximum is 350. The median is 130.5.

Step 3 Find the first quartile and the third quartile.

75 80 125 126 135 140 140 350

$$\text{first quartile } (Q_1) = \frac{80 + 125}{2} = 102.5$$

$$\text{third quartile } (Q_3) = \frac{140 + 140}{2} = 140$$

The first quartile is 102.5. The third quartile is 140.

Think

How do you find the first quartile for an even number of values?
The first quartile is the median of the lower half of the data, so you find the mean of the middle two values in the lower half.

 Got It? 1. What are the minimum, first quartile, median, third quartile, and maximum of each data set?
a. 95 85 75 85 65 60 100 105 75 85 75
b. 11 19 7 5 21 53

A **box-and-whisker plot** is a graph that summarizes a set of data by displaying it along a number line. It consists of three parts: a box and two whiskers.

Box-and-Whisker Plot

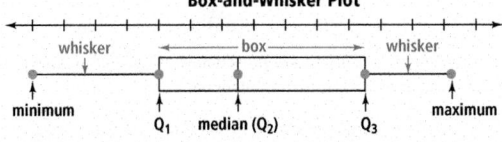

- The left whisker extends from the minimum to the first quartile. It represents about 25% of the data.
- The box extends from the first quartile to the third quartile and has a vertical line through the median. The length of the box represents the interquartile range. It contains about 50% of the data.
- The right whisker extends from the third quartile to the maximum. It represents about 25% of the data.

2 Guided Instruction

Each Problem is worked out and supported online.

Problem 1
Summarizing a Data Set
Animated

Problem 3
Interpreting Box-and-Whisker Plots
Animated

Problem 2
Making a Box-and-Whisker Plot
Animated

Problem 4
Finding a Percentile Rank

Support in Algebra 1 Companion
- Vocabulary
- Key Concepts
- Got It?

Problem 2

Q Are the years from the data table represented in the box-and-whisker plot? Explain. **[No, only the acres are represented in the plot.]**

Q Why is it important to use a number line when creating a box-and-whisker plot? **[It is important so that the width of the box and the length of the whiskers are to scale and accurately show the spread of the data.]**

Q Because the whiskers are relatively long and the box is relatively compact, what is indicated about the distribution of the data? **[It indicates that while the middle 50% of the data is not very dispersed, the upper and lower quarters are more spread out.]**

Got It?

Q What does the long whisker on the right indicate about the data? **[The upper quartile of the data is more spread out in relation to the spread of the other quartiles.]**

Problem 3

Q What do the ranges tell you about the average monthly rainfall for each city? **[The ranges tell you that there is greater variation in the amount of rainfall in Miami than in New Orleans.]**

Q Do you need to compute the actual interquartile range for each city in order to determine which city has the greater interquartile range? Explain. **[No, you can determine which is greater just by looking at the lengths of the boxes.]**

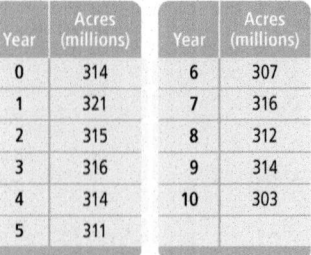

Problem 2 Making a Box-and-Whisker Plot

Agriculture The table at the right shows the amount of crops harvested in the United States for a certain period. What box-and-whisker plot represents the data?

Crops Harvested

Year	Acres (millions)	Year	Acres (millions)
0	314	6	307
1	321	7	316
2	315	8	312
3	316	9	314
4	314	10	303
5	311		

SOURCE: U.S. Department of Agriculture

Know
A set of data

Need
A box-and-whisker plot

Plan
Find the minimum, maximum, and quartiles of the data. Use these numbers to make the box-and-whisker plot.

Step 1 Order the data to find the minimum, maximum, and quartiles.

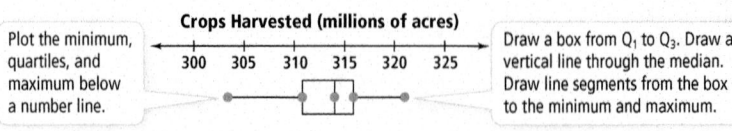

Step 2 Draw the box-and-whisker plot.

Crops Harvested (millions of acres)

Plot the minimum, quartiles, and maximum below a number line.

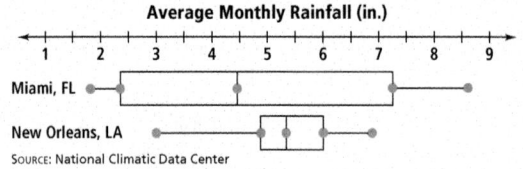

Draw a box from Q_1 to Q_3. Draw a vertical line through the median. Draw line segments from the box to the minimum and maximum.

Got It? 2. What box-and-whisker plot represents the following monthly sales, in millions of dollars, of audio devices: 15 4 9 16 10 16 8 14 25 34?

Problem 3 Interpreting Box-and-Whisker Plots

Weather Use the box-and-whisker plots below. What do the interquartile ranges tell you about the average monthly rainfall for each city?

Think

Why is the interquartile range useful?
It represents the middle of the data set, so it is not affected by the minimum, maximum, or any outliers.

Average Monthly Rainfall (in.)

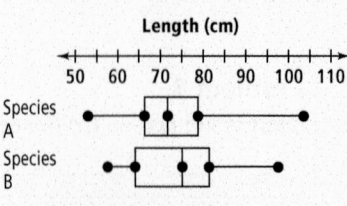

SOURCE: National Climatic Data Center

The box for Miami is longer, so Miami has the greater interquartile range. This greater range means the middle 50% of Miami's monthly rainfalls vary more widely than those of New Orleans.

Additional Problems

1. What are the minimum, first quartile, median, third quartile, and maximum of the data set below?

27 12 20 15 40 33 19 26

ANSWER minimum: 12; first quartile: 17; median: 23; third quartile: 30; maximum: 40

2. The table shows the times of 9 runners in a 200-meter race. What box-and-whisker plot represents the data?

Runner	Time (sec)
Amy	33
Kathy	40
Luisa	34
Angel	30
Roberta	36
Maryanne	32
Ping	34
Cindy	38
Peggy	35

ANSWER

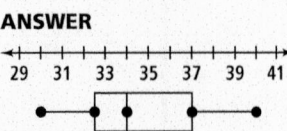

3. Use the box-and-whisker plots below. Which species of snake has a greater range in average length? Which species has a greater interquartile range?

Length (cm)

Species A

Species B

ANSWER Species A has a greater range in average length. Species B has a greater interquartile range.

4. Of 40 students, 9 are taller than 5 ft 10 in. What is the percentile rank of a height of 5 ft 10 in.?

A. 22.5

B. 40

C. 60

D. 77.5

ANSWER D

 **Got It? 3.** What do the medians tell you about the average monthly rainfalls for Miami and New Orleans?

Percentiles separate data sets into 100 equal parts. The **percentile rank** of a data value is the percentage of data values that are less than or equal to that value.

Problem 4 Finding a Percentile Rank

Multiple Choice Of 25 test scores, eight are less than or equal to 75. What is the percentile rank of a test score of 75?

Ⓐ 8   Ⓑ 17   Ⓒ 32   Ⓓ 75

Think

How else could you find the percentile rank?
You could solve the proportion $\frac{8}{25} = \frac{p}{100}$ for p.

$\frac{8}{25}$ Write the ratio of the number of test scores less than or equal to 75 compared to the total number of test scores.

$\frac{8}{25} = 0.32$ Rewrite the fraction as a percent.

$= 32\%$

The percentile rank of 75 is 32. The correct answer is C.

Got It? 4. a. Of the 25 scores in Problem 4, there are 15 scores less than or equal to 85. What is the percentile rank of 85?

b. Reasoning Is it possible to have a percentile rank of 0? Explain.

Lesson Check

Do you know HOW?

Identify the minimum, first quartile, median, third quartile, and maximum of each data set. Then make a box-and-whisker plot of each data set.

1. file sizes (megabytes): 54 100 84 124 188 48 256

2. daily attendance: 29 24 28 32 30 31 26 33

3. In the box-and-whisker plots below, which class has the greater interquartile range of arm spans?

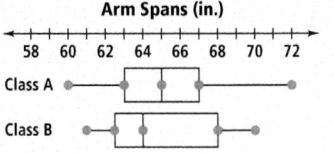

Do you UNDERSTAND?

4. Vocabulary Which portion of a box-and-whisker plot represents the interquartile range?

5. Students taking a make-up test receive the following grades: 77, 89, 88, 67, 91, 95, 83, 79, 81, and 65. Which grade has a percentile rank of 70?

6. Reasoning About what percent of the data in a data set falls between the minimum value and the third quartile? Explain.

7. Error Analysis A test is graded on a scale from 0 to 100. Your friend says that if you score a 78, your percentile rank must be 78. Is your friend correct? Explain.

Got It?

Q Does each point and vertical line indicate a value from a data set? Explain. **[Not always; the quartiles may have been found by taking the mean of two data values.]**

Problem 4

Q What percentage scored better than 75 on the test? Explain. **[68%; 17/25 = 0.68]**

Q If a student selects choice D, what error did he likely make? **[He assumed that the score on the test was equal to the percentile.]**

Got It?

Q What is the division problem to solve 4a? **[15/25]**

3 Lesson Check

Do you know HOW?
• If students have difficulty with Exercise 3, then suggest that they use visual inspection rather than computation.

Do you UNDERSTAND?
• If students have difficulty with Exercise 7, then have them make a data set to use as an example when explaining the error.

Close

Q What information about a data set can be found by looking at a box-and-whisker plot? **[You can usually determine the dispersion of the data set. You can find the minimum, maximum, median, quartiles, and range.]**

Answers

Got It? (continued)

2.

Monthly Sales (millions of $)

3. The median tells you the middle value of the data. So in Miami the monthly rainfall is below 4.5 in. for half the months and above 4.5 in. for half the months. For New Orleans the monthly rainfall is below about 5.3 in. for half the months and above 5.3 in. for the other half of the months.

4. a. 60

b. No; since the percentile rank is the percent of scores that fall at or below a given score there is always at least 1 value associated with a given value. There is no 0 percentile; the lowest score is the first percentile.

Lesson Check

1. 48, 54, 100 188, 256

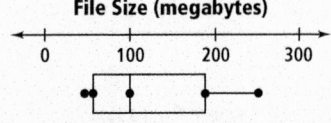
File Size (megabytes)

2. 24, 27, 29.5, 31.5, 33

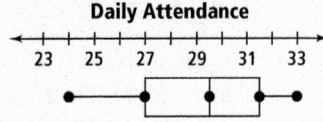
Daily Attendance

3. Class B

4. the middle box

5. 88

6. 75%; the third quartile is the value that divides the data so that about 75% of the data lies below and about 25% of the data lies above.

7. No; the test is scored on point values from 0 to 100, whereas the percentile rank tells you how you did in reference to the rest of the group.

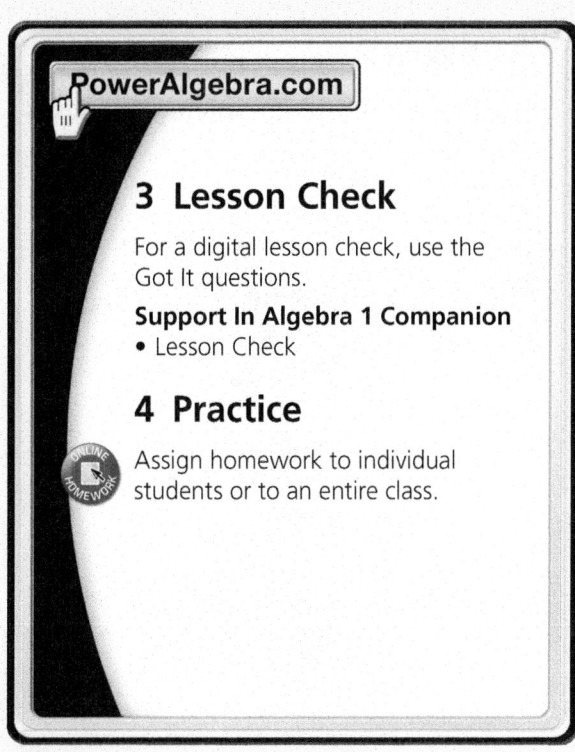

3 Lesson Check

For a digital lesson check, use the Got It questions.

Support In Algebra 1 Companion
• Lesson Check

4 Practice

Assign homework to individual students or to an entire class.

4 Practice

ASSIGNMENT GUIDE

Basic: 8–21 all, 24

Average: 9–17 odd, 19–24

Advanced: 9–17 odd, 19–26

Standardized Test Prep: 27–30

Mixed Review: 31–33

Reasoning exercises have blue headings.

Applications exercises have red headings.

EXERCISE 21: Use the Think About a Plan worksheet in the **Practice and Problem Solving Workbook** (also available in the Teaching Resources in print and online) to further support students' development in becoming independent learners.

HOMEWORK QUICK CHECK

To check students' understanding of key skills and concepts, go over Exercises 11, 13, 19, 20, and 21.

Practice and Problem-Solving Exercises

A) Practice Find the minimum, first quartile, median, third quartile, and maximum of each data set. ◀ See Problem 1.

8. 12 10 11 7 9 10 5

9. 4.5 3.2 6.3 5.2 5 4.8 6 3.9 12

10. 55 53 67 52 50 49 51 52 52

11. 101 100 100 105 101 102 104

Make a box-and-whisker plot to represent each set of data. ◀ See Problem 2.

12. song lengths (s): 227 221 347 173 344 438 171 129 165 333

13. movie ratings: 1 5 1 2.5 3 2 3.5 2 3 1.5 4 2 4 1 3 4.5

14. weekly museum visitors: 531 469 573 206 374 421 505 489 702

15. camera prices: $280 $220 $224 $70 $410 $90 $30 $120

16. Fuel Use Use the box-and-whisker plots below. What do they tell you about the fuel efficiencies for each type of vehicle? Explain. ◀ See Problem 3.

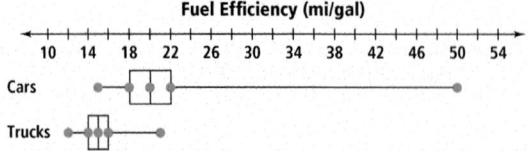

Fuel Efficiency (mi/gal)

10 14 18 22 26 30 34 38 42 46 50 54

Cars

Trucks

17. Of 10 test scores, six are less than or equal to 80. What is the percentile rank of a test score of 80? ◀ See Problem 4.

18. Of 35 judges' scores awarded during a gymnastics event, 28 are less than or equal to 7.5. What is the percentile rank of a score of 7.5?

B) Apply **19. Think About a Plan** You are one of the finalists at a science fair. The scores of the other finalists are 87, 89, 81, 85, 87, 83, 86, 94, 90, 97, 80, 89, 85, and 88. Write an inequality that represents your possible scores if your percentile rank is 80.
- What percent of the scores must be less than or equal to your score?
- What is the total number of finalists' scores?

20. Writing Explain the difference between *range* and *interquartile range*.

21. Basketball The heights of the players on a basketball team are 74 in., 79 in., 71.5 in., 81 in., 73 in., 76 in., 78 in., 71 in., 72 in., and 73.5 in. When the 76-in.-tall player is replaced, the percentile rank of the 73.5-in.-tall player becomes 60. Write an inequality that represents the possible heights of the replacement player.

22. Open-Ended Make a data set of 10 numbers that has a median of 22, an interquartile range of 10, and a minimum less than 4.

23. Reasoning Must the third quartile of a data set be less than the maximum value? Explain.

Answers

Practice and Problem-Solving Exercises

8. 5, 7, 10, 11, 12

9. 3.2, 4.2, 5, 6.15, 12

10. 49, 50.5, 52, 54, 67

11. 100, 100, 101, 104, 105

12.

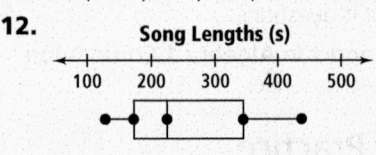

Song Lengths (s)

100 200 300 400 500

13.

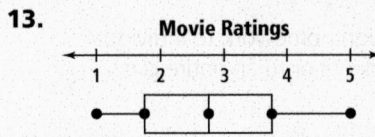

Movie Ratings

1 2 3 4 5

14.

Weekly Museum Visitors

200 300 400 500 600 700

15.

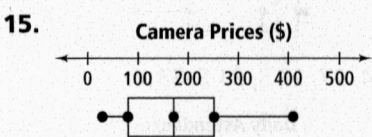

Camera Prices ($)

0 100 200 300 400 500

16. The fuel efficiency in mi/gal of cars goes from a low of 14.5 to a high of about 50, with the middle 50% of cars being in the range of 18 to 22 mi/gal. Trucks have a low of about 12 mi/gal to a high of about 22 mi/gal with the middle 50% being between 14 and 16 mi/gal. The range of the cars is much greater than that of trucks.

17. 60

18. 80

19. $90 \le x < 94$

20. The range gives the difference between the greatest and least values, while the interquartile range gives the difference between the third and first quartiles.

21. $0 < h \le 73.5$

22. Check students' work.

23. It could also be equal to the maximum value, which could happen if the top quarter of the scores all have the same value.

24. Packaging A cereal company is choosing between two devices to package their cereal into bags. The box-and-whisker plots at the right show the weights of the bags packed by each device.

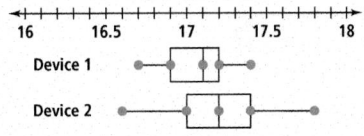

Bag Weight (oz)

Device 1

Device 2

a. Which device produces packages with a more consistent weight? Explain.

b. Which device should be chosen if the manufacturer wants to minimize the number of packages with weights less than 17 oz? More than 17.2 oz? Explain.

 **Challenge**

25. Reasoning Can you find the mean, median, and mode of a data set by looking at a box-and-whisker plot? Explain.

26. Of 100 people that take a test, nine have scores greater than 93. What is the percentile rank of a score of 93?

Standardized Test Prep

GRIDDED RESPONSE

SAT/ACT

27. During one week, the employees of a small business work 17, 21, 42, 29, 12, 17, 18, 19, 27, and 36 h. What is the third quartile of this data set?

28. What is the range of the data set 100, 32, 101, 96, 89, 120, and 40?

29. Jared can clear his driveway of snow in 36 min. It takes his brother 48 min. To the nearest minute, how long does it take to clear the driveway if they work together?

30. To the nearest hundredth, what is the value of $\sqrt{15} \cdot \frac{7}{\sqrt{3}}$?

Mixed Review

Find the mean, median, and mode of each data set.

 See Lesson 12-3.

31. prize pumpkin weights (lb): 948 627 731 697 988 643 719 627

32. daily customers: 47 41 22 17 55 34 71 46 39 41 38 60 52

Get Ready! To prepare for Lesson 12-5, do Exercise 33.

33. Bowling Make a scatter plot of the data below. Draw a trend line and write its equation. Predict the number of tenpin bowling establishments in 2015.

See Lesson 5-7.

Tenpin Bowling					
Year	2002	2003	2004	2005	2006
Bowling Establishments	5973	5811	5761	5818	5566

Source: United States Bowling Congress

24. a. Device 1; the range is the smallest.

b. Device 2; Device 1; Device 2 has 25% of its packages below 17 oz, while Device 1 has more than that. Device 1 has 25% packages greater than 17.2 oz, while Device 2 has about 50% of its packages greater.

25. You can only find the median, which is the value at the line in the box.

26. 91

27. 29

28. 88

29. 21

30. 15.65

31. 747.5, 708, 627

32. 43.3, 41, 41

33.

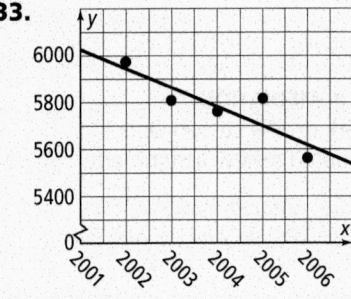

Answers may vary. Sample:
$y = -81x + 167{,}509$; about 4300 bowling establishments

Additional Instructional Support

Algebra 1 Companion

Students can use the **Algebra 1 Companion** worktext (4 pages) as you teach the lesson. Use the Companion to support

- New Vocabulary
- Key Concepts
- Got It for each Problem
- Lesson Check

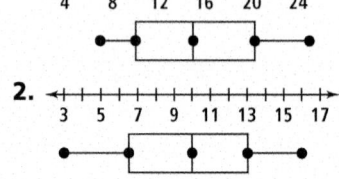

ELL Support

Focus on Language What other words sound like *quartile*? Ideas might be *quart*, *quarter*, or *quartet*. What does it mean to predict? Ask students to predict what the root word "quart" means. Quart means a *fourth*. Ask: Why do you think this is called a quartile? A quartile divides a set of data into four equal parts. Provide students with multiple sets of data to separate into quartiles. When they are proficient at the concept, ask, when a set of data is divided into fourths, in which fourth is the median? Then introduce the term *interquartile range*. Ask: What did you learn about *range* in the last lesson?

5 Assess & Remediate

Lesson Quiz

1. What are the minimum, first quartile, median, third quartile, and maximum of the data set below? Make a box-and-whisker plot for the data.

   7 18 22 10 25 12 10 19 15

2. The table shows the number of sales by 8 salespeople over the past month. What box-and-whisker plot represents the data?

Salesperson	Number of Sales
Nancy	11
Carlos	3
Orlando	8
Russell	12
Betty	16
Misty	5
Carmen	14
Paula	9

3. **Do you UNDERSTAND?** Of 52 players shooting free throws, 39 made more than 60%. What is the percentile rank of a 60% free throw percentage?

ANSWERS TO LESSON QUIZ

1. minimum: 7; first quartile: 10; median: 15; third quartile: 20.5; maximum: 25

2.

3. 25

PRESCRIPTION FOR REMEDIATION

Use the student work on the Lesson Quiz to prescribe a differentiated review assignment.

Points	Differentiated Remediation
0–1	Intervention
2	On-level
3	Extension

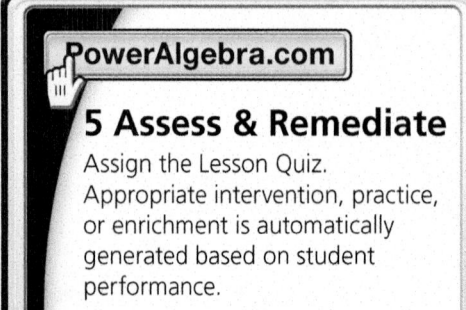

PowerAlgebra.com

5 Assess & Remediate

Assign the Lesson Quiz. Appropriate intervention, practice, or enrichment is automatically generated based on student performance.

Intervention

- **Reteaching** (2 pages) Provides reteaching and practice exercises for the key lesson concepts. Use with struggling students or absent students.

- **English Language Learner Support** Helps students develop and reinforce mathematical vocabulary and key concepts.

All-in-One Resources/Online
Reteaching

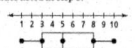

All-in-One Resources/Online
English Language Learner Support

Differentiated Remediation *continued*

On-Level

- **Practice** (2 pages) Provides extra practice for each lesson. For simpler practice exercises, use the Form K Practice pages found in the All-in-One Teaching Resources and online.

- **Think About a Plan** Helps students develop specific problem-solving skills and strategies by providing scaffolded guiding questions.

- **Standardized Test Prep** Focuses on all major exercises, all major question types, and helps students prepare for the high-stakes assessments.

Extension

- **Enrichment** Provides students with interesting problems and activities that extend the concepts of the lesson.

- **Activities, Games, and Puzzles** Worksheets that can be used for concepts development, enrichment, and for fun!

Practice and Problem Solving Wkbk/All-in-One Resources/Online
Practice page 1

Practice and Problem Solving Wkbk/All-in-One Resources/Online
Practice page 2

All-in-One Resources/Online
Enrichment

Practice and Problem Solving Wkbk/All-in-One Resources/Online
Think About a Plan

Practice and Problem Solving Wkbk/All-in-One Resources/Online
Standardized Test Prep

Online Teacher Resource Center
Activities, Games, and Puzzles

Guided Instruction

PURPOSE To explore methods of collecting data
PROCESS Students

- select a sample that is a good representation of the entire group.
- study the smaller portion of an entire group, and make predictions from the study.
- design and conduct their own survey, asking questions that are not opinionated and/or biased.

DISCUSS Have students identify ways that surveys are used in real-world settings. Ask them to tell the advantages and disadvantages of using samples. Ask how the media or how advertisers use the results of surveys to sway opinions.

Activity 1

In this Activity students examine a survey and look at ways to improve the survey.

> **Q** What is the population in this survey? **[all of the students in your school]**
>
> **Q** Is it feasible to study the entire population? Why or why not? **[In the case of most schools, it would be unrealistic to survey each and every individual; therefore, it would be necessary to utilize a sample group.]**

Activity 2

In this Activity students design and conduct their own survey.

> **Q** In Exercise 8, it says to summarize your results in a graph. What are some of the types of graph you could use? **[Samples: line plot, line graph, stem-and-leaf plot, circle graph, bar graph, box-and-whisker plot, histogram, and Venn diagram]**

Concept Byte
Use With Lesson 12-5

Designing Your Own Survey

You have learned how to organize, display, and summarize data. In this activity you will explore methods of collecting data.

Suppose a statistician is trying to predict how a town will vote in an upcoming election. She could ask every person in the town, but this method takes too much time and work. Instead, she might rely on an information-gathering survey that is sent to only some people in the town. She can then use the results to predict how other people in the town might vote.

When you design a survey, you need to make sure that the people you survey are representative of the group you want to study.

Activity 1

Suppose you want to find out how many hours of exercise the students at your school get each week. At the school gym you ask everybody you see, "How many hours of exercise do you get every week?"

1. Will the results of your survey be representative of your entire school? Explain.

2. Is there a better location to conduct your survey?

3. Suppose you asked, "Do you work out every day like a healthy person, or are you a lazy couch potato who only works out once in a while?" Do you think the results of your survey would change? Explain your reasoning.

Activity 2

In this activity, you will design and conduct a survey.

4. Select a topic for your survey. You could ask about favorite sporting events, snacks, musical instruments, or another topic of your choice.

5. **Writing** What question will you ask? Will your question influence the opinion of the people you are surveying?

6. What group of people do you want to study? Are you going to ask the entire group, or just a portion of the whole group?

7. **Data Collection** Complete your survey.

8. **Writing** Summarize your results with a graph and a brief description.

9. **Reasoning** Are the people you surveyed representative of the group you want to study? Explain.

Answers

Activity 1

1. No; your results will be skewed because you are only asking people who regularly exercise and not those who do not.

2. yes; at an exercise-neutral place

3. Yes; you are asking a leading question that makes a person want to answer one way or another.

Activity 2

4–9. Check students' work.

12-5 Samples and Surveys

Objective To classify data and analyze samples and surveys

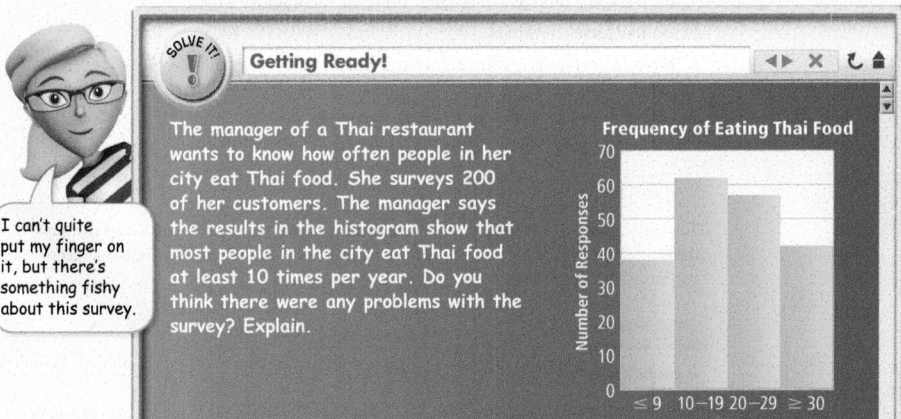

SOLVE IT!

Getting Ready!

The manager of a Thai restaurant wants to know how often people in her city eat Thai food. She surveys 200 of her customers. The manager says the results in the histogram show that most people in the city eat Thai food at least 10 times per year. Do you think there were any problems with the survey? Explain.

Frequency of Eating Thai Food

I can't quite put my finger on it, but there's something fishy about this survey.

In the Solve It, the restaurant manager collected data from the customers of the restaurant. In this lesson, you will learn about ways to collect data.

Lesson Vocabulary
• quantitative
• qualitative
• univariate
• bivariate
• population
• sample
• bias

Essential Understanding When collecting data to solve a problem, you need to make sure that your methods are fair and that you accurately represent the results.

You can collect data using measurements or categories. **Quantitative** data measure quantities and can be described numerically, such as test scores and ages. **Qualitative** data name qualities and can be words or numbers, such as sports or ZIP codes.

Types of Data	Description	Examples
Quantitative	Has units and can be measured and numerically compared	**Age:** 13 yr **Weight:** 214 g **Time:** 23 min
Qualitative	Describes a category and cannot be measured or numerically compared	**Hair color:** brown **Attitude:** optimistic **ZIP code:** 02125

PowerAlgebra.com | Lesson 12-5 Samples and Surveys | 741

---

1 Interactive Learning

Solve It!

PURPOSE To analyze the composition and results of a statistical survey
PROCESS Students may consider both the sample method and the statistical interpretation of the study.

FACILITATE

Q Do you think that the responses of the customers of her restaurant accurately reflect the responses of other people in the city? Explain. **[No, the customers of her restaurant probably like Thai food, whereas many other people in the city may not like Thai food.]**

Q Do you think that the intervals used in the histogram give the restaurant owner a clear display of the survey results? Explain. **[Smaller intervals, such as 5, might show the data better. In the interval with the most frequency, 60 customers ate Thai food 10 to 19 times per year. The restaurant owner might want to know if more of those 60 people ate 10–14 times a year, or more ate 15–19 times a year.]**

ANSWER See Solve It in Answers on next page.
CONNECT THE MATH In the Solve It, students analyze a histogram of survey results and consider how accurately the results reflect the intended population. Students learn in the lesson about ways to collect reliable data and the difference between quantitative and qualitative data.

12-5 Preparing to Teach

BIG idea Data Collection and Analysis **UbD**

ESSENTIAL UNDERSTANDINGS

• When collecting data, it is important for the results to accurately represent the situation.
• Surveys can use random, systematic, or stratified sampling methods.

Math Background

While the purpose of descriptive statistics is to summarize and describe a set of data, the purpose of inferential statistics is to make conclusions that extend beyond the actual data at hand. For example, when a survey is taken, the results gained from a sample might be used to draw conclusions about the population from which the sample was drawn. Another example of inferential statistics involves the use of bivariate data. The two variables in a bivariate set of data

can be examined to determine how change in one of the variables effects change in the other variable. This relationship between the two variables can then be used to make predictions for values of the variables that are not included in the data set.

Support Student Learning

Use the **Algebra 1 Companion** to engage and support students during instructions. See Lesson Resources at the end of this lesson for details.

PowerAlgebra.com

1 Interactive Learning

Solve It!

Step out how to solve the Problem with helpful hints and an online question. Other questions are listed above in Interactive Learning.

2 Guided Instruction

Problem 1

> **Q** What is a data set involving movies that would be quantitative in nature? **[Answers may vary: Sample: Amount of box office revenues for movies opening one weekend.]**
>
> **Q** What is a data set involving students who take Spanish at different schools that would be qualitative? **[Answers may vary: Sample: the name of the Spanish textbook used]**

Got It?   ERROR PREVENTION

If students are confusing the two types of data, suggest that they create a sample data set to consider. For example, with eye color, they might create the set: {blue, green, brown, blue, hazel}.

Problem 2

> **Q** What is a sample data set for 2A? **[Answers may vary. Sample: {1.008, 4.003, 6.941}]**
>
> **Q** What is a sample data set for 2B? **[Answers may vary. Sample: {(8, 2), (27, 3), (64, 4)}]**

Got It?

> **Q** What variable(s) is being measured in 2a? in 2b? **[height of a mammal and weight of a mammal; cost of Internet service]**

The problem with many surveys lies with the sample used in taking the survey. You can demonstrate this idea in your classroom. Explain that all the students in the class represent a population. Use the following samples and question to clarify a representative sample.

 **Problem 1** Classifying Data

Think

Are the data numerical measurements?
Movie titles and jersey numbers are not numerical measurements, but a number of students is.

Is each data set *qualitative* or *quantitative*?

A favorite movies

The data are not numerical quantities. These are qualitative data.

B numbers of students in different schools who take Spanish

The data are numerical quantities. These are quantitative data.

C football jersey numbers

The data are numerical but not measurements. They are qualitative data.

Got It? **1.** Is each data set *qualitative* or *quantitative*? Explain.
    a. costs of CDs   **b.** eye colors

The kind of data you are working with determines the type of graph you use to display the data. A set of data that uses only one variable is **univariate**. A set of data that uses two variables is **bivariate**.

Problem 2 Identifying Types of Data

Think

Does the data set involve one or two variables?
One variable means the data set is univariate. Two variables means the data set is bivariate.

Is each data set *univariate* or *bivariate*?

A the atomic weights of the elements in the periodic table

There is only one variable, atomic weight. The data set is univariate.

B the edge lengths and volumes of cubes

There are two variables, edge length and volume. The data set is bivariate.

Got It? **2.** Is each data set *univariate* or *bivariate*? Explain.
    a. heights and weights of mammals
    b. the cost of Internet service from several different providers

Statisticians collect information about specific groups of objects or people. The entire group that you want information about is called a **population**. When a population is too large to survey, statisticians survey a part of it to find characteristics of the whole. The part that is surveyed is called a **sample**.

Three sampling methods are shown on the next page. When designing a survey, you should choose a sample that reflects the population.

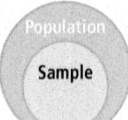

Answers

Solve It!

Answers may vary. Sample: The manager wanted to know how often people in her city eat Thai food, but she only surveyed her customers. This is a biased sample as the people she is surveying already eat Thai food.

Got It?

1. a. quantitative; numerical quantities
   b. qualitative; not numerical
2. a. Bivariate; there are two variables.
   b. Univariate; there is only one variable.

 PowerAlgebra.com

2 Guided Instruction

Each Problem is worked out and supported online.

Problem 1
Classifying Data
Animated

Problem 2
Identifying Types of Data

Problem 3
Choosing a Sample
Animated

Problem 4
Determining Bias in a Survey Question
Animated

Problem 5
Determining Bias in a Sample

Support in Algebra 1 Companion
• Vocabulary
• Key Concepts
• Got It?

Name	Sampling Method	Example
Random	Survey a population at random.	Survey people whose names are drawn out of a hat.
Systematic	Select a number *n* at random. Then survey every *n*th person.	Select the number 5 at random. Survey every fifth person.
Stratified	Separate a population into smaller groups, each with a certain characteristic. Then survey at random within each group.	Separate a high school into four groups by grade level. Survey a random sample of students from each grade.

 Problem 3 Choosing a Sample

DVD Rentals You want to find out how many DVDs students at your school rent in a month. You interview every tenth teenager you see at a mall. What sampling method are you using? Is this a good sample?

Think

What population are you trying to represent with this sample?
You want to collect information about the students at your school.

Since you are interviewing every tenth teenager, this method is systematic. This is not a good sample because it will likely include teenagers who do not attend your school.

Got It? 3. You revise your plan and interview all students leaving a school assembly who are wearing the school colors. Will this plan give a good sample? Explain.

A survey question has **bias** when it contains assumptions that may or may not be true. Bias can influence opinion and can make one answer seem better than another. Survey questions must be carefully worded to avoid bias.

 Problem 4 Determining Bias in a Survey Question

Movies A reporter wants to find out what kinds of movies are most popular with local residents. The reporter asks, "Do you prefer exciting action movies or boring documentaries?" Is the question biased? Explain.

Know	Need	Plan
The survey question	To determine whether the question is biased	Check the question for adjectives or phrases that make one category seem more appealing.

The question is biased because the words *exciting* and *boring* make action films sound more interesting than documentaries.

Got It? 4. Reasoning How can the question in Problem 4 be reworded so that it is not biased?

Note: you may need to adjust the numbers in the following to better represent your class.
- Name four girls. Ask: Is this a representative sample of the class?
- Name three girls, one boy. Ask the question.
- Name two girls with long hair, two boys with short hair. Ask the question.

Continue naming a sample until the class agrees that the sample is representative of the class.

Problem 3

Q What kind of data will you be collecting in this survey? **[univariate quantitative data]**

Q How could you revise this systematic sample so that it will result in a good sample? **[You could interview every tenth student that you encounter in the school lunchroom.]**

Got It?

Ask students to describe a stratified sampling method that would result in a good sample of the student population.

Problem 4

Q If you were to use the survey question as given, what results might you expect? **[Answers may vary. Sample: I would expect a majority of the responses to be in favor of action movies.]**

Q For what purpose might a surveyor use this biased question? **[Answers may vary. Sample: He might want to convince the local theater to show only action movies.]**

Got It?

Ask students to devise an unbiased sampling method and unbiased questions for a survey that would be useful to a video store owner who would like to adapt his inventory to the interests of his customers.

Additional Problems

1. Is each data set *qualitative* or *quantitative*?
a. hair color
b. lengths of boards
c. ages of students
ANSWER a. qualitative
b. quantitative
c. quantitative

2. Is each data set *univariate* or *bivariate*?
a. the radius of a circle and the area of the circle
b. the cost of renting a taxi based on the number of miles driven
ANSWER a. bivariate
b. bivariate

3. A grocery store owner wants to know how much customers are spending on average. He surveys every customer who uses a discount coupon. What sampling method is the store owner using? Is this a good sample?
ANSWER Stratified sample; sample answer: This sample may not represent his customers well; customers who use discount coupons may be more interested in bargains and low-cost items.

4. A reporter wants to find out how many voters support the construction of a new highway. She asks randomly selected voters the question: "Do you support the economic growth that the new highway will bring, or are you opposed to the project?" Is the question biased? Explain.
ANSWER Sample answer: Yes, the question is biased by saying that the highway will lead to economic growth.

5. Micah wants to know what outdoor activities people in the community enjoy on the weekends. He interviews every fifth person at a local bike trail on Saturday. How might this cause bias in the results of the survey?
ANSWER Sample answer: The sample might be biased toward bike riding since the members of the sample were found at a bike trail.

Problem 5

Tell students that while the word *bias* in common English usage suggests something unfair or morally wrong, the word *bias* in statistical terms is a purely mathematical concept. Although some people may intentionally create bias in their samples, most bias in a sample is due to the difficulty in obtaining a representative random sample.

Got It?

> **Q** How could you create a less biased sample?
> **[Answers may vary. Sample: I would ask each classmate the question in person so that it is no longer a voluntary-response sample.]**

3 Lesson Check

Do you know HOW?

• If students have difficulty with Exercises 1-3, then have them refer to the summary table of sampling methods.

Do you UNDERSTAND?

• If students have difficulty with Exercise 6, then have them provide an example of both univariate data and bivariate data.

Close

> **Q** What characteristics does a good survey have?
> **[A good survey gathers data from a sample that possesses the same characteristics as the population being studied, using a survey question that does not influence opinion in any way.]**

Samples can also be biased. For example, all voluntary-response samples are biased because you cannot be sure that the people who choose to respond are representative of the population. The location where a survey is conducted can also cause a sample to be biased.

 **Problem 5** Determining Bias in a Sample

Sports You want to determine what percent of teens ages 14 to 18 watch wrestling on TV. At a high school wrestling match, you ask every third teenager whether he or she watches wrestling on TV. How might this cause bias in the results of your survey?

The sample chosen is not representative of the population. People who attend a high school wrestling match may be more likely to watch wrestling on TV.

Think

Ask yourself whether the sample and the population have similar characteristics. If not, the sample is biased.

 Got It? 5. You want to know how many of your classmates have cell phones. To determine this, you send every classmate an e-mail asking, "Do you own a cell phone?" How might this method of gathering data affect the results of your survey?

 **Lesson Check**

Do you know HOW?

Determine whether each sampling method is *random*, *systematic*, or *stratified*.

  1. You survey every tenth student who enters the cafeteria.

  2. You draw student ID numbers out of a hat and survey those students.

  3. You survey two students at random from each class.

Do you UNDERSTAND?

  4. Vocabulary Is a data set of your class's test scores *qualitative* or *quantitative* data?

  5. Writing Explain why "Do you prefer delicious fruit or plain vegetables for a snack food?" is a biased survey question.

  6. Compare and Contrast What is the difference between univariate data and bivariate data? Give an example of each type of data.

Practice and Problem-Solving Exercises

A Practice Determine whether each data set is *qualitative* or *quantitative*. ◀ See Problem 1.

  7. favorite recording stars   **8.** best-selling DVDs

  9. numbers of gigabytes in memory cards   **10.** prices of TVs

Determine whether each data set is *univariate* or *bivariate*. ◀ See Problem 2.

  11. numbers of CDs your classmates own   **12.** ages and heights of your friends

  13. Zip codes of your relatives   **14.** circumferences and radii of circles

---

3 Lesson Check

For a digital lesson check, use the Got It? questions.

Support in Algebra 1 Companion
• Lesson Check

4 Practice

Assign homework to individual students or to an entire class.

Answers

Got It? (continued)

3. No; if you are using a stratified sampling method, you should sample at random from each group.

4. Answers may vary. Sample: Do you prefer action movies or documentaries?

5. Students who have e-mail may be more likely to have a cell phone.

Lesson Check

1. systematic

2. random

3. stratified

4. quantitative

5. The words *delicious* and *plain* are biased and might influence a respondent's answer.

6. Univariate data involves one variable and bivariate data involves two variables.

Practice and Problem-Solving Exercises

7. qualitative

8. qualitative

9. quantitative

10. quantitative

11. univariate

12. bivariate

13. univariate

14. bivariate

Determine whether the sampling method is *random*, *systematic*, or *stratified*. See Problem 3.
Tell whether the method will produce a good sample.

15. A pollster randomly selects 100 people from each town in a certain candidate's district to see if they support the candidate.

16. A factory tests the quality of every thirtieth shirt made.

17. A printing company randomly selects 10 of 450 books it printed to see if all the books were printed properly.

Determine whether each question is biased. Explain your answer. See Problem 4.

18. Since global warming is a big problem, do you support government funding of studies on global warming?

19. Where would you most like to go on vacation?

20. Do you prefer shopping online or the excitement of going to stores with friends?

21. You want to find out how much time people in your town spend doing volunteer work. You call 100 homes in the community during the day. Of those surveyed, 85% are over the age of 60. How might this create bias in your survey results? See Problem 5.

22. You want to find out how many people in your neighborhood have pets in their homes. You ask every fourth person at the local dog park. How might this create bias in your survey results?

B Apply

23. Reasoning You review the results of survey questions given to two random samples of students from your school. The results are shown in the table below. Why are the results not the same?

Favorite Color

Color	Red	Blue	Green	Yellow	Pink	Purple	Black
Group A	8	6	4	2	5	4	1
Group B	7	7	3	0	6	5	2

24. Think About a Plan You want to find out what types of music students would like to listen to at the next school dance. How would you conduct a survey to find the music preferences of your entire school?
  • What sampling method can you use to choose an unbiased sample?
  • How can you write survey questions that are not biased?

25. Travel A travel agent wants to determine whether a trip to France is a popular vacation for young adults. How could each factor described below create bias in the survey results?
  a. The agent interviews people at an international airport.
  b. The agent asks, "Would you prefer to vacation in France or in Italy?"
  c. Of the people interviewed, 86% took a French class in high school.

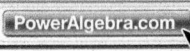

4 Practice

ASSIGNMENT GUIDE
Basic: 7–26 all, 28–34 even
Average: 7–21 odd, 23–38
Advanced: 7–21 odd, 23–40
Standardized Test Prep: 41–44
Mixed Review: 45–52

Reasoning exercises have blue headings.

Applications exercises have red headings.

EXERCISE 25: Use the Think About a Plan worksheet in the **Practice and Problem Solving Workbook** (also available in the Teaching Resources in print and online) to further support students' development in becoming independent learners.

HOMEWORK QUICK CHECK
To check students' understanding of key skills and concepts, go over Exercises 9, 19, 24, 25, and 26.

---

15. stratified; not a good sample as it assumes each town has a similar number of voters

16. systematic; not a good sample because it does not include randomness

17. random; good sample

18. biased; question is influenced by the wording

19. not biased; respondent is not influenced by question

20. biased; wording of choices is biased

21. During the day many people are at work so your sample is not representative of the population.

22. You are asking people who are apt to have a pet because they are at a dog park.

23. Because each sample is random, it would not be expected to be exactly the same.

24. You could use a random sample of the whole school or you could use a stratified sample of each class (freshmen, sophomores, etc.). Your question might be "What type of music do you want to hear at the dance?"

25. a. People at an airport are more likely to be travelers.

  b. Your question is influencing the result. Respondents might prefer "neither."

  c. The sample is biased as it includes mostly people who might prefer France.

Answers

Practice and Problem-Solving Exercises
(continued)

26. The way the question is posed may influence the answer. A better question would be "At what age do you think a person should be able to vote?"

27. people who are customers at the store; every fifteenth customer; systematic

28. school population; club members; stratified

29. attendees at the game; random attendees; random

30. all the restaurant's customers; every third customer; systematic

31. quantitative; univariate

32. quantitative; univariate

33. qualitative; bivariate

34. qualitative; bivariate

35. **a.** Responses are voluntary and there are sports that are not listed.

    b. no for the reasons listed in part (a)

36. **a.** Biased; you are surveying customers who are probably bike riders.

    b. Biased; your survey is not representative of all town residents as you are excluding many.

    c. Biased; you are sampling only classmates who are not representative of the whole town.

    d. Biased; you are sampling only those residents who are customers of that shop rather than the whole town; you are probably only getting people from that particular part of town.

37. Response is voluntary and only those who like the scent are probably going to return the card.

---

26. **Error Analysis** Malik is conducting a survey about the legal voting age in the United States. His question is, "Isn't the legal voting age too high?" When his friends suggested that his question was biased, he revised it to be, "Don't you think the legal voting age should be lower?" Describe and correct the error in his rewritten survey question.

In each situation, identify the population and sample. Tell whether each sample is a *random*, *systematic*, or *stratified* sample.

27. For one month, the owner of a sporting goods store asks every fifteenth customer which sport he or she most enjoys watching on TV.

28. One student from each club is chosen at random to represent the school at the school fair.

29. At a high school football game, every spectator places his or her ticket stub in a bowl. After the game, the coach chooses ten people to march in the victory parade.

30. A restaurant asks every third customer to complete an evaluation form.

Classify the data as *qualitative* or *quantitative* and as *univariate* or *bivariate*.

31. average number of visitors per day at each of six different theme parks

32. monthly low temperatures in Rochester, New York

33. names of U.S. presidents and the states they were born in

34. favorite color and a person's gender

35. **Sports** A student posts a survey on a Web site asking readers to choose their favorite sport to play from a list of five sports. The results are shown at the right.
    a. What biases might exist as a result of the design of this survey?
    b. Do you believe the results of this survey are valid? Explain your answer.

    Students' Favorite Sports

Golf	Basketball
Swimming	Baseball
Tennis	

36. **Writing** You are writing an article for the school newspaper about support for the mayor's proposal for bike paths. For each situation below, determine whether the data collection method will result in an unbiased sample of town residents. Explain your answer.
    a. You survey every tenth person leaving a bicycle repair store.
    b. You call homes in your neighborhood every morning Monday through Friday for one week.
    c. You send an e-mail to 100 classmates chosen at random.
    d. You poll every fifth person at a popular local sandwich shop.

37. **Market Research** A perfume company sends a sample of a new scent to 500 homes. Each responder who sends back a response card saying how much she likes the scent will have a chance to win a bottle of perfume. How will this affect the results?

38. Elections A radio station asks its listeners to call and tell who their favorite candidate is in an upcoming election. Sixty-eight percent of the callers prefer a certain candidate, so the radio station announces that the candidate will win the election. Is the conclusion valid? Explain.

Challenge **39. Data Collection** You want to find out what kinds of pets the families of students attending your school have.
   a. Write an unbiased question for your survey. Will you be collecting quantitative or qualitative data?
   b. Choose a population and sampling method. Describe them both.
   c. Collect the data as you described and display the results in a graph.

40. Writing A toothpaste company reports that four out of five dentists recommend their toothpaste. What information do you need to know about the survey to determine whether the results are unbiased?

Standardized Test Prep

SAT/ACT
41. What is the solution of the equation $\frac{x}{2} - 11 = 19$?
   Ⓐ 8   Ⓑ 16   Ⓒ 30   Ⓓ 60

42. What is 0.0000212 written in scientific notation?
   Ⓕ 2.12×10^5 Ⓖ 2.12×10^{-5} Ⓗ 21.2×10^{-6} Ⓘ 2.12×10^{-6}

43. 40% of what number is 50?
   Ⓐ 155   Ⓑ 125   Ⓒ 20   Ⓓ 2

Short
Response
44. A reporter is trying to predict who will win an open seat on the city council. Her plan is to ask 20 coworkers who they think will win. Will this plan give a good sample? Explain.

Mixed Review

45. Of 30 test scores, 12 are less than or equal to 85. What is the percentile rank of a test score of 85?   ◀ See Lesson 12-4.

46. There are 15 bands in a competition. The judges give 9 bands a score of 7.5 or lower. What is the percentile rank of 7.5?

Solve each inequality.   ◀ See Lesson 3-4.

47. $4 - 3a < 3a - 2$ **48.** $3(x - 2) \le 6x + 3$ **49.** $2.7 + 2b > 3.4 - 1.5b$

Get Ready! To prepare for Lesson 12-6, do Exercises 50–52.

Write each fraction in simplest form.   ◀ See p. 789.

50. $\frac{5 \cdot 4 \cdot 3 \cdot 2 \cdot 1}{3 \cdot 2 \cdot 1}$ **51.** $\frac{7 \cdot 6 \cdot 5 \cdot 4 \cdot 3 \cdot 2 \cdot 1}{5 \cdot 4 \cdot 3 \cdot 2 \cdot 1}$ **52.** $\frac{6 \cdot 5 \cdot 4 \cdot 3 \cdot 2 \cdot 1}{5 \cdot 4 \cdot 3 \cdot 2 \cdot 1}$

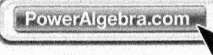
38. No; it is a voluntary response.
39. a. Answers may vary. Sample: Does your family have a pet? If so, what kind of pet is it?; qualitative
   b. Check students' work.
   c. Check students' work.
40. How was the survey done and what question did they ask?
41. D
42. G
43. B
44. [2] No; her sample is not representative of the population.
   [1] correct answer, with a vague explanation

45. 40
46. 60
47. $a > 1$
48. $x \ge -3$
49. $b > 0.2$
50. 20
51. 42
52. 6

Additional Instructional Support

Algebra 1 Companion

Students can use the **Algebra 1 Companion** worktext (4 pages) as you teach the lesson. Use the Companion to support

- New Vocabulary
- Key Concepts
- Got It for each Problem
- Lesson Check

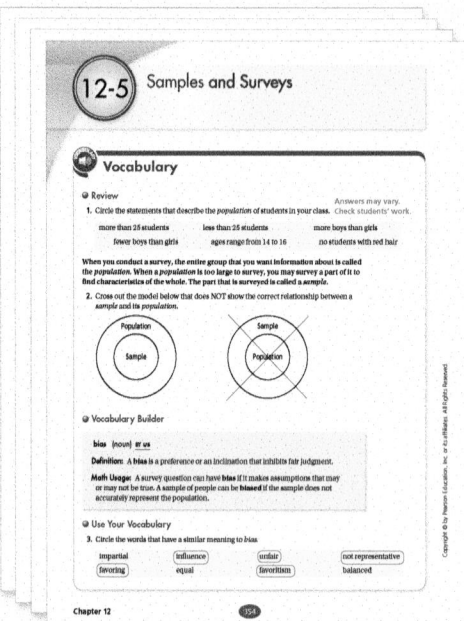

ELL Support

Focus on Language Have a discussion about the roots of the words *qualitative* (*quality*) and *quantitative* (*quantity*). Ask students for examples of quality versus quantity. Then ask them to write a paragraph that compares qualitative and quantitative data using their own words. Tell them to include examples. Repeat with *univariate* and *bivariate*. First discuss the prefixes and root words.

Focus on Communication Place students in pairs either academically or by language levels so a more proficient student is with a less proficient student. Have students read their paragraphs comparing qualitative and quantitative data to each other. Encourage them to question one another.

5 Assess & Remediate

Lesson Quiz

1. Is each data set *qualitative* or *quantitative*?
   a. the favorite kinds of music of students in your homeroom
   b. the number of goals scored by a team
   c. the screen sizes of the monitors at a computer store

2. Is each data set *univariate* or *bivariate*?
   a. the number of pets your classmates have in their families
   b. the number of ice cream cones sold based on the outside temperature

3. **Do you UNDERSTAND?** Miss Vickers is planning a field trip for her class. She puts her students' names in a hat and pulls out 10 names and asks the students whether they prefer the zoo, the aquarium, or the nature center. What sampling method does she use?

4. A city planner wants to find out the average commute time for downtown workers. She interviews randomly selected passengers getting off the bus on a Monday morning. How might this create bias in the results of the survey? Explain.

ANSWERS TO LESSON QUIZ

1. a. qualitative;   b. quantitative;
   c. quantitative

2. a. univariate;   b. bivariate

3. random sampling

4. Sample answer: The sample is biased to include only bus riders. The results for those who car-pool, drive alone, ride the train, or bicycle are not taken into account.

PRESCRIPTION FOR REMEDIATION

Use the student work on the Lesson Quiz to prescribe a differentiated review assignment.

Points	Differentiated Remediation
0–2	Intervention
3	On-level
4	Extension

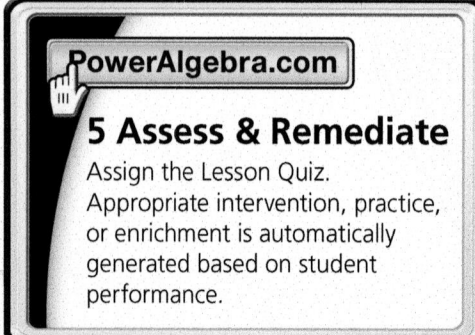

PowerAlgebra.com

5 Assess & Remediate

Assign the Lesson Quiz. Appropriate intervention, practice, or enrichment is automatically generated based on student performance.

Intervention

- **Reteaching** (2 pages) Provides reteaching and practice exercises for the key lesson concepts. Use with struggling students or absent students.

- **English Language Learner Support** Helps students develop and reinforce mathematical vocabulary and key concepts.

All-in-One Resources/Online
Reteaching

12-5 Reteaching
Samples and Surveys

In order to determine the patterns of a large group, a sample of the population can be taken representing the large group's patterns. Three different ways of selecting a sample are discussed in this lesson.

Problem

A high school is trying to determine the favorite subject of the student body. What are ways that the school can select samples to survey the student body in a random method, systematic method, and a stratified method?

There are various other correct answers for each type of sampling. The answers below are examples of how the school can select samples of the school population to survey.

Random: The school can place every student's name in a box and randomly select names out of the box to take the survey. A random sample is selected in such a way that every possible sample has an equal chance of being selected from the population.

Systematic: The school selects every eighth student that walks in the door in the morning to take the survey. A systematic sample is selected according to a specified item or time interval.

Stratified: The school can divide the school by grade and randomly select students in each grade to take the survey. Stratified sampling involves dividing the group up into subgroups and then sampling each of the subgroups.

Questions can be worded in such a way that will bias the answer. Words or descriptions can be included in the survey question to make certain choices more or less attractive than others. For a survey question to be a good question, bias should be avoided.

Problem

A market research company is conducting research regarding which fast food restaurant is the most popular. The company decides to spend several weekends in various popular fast food restaurants to ask the customers what their favorite fast food restaurant is. Is this survey biased? Explain why or why not. If the survey is biased, how can the company change their method to make it unbiased?

The survey is biased because the majority of people are probably in their favorite fast food restaurant. The company could make it more unbiased by conducting the survey in a more neutral location such as a shopping mall.

All-in-One Resources/Online
English Language Learner Support

12-5 ELL Support
Samples and Surveys

| bivariate | qualitative | quantitative | univariate |

Choose the word from the list that is defined by each phrase.

1. Data that measures quantity and can be described numerically.   _quantitative_
2. A set of data that uses two variables.   _bivariate_
3. Data that measures quality and can be words or numbers   _qualitative_
4. A set of data that only uses one variable   _univariate_

Use a word from the list above to complete each sentence.

5. Prices of DVDs is ___quantitative___ data.
6. Perimeter and area of a triangle is a ___bivariate___ data set.
7. Favorite kind of pizza is ___qualitative___ data.
8. The cost of a health club membership from several different health clubs is a ___univariate___ data set.

Multiple Choice

9. Which of the following is an example of quantitative data?   B
   A. dark chocolate
   B. 5 oz. chocolate
   C. smooth texture
   D. strong taste

10. Which of the following is an example of a bivariate data set?   F
    F. age and height of a classmate
    G. gender of a classmate
    H. home phone number of a classmate
    I. classmate's favorite color

Differentiated Remediation *continued*

On-Level

- **Practice** (2 pages) Provides extra practice for each lesson. For simpler practice exercises, use the Form K Practice pages found in the All-in-One Teaching Resources and online.

- **Think About a Plan** Helps students develop specific problem-solving skills and strategies by providing scaffolded guiding questions.

- **Standardized Test Prep** Focuses on all major exercises, all major question types, and helps students prepare for the high-stakes assessments.

Extension

- **Enrichment** Provides students with interesting problems and activities that extend the concepts of the lesson.

- **Activities, Games, and Puzzles** Worksheets that can be used for concepts development, enrichment, and for fun!

Practice and Problem Solving Wkbk/ All-in-One Resources/Online
Practice page 1

Practice and Problem Solving Wkbk/ All-in-One Resources/Online
Practice page 2

All-in-One Resources/Online
Enrichment

Practice and Problem Solving Wkbk/ All-in-One Resources/Online
Think About a Plan

Practice and Problem Solving Wkbk/ All-in-One Resources/Online
Standardized Test Prep

Online Teacher Resource Center
Activities, Games, and Puzzles

Guided Instruction

PURPOSE To examine graphs that are well-suited to the data and to recognize when other types of graphs are a poor choice or drawn so as to be misleading

PROCESS Students will compare two presentations of the same data and analyze which of the two presentations may be misleading.

DISCUSS Ask students when misleading graphs may be helpful in the workplace. Tie in the concept of misleading graphs to the concept of writing a persuasive letter. When is it beneficial to use a misleading graph?

Activity 1
In this Activity students compare two line graphs which depict a company's monthly profits.

> **Q** Do the graphs show the same data? **[yes]**
>
> **Q** In what situation would the graph on the left be best to use? **[Answers will vary. Sample: When trying to show that there was a steady increase in profit and a large increase in recent months.]**
>
> **Q** In what situation would the graph on the right be best to use? **[Answers will vary. Sample: When trying to show that there was not much of an increase in the profit.]**

Activity 2
In this Activity students examine a bar graph which shows the results of a survey conducted by a local newspaper.

> **Q** What is wrong with the use of the word "many" by the columnist in Exercise 5? **[It is a subjective term.]**

VISUAL LEARNERS
Have students redraw the graph from Activity 2 so that it is not misleading.

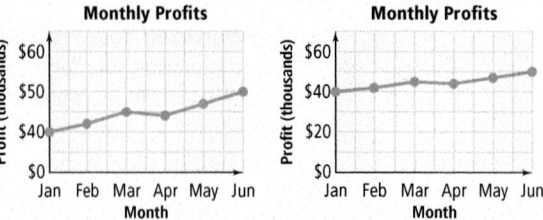

Concept Byte
Use With Lesson 12-5

Misleading Graphs and Statistics

There are many ways to graph data that show the data accurately. There are also ways to graph data that are misleading.

Activity 1

A company uses the two graphs below to display its monthly profits.

1. How are the scales of the axes different in the two graphs?

2. An investor looks at the graph on the left and concludes that the company's profits doubled from January to June. Is the investor correct? Explain.

3. Another investor looks at the graph on the right and concludes that the company's profits increased about 25% from January to June. Is the investor correct? Explain.

4. Reasoning Which graph most accurately displays the data? Explain.

Activity 2

A local newspaper conducts a survey about where people in your town go on vacation. The paper uses the graph at the right to display the results.

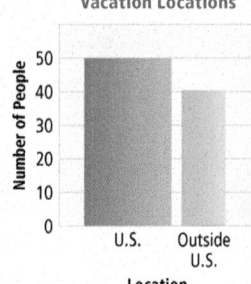

5. A columnist writes that many more people vacation in the United States than outside the United States. Do you think the graph supports the columnist's statement? Explain.

6. According to the graph, how many people vacation in the United States? How many people vacation outside the United States?

7. How do the areas of the bars in the graph compare?

8. Why is the graph misleading?

9. Reasoning How could you redraw the graph so that it is not misleading? Explain your answer.

Answers

Activity 1

1. The graph on the left has a vertical scale that does not start at zero.

2. No; the scale does not start at zero.

3. Yes; the percent increase was about $\frac{10}{40}$ or 25%.

4. The graph on the right; because the vertical scale starts at 0, the appearance of the growth in profit is not misleading.

Activity 2

5. Yes; the graph uses different widths for each category, so at quick glance the graph appears to support the columnist.

6. 50 people; 40 people

7. Because the widths of the bars are not the same, the area of the U.S. bar is exaggerated.

8. The areas of the bars do not accurately reflect the true percentages.

9. Make the width of the bars the same.

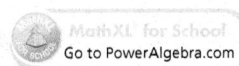

Do you know HOW?

Find each sum or difference.

1. $\begin{bmatrix} -2 & 3 \\ 0 & 4 \\ -1 & 1 \end{bmatrix} + \begin{bmatrix} 4 & -1 \\ 3 & 0 \\ -3 & 2 \end{bmatrix}$

2. $\begin{bmatrix} 0 & -2 \\ 3 & 1 \\ -4 & 3 \end{bmatrix} - \begin{bmatrix} -1 & 0 \\ 2 & 5 \\ -4 & 3 \end{bmatrix}$

Find each product.

3. $-2\begin{bmatrix} 3 & 0 \\ -2 & 1 \end{bmatrix}$

4. $3\begin{bmatrix} -1 & 3 \\ 0 & 2 \end{bmatrix}$

Tell whether each histogram is *uniform*, *symmetric*, or *skewed*.

5.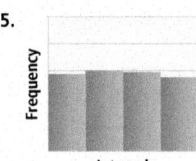
   Interval

6.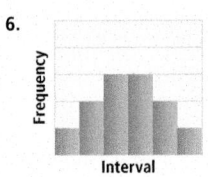
   Interval

7. **Gymnastics** A gymnast's scores from his tryouts are listed below. Make a frequency table and a histogram that represent the data.
   8.8 9.1 3.5 6.9 7.3 9.6 9.0 5.7 7.2 4.3 8.9 9.5

8. **Basketball** A basketball player's points per game are listed below. Make a cumulative frequency table that represents the data.
   16 8 19 12 9 10 11 9 12 23 5 20 13 6 17

9. **Music** The hours per week that a school band practiced are listed below. What are the mean, median, mode, and range of their practice times? Which measure of central tendency best describes their practice times?
   7 5 9 7 4 6 10 8 5 7 8 7 3 12 15 13 8

Identify the minimum, first quartile, median, third quartile, and maximum of each data set. Then make a box-and-whisker plot of each data set.

10. daily visitors: 34 29 32 25 97 93 112 108 90

11. commute (mi): 8 33 28 7 42 9 30 38 22 6 37

12. **Movies** Of the ratings for ten movies, eight ratings are less than or equal to 7. What is the percentile rank of a rating of 7?

Determine whether each data set is *qualitative* or *quantitative*.

13. favorite books

14. prices of DVDs

15. **Business** A software business e-mails every thousandth name on an e-mail list to find out what software the people are using. Is the survey plan *random*, *systematic*, or *stratified*? Will it give a good sample? Explain.

Do you UNDERSTAND?

16. **Reasoning** When you compare two sets of data, will the set with the greater interquartile range always have the greater range? Explain and give an example.

17. **Writing** When is each measure of central tendency most useful?

18. **Error Analysis** A student wrote the matrix equation at the right. Describe and correct the mistake.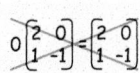

19. **Open-Ended** Describe a problem that you could solve by conducting a survey. Write an unbiased survey question, and explain how to choose a good sample for your survey.

20. **Reasoning** Which measure of central tendency would be most appropriate for qualitative data? Explain your answer.

Answers

Mid-Chapter Quiz

1. $\begin{bmatrix} 2 & 2 \\ 3 & 4 \\ -4 & 3 \end{bmatrix}$

2. $\begin{bmatrix} 1 & -2 \\ 1 & -4 \\ 0 & 0 \end{bmatrix}$

3. $\begin{bmatrix} -6 & 0 \\ 4 & -2 \end{bmatrix}$

4. $\begin{bmatrix} -3 & 9 \\ 0 & 6 \end{bmatrix}$

5. uniform

6. symmetric

7. Answers may vary. Sample:

Gymnasts' Scores

Score	Frequency
3.0–4.9	2
5.0–6.9	2
7.0–8.9	4
9.0–10.9	4

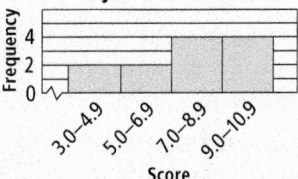

Gymnasts' Scores

8.

Points Per Game

Points	Frequency	Cumulative Frequency
5–9	5	5
10–14	5	10
15–19	3	13
20–24	2	15

9. 7.9, 7, 7, 12; since there are no outliers, the mean is best.

10. 25, 30.5, 90, 102.5, 112

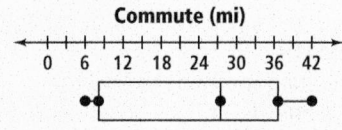

Daily Visitors

11. 6, 8, 28, 37, 42

Commute (mi)

12. 80

13. qualitative

14. quantitative

15. Systematic; because you do not know who the e-mail list will go to and since the response will be voluntary, it is probably not a good sample.

16. No; answers may vary. Sample: The data set consisting of 1, 2, 5, 10 and 15 has an interquartile range of 11 and a range of 14, but the data set consisting of 1, 3, 4, 5 and 20 has an interquartile range of 10.5 and a range of 19. The first set has a larger interquartile range but not a larger range.

17. The mean is more useful when the data has no outliers. The median is better if the data has outliers. The mode is most useful when data is qualitative.

18. Since the matrix is being multiplied by 0, the result should be $\begin{bmatrix} 0 & 0 \\ 0 & 0 \end{bmatrix}$.

19. Check students' work.

20. The mode; qualitative data is not numeric so it makes no sense to find a mean or a median.

1 Interactive Learning

Solve It!

PURPOSE To determine the number of possible ways to choose four objects with regard to order

PROCESS Students may
- make an organized list (partial or complete).
- make a tree diagram (partial or complete).
- use mathematical reasoning.

FACILITATE

Q How many orders are possible if Tilting Towers is the first ride and Splash Down is the second ride? Explain. **[Two orders; you can reverse the Ferris Wheel and Loop-de-Loop.]**

Q How many orders are possible if Tilting Towers is the first ride? Explain. **[Six orders; the remaining three rides can be arranged into 6 different orders.]**

ANSWER See Solve It in Answers on next page.

CONNECT THE MATH

You can use counting methods to find the number of ways objects can be chosen with and without regard to order. In the lesson, students learn formulas for calculating permutations and combinations.

Review how to make and read a tree diagram.

Q If the tree diagram had been made with drama as the movie listed first, would the list of Order of Movies be different from what is shown? Explain. **[No; the same six possible orders would be listed, but in a different order.]**

12-6 Permutations and Combinations

Objective To find permutations and combinations

Getting Ready! ◄► ✗ ↺ ⬆

At an amusement park, you want to go on all of the rides shown on the signpost. In how many different orders can you go on the rides? Describe how you found the answer.

Making a list could take a long time. Is there a faster way?

Lesson Vocabulary
- Multiplication Counting Principle
- permutation
- *n* factorial
- combination

Essential Understanding You can use counting methods to find the number of possible ways to choose objects with and without regard to order.

One way to find the possible orders of objects is to make an organized list. Another way is to make a tree diagram. Both methods help you see if you have thought of all the possibilities.

The tree diagram below shows all the possible orders for watching three movies (a comedy, a drama, and an action film).

First Movie	Second Movie	Third Movie	Order of Movies
comedy	drama	action	comedy, drama, action
	action	drama	comedy, action, drama
drama	comedy	action	drama, comedy, action
	action	comedy	drama, action, comedy
action	comedy	drama	action, comedy, drama
	drama	comedy	action, drama, comedy

There are six possible orders for watching the three movies.

When one event does not affect the result of a second event, the events are *independent*. When events are independent, you can find the number of outcomes using the Multiplication Counting Principle.

12-6 Preparing to Teach

BIG idea Probability   **UbD**

ESSENTIAL UNDERSTANDINGS
- Counting methods can be used to find the number of possible ways to choose objects with and without regard to order.
- Permutation and combination notation can be used to represent real-world situations.

Math Background

For permutations, teach students to read the notation $_nP_r$ as the number of permutations of n objects arranged r at a time. This helps students understand the underlying process represented by the special notation. In particular, it allows them to find the sample space in cases where permutations and combinations figure in probability problems.

To help students understand the differences between permutations and combinations, explain that in a permutation the order of the object is important and in a combination order does not matter. Therefore, there are fewer combinations

than permutations, and the combinations are a subset of the permutations.

Combinatorics is a branch of mathematics that deals with discrete and usually finite sets of objects. Enumerating all of the possible permutations or combinations of a finite set is the most elementary concept in this field of mathematics. The more advanced concepts of combinations have become very important as they have been applied to the development of the computer sciences. Students will encounter combinations again when they study the Binomial Expansion Theorem in a future algebra course.

Support Student Learning

Use the **Algebra 1 Companion** to engage and support students during instructions. See Lesson Resources at the end of this lesson for details.

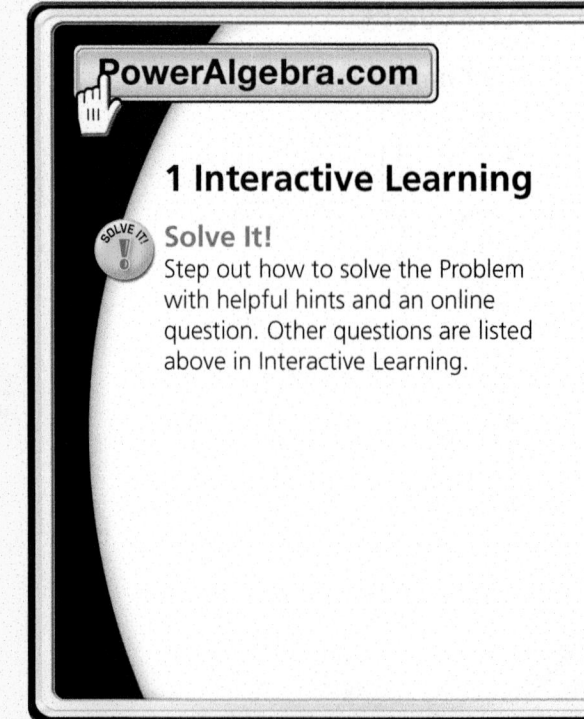

PowerAlgebra.com

1 Interactive Learning

Solve It!

Step out how to solve the Problem with helpful hints and an online question. Other questions are listed above in Interactive Learning.

Key Concept Multiplication Counting Principle

If there are *m* ways to make a first selection and *n* ways to make a second selection, then there are *m · n* ways to make the two selections.

Example

For 5 shirts and 8 pairs of shorts, the number of possible outfits is 5 · 8 = 40.

 **Problem 1** Using the Multiplication Counting Principle

Shopping Use the diagram below. How many ways are there to get from the first floor to the third floor using only escalators?

Think

What is another way to solve this problem?
You can draw a diagram like the tree diagram on the previous page to show all of the possible escalator routes.

2 · 3 = 6

Routes by escalator from first floor to second floor

Routes by escalator from second floor to third floor

Routes by escalator from first floor to third floor

There are 6 possible ways to get from the first floor to the third floor using only escalators.

Got It? 1. a. A pizza shop offers 8 vegetable toppings and 6 meat toppings. How many different pizzas can you order with one meat topping and one vegetable topping?

b. Reasoning Is a tree diagram a convenient way to find the answer to part (a)? Explain.

A **permutation** is an arrangement of objects in a specific order. Here are the possible permutations of the letters A, B, and C without repeating any letters.

ABC   ACB   BAC   BCA   CAB   CBA

---

2 Guided Instruction

Take Note

Apply the Multiplication Counting Principle to the scenario introduced in the Solve It. Elicit from students that there are four selections that must be made. When choosing your first ride, you have four choices. When choosing your second ride, you have three choices. When choosing your third ride, you have two choices. When choosing your last ride, you have only one choice.

Problem 1

Q How many selections are there to make? What are the selections? **[Two; the first selection is which escalator to take from floor 1 to floor 2 and the second selection is which escalator to take from floor 2 to floor 3.]**

Q How many choices do you have when making your first selection? Explain. **[You have two choices because there are two escalators.]**

Q How many choices do you have when making your second selection? Explain. **[You have three choices because there are three escalators.]**

Got It?   VISUAL LEARNERS

Suggest that students make a box for each selection that must be made, and then fill in each box with the number of choices for each selection. For example:

$$\boxed{8} \cdot \boxed{6} =$$

Answers

Solve It!

24 ways; explanations may vary.

Got It?

1. a. 48

    b. No; the tree diagram would be very large, so using the Multiplication Counting Principle would be easier.

---

2 Guided Instruction

Each Problem is worked out and supported online.

Problem 1
Using the Multiplication Counting Principle

Problem 2
Finding Permutations

Alternate Problem 2
Finding Permutations
Animated

Problem 3
Using Permutation Notation
Animated

Problem 4
Using Combination Notation
Animated

Alternate Problem 4
Using Combination Notation

Support in Algebra 1 Companion
• Vocabulary
• Key Concepts
• Got It?

Problem 2

> **Q** How many total selections must be made? Explain.
> [Nine; you must select one player for each of the nine positions in the batting.]

Got It?

> **Q** A student says the answer is $8 \cdot 8 \cdot 8 \cdot 8 \cdot 8 \cdot 8 \cdot 8 \cdot 8 = 16{,}777{,}216$. How would you respond?
> [The first swimmer has 8 choices, but after that swimmer takes a lane, the second swimmer has only 7 choices, and so on.]

Take Note

Show students how Problem 2 can be solved using permutation notation in which 9 players are arranged 9 at a time. Hence,

$$_9P_9 = \frac{9!}{(9-9)!} = \frac{9!}{0!} = \frac{9!}{1}$$

Problem 3

> **Q** How many objects are there from which to choose? [seven]
> **Q** How many of the objects are going to be arranged at a time? [five]
> **Q** If the question were changed to "How many sets of 5 songs are possible?" would the answer still be 2520? Explain. [No, the answer would be less since the different orders of the songs would not be counted.]

 **Problem 2** Finding Permutations

Baseball How many different batting orders can you have with 9 players?

There are 9 choices for the first batter, 8 for the second, and so on.

$$9 \cdot 8 \cdot 7 \cdot 6 \cdot 5 \cdot 4 \cdot 3 \cdot 2 \cdot 1 = 362{,}880 \quad \text{Use a calculator.}$$

There are 362,880 possible batting orders.

 Got It? 2. A swimming pool has 8 lanes. In how many ways can 8 swimmers be assigned lanes for a race?

A short way to write the product in Problem 2 is 9!, read "nine factorial." For any positive integer n, the expression **n factorial** is written as $n!$ and is the product of the integers from n down to 1. The value of 0! is defined to be 1.

You can use factorials to write a formula for the number of permutations of n objects arranged r at a time.

take note **Key Concept** Permutation Notation

The expression $_nP_r$ represents the number of permutations of n objects arranged r at a time.

$$_nP_r = \frac{n!}{(n-r)!}$$

Example $_8P_2 = \frac{8!}{(8-2)!} = \frac{8!}{6!} = \frac{8 \cdot 7 \cdot 6 \cdot 5 \cdot 4 \cdot 3 \cdot 2 \cdot 1}{6 \cdot 5 \cdot 4 \cdot 3 \cdot 2 \cdot 1} = 56$

 **Problem 3** Using Permutation Notation

Music A band has 7 new songs and wants to put 5 of them on a demo CD. How many arrangements of 5 songs are possible?

To find the number of possible arrangements, find the value of $_7P_5$.

Method 1 Use the formula for permutations.

$$_7P_5 = \frac{7!}{(7-5)!} = \frac{7!}{2!} = \frac{7 \cdot 6 \cdot 5 \cdot 4 \cdot 3 \cdot 2 \cdot 1}{2 \cdot 1} \quad \text{Write using factorials.}$$

$$= 2520 \quad \text{Simplify.}$$

Method 2 Use a graphing calculator.

Press .

$$_7P_5 = 2520$$

There are 2520 possible arrangements of 5 songs.

> 7 nPr 5
>
> 2520

Additional Problems

1. A car manufacturer offers 4 different kinds of interiors and 9 different color options. How many different cars are possible with one kind of interior and one color?

ANSWER 36

2. How many different ways can 8 players finish a race if there are no ties?

ANSWER 40,320

3. There are 6 students running for 3 different student council positions: president, vice president, and treasurer. How many different ways can the three offices be filled?

ANSWER 120

4. Ten employees are eligible for 4 promotions. How many different ways can the promotions be earned if the order is not important?

ANSWER 210

Answers

Got It? (continued)

  2. 40,320 ways

Plan

How do you use the Multiplication Counting Principle to find the number of permutations?
Multiply the number of ways to make each selection.

Think

How can you think about this problem in a different way?
You can use the Multiplication Counting Principle. There are 7 choices for the first song, 6 for the second, 5 for the third, 4 for the fourth, and 3 for the fifth.

Got It? 3. There are 6 students in a classroom with 8 desks. How many possible seating arrangements are there?

A **combination** is a selection of objects without regard to order. For example, if you are selecting two side dishes from a list of five, the order in which you choose the side dishes does not matter.

Key Concept   Combination Notation

The expression $_nC_r$ represents the number of combinations of n objects chosen r at a time.

$$_nC_r = \frac{n!}{r!(n-r)!}$$

Example $_8C_2 = \frac{8!}{2!(8-2)!} = \frac{8!}{2!6!} = \frac{8 \cdot 7 \cdot 6 \cdot 5 \cdot 4 \cdot 3 \cdot 2 \cdot 1}{(2 \cdot 1)(6 \cdot 5 \cdot 4 \cdot 3 \cdot 2 \cdot 1)} = 28$

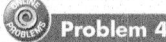 **Problem 4** Using Combination Notation

Multiple Choice Twenty people report for jury duty. How many different 12-person juries can be chosen?

(A) 20   (B) 240   (C) 125,970   (D) 479,001,600

You need the number of combinations of 20 jurors chosen 12 at a time. Find $_{20}C_{12}$.

$_{20}C_{12} = \frac{20!}{12!(20-12)!} = \frac{20!}{12!8!}$ Write using factorials.

$\qquad = 125,970$ Simplify using a calculator.

There are 125,970 different 12-person juries. The correct answer is C.

 Got It? 4. In how many different ways can you choose 3 types of flowers for a bouquet from a selection of 15 types of flowers?

 ## Lesson Check

Do you know HOW?

Find the value of each expression.

1. 7!   2. 13!   3. $_6P_3$

4. $_{10}P_4$ 5. $_5C_3$ 6. $_7C_3$

7. How many outfits can you make with 6 shirts and 4 pairs of pants?

Do you UNDERSTAND?

8. **Vocabulary** Would you use permutations or combinations to find the number of possible arrangements of 10 students in a line? Why?

9. **Compare and Contrast** How are permutations and combinations similar? How are they different?

10. **Reasoning** Explain why $_nC_n$ is equal to 1.

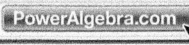

Take Note
A combination only counts each possible distinct group of objects and can be viewed as a permutation with the redundancies "divided out."

Problem 4

> Q If a classmate selects answer choice B, what mistake did she likely make? **[She used the Multiplication Counting Principle, which is not the way to calculate the number of combinations.]**

Got It?

> Q What is the division problem after the factorial is applied? $[\frac{15 \cdot 14 \cdot 13}{6}]$

3 Lesson Check

Do you know HOW?
• If students have difficulty with Exercise 7, then review the Multiplication Counting Principle.

Do you UNDERSTAND?
• In Exercise 10, ask why $_nP_n$ is *not* equal to 1.

Close

> Q Why is the number of combinations of n objects chosen r at a time less than the number of permutations of n objects chosen r at a time? **[A combination counts each distinct group only once, while a permutation counts all possible arrangements of each distinct group.]**

Answers

Got It? (continued)
3. 20,160
4. 455 ways

Lesson Check
1. 5040
2. 6,227,020,800
3. 120
4. 5040
5. 10
6. 35

7. 24 outfits

8. permutations

9. Permutations are used to count in situations where order is important. Combinations are used to count in situations where selection, not order, is important.

10. There is only one way to take n things, n at a time.

Also, $_nC_n = \frac{n!}{n!(n-n)!} = \frac{1}{0!} = \frac{1}{1} = 1$.

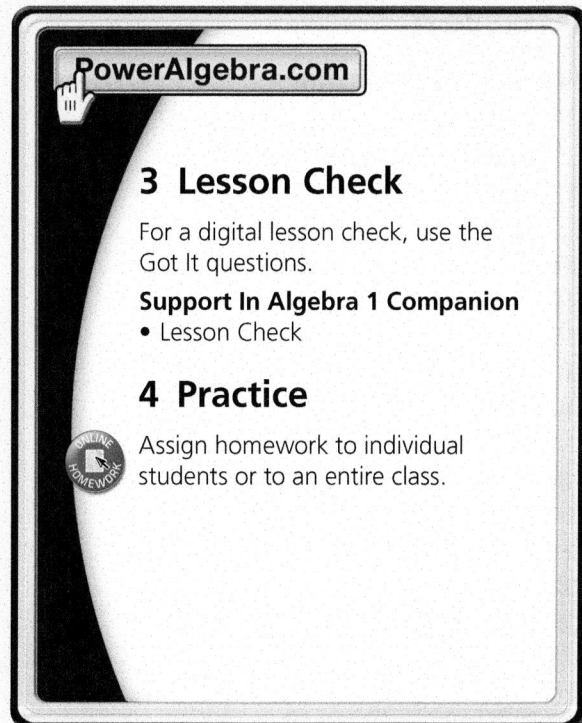

4 Practice

Practice and Problem-Solving Exercises

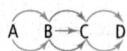 Practice

ASSIGNMENT GUIDE

Basic: 11–39 all, 40–46 even, 53–55

Average: 11–39 odd, 40–61

Advanced: 11–39 odd, 40–65

Standardized Test Prep: 66–69

Mixed Review: 70–81

Reasoning exercises have blue headings.

Applications exercises have red headings.

EXERCISE 55: Use the Think About a Plan worksheet in the **Practice and Problem Solving Workbook** (also available in the Teaching Resources in print and online) to further support students' development in becoming independent learners.

HOMEWORK QUICK CHECK

To check students' understanding of key skills and concepts, go over Exercises 11, 27, 46, 53, and 55.

11. Telephones A seven-digit telephone number can begin with any digit except 0 or 1. There are no restrictions on digits after the first digit.
   a. How many possible choices are there for the first digit? For each digit after the first digit?
   b. How many different seven-digit telephone numbers are possible?
   ◀ *See Problem 1.*

12. Use the diagram and the Multiplication Counting Principle to find each of the following:
   a. the number of routes from A to C
   b. the number of routes from A to D
   A B→C D

13. Sports In an ice-skating competition, the order in which competitors skate is determined by a drawing. Suppose there are 10 skaters in the finals. How many different orders are possible for the final program?
   ◀ *See Problem 2.*

14. Photography Suppose you are lining up with 4 cousins for a photo. How many different arrangements are possible?

Find the value of each expression.   ◀ *See Problem 3.*

15. $_8P_4$ **16.** $_9P_3$ **17.** $_7P_6$ **18.** $_8P_5$ **19.** $_7P_2$

20. $_5P_5$ **21.** $_6P_1$ **22.** $_{11}P_0$ **23.** $_{10}P_2$ **24.** $_{12}P_9$

25. Reading You have 10 books on your bookshelf. In how many orders can you read 4 of the books on a summer vacation?

26. Student Government A student council has 24 members. The council is selecting a 3-person committee to plan a car wash. Each person on the committee will have one task: one person will find a location, another person will organize publicity, and the third person will schedule volunteers. In how many different ways can 3 students be chosen and given a task?

Find the value of each expression.   ◀ *See Problem 4.*

27. $_6C_6$ **28.** $_5C_4$ **29.** $_9C_1$ **30.** $_7C_2$ **31.** $_8C_5$

32. $_3C_0$ **33.** $_8C_6$ **34.** $_7C_5$ **35.** $_{10}C_9$ **36.** $_{15}C_4$

37. Law For some civil cases, at least 9 of 12 jurors must agree on a verdict. How many combinations of 9 jurors are possible on a 12-person jury?

38. Gift Certificates For your birthday you received a gift certificate from a music store for 3 CDs. There are 8 CDs you would like to have. How many different groups of 3 CDs can you select from the 8 you want?

39. Quilting There are 30 fabrics available at a quilt store. How many different groups of 5 fabrics can you choose for a quilt?

Answers

Practice and Problem-Solving Exercises

11. a. 8, 10
   b. 8×10^6 or 8,000,000

12. a. 4
   b. 8

13. 3,628,800

14. 120

15. 1680

16. 504

17. 5040

18. 6720

19. 42

20. 120

21. 6

22. 1

23. 90

24. 79,833,600

25. 5040 ways

26. 12,144 ways

27. 1

28. 5

29. 9

30. 21

31. 56

32. 1

33. 28

34. 21

35. 10

36. 1365

37. 220 ways

38. 56 groups

39. 142,506 groups

Determine which value is greater.

40. $_8P_6$ or $_6P_2$ **41.** $_9P_7$ or $_9P_2$ **42.** $_{10}P_3$ or $_8P_4$

43. $_9C_6$ or $_9P_6$ **44.** $_{11}C_5$ or $_{11}C_8$ **45.** $_7C_4$ or $_8C_5$

46. Think About a Plan Draw four points like those in Figure 1. Draw line segments so that every point is joined to every other point. How many line segments did you draw? How many segments would you need to join each point to all the others in Figure 2?
- How many points are there in Figure 2?
- Should you use combinations or permutations to find the number of segments that join pairs of points?

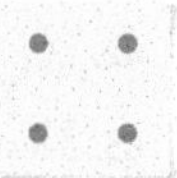

Figure 1 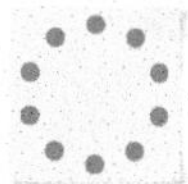   Figure 2

47. a. Lena wants a password that uses the 4 letters of her name. How many permutations are possible using each letter only once?
  b. Writing Is creating a password based on your name a good idea? Explain your reasoning.

48. License Plates In one state, a regular license plate has a two-digit number that is fixed by county, then one letter, and then four one-digit numbers.
  a. How many different license plates are possible in each county?
  b. Suppose there are 92 counties in the state. How many license plates are possible in the entire state?

Find the number of arrangements of letters taken three at a time that can be formed from each set of cards.

49.    **50.**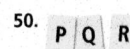

51.    **52.**

Reasoning Explain whether each situation is a permutation problem or a combination problem.

53. A locker contains 8 books. You select 3 books at random. How many different sets of books can you select?

54. You take 4 books out of the school library to read during spring vacation. In how many different orders can you read the 4 books?

55. Media The call signs of radio and television stations in the United States generally begin with the letter W east of the Mississippi River and the letter K west of the Mississippi. Repetition of letters is allowed.
  a. How many different call signs are possible if each station uses a W or K followed by 3 letters?
  b. How many different call signs are possible if each station uses a W or K followed by 4 letters?

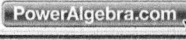

40. $_8P_6$
41. $_9P_7$
42. $_8P_4$
43. $_9P_6$
44. $_{11}C_5$
45. $_8C_5$
46. 6 segments; 45 segments
47. a. 24 ways
  b. No; there is a limited number of ways that you can arrange the letters so someone can figure it out.

48. a. 26×10^4 or 260,000 license plates
  b. 23,920,000 plates
49. 60
50. 6
51. 210
52. 24
53. $_8C_3 = 56$
54. $4! = 24$
55. a. 35,152 call signs
  b. 913,952 call signs

Answers

Practice and Problem-Solving Exercises
(continued)

56. 3

57. 2

58. 5

59. 4

60. 8

61. 1

62. always

63. sometimes

64. always

65. a. 15

    b. 4; 3

    c. 4

    d. 60

66. 72 different lunches

67. 0.073

68. 8

69. 834

70. qualitative

71. quantitative

72. quantitative

73. qualitative

74. 0.81, −6.81

75. 6.70, 0.30

76. 1.46, −5.46

77. −1, −1.67

78. 32%

79. 9%

80. 22.5%

81. 18%

Find the value of each expression.

56. $\dfrac{_5P_3}{_5P_2}$

57. $\dfrac{_4P_3}{_4P_2}$

58. $\dfrac{_7P_3}{_7P_2}$

59. $_2C_2 + {}_2C_1 + {}_2C_0$

60. $_3C_3 + {}_3C_2 + {}_3C_1 + {}_3C_0$

61. $_{90}C_{90}$

Challenge Determine whether each statement is *always*, *sometimes*, or *never* true. Assume $n \neq 0$.

62. $_nC_1 = n$

63. $_3C_x > x$

64. $_nC_{(n-1)} = n$

65. A test has 10 questions. You must answer a total of 7 questions, including exactly 4 of the first 6 questions.
    a. In how many ways can you choose 4 of the first 6 questions?
    b. How many questions are left after you have answered 4 of the first 6 questions? How many must you still answer?
    c. In how many ways can you choose questions to finish the test?
    d. How many different ways are there of completing the test (meeting all of its requirements)?

Standardized Test Prep

GRIDDED RESPONSE

SAT/ACT

66. The school cafeteria serves lunches consisting of 1 main dish, 1 vegetable, 1 salad, and 1 dessert. The menu has choices of 2 main dishes, 3 vegetables, 3 salads, and 4 desserts. How many different lunches are possible?

67. What is 7.3×10^{-2} written in standard form?

68. How many elements are in the union of the two sets $M = \{4, 5, -6, 7, 8\}$ and $N = \{-4, 5, 6, 7, -8\}$?

69. You deposit $500 in an account earning 5.25% annual interest. You make no further deposits to the account and the interest is compounded annually. What is the balance in dollars after 10 yr? Round to the nearest dollar.

Mixed Review

Determine whether each data set is *qualitative* or *quantitative*. ◀ See Lesson 12-5.

70. ZIP codes   **71.** race times   **72.** heights of people   **73.** emotions

Use the quadratic formula to solve each equation. If necessary, round answers to the nearest hundredth. ◀ See Lesson 9-6.

74. $2x^2 + 12x - 11 = 0$ **75.** $x^2 - 7x + 2 = 0$ **76.** $x^2 + 4x - 8 = 0$ **77.** $3x^2 + 8x + 5 = 0$

Get Ready! To prepare for Lesson 12-7, do Exercises 78–81.

Rewrite each decimal or fraction as a percent. ◀ See p. 793

78. 0.32   **79.** 0.09   **80.** $\dfrac{45}{200}$ **81.** $\dfrac{9}{50}$

Additional Instructional Support

Algebra 1 Companion

Students can use the **Algebra 1 Companion** worktext (4 pages) as you teach the lesson. Use the Companion to support

- New Vocabulary
- Key Concepts
- Got It for each Problem
- Lesson Check

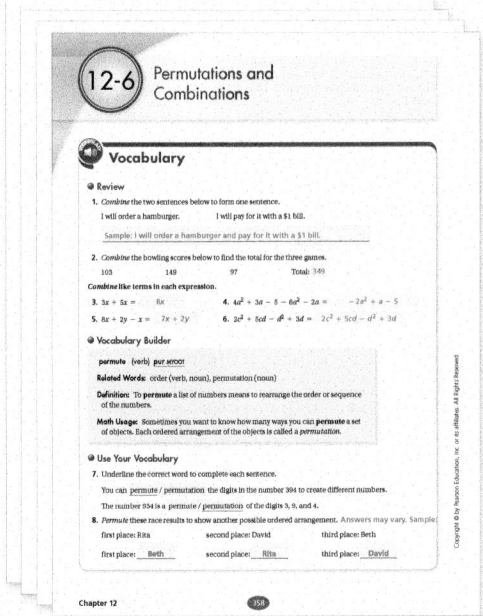

ELL Support

Use Role Playing Demonstrate a handshake. Then write the following on the board: There are 8 students on a debate team. Each student shakes the hand of another student one time. Students can act out the handshakes. Other options are to draw a picture or diagram to show how many handshakes will take place.

Use Manipulatives Place students into heterogeneous pairs. Give students four letter tiles, counters, or some other unique items. Model placing the objects in some order. Record the order before moving the objects into another order. Think aloud as you work. Then let students do the work as you monitor. Increase the number of objects to make it more challenging.

5 Assess & Remediate

Lesson Quiz

1. A deli offers 3 different kinds of bread and 8 different kinds of toppings on its submarine sandwiches. How many different sandwiches are possible?

2. How many different ways can 6 students stand in line for the water fountain?

3. There are 8 swimmers competing in a race. Prizes are awarded for the swimmers who finish in first, second, and third place. How many different ways can the swimmers finish first, second, and third?

4. There are 7 movies that Christine wants to see over break. She only has time to see 4 of the movies. How many different groups of 4 movies are possible if the order in which they are seen is not important?

5. **Do you UNDERSTAND?** In a restaurant, you can order any three appetizers from a list of seven. Which represents the number of different choices you have, $_7P_3$ or $_7C_3$? Explain.

ANSWERS TO LESSON QUIZ

1. 24
2. 720
3. 336
4. 35
5. The order does not matter, so you have $_7C_3$ or 35 choices.

PRESCRIPTION FOR REMEDIATION

Use the student work on the Lesson Quiz to prescribe a differentiated review assignment.

Points	Differentiated Remediation
0–2	Intervention
3–4	On-level
5	Extension

PowerAlgebra.com

5 Assess & Remediate

Assign the Lesson Quiz. Appropriate intervention, practice, or enrichment is automatically generated based on student performance.

Intervention

- **Reteaching** (2 pages) Provides reteaching and practice exercises for the key lesson concepts. Use with struggling students or absent students.

- **English Language Learner Support** Helps students develop and reinforce mathematical vocabulary and key concepts.

All-in-One Resources/Online
Reteaching

12-6 Reteaching
Permutations and Combinations

All-in-One Resources/Online
English Language Learner Support

12-6 ELL Support
Permutations and Combinations

Differentiated Remediation *continued*

On-Level

- **Practice** (2 pages) Provides extra practice for each lesson. For simpler practice exercises, use the Form K Practice pages found in the All-in-One Teaching Resources and online.

- **Think About a Plan** Helps students develop specific problem-solving skills and strategies by providing scaffolded guiding questions.

- **Standardized Test Prep** Focuses on all major exercises, all major question types, and helps students prepare for the high-stakes assessments.

Extension

- **Enrichment** Provides students with interesting problems and activities that extend the concepts of the lesson.

- **Activities, Games, and Puzzles** Worksheets that can be used for concepts development, enrichment, and for fun!

Practice and Problem Solving Wkbk/All-in-One Resources/Online
Practice page 1

12-6 Practice — Form G
Permutations and Combinations

1. A six-character license plate number can begin with any two letters and end with four one-digit numbers.
   a. How many possible choices are there for the first two characters? For the last four characters? 676; 10,000
   b. How many different six-character license plate numbers are possible? 6,760,000

2. Use the map at the right and the Multiplication Counting Principle to find each of the following:
   a. the number of routes from Piketon to Dublin 3
   b. the number of routes from Piketon to Blaise 6
   c. the number of routes from Blaise to Piketon 6

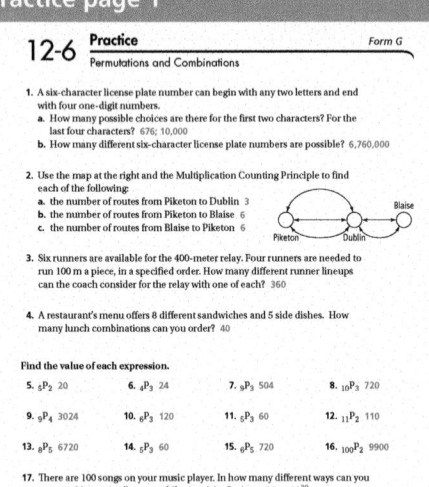

3. Six runners are available for the 400-meter relay. Four runners are needed to run 100 m a piece, in a specified order. How many different runner lineups can the coach consider for the relay with one of each? 360

4. A restaurant's menu offers 8 different sandwiches and 5 side dishes. How many lunch combinations can you order? 40

Find the value of each expression.

5. $_5P_2$ 20   6. $_4P_3$ 24   7. $_9P_3$ 504   8. $_{10}P_3$ 720

9. $_9P_4$ 3024   10. $_6P_3$ 120   11. $_5P_3$ 60   12. $_{11}P_2$ 110

13. $_8P_5$ 6720   14. $_5P_3$ 60   15. $_6P_5$ 720   16. $_{100}P_2$ 9900

17. There are 100 songs on your music player. In how many different ways can you arrange 20 songs to listen to while exercising? about 1.3×10^{39}

Find the value of each expression.

18. $_6C_3$ 10   19. $_{10}C_8$ 45   20. $_5C_5$ 5   21. $_9C_4$ 126

22. $_6C_3$ 20   23. $_7C_6$ 21   24. $_4C_3$ 4   25. $_8C_4$ 70

26. $_6C_5$ 6   27. $_5C_4$ 5   28. $_7C_3$ 35   29. $_{10}C_3$ 120

Practice and Problem Solving Wkbk/All-in-One Resources/Online
Practice page 2

12-6 Practice (continued) — Form G
Permutations and Combinations

30. There are 15 slips of paper in a jar. Each slip has a different name on it. How many ways can you draw 5 names from the jar? 3003

Find the number of combinations of numbers taken four at a time can be formed from each set of cards.

31. | 23 | 24 | 25 | 26 | 27 | 5

32. | 10 | 11 | 12 | 13 | 14 | 15 | 15

33. | 9 | 11 | 13 | 15 | 17 | 19 | 15

34. | 5 | 6 | 7 | 8 | 1

Explain whether each situation is a combination problem or a permutation problem.

35. Your friends rented 6 different video games. In how many different orders can you play the 6 games? permutation

36. There are 20 games to choose from at the local game store. How many different sets of 4 games could you choose to rent? combination

37. The Aluru family has a garage door that opens with a 4-digit PIN. They decide to base the code on Mrs. Aluru's birthday: 01/24/63. How many PINs are there that use four of the digits in Mrs. Aluru's birthday? permutation

38. You have 10 photographs to choose from. How many different ways can you arrange 5 of the photographs in a single row above the sofa? permutation

39. There are 6 class periods in the school day. There are 10 subjects to choose from. How many different class schedules are possible? permutation

Determine which value is greater.

40. $_5P_6$ or $_5P_3$ $_5P_6$ 41. $_9C_9$ or $_9C_5$ $_9C_5$ 42. $_{10}C_4$ or $_{10}C_6$ The values are equal.   43. $_{10}P_4$ or $_6P_6$ $_{10}P_4$

Practice and Problem Solving Wkbk/All-in-One Resources/Online
Think About a Plan

12-6 Think About a Plan
Permutations and Combinations

Media The call signs of radio and television stations in the United States generally begin with the letter W east of the Mississippi River and the letter K west of the Mississippi. Repetition of letters is allowed.
   a. How many different call signs are possible if each station uses a W or K followed by 3 letters?
   b. How many different call signs are possible if each station uses a W or K followed by 4 letters?

1. How many different call signs are possible if a station uses a W followed by 3 letters? Use the formula for permutations. 17,576

2. How many different call signs are possible if a station uses K followed by 3 letters? Compare this answer to the one above. 17,576; The values are the same.

3. How would you combine your answers above to determine how many different call signs are possible if each station uses a W or K followed by 3 letters? Add them.

4. How many different call signs are possible if each station uses a W or K followed by 3 letters? 35,152

5. How many different call signs are possible if a station uses a W followed by 4 letters? Use the formula for permutations. 456,976

6. How many different call signs are possible if each station uses a W or K followed by 4 letters? 913,952

Practice and Problem Solving Wkbk/All-in-One Resources/Online
Standardized Test Prep

12-6 Standardized Test Prep
Permutations and Combinations

Multiple Choice

For Exercises 1–7, choose the correct letter.

1. What is the value of $_5P_3$? C
   A. 20   B. 40   C. 60   D. 120

2. What is the value of $_{10}C_6$? F
   F. 210   G. 5040   H. 151,200   I. 3,628,800

3. There are 12 people on the basketball team. How many different 5-person starting lineups can be chosen? B
   A. 120   B. 792   C. 95,040   D. 3,991,680

4. The manager of a baseball team has 15 players to choose from for his 9-person batting order. How many different ways can he arrange the players in the lineup? I
   F. 5005   G. 362,880   H. 3,603,600   I. 1,816,214,400

5. For a road trip, a friend is going to place 5 CDs into her CD player. She has 9 CDs to choose from. How many different selections of CDs can she make? A
   A. 126   B. 3024   C. 15,120   D. 362,880

6. There are 8 students on the ballot who are running for student council. Four students will be selected for the council. How many different groups of students can be selected for the council? F
   F. 24   G. 70   H. 1680   I. 40,320

7. A website requires a 4-digit numerical password in which the digits cannot repeat. How many possible passwords are there? B
   A. 24   B. 5040   C. 151,200   D. 3,628,800

Short Response

8. A restaurant serves 4 different sandwiches, 3 different sides, and 3 different beverages for lunch. How many possible meals are there? Show your work.
   $4! + 3! + 3! = 36$
   [2] Answer is correct and work is shown.
   [1] Answer does not show work or is not correct.
   [0] Answer is incorrect and work is incorrect.

All-in-One Resources/Online
Enrichment

12-6 Enrichment
Permutations and Combinations

The triangle on the right is called Pascal's Triangle. It has many patterns and applications associated with it. You will explore one application here.

```
        1
       1  1
      1  2  1
     1  3  3  1
    1  4  6  4  1
   1  5 10 10  5  1
```

1. Identify three patterns that you observe in Pascal's Triangle.
   Sample: Every row starts and ends with 1; the sum of every pair of numbers in a row is the value of the number between those numbers in the next row; the numbers in a row are symmetric

2. Complete the next two rows of the triangle.
   1 6 15 20 15 6 1
   1 7 21 35 35 21 7 1

3. A family is expecting kittens. They would like to know how many different ways five kittens can be born. For example, all five kittens could be female, or one kitten could be male and the rest females. Complete the chart below to determine how many different combinations are possible.

5 Kittens 0 Females	5 Kittens 1 Female	5 Kittens 2 Females	5 Kittens 3 Females	5 Kittens 4 Females	5 Kittens 5 Females
$_5C_0$	$_5C_1$	$_5C_2$	$_5C_3$	$_5C_4$	$_5C_5$
1	5	10	10	5	1

4. Compare the numbers in your table to Pascal's Triangle. How are they related?
   The numbers are the same as the numbers in row 6 of Pascal's Triangle.

5. Use Pascal's Triangle to determine how many different ways(combinations) the family could have 7 kittens with four females. 35

Online Teacher Resource Center
Activities, Games, and Puzzles

12-6 Game: A Winning Combination
Permutations and Combinations

Provide the host with the following questions and answers.

1. How many positive three-digit numbers are possible by using each digit once? (Allow 0 as a first digit.) **Answer:** 720
2. How many types of confetti can a party store make by selecting from 3 of 7 colors? **Answer:** 35
3. How many basketball teams of 5 different positions are possible from 10 eligible players? **Answer:** 30,240
4. How many arrangements of 3 different numbers are possible on a lock that uses 36 numbers? **Answer:** 42,840
5. In how many ways can you answer 6 out of 10 questions on a test? **Answer:** 210
6. How many triangles are possible by selecting any 3 points of a hexagon? **Answer:** 20
7. In how many ways can you rank 5 favorite TV shows from a sample of 10 shows? **Answer:** 30,240
8. In how many ways can you invite 3 of your 6 friends to dinner? **Answer:** 20
9. In how many ways can the judges of a contest award 3 prizes to 6 eligible contestants? **Answer:** 120
10. In how many ways can you put 4 party invitations into 4 envelopes? **Answer:** 24
11. How many four-letter computer passwords are possible from the letters A–Z and the digits 0–9 without repeating any characters? **Answer:** 1,413,720
12. In how many ways can a sailboat captain choose 4 flags from 10 to hoist on a mast? **Answer:** 5040
13. In how many ways can a boating club form a crew of 8 different positions from 12 eligible club members? **Answer:** 19,958,400
14. How many schedules of 5 class subjects can you make from a selection of 12 subjects? **Answer:** 95,040
15. In how many ways can you arrange the letters of the word DISCOVERY? **Answer:** 362,880
16. How many varieties of pizza with two toppings can you make from eight toppings? **Answer:** 28
17. In how many ways can 4 students take their places in 6 seats on a bus? **Answer:** 360
18. How many musical arrangements of 3 notes can you play from 12 notes? **Answer:** 1320
19. How many school committees of 3 persons (president, treasurer, and secretary) can your teacher form from 8 eligible persons? **Answer:** 336
20. In how many ways can a teacher assign eight tutors to eight classes? **Answer:** 40,320
21. In how many ways can you choose 3 songs from a list of the top 10 songs? **Answer:** 120
22. In how many ways can you choose 5 friends from a group of 10 to wait in line at a movie theater? **Answer:** 30,240
23. How many seven-digit cell phone numbers are possible with no repeated digits? (Allow 0 for a first digit.) **Answer:** 604,800
24. In how many ways can 3 of your friends have different birthdays? (Assume that there are 365 days in a year.) **Answer:** 48,228,180
25. How many relay teams of 4 persons can you make from a group of 10 runners if the order is not important? **Answer:** 210

12-7 Theoretical and Experimental Probability

Objective To find theoretical and experimental probabilities

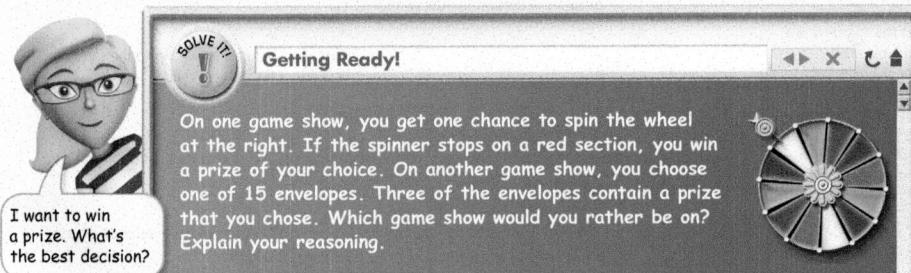

SOLVE IT!

Getting Ready!

On one game show, you get one chance to spin the wheel at the right. If the spinner stops on a red section, you win a prize of your choice. On another game show, you choose one of 15 envelopes. Three of the envelopes contain a prize that you chose. Which game show would you rather be on? Explain your reasoning.

I want to win a prize. What's the best decision?

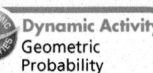
Dynamic Activity
Geometric Probability

Lesson Vocabulary
• outcome
• sample space
• event
• probability
• theoretical probability
• complement of an event
• odds
• experimental probability

In the Solve It, spinning red and choosing the right envelope are desired outcomes. An **outcome** is the result of a single trial, such as spinning a wheel. The **sample space** is all the possible outcomes. An **event** is any outcome or group of outcomes. The outcomes that match a given event are favorable outcomes.

Here is how these terms apply to rolling an even number on a number cube.

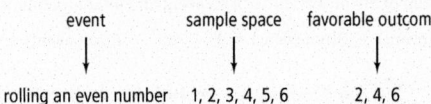

event	sample space	favorable outcomes
↓	↓	↓
rolling an even number	1, 2, 3, 4, 5, 6	2, 4, 6

Essential Understanding The **probability** of an event, or P(event), tells you how likely it is that the event will occur. You can find probabilities by reasoning mathematically or by using data collected from an experiment.

In the number-cube example above, the outcomes in the sample space are equally likely to occur. When all possible outcomes are equally likely, you can find the *theoretical probability* of an event using the following formula.

theoretical probability $P(\text{event}) = \dfrac{\text{number of favorable outcomes}}{\text{number of possible outcomes}}$

$$P(\text{rolling an even number}) = \frac{3}{6} = \frac{1}{2}$$

You can write the probability of an event as a fraction, a decimal, or a percent. The probability of an event ranges from 0 to 1.

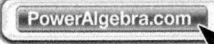

equally likely to occur
or not occur

impossible ———————————————— certain

0 ←— less likely   0.5   more likely —→ 1

12-7 Preparing to Teach

BIG idea Probability   **UbD**
ESSENTIAL UNDERSTANDINGS
• The probability of an event, or P(event) tells how likely it is that the event will occur.
• Probabilities can be found by reasoning mathematically or by using experimental data.

Math Background
Probability is an application of ratios that compares the number of favorable outcomes to the total number of possible outcomes.

The principle that the experimental probability approaches the theoretical probability as the number of trials increases is called the Law of Large Numbers. An experiment that gives students hands-on experience with the Law of Large Numbers

is flipping a coin and recording heads or tails.

Two applications of probability in everyday life are risk assessment and quality control. In quality control, manufacturers use experimental probability to predict the percentage of defective products that will be produced. In risk assessment, statisticians determine the probability of an event occurring and the consequences of its occurrence as a first step in a process called risk management.

Support Student Learning
Use the **Algebra 1 Companion** to engage and support students during instructions. See Lesson Resources at the end of this lesson for details.

---

1 Interactive Learning

Solve It!
PURPOSE To determine and compare the probability of two events
PROCESS Students may analyze each event by considering the number of favorable outcomes compared to the number of possible outcomes.

FACILITATE

Q How many different spaces can the wheel stop on? **[12]**

Q How many of the total number of spaces on the wheel would earn you a prize? **[2]**

Q How many different envelopes can you choose from on the second game show? **[15]**

Q How many of the total number of envelopes would earn you a prize? **[3]**

ANSWER See Solve It in Answers on next page.
CONNECT THE MATH In the Solve It, students look at two situations involving a spinner and a set of envelopes to name their possible outcomes. In the lesson, students use the total of possible outcomes to compute the probability of an event.

2 Guided Instruction

To help students make the distinction between impossible and certain probability, give students the following examples related to a standard six-sided number cube and have them identify which describes the situation, *impossible* or *certain*.
• roll a 7 (impossible)
• roll a number less than 10 (certain)
• roll a number greater than 12 (impossible)
• roll a 0 (impossible)
• roll a number between 0 and 7 (certain)

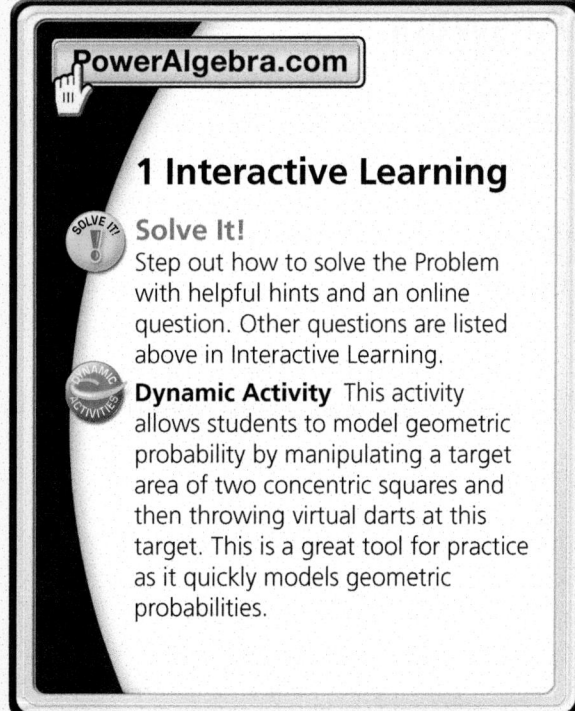

PowerAlgebra.com

1 Interactive Learning

SOLVE IT!
Solve It!
Step out how to solve the Problem with helpful hints and an online question. Other questions are listed above in Interactive Learning.

Dynamic Activity This activity allows students to model geometric probability by manipulating a target area of two concentric squares and then throwing virtual darts at this target. This is a great tool for practice as it quickly models geometric probabilities.

Problem 1

Q What planets are nearer to the sun than Earth is? **[Mercury and Venus]**

Q If you were to randomly draw a name 20 times, how many of those times would you expect to draw either Mercury or Venus? **[approximately 5 times]**

Q If you were to randomly draw a name 20 times, is it possible that you might draw Mercury or Venus 10 times? Explain. **[Yes, it is possible to draw them 10 times, or any number of times from 0 to 20. However, the theoretical probability of drawing Mercury or Venus each time is $\frac{1}{4}$.]**

Got It?   VISUAL LEARNERS

Q What is the theoretical probability that you will select Earth? **[1/8]**

Problem 2

Q What is the sum of P(drink A) and P(not Drink A)? Explain. **[The sum is one, because one of these two events must occur.]**

Q What is another way to write P(not drink A) for this situation? **[P(drink B, C, or D)]**

Got It?

The total number of favorable and unfavorable outcomes for an event is equal to the total number of possible outcomes for that event.

 **Problem 1** Finding Theoretical Probability

Astronomy Our solar system's 8 planets, in order of least to greatest distance from the sun, are Mercury, Venus, Earth, Mars, Jupiter, Saturn, Uranus, and Neptune. You will randomly draw one of the names of the planets and write a report on that planet. What is the theoretical probability that you will select a planet whose distance from the sun is less than Earth's?

Think

Does a "favorable outcome" always mean that something good happens?
No. For example, if you are determining the probability of losing a game, the "favorable" outcomes are the outcomes where you lose.

$P(\text{event}) = \dfrac{\text{number of favorable outcomes}}{\text{number of possible outcomes}}$

$= \dfrac{2}{8}$ Two planets out of 8 are nearer to the sun than Earth: Mercury and Venus.

$= \dfrac{1}{4}$ Simplify.

The probability of selecting a planet whose distance from the sun is less than Earth's is $\frac{1}{4}$.

 Got It? 1. In Problem 1, what is the theoretical probability that you will select a planet whose distance from the sun is greater than Earth's?

The **complement of an event** consists of all outcomes in the sample space that are not in the event. The possible outcomes for rolling a number cube are 1, 2, 3, 4, 5, and 6. The outcomes for rolling an even number are 2, 4, and 6. The outcomes for the complement of rolling an even number are 1, 3, and 5.

The sum of the probabilities of an event and its complement is 1.

$P(\text{event}) + P(\text{not event}) = 1$ or $P(\text{not event}) = 1 - P(\text{event})$

 Problem 2 Finding the Probability of the Complement of an Event

Consumer Research In a taste test, 50 participants are randomly given a beverage to sample. There are 20 samples of Drink A, 10 samples of Drink B, 10 samples of Drink C, and 10 samples of Drink D. What is the probability of a participant not getting Drink A?

Think

How else can you find P(not Drink A)?
You can divide the number of other drink samples by the total number of samples.
P(not Drink A)
$= \frac{10 + 10 + 10}{50}$
$= \frac{30}{50} = \frac{3}{5}$

$P(\text{Drink A}) = \dfrac{\text{number of samples of Drink A}}{\text{total number of samples}} = \dfrac{20}{50} = \dfrac{2}{5}$ Find P(Drink A).

$P(\text{not Drink A}) = 1 - P(\text{Drink A})$ Use the complement formula.

$= 1 - \dfrac{2}{5} = \dfrac{3}{5}$ Substitute and simplify.

The probability of not getting Drink A is $\frac{3}{5}$.

 Got It? 2. Reasoning Suppose a taste test is repeated with the same number of samples of Drink A, but more samples of other drinks. What happens to P(not Drink A)?

Answers

Solve It!

Answers may vary. Sample: on the game show where you pick the envelope because you have a $\frac{3}{15}$, or 20% chance of winning; using the wheel you only have a $\frac{2}{12}$, or $16\frac{2}{3}$% chance of winning.

Got It?

1. $\frac{5}{8}$

2. It will be $1 - \dfrac{20}{50 + x}$, where x is the number of other samples added. The probability will increase.

3. 3 : 1

4. 98%

 PowerAlgebra.com

2 Guided Instruction

Each Problem is worked out and supported online.

Problem 1
Finding Theoretical Probability

Problem 2
Finding the Probability of the Complement of an Event
Animated

Problem 3
Finding Odds
Animated

Problem 4
Finding Experimental Probability

Problem 5
Using Experimental Probability
Animated

Support in Algebra 1 Companion
• Vocabulary
• Key Concepts
• Got It?

Odds describe the likelihood of an event as a ratio comparing the number of favorable and unfavorable outcomes.

$$\text{odds in favor of an event} = \frac{\text{number of favorable outcomes}}{\text{number of unfavorable outcomes}}$$

$$\text{odds against an event} = \frac{\text{number of unfavorable outcomes}}{\text{number of favorable outcomes}}$$

 Problem 3 Finding Odds

What are the odds in favor of the spinner landing on a number greater than or equal to 6?

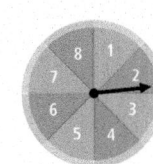

Favorable outcomes: 6, 7, 8   Total: 3
Unfavorable outcomes: 1, 2, 3, 4, 5   Total: 5

The odds in favor of the event are $\frac{3}{5}$, or 3 : 5.

Got It? 3. What are the odds against the spinner landing on a number less than 3?

Think

How is finding odds different from finding probability?
To find odds, you compare favorable and unfavorable outcomes. To find probability, you compare favorable outcomes and all possible outcomes.

Experimental probability is based on data collected from repeated trials.

experimental probability $P(\text{event}) = \dfrac{\text{number of times the event occurs}}{\text{number of times the experiment is done}}$

 Problem 4 Finding Experimental Probability

Quality Control After receiving complaints, a skateboard manufacturer inspects 1000 skateboards at random. The manufacturer finds no defects in 992 skateboards. What is the probability that a skateboard selected at random has no defects? Write the probability as a percent.

$$P(\text{no defects}) = \frac{\text{number of skateboards with no defects}}{\text{number of skateboards examined}}$$

$$= \frac{992}{1000} \qquad\qquad \text{Substitute.}$$

$$= 0.992 \qquad\qquad \text{Write as a decimal.}$$

$$= 99.2\% \qquad\qquad \text{Change to percent.}$$

The probability that a skateboard selected at random has no defects is 99.2%.

Got It? 4. Suppose the manufacturer in Problem 4 inspects 2500 skateboards. There are 2450 skateboards with no defects. What is the probability that a skateboard selected at random has no defects? Write the probability as a percent.

Think

How is the formula for experimental probability similar to the formula for theoretical probability?
In each formula, you divide a number of items corresponding to an event by a total number of items.

Problem 3

Q For what event would the odds be 1 : 1? **[Answers may vary. Sample: the spinner landing on an even number]**

Q If you are told that the odds are 1 : 50 for winning a game, what assumptions can you make about the game? **[For every 50 unfavorable outcomes, there is only 1 favorable outcome.]**

Got It?

Q What is the product of the odds for and against an event? **[The product is 1.]**

Problem 4

Q What is the probability that a skateboard selected at random does have defects? **[$\frac{8}{1000} = 0.8\%$]**

Q Given this probability, if the manufacturer surveys 100 previous customers, how many of the customers will likely report that they bought a skateboard with a defect? Explain. **[either one or none; 100 · 0.8% = 0.8]**

Got It?
Explain that a skateboard manufacturer must decide how many skateboards to inspect in order to obtain an accurate percentage of how many skateboards actually have defects.

Additional Problems

1. Kristy spins the game spinner below. What is the theoretical probability that she spins a number less than 4?

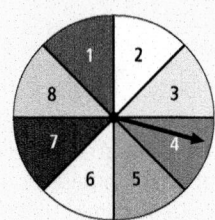

ANSWER $\frac{3}{8}$

2. A final exam contains 15 multiple choice questions, 10 true/false questions, 10 short answer questions, and 5 essay questions. Suppose Mrs. Wilson selects a question at random to review with her class. What is the probability that it is not a multiple choice?

ANSWER $\frac{5}{8}$

3. A jar contains 7 green marbles and 5 red marbles. If a marble is selected at random, what are the odds in favor of selecting a green marble?

ANSWER 7 : 5

4. In a survey on favorite pets, 28 people chose dogs as their favorite pet, 15 chose cats, 4 chose birds, and 3 chose fish. If a survey participant is selected at random, what is the probability that he or she prefers dogs as a pet?

ANSWER 56%

5. A quality control worker samples 500 LCD monitors and finds cosmetic defects in 3 of them. If the company manufactures a run of 12,000 monitors, how many of them would you expect to have a cosmetic defect?

ANSWER 72

Problem 5

> **Q** What is the probability that another home randomly selected from the town owns a dog? $[\frac{197}{500}]$
>
> **Q** How many households likely do not own a dog? Explain. **[24,800 − 9770 = 15,030 households likely do not own a dog.]**

Got It?

Show students that they can also solve this problem by setting up and solving the proportion:

$$\frac{692}{700} = \frac{x}{35,400}$$

3 Lesson Check

Do you know HOW?

- If students have difficulty with Exercises 1-4, then have them review Problem 1 to write a fraction in simplest form.

Do you UNDERSTAND?

- If students have difficulty with Exercise 7, then have them give their answer in terms of a specific situation.

Close

> **Q** How might a game show producer use experimental probability to determine if a spinner used to award prizes has a defect? **[The producer might conduct a large number of trials to determine if the experimental probability is close to the theoretical probability of winning a prize.]**

You can use experimental probability to make a prediction. Predictions are not exact, so round your results.

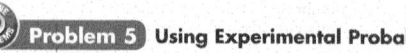 **Problem 5** Using Experimental Probability

Pets You ask 500 randomly selected households in your town if they have a dog. Of the 500 households, 197 respond that they do have a dog. If your town has 24,800 households, about how many households are likely to have a dog?

Know	Need	Plan
• 197 of 500 respondents own a dog • Your town has 24,800 households	Likely number of households that own a dog	Find the experimental probability that a household owns a dog. Then multiply it by the total number of households.

$$P(\text{own dog}) = \frac{\text{number of respondents that own a dog}}{\text{number of households surveyed}} = \frac{197}{500} = 0.394$$

households with dog = $P(\text{own dog}) \cdot$ total number of households

$$= 0.394 \cdot 24,800 \qquad \text{Substitute.}$$
$$= 9771.2 \qquad \text{Simplify.}$$

It is likely that approximately 9770 households in your town own a dog.

 Got It? 5. A manufacturer inspects 700 light bulbs and finds that 692 of the light bulbs work. There are about 35,400 light bulbs in the manufacturer's warehouse. About how many of the light bulbs in the warehouse are likely to work?

 Lesson Check

Do you know HOW?

Find the theoretical probability of each event when rolling a number cube.

1. $P(4)$

2. $P(\text{less than 3})$

3. $P(\text{not 3})$

4. $P(\text{not greater than 4})$

5. What are the odds in favor of rolling a 4 on a number cube?

6. You toss a dart at a dartboard 500 times. You hit the bull's-eye 80 times. What is the experimental probability that you hit the bull's-eye?

Do you UNDERSTAND?

7. **Vocabulary** What is the difference between theoretical probability and experimental probability?

8. **Error Analysis** Eric calculated the probability of getting a number less than 3 when randomly choosing an integer from 1 to 10. Describe and correct his error.

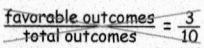

9. **Open-Ended** Describe a real-world situation in which one event is nearly certain to occur and another event is highly unlikely.

---

3 Lesson Check

For a digital lesson check, use the Got It questions.

Support in Algebra 1 Companion
- Lesson Check

4 Practice

Assign homework to individual students or to an entire class.

Answers

Got It? (continued)

5. about 34,995 light bulbs

Lesson Check

1. $\frac{1}{6}$
2. $\frac{1}{3}$
3. $\frac{5}{6}$
4. $\frac{2}{3}$
5. 1 : 5
6. 16%
7. Theoretical probability is based on the number of favorable outcomes when all of the outcomes are equally likely. Experimental probability is based on the results of an experiment.
8. There are only two outcomes that are favorable, getting a 1 or a 2, therefore the probability is $\frac{2}{10}$, or $\frac{1}{5}$.
9. Check students' work.

Practice and Problem-Solving Exercises

See Problems 1 and 2.

A Practice

The spinner at the right is divided into six equal parts. Find the theoretical probability of landing on the given section(s) of the spinner.

10. P(blue)   **11.** P(white)   **12.** P(5)   **13.** P(not less than 3)

14. P(8)   **15.** P(even)   **16.** P(not 2)   **17.** P(less than 5)

18. P(not green)   **19.** P(not red)   **20.** P(even or odd)   **21.** P(greater than 4)

Use the spinner at the right above. Find the odds.

See Problem 3.

22. odds in favor of even number   **23.** odds against 2   **24.** odds against a factor of 6

25. odds against green   **26.** odds in favor of blue   **27.** odds in favor of a multiple of 5

The results of a survey of 100 randomly selected students at a 2000-student high school are shown at the right. Find the experimental probability that a student selected at random has the given plans after graduation.

See Problem 4.

Plans for After Graduation

Response	Number of Responses
Go to community college	24
Go to 4-year college	43
Take a year off before college	12
Go to trade school	15
Do not plan to go to college	6

28. P(community college)

29. P(4-year college)

30. P(trade school)

31. P(not trade school)

32. P(trade school or community college)

33. A park has about 500 trees. You find that 27 of 67 randomly chosen trees are oak trees. About how many trees in the entire park are likely to be oak trees?

See Problem 5.

B Apply

34. Error Analysis A spinner has 3 red and 5 blue sections of equal size. A friend says the odds in favor of spinning blue are 3 : 5. Describe and correct the error.

35. Think About a Plan The United States has a land area of about 3,536,278 mi². Illinois has a land area of about 57,918 mi². What is the probability that a location in the United States chosen at random is not in Illinois? Give your answer to the nearest tenth of a percent.
   • How can you solve this problem using the complement of an event?
   • How do you write a fraction as a percent?

36. Transportation Out of 80 workers surveyed at a company, 17 walk to work.
   a. What is the experimental probability that a randomly selected worker at that company walks to work?
   b. Predict about how many of the 3600 workers at the company walk to work.

37. Open-Ended Suppose your teacher chooses a student at random from your algebra class. What is the probability that a boy is not selected?

38. Reasoning The odds in favor of Event A are equal to the odds against Event A. What is the probability of Event A? Explain.

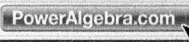
| Lesson 12-7   Theoretical and Experimental Probability | 761 |

---

4 Practice

ASSIGNMENT GUIDE

Basic: 10–36 all, 38

Average: 11–33 odd, 34–41

Advanced: 11–33 odd, 34–46

Standardized Test Prep: 47–49

Mixed Review: 50–59

Reasoning exercises have blue headings.

Applications exercises have red headings.

EXERCISE 36: Use the Think About a Plan worksheet in the **Practice and Problem Solving Workbook** (also available in the Teaching Resources in print and online) to further support students' development in becoming independent learners.

HOMEWORK QUICK CHECK

To check students' understanding of key skills and concepts, go over Exercises 23, 29, 34, 35, and 36.

Practice and Problem-Solving Exercises

10. $\frac{1}{2}$

11. 0

12. $\frac{1}{6}$

13. $\frac{2}{3}$

14. 0

15. $\frac{1}{2}$

16. $\frac{5}{6}$

17. $\frac{2}{3}$

18. $\frac{5}{6}$

19. $\frac{2}{3}$

20. 1

21. $\frac{1}{3}$

22. 3 : 3

23. 5 : 1

24. 2 : 4

25. 5 : 1

26. 3 : 3

27. 1 : 5

28. 24%

29. 43%

30. 15%

31. 85%

32. 39%

33. about 201 trees

34. Those are the odds against. The odds in favor of spinning blue are 5 : 3.

35. 98.4%

36. a. $\frac{17}{80}$
    b. 765 workers

37. Check students' work.

38. 50%; since the number of favorable outcomes equals the number of unfavorable outcomes, the probability will be equal to $\frac{n}{2n} = \frac{1}{2}$.

Answers

Practice and Problem-Solving Exercises
(continued)

39. 40%

40. 3 : 7

41. 25%

42. 30%; there are 3*n* blue marbles and 10*n* total marbles, where *n* is a positive integer. Therefore the probability of choosing a blue marble is $\frac{3}{10}$.

43. $\frac{3}{16}$

44. $\frac{3}{8}$

45. $\frac{5}{8}$

46. $\frac{7}{16}$

47. B

48. G

49. [2] Since order does not make a different group, this is a combination problem.
$$_{11}C_5 = \frac{11!}{5!(11-5)!} = 462$$
There are 462 different groups the coach can choose.

[1] correct methods used with minor computational error

50. 840

51. 6

52. 30

53. 9

54. 5

55. {1, 4, 5, 6, 7, 10}

56. {4, 6}

57. {0, 2, 4, 5, 6, 7, 8, 10}

58. {4, 10}

59. {0, 1, 2, 4, 6, 7, 8, 10}

Football The stem-and-leaf plot at the right shows the difference between the points scored by the winning and losing teams in the Super Bowl during one 20-yr period.

39. Find the probability that the winning team won by less than 10 points.

40. Find the odds that the winning team won by 10 to 15 points.

41. Find the probability that the winning team won by more than 20 points.

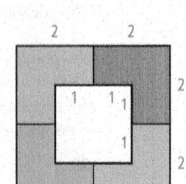

Difference Between Winning and Losing Super Bowl Scores

0	1 3 3 3 3 4 7 7
1	0 1 2 3 4 5 7
2	3 7 7
3	5
4	5

Key: 1 | 0 means 10 points

Challenge

42. Reasoning The odds in favor of choosing a red marble from a bag of red and blue marbles are 7 : 3. What is the probability of choosing a blue marble? Explain.

Geometry Use the figure at the right. Assume that the white square is centered in the large square. If you randomly choose a point inside the figure, what is the probability that it will be in the region described?

43. *P*(red)

44. *P*(blue)

45. *P*(not blue)

46. *P*(green or white)

Standardized Test Prep

SAT/ACT

47. What is the median of the following class sizes: 29, 31, 28, 25, 27, 33, 33, 26?
- Ⓐ 28
- Ⓑ 28.5
- Ⓒ 29
- Ⓓ 33

48. If $y = 10$ when $x = 5$, and *y* varies inversely with *x*, which equation relates *x* and *y*?
- Ⓕ $xy = 5$
- Ⓖ $y = \frac{50}{x}$
- Ⓗ $xy = 2$
- Ⓘ $y = \frac{2}{x}$

Short Response

49. A basketball team has 11 players. How many different 5-player groups can the coach choose to play during a game? Show your work.

Mixed Review

Find the number of permutations or combinations. 🔁 See Lesson 12-6.

50. $_7P_4$ **51.** $_3P_3$ **52.** $_6P_2$ **53.** $_9C_1$ **54.** $_5C_4$

Get Ready! To prepare for Lesson 12-8, do Exercises 55–59.

Find each union or intersection. Let $J = \{4, 5, 6, 7\}$, $K = \{1, 4, 7, 10\}$, and 🔁 See Lesson 3-8.
$L = \{x \mid x$ is an even whole number less than 12$\}$.

55. $J \cup K$ **56.** $J \cap L$ **57.** $J \cup L$ **58.** $L \cap K$ **59.** $K \cup L$

Differentiated Remediation

Additional Instructional Support

Algebra 1 Companion

Students can use the **Algebra 1 Companion** worktext (4 pages) as you teach the lesson. Use the Companion to support

- New Vocabulary
- Key Concepts
- Got It for each Problem
- Lesson Check

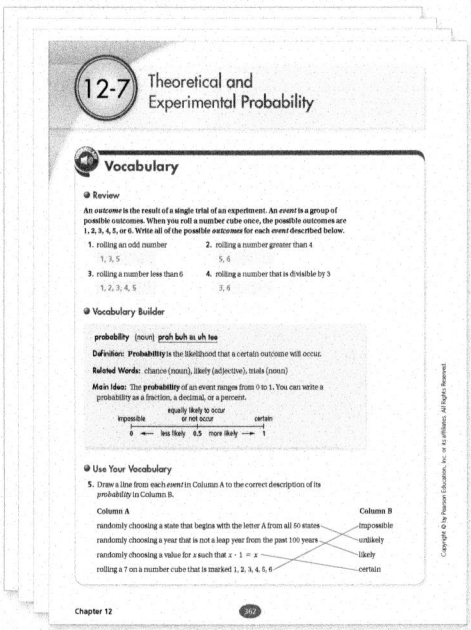

ELL Support

Use Manipulatives Have students work in pairs. Give each pair a coin to toss. What are the possible outcomes, or results, of a toss or event? What is the sample space? Ask students to predict the outcome (the number of heads or tails) if the coin is tossed 20 times. What is a prediction? How can you make an accurate prediction? Show students how to find theoretical probability before telling students to toss the coin and record the results. Repeat with a number cube.

5 Assess & Remediate

Lesson Quiz

1. The ages of the people on a bus are 24, 38, 47, 29, 51, 44, 40, 31, 36, and 43. If a bus passenger is selected at random, what is the probability that he or she is younger than 30?

2. **Do you UNDERSTAND?** Alexandra has scarves in the colors shown below. Suppose Alexandra selects a scarf at random. Find each probability.

Red	4
Blue	3
Silver	7
Black	6

   a. $P(\text{red})$
   b. $P(\text{silver or blue})$
   c. $P(\text{not black})$
   d. $P(\text{not silver and not black})$

3. A random selection of 250 motherboards reveals defects in 2 of them. Suppose the manufacturing company produces a run of 8000 motherboards. How many of them should the company expect to have defects?

ANSWERS TO LESSON QUIZ

1. $\frac{1}{5}$

2. a. $\frac{1}{5}$ b. $\frac{1}{2}$ c. $\frac{7}{10}$ d. $\frac{7}{20}$

3. 64

PRESCRIPTION FOR REMEDIATION

Use the student work on the Lesson Quiz to prescribe a differentiated review assignment.

Points	Differentiated Remediation
0–1	Intervention
2	On-level
3	Extension

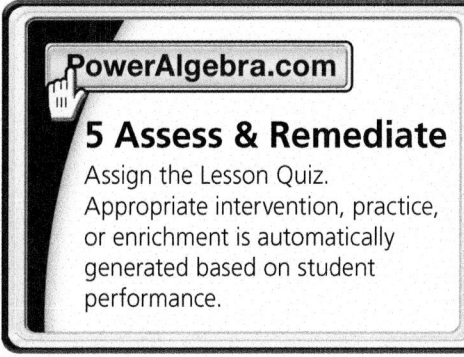

PowerAlgebra.com

5 Assess & Remediate

Assign the Lesson Quiz. Appropriate intervention, practice, or enrichment is automatically generated based on student performance.

Intervention

- **Reteaching** (2 pages) Provides reteaching and practice exercises for the key lesson concepts. Use with struggling students or absent students.

- **English Language Learner Support** Helps students develop and reinforce mathematical vocabulary and key concepts.

All-in-One Resources/Online
Reteaching

12-7 Reteaching
Theoretical and Experimental Probability

You can find **theoretical probability** by using the following formula.

$P(\text{event}) = \frac{\text{number of favorable outcomes}}{\text{number of possible outcomes}}$

Experimental probability relies on data from repeated trials. You can find experimental probability by using the following formula.

$P(\text{event}) = \frac{\text{number of times the event occurs}}{\text{number of times the experiment is done}}$

Problem

You choose a crayon at random from a bag containing 4 green crayons, 1 red crayon, 2 blue crayons, and 5 yellow crayons. What is the probability that your crayon will be blue?

There are $4 + 1 + 2 + 5$, or 12 crayons. Two crayons are blue.

$P(\text{blue}) = \frac{\text{number of favorable outcomes}}{\text{number of possible outcomes}}$
$= \frac{2}{12} \text{ or } \frac{1}{6}$

Exercises

You spin a spinner that has 12 equal-sized sections numbered 1 to 12. Find the theoretical probability of landing on the given section(s) of the spinner.

1. $P(6) \ \frac{1}{12}$ 2. $P(\text{odd number}) \ \frac{1}{2}$ 3. $P(\text{greater than 8}) \ \frac{1}{3}$

4. $P(\text{less than 9}) \ \frac{2}{3}$ 5. $P(\text{multiple of 3}) \ \frac{1}{4}$ 6. $P(\text{multiple of 5}) \ \frac{1}{6}$

7. $P(\text{greater than 10}) \ \frac{1}{6}$ 8. $P(\text{less than 4}) \ \frac{1}{4}$ 9. $P(\text{not 1}) \ \frac{11}{12}$

All-in-One Resources/Online
English Language Learner Support

12-7 ELL Support
Theoretical and Experimental Probability

Concept List

complement of an event	event	experimental probability
odds against an event	odds in favor of an event	outcome
probability	sample space	theoretical probability

Choose the concept from the list above that best represents the item in each box.

1.	2.	3.
$P(\text{event}) = \frac{\text{number of times event occurs}}{\text{number of times experiment is done}}$	$\frac{\text{number of unfavorable outcomes}}{\text{number of favorable outcomes}}$	
experimental probability	odds against an event	outcome or event
4.	**5.**	**6.**
$\frac{\text{number of favorable outcomes}}{\text{number of possible outcomes}}$	$P(\text{event}) + P(\text{not event}) = 1$	1, 2, 3, 4, 5, 6
theoretical probability	complement of an event	any outcome or group of outcomes event
7.	**8.**	**9.**
$\frac{\text{number of favorable outcomes}}{\text{number of unfavorable outcomes}}$		$P(\text{event})$
odds in favor of an event	all possible outcomes sample space	probability

Differentiated Remediation *continued*

On-Level

- **Practice** (2 pages) Provides extra practice for each lesson. For simpler practice exercises, use the Form K Practice pages found in the All-in-One Teaching Resources and online.

- **Think About a Plan** Helps students develop specific problem-solving skills and strategies by providing scaffolded guiding questions.

- **Standardized Test Prep** Focuses on all major exercises, all major question types, and helps students prepare for the high-stakes assessments.

Extension

- **Enrichment** Provides students with interesting problems and activities that extend the concepts of the lesson.

- **Activities, Games, and Puzzles** Worksheets that can be used for concepts development, enrichment, and for fun!

Practice and Problem Solving Wkbk/All-in-One Resources/Online
Practice page 1

12-7 Practice — Form G
Theoretical and Experimental Probability

You spin a spinner that has 15 equal-sized sections numbered 1 to 15. Find the theoretical probability of landing on the given section(s) of the spinner.

1. $P(15)$ $\frac{1}{15}$
2. $P(\text{odd number})$ $\frac{8}{15}$
3. $P(\text{even number})$ $\frac{7}{15}$
4. $P(\text{not 5})$ $\frac{14}{15}$
5. $P(\text{less than 5})$ $\frac{4}{15}$
6. $P(\text{greater than 8})$ $\frac{7}{15}$
7. $P(\text{multiple of 5})$ $\frac{1}{5}$
8. $P(\text{less than 16})$ 1
9. $P(\text{prime number})$ $\frac{2}{5}$

10. You roll a number cube. What is the probability that you will roll a number less than 5? $\frac{2}{3}$

11. The probability that a spinner will land on a red section is $\frac{1}{6}$. What is the probability that the spinner will not land on a red section? $\frac{5}{6}$

You choose a marble at random from a bag containing 2 red marbles, 4 green marbles, and 3 blue marbles. Find the odds.

12. odds in favor of red $2:7$
13. odds in favor of blue $1:2$
14. odds against green $5:4$
15. odds against red $7:2$
16. odds in favor of green $4:5$
17. odds against blue $2:1$

18. You roll a number cube. What are the odds that you will roll an even number? $1:1$

Practice and Problem Solving Wkbk/All-in-One Resources/Online
Practice page 2

12-7 Practice (continued) — Form G
Theoretical and Experimental Probability

One hundred twenty randomly selected students at Roosevelt High School were asked to name their favorite sport. The results are shown in the table. Find the experimental probability that a student selected at random makes the given response.

Favorite Sport Survey	
Sport	Number of Responses
Basketball	30
Baseball	22
Football	34
Soccer	20
Other	14

19. $P(\text{basketball})$ $\frac{1}{4}$
20. $P(\text{soccer})$ $\frac{1}{6}$
21. $P(\text{baseball})$ $\frac{11}{60}$
22. $P(\text{football})$ $\frac{17}{60}$

23. A meteorologist says that the probability of rain today is 35%. What is the probability that it will not rain? 65%

24. Hank usually makes 11 out of every 20 of his free throws. What is the probability that he will miss his next free throw? $\frac{9}{20}$

25. There are 250 freshmen at Central High School. You survey 50 randomly selected freshmen and find that 35 plan to go to the school party on Friday. How many freshmen are likely to be at the party? 175 freshmen

26. The Widget Company randomly selects its widgets and checks for defects. If 5 of the 300 selected widgets are defective, how many defective widgets would you expect in the 1500 widgets manufactured today? 25 defective widgets

---

All-in-One Resources/Online
Enrichment

12-7 Enrichment
Theoretical and Experimental Probability

A dart is thrown at random and hits the square at the right. The probability that the dart will hit the shaded part is the ratio of area of the shaded part to the area of the whole square.

$$P(\text{shaded part}) = \frac{\text{area of shaded part}}{\text{area of the whole}}$$

A dart is thrown at random and hits the geometric shape. Find the probability that it will hit the shaded area.

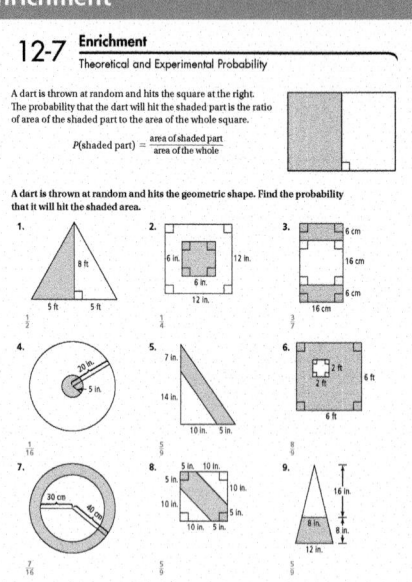

Practice and Problem Solving Wkbk/All-in-One Resources/Online
Think About a Plan

12-7 Think About a Plan
Theoretical and Experimental Probability

Transportation Out of 80 workers surveyed at a company, 17 walk to work.
a. What is the experimental probability that a randomly selected worker at that company walks to work?
b. Predict about how many of the 3600 workers at the company walk to work.

Understanding the Problem

1. Write a fraction that represents the probability that a randomly selected worker at the company walks to work.

$$P(\text{walks to work}) = \frac{\text{number surveyed who walk to work}}{\text{total number surveyed}} = \frac{17}{80}$$

Planning the Solution

2. Let w represent the number of workers who walk to work. Write an equation that could be used to predict the total number of workers who walk to work.

$$w = \frac{17}{80} \times 3600$$

Getting an Answer

3. Solve the equation.
765 walkers

4. Is your answer reasonable? Explain.
Answers may vary. Sample: Yes; just less than one-fourth of the workers surveyed walked to work and 765 is just less than one-fourth of the total number of workers.

5. The experimental probability is $\frac{17}{80}$, and I predict that approximately 765 workers walk to work.

Practice and Problem Solving Wkbk/All-in-One Resources/Online
Standardized Test Prep

12-7 Standardized Test Prep
Theoretical and Experimental Probability

Multiple Choice

For Exercises 1–5, choose the correct letter.

1. A letter from the word *MISSISSIPPI* is selected at random. What is the probability that the letter is *P*? C
A. $\frac{2}{11}$ B. $\frac{1}{9}$ C. $\frac{4}{11}$ D. $\frac{2}{9}$

2. You spin a spinner that has 8 equal-sized sections numbered 1 to 8. Which event is least likely to occur? I
F. The number is even.
G. The number is greater than 3.
H. The number is less than 3.
I. The number is a multiple of 5.

3. You toss a number cube. What are the odds against getting a number less than 3? A
A. $2:1$ B. $1:2$ C. $3:1$ D. $1:3$

4. A meteorologist says that the probability of snow today is 45%. What is the probability that it will *not* snow? H
F. $\frac{9}{11}$ G. $\frac{9}{20}$ H. $\frac{11}{20}$ I. $\frac{9}{11}$

5. What is the probability that a number picked from the set $\{-4, -3, -2, -1, 0, 1, 2, 3, 4, 5\}$ will be a solution of $2x + 5 > 1$? C
A. 20%   B. 30%   C. 70%   D. 80%

Short Response

6. A pizza restaurant is having a contest. The restaurant advertises that one out of every 25 customers will win a small pizza.
a. What is the probability that a customer will win? $\frac{1}{25}$
b. If the restaurant has 275 customers on Monday, how many winners would you expect? 11 winners

[2] Both parts answered correctly.
[1] One part answered correctly.
[0] Neither part answered correctly.

Online Teacher Resource Center
Activities, Games, and Puzzles

12-7 Activity: Probability and Area
Theoretical and Experimental Probability

In this activity, you will use experimental probability to estimate area.

The grid at the right has 36 squares for a total area of 36 square units. Each square has a dot inside it. The coordinates of each dot are expressed by the ordered pair (column number, row number). For example, (5, 1) is the dot in the 5th column and 1st row of the grid. By rolling a number cube twice, you can randomly generate the coordinates of a dot.

1. Suppose you roll a number cube 18 times to generate the coordinates of nine dots: (1, 1), (2, 1), (2, 6), (3, 3), (3, 5), (4, 3), (5, 2), (5, 5), (6, 1). What is the experimental probability that a dot will be *on* or *inside* the circle? $\frac{7}{9}$

2. To estimate the area of the circle, use the following formula.
estimated area = total area × experimental probability
What is the estimated area of the circle? 28 units²

Roll a number cube 20 times until you generate the 10 coordinates of 10 different dots. (Coordinates may appear more than once.) Estimate the area of each figure below by using the experimental probability that a dot is *on* or *inside* the figure. (To save time, use the same 10 ordered pairs for all exercises.) Then select 10 more dots in each figure and estimate each area again. Compare your results with the actual area. Discuss your results with classmates. Answers may vary.

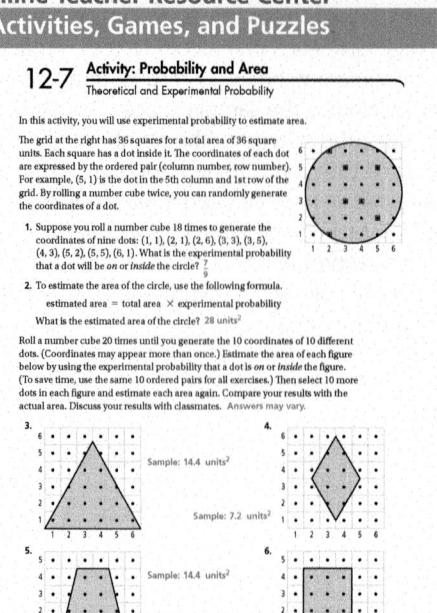

Conducting Simulations

A *simulation* is a model of a real-life situation. One way to do a simulation is to use random numbers generated by a graphing calculator or computer program.

On a graphing calculator, the command **RANDINT** generates random integers. To create a list of random integers, press (math) ◁ (5). The calculator will display **RANDINT(**. After the parenthesis, type (0) (,) (9) (9), and press (enter) repeatedly to create random 1- and 2-digit numbers from 0 to 99.

Activity 1

About 40% of people in the United States have type A blood. Estimate the probability that the next two people who donate blood in a blood drive have type A blood.

53	18	33	75
93	34	36	45
25	71	47	46
66	13	63	36
21	59	27	07
83	25	72	24
73	52	59	81
14	09	40	64
81	72	02	38
21	09	92	10

Step 1 To simulate this situation, let a 2-digit number represent 2 people. Use a calculator to generate 40 random 2-digit numbers, like the example at the right.

Step 2 Since about 40% of people in the United States have type A blood, 40% of the digits 0–9 can be used to represent these people. Let 0, 1, 2, and 3 represent people with type A blood, and let 4, 5, 6, 7, 8, and 9 represent people without type A blood. So, the 2-digit number 53 represents one person without type A blood (the digit 5) and one person with type A blood (the digit 3).

Step 3 In the example at the right, the six numbers in red represent two consecutive people who have type A blood. The other 2-digit numbers have at least one digit that represents a person of a blood type other than type A.

$$P(\text{two consecutive people of blood type A}) = \frac{\text{number of times the event occurs}}{\text{number of times the experiment is done}}$$

$$= \frac{6}{40} = 0.15$$

> Convert 1-digit numbers like 9 into 2-digit numbers by adding a leading zero.

You can also simulate situations using other methods, such as rolling number cubes, spinning spinners, or flipping coins.

Activity 2

A cereal company has a promotion in which 1 in every 6 boxes contains a movie ticket.

Step 1 Roll two number cubes to represent two boxes of the cereal. Let 1 represent a winning box and let 2, 3, 4, 5, and 6 represent a nonwinning box.

Step 2 Record the result. Repeat this process 30 times. Use your results to estimate the probability that both boxes contain a movie ticket.

| PowerAlgebra.com | Concept Byte   Conducting Simulations | 763 |

Guided Instruction

PURPOSE To learn what a simulation is, why simulations are used, and some of the different methods that can be used to simulate experiments

PROCESS Students will

• conduct a simulation using random numbers.

• conduct a simulation using a number cube.

DISCUSS There are many real-life situations that involve a certain degree of uncertainty. Simulations are models that provide a means of studying the probability of occurrences in these real-life situations. Graphing calculators are popular for conducting simulations because they have functions that can randomly generate integers.

Activity 1

In this Activity students conduct a simulation with random numbers.

Q Why are two-digit numbers being generated in Step 1? **[Because each digit of the two-digit number represents a person.]**

Q Could a different number of random integers (other than 40) have been generated in this simulation? Explain. **[Yes, however, you want to be sure to generate enough numbers so that you get reliable results.]**

Q Will each person that follows these steps get exactly the same results? Explain. **[No, because the integers are being randomly generated by the calculator.]**

Activity 2

In this Activity students conduct a simulation with a number cube.

Q Why is a number cube a good choice for this simulation? **[Because there are six sides of a number cube, and one in every six boxes of cereal contains a ticket.]**

Q Does it matter which number you select to represent a winning box? **[No, it is arbitrary.]**

Q Why are two number cubes being rolled? **[One cube is used to represent your own box of cereal, and the other cube is used to represent your friend's box of cereal.]**

1 Interactive Learning

Solve It!

PURPOSE To determine the probability of a compound event using simple probability

PROCESS Students may use simple probability by determining the number of favorable outcomes and comparing it to the number of possible outcomes.

FACILITATE

Q How many songs on the music device are rock songs? How many are performed by an artist whose name begins with the letter A? **[27; 28]**

Q How many songs on the music device are rock songs that are performed by an artist whose name begins with the letter A? **[16]**

ANSWER See Solve It in Answers on next page.

CONNECT THE MATH Students explore a compound event in the Solve It. In the lesson, students will learn about compound events, mutually exclusive events, overlapping events, independent events, and dependent events and how the type of event affects the probability of the event.

2 Guided Instruction

Take Note

Use Venn diagrams and the data provided in the Solve It to illustrate the concepts of mutually exclusive and overlapping events.

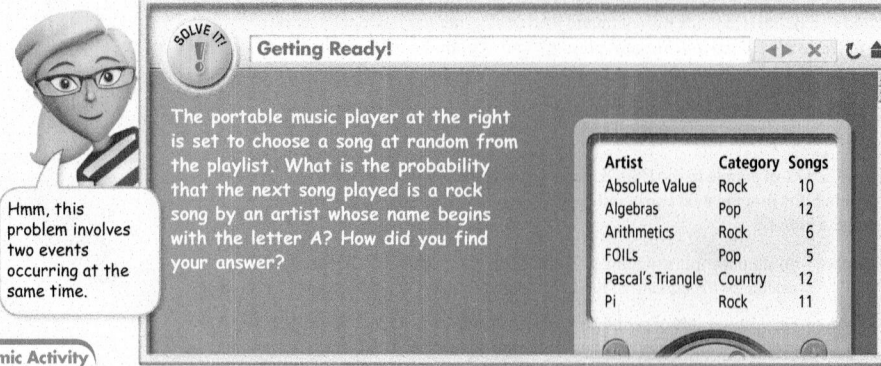

12-8 Probability of Compound Events

Objectives To find probabilities of mutually exclusive and overlapping events
To find probabilities of independent and dependent events

Dynamic Activity
Independent and Dependent Events

Lesson Vocabulary
- compound event
- mutually exclusive events
- overlapping events
- independent events
- dependent events

In the Solve It, you found the probability that the next song is both a rock song and also a song by an artist whose name begins with the letter A. This is an example of a **compound event,** which consists of two or more events linked by the word *and* or the word *or*.

Essential Understanding You can write the probability of a compound event as an expression involving probabilities of simpler events. This may make the compound probability easier to find.

When two events have no outcomes in common, the events are **mutually exclusive events.** If A and B are mutually exclusive events, then $P(A \text{ and } B) = 0$. When events have at least one outcome in common, they are **overlapping events.**

You need to determine whether two events A and B are mutually exclusive before you can find $P(A \text{ or } B)$.

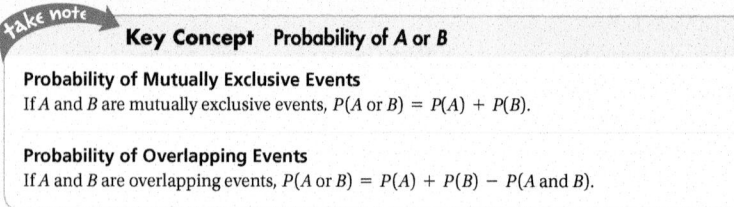

Key Concept   Probability of A or B

Probability of Mutually Exclusive Events
If A and B are mutually exclusive events, $P(A \text{ or } B) = P(A) + P(B)$.

Probability of Overlapping Events
If A and B are overlapping events, $P(A \text{ or } B) = P(A) + P(B) - P(A \text{ and } B)$.

12-8 Preparing to Teach

BIG idea Probability   UbD

ESSENTIAL UNDERSTANDINGS
- The probability of a compound event can sometimes be found from expressions of the probabilities of simpler events.
- Different methods must be used for finding the probability of two dependent events compared to finding the probability of two independent events.

Math Background

A compound event in the study of probability is an event that consists of two or more simple probability events. When two simple events constitute a compound event, the two events can be either a union in which one or the other event occurs, or an intersection in which both of the events occur. The two events are said to be mutually exclusive if the probability of both events occurring is zero. The two

events are said to be independent if the probability of one event occurring is not dependent on the other event occurring. Have students look at compound probability problems by first determining whether the first event affects the second event. Once students determine whether the events are dependent or independent, they can select the appropriate equation. It may sometimes be difficult to determine whether events are independent, but it is crucial mathematicaly: $P(A \text{ and } B) = P(A) \cdot P(B)$ if and only if A and B are independent events.

Support Student Learning

Use the **Algebra 1 Companion** to engage and support students during instructions. See Lesson Resources at the end of this lesson for details.

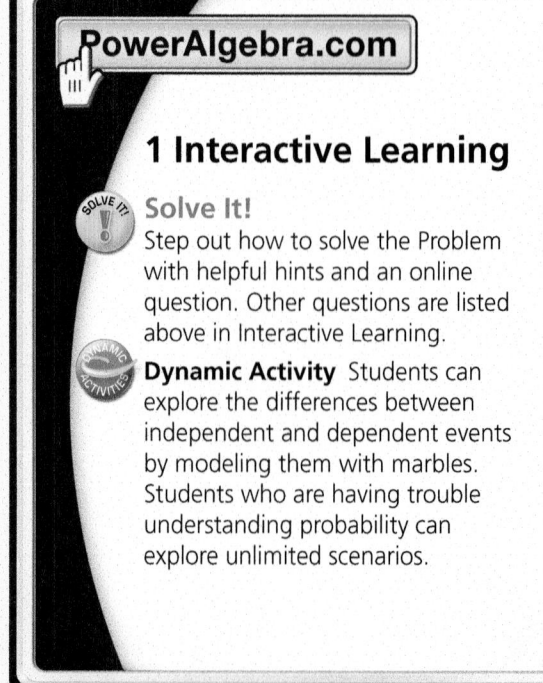

PowerAlgebra.com

1 Interactive Learning

Solve It!
Step out how to solve the Problem with helpful hints and an online question. Other questions are listed above in Interactive Learning.

Dynamic Activity Students can explore the differences between independent and dependent events by modeling them with marbles. Students who are having trouble understanding probability can explore unlimited scenarios.

 **Problem 1** Mutually Exclusive and Overlapping Events

Suppose you spin a spinner that has 20 equal-sized sections numbered from 1 to 20.

Ⓐ What is the probability that you spin a 2 or a 5?

Because the spinner cannot land on both 2 and 5, the events are mutually exclusive.

$$P(2 \text{ or } 5) = P(2) + P(5)$$

$$= \frac{1}{20} + \frac{1}{20} \quad \text{Substitute.}$$

$$= \frac{2}{20} = \frac{1}{10} \quad \text{Simplify.}$$

The probability that you spin a 2 or a 5 is $\frac{1}{10}$.

Ⓑ What is the probability that you spin a number that is a multiple of 2 or 5?

Since a number can be a multiple of 2 and a multiple of 5, such as 10, the events are overlapping.

$$P(\text{multiple of 2 or multiple of 5})$$

$$= P(\text{multiple of 2}) + P(\text{multiple of 5}) - P(\text{multiple of 2 and 5})$$

$$= \frac{10}{20} + \frac{4}{20} - \frac{2}{20} \quad \text{Substitute.}$$

$$= \frac{12}{20} = \frac{3}{5} \quad \text{Simplify.}$$

The probability that you spin a number that is a multiple of 2 or a multiple of 5 is $\frac{3}{5}$.

How many multiples are there?
There are 10 multiples of 2: 2, 4, 6, 8, 10, 12, 14, 16, 18, and 20. There are 4 multiples of 5: 5, 10, 15, and 20. There are 2 multiples of 2 and 5: 10 and 20.

Got It? **1.** Suppose you roll a standard number cube.
a. What is the probability that you roll an even number or a number less than 4?
b. What is the probability that you roll a 2 or an odd number?

A standard set of checkers has an equal number of red and black checkers. The diagram at the right shows the possible outcomes when randomly choosing a checker, putting it back, and choosing again. The probability of getting a red on either choice is $\frac{1}{2}$. The first choice, or event, does not affect the second event. The events are *independent*.

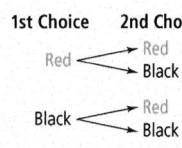

1st Choice 2nd Choice

Two events are **independent events** if the occurrence of one event does not affect the probability of the second event.

 Key Concept Probability of Two Independent Events

If A and B are independent events, $P(A \text{ and } B) = P(A) \cdot P(B)$.

2 Guided Instruction

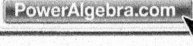 Each Problem is worked out and supported online.

Problem 1
Mutually Exclusive and Overlapping Events

Problem 2
Finding the Probability of Independent Events
Animated

Problem 3
Selecting With Replacement
Animated

Problem 4
Selecting Without Replacement
Animated

Problem 5
Finding the Probability of a Compound Event
Animated

Support in Algebra 1 Companion
• Vocabulary
• Key Concepts
• Got It?

Problem 1

Q Is it possible for the spinner to land on both 2 and 5 during the same spin? Explain. **[No; there is only one number on each section.]**

Q If you used the formula for overlapping events to determine the probability in 1A, would you still arrive at the same answer? **[Yes; the probability of landing on both 2 and 5 is zero, so you would get the same answer.]**

Q Is it possible to land on both a multiple of 2 and a multiple of 5? Explain. **[Yes; the numbers 10 and 20 are multiples of both 2 and 5.]**

Q If you used the formula for mutually exclusive events to determine the probability in 1B, would you still arrive at the same answer? **[No, because you would count some of the sections twice as favorable outcomes.]**

Got It?

Q Which formula should you use to compute the probability in 1a? 1b? **[formula for overlapping events; formula for mutually exclusive events]**

Take Note

Ask students to state several more examples and a nonexample of independent events.

Answers

Solve It!

$\frac{2}{7}$; explanations may vary.

Got It?

1. a. $\frac{5}{6}$

b. $\frac{2}{3}$

Problem 2
The probability can be calculated by interpreting this event as a simple event.

> **Q** What is the total number of outcomes possible when the two number cubes are rolled simultaneously? Explain. **[Using the Multiplication Counting Principle, there are 6 · 6 = 36 possible outcomes.]**
>
> **Q** What is the total number of favorable outcomes possible when the two number cubes are rolled simultaneously? **[Using the Multiplication Counting Principle, there are 1 · 3 = 3 possible favorable outcomes.]**

Got It?
Ask students to describe an event involving the number cubes that has a probability of $\frac{1}{2}$.

Problem 3
Show students that the probability can be computed using the Multiplication Counting Principle. The number of ways to choose a dotted tile first and then a dragon is 4 · 3 = 12 ways. The number of ways to choose two tiles is 15 · 15 = 225. Therefore, the probability is $\frac{12}{225} = \frac{4}{75}$.

Got It?

> **Q** What is the probability of choosing a bird tile? a flower tile? $[\frac{2}{15}; \frac{1}{15}]$

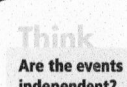

Think

Are the events independent?
Yes. The outcome of rolling one number cube does not affect the outcome of rolling another number cube.

Plan

Why are the events independent when you select with replacement?
When you replace the tile, the conditions for the second selection are exactly the same as for the first selection.

Problem 2 Finding the Probability of Independent Events

Suppose you roll a red number cube and a blue number cube. What is the probability that you will roll a 3 on the red cube and an even number on the blue cube?

$P(\text{red } 3) = \frac{1}{6}$ Only one of the six numbers is a 3.

$P(\text{blue even}) = \frac{3}{6} = \frac{1}{2}$ Three of the six numbers are even.

$P(\text{red 3 and blue even}) = P(\text{red 3}) \cdot P(\text{blue even})$

$= \frac{1}{6} \cdot \frac{1}{2} = \frac{1}{12}$ Substitute and then simplify.

The probability is $\frac{1}{12}$.

Got It? **2.** You roll a red number cube and a blue number cube. What is the probability that you roll a 5 on the red cube and a 1 or 2 on the blue cube?

Problem 3 Selecting With Replacement

Games You choose a tile at random from the game tiles shown. You replace the first tile and then choose again. What is the probability that you choose a dotted tile and then a dragon tile?

Because you replace the first tile, the events are independent.

$P(\text{dotted}) = \frac{4}{15}$ 4 of the 15 tiles are dotted.

$P(\text{dragon}) = \frac{3}{15} = \frac{1}{5}$ 3 of the 15 tiles are dragons.

$P(\text{dotted and dragon}) = P(\text{dotted}) \cdot P(\text{dragon})$

$= \frac{4}{15} \cdot \frac{1}{5}$ Substitute.

$= \frac{4}{75}$ Simplify.

The probability that you will choose a dotted tile and then a dragon tile is $\frac{4}{75}$.

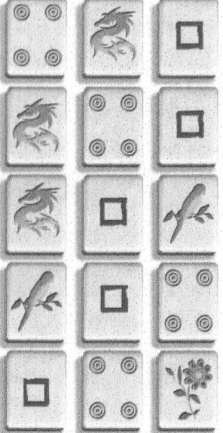

Got It? **3.** In Problem 3, what is the probability that you randomly choose a bird and then, after replacing the first tile, a flower?

Two events are **dependent events** if the occurrence of one event affects the probability of the second event. For example, suppose in Problem 3 that you do *not* replace the first tile before choosing another. This changes the set of possible outcomes for your second selection.

Additional Problems

1. A dartboard has 12 equally sized sections numbered from 1 to 12.

   a. What is the probability of throwing a dart that lands on an odd number?

   b. What is the probability of throwing a dart that lands on a multiple of 3?

   ANSWER a. $\frac{1}{2}$ **b.** $\frac{1}{3}$

2. Suppose you roll a number cube and flip a coin. What is the probability of rolling a number greater than 2 and flipping heads?

   ANSWER $\frac{1}{3}$

3. A bag contains 4 red chips, 3 green chips, 6 blue chips, and 5 black chips. Andrew selects a chip at random. He replaces the chip and then selects another one at random. What is the probability that he selects a red chip, then a black chip?

   ANSWER $\frac{5}{81}$

4. Refer to the information given in Additional Problem 3. Suppose Andrew selects a chip at random, does not replace it, then selects another chip at random. What is the probability that he selects a blue chip, then a green chip?

   ANSWER $\frac{1}{17}$

5. Justin has 8 rock songs, 3 hip hop songs, 5 classical music songs, and 4 country songs in a playlist on his mp3 player. Suppose he plays songs at random from the playlist. If the mp3 player will not play the same song twice in a row, what is the probability that he will hear a rock song followed by a country song?

   ANSWER $\frac{8}{95}$

Key Concept **Probability of Two Dependent Events**

If A and B are dependent events, $P(A \text{ then } B) = P(A) \cdot P(B \text{ after } A)$.

 Problem 4 Selecting Without Replacement ⊕ᴿᴵᴰᴰᴱᴰ ᴿᴱˢᴾᴼᴺˢᴱ

Games Suppose you choose a tile at random from the tiles shown in Problem 3. Without replacing the first tile, you select a second tile. What is the probability that you choose a dotted tile and then a dragon tile?

Because you do not replace the first tile, the events are dependent.

$P(\text{dotted}) = \frac{4}{15}$ 4 of the 15 tiles are dotted.

$P(\text{dragon after dotted}) = \frac{3}{14}$ 3 of the 14 remaining tiles are dragons.

$P(\text{dotted then dragon}) = P(\text{dotted}) \cdot P(\text{dragon after dotted})$

$= \frac{4}{15} \cdot \frac{3}{14} = \frac{2}{35}$ Substitute and then simplify.

The probability that you will choose a dotted tile and then a dragon tile is $\frac{2}{35}$.

Think

How is P(dragon after dotted) different from P(dragon)?
After selecting the first tile without replacement, there is one less tile to choose from for the second choice.

✓ **Got It? 4.** In Problem 4, what is the probability that you will randomly choose a flower and then, without replacing the first tile, a bird?

 Problem 5 Finding the Probability of a Compound Event

Essay Contest One freshman, 2 sophomores, 4 juniors, and 5 seniors receive top scores in a school essay contest. To choose which 2 students will read their essays at the town fair, 2 names are chosen at random from a hat. What is the probability that a junior and then a senior are chosen?

Know	Need	Plan
Grade levels of the 12 students	P(junior then senior)	Determine whether the events are dependent or independent and use the formula that applies.

The first outcome affects the probability of the second. So the events are dependent.

$P(\text{junior}) = \frac{4}{12} = \frac{1}{3}$ 4 of the 12 students are juniors.

$P(\text{senior after junior}) = \frac{5}{11}$ 5 of the 11 remaining students are seniors.

$P(\text{junior then senior}) = P(\text{junior}) \cdot P(\text{senior after junior})$

$= \frac{1}{3} \cdot \frac{5}{11} = \frac{5}{33}$ Substitute and then simplify.

The probability that a junior and then a senior are chosen is $\frac{5}{33}$.

PowerAlgebra.com | **Lesson 12-8** Probability of Compound Events | **767**

Take Note
Ask students to state several more examples and a nonexample of dependent events.

Problem 4
Show students that the probability can be computed using the Multiplication Counting Principle. The number of ways to choose a dotted tile first and then a dragon is $4 \cdot 3 = 12$ ways. The number of ways to choose two tiles is $15 \cdot 14 = 210$. Therefore, the probability is $\frac{12}{210} = \frac{2}{35}$.

Got It?

Q What is the probability that you will choose a flower and then, without replacing the first tile, another flower? **[The probability is zero.]**

Problem 5

Q If the first name were replaced prior to the second name being chosen, what might occur? **[One student would need to read his or her essay twice.]**

Q What is the probability of choosing both of the sophomores to read their essays? Explain. **[$\frac{2}{12} \cdot \frac{1}{11} = \frac{2}{132} = \frac{1}{66}$]**

Answers

Got It? (continued)

2. $\frac{2}{225}$

3. $\frac{1}{18}$

4. $\frac{1}{105}$

Got It?

Q In problem 5, what is the probability that no seniors or juniors are chosen? $[\frac{1}{22}]$

3 Lesson Check

Do you know HOW?
- If students have difficulty with Exercise 3, then have them review Problem 3 to understand how to handle replacement.

Do you UNDERSTAND?
- If students have difficulty with Exercise 4, then have them also provide an example of a compound event composed of two mutually exclusive events when you spin a spinner with the integers from 1 through 8.

Close

Q How does finding the probability of selecting with replacement compare to finding the probability of selecting without replacement? **[When you select with replacement, the total number of possible outcomes is the same for each event. When you select without replacement, the total number of possible outcomes decreases after each event.]**

 Got It? 5. a. In Problem 5, what is the probability that a senior and then a junior are chosen?

b. Reasoning Is P(junior then senior) different from P(senior then junior)? Explain.

 **Lesson Check**

Do you know HOW?
Use the cards below.

 B 1 5 D 10

1. You choose a card at random. What is each probability?
   a. P(B or number)   **b.** P(red or 5)
   c. P(red or yellow)   **d.** P(yellow or letter)

2. What is the probability of choosing a yellow card and then a D if the first card *is not* replaced before the second card is drawn?

3. What is the probability of choosing a yellow card and then a D if the first card is replaced before the second card is drawn?

Do you UNDERSTAND?
4. Vocabulary What is an example of a compound event composed of two overlapping events when you spin a spinner with the integers from 1 through 8?

5. Reasoning Are an event and its complement mutually exclusive or overlapping? Use an example to explain.

6. Open-Ended What is a real-world example of two independent events?

7. Error Analysis Describe and correct the error below in calculating P(yellow or letter) from Exercise 1, part (d).

$$P(\text{yellow or letter}) = P(\text{yellow}) \text{ or } P(\text{letter})$$
$$= \frac{3}{5} + \frac{2}{5}$$
$$= 1$$

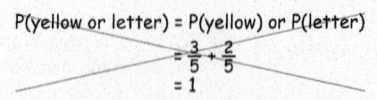 **Practice and Problem-Solving Exercises**

A Practice You spin the spinner at the right, which is divided into equal sections. Find each probability.   ◆ See Problem 1.

8. P(4 or 7)   **9.** P(even or red)   **10.** P(odd or 10)

11. P(3 or red)   **12.** P(red or less than 3)   **13.** P(odd or multiple of 3)

14. P(7 or blue)   **15.** P(red or more than 8)   **16.** P(greater than 6 or blue)

You roll a blue number cube and a green number cube. Find each probability.   ◆ See Problem 2.

17. P(blue even and green even)   **18.** P(blue and green both less than 6)

19. P(green less than 7 and blue 4)   **20.** P(blue 1 or 2 and green 1)

You choose a tile at random from a bag containing 2 A's, 3 B's, and 4 C's. You replace the first tile in the bag and then choose again. Find each probability.   ◆ See Problem 3.

21. P(A and A)   **22.** P(A and B)   **23.** P(B and B)   **24.** P(C and C)   **25.** P(B and C)

---

3 Lesson Check

For a digital lesson check, use the Got It questions.

Support In Algebra 1 Companion
- Lesson Check

4 Practice

Assign homework to individual students or to an entire class.

Answers

Got It? (continued)

5. a. $\frac{5}{33}$
  b. No; the numerators and the denominators are the same, so the product is the same.

Lesson Check

1. a. $\frac{4}{5}$
  b. $\frac{3}{5}$
  c. 1
  d. $\frac{4}{5}$

2. $\frac{3}{20}$

3. $\frac{3}{25}$

4. Answers may vary. Sample: find the probability of spinning a number less than 5 that is even.

5. Mutually exclusive; answers may vary. Sample: The complement of being even on a number die is being odd, and even and odd are mutually exclusive.

6. Check students' work.

7. Because a tile can be both yellow and a letter, the formula should be P(yellow or letter) = P(yellow) + P(letter) − P(yellow and letter) = $\frac{3}{5} + \frac{2}{5} - \frac{1}{5} = \frac{4}{5}$.

Practice and Problem-Solving Exercises

8. $\frac{1}{5}$ **9.** $\frac{4}{5}$ **10.** $\frac{3}{5}$ **11.** $\frac{1}{2}$

12. $\frac{7}{10}$ **13.** $\frac{3}{5}$ **14.** $\frac{3}{5}$ **15.** $\frac{7}{10}$

16. $\frac{3}{5}$ **17.** $\frac{1}{4}$ **18.** $\frac{25}{36}$ **19.** $\frac{1}{6}$

20. $\frac{1}{18}$ **21.** $\frac{4}{81}$ **22.** $\frac{2}{27}$ **23.** $\frac{1}{9}$

24. $\frac{16}{81}$ **25.** $\frac{4}{27}$

You pick a coin at random from the set shown at the right and then pick a second coin without replacing the first. Find each probability.

◀ See Problem 4.

26. P(dime then nickel)

27. P(quarter then penny)

28. P(penny then dime)

29. P(penny then quarter)

30. P(penny then nickel)

31. P(dime then penny)

32. P(dime then dime)

33. P(quarter then quarter)

34. Cafeteria Each day, you, Terry, and 3 other friends randomly choose one of your 5 names from a hat to decide who throws away everyone's lunch trash. What is the probability that you are chosen on Monday and Terry is chosen on Tuesday?

◀ See Problem 5.

35. Free Samples Samples of a new drink are handed out at random from a cooler holding 5 citrus drinks, 3 apple drinks, and 3 raspberry drinks. What is the probability that an apple drink and then a citrus drink are handed out?

B Apply

Are the two events *dependent* **or** *independent***? Explain.**

36. Toss a penny. Then toss a nickel.

37. Pick a name from a hat. Without replacement, pick a different name.

38. Pick a ball from a basket of yellow and pink balls. Return the ball and pick again.

39. Writing Use your own words to explain the difference between independent and dependent events. Give an example of each.

40. Reasoning A bag holds 20 yellow mints and 80 other green or pink mints. You choose a mint at random, eat it, and choose another.
a. Find the number of pink mints if P(yellow then pink) $= P$(green then yellow).
b. What is the least number of pink mints if P(yellow then pink) $> P$(green then yellow)?

41. Think About a Plan An acre of land is chosen at random from each of the three states listed in the table at the right. What is the probability that all three acres will be farmland?
• Does the choice of an acre from one state affect the choice from the other states?
• How must you rewrite the percents to use a formula from this lesson?

Percent of State That Is Farmland	
Alabama	27%
Florida	27%
Indiana	65%

42. Phone Poll A pollster conducts a survey by phone. The probability that a call does not result in a person taking this survey is 85%. What is the probability that the pollster makes 4 calls and none result in a person taking the survey?

43. Open-Ended Find the number of left-handed students and the number of right-handed students in your class. Suppose your teacher randomly selects one student to take attendance and then a different student to work on a problem on the board.
a. What is the probability that both students are left-handed?
b. What is the probability that both students are right-handed?
c. What is the probability that the first student is right-handed and the second student is left-handed?

26. $\frac{1}{8}$ **27.** $\frac{1}{36}$ **28.** $\frac{1}{12}$ **29.** $\frac{1}{36}$

30. $\frac{1}{12}$ **31.** $\frac{1}{12}$ **32.** $\frac{1}{12}$ **33.** 0

34. $\frac{1}{25}$ **35.** $\frac{3}{22}$

36. Independent; the outcome of the first event does not affect the second event.

37. Dependent; the outcome of the first event affects the outcome of the second.

38. Independent; the outcome of the first event does not affect the second event.

39. For independent events, the outcome of the first event does not affect the outcome of the second event, while for dependent events, the outcome is affected. An example of two independent events is the rolling of two number cubes. An example of two dependent events is picking two cards from a deck without replacing the first one.

40. a. 40 pink mints
b. 41 pink mints

41. about 4.7%

42. about 52.2%

43. a–c. Check students' work.

4 Practice

ASSIGNMENT GUIDE

Basic: 8–35 all, 36–40 even, 41–42

Average: 9–35 odd, 36–43

Advanced: 9–35 odd, 36–45

Standardized Test Prep: 46–48

Mixed Review: 49–55

Reasoning exercises have blue headings.

Applications exercises have red headings.

EXERCISE 42: Use the Think About a Plan worksheet in the **Practice and Problem Solving Workbook** (also available in the Teaching Resources in print and online) to further support students' development in becoming independent learners.

HOMEWORK QUICK CHECK

To check students' understanding of key skills and concepts, go over Exercises 13, 27, 40, 41, and 42.

Answers

Practice and Problem-Solving Exercises
(continued)

44. a. $\frac{1}{36}$

  b. $\frac{1}{36}$

  c. $\frac{1}{6}$

45. a. 12

  b. $\frac{5}{6}$

  c. $\frac{1}{3}$

46. D

47. I

48. [4] **a.** Samples from either the nutrition club or the wrestling team could lead to biased results because each is not representative of the whole student population. A sample from each homeroom is better because this sample is more representative.

  b. Would you rather have pizza or a less-popular choice? What is your first choice for a menu item for the cafeteria?

  [3] Answers for both parts are given, but reasons are not given for part (a).

  [2] Either part (a) or part (b) is correct.

  [1] Answers for part (a) are given but no reasons are supplied. Part (b) is incorrect or part (a) is incorrect and only one question is given for part (b).

49. $\frac{11}{21}$

50. $\frac{4}{21}$

51. $\frac{2}{7}$

52. $\frac{8}{21}$

53. -22

54. $\frac{a+5}{5(a-5)}$

55. $\frac{7(y+1)}{7y+1}$

 **Challenge**   **44.** Suppose you roll a red number cube and a yellow number cube.
  a. What is P(red 1 and yellow 1)?
  b. What is P(red 2 and yellow 2)?
  c. What is the probability of rolling any matching pair of numbers? (*Hint:* Add the probabilities of each of the six matches.)

45. A two-digit number is formed by randomly selecting from the digits 1, 2, 3, and 5 without replacement.
  a. How many different two-digit numbers can be formed?
  b. What is the probability that a two-digit number contains a 2 or a 5?
  c. What is the probability that a two-digit number is prime?

Standardized Test Prep

 SAT/ACT   **46.** You take a three-question true-or-false quiz. You guess on all the questions. What is the probability that you will get a perfect score?

  Ⓐ 1   Ⓑ $\frac{1}{2}$ Ⓒ $\frac{1}{4}$ Ⓓ $\frac{1}{8}$

47. You have a bag containing 3 green marbles, 4 red marbles, and 2 yellow marbles. You select 1 marble randomly. What are the odds against selecting a green or yellow marble?

  Ⓕ 5 : 4   Ⓖ 9 : 4   Ⓗ 4 : 9   Ⓘ 4 : 5

Extended Response   **48.** A survey at your school is being taken to gather student input on the items offered by the cafeteria.
  a. Possible sampling methods are asking the nutrition club, asking the boys' wrestling team, and asking 5 students from each homeroom. Explain whether or not each sample could lead to biased results.
  b. Write a question designed to encourage respondents to favor more pizza. Then write another question about menu choices that is unbiased.

Mixed Review

You select a number at random from the integers 10 through 30, inclusive. Find each probability.   ◈ See Lesson 12-7.

49. P(number is even)   **50.** P(number is a multiple of 6)

51. P(number is prime)   **52.** P(number is less than 18)

Simplify each complex fraction.   ◈ See Lesson 11-2.

53. $\dfrac{\frac{-12q-10}{6q+5}}{11}$ **54.** $\dfrac{\frac{3a+2}{a^2-10a+25}}{\frac{15a+10}{a^2-25}}$ **55.** $\dfrac{\frac{7y^2+6y-1}{y+3}}{\frac{49y^2-1}{7y+21}}$

Additional Instructional Support

Algebra 1 Companion

Students can use the **Algebra 1 Companion** worktext (4 pages) as you teach the lesson. Use the Companion to support

- New Vocabulary
- Key Concepts
- Got It for each Problem
- Lesson Check

ELL Support

Assess Understanding Divide students into 8 groups and assign them a lesson from the chapter. Have each group define each vocabulary word from the lesson, breaking the word down into parts (prefix, suffix, root word) if possible. Then have groups present their words. Model an example, such as *scalar*, if desired. Have students discuss their words. Use the opportunity for students to restate definitions or rephrase them in their own words. Students can write the words and definitions on cards and post on a word wall.

5 Assess & Remediate

Lesson Quiz

1. The table below shows the distribution of letter tiles in a board game. Players select a letter tile at random. Find each probability.

Letter Distribution

Letter	Number
A	4
E	7
I	3
O	4
U	2

a. $P(A)$　**b.** $P(\text{vowel})$　**c.** $P(I \text{ or } U)$

2. Suppose you roll a number cube and spin a spinner with four equal-sized sections labeled 1, 2, 3, 4. What is the probability you roll a prime number and spin a prime number?

3. Do you UNDERSTAND? Reagan rolls a number cube and spins the spinner below. What is the probability of spinning a number greater than 5 and rolling an even number?

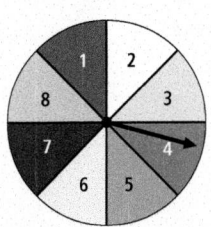

ANSWERS TO LESSON QUIZ

1. a. $\frac{1}{5}$　**b.** 1　**c.** $\frac{1}{4}$

2. $\frac{1}{4}$　**3.** $\frac{3}{16}$

PRESCRIPTION FOR REMEDIATION

Use the student work on the Lesson Quiz to prescribe a differentiated review assignment.

Points	Differentiated Remediation
0–1	Intervention
2	On-level
3	Extension

PowerAlgebra.com

5 Assess & Remediate

Assign the Lesson Quiz. Appropriate intervention, practice, or enrichment is automatically generated based on student performance.

Intervention

- **Reteaching** (2 pages) Provides reteaching and practice exercises for the key lesson concepts. Use with struggling students or absent students.

- **English Language Learner Support** Helps students develop and reinforce mathematical vocabulary and key concepts.

All-in-One Resources/Online
Reteaching

12-8 Reteaching
Probability of Compound Events

All-in-One Resources/Online
English Language Learner Support

12-8 ELL Support
Probability of Compound Events

Differentiated Remediation *continued*

On-Level

- **Practice** (2 pages) Provides extra practice for each lesson. For simpler practice exercises, use the Form K Practice pages found in the All-in-One Teaching Resources and online.

- **Think About a Plan** Helps students develop specific problem-solving skills and strategies by providing scaffolded guiding questions.

- **Standardized Test Prep** Focuses on all major exercises, all major question types, and helps students prepare for the high-stakes assessments.

Extension

- **Enrichment** Provides students with interesting problems and activities that extend the concepts of the lesson.

- **Activities, Games, and Puzzles** Worksheets that can be used for concepts development, enrichment, and for fun!

Practice and Problem Solving Wkbk/All-in-One Resources/Online
Practice page 1

Practice and Problem Solving Wkbk/All-in-One Resources/Online
Practice page 2

All-in-One Resources/Online
Enrichment

Practice and Problem Solving Wkbk/All-in-One Resources/Online
Think About a Plan

Practice and Problem Solving Wkbk/All-in-One Resources/Online
Standardized Test Prep

Online Teacher Resource Center
Activities, Games, and Puzzles

Concept Byte

Conditional Probability

Use With Lesson 12-8

A **conditional probability** contains a condition that may limit the sample space for an event. You can write a conditional probability using the notation $P(B \mid A)$, read "the probability of event B, given event A."

Activity 1

The table shows sales at a car dealership. Use the table to answer the following questions.

Car Sales

	$15,000 or Less	More Than $15,000
Domestic	15	8
Foreign	11	12

1. How many domestic cars were sold?

2. How many foreign cars were sold?

3. How many cars were sold for $15,000 or less?

4. How many cars were sold for more than $15,000?

To find a conditional probability like $P(\text{domestic} \mid \$15,000 \text{ or less})$, which is the probability that a car is domestic given it costs $15,000 or less, first determine the sample space. There are 26 cars that are $15,000 or less. Of those 26 cars, 15 are domestic. So, $P(\text{domestic} \mid \$15,000 \text{ or less}) = \frac{15}{26}$.

5. **a.** What is $P(\text{foreign} \mid \$15,000 \text{ or less})$ and $P(\$15,000 \text{ or less} \mid \text{foreign})$?
   b. Reasoning Are the probabilities the same? Why or why not?

6. **Data Collection** Conduct a survey of at least ten people. Find out if they are right- or left-handed. Also find out if each person has any left-handed family members.
   a. Copy the table at the right and record your data.
   b. Find $P(\text{left-handed} \mid \text{left-handed family members})$.
   c. Find $P(\text{no left-handed family members} \mid \text{left-handed})$.
   d. Interpret your results.

	Left-Handed Family Members	No Left-Handed Family Members
Left-handed		
Right-handed		

7. **Reasoning** Consider the theoretical probabilities for a pair of number cubes. Does $P(\text{even on cube 1} \mid \text{odd on cube 2}) = P(\text{odd on cube 2} \mid \text{even on cube 1})$? Explain your answer.

8. Consider the table at the right. Find each probability.
   a. $P(\text{female recipient} \mid \text{associate's degree})$
   b. $P(\text{male recipient} \mid \text{bachelor's degree})$
   c. $P(\text{advanced degree} \mid \text{female recipient})$
   d. $P(\text{female recipient} \mid \text{advanced degree})$

Projected Number of Degree Recipients in 2015 (thousands)

Degree	Male	Female
Associate's	288	467
Bachelor's	720	980
Advanced	377	506

SOURCE: U.S. Department of Education

Guided Instruction

PURPOSE To apply conditional probability to real-world situations

PROCESS Students will explore real-life situations that involve conditional probabilities.

DISCUSS Reinforce the benefits of organizing the outcomes of the events in conditional probability problems by appropriately using tables and tree diagrams.

Activity 1

In this Activity students are guided through several situations in which conditional probabilities apply.

Q How is the data organized in each of these situations and why? **[Tables: they provide a means of keeping track of the number of occurrences of events, as well as the sample spaces.]**

Q In Exercise 6, why do you suppose it is suggested that at least ten people be surveyed? **[You need to have ample people to survey in order to have accurate results.]**

Q In Exercise 7, what kinds of events are represented by the roll of the pair of number cubes? **[independent events]**

Answers

Activity 1

1. 23

2. 23

3. 26

4. 20

5. **a.** $\frac{11}{26}$, $\frac{11}{23}$
   b. No; the sample spaces are different.

6. **a–d.** Check students' work.

7. Yes; the probability of being odd is the same as the probability of being even and the two events are independent.

8. **a.** $\frac{467}{755}$
   b. $\frac{36}{85}$
   c. $\frac{506}{1953}$
   d. $\frac{506}{883}$

Guided Instruction

Activity 2

In this Activity students use tree diagrams to solve problems involving conditional probability.

> **Q** Why is the disc throw the first branch of the tree diagram? **[Because the disc is always being thrown. Whether or not the dog catches the disc is based upon the throw.]**
>
> **Q** Why is a tree diagram a good way of displaying the events in this situation? **[Because of the way in which the outcomes of the events depend on one another.]**
>
> **Q** How can you use the tree diagram to find $P(C \mid M)$? **[$P(C \mid M)$ is the probability along the line that connects node M to node C.]**
>
> **Q** How can you use the tree diagram to find $P(M$ and $C)$? **[Multiply the probability along the line that goes to M and the line that connects M and C.]**

You can use tree diagrams to solve problems involving conditional probability and events that are not equally likely.

Activity 2

A dog owner throws a flying disc to a dog. The following statements are true.
- The dog catches the disc 40% of the time if the owner throws it 20 ft or less.
- The dog catches the disc 75% of the time if the owner throws it more than 20 ft.
- 80% of the time, the dog's owner throws the disc more than 20 ft.

You can organize these probabilities in a tree diagram.

L represents a throw that is less than or equal to 20 ft.
M represents a throw that is greater than 20 ft.
C represents that the dog catches the disc.
N represents that the dog does not catch the disc.

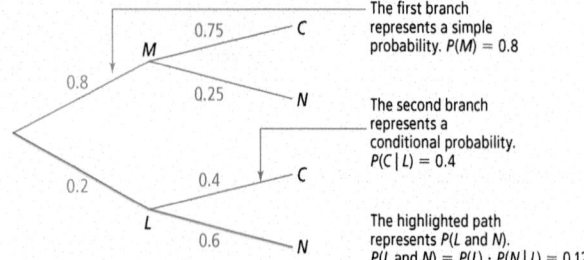

Use the tree diagram to answer the following questions.

9. What is $P(C \mid M)$?

10. What is $P(N \mid L)$?

11. What is $P(M$ and $C)$?

12. **a.** Suppose the dog returns the disc 90% of the time after she catches it, and 15% of the time when she does not catch the disc. Copy the tree diagram above and extend it to include this information.

    b. Use your tree diagram to find the probability that the disc was thrown more than 20 ft, caught by the dog, and returned to the owner.

13. **Data Collection** Take a survey of at least 20 people. Record their genders and whether or not their first names end with a vowel (including y).

    a. Make a tree diagram using gender as the first branch and last letter of first name as the second branch.

    b. Find $P(\text{female} \mid \text{ends in vowel})$ and $P(\text{ends in vowel} \mid \text{male})$.

    c. Interpret your results.

    d. **Reasoning** Do you think it makes more sense to have gender as the first branch or second branch? Explain.

Answers

Activity 2

9. 0.75

10. 0.6

11. 0.6

12. a.

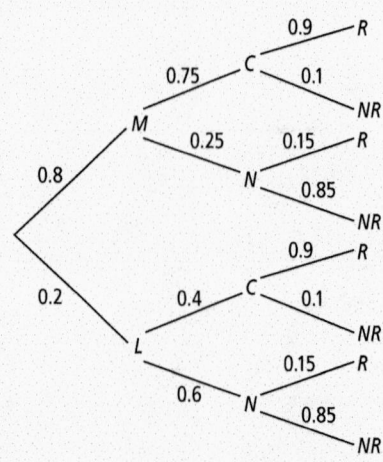

b. 0.54

13. a–d. Check Students' work.

12 *Pull It* **All Together**

To solve these problems you will pull together many concepts and skills that you have studied about data analysis and probability.

BIG idea Data Collection and Analysis

When you collect data, you should use a sampling technique free of bias. You can use standard measures to describe data sets and make estimates, decisions, or predictions.

BIG idea Data Representation

You can use matrices, frequency tables, histograms, box-and-whisker plots, tree diagrams, and other representations to describe different types of data sets.

Task 1

You are writing an article on gaming systems for your school newspaper. You take a survey of 250 people ages 13 to 18 and ask whether they have a home gaming system, a portable gaming system, or no gaming system. The results of your survey are shown in the matrix at the right.

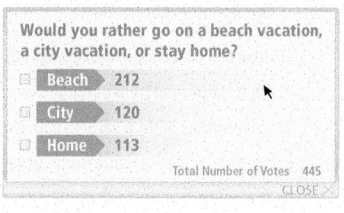

	Age
	13 14 15 16 17 18
Home gaming	12 22 26 32 24 26
Portable gaming	5 5 4 9 7 6
No gaming	18 12 8 6 12 16

  a. Make a histogram that represents the number of students who have gaming systems, either home or portable. Is the histogram *uniform, symmetric,* or *skewed*?

  b. What is another way you could have drawn the histogram in part (a)? Explain.

  c. Display some or all of the data using a different representation. Explain your choice.

  d. If a person needed to know as much specific data as possible, what kind of data display would you show the person? Why?

  e. What is the experimental probability that the next person you survey does *not* have a gaming system?

BIG idea Probability

You can find theoretical and experimental probabilities to make decisions or predictions about future events.

Task 2

The Web site at the right shows the results of an online survey that asks, "Would you rather go on a beach vacation, a city vacation, or stay at home?"

  a. Is the survey question biased? Why or why not?

  b. Based on the survey, what are the odds that a person will want to stay at home for vacation?

  c. Based on the survey, what is the probability that a person will travel for vacation?

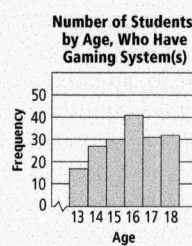

Would you rather go on a beach vacation, a city vacation, or stay home?

☐ **Beach** 212
☐ **City** 120
☐ **Home** 113

Total Number of Votes 445

CLOSE ✕

Performance Task   UbD

Pull It All Together

The concepts and skills required to solve these problems are from several lessons within this chapter and from the previous chapter. As students solve these problems, they will demonstrate their reasoning strategies and their growth as independent problem solvers.

The following questions are designed for you to:

- Help support students as they do the Tasks.
- Gauge the amount of support students need as they progress to becoming independent problem solvers.

Task 1

- What should be the intervals on the histogram?
- What makes various data displays good choices to display data?
- How can you use the graph to help you make a prediction about the next person that is surveyed?

Task 2

- What makes a survey question biased?
- Are there any other possible vacations that someone may prefer?
- How can you find the probability a person chosen at random falls into a specific category?

Assess Performance   UbD

Pull It All Together

See p. 67 for a holistic scoring rubric to gauge a student's progress on Understanding the Problem, Planning a Solution, Getting an Answer, and Assessing Autonomy.

SOLUTION OUTLINES

Task 1

a. First step: Find the total number of students at each age who have gaming systems. (Answer: 13: 12 + 5 = 17; 14: 22 + 5 = 27; 15: 26 + 4 = 30; 16: 32 + 9 = 41; 17: 24 + 7 = 31; 18: 26 + 6 = 32)

Second step: Make a frequency table to organize your information from the first step. Answer:

Number of Students, by Age, Who Have Gaming System(s)

Age	Frequency
13	17
14	27
15	30
16	41
17	31
18	32

Third step: Make a histogram using your frequency table from the second step. Answer:

Number of Students, by Age, Who Have Gaming System(s)

(histogram with x-axis: Age 13 14 15 16 17 18; y-axis: Frequency 0–50)

Fourth step: Determine whether the histogram is *uniform, symmetric,* or *skewed*. (Answer: Because the peak of the histogram is not in the center, the histogram is *skewed*.)

b. Answers may vary. Sample: You could have used a different interval, such as intervals of 2, to show the age groups of the students surveyed.

c. Answers may vary. Sample: You can display the data in a cumulative frequency table to show the total number of students, at a given age or younger, who have gaming systems.

Number of Students, by Age, Who Have Gaming System(s)

Age	Frequency	Cumulative Frequency
13	17	17
14	27	44
15	30	74
16	41	115
17	31	146
18	32	178

Solution Outlines continued on next page.

Essential Questions **UbD**

BIG idea **Data Collection and Analysis**

ESSENTIAL QUESTION How can collecting and analyzing data help you make decisions or predictions?

ANSWER When you collect data, you should use a sampling technique free of bias. You can use standard measures to describe data sets and make estimates, decisions, or predictions.

BIG idea **Data Representation**

ESSENTIAL QUESTION How can you make and interpret different representations of data?

ANSWER You can use matrices, frequency tables, histograms, box-and-whisker plots, tree diagrams, and other representations to describe different types of data sets.

BIG idea **Probability**

ESSENTIAL QUESTION How is probability related to real-world events?

ANSWER You can find theoretical and experimental probabilities to make decisions or predictions about future events.

---

(12) Chapter Review

Connecting **BIG** ideas and Answering the Essential Questions

1. Data Collection and Analysis
When you collect data, you should use a sampling technique free of bias. You can use standard measures to describe data sets and make estimates, decisions, or predictions.

Data Analysis (Lessons 12-3 and 12-4)
11 12 14 16 11 10 13 7
Mean: 11.75   Median: 11.5
Mode: 11   Range: 9

Samples and Surveys (Lesson 12-5)
Data Types: qualitative, quantitative, univariate, bivariate
Sample Types: random, systematic, stratified

2. Data Representation
You can use matrices, frequency tables, histograms, box-and-whisker plots, tree diagrams, and other representations to describe different types of data sets.

Data Displays (Lessons 12-1, 12-2, 12-4, and 12-6)

3. Probability
You can find theoretical and experimental probabilities to make decisions or predictions about future events.

Theoretical and Experimental Probability (Lesson 12-7)
Theoretical: $\frac{\text{number of favorable outcomes}}{\text{number of possible outcomes}}$
Experimental: $\frac{\text{number of times event occurs}}{\text{number of times experiment is done}}$

Probability of Compound Events (Lesson 12-8)
Independent:
$P(A \text{ and } B) = P(A) \cdot P(B)$
Dependent:
$P(A \text{ then } B) = P(A) \cdot P(B \text{ after } A)$

Chapter Vocabulary

- bias (p. 743)
- bivariate (p. 742)
- box-and-whisker plot (p. 735)
- combination (p. 753)
- complement of an event (p. 758)
- compound event (p. 764)
- dependent events (p. 766)
- element (p. 714)
- frequency (p. 720)
- histogram (p. 721)
- independent events (p. 765)
- interquartile range (p. 734)
- matrix (p. 714)
- measure of central tendency (p. 726)
- outcome (p. 757)
- outlier (p. 726)
- overlapping events (p. 764)
- percentile (p. 737)
- permutation (p. 751)
- population (p. 742)
- probability (p. 757)
- qualitative (p. 741)
- quantitative (p. 741)
- quartile (p. 734)
- range of a set of data (p. 728)
- sample (p. 742)
- scalar multiplication (p. 715)
- univariate (p. 742)

Choose the correct term to complete each sentence.

1. Each numerical item of data in a matrix is called a(n) ? .

2. The number of data values in an interval is the ? of the interval.

3. A(n) ? is a data value much greater or less than the other values in a data set.

4. The median of the lower half of an ordered data set is the first ? .

Summative Questions **UbD**

Use the following prompts as you review this chapter with your students. The prompts are designed to help you assess your students' understanding of the BIG Ideas they have studied.

- How can you show data in a display?
- What measures describe data?
- How do you find simple probability?
- How do you find probabilities of compound events?

SOLUTION OUTLINES (continued)

d. Answers may vary. Sample: a box-and-whisker plot, with the students' ages on the number line and with one plot for each category: home gaming, portable gaming, and no gaming; each plot gives the minimum, maximum, and median numbers of students who have and do not have a gaming system. The plots also divide the numbers of students into four quartiles. In addition, you can compare the information in each plot to the information in the other plots.

e. First step: Find the total number of students who do not have a gaming system. (Answer:
$18 + 12 + 8 + 6 + 12 + 16 = 72$)
Second step: Find the experimental probability that the next person you survey does not have a gaming system.
(Answer: $P(\text{no gaming system}) =$
$\frac{\text{number of students who do not have systems}}{\text{total number of students surveyed}}$
$= \frac{72}{250} = 0.288 = 28.8\%$)

Task 2

a. The question is not biased because it does not contain any words that make one option sound better than the other options.

b. First step: Find the number of people who want to stay at home for vacation. (Answer: 113)
Second step: Find the number of people who do not want to stay at home for vacation. (Answer: $212 + 120 = 332$)
Third step: Find the odds that a person will want to stay at home for vacation. (Answer: 113:332)

c. First step: Find the total number of people who would travel for vacation. (Answer: 332)
Second step: Find the probability that a person will travel for vacation.
(Answer: $\frac{332}{445} \approx 0.746 = 74.6\%$)

12-1 Organizing Data Using Matrices

Quick Review

You can use **matrices** to organize data. To add or subtract matrices that are the same size, add or subtract the corresponding **elements**. To multiply a matrix by a **scalar**, multiply each element by the scalar.

Example

What is the difference?

$$\begin{bmatrix} 3 & 2 \\ -1 & 5 \\ 2 & -2 \end{bmatrix} - \begin{bmatrix} 2 & 4 \\ 4 & -3 \\ 1 & 0 \end{bmatrix} = \begin{bmatrix} 3-2 & 2-4 \\ -1-4 & 5-(-3) \\ 2-1 & -2-0 \end{bmatrix}$$

$$= \begin{bmatrix} 1 & -2 \\ -5 & 8 \\ 1 & -2 \end{bmatrix}$$

Exercises

Find each sum, difference, or product.

5. $\begin{bmatrix} -5 & 1 \\ 0 & 8 \end{bmatrix} - \begin{bmatrix} 7 & -6 \\ -4 & 2 \end{bmatrix}$

6. $\begin{bmatrix} 0.4 & 1.5 \\ 3.2 & -3 \\ 1.5 & -2.1 \end{bmatrix} + \begin{bmatrix} 4 & 3 \\ 6.3 & -7.2 \\ 1.9 & -0.5 \end{bmatrix}$

7. $-4.2 \begin{bmatrix} 3 & 1.1 \\ 3 & -2 \\ -1 & 2.9 \end{bmatrix}$

12-2 Frequency and Histograms

Quick Review

The **frequency** of an interval is the number of data values in that interval. A **histogram** is a graph that groups data into intervals and shows the frequency of values in each interval.

Example

Below are the prices of the television models sold at an electronics store. What is a histogram of the data?

$1399 $1349 $999 $2149 $149 $279 $449 $379 $1379
$799 $3199 $1099 $499 $899 $949 $1799 $1699 $3499

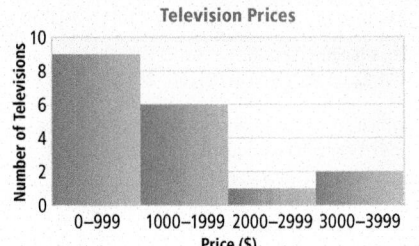

Exercises

Use the data to make a histogram.

8. customers: 141 128 132 141 152 169 121 133 131
156 142 136 135 144 135 153

9. workout times (min): 41 29 46 39 37 44 33 51 42 30

Tell whether each histogram is *uniform*, *symmetric*, or *skewed*.

10.

11.

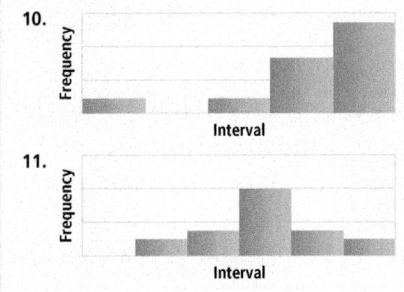

PowerAlgebra.com

Answers

Chapter Review

1. element
2. frequency
3. outlier
4. quartile

5. $\begin{bmatrix} -12 & 7 \\ 4 & 6 \end{bmatrix}$

6. $\begin{bmatrix} 4.4 & 4.5 \\ 9.5 & -10.2 \\ 3.4 & -2.6 \end{bmatrix}$

7. $\begin{bmatrix} -12.6 & -4.62 \\ -12.6 & 8.4 \\ 4.2 & -12.18 \end{bmatrix}$

8.

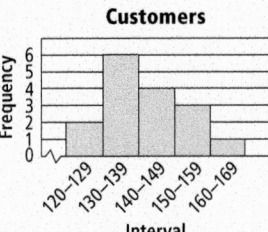

9.

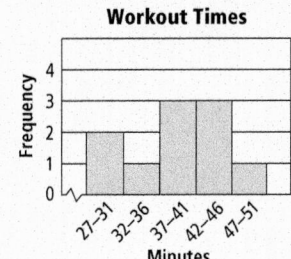

10. skewed
11. symmetric

Answers

Chapter Review (continued)

12. 26.3, 26, 23 and 25 and 29, 9

13. 12.1, 12, 12, 2

14. 11.1, 11.3, 13.4; mean or median

15. 27

16.

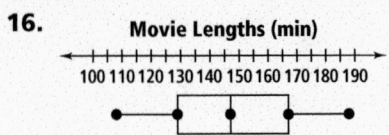

Movie Lengths (min)

100 110 120 130 140 150 160 170 180 190

17.

Dog Weights (lb)

10 20 30 40 50 60 70 80 90

18.

Book Lengths (Number of Pages)

140 180 220 260 300 340 380 420

19. B; the box in A is from about 90 to 110, where the box in B is from about 75 to 125.

12-3 Measures of Central Tendency and Dispersion

Quick Review

The **mean** of a data set equals $\frac{\text{sum of the data values}}{\text{total number of data values}}$. The **median** is the middle value in the data set when the values are arranged in order. The **mode** is the data item that occurs the most times. The **range of a set of data** is the difference between the greatest and least data values.

Example

The quality ratings of 9 movies showing at a movie theater near you are 5.6, 7.9, 7.0, 5.9, 7.8, 6.2, 6.4, 5.2, and 5.6. What are the mean, median, mode, and range of the data?

mean:

$$\frac{5.6 + 7.9 + 7.0 + 5.9 + 7.8 + 6.2 + 6.4 + 5.2 + 5.6}{9} = 6.4$$

5.2 5.6 5.6 5.9 6.2 6.4 7.0 7.8 7.9   Order the data.

median: 6.2   6.2 is the middle value.

mode: 5.6   5.6 occurs most often.

range: 7.9 − 5.2 = 2.7   Find difference between greatest and least values.

Exercises

Find the mean, median, mode, and range of each data set.

12. points scored by a football team: 23 31 26 27 25 28 23 23 25 29 29 29 25 22 30

13. clips per package: 12 12 13 12 12 12 12 12 13 12 11 12 12 12 12 12

14. **Cats** A veterinarian examines 9 cats. The weights of the cats are 13.4 lb, 13.1 lb, 10.4 lb, 6.8 lb, 11.4 lb, 10.8 lb, 13.4 lb, 11.3 lb, and 9.3 lb. Find the mean, median, and mode of the data. Which measure of central tendency best describes the data?

15. **Basketball** A basketball player scores 22, 19, 25, and 17 points in four games. How many points does the basketball player need to score in the fifth game to average 22 points scored per game?

12-4 Box-and-Whisker Plots

Quick Review

A **box-and-whisker plot** organizes data values into four groups using the minimum value, the first quartile, the median, the third quartile, and the maximum value.

Example

What box-and-whisker plot represents the test scores below?

62 57 78 69 85 43 94 82 61 90 83 51 67 88 55

Arrange the data in order from least to greatest.

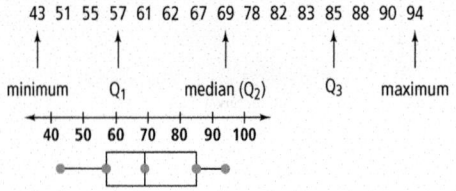

43 51 55 57 61 62 67 69 78 82 83 85 88 90 94

minimum   Q₁   median (Q₂)   Q₃   maximum

40 50 60 70 80 90 100

Exercises

Make a box-and-whisker plot of each data set.

16. movie lengths (min):
125 117 174 131 142 108 188 162 155 167 129 133 147 175 150

17. dog weights (lb):
23 15 88 34 33 49 52 67 42 71 28

18. book lengths (pages):
178 223 198 376 284 156 245 202 315 266

19. Which box-and-whisker plot represents the data set with the greater interquartile range? Explain.

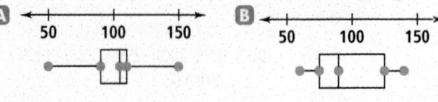

A   50 100 150   **B**   50 100 150

12-5 Samples and Surveys

Quick Review

You can obtain information about a **population** of people by surveying a smaller part of it, called a **sample**. The sample should be representative of the population. An unrepresentative sample or a poorly worded question can result in **bias**.

Example

A survey asks, "Should Plainville make itself proud by building a beautiful new library?" Is the question biased?

The question is biased. The words *proud* and *beautiful* make it clear that the answer is expected to be yes.

Exercises

Determine whether the sampling method is *random*, *systematic*, or *stratified*. Tell whether the method will give a good sample. Then write an unbiased survey question for the situation.

20. Movies An interviewer outside a movie theater asks every third person in line whether he or she will see more or fewer movies in the coming year.

21. Student Government Ten randomly chosen students in each class (freshman, sophomore, junior, and senior) are asked whom they support for student council president.

12-6 Permutations and Combinations

Quick Review

If there are m ways to make a first selection and n ways to make a second selection, then there are $m \cdot n$ ways to make the two selections.

A **permutation** is an arrangement of objects in a specific order. The number of permutations of n objects arranged r at a time, $_nP_r$, equals $\frac{n!}{(n-r)!}$.

A **combination** is a selection of objects without regard to order. The number of combinations of n objects chosen r at a time, $_nC_r$, equals $\frac{n!}{r!(n-r)!}$.

Example

In how many ways can you choose 3 people to serve on a committee out of a group of 7 volunteers?

The order does not matter, so this is a combination problem.

$_7C_3 = \frac{7!}{3!(7-3)!} = \frac{7!}{3!4!}$ Write using factorials.

$= \frac{7 \cdot 6 \cdot 5 \cdot 4 \cdot 3 \cdot 2 \cdot 1}{(3 \cdot 2 \cdot 1)(4 \cdot 3 \cdot 2 \cdot 1)}$ Write the factorials as products.

$= 35$ Simplify.

There are 35 ways to choose 3 people out of a group of 7.

Exercises

Find the number of permutations.

22. $_9P_5$ **23.** $_3P_2$ **24.** $_8P_3$

25. $_5P_2$ **26.** $_6P_4$ **27.** $_7P_2$

Find the number of combinations.

28. $_8C_2$ **29.** $_9C_4$ **30.** $_5C_3$

31. $_6C_3$ **32.** $_7C_3$ **33.** $_5C_4$

34. Side Dishes You can choose any 2 of the following side dishes with your dinner: mashed potatoes, cole slaw, french fries, applesauce, or rice. How many different combinations of side dishes can you choose?

35. Talent Show There are 8 groups participating in a talent show. In how many different orders can the groups perform?

36. Clothing You have 6 shirts, 7 pairs of pants, and 3 pairs of shoes. How many different outfits can you wear?

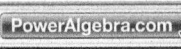
20. Systematic; good sample; do you plan on seeing more or fewer movies in the coming year?

21. Stratified; good sample; who do you support for student council president?

22. 15,120

23. 6

24. 336

25. 20

26. 360

27. 42

28. 28

29. 126

30. 10

31. 20

32. 35

33. 5

34. 10

35. 40,320 ways

36. 126 outfits

Answers

Chapter Review (continued)

37. $\frac{1}{2}$

38. $\frac{1}{2}$

39. $\frac{1}{6}$

40. $\frac{5}{6}$

41. 0

42. $\frac{1}{3}$

43. about 93.3%

44. $\frac{2}{7}$

45. $\frac{2}{7}$

46. $\frac{1}{36}$

47. $\frac{1}{4}$

48. Dependent; the outcome of the first event affects the outcome of the second event.

49. Independent; the outcome of the spinner does not affect the outcome of the pick.

12-7 Theoretical and Experimental Probability

Quick Review

An **event** is an **outcome** or group of outcomes. The **probability** of an event, which indicates how likely it is to occur, is written $P(\text{event})$. When all possible outcomes are equally likely, the **theoretical probability** of an event is given by $P(\text{event}) = \frac{\text{number of favorable outcomes}}{\text{number of possible outcomes}}$.

Example

What is the theoretical probability that a randomly chosen date is a day beginning with a T?

There are 2 favorable outcomes, Tuesday and Thursday.

There are 7 possible outcomes, the 7 days of the week.

$$P(\text{day beginning with a T}) = \frac{\text{number of favorable outcomes}}{\text{number of possible outcomes}}$$
$$= \frac{2}{7}$$

The probability of a day beginning with a T is $\frac{2}{7}$.

Exercises

The spinner at the right is divided into six equal sections. Find the theoretical probability of landing on the given sections of the spinner.

37. $P(\text{even})$ **38.** $P(\text{odd})$

39. $P(5)$ **40.** $P(\text{not } 3)$

41. $P(7)$ **42.** $P(\text{more than } 4)$

43. **Apples** An apple farmer finds that he has to throw out 15 bad apples from the 225 he has picked. What is the experimental probability that the next apple he picks will be good?

12-8 Probability of Compound Events

Quick Review

You can use a formula to find the probability of a **compound event** involving two events A and B.

Mutually exclusive events: $P(A \text{ or } B) = P(A) + P(B)$

Overlapping events:
$P(A \text{ or } B) = P(A) + P(B) - P(A \text{ and } B)$

Independent events: $P(A \text{ and } B) = P(A) \cdot P(B)$

Dependent events: $P(A \text{ then } B) = P(A) \cdot P(B \text{ after } A)$

Example

You roll a number cube and flip a coin. What is the probability that you roll a 5 and the coin comes up heads?

Rolling a 5 and flipping heads are independent events.

$P(5 \text{ and heads}) = P(5) \cdot P(\text{heads}) = \frac{1}{6} \cdot \frac{1}{2} = \frac{1}{12}$

The probability of rolling a 5 and flipping heads is $\frac{1}{12}$.

Exercises

You randomly pick two marbles from a bag containing 3 yellow marbles and 4 red marbles. You pick the second marble without replacing the first marble. Find each probability.

44. $P(\text{red then red})$ **45.** $P(\text{yellow then red})$

You roll a number cube twice. Find each probability.

46. $P(6 \text{ then } 3)$ **47.** $P(\text{odd then even})$

Are the two events *dependent* or *independent*? Explain.

48. You pick one of 7 names from a hat and then pick a second name without replacing the first one.

49. You spin a spinner with 5 equal sections and pick a marble from a bag containing 2 green marbles and 4 blue marbles.

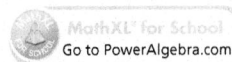

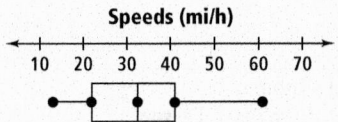

Do you know HOW?

Simplify.

1. $\begin{bmatrix} 0 & -3 \\ 2 & 0 \\ 1 & -1 \end{bmatrix} - \begin{bmatrix} 2 & 0 \\ -1 & 1 \\ -2 & 3 \end{bmatrix}$ 2. $-3\begin{bmatrix} 1 & 2 & -1 \\ 0 & -2 & 3 \\ -3 & 1 & 0 \end{bmatrix}$

Tell whether each histogram is *uniform, symmetric,* or *skewed*.

3.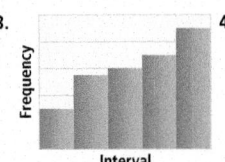

4.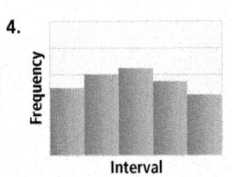

5. **Sports** The 400-m race times (in seconds) for a track team are listed below. Make a frequency table and a histogram that represent their times.

   58 54 63 56 60 58 72 61 60 59 57 52 66 68

6. **Landscaping** The hours a gardener worked over the past 14 weeks are listed below. What are the mean, median, mode, and range of the hours the gardener worked? Which measure of central tendency best describes the data?

   39 52 41 44 47 36 51 44 50 40 53 46 44 35

7. **Diving** The weights of 8 scuba divers, without tanks, are 85, 103, 94, 97, 88, 91, 104, and 95 kg. A tank weighs 15 kg. What are the mean, median, mode, and range of the divers' weights with tanks?

Identify the minimum, first quartile, median, third quartile, and maximum of each data set. Then make a box-and-whisker plot of each data set.

8. test scores: 87 52 91 66 79 56 73 90 78 51 83

9. speeds (mi/h): 41 19 31 13 48 22 61 30 34 37

10. Out of 10 dogs, 4 weigh no more than 12.5 kg. What is the percentile rank of the weight 12.5 kg?

11. **Cafeteria** A teacher asks a student chosen at random from each table in the cafeteria for his or her opinion of school food. Will this survey method give a good sample? Explain.

12. **Security** Suppose a password contains 4 lowercase letters. How many permutations are possible if no letters are repeated?

13. What is the value of $_6C_3$?

The spinner at the right is divided into four equal sections. Find the theoretical probability of landing on the given section(s) of the spinner.

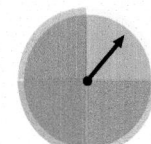

14. $P(\text{orange})$

15. $P(\text{blue})$

16. $P(\text{not green})$

17. Suppose you choose a tile at random from a bag containing 5 X's, 4 Y's, and 3 Z's. You replace the first tile in the bag and choose again. What is the probability of choosing 2 Y's?

18. Suppose you choose a marble at random from a bag containing 3 blue, 5 yellow, and 7 red marbles. You choose a second marble without replacing the first. What is the probability of choosing 2 blue marbles?

Do you UNDERSTAND?

19. **Reasoning** Could a student use the formula $P(A \text{ or } B) = P(A) + P(B) - P(A \text{ and } B)$ to solve a problem about mutually exclusive events and get the correct answer? Explain.

20. **Writing** How do you calculate interquartile range? How is this measure useful?

21. **Open-Ended** Give examples of univariate and bivariate data. How do these types of data differ?

22. **Reasoning** Is it possible for r to be greater than n in $_nC_r$? Explain.

---

9. 13, 22, 32.5, 41, 61

Speeds (mi/h)

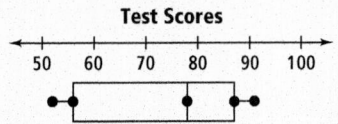

10. 40

11. Yes; assuming all the students are at this lunch, it will be a representative sample.

12. 358,800 passwords

13. 20

14. $\frac{1}{2}$

15. $\frac{1}{4}$

16. $\frac{3}{4}$

17. $\frac{1}{9}$

18. $\frac{1}{35}$

19. Yes; for mutually exclusive events $P(A \text{ and } B) = 0$.

20. The interquartile range is the difference of the third quartile and the first quartile. It tells you between what values the middle 50% of the data lies.

21. Answers may vary. Sample: Univariate data involves one variable, such as height. Bivariate data involves two variables, such as height and weight.

22. No; a combination of the form $_nC_r$ means how many ways you can arrange n things taken r at a time. It does not make sense if $r > n$.

Answers

Chapter Test

1. $\begin{bmatrix} -2 & -3 \\ 3 & -1 \\ 3 & -4 \end{bmatrix}$

2. $\begin{bmatrix} -3 & -6 & 3 \\ 0 & 6 & -9 \\ 9 & -3 & 0 \end{bmatrix}$

3. skewed

4. uniform or symmetric

5.

400-Meter Race Times

Time(s)	Frequency
50–54	2
55–59	5
60–64	4
65–69	2
70–74	1

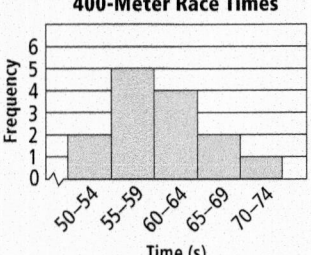

6. 44.4, 44, 44, 18; mean, since there are no outliers

7. 109.6, 109.5, no mode, 19

8. 51, 56, 78, 87, 91

Test Scores

Item Number	Lesson
1	5-3
2	7-4
3	12-7
4	4-6
5	9-1
6	1-9
7	3-6
8	4-4
9	11-2
10	6-3
11	5-3
12	9-1
13	4-5
14	6-5
15	2-5
16	9-1
17	6-1
18	10-2
19	9-1
20	5-3
21	5-6
22	9-1
23	12-4
24	2-3
25	6-2
26	2-9
27	12-5
28	9-6
29	1-4
30	12-3
31	8-1
32	10-3
33	4-5
34	9-1
35	3-7
36	4-5
37	3-8
38	7-5
39	5-6
40	5-7
41	2-5
42	4-2
43	7-5
44	8-8
45	12-6
46	2-8
47	12-2

End-of-Course Assessment
to Prepare for the Algebra I ADP End-of-Course Exam

The following items should be completed *without* a calculator. For multiple choice questions, write the letter of the correct answer on your paper. For all other questions, show your work and clearly explain your answer.

1. Which equation represents a line with a greater slope and lesser y-intercept than the line shown?

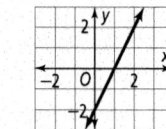

- (A) $y = x - 1$
- (B) $y = -x - 1$
- (C) $y = -2x - 2$
- (D) $y = 3x - 3$

2. Which expression is equivalent to $3(x^2 + 1) - 5x(x^2 + x + 1)$?

- (A) $-5x^3 + 8x^2 + 5x + 3$
- (B) $-5x^3 - 2x^2 - 5x + 3$
- (C) $-10x^3 + x^2 - 7x + 6$
- (D) $5x^3 - 2x^2 - 5x + 3$

3. You roll a pair of number cubes. What is the probability of rolling odd numbers on both cubes?

- (A) $\frac{1}{12}$
- (B) $\frac{1}{6}$
- (C) $\frac{1}{4}$
- (D) $\frac{2}{3}$

4. What is the greatest value in the range of $f(x) = x^2 - 3$ for the domain $\{-3, 0, 1, 2\}$?

- (A) -3 (C) 2
- (B) 0 (D) 6

5. Which equation best represents the graph at the right?

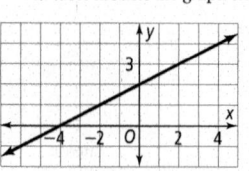

- (A) $y = x^2$
- (B) $y = -x^2$
- (C) $y = x^2 - 2$
- (D) $y = x^2 + 2$

6. Which table models the graph shown below?

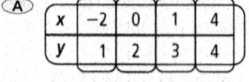

- (A)

x	-2	0	1	4
y	1	2	3	4

- (B)

x	-6	-3	0	6
y	-1	0.5	2	5

- (C)

x	-1	0	3	4
y	-6	-4	2	4

- (D)

x	0	0.5	1	2
y	-4	-3	-2	0

7. Which of the graphs below represents the solution set of $-3 < x + 3 \le 7$?

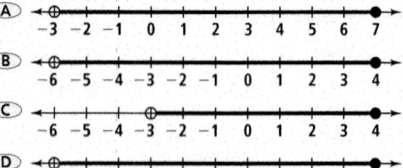

Answers

End-of-Course Test

1. D

2. B

3. C

4. D

5. C

6. B

7. B

8. Consider the graph shown below. Which statement is always a correct conclusion about the coordinates of the points on the graph?

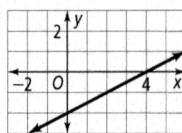

- (A) The x-values are always 2 less than the y-values.
- (B) The y-values are always 4 more than the x-values.
- (C) For positive values of x, the x-values are always greater than the y-values.
- (D) For positive values of x, the y-values are always greater than the x-values.

9. Which expression is equivalent to $\frac{4x^2 - 9}{6x^2 + 9x}$?

- (A) $\frac{2x - 3}{x + 3}$
- (B) $\frac{2}{3 + x}$
- (C) $\frac{2x + 3}{3x}$
- (D) $\frac{2x - 3}{3x}$

10. Which ordered pair is a solution of the given system?
$$2x + 5y = -11$$
$$10x + 3y = 11$$

- (A) $(3, -2)$
- (C) $(-2, 3)$
- (B) $(-3, 2)$
- (D) $(2, -3)$

11. What is the slope-intercept form of the equation $-3x + 4y = 8$?

- (A) $y = 3x + 2$
- (B) $y = 3x + 8$
- (C) $y = \frac{3}{4}x + 2$
- (D) $y = -\frac{3}{4}x + 2$

12. What is the y-coordinate of the vertex of the function $y = 2x^2 + 5x - 8$?

13. Lisa is driving a car at an average speed of 55 mi/h.
- **a.** What is Lisa's average speed in feet per second?
- **b.** How many feet will Lisa travel in 40 min?

14. What is a linear inequality that describes the graph below?

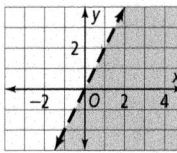

- (A) $y \leq 2x$
- (C) $y > 2x$
- (B) $y < 2x$
- (D) $y \geq 2x$

15. What equation do you get when you solve $2x^2y - 4y = -24$ for y?

- (A) $y = -\frac{12}{x^2 - 2}$
- (B) $y = \frac{12}{x^2 + 2}$
- (C) $y = \frac{12}{x^2 - 2}$
- (D) $y = -x^2 - 22$

16. What is the minimum point of the parabola graphed below?

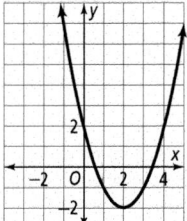

- (A) $(-2, 2)$
- (B) $(2, -2)$
- (C) $(0, 2)$
- (D) There is no minimum.

8. C
9. D
10. D
11. C
12. −11.125
13. a. 80.$\overline{6}$ ft/s
      b. 193,600 ft
14. B
15. A
16. B

Answers

17. C

18. B

19. C

20. D

21. B

22. A

23. Team A scored less than 40 points in about half of their games and more than 40 points in about half of their games, while Team B scored less than 35 points in about half of their games and more than 35 points in about half of their games.

24. B

---

17. What is the graph of the given system of equations?

$$2x + y = -3$$
$$-x + y = -1$$

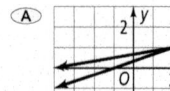 Ⓐ
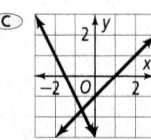 Ⓒ

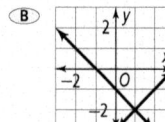 Ⓑ
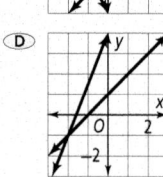 Ⓓ

18. What is the simplified form of $\sqrt{27n^3}$?

Ⓐ $3n\sqrt{3n^2}$

Ⓑ $3n\sqrt{3n}$

Ⓒ $3n^2\sqrt{3n}$

Ⓓ $3n^2\sqrt{3}$

19. What is the vertex of the parabola graphed below?

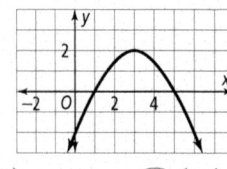

Ⓐ $(0, -1)$ Ⓒ $(3, 2)$

Ⓑ $(1, 0)$ Ⓓ $(5, 0)$

20. A line passes through the point $(-3, -2)$ and has slope 2. What is an equation of the line?

Ⓐ $y = 2x - 0.5$

Ⓑ $y = 2x + 0.5$

Ⓒ $y = 2x + 1$

Ⓓ $y = 2x + 4$

21. What equation describes a line that is parallel to the line below and passes through the point $(-2, 1)$?

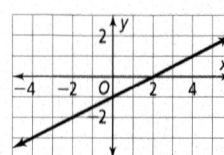

Ⓐ $y = 2x + 2$

Ⓑ $y = \frac{1}{2}x + 2$

Ⓒ $y = \frac{1}{2}x + 1$

Ⓓ $y = 2x + 3$

22. What is an equation of the axis of symmetry for the graph of the function $f(x) = 2x^2 + 4x - 5$?

Ⓐ $x = -1$

Ⓑ $x = 1$

Ⓒ $x = -2$

Ⓓ $x = 2$

23. The box-and-whisker plots below show the points scored by two college football teams in games over the course of one season. What do the medians tell you about each team's points per game?

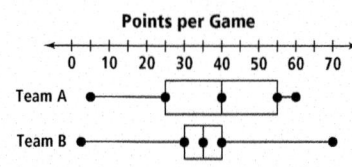

24. What is the solution of the equation $\frac{4x + 3}{3} - \frac{2x - 1}{2} = 3$?

Ⓐ 0

Ⓑ 4.5

Ⓒ 7

Ⓓ 8

A calculator may be used for the following questions. For multiple choice questions, write the letter of the correct answer on your paper. For all other questions, show your work and clearly explain your answer.

25. The width of a rectangle is 10 in. less than its length. If the perimeter of the rectangle is 36 in., what is its width in inches?

26. Erin surveyed 256 people to find out what type of bread they prefer. Her results are shown in the table below. Based on her data, which statement is true?

Bread Preference

Type of Bread	Percent
Wheat	32
Whole grain	26
White	20
Rye	22

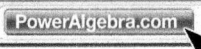

(A) Exactly 26 people prefer whole grain.

(B) More than half of the people prefer white or rye.

(C) About 80 people prefer wheat.

(D) About $\frac{1}{20}$ of the people prefer white.

27. Is the question "Do you prefer delicious steak or ordinary meatloaf for dinner?" biased? Explain.

28. What are the solutions of the equation $3x^2 + 11x - 4 = 0$?

(A) $\frac{1}{3}, 4$

(B) $\frac{1}{3}, -4$

(C) $-\frac{1}{3}, 4$

(D) $3, -4$

29. Which is NOT a rational number?

(A) 4

(B) $\sqrt{25}$

(C) $6.\overline{3}$

(D) $\sqrt{35}$

30. How does the mean of the data set below change if each value is increased by 8?
105 110 104 107 102 106 133 81

(A) The mean increases by 1.

(B) The mean increases by 8.

(C) The mean decreases by 8.

(D) The mean does not change.

31. What is $(2x^2 - 4x + 8) - (3x^2 + 10x + 2)$?

(A) $-x^2 - 14x - 6$

(B) $-x^2 + 6x + 6$

(C) $-x^2 - 14x + 6$

(D) $5x^2 + 6x + 10$

32. What is the simplified form of $\sqrt{32} + \sqrt{50}$?

(A) $\sqrt{82}$

(B) $9\sqrt{2}$

(C) $8\sqrt{4} + 10\sqrt{5}$

(D) $2\sqrt{8} + 5\sqrt{2}$

33. An airplane flies 500 mi/h in still air. Flying with the jet stream, the plane travels 1200 mi from City A to City B. The plane then returns to City A, flying against the jet stream. The round-trip flight time is 5 h. What is the speed of the jet stream in miles per hour?

(A) 25 mi/h

(B) 100 mi/h

(C) 150 mi/h

(D) 223 mi/h

34. A new toy store is opening next week, and the owner is deciding how to price one of the toys. The equation $S = -32p^2 + 960p$ predicts the totals sales S as a function of the toy's price p, where S and p are in dollars. What price will produce the highest total sales?

(A) $12

(B) $15

(C) $30

(D) $32

25. 4 in.

26. C

27. Yes; *delicious* and *ordinary* are biased and the question leads you to pick the steak.

28. B

29. D

30. B

31. C

32. B

33. B

34. B

Answers

End-of-Course Test (continued)

35. A

36. a. $5p + 18 = 153$

    b. $27

37. A

38. B

39. C

40. B

---

35. Which of the following is the solution set for the equation $|p - 2| = 7$?

  (A) $\{-5, 9\}$

  (B) $\{-9, 9\}$

  (C) $\{-5\}$

  (D) $\{9\}$

36. Natalia spent $153 of her savings at the mall. She bought clothes, a few paperback novels, and an $18 DVD. She spent 4 times as much on clothes as she did on the paperbacks.

  a. Write an equation that can be used to determine how much money Natalia spent on the paperback novels.

  b. Use the equation to determine how much Natalia spent on paperbacks.

37. Keysha randomly surveyed 150 people at a football game last weekend to find out whether they like hot dogs, hamburgers, or nachos. She recorded her results in the Venn diagram below. Of the 850 people at the game, how many should she expect to like both hot dogs and hamburgers?

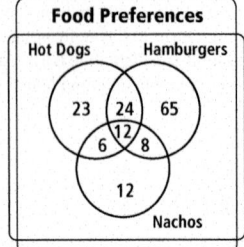

Food Preferences

Hot Dogs   Hamburgers

23   24   65

12

6   8

12

Nachos

  (A) 204

  (B) 281

  (C) 306

  (D) 782

38. What is the simplified form of $\frac{5x^2y^3}{3x^3y^4}$?

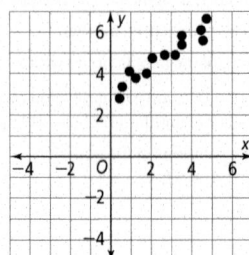

  (A) $\frac{5x^5y^7}{3}$

  (B) $\frac{5}{3xy}$

  (C) $\frac{5x^2y^3}{3x^3y^4}$

  (D) $\frac{5y^7}{3x^5}$

39. Line p passes through points $(5, -4)$ and $(2, 7)$. What is the slope of a line that is perpendicular to line p?

  (A) $-\frac{11}{3}$

  (B) $-\frac{3}{11}$

  (C) $\frac{3}{11}$

  (D) $\frac{11}{3}$

40. Which of the following is an equation of a reasonable trend line for the scatter plot shown?

  (A) $y = \frac{1}{3}x + 8$

  (B) $y = \frac{2}{3}x + 3$

  (C) $y = \frac{1}{2}x - 3$

  (D) $y = 3x + 3$

41. The sides of a square are all increased by 2 in. The area of the new square is 49 in.^{2}. What is the length of a side of the original square?

(A) 2 in.

(B) 4.5 in.

(C) 5 in.

(D) 9 in.

42. Which of the following sets of points does NOT represent a function?

(A) $\{(-2, 0), (-1, 1), (0, 4), (1, -2), (2, -6)\}$

(B) $\{(-5, 0), (-4, 0), (-3, 0), (-2, 0), (-1, 0)\}$

(C) $\{(0, 1), (1, 10), (1, 100), (10, 100), (100, 1000)\}$

(D) $\{(2, 4), (3, 9), (4, 16), (5, 25), (6, 36)\}$

43. How do you write $\frac{8x^2y^{-3}z^2}{10x^{-1}y^2z}$ using only positive exponents?

(A) $\frac{4xyz}{5}$

(B) $\frac{4x^3}{5yz}$

(C) $\frac{4x^3z}{5y^5}$

(D) $\frac{4xz}{5y}$

44. A rectangular prism has a volume of $6x^4 - 13x^3 - 5x^2$. What expressions can represent the dimensions of the prism? Use factoring.

45. Lucia has 8 shirts, 4 sweaters, and 5 jackets. How many different outfits can she make using one item from each category?

(A) 17

(B) 40

(C) 160

(D) 185

46. Ricardo's art class is making a tile mosaic using similar right triangles.

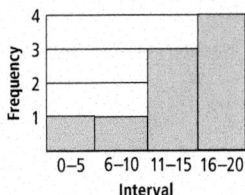

Tile A and Tile B are similar. What is the area of Tile B?

(A) 4 in.^{2}

(B) 5 in.^{2}

(C) 6 in.^{2}

(D) 12 in.^{2}

47. What type of histogram is shown below?

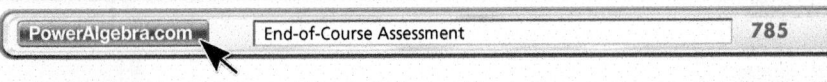

(A) skewed

(B) uniform

(C) symmetric

(D) none of these

41. C

42. C

43. C

44. x^2; $3x + 1$; $2x - 5$

45. C

46. A

47. A

Skills **Handbook**

Prime Numbers and Composite Numbers

A prime number is a whole number greater than 1 that has exactly two factors, the number 1 and itself.

Prime number	2	5	17	29
Factors	1, 2	1, 5	1, 17	1, 29

A composite number is a number that has more than two factors. The number 1 is neither prime nor composite.

Composite number	6	15	48
Factors	1, 2, 3, 6	1, 3, 5, 15	1, 2, 3, 4, 6, 8, 12, 16, 24, 48

Example 1

Is 51 prime or composite?

$51 = 3 \cdot 17$ Try to find factors other than 1 and 51.

51 is a composite number.

You can use a factor tree to find the prime factors of a number. When all the factors are prime numbers, it is called the prime factorization of the number.

Example 2

Use a factor tree to write the prime factorization of 28.

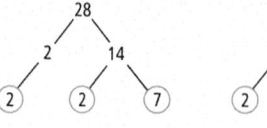

The order of listing the factors may be different, but the prime factorization is the same.

The prime factorization of 28 is $2 \cdot 2 \cdot 7$.

Exercises

Is each number prime or composite?

1. 9	**2.** 16	**3.** 34	**4.** 61	**5.** 7	**6.** 13
7. 12	**8.** 40	**9.** 57	**10.** 64	**11.** 120	**12.** 700

List all the factors of each number.

13. 46	**14.** 32	**15.** 11	**16.** 65	**17.** 27	**18.** 29

Use a factor tree to write the prime factorization of each number.

19. 18	**20.** 20	**21.** 27	**22.** 54	**23.** 64	**24.** 96

Answers

Prime Numbers and Composite Numbers

1. composite   **2.** composite

3. composite   **4.** prime

5. prime   **6.** prime

7. composite   **8.** composite

9. prime   **10.** composite

11. composite   **12.** composite

13. 1, 2, 23, 46   **14.** 1, 2, 4, 8, 16, 32

15. 1, 11   **16.** 1, 5, 13, 65

17. 1, 3, 9, 27   **18.** 1, 29

19. $2 \cdot 3 \cdot 3$ **20.** $2 \cdot 2 \cdot 5$

21. $3 \cdot 3 \cdot 3$ **22.** $2 \cdot 3 \cdot 3 \cdot 3$

23. $2 \cdot 2 \cdot 2 \cdot 2 \cdot 2 \cdot 2$

24. $2 \cdot 2 \cdot 2 \cdot 17$

Factors and Multiples

A common factor is a number that is a factor of two or more numbers. The greatest common factor (GCF) is the greatest number that is a common factor of two or more numbers.

Example 1

Find the GCF of 24 and 64.

Method 1 List all the factors of each number.

Factors of 24	1, 2, 3, 4, 6, 8, 12, 24	Find the common factors: 1, 2, 4, 8.
Factors of 64	1, 2, 4, 8, 16, 32, 64	The greatest common factor is 8.

The GCF of 24 and 64 is 8.

Method 2 Use the prime factorization of each number.

$24 = 2 \cdot 2 \cdot 2 \cdot 3$ Find the prime factorization of each number.

$64 = 2 \cdot 2 \cdot 2 \cdot 2 \cdot 2 \cdot 2$

$GCF = 2 \cdot 2 \cdot 2 = 8$ The product of the common prime factors is the GCF.

A common multiple is a number that is a multiple of two or more numbers. The least common multiple (LCM) is the least number that is a common multiple of two or more numbers.

Example 2

Find the LCM of 12 and 18.

Method 1 List the multiples of each number.

Multiples of 12	12, 24, 36, . . .	List the multiples of each number until you find
Multiples of 18	18, 36, . . .	the first common multiple.

The LCM of 12 and 18 is 36.

Method 2 Use the prime factorization of each number.

$12 = 2 \cdot 2 \cdot 3$

$18 = 2 \cdot 3 \cdot 3$

$LCM = 2 \cdot 2 \cdot 3 \cdot 3 = 36$ Use each prime factor the greatest number of times it appears in either number.

Exercises

Find the GCF of each set of numbers.

1. 12 and 22   **2.** 7 and 21   **3.** 24 and 48   **4.** 42, 63, and 105

Find the LCM of each set of numbers.

5. 16 and 20   **6.** 14 and 21   **7.** 11 and 33   **8.** 6, 7, and 12

Factors and Multiples

1. 2   **2.** 7
3. 24   **4.** 21
5. 80   **6.** 42
7. 33   **8.** 84

Using Estimation

To make sure the answer to a problem is reasonable, you can estimate before you calculate. If the answer is close to your estimate, the answer is probably correct.

Example 1

Estimate to find whether each calculation is correct.

a. Calculation		Estimate
$126.91	≈	$130
$14.05	≈	$10
+$25.14	≈	+$30
$266.10		$170

b. Calculation		Estimate
372.85	≈	370
−227.31	≈	−230
145.54		140

The answer is not close to the estimate. It is not reasonable. The calculation is incorrect.

The answer is close to the estimate. It is reasonable. The calculation is correct.

For some situations, like estimating a grocery bill, you may not need an exact answer. A *front-end estimate* will give you a good estimate that is usually closer to the exact answer than an estimate you would get by rounding alone. Add the front-end digits, estimate the sum of the remaining digits by rounding, and then combine sums.

Example 2

Tomatoes cost $3.54, squash costs $2.75, and lemons cost $1.20. Estimate the total cost of the produce.

Add the front-end digits.	3.54	→	0.50	Estimate by rounding. Then add.
	2.75	→	0.80	
	+1.20	→	+0.20	
	6		1.50	

Since $6 + 1.50 = 7.50$, the total cost is about $7.50.

Exercises

Estimate by rounding.

1. the sum of $15.70, $49.62, and $278.01

2. $563 - 125$

3. the sum of $163.90, $107.21, and $33.56

4. $824 - 467$

Use front-end estimation to find each sum or difference.

5. $1.65 + $5.42 + $9.89

6. $1.369 + 7.421 + 2.700$

7. $9.563 - 2.480$

8. $1.17 + 3.92 + 2.26$

9. $8.611 - 1.584$

10. $2.52 + $3.04 + $5.25

11. Ticket prices at an amusement park cost $11.25 for adults and $6.50 for children under 12. Estimate the cost for three children and one adult.

Answers

Using Estimation

Answers may vary for Exercises 1–11. Samples are given.

1. $350

2. 440

3. $300

4. 350

5. $17

6. 11.500

7. 6.90

8. 7.4

9. 7

10. $10.80

11. $30.80

Simplifying Fractions

A fraction can name a part of a group or region. The region below is divided into 10 equal parts and 6 of the equal parts are shaded.

$\dfrac{6}{10}$ ← Numerator
   ← Denominator   Read as "six tenths."

Two fractions that represent the same value are called equivalent fractions. You can find a fraction that is equivalent to a given fraction by multiplying the numerator and the denominator of the given fraction by the same nonzero number.

Example 1

Write five fractions that are equivalent to $\frac{3}{5}$.

$\frac{3}{5} = \frac{3 \cdot 2}{5 \cdot 2} = \frac{6}{10}$ $\frac{3}{5} = \frac{3 \cdot 3}{5 \cdot 3} = \frac{9}{15}$ $\frac{3}{5} = \frac{3 \cdot 4}{5 \cdot 4} = \frac{12}{20}$ $\frac{3}{5} = \frac{3 \cdot 5}{5 \cdot 5} = \frac{15}{25}$ $\frac{3}{5} = \frac{3 \cdot 6}{5 \cdot 6} = \frac{18}{30}$

The fraction $\frac{3}{5}$ is in simplest form because its numerator and denominator are relatively prime, which means their only common factor is 1. To write a fraction in simplest form, divide its numerator and its denominator by their greatest common factor (GCF).

Example 2

Write $\frac{6}{24}$ in simplest form.

Step 1 Find the GCF of 6 and 24.

$6 = 2 \cdot 3$ Multiply the common prime factors, 2 and 3.
$24 = 2 \cdot 2 \cdot 2 \cdot 3$ GCF = 2 · 3 = 6.

Step 2 Divide the numerator and the denominator of $\frac{6}{24}$ by the GCF, 6.

$\frac{6}{24} = \frac{6 \div 6}{24 \div 6} = \frac{1}{4}$ Simplify.

Exercises

Write five fractions that are equivalent to each fraction.

1. $\frac{4}{7}$ **2.** $\frac{9}{16}$ **3.** $\frac{3}{8}$ **4.** $\frac{8}{17}$ **5.** $\frac{5}{6}$ **6.** $\frac{7}{10}$

Complete each statement.

7. $\frac{3}{7} = \frac{\blacksquare}{21}$ **8.** $\frac{5}{8} = \frac{20}{\blacksquare}$ **9.** $\frac{11}{12} = \frac{44}{\blacksquare}$ **10.** $\frac{12}{16} = \frac{\blacksquare}{4}$ **11.** $\frac{50}{100} = \frac{1}{\blacksquare}$

Is each fraction in simplest form? If not, write the fraction in simplest form.

12. $\frac{4}{12}$ **13.** $\frac{3}{16}$ **14.** $\frac{5}{30}$ **15.** $\frac{9}{72}$ **16.** $\frac{11}{22}$ **17.** $\frac{24}{25}$

Write each fraction in simplest form.

18. $\frac{8}{16}$ **19.** $\frac{7}{14}$ **20.** $\frac{6}{9}$ **21.** $\frac{20}{30}$ **22.** $\frac{8}{20}$ **23.** $\frac{12}{40}$

Simplifying Fractions

1. $\frac{8}{14}, \frac{12}{21}, \frac{16}{28}, \frac{20}{35}, \frac{24}{42}$

2. $\frac{18}{32}, \frac{27}{48}, \frac{36}{64}, \frac{45}{80}, \frac{54}{96}$

3. $\frac{6}{16}, \frac{9}{24}, \frac{12}{32}, \frac{15}{40}, \frac{18}{48}$

4. $\frac{16}{34}, \frac{24}{51}, \frac{32}{68}, \frac{40}{85}, \frac{48}{102}$

5. $\frac{10}{12}, \frac{15}{18}, \frac{20}{24}, \frac{25}{30}, \frac{30}{36}$

6. $\frac{14}{20}, \frac{21}{30}, \frac{28}{40}, \frac{35}{50}, \frac{42}{60}$

7. 9   **8.** 32

9. 48   **10.** 3

11. 2   **12.** no; $\frac{1}{3}$

13. yes   **14.** no; $\frac{1}{6}$

15. no; $\frac{1}{8}$ **16.** no; $\frac{1}{2}$

17. yes   **18.** $\frac{1}{2}$

19. $\frac{1}{2}$ **20.** $\frac{2}{3}$

21. $\frac{2}{3}$ **22.** $\frac{2}{5}$

23. $\frac{3}{10}$

Fractions and Decimals

You can write a fraction as a decimal.

Example 1

Write $\frac{3}{5}$ as a decimal.

$$5\overline{)3.0}^{\,0.6} \qquad \text{Divide the numerator by the denominator.}$$

So $\frac{3}{5} = 0.6$.

You can write a decimal as a fraction.

Example 2

Write 0.38 as a fraction.

$0.38 = 38$ hundredths $= \frac{38}{100} = \frac{19}{50}$

Some fractions can be written as decimals that repeat, but do not end.

$$
\begin{array}{r}
0.2727\ldots \\
11\overline{)3.0000\ldots} \\
\underline{2.2} \\
80 \\
\underline{77} \\
30 \\
\underline{22} \\
80 \\
\underline{77} \\
3
\end{array}
$$

Example 3

Write $\frac{3}{11}$ as a decimal.

Divide the numerator by the denominator, as shown at the right. The remainders 8 and 3 keep repeating. Therefore 2 and 7 will keep repeating in the quotient.

$\frac{3}{11} = 0.2727\ldots = 0.\overline{27}$

You can write a repeating decimal as a fraction.

Example 4

Write 0.363636... as a fraction.

Let $x = 0.363636\ldots$

$$
\begin{aligned}
100x &= 36.36363636\ldots && \text{When 2 digits repeat, multiply by 100.} \\
99x &= 36 && \text{Subtract } x = 0.363636. \\
x &= \frac{36}{99}, \text{ or } \frac{4}{11} && \text{Divide each side by 99.}
\end{aligned}
$$

Exercises

Write each fraction or mixed number as a decimal.

1. $\frac{3}{10}$ 2. $\frac{13}{12}$ 3. $\frac{4}{20}$ 4. $\frac{25}{75}$ 5. $\frac{5}{7}$ 6. $4\frac{3}{25}$

Write each decimal as a fraction in simplest form.

7. 0.07 8. 0.25 9. 0.875 10. 0.4545 11. 6.333 12. 7.2626

Answers

Fractions and Decimals

1. 0.3
2. $1.08\overline{3}$
3. 0.2
4. $0.\overline{3}$
5. $0.\overline{714285}$
6. 4.12
7. $\frac{7}{100}$
8. $\frac{1}{4}$
9. $\frac{7}{8}$
10. $\frac{5}{11}$
11. $6\frac{1}{3}$
12. $7\frac{26}{99}$

Adding and Subtracting Fractions

You can add and subtract fractions when they have the same denominator.
Fractions with the same denominator are called like fractions.

Example 1

a. Add $\frac{4}{5} + \frac{3}{5}$.

$\frac{4}{5} + \frac{3}{5} = \frac{4+3}{5} = \frac{7}{5} = 1\frac{2}{5}$ ← Add or subtract the numerators and keep the same denominator.

b. Subtract $\frac{5}{9} - \frac{2}{9}$.

→ $\frac{5}{9} - \frac{2}{9} = \frac{5-2}{9} = \frac{3}{9} = \frac{1}{3}$

Fractions with unlike denominators are called unlike fractions. To add or subtract unlike fractions, find the least common denominator (LCD) and write equivalent fractions with the same denominator. Then add or subtract the like fractions.

Example 2

Add $\frac{3}{4} + \frac{5}{6}$.

$\frac{3}{4} + \frac{5}{6} = \frac{9}{12} + \frac{10}{12}$ Find the LCD. The LCD is the least common multiple (LCM) of the denominators. The LCD of 4 and 6 is 12. Write equivalent fractions.

$= \frac{9+10}{12} = \frac{19}{12}$, or $1\frac{7}{12}$ Add like fractions and simplify.

To add or subtract mixed numbers, add or subtract the fractions. Then add or subtract the whole numbers. Sometimes when subtracting mixed numbers you have to regroup so that you can subtract the fractions.

Example 3

Subtract $5\frac{1}{4} - 3\frac{2}{3}$.

$5\frac{1}{4} - 3\frac{2}{3} = 5\frac{3}{12} - 3\frac{8}{12}$ Write equivalent fractions with the same denominator.

$= 4\frac{15}{12} - 3\frac{8}{12}$ Write $5\frac{3}{12}$ as $4\frac{15}{12}$ so you can subtract the fractions.

$= 1\frac{7}{12}$ Subtract the fractions. Then subtract the whole numbers.

Exercises

Add or subtract. Write each answer in simplest form.

1. $\frac{2}{7} + \frac{3}{7}$
2. $\frac{3}{8} + \frac{7}{8}$
3. $\frac{6}{5} + \frac{9}{5}$
4. $\frac{4}{9} + \frac{8}{9}$
5. $6\frac{2}{3} + 3\frac{4}{5}$

6. $1\frac{4}{7} + 2\frac{3}{14}$
7. $4\frac{5}{6} + 1\frac{7}{18}$
8. $2\frac{4}{5} + 3\frac{6}{7}$
9. $4\frac{2}{3} + 1\frac{6}{11}$
10. $3\frac{7}{9} + 5\frac{4}{11}$

11. $8 + 1\frac{2}{3}$
12. $8\frac{1}{5} + 3\frac{3}{4}$
13. $11\frac{3}{8} + 2\frac{1}{16}$
14. $\frac{7}{8} - \frac{3}{8}$
15. $\frac{9}{10} - \frac{3}{10}$

16. $\frac{17}{5} - \frac{2}{5}$
17. $\frac{11}{7} - \frac{2}{7}$
18. $\frac{5}{11} - \frac{4}{11}$
19. $8\frac{5}{8} - 6\frac{1}{4}$
20. $3\frac{2}{3} - 1\frac{8}{9}$

21. $8\frac{5}{6} - 5\frac{1}{2}$
22. $12\frac{3}{4} - 4\frac{5}{6}$
23. $17\frac{2}{7} - 8\frac{2}{9}$
24. $7\frac{3}{4} - 3\frac{3}{8}$
25. $4\frac{1}{12} - 1\frac{11}{12}$

Adding and Subtracting Fractions

1. $\frac{5}{7}$
2. $1\frac{1}{4}$
3. 3
4. $1\frac{1}{3}$
5. $10\frac{7}{15}$
6. $3\frac{11}{14}$
7. $6\frac{2}{9}$
8. $6\frac{23}{35}$
9. $6\frac{7}{33}$
10. $9\frac{14}{99}$
11. $9\frac{2}{3}$
12. $11\frac{19}{20}$
13. $13\frac{7}{16}$
14. $\frac{1}{2}$
15. $\frac{3}{5}$
16. 3
17. $1\frac{2}{7}$
18. $\frac{1}{11}$
19. $2\frac{3}{8}$
20. $1\frac{7}{9}$
21. $3\frac{1}{3}$
22. $7\frac{11}{12}$
23. $9\frac{4}{63}$
24. $4\frac{3}{8}$
25. $2\frac{1}{6}$

Multiplying and Dividing Fractions

To multiply two or more fractions, multiply the numerators, multiply the denominators, and simplify the product, if necessary.

Example 1

Multiply $\frac{3}{7} \cdot \frac{5}{6}$.

Method 1 Multiply the numerators and the denominators. Then simplify.

$$\frac{3}{7} \cdot \frac{5}{6} = \frac{3 \cdot 5}{7 \cdot 6} = \frac{15}{42} = \frac{15 \div 3}{42 \div 3} = \frac{5}{14}$$

Method 2 Simplify before multiplying.

$$\frac{{}^1\!3}{7} \cdot \frac{5}{6_2} = \frac{1 \cdot 5}{7 \cdot 2} = \frac{5}{14}$$

To multiply mixed numbers, change the mixed numbers to improper fractions and multiply the fractions. Write the product as a mixed number.

Example 2

Multiply $2\frac{4}{5} \cdot 1\frac{2}{3}$.

$$2\frac{4}{5} \cdot 1\frac{2}{3} = \frac{14}{5} \cdot \frac{5^1}{3} = \frac{14}{3} = 4\frac{2}{3}$$

To divide fractions, change the division problem to a multiplication problem. Remember that $8 \div \frac{1}{4}$ is the same as $8 \cdot 4$. To divide mixed numbers, change the mixed numbers to improper fractions and divide the fractions.

Example 3

a. Divide $\frac{4}{5} \div \frac{3}{7}$.

$\frac{4}{5} \div \frac{3}{7} = \frac{4}{5} \cdot \frac{7}{3}$ Multiply by the reciprocal of the divisor.

$= \frac{28}{15}$ Simplify.

$= 1\frac{13}{15}$ Write as a mixed number.

b. Divide $4\frac{2}{3} \div 7\frac{3}{5}$.

$4\frac{2}{3} \div 7\frac{3}{5} = \frac{14}{3} \div \frac{38}{5}$ Change to improper fractions.

$= \frac{14^7}{3} \cdot \frac{5}{38_{19}}$ Simplify.

$= \frac{35}{57}$ Multiply.

Exercises

Multiply or divide. Write your answers in simplest form.

1. $\frac{2}{5} \cdot \frac{3}{4}$ 2. $\frac{3}{7} \cdot \frac{4}{3}$ 3. $1\frac{1}{2} \cdot 5\frac{3}{4}$ 4. $3\frac{4}{5} \cdot 10$ 5. $5\frac{1}{4} \cdot \frac{2}{3}$

6. $4\frac{1}{2} \cdot 7\frac{1}{2}$ 7. $3\frac{2}{3} \cdot 6\frac{9}{10}$ 8. $6\frac{1}{2} \cdot 7\frac{2}{3}$ 9. $2\frac{2}{5} \cdot 1\frac{1}{6}$ 10. $4\frac{1}{9} \cdot 3\frac{3}{8}$

11. $\frac{3}{5} \div \frac{1}{2}$ 12. $\frac{4}{5} \div \frac{9}{10}$ 13. $2\frac{1}{2} \div 3\frac{1}{2}$ 14. $1\frac{4}{5} \div 2\frac{1}{2}$ 15. $3\frac{1}{6} \div 1\frac{3}{4}$

16. $5 \div \frac{3}{8}$ 17. $\frac{4}{9} \div \frac{3}{5}$ 18. $\frac{5}{8} \div \frac{3}{4}$ 19. $2\frac{1}{5} \div 2\frac{1}{2}$ 20. $6\frac{1}{2} \div \frac{1}{4}$

Answers

Multiplying and Dividing Fractions

1. $\frac{3}{10}$ 2. $\frac{4}{7}$

3. $8\frac{5}{8}$ 4. 38

5. $3\frac{1}{2}$ 6. $33\frac{3}{4}$

7. $25\frac{3}{10}$ 8. $49\frac{5}{6}$

9. $2\frac{4}{5}$ 10. $13\frac{7}{8}$

11. $1\frac{1}{5}$ 12. $\frac{8}{9}$

13. $\frac{5}{7}$ 14. $\frac{18}{25}$

15. $1\frac{17}{21}$ 16. $13\frac{1}{3}$

17. $\frac{20}{27}$ 18. $\frac{5}{6}$

19. $\frac{22}{25}$ 20. 26

Fractions, Decimals, and Percents

Percent means per hundred. 50% means 50 per hundred. $50\% = \frac{50}{100} = 0.50$.

You can write a fraction as a percent by writing the fraction as a decimal first. Then move the decimal point two places to the right and write a percent sign.

Example 1

Write each number as a percent.

a. $\frac{3}{5}$

$\frac{3}{5} = 0.6$

$0.6 = 60\%$

b. $\frac{7}{20}$

$\frac{7}{20} = 0.35$

$0.35 = 35\%$

c. $\frac{2}{3}$

$\frac{2}{3} = 0.66\overline{6}$

$0.66\overline{6} = 66.\overline{6}\% \approx 66.7\%$

You can write a percent as a decimal by moving the decimal point two places to the left and removing the percent sign. You can write a percent as a fraction with a denominator of 100. Then simplify the fraction, if possible.

Example 2

Write each percent as a decimal and as a fraction or mixed number.

a. 25%

$25\% = 0.25$

$25\% = \frac{25}{100} = \frac{1}{4}$

b. $\frac{1}{2}\%$

$\frac{1}{2}\% = 0.5\% = 0.005$

$\frac{1}{2}\% = \frac{\frac{1}{2}}{100} = \frac{1}{2} \div 100$

$= \frac{1}{2} \cdot \frac{1}{100} = \frac{1}{200}$

c. 360%

$360\% = 3.6$

$360\% = \frac{360}{100} = \frac{18}{5} = 3\frac{3}{5}$

Exercises

Write each number as a percent. If necessary, round to the nearest tenth.

1. 0.56   **2.** 0.09   **3.** 6.02   **4.** 5.245   **5.** 8.2   **6.** 0.14

7. $\frac{1}{7}$ **8.** $\frac{9}{20}$ **9.** $\frac{1}{9}$ **10.** $\frac{5}{6}$ **11.** $\frac{3}{4}$ **12.** $\frac{7}{8}$

Write each percent as a decimal.

13. 7%   **14.** 8.5%   **15.** 0.9%   **16.** 250%   **17.** 83%   **18.** 110%

19. 15%   **20.** 72%   **21.** 0.03%   **22.** 36.2%   **23.** 365%   **24.** 101%

Write each percent as a fraction or mixed number in simplest form.

25. 19%   **26.** $\frac{3}{4}\%$ **27.** 450%   **28.** $\frac{4}{5}\%$ **29.** 64%   **30.** $\frac{2}{3}\%$

31. 24%   **32.** 845%   **33.** $\frac{3}{8}\%$ **34.** 480%   **35.** 60%   **36.** 350%

Fractions, Decimals, and Percents

1. 56%   **2.** 9%

3. 602%   **4.** 524.5%

5. 820%   **6.** 14%

7. 14.3%   **8.** 45%

9. 11.1%   **10.** 83.3%

11. 75%   **12.** 87.5%

13. 0.07   **14.** 0.085

15. 0.009   **16.** 2.5

17. 0.83   **18.** 1.10

19. 0.15   **20.** 0.72

21. 0.0003   **22.** 0.362

23. 3.65   **24.** 1.01

25. $\frac{19}{100}$ **26.** $\frac{3}{400}$

27. $4\frac{1}{2}$ **28.** $\frac{1}{125}$

29. $\frac{16}{25}$ **30.** $\frac{1}{150}$

31. $\frac{6}{25}$ **32.** $8\frac{9}{20}$

33. $\frac{3}{800}$ **34.** $4\frac{4}{5}$

35. $\frac{3}{5}$ **36.** $3\frac{1}{2}$

Exponents

You can express $2 \cdot 2 \cdot 2 \cdot 2 \cdot 2$ as 2^5. The raised number 5 shows the number of times 2 is used as a factor. The number 2 is the base. The number 5 is the exponent.

$2^5 \leftarrow$ exponent
$\uparrow$
base

Factored Form: $2 \cdot 2 \cdot 2 \cdot 2 \cdot 2$ Exponential Form: 2^5 Standard Form: 32

A number with an exponent of 1 is the number itself: $8^1 = 8$.
Any number, except 0, with an exponent of 0 is 1: $5^0 = 1$.

Example 1

Write each expression using exponents.

a. $8 \cdot 8 \cdot 8 \cdot 8 \cdot 8$ **b.** $2 \cdot 9 \cdot 9 \cdot 9 \cdot 9 \cdot 9 \cdot 9$ **c.** $6 \cdot 6 \cdot 10 \cdot 10 \cdot 10 \cdot 6 \cdot 6$

Count the number of times each number is used as a factor.

$= 8^5$ $= 2 \cdot 9^6$ $= 6^4 \cdot 10^3$

Example 2

Write each expression in standard form.

a. 2^3 **b.** $8^2 \cdot 3^4$ **c.** $10^3 \cdot 15^2$

Write each expression in factored form and multiply.

$2 \cdot 2 \cdot 2 = 8$ $8 \cdot 8 \cdot 3 \cdot 3 \cdot 3 \cdot 3 = 5184$ $10 \cdot 10 \cdot 10 \cdot 15 \cdot 15 = 225{,}000$

For powers of 10, the exponent tells how many zeros are in the number in standard form.

$10^1 = 10$ $10^3 = 10 \cdot 10 \cdot 10 = 1000$ $10^5 = 10 \cdot 10 \cdot 10 \cdot 10 \cdot 10 = 100{,}000$

You can use powers of 10 to write numbers in expanded form.

Example 3

Write 739 in expanded form using powers of 10.

$739 = 700 + 30 + 9 = (7 \cdot 100) + (3 \cdot 10) + (9 \cdot 1) = (7 \cdot 10^2) + (3 \cdot 10^1) + (9 \cdot 10^0)$

Exercises

Write each expression using exponents.

1. $6 \cdot 6 \cdot 6 \cdot 6$ **2.** $7 \cdot 7 \cdot 7 \cdot 7 \cdot 7$ **3.** $5 \cdot 2 \cdot 2 \cdot 2 \cdot 2$

4. $3 \cdot 3 \cdot 3 \cdot 3 \cdot 3 \cdot 14 \cdot 14$ **5.** $4 \cdot 4 \cdot 3 \cdot 3 \cdot 2$ **6.** $3 \cdot 5 \cdot 5 \cdot 7 \cdot 7 \cdot 7$

Write each number in standard form.

7. 4^3 **8.** 9^4 **9.** 12^2 **10.** $6^2 \cdot 7^1$ **11.** $11^2 \cdot 3^3$

Write each number in expanded form using powers of 10.

12. 658   **13.** 1254   **14.** 7125   **15.** 83,401   **16.** 294,863

Answers

Exponents

1. 6^4 **2.** 7^5

3. $5 \cdot 2^4$ **4.** $3^5 \cdot 14^2$

5. $4^2 \cdot 3^2 \cdot 2$ **6.** $3 \cdot 5^2 \cdot 7^3$

7. 64   **8.** 6561

9. 141   **10.** 252

11. 3267

12. $(6 \cdot 10^2) + (5 \cdot 10^1) + (8 \cdot 10^0)$

13. $(1 \cdot 10^3) + (2 \cdot 10^2) + (5 \cdot 10^1) \cdot (4 \cdot 10^0)$

14. $(7 \cdot 10^3) + (1 \cdot 10^2) + (2 \cdot 10^1) + (5 \cdot 10^0)$

15. $(8 \cdot 10^4) + (3 \cdot 10^3) + (4 \cdot 10^2) + (0 \cdot 10^1) + (1 \cdot 10^0)$

16. $(2 \cdot 10^5) + (9 \cdot 10^4) + (4 \cdot 10^3) + (8 \cdot 10^2) + (6 \cdot 10^1) + (3 \cdot 10^0)$

erimeter, Area, and Volume

 perimeter of a figure is the distance around the figure. The area of a figure is the
 mber of square units contained in the figure. The volume of a three-dimensional
 ure is the number of cubic units contained in the figure.

xample 1

d the perimeter of each figure.

a. 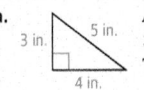 Add the measures of the sides.
$3 + 4 + 5 = 12$
The perimeter is 12 in.

b. Use the formula $P = 2\ell + 2w$.
$P = 2(3) + 2(4)$
$= 6 + 8 = 14$
The perimeter is 14 cm.

xample 2

d the area of each figure.

a. 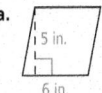 Use the formula $A = bh$.
$A = 6 \cdot 5 = 30$
The area is 30 in.^{2}.

b. Use the formula $A = \frac{1}{2}(bh)$.
$A = \frac{1}{2}(7 \cdot 6) = 21$
The area is 21 in.^{2}.

xample 3

d the volume of each figure.

a. 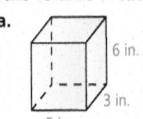 Use the formula $V = Bh$.
B = area of the base
$= 3 \cdot 5 = 15$
$V = 15 \cdot 6 = 90$ in.^{3}
The volume is 90 in.^{3}.

b. 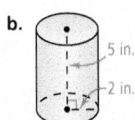 Use the formula $V = \pi r^2 h$.
$V = 3.14 \cdot 2^2 \cdot 5$
$= 3.14 \cdot 4 \cdot 5 = 62.8$ in.^{3}
The volume is 62.8 in.^{3}.

xercises

 r Exercises 1–2, find the perimeter of each figure. For Exercises 3–4, find the
 ea of each figure. For Exercises 5–7, find the volume of each figure.

2.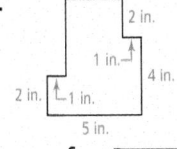

3.

4.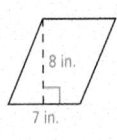

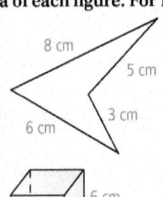

6.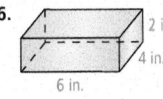

7.

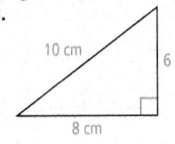

Perimeter, Area, and Volume

1. 22 cm   **2.** 22 in.

3. 24 cm^2 **4.** 56 in.^{2}

5. 216 cm^3 **6.** 48 cm^3

7. 352 cm^3

Line Plots

A line plot is created by placing a mark above a number line corresponding to each data value. Line plots have two main advantages:

- You can see the frequency of data values.
- You can see how the data values compare.

Example

The table at the right gives the heights, in inches, of a group of 25 adults. Display the data in a line plot. Describe the data shown in the line plot.

Heights of Adults (in.)				
59	60	63	63	64
64	64	65	65	65
67	67	67	67	68
68	68	69	70	70
71	72	73	73	77

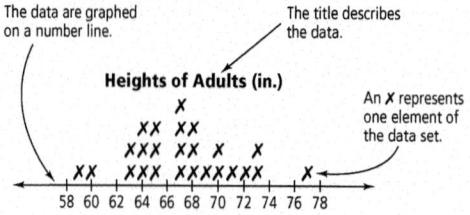

The data are graphed on a number line.

The title describes the data.

Heights of Adults (in.)

An **X** represents one element of the data set.

The line plot shows that most of the heights are concentrated around 67 in., the maximum value is 77 in., and the minimum value is 59 in.

Exercises

Display each set of data in a line plot.

1. 3, 6, 4, 3, 6, 0, 4, 5, 0, 4, 6, 1, 5, 1, 0, 5, 5, 6, 5, 3

2. 19, 18, 18, 18, 19, 20, 19, 18, 18, 17, 18, 20, 19, 17

Draw a line plot for each frequency table.

3.

Number	1	2	3	4	5	6
Frequency	4	1	0	5	7	2

4.

Number	12	13	15	16	18	19
Frequency	2	5	1	3	6	3

5. **Olympics** The numbers of gold medals won by different countries during the 2002 Winter Olympics are listed below.

1, 1, 1, 2, 2, 2, 3, 3, 3, 3, 4, 4, 4, 5, 7, 10, 12, 13

Display the data in a line plot. Describe the data shown in the line plot.

Answers

Line Plots National

1.

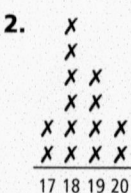

2.

3.

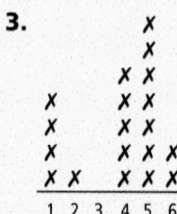

4.

5. **Gold Medals Won**

The line plot shows that most of the countries won about 3 gold medals. The maximum number of gold medals that a country won was 13, and the minimum was 1.

Bar Graphs

Bar graphs are used to display and compare data. The horizontal axis shows categories and the vertical axis shows amounts. A multiple bar graph includes a key.

Example

Draw a bar graph for the data in the table below.

Median Household Income

Town	2 person	3 person	4 person
Mason	$62,690	$68,070	$77,014
Barstow	$68,208	$82,160	$99,584
York	$51,203	$58,902	$67,911
Rexford	$52,878	$54,943	$63,945
Onham	$54,715	$61,437	$69,260

The categories (in the first column) are placed on the horizontal scale. The amounts (in the second, third, and fourth columns) are used to create the scale on the vertical scale and to draw each bar.

Graph the data for each town. Use the values in the top row to create the key.

The highest median income is $99,584. A reasonable range for the vertical scale is $0 to $108,000.

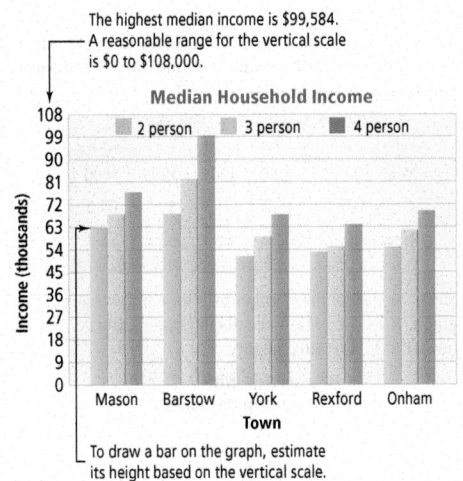

To draw a bar on the graph, estimate its height based on the vertical scale.

Exercises

1. Draw a bar graph for the data in the table below.

Highest Temperatures (°F)

Town	March	June	August
Mason	61	86	83
Barstow	84	104	101
York	89	101	102
Rexford	88	92	93
Onham	81	104	100

2. a. Reasoning If one more column of data were added to the table in the example, how would the bar graph be different?

   b. If one more row of data were added to the table in the example, how would the bar graph be different?

PowerAlgebra.com   Skills Handbook   797

Bar Graphs

1.

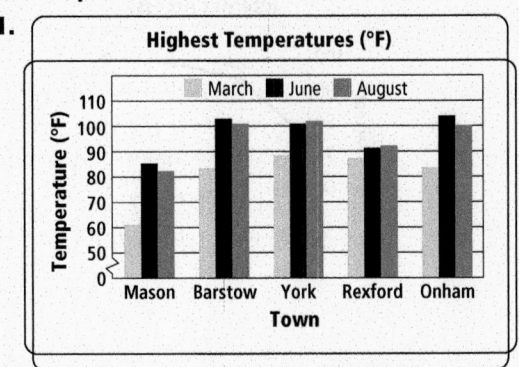

2. a. Each town would have one more bar and a new key element for the new month would be added.

   b. There would be another group of three bars added for the new town.

Line Graphs

Line graphs are used to display the change in a set of data over a period of time. A multiple-line graph shows change in more than one category of data over time. You can use a line graph to look for trends and make predictions.

Example

The data in the table below show the number of households, in thousands, that have cable TV and the number of households that subscribe to newspapers in a certain city. Graph the data.

Households With Cable TV and Newspapers (thousands)

Year	1980	1990	1995	2000	2005
Cable TV	15.2	51.9	60.5	68.6	73.9
Newspapers	62.2	62.3	58.2	55.8	53.3

Since the data show changes over time for two sets of data, use a double line graph. The horizontal scale displays years. The vertical axis shows the number of households for each category.

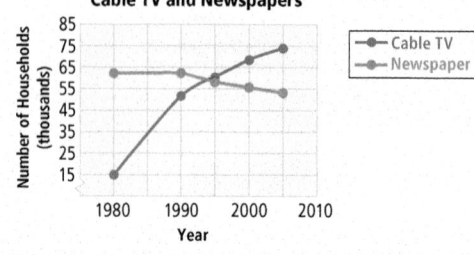

Households With Cable TV and Newspapers

Notice that there is a *break* in the vertical axis. You can use a zigzag line to indicate a break from 0 to 15 since there is no data less than 15 to graph.

Exercises

Graph the data in each table.

1.

Market Share (percent)

Year	2004	2005	2006	2007
Rap/Hip Hop	12.1	13.3	11.4	10.8
Pop	10.0	8.1	7.1	10.7

SOURCE: Recording Industry of America

2.

Percent of Schools With Internet Access

Year	1997	1999	2001	2003
Elementary	75	94	99	100
Secondary	89	98	100	100

SOURCE: National Center for Education Statistics

798

Answers

Line Graphs

1.

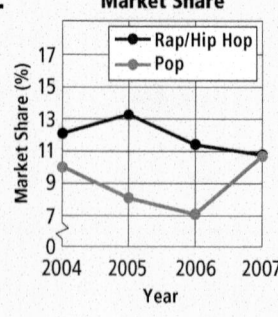

Market Share

2.

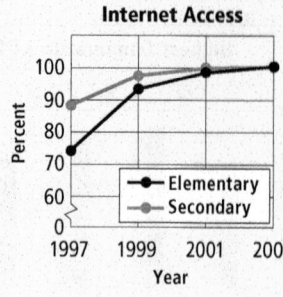

Schools With Internet Access

Circle Graphs

A circle graph is an efficient way to present certain types of data. The entire circle represents all of the data. Each section of the circle represents a part of the whole and can be labeled with the actual data or the data expressed as a fraction, decimal, or percent. The angles at the center are central angles, and each angle is proportional to the percent or fraction of the total.

Example

Students at a high school were asked to pick their favorite instrument. The table at the right shows the number of students who chose each instrument. Draw a circle graph for the data.

Favorite Musical Instruments

Instrument	Number of Students
Bass	35
Drums	103
Piano	150
Guitar	182

Step 1 Add to find the total number.

$35 + 103 + 150 + 182 = 470$

Step 2 For each central angle, set up a proportion to find the measure. Use a calculator to solve each proportion.

$\frac{35}{470} = \frac{a}{360°}$ $\frac{103}{470} = \frac{b}{360°}$ $\frac{150}{470} = \frac{c}{360°}$ $\frac{182}{470} = \frac{d}{360°}$

$a \approx 27°$ $b \approx 79°$ $c \approx 115°$ $d \approx 139°$

Step 3 Use a compass to draw a circle. Draw the approximate central angles using a protractor.

Step 4 Label each sector.

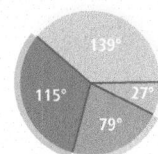

Favorite Musical Instruments

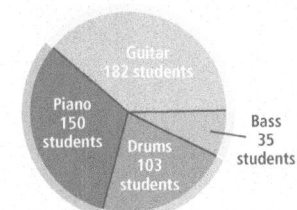

Exercises

1. a. Use the data in the table to draw a circle graph.

b. Approximately what percent of students ride the bus?

Methods of Transportation

Transportation Method	Walk	Bicycle	Bus	Car
Number of Students	252	135	432	81

c. Approximately how many times more students walk than ride in a car?

2. Data Collection Survey your class to find out how they get to school. Use the data to draw a circle graph.

Circle Graphs

1. a. Transportation Mode

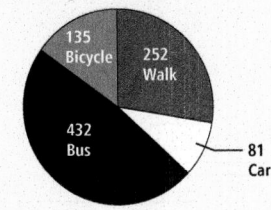

b. 48%

c. 3 times

2. Check students' work.

Stem-and-Leaf Plots

A stem-and-leaf plot is a display of data that uses the digits of the data values. To make a stem-and-leaf plot, separate each number into a stem and a leaf. A stem and leaf for the number 2.39 is shown at the right.

all digits to the left of last digit | last digit

2.3 | 9

stem leaf

You can use a stem-and-leaf plot to organize data. The data below describe the price for the same notebook at several stores.

Notebook Prices: $2.39 $2.47 $2.43 $2.21 $2.33 $2.28 $2.26

Use the first two digits for the "stems."

2.2	1 6 8
2.3	3 9
2.4	3 7

Key: 2.4 | 3 means 2.43

Use the corresponding last digits for the "leaves." Arrange the numbers in order.

You can use a back-to-back stem-and-leaf plot to display two related data sets. The stems are between two vertical bars, and the leaves are on each side. Leaves are in increasing order from the stems. In the back-to-back stem-and-leaf plot below, 3|4|1 represents a commute time of 43 min in Town A and a commute time of 41 min in Town B.

Daily Commute (min)

Town A		Town B
6 6 4 3	4	1 1 4 5 7
9 8 6 4 4 4	5	0 2 2 2 4
5 2 1 0	6	4 5 8 9
8 7 6 6 4 2	7	3 6 7 9 9 9

Key:

7 | 3 means 73

2 | 7 | 3

2 | 7 means 72

Exercises

Make a stem-and-leaf plot for each set of data.

1. 18 35 28 15 36 10 25 22 15

2. 18.6 18.4 17.6 15.7 15.3 17.5

3. 785 776 788 761 768 768 785

4. 0.8 0.2 1.4 3.5 4.3 4.5 2.6 2.2

5. Make a back-to-back stem-and-leaf plot of the test scores of the two classes below.
Class A: 98 78 85 72 94 81 68 83
Class B: 87 91 79 75 90 81 82 100

Answers

Stem-and-Leaf Plots

1.

1	0 5 5 8
2	2 5 8
3	5 6

Key: 1 | 0 means 10

2.

15	3 7
16	
17	5 6
18	4 6

Key: 15 | 3 means 15.3

3.

76	1 8 8
77	6
78	5 5 8

Key: 76 | 1 means 761

4.

0	2 8
1	4
2	2 6
3	5
4	3 5

Key: 0 | 2 means 0.2

5.

Test Scores

Class A		Class B
8	6	
8 2	7	5 9
5 3 1	8	1 2 7
8 4	9	0 1
	10	0

Key:

7 | 5 means 75

2 | 7 | 5

2 | 7 means 72

Reference

Table 1 Measures

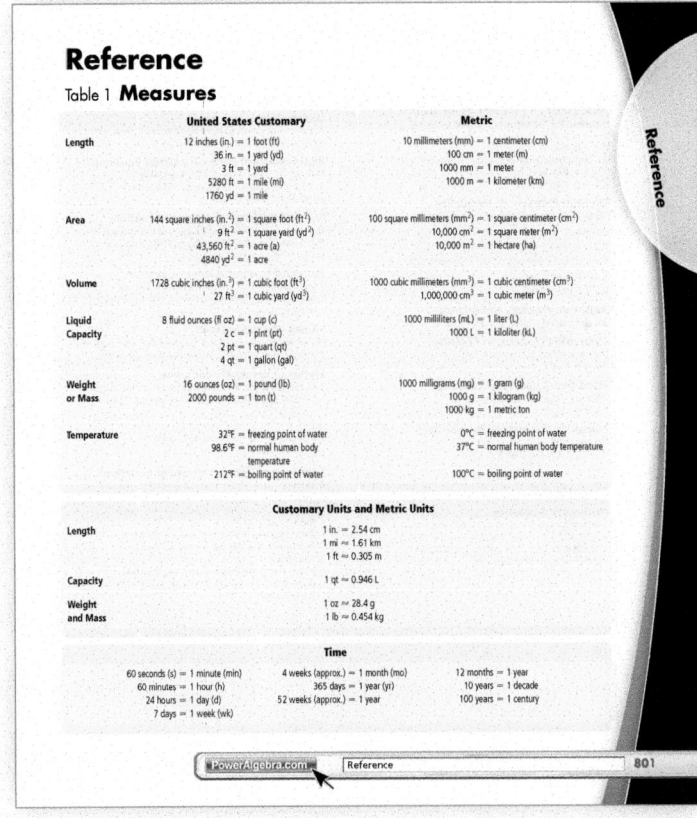

	United States Customary	Metric
Length	12 inches (in.) = 1 foot (ft) 36 in. = 1 yard (yd) 3 ft = 1 yard 5280 ft = 1 mile (mi) 1760 yd = 1 mile	10 millimeters (mm) = 1 centimeter (cm) 100 cm = 1 meter (m) 1000 mm = 1 meter 1000 m = 1 kilometer (km)
Area	144 square inches (in.^{2}) = 1 square foot (ft^2) 9 ft^2 = 1 square yard (yd^2) 43,560 ft^2 = 1 acre (a) 4840 yd^2 = 1 acre	100 square millimeters (mm^2) = 1 square centimeter (cm^2) 10,000 cm^2 = 1 square meter (m^2) 10,000 m^2 = 1 hectare (ha)
Volume	1728 cubic inches (in.^{3}) = 1 cubic foot (ft^3) 27 ft^3 = 1 cubic yard (yd^3)	1000 cubic millimeters (mm^3) = 1 cubic centimeter (cm^3) 1,000,000 cm^3 = 1 cubic meter (m^3)
Liquid Capacity	8 fluid ounces (fl oz) = 1 cup (c) 2 c = 1 pint (pt) 2 pt = 1 quart (qt) 4 qt = 1 gallon (gal)	1000 milliliters (mL) = 1 liter (L) 1000 L = 1 kiloliter (kL)
Weight or Mass	16 ounces (oz) = 1 pound (lb) 2000 pounds = 1 ton (t)	1000 milligrams (mg) = 1 gram (g) 1000 g = 1 kilogram (kg) 1000 kg = 1 metric ton
Temperature	32°F = freezing point of water 98.6°F = normal human body temperature 212°F = boiling point of water	0°C = freezing point of water 37°C = normal human body temperature 100°C = boiling point of water

Customary Units and Metric Units

Length	1 in. ≈ 2.54 cm 1 mi ≈ 1.61 km 1 ft ≈ 0.305 m
Capacity	1 qt ≈ 0.946 L
Weight and Mass	1 oz ≈ 28.4 g 1 lb ≈ 0.454 kg

Time

60 seconds (s) = 1 minute (min) 60 minutes = 1 hour (h) 24 hours = 1 day (d) 7 days = 1 week (wk)	4 weeks (approx.) = 1 month (mo) 365 days = 1 year (yr) 52 weeks (approx.) = 1 year	12 months = 1 year 10 years = 1 decade 100 years = 1 century

Table 2 Reading Math Symbols

Symbols	Words	Symbols	Words
·	multiplication sign, times (×)	$\angle A$	angle A
=	equals	$m\angle A$	measure of angle A
≟	Are the statements equal?	$\triangle ABC$	triangle ABC
≈	is approximately equal to	(x, y)	ordered pair
≠	is not equal to	$x_1, x_2, \ldots$	specific values of the variable x
<	is less than		
>	is greater than	$y_1, y_2, \ldots$	specific values of the variable y
≤	is less than or equal to		
≥	is greater than or equal to	$\bar{x}$	mean of data values of x
≅	is congruent to	σ	standard deviation
±	plus or minus	$f(x)$	f of x; the function value at x
( )	parentheses for grouping	m	slope of a line
[ ]	brackets for grouping	b	y-intercept of a line
{ }	set braces	$a:b$	ratio of a to b
%	percent	$\begin{bmatrix} 1 & 3 \\ 2 & 4 \end{bmatrix}$	matrix
$|a|$	absolute value of a	sin A	sine of $\angle A$
...	and so on	cos A	cosine of $\angle A$
$-a$	opposite of a	tan A	tangent of $\angle A$
π	pi, an irrational number, approximately equal to 3.14	n!	n factorial
°	degree(s)	$_nP_r$	permutations of n objects arranged r at a time
a^n	nth power of a		
$\sqrt{x}$	nonnegative square root of x	$_nC_r$	combinations of n objects chosen r at a time
$\frac{1}{a}, a \neq 0$	reciprocal of a	P(event)	probability of an event
$a^{-n}, a \neq 0$	$\frac{1}{a^n}, a \neq 0$	^	raised to a power (in a spreadsheet formula)
$\overleftrightarrow{AB}$	line through points A and B	*	multiply (in a spreadsheet formula)
$\overline{AB}$	segment with endpoints A and B	/	divide (in a spreadsheet formula)
AB	length of $\overline{AB}$; distance between points A and B		

Properties and Formulas

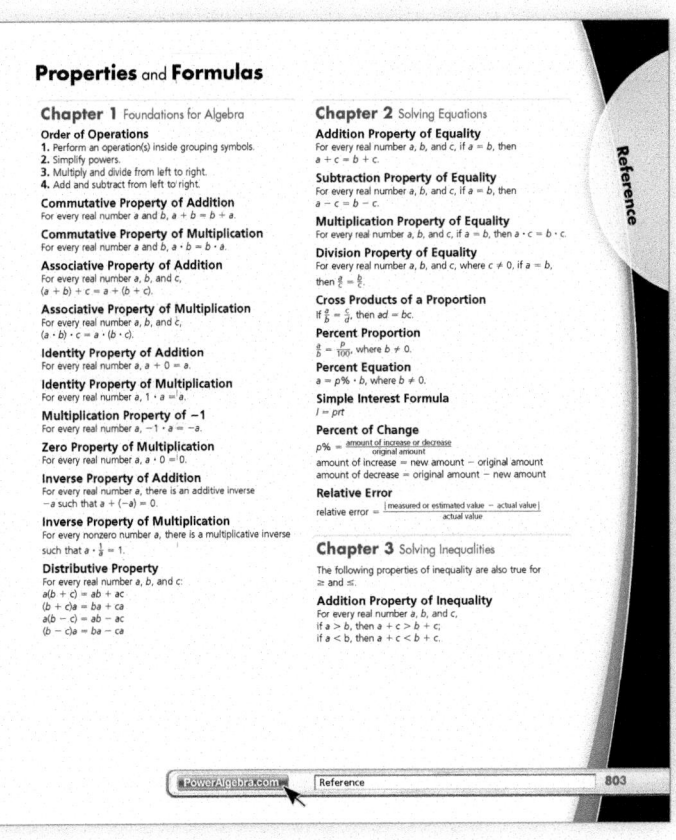

Chapter 1 Foundations for Algebra

Order of Operations
1. Perform an operation(s) inside grouping symbols.
2. Simplify powers.
3. Multiply and divide from left to right.
4. Add and subtract from left to right.

Commutative Property of Addition
For every real number a and b, $a + b = b + a$.

Commutative Property of Multiplication
For every real number a and b, $a \cdot b = b \cdot a$.

Associative Property of Addition
For every real number a, b, and c,
$(a + b) + c = a + (b + c)$.

Associative Property of Multiplication
For every real number a, b, and c,
$(a \cdot b) \cdot c = a \cdot (b \cdot c)$.

Identity Property of Addition
For every real number a, $a + 0 = a$.

Identity Property of Multiplication
For every real number a, $1 \cdot a = a$.

Multiplication Property of −1
For every real number a, $-1 \cdot a = -a$.

Zero Property of Multiplication
For every real number a, $a \cdot 0 = 0$.

Inverse Property of Addition
For every real number a, there is an additive inverse $-a$ such that $a + (-a) = 0$.

Inverse Property of Multiplication
For every nonzero number a, there is a multiplicative inverse such that $a \cdot \frac{1}{a} = 1$.

Distributive Property
For every real number a, b, and c:
$a(b + c) = ab + ac$
$(b + c)a = ba + ca$
$a(b - c) = ab - ac$
$(b - c)a = ba - ca$

Chapter 2 Solving Equations

Addition Property of Equality
For every real number a, b, and c, if $a = b$, then $a + c = b + c$.

Subtraction Property of Equality
For every real number a, b, and c, if $a = b$, then $a - c = b - c$.

Multiplication Property of Equality
For every real number a, b, and c, if $a = b$, then $a \cdot c = b \cdot c$.

Division Property of Equality
For every real number a, b, and c, where $c \neq 0$, if $a = b$, then $\frac{a}{c} = \frac{b}{c}$.

Cross Products of a Proportion
If $\frac{a}{b} = \frac{c}{d}$, then $ad = bc$.

Percent Proportion
$\frac{a}{b} = \frac{p}{100}$, where $b \neq 0$.

Percent Equation
$a = p\% \cdot b$, where $b \neq 0$.

Simple Interest Formula
$I = prt$

Percent of Change
$p\% = \frac{\text{amount of increase or decrease}}{\text{original amount}}$
amount of increase = new amount − original amount
amount of decrease = original amount − new amount

Relative Error
$\text{relative error} = \frac{|\text{measured or estimated value} - \text{actual value}|}{\text{actual value}}$

Chapter 3 Solving Inequalities

The following properties of inequality are also true for $\geq$ and $\leq$.

Addition Property of Inequality
For every real number a, b, and c,
if $a > b$, then $a + c > b + c$,
if $a < b$, then $a + c < b + c$.

Subtraction Property of Inequality
For every real number a, b, and c,
if $a > b$, then $a - c > b - c$;
if $a < b$, then $a - c < b - c$.

Multiplication Property of Inequality
For every real number a, b, and c, where $c > 0$,
if $a > b$, then $ac > bc$;
if $a < b$, then $ac < bc$.
For every real number a, b, and c, where $c < 0$,
if $a > b$, then $ac < bc$;
if $a < b$, then $ac > bc$.

Division Property of Inequality
For every real number a, b, and c, where $c > 0$,
if $a > b$, then $\frac{a}{c} > \frac{b}{c}$;
if $a < b$, then $\frac{a}{c} < \frac{b}{c}$.
For every real number a, b, and c, where $c < 0$,
if $a > b$, then $\frac{a}{c} < \frac{b}{c}$;
if $a < b$, then $\frac{a}{c} > \frac{b}{c}$.

Reflexive Property of Equality
For every real number a, $a = a$.

Symmetric Property of Equality
For every real number a and b,
if $a = b$, then $b = a$.

Transitive Property of Equality
For every real number a, b, and c,
if $a = b$ and $b = c$, then $a = c$.

Transitive Property of Inequality
For every real number a, b, and c,
if $a < b$ and $b < c$, then $a < c$.

Chapter 4 An Introduction to Functions

Arithmetic Sequence
The form for the rule of an arithmetic sequence is
$A(n) = A(1) + (n - 1)d$, where $A(n)$ is the nth term,
$A(1)$ is the first term, n is the term number, and
d is the common difference.

Chapter 5 Linear Functions

Slope
$$\text{slope} = \frac{\text{vertical change}}{\text{horizontal change}} = \frac{\text{rise}}{\text{run}}$$

Direct Variation
A direct variation is a relationship that can be represented by
a function of the form $y = kx$, where $k \neq 0$.

Slope-Intercept Form of a Linear Equation
The slope-intercept form of a linear equation is
$y = mx + b$, where m is the slope and b is the
y-intercept.

Point-Slope Form of a Linear Equation
The point-slope form of the equation of a nonvertical line
that passes through the point (x_1, y_1) with slope m is
$y - y_1 = m(x - x_1)$.

Standard Form of a Linear Equation
The standard form of a linear equation is $Ax + By = C$,
where A, B, and C are real numbers and A and B are not
both zero.

Slopes of Parallel Lines
Nonvertical lines are parallel if they have the same slope and
different y-intercepts. Any two vertical lines are parallel.

Slopes of Perpendicular Lines
Two lines are perpendicular if the product of their slopes is
-1. A vertical line and horizontal line are perpendicular.

Chapter 6 Systems of Equations and Inequalities

Solutions of Systems of Linear Equations
A system of linear equations can have one solution, no
solution, or infinitely many solutions:
- If the lines have different slopes, the lines intersect, so
  there is one solution.
- If the lines have the same slopes and different
  y-intercepts, the lines are parallel, so there are no
  solutions.
- If the lines have the same slopes and the same
  y-intercepts, the lines are the same, so there are infinitely
  many solutions.

Chapter 7 Exponents and Exponential Functions

Zero as an Exponent
For every nonzero number a, $a^0 = 1$.

Negative Exponent
For every nonzero number a and integer n, $a^{-n} = \frac{1}{a^n}$.

Scientific Notation
A number in scientific notation is written as the product of
two factors in the form $a \times 10^n$, where n is an integer and
$1 \leq a < 10$.

Multiplying Powers With the Same Base
For every nonzero number a and integers m and n,
$a^m \cdot a^n = a^{m+n}$.

Dividing Powers With the Same Base
For every nonzero number a and integers m and n,
$\frac{a^m}{a^n} = a^{m-n}$.

Raising a Power to a Power
For every nonzero number a and integers m and n,
$(a^m)^n = a^{mn}$.

Raising a Product to a Power
For every nonzero number a and b and integer n,
$(ab)^n = a^n b^n$.

Raising a Quotient to a Power
For every nonzero number a and b and integer n,
$\left(\frac{a}{b}\right)^n = \frac{a^n}{b^n}$.

Geometric Sequence
The form for the rule of a geometric sequence is
$A(n) = a \cdot r^{n-1}$, where $A(n)$ is the nth term, a is the first
term, n is the term number, and r is the common ratio.

Exponential Growth and Decay
An exponential function has the form $y = a \cdot b^x$, where a is a
nonzero constant, b is greater than 0 and not equal to 1, and
x is a real number.
- The function $y = a \cdot b^x$, where b is the growth factor,
  models exponential growth for $a > 0$ and $b > 1$.
- The function $y = a \cdot b^x$, where b is the decay factor,
  models exponential decay for $a > 0$ and $0 < b < 1$.

Chapter 8 Polynomials and Factoring

Factoring Special Cases
For every nonzero number a and b:
$a^2 - b^2 = (a + b)(a - b)$
$a^2 + 2ab + b^2 = (a + b)(a + b) = (a + b)^2$
$a^2 - 2ab + b^2 = (a - b)(a - b) = (a - b)^2$

Chapter 9 Quadratic Functions and Equations

Graph of a Quadratic Function
The graph of $y = ax^2 + bx + c$, where $a \neq 0$, has the line
$x = \frac{-b}{2a}$ as its axis of symmetry. The x-coordinate of the
vertex is $\frac{-b}{2a}$.

Zero-Product Property
For every real number a and b, If $ab = 0$, then
$a = 0$ or $b = 0$.

Quadratic Formula
If $ax^2 + bx + c = 0$, where $a \neq 0$, then
$x = \frac{-b \pm \sqrt{b^2 - 4ac}}{2a}$.

Property of the Discriminant
For the quadratic equation $ax^2 + bx + c = 0$, where $a \neq 0$,
the value of the discriminant $b^2 - 4ac$ tells you the number
of solutions.
- If $b^2 - 4ac > 0$, there are two real solutions.
- If $b^2 - 4ac = 0$, there is one real solution.
- If $b^2 - 4ac < 0$, there are no real solutions.

Chapter 10 Radical Expressions and Equations

The Pythagorean Theorem
In a right triangle, the sum of the squares of the lengths
of the legs is equal to the square of the length of the
hypotenuse: $a^2 + b^2 = c^2$.

The Converse of the Pythagorean Theorem
If a triangle has sides of lengths a, b, and c, and
$a^2 + b^2 = c^2$, then the triangle is a right triangle with
hypotenuse of length c.

Multiplication Property of Square Roots
For every number $a \geq 0$ and $b \geq 0$, $\sqrt{ab} = \sqrt{a} \cdot \sqrt{b}$.

Division Property of Square Roots
For every number $a \geq 0$ and $b > 0$, $\sqrt{\frac{a}{b}} = \frac{\sqrt{a}}{\sqrt{b}}$.

Trigonometric Ratios
$\text{sine of } \angle A = \frac{\text{length of leg opposite } \angle A}{\text{length of hypotenuse}}$
$\text{cosine of } \angle A = \frac{\text{length of leg adjacent to } \angle A}{\text{length of hypotenuse}}$
$\text{tangent of } \angle A = \frac{\text{length of leg opposite } \angle A}{\text{length of leg adjacent to } \angle A}$

The Distance Formula
The distance d between any two points (x_1, y_1) and
(x_2, y_2) is $d = \sqrt{(x_2 - x_1)^2 + (y_2 - y_1)^2}$.

The Midpoint Formula
The midpoint M of a line segment with endpoints
$A(x_1, y_1)$ and $B(x_2, y_2)$ is $\left(\frac{x_1 + x_2}{2}, \frac{y_1 + y_2}{2}\right)$.

Chapter 11 Rational Expressions and Functions

Inverse Variation
An inverse variation is a relationship that can be represented
by a function of the form $y = \frac{k}{x}$, where $k \neq 0$.

Chapter 12 Data Analysis and Probability

Mean
The mean of a set of data values is $\frac{\text{sum of the data values}}{\text{total number of data values}}$.

Standard Deviation
Standard deviation is a measure of how the values in a data
set vary, or deviate from the mean.
$\sigma = \sqrt{\frac{\Sigma(x - \overline{x})^2}{n}}$

Multiplication Counting Principle
If there are m ways to make a first selection and n ways to
make a second selection, there are $m \cdot n$ ways to make the
two selections.

Permutation Notation
The expression $_nP_r$ represents the number of permutations of
n objects arranged r at a time.
$_nP_r = \frac{n!}{(n - r)!}$

Combination Notation
The expression $_nC_r$ represents the number of combinations
of n objects chosen r at a time.
$_nC_r = \frac{n!}{r!(n - r)!}$

Theoretical Probability
$P(\text{event}) = \frac{\text{number of favorable outcomes}}{\text{number of possible outcomes}}$

Probability of an Event and Its Complement
$P(\text{event}) + P(\text{not event}) = 1$, or
$P(\text{not event}) = 1 - P(\text{event})$

Odds
$\text{Odds in favor of an event} = \frac{\text{number of favorable outcomes}}{\text{number of unfavorable outcomes}}$
$\text{Odds against an event} = \frac{\text{number of unfavorable outcomes}}{\text{number of favorable outcomes}}$

Experimental Probability
$P(\text{event}) = \frac{\text{number of times the event occurs}}{\text{number of times the experiment is done}}$

Probability of Mutually Exclusive Events
If A and B are mutually exclusive events, then
$P(A \text{ or } B) = P(A) + P(B)$.

Probability of Overlapping Events
If A and B are overlapping events, then
$P(A \text{ or } B) = P(A) + P(B) - P(A \text{ and } B)$.

Probability of Two Independent Events
If A and B are independent events, then
$P(A \text{ and } B) = P(A) \cdot P(B)$.

Probability of Two Dependent Events
If A and B are independent events, then
$P(A \text{ then } B) = P(A) \cdot P(B \text{ after } A)$.

Formulas of **Geometry**

You will use a number of geometric formulas as you work through your algebra book. Here are some perimeter, area, and volume formulas.

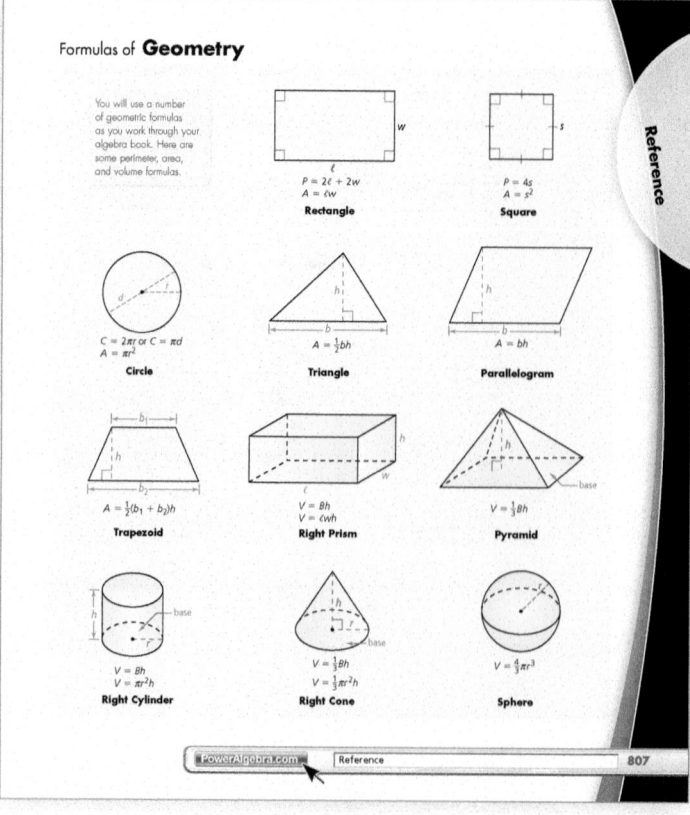

$P = 2\ell + 2w$
$A = \ell w$
Rectangle

$P = 4s$
$A = s^2$
Square

$C = 2\pi r$ or $C = \pi d$
$A = \pi r^2$
Circle

$A = \frac{1}{2}bh$
Triangle

$A = bh$
Parallelogram

$A = \frac{1}{2}(b_1 + b_2)h$
Trapezoid

$V = Bh$
$V = \ell wh$
Right Prism

$V = \frac{1}{3}Bh$
Pyramid

$V = Bh$
$V = \pi r^2 h$
Right Cylinder

$V = \frac{1}{3}Bh$
$V = \frac{1}{3}\pi r^2 h$
Right Cone

$V = \frac{4}{3}\pi r^3$
Sphere

Page 808

Visual Glossary

English

A

Spanish

Absolute value (p. 31) The distance that a number is from zero on a number line.

Valor absoluto (p. 31) La distancia a la que un número está del cero en una recta numérica.

Example −7 is 7 units from 0, so
$|-7| = 7$.

Absolute value function (p. 342) A function with a V-shaped graph that opens up or down. The parent function for the family of absolute value functions is $y = |x|$.

Función de valor absoluto (p. 342) Función cuya gráfica forma una V y que se abre hacia arriba o hacia abajo. La función madre de la familia de funciones de valor absoluto es $y = |x|$.

Example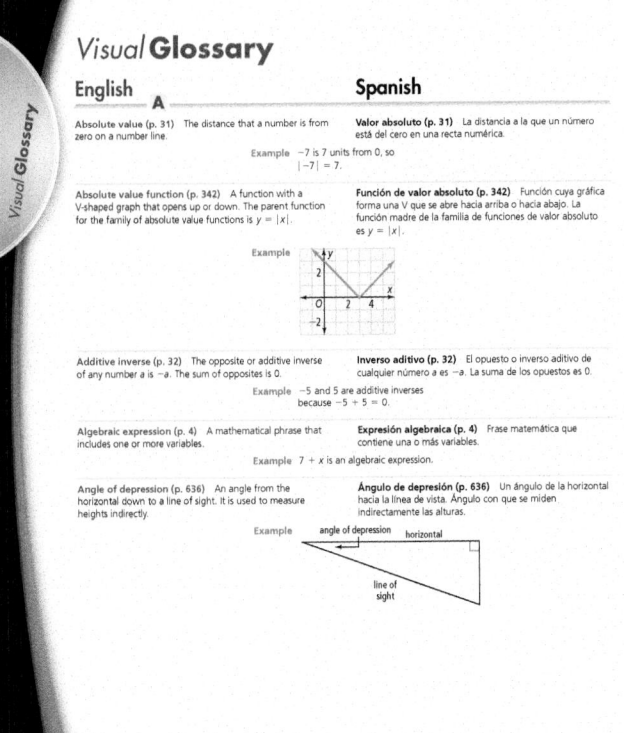

Additive inverse (p. 32) The opposite or additive inverse of any number a is $-a$. The sum of opposites is 0.

Inverso aditivo (p. 32) El opuesto o inverso aditivo de cualquier número a es $-a$. La suma de los opuestos es 0.

Example −5 and 5 are additive inverses
because $-5 + 5 = 0$.

Algebraic expression (p. 4) A mathematical phrase that includes one or more variables.

Expresión algebraica (p. 4) Frase matemática que contiene una o más variables.

Example $7 + x$ is an algebraic expression.

Angle of depression (p. 636) An angle from the horizontal down to a line of sight. It is used to measure heights indirectly.

Ángulo de depresión (p. 636) Un ángulo de la horizontal hacia una línea de vista. Ángulo con que se miden indirectamente las alturas.

Example angle of depression   horizontal

line of
sight

Page 809

English

Spanish

Angle of elevation (p. 636) An angle from the horizontal up to a line of sight. It is used to measure heights indirectly.

Ángulo de elevación (p. 636) Ángulo de la horizontal hacia la línea de vista. Ángulo con que se miden las alturas indirectamente.

Example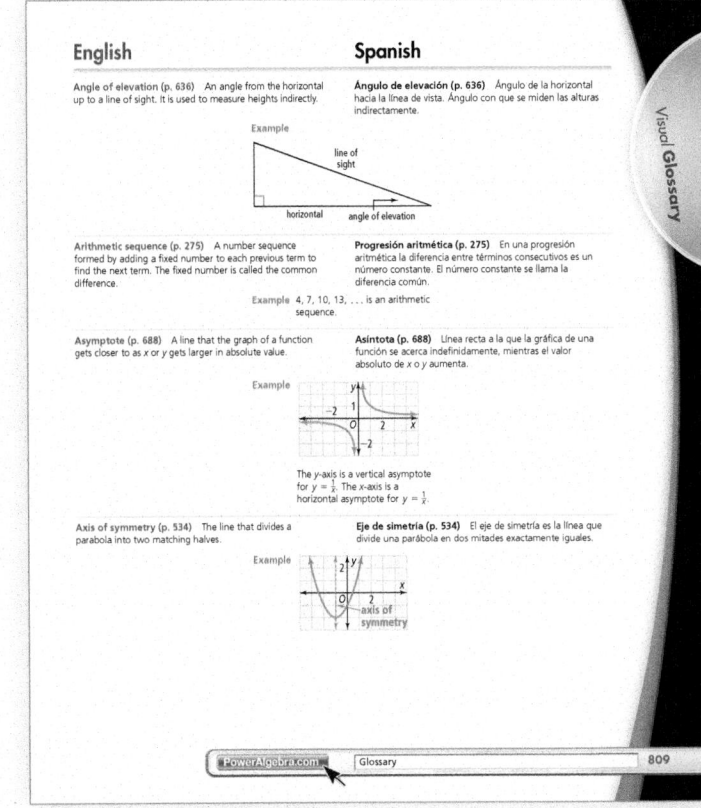

line of
sight

horizontal   angle of elevation

Arithmetic sequence (p. 275) A number sequence formed by adding a fixed number to each previous term to find the next term. The fixed number is called the common difference.

Progresión aritmética (p. 275) En una progresión aritmética la diferencia entre términos consecutivos es un número constante. El número constante se llama la diferencia común.

Example 4, 7, 10, 13, . . . is an arithmetic
sequence.

Asymptote (p. 688) A line that the graph of a function gets closer to as x or y gets larger in absolute value.

Asíntota (p. 688) Línea recta a la que la gráfica de una función se acerca indefinidamente, mientras el valor absoluto de x o y aumenta.

Example

The y-axis is a vertical asymptote
for $y = \frac{1}{x}$. The x-axis is a
horizontal asymptote for $y = \frac{1}{x}$.

Axis of symmetry (p. 534) The line that divides a parabola into two matching halves.

Eje de simetría (p. 534) El eje de simetría es la línea que divide una parábola en dos mitades exactamente iguales.

Example

axis of
symmetry

Page 810

English

B

Spanish

Base (p. 10) A number that is multiplied repeatedly.

Base (p. 10) El número que se multiplica repetidas veces.

Example $4^5 = 4 \cdot 4 \cdot 4 \cdot 4 \cdot 4$. The base
4 is used as a factor 5 times.

Bias (p. 743) A sampling error that causes one option to seem better than another. Survey questions or samples can be biased.

Parcialidad (p. 743) Error de muestreo que hace que una opción parezca mejor que otra. Preguntas en una encuesta o muestras pueden ser parciales.

Binomial (p. 475) A polynomial of two terms.

Binomio (p. 475) Polinomio compuesto de dos términos.

Example $3x + 7$ is a binomial.

Bivariate (p. 742) A set of data that uses two variables is bivariate.

Bivariado (p. 742) Un conjunto de datos que usa dos variables es bivariado.

Box-and-whisker plot (p. 735) A graph that summarizes data along a number line. The left whisker extends from the minimum to the first quartile. The box extends from the first quartile to the third quartile and has a vertical line through the median. The right whisker extends from the third quartile to the maximum.

Gráfica de cajas (p. 735) Gráfica que resume los datos a lo largo de una recta numérica. El brazo izquierdo se extiende desde el valor mínimo del primer cuartil. La caja se extiende desde el primer cuartil hasta el tercer cuartil y tiene una línea vertical que atraviesa la mediana. El brazo derecho se extiende desde el tercer cuartil hasta el valor máximo.

Example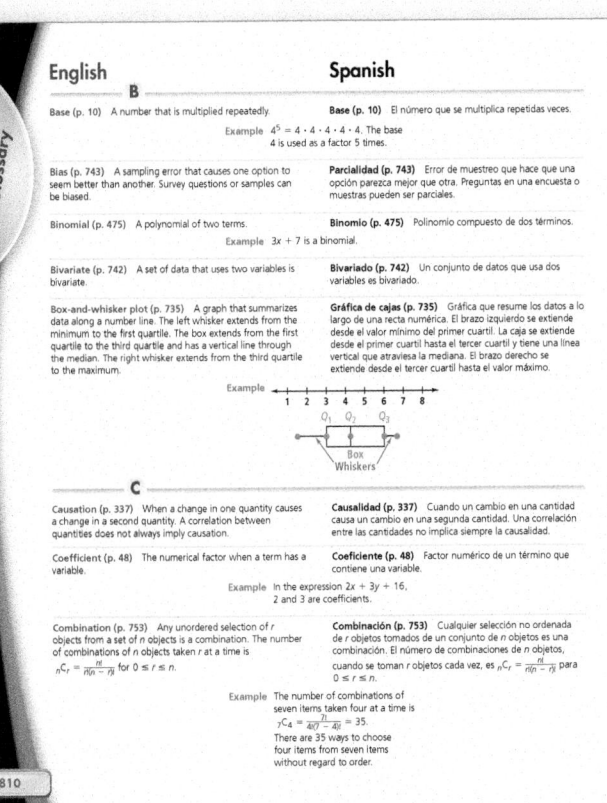

C

Causation (p. 337) When a change in one quantity causes a change in a second quantity. A correlation between quantities does not always imply causation.

Causalidad (p. 337) Cuando un cambio en una cantidad causa un cambio en una segunda cantidad. Una correlación entre las cantidades no implica siempre la causalidad.

Coefficient (p. 48) The numerical factor when a term has a variable.

Coeficiente (p. 48) Factor numérico de un término que contiene una variable.

Example In the expression $2x + 3y + 16$,
2 and 3 are coefficients.

Combination (p. 753) Any unordered selection of r objects from a set of n objects is a combination. The number of combinations of n objects taken r at a time is $_nC_r = \frac{n!}{r!(n-r)!}$ for $0 \le r \le n$.

Combinación (p. 753) Cualquier selección no ordenada de r objetos tomados de un conjunto de n objetos es una combinación. El número de combinaciones de n objetos, cuando se toman r objetos cada vez, es $_nC_r = \frac{n!}{r!(n-r)!}$ para $0 \le r \le n$.

Example The number of combinations of
seven items taken four at a time is
$_7C_4 = \frac{7!}{4!(7-4)!} = 35$.
There are 35 ways to choose
four items from seven items
without regard to order.

Page 811

English

Spanish

Common difference (p. 275) The difference between consecutive terms of an arithmetic sequence.

Diferencia común (p. 275) La diferencia común es la diferencia entre los términos consecutivos de una progresión aritmética.

Example The common difference is 3 in the
arithmetic sequence 4, 7, 10, 13, . . .

Common ratio (p. 453) The fixed number used to find terms in a geometric sequence.

Razón común (p. 453) Número constante que se usa para hallar los términos en una progresión geométrica.

Example The common ratio is $\frac{1}{3}$ in
the geometric sequence
9, 3, 1, $\frac{1}{3}$, . . .

Complement of an event (p. 758) All possible outcomes that are not in the event.
$P(\text{complement of event}) = 1 - P(\text{event})$

Complemento de un suceso (p. 758) Todos los resultados posibles que no se dan en el suceso.
$P(\text{complemento de un suceso}) = 1 - P(\text{suceso})$

Example The complement of rolling a 1 or a 2 on a
number cube is rolling a 3, 4, 5, or 6.

Complement of a set (p. 196) The set of all elements in the universal set that are not in a given set.

Complemento de un conjunto (p. 196) Conjunto de todos los elementos en el conjunto universal que no se incluyen en el conjunto dado.

Example If $U = \{. . . , -3, -2, -1, 0, 1, 2, 3, . . .\}$
and $A = \{0, 1, 2, 3, . . .\}$, then the
complement of A is $A' = \{. . . , -3, -2, -1\}$.

Completing the square (p. 561) A method of solving quadratic equations. Completing the square turns every quadratic equation into the form $x^2 = c$.

Completar el cuadrado (p. 561) Método para solucionar ecuaciones cuadráticas. Cuando se completa el cuadrado, se transforma la ecuación cuadrática a la fórmula $x^2 = c$.

Example $x^2 + 6x - 7 = 9$ is rewritten as
$(x + 3)^2 = 25$ by completing the
square.

Complex fraction (p. 516) A fraction that has a fraction in its numerator or denominator or in both its numerator and denominator.

Fracción compleja (p. 516) Una fracción compleja es una fracción que contiene otra fracción en el numerador o en el denominador, o en ambos.

Example $\frac{\frac{2}{3}}{\frac{1}{2}}$

Compound event (p. 764) An event that consists of two or more events linked by the word and or the word or.

Suceso compuesto (p. 764) Suceso que consiste en dos o más sucesos unidos por medio de la palabra y o la palabra o.

Examples Rolling a 5 on a number cube
and then rolling a 4 is a
compound event.

Page 812

English	Spanish

Compound inequalities (p. 200) Two inequalities that are joined by *and* or *or*.

Desigualdades compuestas (p. 200) Dos desigualdades que están enlazadas por medio de una *y* o una *o*.

Examples $5 < x$ and $x < 10$
$14 < x$ or $x \le -3$

Compound interest (p. 456) Interest paid on both the principal and the interest that has already been paid.

Interés compuesto (p. 456) Interés calculado tanto sobre el capital como sobre los intereses ya pagados.

Example For an initial deposit of $1000 at a 6% interest rate with interest compounded quarterly, the function $y = 1000\left(\frac{0.06}{4}\right)^x$ gives the account balance *y* after *x* years.

Conclusion (p. 602) The conclusion is the part of an *If-then* statement (conditional) that follows *then*.

Conclusión (p. 602) La conclusión es lo que sigue a la palabra *entonces* en un enunciado condicional.

Example In the conditional "If an animal has four legs, then it is a horse," the conclusion is "It is a horse."

Conditional (p. 602) A conditional is an *If-then* statement.

Condicional (p. 602) Un enunciado condicional es del tipo *si . . ., entonces . . .*

Example If an animal has four legs, then it is a horse.

Conditional probability (p. 771) A probability that contains a condition that may limit the sample space for an event. The notation $P(B|A)$ is read "the probability of event *B*, given event *A*."

Probabilidad condicional (p. 771) Probabilidad que contiene una condición que puede limitar el espacio de muestra de un suceso. La notación $P(B|A)$ se lee "la probabilidad del suceso *B*, dado el suceso *A*."

Conjugates (p. 614) The sum and the difference of the same two terms.

Valores conjugados (p. 614) La suma y resta de los mismos dos términos.

Example $(\sqrt{3} + 2)$ and $(\sqrt{3} - 2)$ are conjugates.

Consistent system (p. 361) A system of equations that has at least one solution is consistent.

Sistema consistente (p. 361) Un sistema de ecuaciones que tiene por lo menos una solución es consistente.

Example

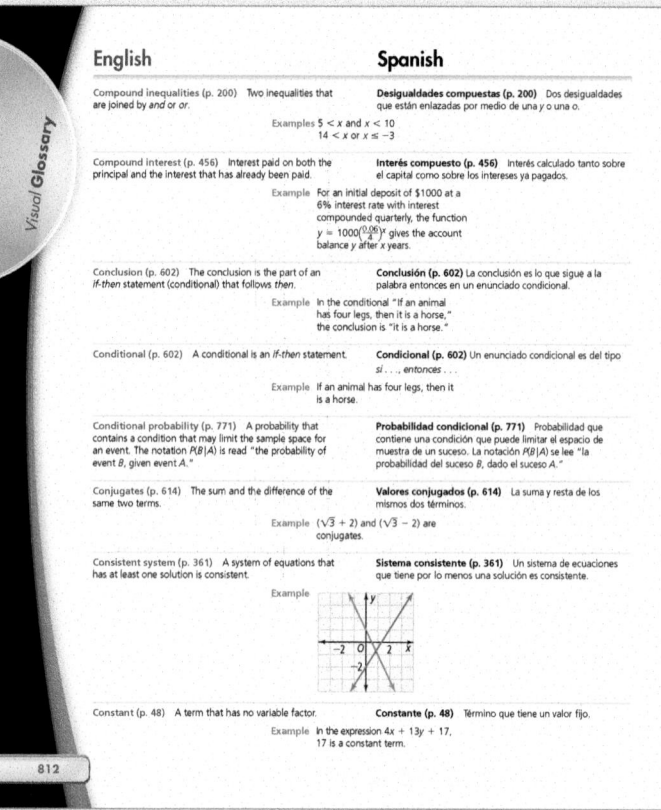

Constant (p. 48) A term that has no variable factor.

Constante (p. 48) Término que tiene un valor fijo.

Example In the expression $4x + 13y + 17$, 17 is a constant term.

Page 813

English	Spanish

Constant of variation for direct variation (p. 299) The nonzero constant *k* in the function $y = kx$.

Constante de variación en variaciones directas (p. 299) La constante *k* cuyo valor no es cero en la función $y = kx$.

Example For the direct variation $y = 24x$, 24 is the constant of variation.

Constant of variation for inverse variation (p. 680) The nonzero constant *k* in the function $y = \frac{k}{x}$.

Constante de variación en variaciones inversas (p. 680) La constante *k* cuyo valor no es cero en la función $y = \frac{k}{x}$.

Example For the inverse variation $y = \frac{8}{x}$, 8 is the constant of variation.

Continuous graph (p. 255) A graph that is unbroken.

Gráfica continua (p. 255) Una gráfica continua es una gráfica ininterrumpida.

Example

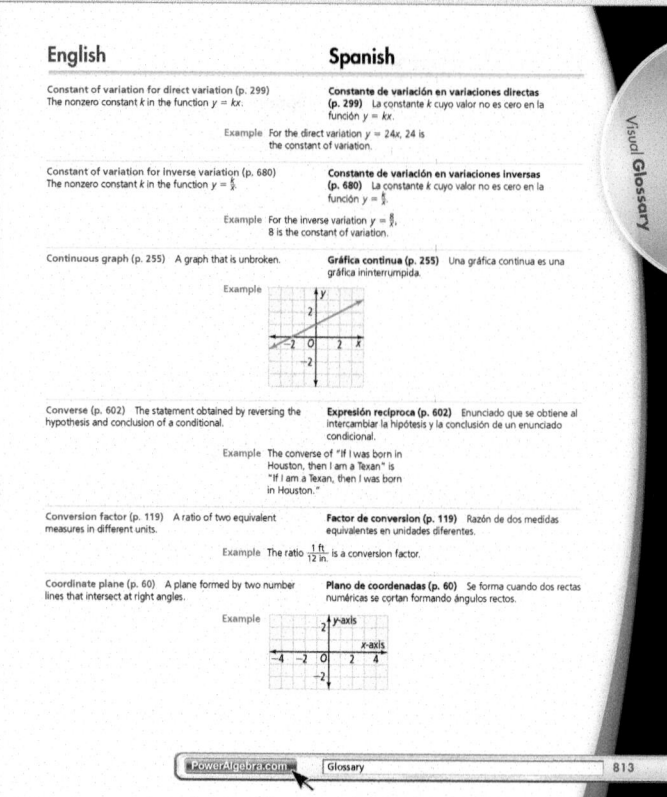

Converse (p. 602) The statement obtained by reversing the hypothesis and conclusion of a conditional.

Expresión recíproca (p. 602) Enunciado que se obtiene al intercambiar la hipótesis y la conclusión de un enunciado condicional.

Example The converse of "If I was born in Houston, then I am a Texan" is "If I am a Texan, then I was born in Houston."

Conversion factor (p. 119) A ratio of two equivalent measures in different units.

Factor de conversión (p. 119) Razón de dos medidas equivalentes en unidades diferentes.

Example The ratio $\frac{1 \, ft}{12 \, in.}$ is a conversion factor.

Coordinate plane (p. 60) A plane formed by two number lines that intersect at right angles.

Plano de coordenadas (p. 60) Se forma cuando dos rectas numéricas se cortan formando ángulos rectos.

Example

Page 814

English	Spanish

Coordinates (p. 60) The numbers that make an ordered pair and identify the location of a point.

Coordenadas (p. 60) Números ordenados por pares que determinan la posición de un punto sobre un plano.

Example

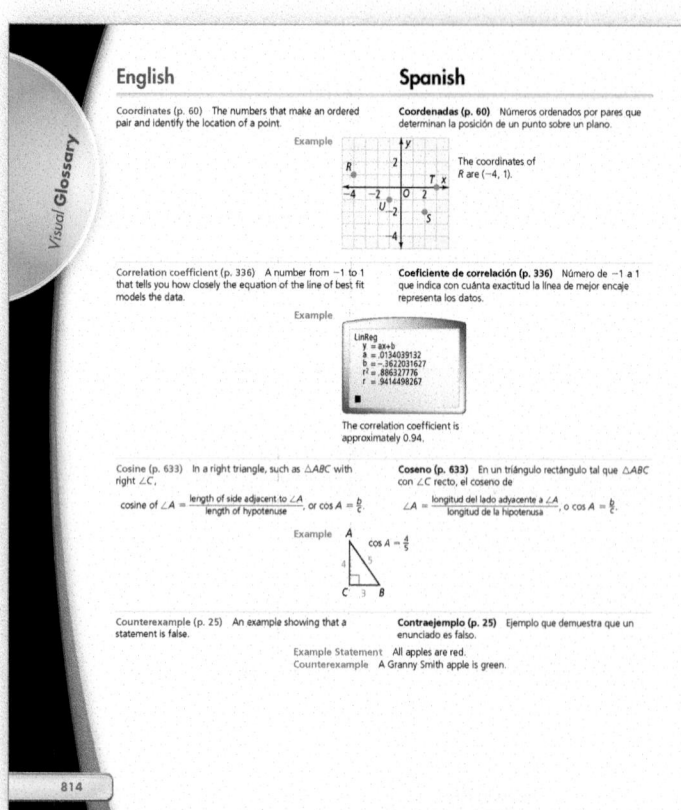

The coordinates of *R* are $(-4, 1)$.

Correlation coefficient (p. 336) A number from -1 to 1 that tells you how closely the equation of the line of best fit models the data.

Coeficiente de correlación (p. 336) Número de -1 a 1 que indica con cuánta exactitud la línea de mejor encaje representa los datos.

Example

The correlation coefficient is approximately 0.94.

Cosine (p. 633) In a right triangle, such as $\triangle ABC$ with right $\angle C$,

cosine of $\angle A = \frac{\text{length of side adjacent to } \angle A}{\text{length of hypotenuse}}$, or $\cos A = \frac{b}{c}$.

Coseno (p. 633) En un triángulo rectángulo tal que $\triangle ABC$ con $\angle C$ recto, el coseno de

$\angle A = \frac{\text{longitud del lado adyacente a } \angle A}{\text{longitud de la hipotenusa}}$, o $\cos A = \frac{b}{c}$.

Example $\cos A = \frac{4}{5}$

Counterexample (p. 25) An example showing that a statement is false.

Contraejemplo (p. 25) Ejemplo que demuestra que un enunciado es falso.

Example Statement All apples are red.
Counterexample A Granny Smith apple is green.

Page 815

English	Spanish

Cross product (of sets) (p. 220) The cross product of two sets *A* and *B*, denoted by $A \times B$, is the set of all ordered pairs with the first element in *A* and with the second element in *B*.

Producto cruzado (de dos conjuntos) (p. 220) El producto cruzado de dos conjuntos *A* y *B*, definido por $A \times B$, es el conjunto de todos los pares ordenados cuyo primer elemento está en *A* y cuyo segundo elemento está en *B*.

Cross products (of a proportion) (p. 125) In a proportion $\frac{a}{b} = \frac{c}{d}$, the products ad and bc. These products are equal.

Productos cruzados (de una proporción) (p. 125) En una proporción $\frac{a}{b} = \frac{c}{d}$, los productos ad y bc. Estos productos son iguales.

Example The cross products for $\frac{3}{4} = \frac{6}{8}$ are $3 \cdot 8$ and $4 \cdot 6$.

Cumulative frequency table (p. 722) A table that shows the number of data values that lie in or below the given intervals.

Tabla de frecuencia cumulativa (p. 722) Tabla que muestra el número de valores de datos que están dentro o por debajo de los intervalos dados.

Example

Interval	Frequency	Cumulative Frequency
0–9	5	5
10–19	8	13
20–29	4	17

D

Decay factor (p. 457) 1 minus the percent rate of change, expressed as a decimal, for an exponential decay situation.

Factor de decremento (p. 457) 1 menos la tasa porcentual de cambio, expresada como decimal, en una situación de reducción exponencial.

Example The decay factor of the function $y = 5(0.3)^x$ is 0.3.

Deductive reasoning (p. 25) A process of reasoning logically from given facts to a conclusion.

Razonamiento deductivo (p. 25) El razonamiento deductivo es un proceso de razonamiento lógico que parte de hechos dados hasta llegar a una conclusión.

Example Based on the fact that the sum of any two even numbers is even, you can deduce that the product of any whole number and any even number is even.

Degree of a monomial (p. 474) The sum of the exponents of the variables of a monomial.

Grado de un monomio (p. 474) La suma de los exponentes de las variables de un monomio.

Example $-4x^3y^2$ is a monomial of degree 5.

Degree of a polynomial (p. 475) The highest degree of any term of the polynomial.

Grado de un polinomio (p. 475) El grado de un polinomio es el grado mayor de cualquier término del polinomio.

Example The polynomial $P(x) = x^6 + 2x^3 - 3$ has degree 6.

Page 816

English	Spanish

Dependent events (p. 766) When the outcome of one event affects the probability of a second event, the events are dependent events.

Sucesos dependientes (p. 766) Dos sucesos son dependientes si el resultado de un suceso afecta la probabilidad del otro.

Example You have a bag with marbles of different colors. If you pick a marble from the bag and pick another without replacing the first, the events are dependent events.

Dependent system (p. 361) A system of equations that does not have a unique solution.

Sistema dependiente (p. 361) Sistema de ecuaciones que no tiene una solución única.

Example The system $\begin{cases} y = 2x + 3 \\ -4x + 2y = 6 \end{cases}$ represents two equations for the same line, so it has many solutions. It is a dependent system.

Dependent variable (p. 240) A variable that provides the output values of a function.

Variable dependiente (p. 240) Variable de la que dependen los valores de salida de una función.

Example In the equation $y = 3x$, y is the dependent variable.

Difference of squares (p. 513) A difference of two squares is an expression of the form $a^2 - b^2$. It can be factored as $(a + b)(a - b)$.

Diferencia de dos cuadrados (p. 513) La diferencia de dos cuadrados es una expresión de la forma $a^2 - b^2$. Se puede factorizar como $(a + b)(a - b)$.

Examples $25a^2 - 4 = (5a + 2)(5a - 2)$
$m^6 - 1 = (m^3 + 1)(m^3 - 1)$

Direct variation (p. 299) A linear function defined by an equation of the form $y = kx$, where $k \neq 0$.

Variación directa (p. 299) Una función lineal definida por una ecuación de la forma $y = kx$, donde $k \neq 0$, representa una variación directa.

Example $y = 18x$ is a direct variation.

Discrete graph (p. 255) A graph composed of isolated points.

Gráfica discreta (p. 255) Una gráfica discreta es compuesta de puntos aislados.

Example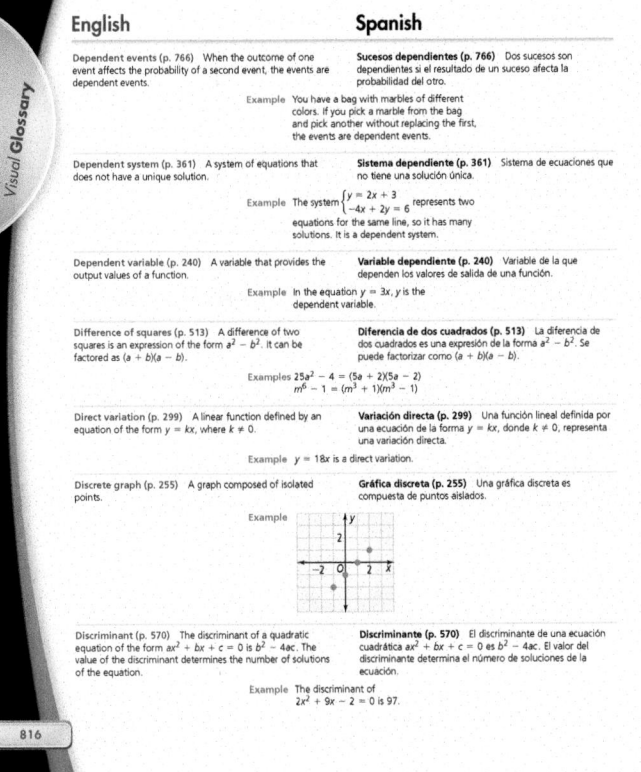

Discriminant (p. 570) The discriminant of a quadratic equation of the form $ax^2 + bx + c = 0$ is $b^2 - 4ac$. The value of the discriminant determines the number of solutions of the equation.

Discriminante (p. 570) El discriminante de una ecuación cuadrática $ax^2 + bx + c = 0$ es $b^2 - 4ac$. El valor del discriminante determina el número de soluciones de la ecuación.

Example The discriminant of $2x^2 + 9x - 2 = 0$ is 97.

Page 817

English	Spanish

Disjoint sets (p. 215) Sets that do not have any elements in common.

Conjuntos ajenos (p. 215) Conjuntos que no tienen elementos en común.

Example The set of positive integers and the set of negative integers are disjoint sets.

Distance Formula (p. 605) The distance d between any two points (x_1, y_1) and (x_2, y_2) is $d = \sqrt{(x_2 - x_1)^2 + (y_2 - y_1)^2}$.

Fórmula de distancia (p. 605) La distancia d entre dos puntos cualesquiera (x_1, y_1) y (x_2, y_2) es $d = \sqrt{(x_2 - x_1)^2 + (y_2 - y_1)^2}$.

Example The distance between $(-2, 4)$ and $(4, 5)$ is
$d = \sqrt{(4 - (-2))^2 + (5 - 4)^2}$
$= \sqrt{(6)^2 + (1)^2}$
$= \sqrt{37}$

Distributive Property (p. 46) For every real number a, b, and c:

Propiedad Distributiva (p. 46) Para cada número real a, b y c:

$a(b + c) = ab + ac \quad (b + c)a = ba + ca$
$a(b - c) = ab - ac \quad (b - c)a = ba - ca$

$a(b + c) = ab + ac \quad (b + c)a = ba + ca$
$a(b - c) = ab - ac \quad (b - c)a = ba - ca$

Examples $3(19 + 4) = 3(19) + 3(4)$
$(19 + 4)3 = 19(3) + 4(3)$
$7(11 - 2) = 7(11) - 7(2)$
$(11 - 2)7 = 11(7) - 2(7)$

Domain (of a relation or function) (p. 268) The possible values for the input of a relation or function.

Dominio (de una relación o función) (p. 268) Posibles valores de entrada de una relación o función.

Example In the function $f(x) = x + 22$, the domain is all real numbers.

E

Element (of a matrix) (p. 714) An item in a matrix.

Elemento (de una matriz) (p. 714) Componente de una matriz.

Example $\begin{bmatrix} 5 & -2 \\ 7 & 3 \end{bmatrix}$
5, 7, -2, and 3 are the four elements of the matrix.

Elements (of a set) (p. 17) Members of a set.

Elementos (p. 17) Partes integrantes de un conjunto.

Example Cats and dogs are elements of the set of mammals.

Page 818

English	Spanish

Elimination method (p. 374) A method for solving a system of linear equations. You add or subtract the equations to eliminate a variable.

Eliminación (p. 374) Método para resolver un sistema de ecuaciones lineales. Se suman o se restan las ecuaciones para eliminar una variable.

Example $3x + y = 19$
$\underline{2x - y = 1}$
$5x + 0 = 20 \quad$ Add the equations to get $x = 4$.
$2(4) - y = 1 \rightarrow$ Substitute 4 for x in the second equation.
$8 - y = 1$
$y = 7 \rightarrow$ Solve for y.

Empty set (p. 195) A set that does not contain any elements.

Conjunto vacío (p. 195) Conjunto que no contiene elementos.

Example The intersection of the set of positive integers and the set of negative integers is the empty set.

Equation (p. 53) A mathematical sentence that uses an equal sign.

Ecuación (p. 53) Enunciado matemático que tiene el signo de igual.

Example $x + 5 = 3x - 7$

Equivalent equations (p. 81) Equations that have the same solution.

Ecuaciones equivalentes (p. 81) Ecuaciones que tienen la misma solución.

Example $\frac{a}{3} = 3$ and $\frac{a}{3} + a = 3 + a$ are equivalent equations.

Equivalent expressions (p. 23) Algebraic expressions that have the same value for all values of the variable(s).

Ecuaciones equivalentes (p. 23) Expresiones algebraicas que tienen el mismo valor para todos los valores de la(s) variable(s).

Example $3a + 2a$ and $5a$ are equivalent expressions.

Equivalent inequalities (p. 171) Inequalities that have the same set of solutions.

Desigualdades equivalentes (p. 171) Las desigualdades equivalentes tienen el mismo conjunto de soluciones.

Example $x + 4 < 7$ and $x < 3$ are equivalent inequalities.

Evaluate (p. 12) To substitute a given number for each variable, and then simplify.

Evaluar (p. 12) Método de sustituir cada variable por un número dado para luego simplificar la expresión.

Example To evaluate $3x + 4$ for $x = 2$, substitute 2 for x and simplify.
$3(2) + 4 = 6 + 4 = 10$

Page 819

English	Spanish

Event (p. 757) Any group of outcomes in a situation involving probability.

Suceso (p. 757) En la probabilidad, cualquier grupo de resultados.

Example When rolling a number cube, there are six possible outcomes. Rolling an even number is an event with three possible outcomes, 2, 4, and 6.

Excluded value (p. 646) A value of x for which a rational expression $f(x)$ is undefined.

Valor excluido (p. 646) Valor de x para el cual una expresión racional es indefinida.

Experimental probability (p. 759) The ratio of the number of times an event actually happens to the number of times the experiment is done.
$P(\text{event}) = \frac{\text{number of times an event happens}}{\text{number of times the experiment is done}}$

Probabilidad experimental (p. 759) La razón entre el número de veces que un suceso sucede en la realidad y el número de veces que se hace el experimento.
$P(\text{suceso}) = \frac{\text{número de veces que sucede un suceso}}{\text{número de veces que se hace el experimento}}$

Example A baseball player's batting average shows how likely it is that a player will get a hit, based on previous times at bat.

Exponent (p. 10) A number that shows repeated multiplication.

Exponente (p. 10) Denota el número de veces que debe multiplicarse.

Example $3^4 = 3 \cdot 3 \cdot 3 \cdot 3$
The exponent 4 indicates that 3 is used as a factor four times.

Exponential decay (p. 457) A situation modeled with a function of the form $y = ab^x$, where $a > 0$ and $0 < b < 1$.

Decremento exponencial (p. 457) Para $a > 0$ y $0 < b < 1$, la función $y = ab^x$ representa el decremento exponencial.

Example $y = 5(0.1)^x$

Exponential function (p. 447) A function that repeatedly multiplies an initial amount by the same positive number. You can model all exponential functions using $y = ab^x$, where a is a nonzero constant, $b > 0$, and $b \neq 1$.

Función exponencial (p. 447) Función que multiplica repetidas veces una cantidad inicial por el mismo número positivo. Todas las funciones exponenciales se pueden representar mediante $y = ab^x$, donde a es una constante con valor distinto de cero, $b > 0$ y $b \neq 1$.

Example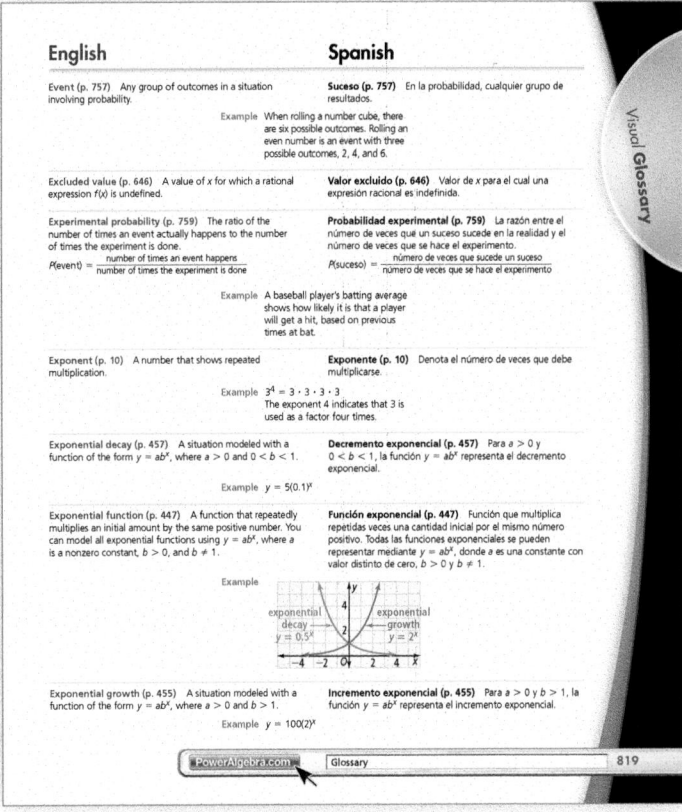

Exponential growth (p. 455) A situation modeled with a function of the form $y = ab^x$, where $a > 0$ and $b > 1$.

Incremento exponencial (p. 455) Para $a > 0$ y $b > 1$, la función $y = ab^x$ representa el incremento exponencial.

Example $y = 100(2)^x$

English | Spanish

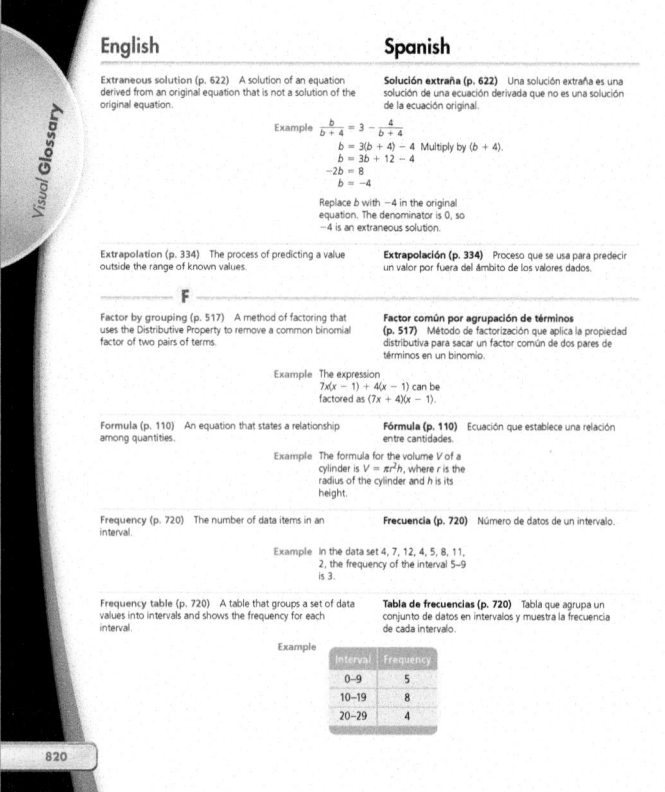

Extraneous solution (p. 622) A solution of an equation derived from an original equation that is not a solution of the original equation.

Solución extraña (p. 622) Una solución extraña es una solución de una ecuación derivada que no es una solución de la ecuación original.

Example $\frac{b}{b+4} = 3 - \frac{4}{b+4}$

$b = 3(b+4) - 4$ Multiply by $(b+4)$.

$b = 3b + 12 - 4$

$-2b = 8$

$b = -4$

Replace b with -4 in the original equation. The denominator is 0, so -4 is an extraneous solution.

Extrapolation (p. 334) The process of predicting a value outside the range of known values.

Extrapolación (p. 334) Proceso que se usa para predecir un valor por fuera del ámbito de los valores dados.

F

Factor by grouping (p. 517) A method of factoring that uses the Distributive Property to remove a common binomial factor of two pairs of terms.

Factor común por agrupación de términos (p. 517) Método de factorización que aplica la propiedad distributiva para sacar un factor común de dos pares de términos en un binomio.

Example The expression $7x(x-1) + 4(x-1)$ can be factored as $(7x+4)(x-1)$.

Formula (p. 110) An equation that states a relationship among quantities.

Fórmula (p. 110) Ecuación que establece una relación entre cantidades.

Example The formula for the volume V of a cylinder is $V = \pi r^2 h$, where r is the radius of the cylinder and h is its height.

Frequency (p. 720) The number of data items in an interval.

Frecuencia (p. 720) Número de datos en un intervalo.

Example In the data set 4, 7, 12, 4, 5, 8, 11, 2, the frequency of the interval 5–9 is 3.

Frequency table (p. 720) A table that groups a set of data values into intervals and shows the frequency for each interval.

Tabla de frecuencias (p. 720) Tabla que agrupa un conjunto de datos en intervalos y muestra la frecuencia de cada intervalo.

Example

Interval	Frequency
0–9	5
10–19	8
20–29	4

English | Spanish

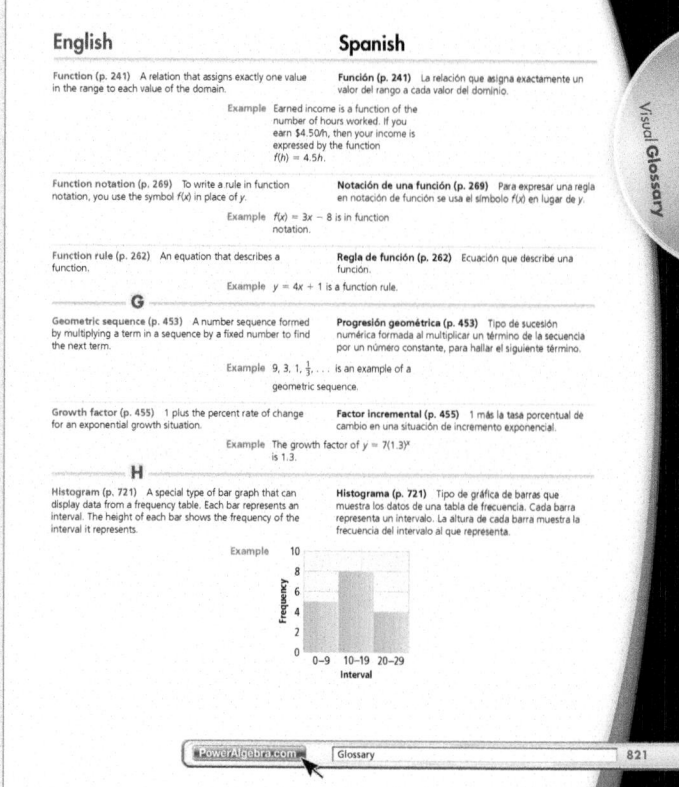

Function (p. 241) A relation that assigns exactly one value in the range to each value of the domain.

Función (p. 241) La relación que asigna exactamente un valor del rango a cada valor del dominio.

Example Earned income is a function of the number of hours worked. If you earn \$4.50/h, then your income is expressed by the function $f(h) = 4.5h$.

Function notation (p. 269) To write a rule in function notation, you use the symbol $f(x)$ in place of y.

Notación de una función (p. 269) Para expresar una regla en notación de función se usa el símbolo $f(x)$ en lugar de y.

Example $f(x) = 3x - 8$ is in function notation.

Function rule (p. 262) An equation that describes a function.

Regla de función (p. 262) Ecuación que describe una función.

Example $y = 4x + 1$ is a function rule.

G

Geometric sequence (p. 453) A number sequence formed by multiplying a term in a sequence by a fixed number to find the next term.

Progresión geométrica (p. 453) Tipo de sucesión numérica formada al multiplicar un término de la secuencia por un número constante, para hallar el siguiente término.

Example $9, 3, 1, \frac{1}{3}, \ldots$ is an example of a geometric sequence.

Growth factor (p. 455) 1 plus the percent rate of change for an exponential growth situation.

Factor incremental (p. 455) 1 más la tasa porcentual de cambio en una situación de incremento exponencial.

Example The growth factor of $y = 7(1.3)^x$ is 1.3.

H

Histogram (p. 721) A special type of bar graph that can display data from a frequency table. Each bar represents an interval. The height of each bar shows the frequency of the interval it represents.

Histograma (p. 721) Tipo de gráfica de barras que muestra los datos en una tabla de frecuencia. Cada barra representa un intervalo. La altura de cada barra muestra la frecuencia del intervalo al que representa.

Example

English | Spanish

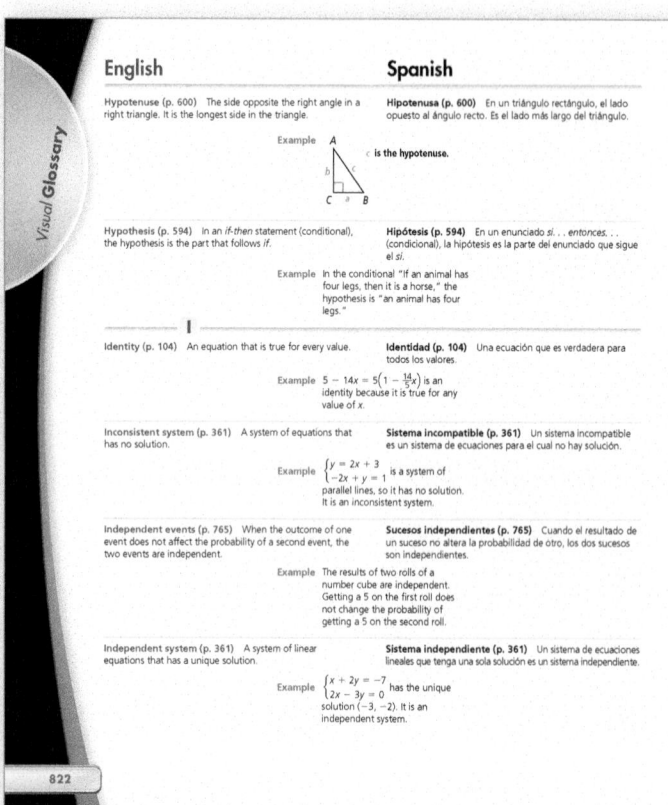

Hypotenuse (p. 600) The side opposite the right angle in a right triangle. It is the longest side in the triangle.

Hipotenusa (p. 600) En un triángulo rectángulo, el lado opuesto al ángulo recto. Es el lado más largo del triángulo.

Example $\overline{c}$ is the hypotenuse.

Hypothesis (p. 594) In an if-then statement (conditional), the hypothesis is the part that follows if.

Hipótesis (p. 594) En un enunciado si... entonces... (condicional), la hipótesis es la parte del enunciado que sigue el si.

Example In the conditional "If an animal has four legs, then it is a horse," the hypothesis is "an animal has four legs."

I

Identity (p. 104) An equation that is true for every value.

Identidad (p. 104) Una ecuación que es verdadera para todos los valores.

Example $5 - 14x = 5\left(1 - \frac{14}{5}x\right)$ is an identity because it is true for any value of x.

Inconsistent system (p. 361) A system of equations that has no solution.

Sistema incompatible (p. 361) Un sistema incompatible es un sistema de ecuaciones para el cual no hay solución.

Example $\begin{cases} y = 2x + 3 \\ -2x + y = 1 \end{cases}$ is a system of parallel lines, so it has no solution. It is an inconsistent system.

Independent events (p. 765) When the outcome of one event does not affect the probability of a second event, the two events are independent.

Sucesos independientes (p. 765) Cuando el resultado de un suceso no altera la probabilidad de otro, los dos sucesos son independientes.

Example The results of two rolls of a number cube are independent. Getting a 5 on the first roll does not change the probability of getting a 5 on the second roll.

Independent system (p. 361) A system of linear equations that has a unique solution.

Sistema independiente (p. 361) Un sistema de ecuaciones lineales que tenga una sola solución es un sistema independiente.

Example $\begin{cases} x + 2y = -7 \\ 2x - 3y = 0 \end{cases}$ has the unique solution $(-3, -2)$. It is an independent system.

English | Spanish

Independent variable (p. 240) A variable that provides the input values of a function.

Variable independiente (p. 240) Variable de la que dependen los valores de entrada de una función.

Example In the equation $y = 3x$, x is the independent variable.

Inductive reasoning (p. 63) Making conclusions based on observed patterns.

Razonamiento inductivo (p. 63) Sacar conclusiones a partir de patrones observados.

Inequality (p. 19) A mathematical sentence that compares the values of two expressions using an inequality symbol.

Desigualdad (p. 19) Expresión matemática que compara el valor de dos expresiones con el símbolo de desigualdad.

Example $3 < 7$

Input (p. 240) A value of the independent variable.

Entrada (p. 240) Valor de una variable independiente.

Example The input is any value of x you substitute into a function.

Integers (p. 18) Whole numbers and their opposites.

Números enteros (p. 18) Números que constan exclusivamente de una o más unidades, y sus opuestos.

Example $\ldots -3, -2, -1, 0, 1, 2, 3, \ldots$

Interpolation (p. 334) The process of estimating a value between two known quantities.

Interpolación (p. 334) Proceso que se usa para estimar el valor entre dos cantidades dadas.

Interquartile range (p. 734) The interquartile range of a set of data is the difference between the third and first quartiles.

Intervalo intercuartil (p. 734) El rango intercuartil de un conjunto de datos es la diferencia entre el tercero y el primer cuartiles.

Example The first and third quartiles of the data set 2, 3, 4, 5, 5, 6, 7, and 7 are 3.5 and 6.5. The interquartile range is $6.5 - 3.5 = 3$.

Intersection (p. 215) The set of elements that are common to two or more sets.

Intersección (p. 215) El conjunto de elementos que son comunes a dos o más conjuntos.

Example If $C = \{1, 2, 3, 4\}$ and $D = \{2, 4, 6, 8\}$, then the intersection of C and D, or $C \cap D$, is $\{2, 4\}$.

Interval notation (p. 203) A notation for describing an interval on a number line. The interval's endpoint(s) are given, and a parenthesis or bracket is used to indicate whether each endpoint is included in the interval.

Notación de intervalo (p. 203) Notación que describe un intervalo en una recta numérica. Los extremos del intervalo se incluyen y se usa un paréntesis o corchete para indicar si cada extremo está incluido en el intervalo.

Example For $-2 \le x < 8$, the interval notation is $[-2, 8)$.

Page 824

English	Spanish

Inverse operations (p. 82) Operations that undo one another.

Example Addition and subtraction are inverse operations. Multiplication and division are inverse operations.

Operaciones inversas (p. 82) Las operaciones que se cancelan una a la otra.

Inverse variation (p. 680) An equation of the form $xy = k$ or $y = \frac{k}{x}$, where $k \neq 0$, is an inverse variation with constant of variation k.

Example The length x and the width y of a rectangle with a fixed area vary inversely. If the area is 40, $xy = 40$.

Variación inversa (p. 680) La ecuación $y = \frac{k}{x}$, ó $xy = k$, donde $k \neq 0$, es una variación inversa con una constante de variación k.

Irrational number (p. 18) A number that cannot be written as a ratio of two integers. Irrational numbers in decimal form are nonterminating and nonrepeating.

Example $\sqrt{11}$ and π are irrational numbers.

Número irracional (p. 18) Número que no puede expresarse como razón de dos números enteros. Los números irracionales en forma decimal no tienen término y no se repiten.

Isolate (p. 82) Using properties of equality and inverse operations to get a variable with a coefficient of 1 alone on one side of the equation.

Example
$$x + 3 = 7$$
$$x + 3 - 3 = 7 - 3$$
$$x = 4$$

Aislar (p. 82) Usar propiedades de igualdad y operaciones inversas para poner una variable con un coeficiente de 1 sola a un lado de la ecuación.

L

Leg (p. 600) Each of the sides that form the right angle of a right triangle.

Example

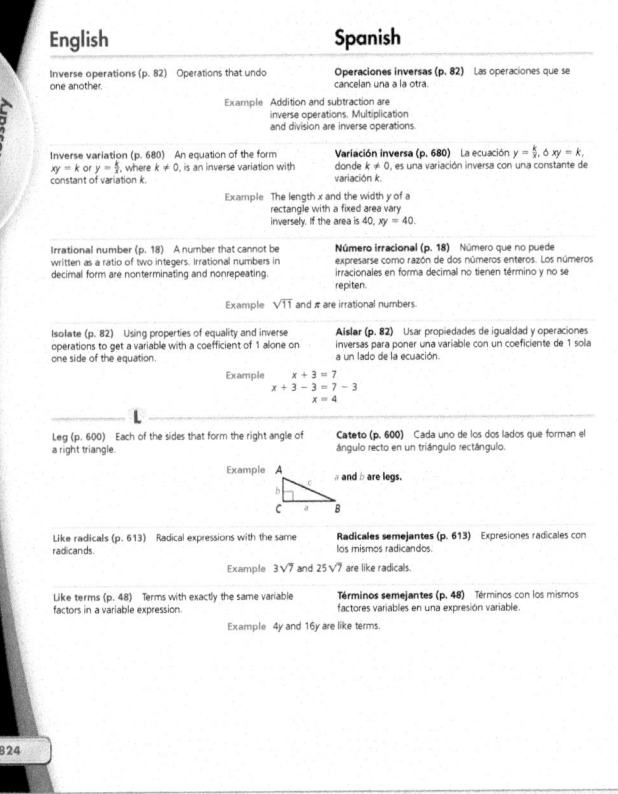

a and b are legs.

Cateto (p. 600) Cada uno de los dos lados que forman el ángulo recto en un triángulo rectángulo.

Like radicals (p. 613) Radical expressions with the same radicands.

Example $3\sqrt{7}$ and $25\sqrt{7}$ are like radicals.

Radicales semejantes (p. 613) Expresiones radicales con los mismos radicandos.

Like terms (p. 48) Terms with exactly the same variable factors in a variable expression.

Example $4y$ and $16y$ are like terms.

Términos semejantes (p. 48) Términos con los mismos factores variables en una expresión variable.

Page 825

English	Spanish

Linear equation (p. 306) An equation whose graph forms a straight line.

Example

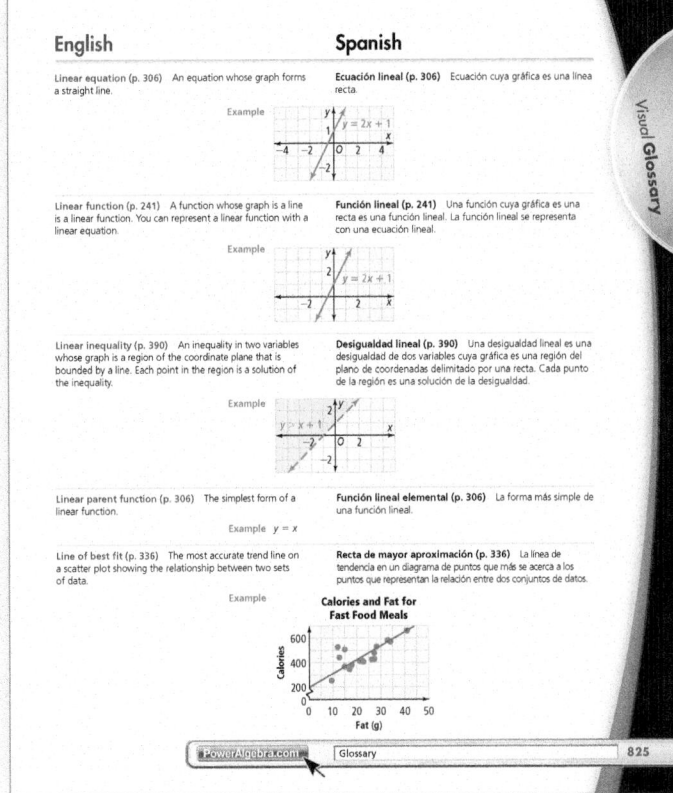

Ecuación lineal (p. 306) Ecuación cuya gráfica es una línea recta.

Linear function (p. 241) A function whose graph is a line is a linear function. You can represent a linear function with a linear equation.

Example

Función lineal (p. 241) Una función cuya gráfica es una recta es una función lineal. La función lineal se representa con una ecuación lineal.

Linear inequality (p. 390) An inequality in two variables whose graph is a region of the coordinate plane that is bounded by a line. Each point in the region is a solution of the inequality.

Example

Desigualdad lineal (p. 390) Una desigualdad lineal es una desigualdad de dos variables cuya gráfica es una región del plano de coordenadas delimitado por una recta. Cada punto de la región es una solución de la desigualdad.

Linear parent function (p. 306) The simplest form of a linear function.

Example $y = x$

Función lineal elemental (p. 306) La forma más simple de una función lineal.

Line of best fit (p. 336) The most accurate trend line on a scatter plot showing the relationship between two sets of data.

Example

Calories and Fat for Fast Food Meals

Recta de mayor aproximación (p. 336) La línea de tendencia en un diagrama de puntos que más se acerca a los puntos que representan la relación entre dos conjuntos de datos.

Page 826

English	Spanish

Literal equation (p. 109) An equation involving two or more variables.

Example $4x + 2y = 18$ is a literal equation.

Ecuación literal (p. 109) Ecuación que incluye dos o más variables.

M

Matrix (p. 714) A matrix is a rectangular array of numbers written within brackets. A matrix with m horizontal rows and n vertical columns is an $m \times n$ matrix.

Example $\begin{bmatrix} 2 & 5 & 6.3 \\ -8 & 0 & -1 \end{bmatrix}$ is a 2×3 matrix.

Matriz (p. 714) Una matriz es un conjunto de números encerrados en corchetes y dispuestos en forma de rectángulo. Una matriz que contenga m filas y n columnas es una matriz $m \times n$.

Maximum (p. 535) The y-coordinate of the vertex of a parabola that opens downward.

Example

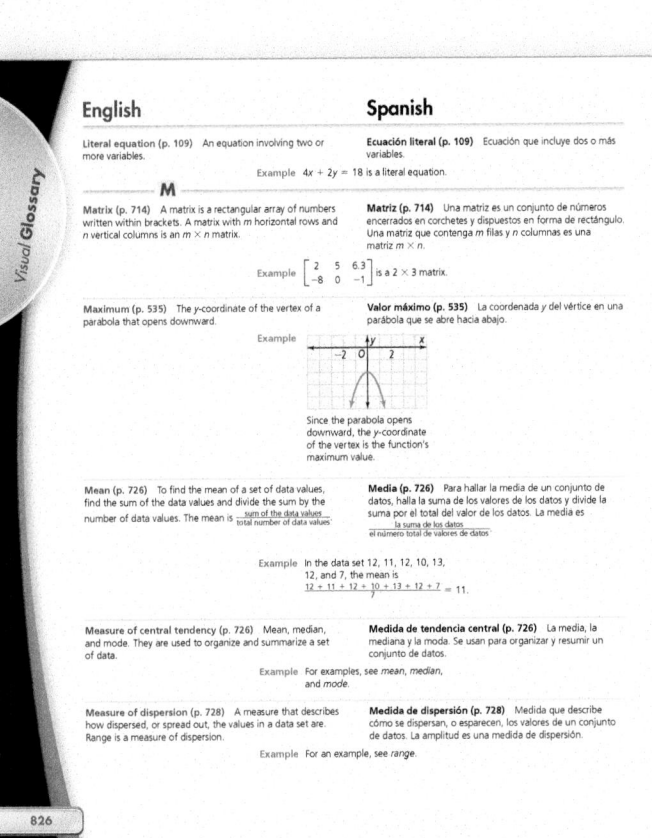

Since the parabola opens downward, the y-coordinate of the vertex is the function's maximum value.

Valor máximo (p. 535) La coordenada y del vértice en una parábola que se abre hacia abajo.

Mean (p. 726) To find the mean of a set of data values, find the sum of the data values and divide the sum by the number of data values. The mean is $\frac{\text{sum of the data values}}{\text{total number of data values}}$.

Example In the data set 12, 11, 12, 10, 13, 12, and 7, the mean is $\frac{12 + 11 + 12 + 10 + 13 + 12 + 7}{7} = 11$.

Media (p. 726) Para hallar la media de un conjunto de datos, halla la suma de los valores de los datos y divide la suma por el total del valor de los datos. La media es $\frac{\text{la suma de los datos}}{\text{el número total de valores de datos}}$.

Measure of central tendency (p. 726) Mean, median, and mode. They are used to organize and summarize a set of data.

Example For examples, see *mean*, *median*, and *mode*.

Medida de tendencia central (p. 726) La media, la mediana y la moda. Se usan para organizar o resumir un conjunto de datos.

Measure of dispersion (p. 728) A measure that describes how dispersed, or spread out, the values in a data set are. Range is a measure of dispersion.

Example For an example, see *range*.

Medida de dispersión (p. 728) Medida que describe cómo se dispersan, o esparecen, los valores de un conjunto de datos. La amplitud es una medida de dispersión.

Page 827

English	Spanish

Median (p. 726) The middle value in an ordered set of numbers.

Example In the data set 7, 10, 11, 12, 12, 12, and 13, the median is 12.

Mediana (p. 726) El valor del medio en un conjunto ordenado de números.

Midpoint (p. 605) The point M that divides a segment $\overline{AB}$ into two equal segments, $\overline{AM}$ and $\overline{MB}$.

Example M is the midpoint of $\overline{XY}$.

Punto medio (p. 605) El punto M que divide un segmento $\overline{AB}$ en dos segmentos iguales, $\overline{AM}$ y $\overline{MB}$.

Midpoint Formula (p. 605) The midpoint M of a line segment with endpoints $A(x_1, y_1)$ and $B(x_2, y_2)$ is $\left(\frac{x_1 + x_2}{2}, \frac{y_1 + y_2}{2}\right)$.

Example The midpoint of a segment with endpoints $A(3, 5)$ and $B(7, 1)$ is $(5, 3)$.

Fórmula del punto medio (p. 605) El punto medio M de un segmento con puntos extremos $A(x_1, y_1)$ y $B(x_2, y_2)$ es $\left(\frac{x_1 + x_2}{2}, \frac{y_1 + y_2}{2}\right)$.

Minimum (p. 535) The y-coordinate of the vertex of a parabola that opens upward.

Example

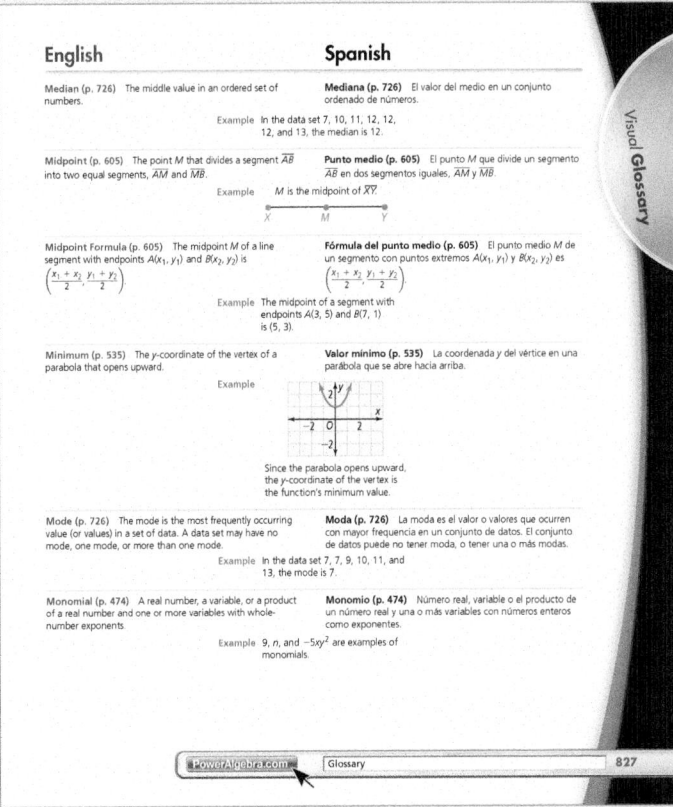

Since the parabola opens upward, the y-coordinate of the vertex is the function's minimum value.

Valor mínimo (p. 535) La coordenada y del vértice en una parábola que se abre hacia arriba.

Mode (p. 726) The mode is the most frequently occurring value (or values) in a set of data. A data set may have no mode, one mode, or more than one mode.

Example In the data set 7, 7, 9, 10, 11, and 13, the mode is 7.

Moda (p. 726) La moda es el valor o valores que ocurren con mayor frequencia en un conjunto de datos. El conjunto de datos puede no tener moda, o tener una o más modas.

Monomial (p. 474) A real number, a variable, or a product of a real number and one or more variables with whole-number exponents.

Example 9, n, and $-5xy^2$ are examples of monomials.

Monomio (p. 474) Número real, variable o el producto de un número real y una o más variables con números enteros como exponentes.

English | Spanish

Multiplication Counting Principle (p. 751) If there are m ways to make the first selection and n ways to make the second selection, then there are $m \cdot n$ ways to make the two selections.

Principio de Conteo en la Multiplicación (p. 751) Si hay m maneras de hacer la primera selección y n maneras de hacer la segunda selección, quiere decir que hay $m \cdot n$ maneras de hacer las dos selecciones.

Example For 5 shirts and 8 pairs of shorts, the number of possible outfits is $5 \cdot 8 = 40$.

Multiplicative inverse (p. 40) Given a nonzero rational number $\frac{a}{b}$, the multiplicative inverse, or reciprocal, is $\frac{b}{a}$. The product of a nonzero number and its multiplicative inverse is 1.

Inverso multiplicativo (p. 40) Dado un número racional $\frac{a}{b}$ distinto de cero, el inverso multiplicativo, o recíproco, es $\frac{b}{a}$. El producto de un número distinto de cero y su inverso multiplicativo es 1.

Example $\frac{4}{3}$ is the multiplicative inverse of $\frac{3}{4}$ because $\frac{3}{4} \times \frac{4}{3} = 1$.

Mutually exclusive events (p. 764) When two events cannot happen at the same time, the events are mutually exclusive. If A and B are mutually exclusive events, then $P(A \text{ or } B) = P(A) + P(B)$.

Sucesos mutuamente excluyentes (p. 764) Cuando dos sucesos no pueden ocurrir al mismo tiempo, son mutuamente excluyentes. Si A y B son sucesos mutuamente excluyentes, entonces $P(A \text{ o } B) = P(A) + P(B)$.

Example Rolling an even number E and rolling a multiple of five M on a standard number cube are mutually exclusive events.

$$P(E \text{ or } M) = P(E) + P(M)$$
$$= \frac{3}{6} + \frac{1}{6}$$
$$= \frac{4}{6}$$
$$= \frac{2}{3}$$

N

Natural numbers (p. 18) The counting numbers.

Números naturales (p. 18) Los números que se emplean para contar.

Example 1, 2, 3, . . .

Negative correlation (p. 333) The relationship between two sets of data, in which one set of data decreases as the other set of data increases.

Correlación negativa (p. 333) Relación entre dos conjuntos de datos en la que uno de los conjuntos disminuye a medida que el otro aumenta.

Example

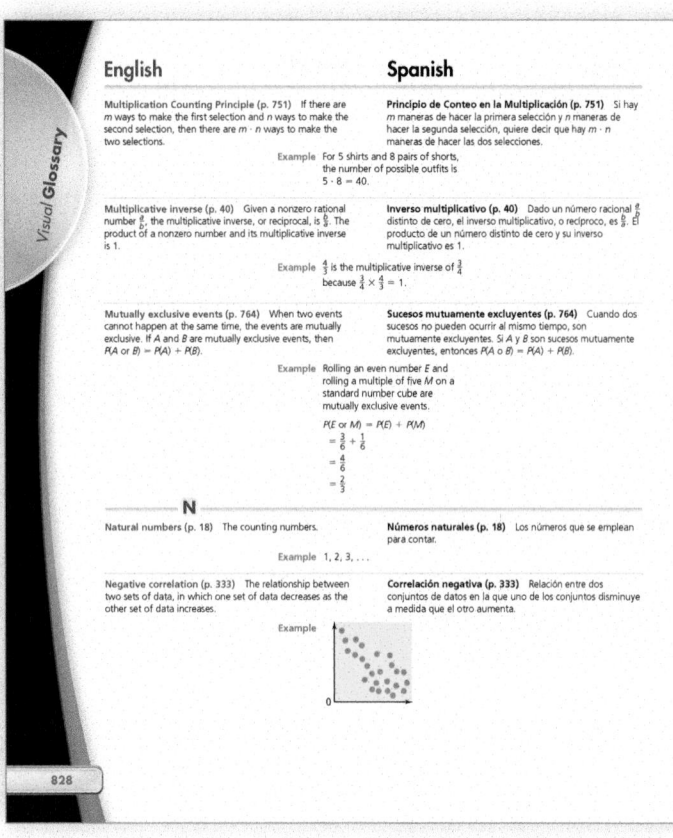

English | Spanish

Negative square root (p. 39) A number of the form $-\sqrt{b}$, which is the negative square root of b.

Raíz cuadrada negativa (p. 39) $-\sqrt{b}$ es la raíz cuadrada negativa de b.

Example -7 is the negative square root of $\sqrt{49}$.

n factorial (p. 752) The product of the integers from n down to 1, for any positive integer n. You write n factorial as $n!$. The value of 0! is defined to be 1.

n factorial (p. 752) Producto de todos los enteros desde n hasta 1, de cualquier entero positivo n. El factorial de n se escribe $n!$. El valor de 0! se define como 1.

Example $4! = 4 \times 3 \times 2 \times 1 = 24$

No correlation (p. 333) There does not appear to be a relationship between two sets of data.

Sin correlación (p. 333) No hay relación entre dos conjuntos de datos.

Example

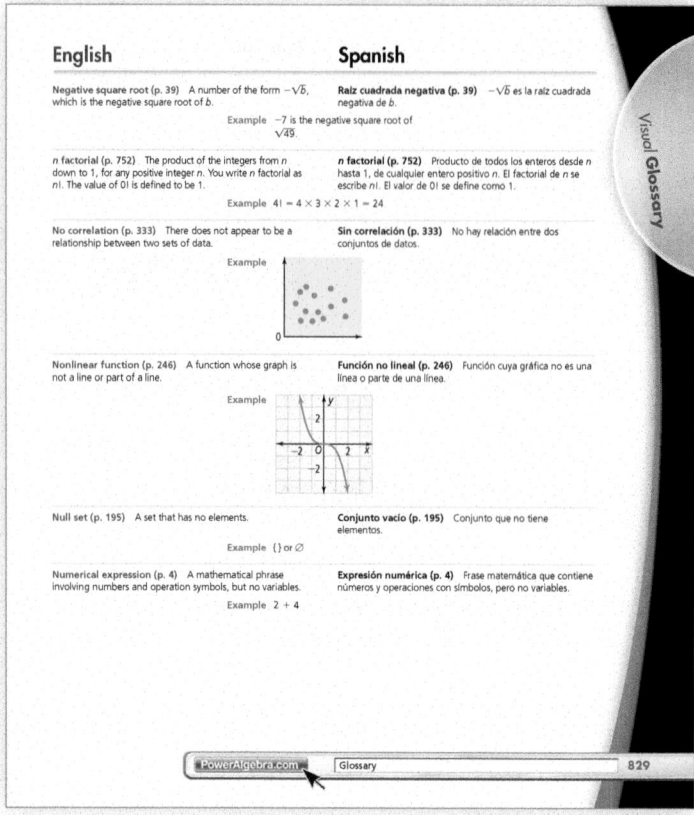

Nonlinear function (p. 246) A function whose graph is not a line or part of a line.

Función no lineal (p. 246) Función cuya gráfica no es una línea o parte de una línea.

Example

Null set (p. 195) A set that has no elements.

Conjunto vacío (p. 195) Conjunto que no tiene elementos.

Example $\{ \}$ or $\varnothing$

Numerical expression (p. 4) A mathematical phrase involving numbers and operation symbols, but no variables.

Expresión numérica (p. 4) Frase matemática que contiene números y operaciones con símbolos, pero no variables.

Example $2 + 4$

English | Spanish

O

Odds (p. 759) A ratio that compares the number of favorable and unfavorable outcomes. Odds in favor are number of favorable outcomes : number of unfavorable outcomes. Odds against are number of unfavorable outcomes : number of favorable outcomes.

Probabilidad a favor (p. 759) Razón que compara el número de resultados favorables y no favorables. Las posibilidades a favor son el número de resultados favorables : número de resultados no favorables. Las posibilidades en contra son el número de resultados no favorables : número de resultados favorables.

Example You have 3 red marbles and 5 blue marbles. The odds in favor of selecting red are 3 : 5.

Open sentence (p. 53) An equation that contains one or more variables and may be true or false depending on the value of its variables.

Enunciado abierto (p. 53) Una ecuación es un enunciado abierto si contiene una o más variables y puede ser verdadera o falsa dependiendo del valor de sus variables.

Example $5 + x = 12$ is an open sentence.

Opposite (p. 32) A number that is the same distance from zero on the number line as a given number, but lies in the opposite direction.

Opuestos (p. 32) Dos números son opuestos si están a la misma distancia del cero en la recta numérica, pero en sentido opuesto.

Example -3 and 3 are opposites.

Opposite reciprocals (p. 328) A number of the form $-\frac{b}{a}$, where $\frac{a}{b}$ is a nonzero rational number. The product of a number and its opposite reciprocal is -1.

Recíproco inverso (p. 328) Número en la forma $-\frac{b}{a}$, donde $\frac{a}{b}$ es un número racional diferente de cero. El producto de un número y su recíproco inverso es -1.

Example $\frac{2}{3}$ and $-\frac{3}{2}$ are opposite reciprocals because $\left(\frac{2}{3}\right)\left(-\frac{3}{2}\right) = -1$.

Ordered pair (p. 60) Two numbers that identify the location of a point.

Par ordenado (p. 60) Un par ordenado de números que denota la ubicación de un punto.

Example The ordered pair $(4, -1)$ identifies the point 4 units to the right on the x-axis and 1 unit down on the y-axis.

Order of operations (p. 11)
1. Perform any operation(s) inside grouping symbols.
2. Simplify powers.
3. Multiply and divide in order from left to right.
4. Add and subtract in order from left to right.

Orden de las operaciones (p. 11)
1. Se hacen las operaciones que están dentro de símbolos de agrupación.
2. Se simplifican todos los términos que tengan exponentes.
3. Se hacen las multiplicaciones y divisiones en orden de izquierda a derecha.
4. Se hacen las sumas y restas en orden de izquierda a derecha.

Example $6 - (4^2 - [2 \cdot 5]) \div 3$
$= 6 - (16 - 10) \div 3$
$= 6 - 6 \div 3$
$= 6 - 2$
$= 4$

English | Spanish

Origin (p. 60) The point at which the axes of the coordinate plane intersect.

Origen (p. 60) Punto de intersección de los ejes del plano de coordenadas.

Example

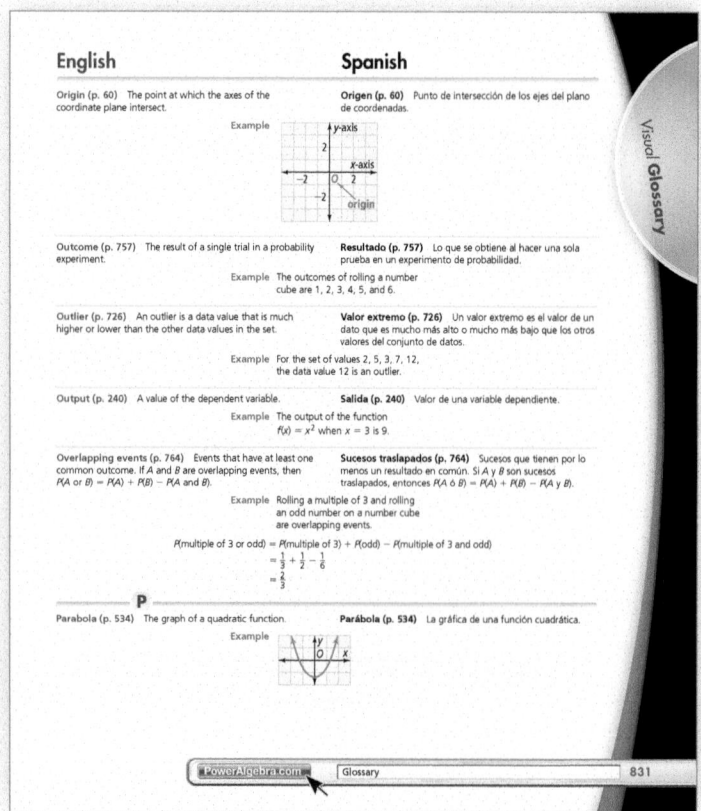

Outcome (p. 757) The result of a single trial in a probability experiment.

Resultado (p. 757) Lo que se obtiene al hacer una sola prueba en un experimento de probabilidad.

Example The outcomes of rolling a number cube are 1, 2, 3, 4, 5, and 6.

Outlier (p. 726) An outlier is a data value that is much higher or lower than the other data values in the set.

Valor extremo (p. 726) Un valor extremo es el valor de un dato que es mucho más alto o mucho más bajo que los otros valores del conjunto de datos.

Example For the set of values 2, 5, 3, 7, 12, the data value 12 is an outlier.

Output (p. 240) A value of the dependent variable.

Salida (p. 240) Valor de una variable dependiente.

Example The output of the function $f(x) = x^2$ when $x = 3$ is 9.

Overlapping events (p. 764) Events that have at least one common outcome. If A and B are overlapping events, then $P(A \text{ or } B) = P(A) + P(B) - P(A \text{ and } B)$.

Sucesos traslapados (p. 764) Sucesos que tienen por lo menos un resultado en común. Si A y B son sucesos traslapados, entonces $P(A \text{ ó } B) = P(A) + P(B) - P(A \text{ y } B)$.

Example Rolling a multiple of 3 and rolling an odd number on a number cube are overlapping events.

$$P(\text{multiple of 3 or odd}) = P(\text{multiple of 3}) + P(\text{odd}) - P(\text{multiple of 3 and odd})$$
$$= \frac{1}{3} + \frac{1}{2} - \frac{1}{6}$$
$$= \frac{2}{3}$$

P

Parabola (p. 534) The graph of a quadratic function.

Parábola (p. 534) La gráfica de una función cuadrática.

Example

English | Spanish

Parallel lines (p. 327) Two lines in the same plane that never intersect. Parallel lines have the same slope.

Rectas paralelas (p. 327) Dos rectas situadas en el mismo plano que nunca se cortan. Las rectas paralelas tienen la misma pendiente.

Example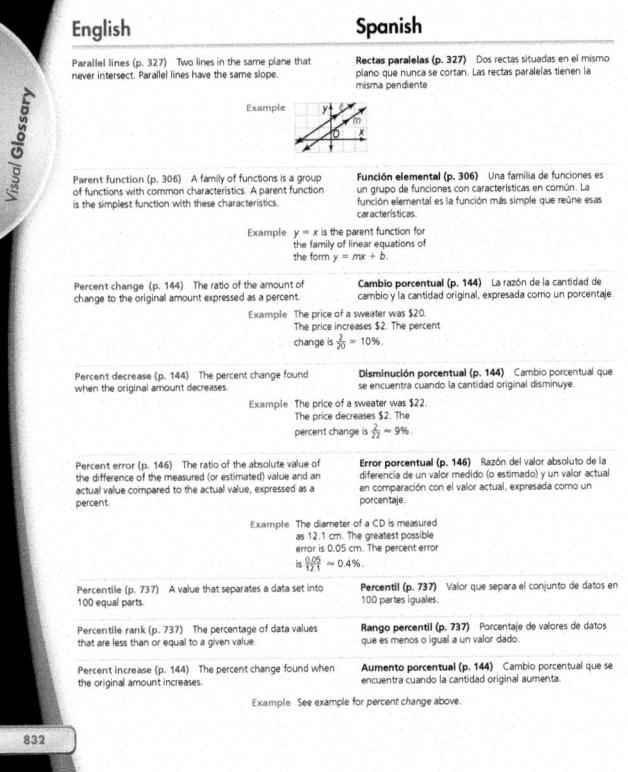

Parent function (p. 306) A family of functions is a group of functions with common characteristics. A parent function is the simplest function with these characteristics.

Función elemental (p. 306) Una familia de funciones es un grupo de funciones con características en común. La función elemental es la función más simple que reúne esas características.

Example $y = x$ is the parent function for the family of linear equations of the form $y = mx + b$.

Percent change (p. 144) The ratio of the amount of change to the original amount expressed as a percent.

Cambio porcentual (p. 144) La razón de la cantidad de cambio y la cantidad original, expresada como un porcentaje.

Example The price of a sweater was $20. The price increases $2. The percent change is $\frac{2}{20} = 10\%$.

Percent decrease (p. 144) The percent change found when the original amount decreases.

Disminución porcentual (p. 144) Cambio porcentual que se encuentra cuando la cantidad original disminuye.

Example The price of a sweater was $22. The price decreases $2. The percent change is $\frac{2}{22} \approx 9\%$.

Percent error (p. 146) The ratio of the absolute value of the difference of the measured (or estimated) value and an actual value compared to the actual value, expressed as a percent.

Error porcentual (p. 146) Razón del valor absoluto de la diferencia de un valor medido (o estimado) y un valor actual en comparación con el valor actual, expresada como un porcentaje.

Example The diameter of a CD is measured as 12.1 cm. The greatest possible error is 0.05 cm. The percent error is $\frac{0.05}{12.1} \approx 0.4\%$.

Percentile (p. 737) A value that separates a data set into 100 equal parts.

Percentil (p. 737) Valor que separa el conjunto de datos en 100 partes iguales.

Percentile rank (p. 737) The percentage of data values that are less than or equal to a given value.

Rango percentil (p. 737) Porcentaje de valores de datos que es menos o igual a un valor dado.

Percent increase (p. 144) The percent change found when the original amount increases.

Aumento porcentual (p. 144) Cambio porcentual que se encuentra cuando la cantidad original aumenta.

Example See example for *percent change* above.

832

English | Spanish

Perfect squares (p. 17) Numbers whose square roots are integers.

Cuadrado perfecto (p. 17) Número cuya raíz cuadrada es un número entero.

Example The numbers 1, 4, 9, 16, 25, 36, . . . are perfect squares because they are the squares of integers.

Perfect square trinomial (p. 511) Any trinomial of the form $a^2 + 2ab + b^2$ or $a^2 - 2ab + b^2$.

Trinomio cuadrado perfecto (p. 511) Todo trinomio de la forma $a^2 + 2ab + b^2$ ó $a^2 - 2ab + b^2$.

Example $(x + 3)^2 = x^2 + 6x + 9$

Permutation (p. 751) An arrangement of some or all of a set of objects in a specific order. You can use the notation $_nP_r$ to express the number of permutations, where n equals the number of objects available and r equals the number of selections to make.

Permutación (p. 751) Disposición de algunos o de todos los objetos de un conjunto en un orden determinado. El número de permutaciones se puede expresar con la notación $_nP_r$, donde n es igual al número total de objetos y r es igual al número de selecciones que han de hacerse.

Example How many ways can you arrange 5 objects 3 at a time?
$$_5P_3 = \frac{5!}{(5-3)!} = \frac{5!}{2!} = \frac{5 \cdot 4 \cdot 3 \cdot 2 \cdot 1}{2 \cdot 1} = 60$$
There are 60 ways to arrange 5 objects 3 at a time.

Perpendicular lines (p. 328) Lines that intersect to form right angles. Two lines are perpendicular if the product of their slopes is -1.

Rectas perpendiculares (p. 328) Rectas que forman ángulos rectos en su intersección. Dos rectas son perpendiculares si el producto de sus pendientes es -1.

Example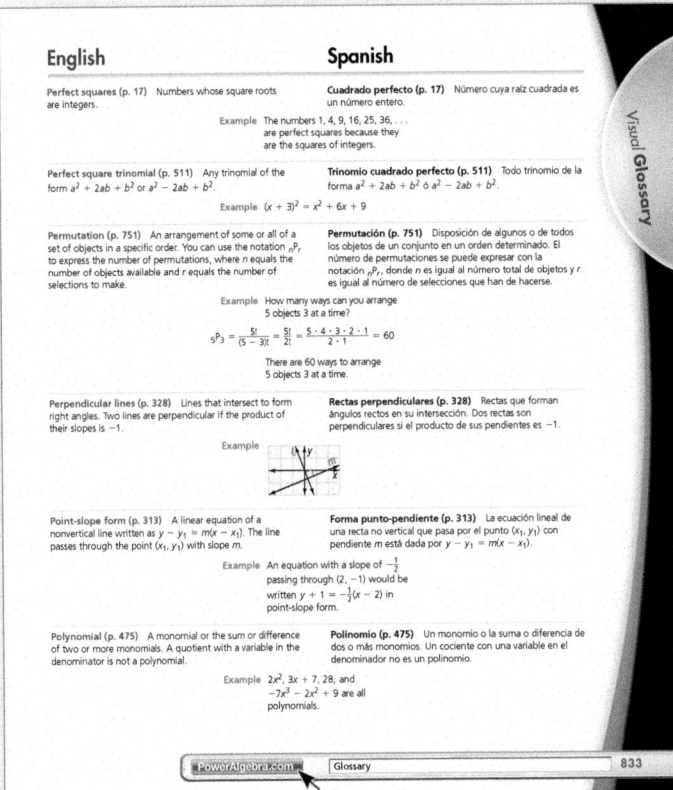

Point-slope form (p. 313) A linear equation of a nonvertical line written as $y - y_1 = m(x - x_1)$. The line passes through the point (x_1, y_1) with slope m.

Forma punto-pendiente (p. 313) La ecuación lineal de una recta no vertical que pasa por el punto (x_1, y_1) con pendiente m está dada por $y - y_1 = m(x - x_1)$.

Example An equation with a slope of $-\frac{1}{2}$ passing through $(2, -1)$ would be written $y + 1 = -\frac{1}{2}(x - 2)$ in point-slope form.

Polynomial (p. 475) A monomial or the sum or difference of two or more monomials. A quotient with a variable in the denominator is not a polynomial.

Polinomio (p. 475) Un monomio o la suma o diferencia de dos o más monomios. Un cociente con una variable en el denominador no es un polinomio.

Example $2x^2$, $3x + 7$, 28, and $-7x^3 - 2x^2 + 9$ are all polynomials.

English | Spanish

Population (p. 742) The entire group that you are collecting information about.

Población (p. 742) El grupo entero del cual juntas información.

Positive correlation (p. 333) The relationship between two sets of data in which both sets of data increase together.

Correlación positiva (p. 333) La relación entre dos conjuntos de datos en la que ambos conjuntos incrementan a la vez.

Example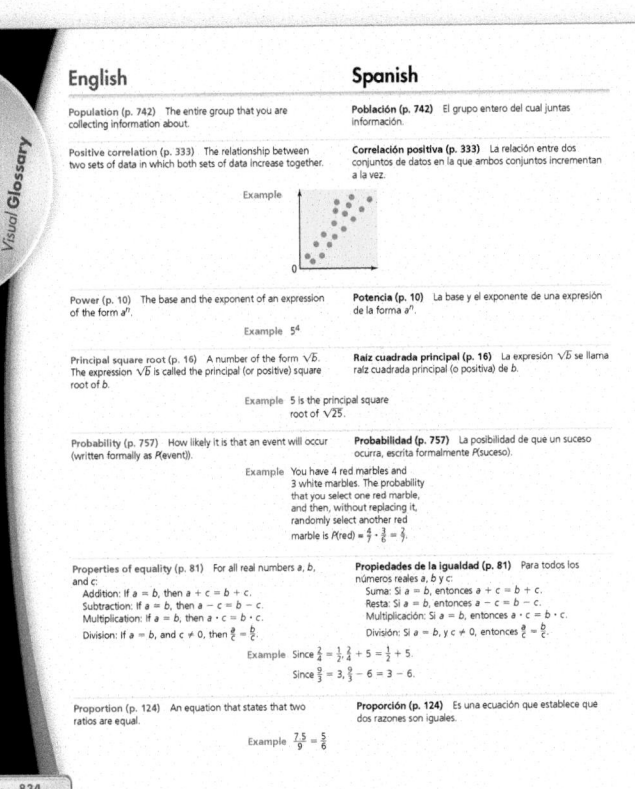

Power (p. 10) The base and the exponent of an expression of the form a^n.

Potencia (p. 10) La base y el exponente de una expresión de la forma a^n.

Example 5^4

Principal square root (p. 16) A number of the form $\sqrt{b}$. The expression $\sqrt{b}$ is called the principal (or positive) square root of b.

Raíz cuadrada principal (p. 16) La expresión $\sqrt{b}$ se llama raíz cuadrada principal (o positiva) de b.

Example 5 is the principal square root of $\sqrt{25}$.

Probability (p. 757) How likely it is that an event will occur (written formally as P(event)).

Probabilidad (p. 757) La posibilidad de que un suceso ocurra, escrita formalmente P(suceso).

Example You have 4 red marbles and 3 white marbles. The probability that you select one red marble, and then, without replacing it, randomly select another red marble is $P(\text{red}) = \frac{4}{7} \cdot \frac{3}{6} = \frac{2}{7}$.

Properties of equality (p. 81) For all real numbers a, b, and c:
Addition: If $a = b$, then $a + c = b + c$.
Subtraction: If $a = b$, then $a - c = b - c$.
Multiplication: If $a = b$, then $a \cdot c = b \cdot c$.
Division: If $a = b$, and $c \neq 0$, then $\frac{a}{c} = \frac{b}{c}$.

Propiedades de la igualdad (p. 81) Para todos los números reales a, b y c:
Suma: Si $a = b$, entonces $a + c = b + c$.
Resta: Si $a = b$, entonces $a - c = b - c$.
Multiplicación: Si $a = b$, entonces $a \cdot c = b \cdot c$.
División: Si $a = b$, y $c \neq 0$, entonces $\frac{a}{c} = \frac{b}{c}$.

Example Since $\frac{2}{4} = \frac{1}{2}$, $\frac{2}{4} + 5 = \frac{1}{2} + 5$. Since $\frac{3}{3} = 3$, $\frac{3}{3} - 6 = 3 - 6$.

Proportion (p. 124) An equation that states that two ratios are equal.

Proporción (p. 124) Es una ecuación que establece que dos razones son iguales.

Example $\frac{7.5}{9} = \frac{5}{6}$

834

English | Spanish

Pythagorean Theorem (p. 600) In any right triangle, the sum of the squares of the lengths of the legs is equal to the square of the length of the hypotenuse: $a^2 + b^2 = c^2$.

Teorema de Pitágoras (p. 600) En un triángulo rectángulo, la suma de los cuadrados de los catetos es igual al cuadrado de la hipotenusa: $a^2 + b^2 = c^2$.

Example 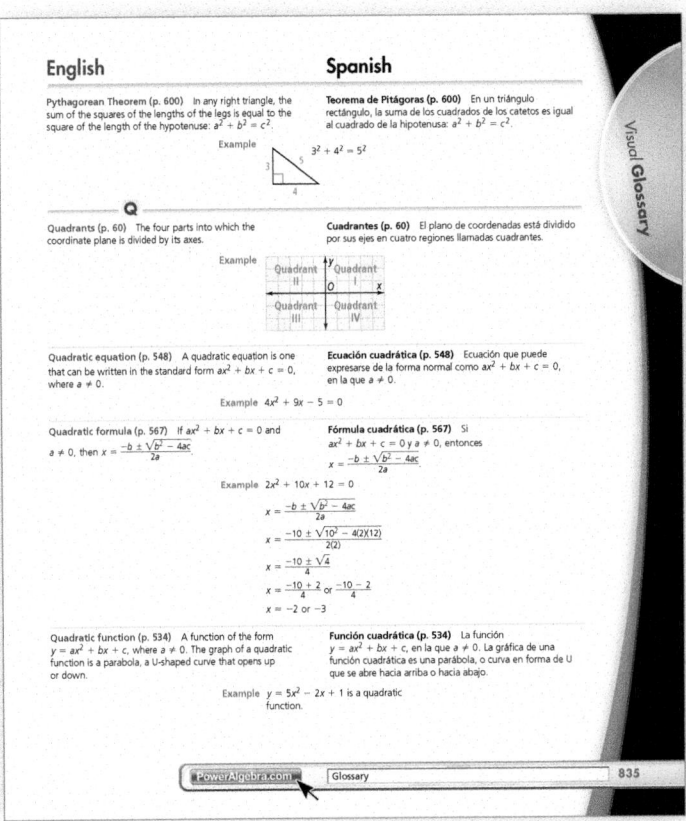 $3^2 + 4^2 = 5^2$

Q

Quadrants (p. 60) The four parts into which the coordinate plane is divided by its axes.

Cuadrantes (p. 60) El plano de coordenadas está dividido por sus ejes en cuatro regiones llamadas cuadrantes.

Example

Quadratic equation (p. 548) A quadratic equation is one that can be written in the standard form $ax^2 + bx + c = 0$, where $a \neq 0$.

Ecuación cuadrática (p. 548) Ecuación que puede expresarse de la forma normal como $ax^2 + bx + c = 0$, en la que $a \neq 0$.

Example $4x^2 + 9x - 5 = 0$

Quadratic formula (p. 567) If $ax^2 + bx + c = 0$ and $a \neq 0$, then $x = \frac{-b \pm \sqrt{b^2 - 4ac}}{2a}$.

Fórmula cuadrática (p. 567) Si $ax^2 + bx + c = 0$ y $a \neq 0$, entonces $x = \frac{-b \pm \sqrt{b^2 - 4ac}}{2a}$.

Example $2x^2 + 10x + 12 = 0$
$$x = \frac{-b \pm \sqrt{b^2 - 4ac}}{2a}$$
$$x = \frac{-10 \pm \sqrt{10^2 - 4(2)(12)}}{2(2)}$$
$$x = \frac{-10 \pm \sqrt{4}}{4}$$
$$x = \frac{-10 + 2}{4} \text{ or } \frac{-10 - 2}{4}$$
$$x = -2 \text{ or } -3$$

Quadratic function (p. 534) A function of the form $y = ax^2 + bx + c$, where $a \neq 0$. The graph of a quadratic function is a parabola, a U-shaped curve that opens up or down.

Función cuadrática (p. 534) La función $y = ax^2 + bx + c$, en la que $a \neq 0$. La gráfica de una función cuadrática es una parábola, o curva en forma de U que se abre hacia arriba o hacia abajo.

Example $y = 5x^2 - 2x + 1$ is a quadratic function.

English / Spanish

Quadratic parent function (p. 534) The simplest quadratic function $f(x) = x^2$ or $y = x^2$.

Función cuadrática madre (p. 534) La función cuadrática más simple $f(x) = x^2$ o $y = x^2$.

Example $y = x^2$ is the parent function for the family of quadratic equations of the form $y = ax^2 + bx + c$.

Qualitative (p. 741) Data that name qualities are qualitative.

Cualitativo (p. 741) Los datos que indican cualidades son cualitativos.

Example The data red, blue, red, green, blue, and blue are qualitative data.

Quantitative (p. 741) Data that measure quantity and can be described numerically are quantitative.

Cuantitativo (p. 741) Los datos que miden cantidades y pueden ser descritos numéricamente son cuantitativos.

Example The data 5 ft, 4 ft, 7 ft, 4 ft, 8 ft, and 10 ft are quantitative.

Quantity (p. 4) Anything that can be measured or counted.

Cantidad (p. 4) Cualquier cosa que se puede medir o contar.

Example A dozen is another way to describe a quantity of 12 eggs.

Quartile (p. 734) A quartile is a value that separates a finite data set into four equal parts. The second quartile (Q_2) is the median of the data set. The first and third quartiles (Q_1 and Q_3) are the medians of the lower half and upper half of the data, respectively.

Cuartil (p. 734) Un cuartil es el valor que separa un conjunto de datos finitos en cuatro partes iguales. El segundo cuartil (Q_2) es la mediana del conjunto de datos. El primer cuartil y el tercer cuartil (Q_1 y Q_3) son medianas de la mitad inferior y de la mitad superior de los datos, respectivamente.

Example For the data set 2, 3, 4, 5, 5, 6, 7, 7, the first quartile is 3.5, the second quartile (or median) is 5, and the third quartile is 6.5.

R

Radical (p. 16) An expression made up of a radical symbol and a radicand.

Radical (p. 16) Expresión compuesta por un símbolo radical y un radicando.

Example $\sqrt{a}$

Radical equation (p. 620) An equation that has a variable in a radicand.

Ecuación radical (p. 620) Ecuación que tiene una variable en un radicando.

Example $\sqrt{x} - 2 = 12$
$\sqrt{x} = 14$
$(\sqrt{x})^2 = 14^2$
$x = 196$

Radical expression (p. 606) Expression that contains a radical.

Expresión radical (p. 606) Expresiones que contienen radicales.

Example $\sqrt{3}$, $\sqrt{5x}$, and $\sqrt{x-10}$ are examples of radical expressions.

English / Spanish

Radicand (p. 16) The expression under the radical sign is the radicand.

Radicando (p. 16) La expresión que aparece debajo del signo radical es el radicando.

Example The radicand of the radical expression $\sqrt{x+2}$ is $x + 2$.

Range (of a relation or function) (p. 268) The possible values of the output, or dependent variable, of a relation or function.

Rango (de una relación o función) (p. 268) El conjunto de todos los valores posibles de la salida, o variable dependiente, de una relación o función.

Example In the function $y = |x|$, the range is the set of all nonnegative numbers.

Range of a set of data (p. 728) The difference between the greatest and the least data values for a set of data.

Rango de un conjunto de datos (p. 728) Diferencia entre el valor mayor y el menor en un conjunto de datos.

Example For the set 2, 5, 8, 12, the range is $12 - 2 = 10$.

Rate (p. 118) A ratio of a to b where a and b represent quantities measured in different units.

Tasa (p. 118) La relación que existe entre a y b cuando a y b son cantidades medidas con distintas unidades.

Example Traveling 125 miles in 2 hours results in the rate $\frac{125 \text{ miles}}{2 \text{ hours}}$ or 62.5 mi/h.

Rate of change (p. 292) The relationship between two quantities that are changing. The rate of change is also called slope.

Tasa de cambio (p. 292) La relación entre dos cantidades que cambian. La tasa de cambio se llama también pendiente.

rate of change $= \frac{\text{change in the dependent variable}}{\text{change in the independent variable}}$

tasa de cambio $= \frac{\text{cambio en la variable dependiente}}{\text{cambio en la variable independiente}}$

Example Video rental for 1 day is \$1.99.
Video rental for 2 days is \$2.99.
rate of change $= \frac{2.99 - 1.99}{2 - 1}$
$= \frac{1.00}{1}$
$= 1$

Ratio (p. 118) A ratio is the comparison of two quantities by division.

Razón (p. 118) Una razón es la comparación de dos cantidades por medio de una división.

Example $\frac{2}{7}$ and 7 : 3 are ratios.

Rational equation (p. 673) An equation containing rational expressions.

Ecuación racional (p. 673) Ecuación que contiene expresiones racionales.

Example $\frac{1}{x} = \frac{3}{2x-1}$ is a rational equation.

English / Spanish

Rational expression (p. 646) A ratio of two polynomials. The value of the variable cannot make the denominator equal to 0.

Expresión racional (p. 646) Una razón de dos polinomios. El valor de la variable no puede hacer el denominador igual a 0.

Example $\frac{3}{x^2 + x}$, where $x \neq 0$

Rational function (p. 687) A function that can be written in the form $f(x) = \frac{\text{polynomial}}{\text{polynomial}}$. The value of the variable cannot make the denominator equal to 0.

Función racional (p. 687) Función que puede expresarse de forma $f(x) = \frac{\text{polinomio}}{\text{polinomio}}$. El valor de la variable no puede hacer el denominador igual a 0.

Example $y = \frac{x}{x^2 + 2}$

Rationalize the denominator (p. 609) To rationalize the denominator of an expression, rewrite it so there are no radicals in any denominator and no denominators in any radical.

Racionalizar el denominador (p. 609) Para racionalizar el denominador de una expresión, ésta se escribe de modo que no haya radicales en ningún denominador y no haya denominadores en ningún radical.

Example $\frac{2}{\sqrt{5}} = \frac{2}{\sqrt{5}} \cdot \frac{\sqrt{5}}{\sqrt{5}} = \frac{2\sqrt{5}}{\sqrt{25}} = \frac{2\sqrt{5}}{5}$

Rational number (p. 18) A real number that can be written as a ratio of two integers. Rational numbers in decimal form are terminating or repeating.

Número racional (p. 18) Número real que puede expresarse como la razón de dos números enteros. Los números racionales en forma decimal son exactos o periódicos.

Example $\frac{2}{3}$, 1.548, and 2.292929 . . . are all rational numbers.

Real number (p. 18) A number that is either rational or irrational.

Número real (p. 18) Un número que es o racional o irracional.

Example 5, -3, $\sqrt{11}$, 0.666 . . . , $5\frac{4}{11}$, 0, and π are all real numbers.

Reciprocal (p. 41) Given a nonzero rational number $\frac{a}{b}$, the reciprocal, or multiplicative inverse, is $\frac{b}{a}$. The product of a nonzero number and its reciprocal is 1.

Recíproco (p. 41) El recíproco, o inverso multiplicativo, de un número racional $\frac{a}{b}$ cuyo valor no es cero es $\frac{b}{a}$. El producto de un número que no es cero y su valor recíproco es 1.

Example $\frac{3}{2}$ and $\frac{2}{3}$ are reciprocals because $\frac{3}{2} \times \frac{2}{3} = 1$.

Relation (p. 268) Any set of ordered pairs.

Relación (p. 268) Cualquier conjunto de pares ordenados.

Example $\{(0, 0), (2, 3), (2, -7)\}$ is a relation.

English / Spanish

Relative error (p. 146) The ratio of the absolute value of the difference of a measured (or estimated) value and an actual value compared to the actual value.

Error relativo (p. 146) Razón del valor absoluto de la diferencia de un valor medido (o estimado) y un valor actual en comparación con el valor actual.

Example You estimated that a plant would be 5 in. tall 3 months after it was planted. The plant was actually 5.5 in. tall 3 months after it was planted. The relative error is
$\frac{|5 - 5.5|}{5.5} = \frac{|-0.5|}{5.5} = \frac{0.5}{5.5} = \frac{1}{11}$, or about 9%.

Root of the equation (p. 548) A solution of an equation.

Raíz de la ecuación (p. 548) Solución de una ecuación.

Roster form (p. 194) A notation for listing all of the elements in a set using set braces and commas.

Lista (p. 194) Una notación en la que se enlistan todos los elementos en un conjunto usando llaves y comas.

Example The set of prime numbers less than 10, expressed in roster form, is $\{2, 3, 5, 7\}$.

S

Sample (p. 742) The part of a population that is surveyed.

Muestra (p. 742) Porción que se estudia de una población.

Example Let the set of all males between the ages of 19 and 34 be the population. A random selection of 900 males between those ages would be a sample of the population.

Sample space (p. 757) All possible outcomes in a situation.

Espacio muestral (p. 757) Todos los resultados posibles de una ecuación.

Example When you roll a number cube, the sample space is $\{1, 2, 3, 4, 5, 6\}$.

Scalar (p. 715) A real number is called a scalar for certain special uses, such as multiplying a matrix. See Scalar multiplication.

Escalar (p. 715) Un número real se llama escalar en ciertos casos especiales, como en la multiplicación de una matriz. Ver Scalar multiplication.

Example $2.5 \begin{bmatrix} 1 & 0 \\ -2 & 3 \end{bmatrix} = \begin{bmatrix} 2.5(1) & 2.5(0) \\ 2.5(-2) & 2.5(3) \end{bmatrix}$
$= \begin{bmatrix} 2.5 & 0 \\ -5 & 7.5 \end{bmatrix}$

English / Spanish

Scalar multiplication (p. 715) Scalar multiplication is an operation that multiplies a matrix A by a scalar c. To find the resulting matrix cA, multiply each element of A by c.

Multiplicación escalar (p. 715) La multiplicación escalar es la que multiplica una matriz A por un número escalar c. Para hallar la matriz resultante cA, multiplica cada elemento de A por c.

Example $2.5 \begin{bmatrix} 1 & 0 \\ -2 & 3 \end{bmatrix} = \begin{bmatrix} 2.5(1) & 2.5(0) \\ 2.5(-2) & 2.5(3) \end{bmatrix}$
$= \begin{bmatrix} 2.5 & 0 \\ -5 & 7.5 \end{bmatrix}$

Scale (p. 132) The ratio of any length in a scale drawing to the corresponding actual length. The lengths may be in different units.

Escala (p. 132) Razón de cualquier longitud de un dibujo a escala a la longitud real correspondiente. Las longitudes pueden tener diferentes unidades.

Example For a drawing in which a 2-in. length represents an actual length of 18 ft, the scale is 1 in. : 9 ft.

Scale drawing (p. 132) An enlarged or reduced drawing similar to an actual object or place.

Dibujo a escala (p. 132) Dibujo que muestra de mayor o menor tamaño un objeto o lugar dado.

Example

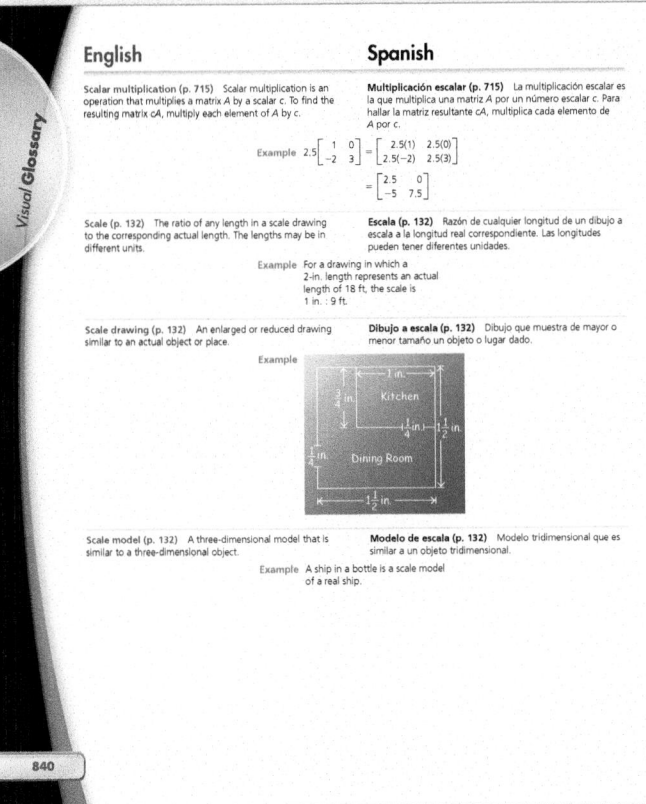

Scale model (p. 132) A three-dimensional model that is similar to a three-dimensional object.

Modelo de escala (p. 132) Modelo tridimensional que es similar a un objeto tridimensional.

Example A ship in a bottle is a scale model of a real ship.

Scatter plot (p. 333) A graph that relates two different sets of data by displaying them as ordered pairs.

Diagrama de puntos (p. 333) Gráfica que muestra la relación entre dos conjuntos. Los datos de ambos conjuntos se presentan como pares ordenados.

Example

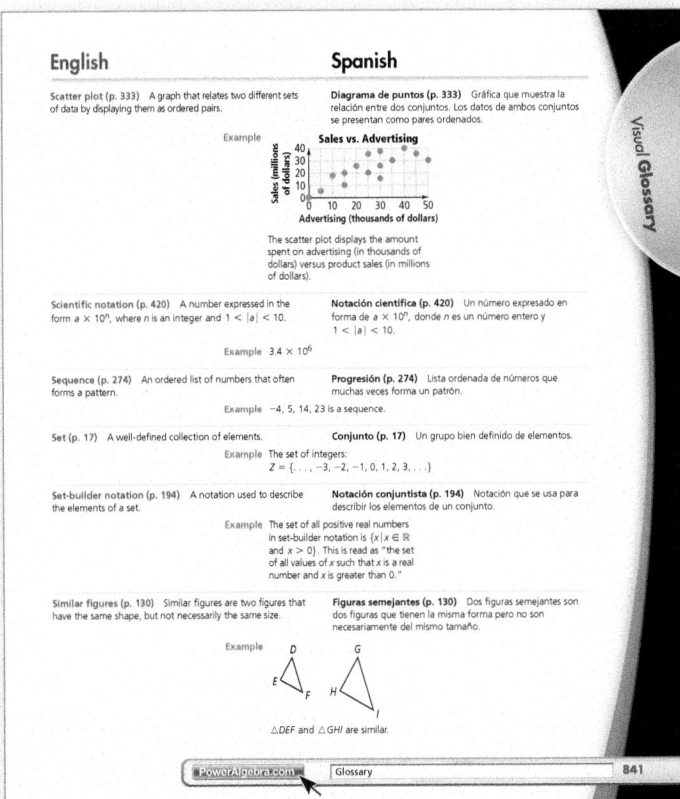

The scatter plot displays the amount spent on advertising (in thousands of dollars) versus product sales (in millions of dollars).

Scientific notation (p. 420) A number expressed in the form $a \times 10^n$, where n is an integer and $1 < |a| < 10$.

Notación científica (p. 420) Un número expresado en forma de $a \times 10^n$, donde n es un número entero y $1 < |a| < 10$.

Example 3.4×10^6

Sequence (p. 274) An ordered list of numbers that often forms a pattern.

Progresión (p. 274) Lista ordenada de números que muchas veces forma un patrón.

Example -4, 5, 14, 23 is a sequence.

Set (p. 17) A well-defined collection of elements.

Conjunto (p. 17) Un grupo bien definido de elementos.

Example The set of integers:
$Z = \{\ldots, -3, -2, -1, 0, 1, 2, 3, \ldots\}$

Set-builder notation (p. 194) A notation used to describe the elements of a set.

Notación conjuntista (p. 194) Notación que se usa para describir los elementos de un conjunto.

Example The set of all positive real numbers in set-builder notation is $\{x \mid x \in \mathbb{R} \text{ and } x > 0\}$. This is read as "the set of all values of x such that x is a real number and x is greater than 0."

Similar figures (p. 130) Similar figures are two figures that have the same shape, but not necessarily the same size.

Figuras semejantes (p. 130) Dos figuras semejantes son dos figuras que tienen la misma forma pero no son necesariamente del mismo tamaño.

Example

$\triangle DEF$ and $\triangle GHI$ are similar.

Simple interest (p. 139) Interest paid only on the principal.

Interés simple (p. 139) Interés basado en el capital solamente.

Example The interest on $1000 at 6% for 5 years is $1000(0.06)5 = $300.

Simplify (p. 10) To replace an expression with its simplest name or form.

Simplificar (p. 10) Reemplazar una expresión por su versión o forma más simple.

Example $\frac{3 + 5}{8}$.

Sine (p. 633) In a right triangle, such as $\triangle ABC$, with right $\angle C$,
$\text{sine of } \angle A = \frac{\text{length of side opposite } \angle A}{\text{length of hypotenuse}}$ or $\sin A = \frac{a}{c}$.

Seno (p. 633) En un triángulo rectángulo tal que $\triangle ABC$ con $\angle C$ recto,
$\text{el seno de } \angle A = \frac{\text{longitud del lado opuesto a } \angle A}{\text{longitud de la hipotenusa}}$, o $\text{sen } A = \frac{a}{c}$.

Example $\sin A = \frac{4}{5}$

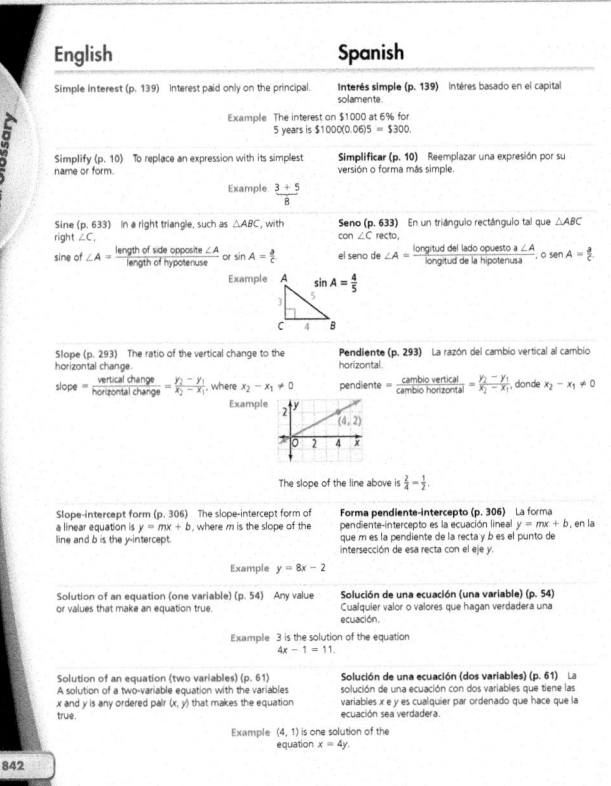

Slope (p. 293) The ratio of the vertical change to the horizontal change.
$\text{slope} = \frac{\text{vertical change}}{\text{horizontal change}} = \frac{y_2 - y_1}{x_2 - x_1}$, where $x_2 - x_1 \neq 0$

Pendiente (p. 293) La razón del cambio vertical al cambio horizontal.
$\text{pendiente} = \frac{\text{cambio vertical}}{\text{cambio horizontal}} = \frac{y_2 - y_1}{x_2 - x_1}$, donde $x_2 - x_1 \neq 0$

Example

The slope of the line above is $\frac{2}{4} = \frac{1}{2}$.

Slope-intercept form (p. 306) The slope-intercept form of a linear equation is $y = mx + b$, where m is the slope of the line and b is the y-intercept.

Forma pendiente-intercepto (p. 306) La forma pendiente-intercepto es la ecuación lineal $y = mx + b$, en la que m es la pendiente de la recta y b es el punto de intersección de esa recta con el eje y.

Example $y = 8x - 2$

Solution of an equation (one variable) (p. 54) Any value or values that make an equation true.

Solución de una ecuación (una variable) (p. 54) Cualquier valor o valores que hagan verdadera una ecuación.

Example 3 is the solution of the equation $4x - 1 = 11$.

Solution of an equation (two variables) (p. 61) A solution of a two-variable equation with the variables x and y is any ordered pair (x, y) that makes the equation true.

Solución de una ecuación (dos variables) (p. 61) La solución de una ecuación con dos variables que tiene las variables x e y es cualquier par ordenado que hace que la ecuación sea verdadera.

Example $(4, 1)$ is one solution of the equation $x = 4y$.

Solution of an inequality (one variable) (p. 165) Any value or values of a variable in the inequality that makes an inequality true.

Solución de una desigualdad (una variable) (p. 165) Cualquier valor o valores de una variable de la desigualdad que hagan verdadera la desigualdad.

Example The solution of the inequality $x < 9$ is all numbers less than 9.

Solution of an inequality (two variables) (p. 390) Any ordered pair that makes the inequality true.

Solución de una desigualdad (dos variables) (p. 390) Cualquier par ordenado que haga verdadera la desigualdad.

Example Each ordered pair in the yellow area and on the solid red line is a solution of $3x - 5y \leq 10$.

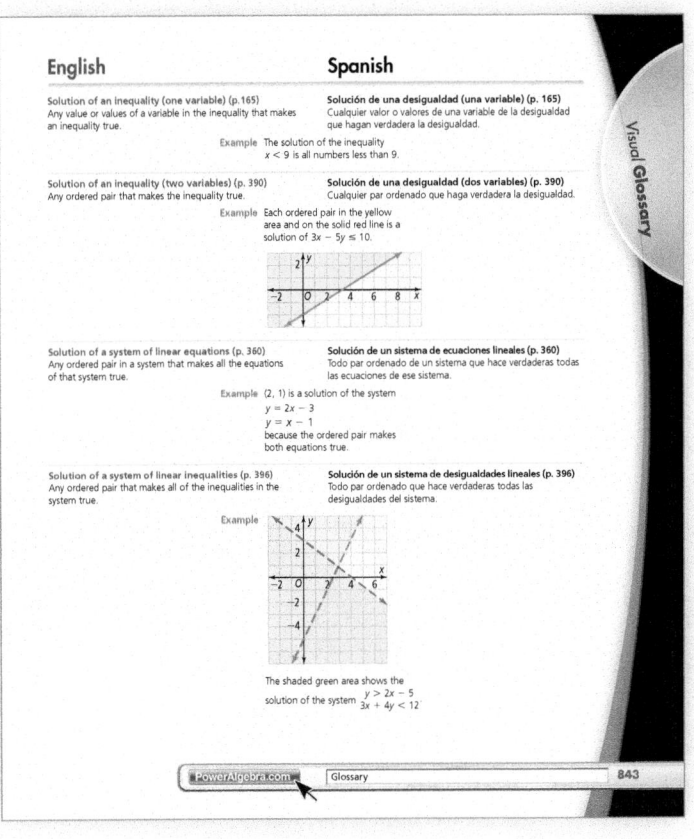

Solution of a system of linear equations (p. 360) Any ordered pair in a system that makes all the equations of that system true.

Solución de un sistema de ecuaciones lineales (p. 360) Todo par ordenado de un sistema que hace verdaderas todas las ecuaciones de ese sistema.

Example $(2, 1)$ is a solution of the system
$y = 2x - 3$
$y = x - 1$
because the ordered pair makes both equations true.

Solution of a system of linear inequalities (p. 396) Any ordered pair that makes all of the inequalities in the system true.

Solución de un sistema de desigualdades lineales (p. 396) Todo par ordenado que hace verdaderas todas las desigualdades del sistema.

Example

The shaded green area shows the solution of the system
$y > 2x - 5$
$3x + 4y < 12$

English | Spanish

Square root (p. 16) A number a such that $a^2 = b$. $\sqrt{b}$ is the principal square root. $-\sqrt{b}$ is the negative square root.

Raíz cuadrada (p. 16) Si $a^2 = b$, entonces a es la raíz cuadrada de b. $\sqrt{b}$ es la raíz cuadrada principal. $-\sqrt{b}$ es la raíz cuadrada negativa.

Example -3 and 3 are square roots of 9.

Square root function (p. 629) A function that contains the independent variable in the radicand.

Función de raíz cuadrada (p. 629) Una función que contiene la variable independiente en el radicando.

Example $y = \sqrt{2x}$ is a square root function.

Standard deviation (p. 733) A measure of how data varies, or deviates, from the mean.

Desviación típica (p. 733) Medida de cómo los datos varían, o se desvían, de la media.

Example Use the following formula to find the standard deviation.

$$\sigma = \sqrt{\frac{\sum(x-\bar{x})^2}{n}}$$

Standard form of a linear equation (p. 320) The standard form of a linear equation is $Ax + By = C$, where A, B, and C are real numbers and A and B are not both zero.

Forma normal de una ecuación lineal (p. 320) La forma normal de una ecuación lineal es $Ax + By = C$, donde A, B y C son números reales, y donde A y B no son iguales a cero.

Example $6x - y = 12$

Standard form of a polynomial (p. 475) The form of a polynomial that places the terms in descending order by degree.

Forma normal de un polinomio (p. 475) Cuando el grado de los términos de un polinomio disminuye de izquierda a derecha, está en forma normal, o en orden descendente.

Example $15x^3 + x^2 + 3x + 9$

Standard form of a quadratic equation (p. 548) The standard form of a quadratic equation is $ax^2 + bx + c = 0$, where $a \neq 0$.

Forma normal de una ecuación cuadrática (p. 548) Cuando una ecuación cuadrática se expresa de forma $ax^2 + bx + c = 0$.

Example $-x^2 + 2x - 9 = 0$

Standard form of a quadratic function (p. 534) The standard form of a quadratic function is $f(x) = ax^2 + bx + c$, where $a \neq 0$.

Forma normal de una función cuadrática (p. 534) La forma normal de una función cuadrática es $f(x) = ax^2 + bx + c$, donde $a \neq 0$.

Example $f(x) = 2x^2 - 5x + 2$

Stem-and-leaf plot (p. 722) A display of data made by using the digits of the values.

Diagrama de tallo y hojas (p. 722) Un arreglo de los datos que usa los dígitos de los valores.

Example

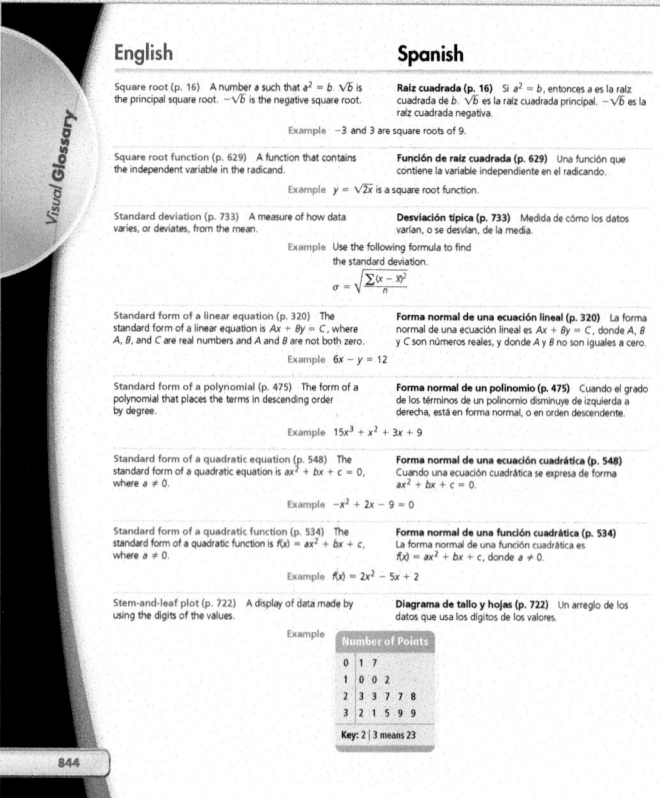

English | Spanish

Subset (p. 17) A subset of a set consists of elements from the given set.

Subconjunto (p. 17) Un subconjunto de un conjunto consiste en elementos del conjunto dado.

Example If $B = \{1, 2, 3, 4, 5, 6, 7\}$ and $A = \{1, 2, 5\}$, then A is a subset of B.

Substitution method (p. 368) A method of solving a system of equations by replacing one variable with an equivalent expression containing the other variable.

Método de sustitución (p. 368) Método para resolver un sistema de ecuaciones en el que se reemplaza una variable por una expresión equivalente que contenga la otra variable.

Example If $y = 2x + 5$ and $x + 3y = 7$, then $x + 3(2x + 5) = 7$.

System of linear equations (p. 360) Two or more linear equations using the same variables.

Sistema de ecuaciones lineales (p. 360) Dos o más ecuaciones lineales que usen las mismas variables.

Example $y = 5x + 7$
$y = \frac{1}{2}x - 3$

System of linear inequalities (p. 396) Two or more linear inequalities using the same variables.

Sistema de desigualdades lineales (p. 396) Dos o más desigualdades lineales que usen las mismas variables.

Example $y \leq x + 1$
$y < 5x$

T

Tangent (p. 633) In a right triangle, such as $\triangle ABC$ with right $\angle C$,

tangent of $\angle A = \dfrac{\text{length of side opposite to } \angle A}{\text{length of side adjacent to } \angle A}$, or $\tan A = \frac{a}{b}$.

Tangente (p. 633) En un triángulo rectángulo tal que $\triangle ABC$, con $\angle C$ recto,

la tangente de $\angle A = \dfrac{\text{longitud del lado opuesto a } \angle A}{\text{longitud del lado adyacente a } \angle A}$,

o la $\tan A = \frac{a}{b}$.

Example

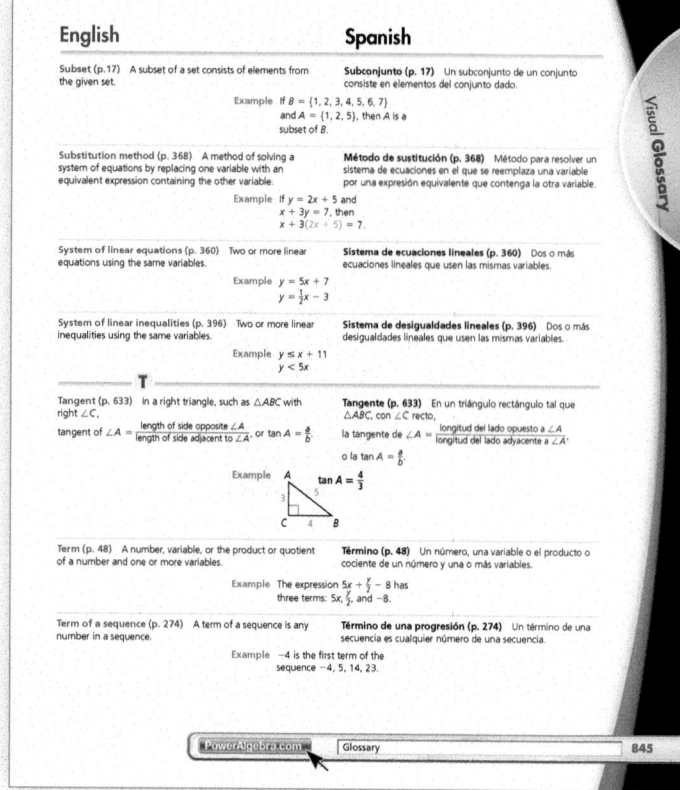

Term (p. 48) A number, variable, or the product or quotient of a number and one or more variables.

Término (p. 48) Un número, una variable o el producto o cociente de un número y una o más variables.

Example The expression $5x + \frac{y}{2} - 8$ has three terms: $5x$, $\frac{y}{2}$, and -8.

Term of a sequence (p. 274) A term of a sequence is any number in a sequence.

Término de una progresión (p. 274) Un término de una secuencia es cualquier número de una secuencia.

Example -4 is the first term of the sequence -4, 5, 14, 23.

English | Spanish

Theoretical probability (p. 757) The ratio of the number of favorable outcomes to the number of possible outcomes if all outcomes have the same chance of happening.

$P(\text{event}) = \dfrac{\text{number of favorable outcomes}}{\text{number of possible outcomes}}$

Probabilidad teórica (p. 757) Si cada resultado tiene la misma probabilidad de darse, la probabilidad teórica de un suceso se calcula como la razón del número de resultados favorables al número de resultados posibles.

$P(\text{suceso}) = \dfrac{\text{número de resultados favorables}}{\text{número de resultados posibles}}$

Example In tossing a coin, the events of getting heads or tails are equally likely. The likelihood of getting heads is $P(\text{heads}) = \frac{1}{2}$.

Translation (p. 342) A transformation that shifts a graph horizontally, vertically, or both.

Traslación (p. 342) Proceso de mover una gráfica horizontalmente, verticalmente o en ambos sentidos.

Example

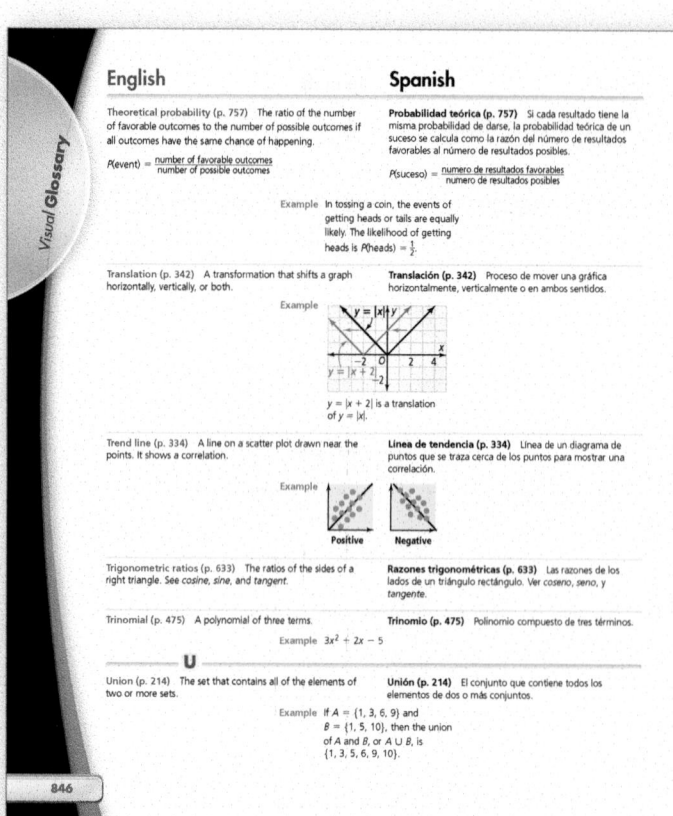

$y = |x + 2|$ is a translation of $y = |x|$.

Trend line (p. 334) A line on a scatter plot drawn near the points. It shows a correlation.

Línea de tendencia (p. 334) Línea de un diagrama de puntos que se traza cerca de los puntos para mostrar una correlación.

Example

Positive   Negative

Trigonometric ratios (p. 633) The ratios of the sides of a right triangle. See cosine, sine, and tangent.

Razones trigonométricas (p. 633) Las razones de los lados de un triángulo rectángulo. Ver coseno, seno, y tangente.

Trinomial (p. 475) A polynomial of three terms.

Trinomio (p. 475) Polinomio compuesto de tres términos.

Example $3x^2 + 2x - 5$

U

Union (p. 214) The set that contains all of the elements of two or more sets.

Unión (p. 214) El conjunto que contiene todos los elementos de dos o más conjuntos.

Example If $A = \{1, 3, 6, 9\}$ and $B = \{1, 5, 10\}$, then the union of A and B, or $A \cup B$, is $\{1, 3, 5, 6, 9, 10\}$.

English | Spanish

Unit analysis (p. 119) Including units for each quantity in a calculation to determine the unit of the answer.

Análisis de unidades (p. 119) Incluir unidades para cada cantidad de un cálculo como ayuda para determinar la unidad que se debe usar para la respuesta.

Example To change 10 ft to yards, multiply by the conversion factor $\frac{1 \text{ yd}}{3 \text{ ft}}$.

$10 \text{ ft} \left(\frac{1 \text{ yd}}{3 \text{ ft}}\right) = 3\frac{1}{3} \text{ yd}$

Unit rate (p. 119) A rate with a denominator of 1.

Razón en unidades (p. 119) Razón cuyo denominador es 1.

Example The unit rate for 120 miles driven in 2 hours is 60 mi/h.

Univariate (p. 742) A set of data that uses only one variable is univariate.

Univariado (p. 742) Un conjunto de datos que tiene sólo una variable es univariado.

Universal set (p. 196) The set of all possible elements from which subsets are formed.

Conjunto universal (p. 196) Conjunto de todos los posibles elementos específicos del cual se forma un subconjunto.

Unlike radicals (p. 613) Radical expressions that do not have the same radicands.

Radicales no semejantes (p. 613) Expresiones radicales que no tienen radicandos semejantes.

Example $\sqrt{2}$ and $\sqrt{3}$ are unlike radicals.

V

Variable (p. 4) A symbol, usually a letter, that represents one or more numbers.

Variable (p. 4) Símbolo, generalmente una letra, que representa uno o más valores de una cantidad.

Example x is the variable in the equation $9 - x = 3$.

Vertex (p. 535) The highest or lowest point on a parabola. The axis of symmetry intersects the parabola at the vertex.

Vértice (p. 535) El punto más alto o más bajo de una parábola. El punto de intersección del eje de simetría y la parábola.

Example

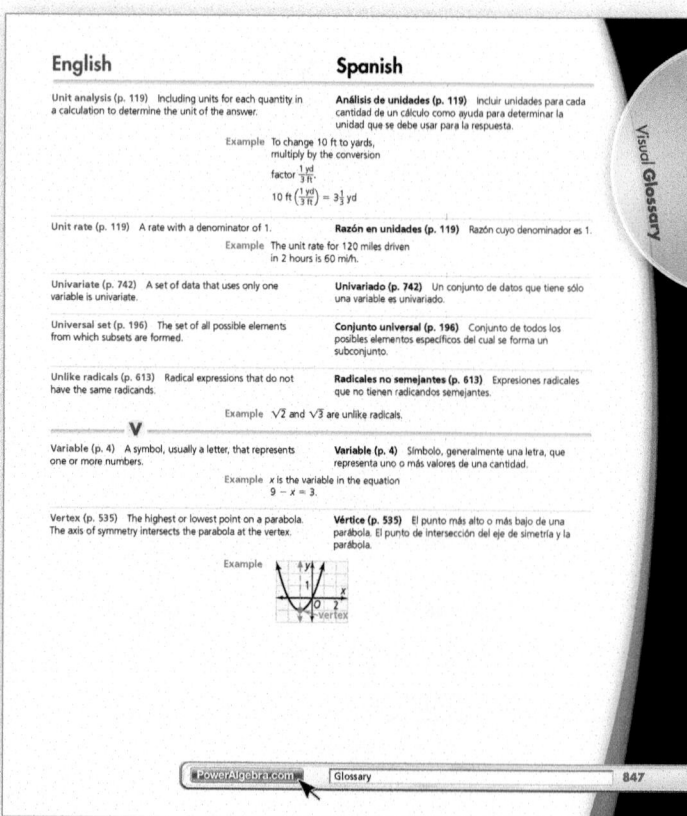

English

Spanish

Vertical-line test (p. 269) The vertical-line test is a method used to determine if a relation is a function or not. If a vertical line passes through a graph more than once, the graph is not the graph of a function.

Prueba de la recta vertical (p. 269) La prueba de recta vertical es un método que se usa para determinar si una relación es una función o no. Si una recta vertical pasa por el medio de una gráfica más de una vez, la gráfica no es una gráfica de una función.

Example

A line would pass through (3, 0) and (3, 2), so the relation is not a function.

— W —

Whole numbers (p. 18) The nonnegative integers.

Números enteros positivos (p. 18) Todos los números enteros que no son negativos.

Example 0, 1, 2, 3, . . .

— X —

x-axis (p. 60) The horizontal axis of the coordinate plane.

Eje x (p. 60) El eje horizontal del plano de coordenadas.

Example

x-coordinate (p. 60) The first number in an ordered pair, specifying the distance left or right of the y-axis of a point in the coordinate plane.

Coordenada x (p. 60) El primer número de un par ordenado, que indica la distancia a la izquierda o a la derecha del eje y de un punto en el plano coordenadas.

Example In the ordered pair (4, −1), 4 is the x-coordinate.

x-intercept (p. 320) The x-coordinate of a point where a graph crosses the x-axis.

Intercepto en x (p. 320) Coordenada x por donde la gráfica cruza el eje de las x.

Example The x-intercept of $3x + 4y = 12$ is 4.

English

Y

y-axis (p. 60) The vertical axis of the coordinate plane.

Spanish

Eje y (p. 60) El eje vertical del plano de coordenadas.

Example

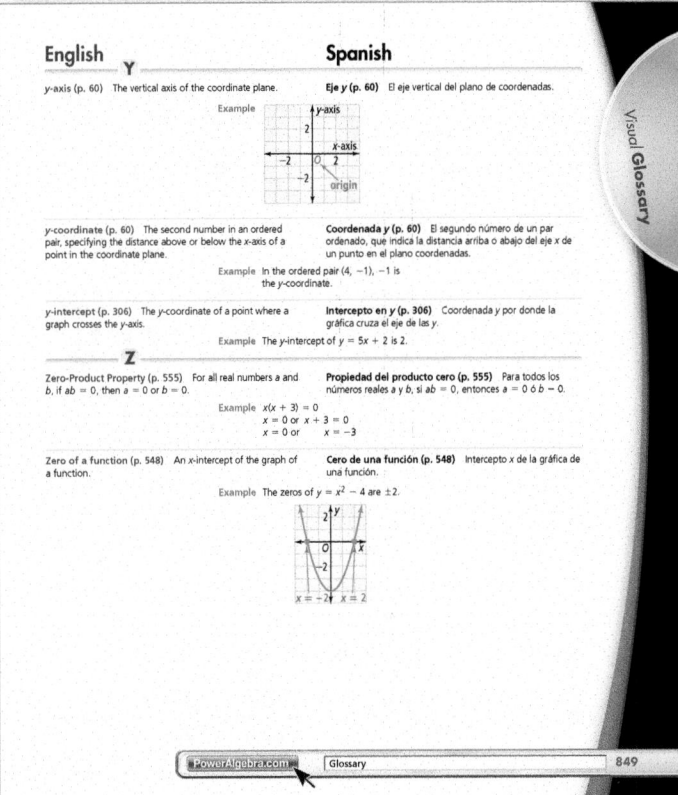

y-coordinate (p. 60) The second number in an ordered pair, specifying the distance above or below the x-axis of a point in the coordinate plane.

Coordenada y (p. 60) El segundo número de un par ordenado, que indica la distancia arriba o abajo del eje x de un punto en el plano coordenadas.

Example In the ordered pair (4, −1), −1 is the y-coordinate.

y-intercept (p. 306) The y-coordinate of a point where a graph crosses the y-axis.

Intercepto en y (p. 306) Coordenada y por donde la gráfica cruza el eje de las y.

Example The y-intercept of $y = 5x + 2$ is 2.

— Z —

Zero-Product Property (p. 555) For all real numbers a and b, if $ab = 0$, then $a = 0$ or $b = 0$.

Propiedad del producto cero (p. 555) Para todos los números reales a y b, si $ab = 0$, entonces $a = 0$ ó $b = 0$.

Example $x(x + 3) = 0$
$x = 0$ or $x + 3 = 0$
$x = 0$ or $x = −3$

Zero of a function (p. 548) An x-intercept of the graph of a function.

Cero de una función (p. 548) Intercepto x de la gráfica de una función.

Example The zeros of $y = x^2 − 4$ are ±2.

PowerAlgebra.com   Glossary

Selected Answers

Chapter 1

Get Ready! p. 1

1. 6 **2.** 5 **3.** 1 **4.** 20 **5.** 15 **6.** 44 **7.** 72 **8.** 150 **9.** 400 **10.** 8 **11.** \$294 **12.** $\frac{4}{5}$ **13.** $\frac{5}{7}$ **14.** $\frac{1}{7}$ **15.** $\frac{12}{13}$ **16.** 0.7 **17.** 0.6 **18.** 0.65 **19.** 0.93 **20.** $0.4\overline{6}$ **21.** $\frac{11}{14}$ **22.** $10\frac{7}{15}$ **23.** $\frac{1}{10}$ **24.** $3\frac{11}{12}$ **25.** Answers may vary. Sample: 20 + 15 **26.** Answers may vary. Sample: A simplified expression is one that is briefer or easier to work with than the original expression. **27.** Answers may vary. Sample: To evaluate an expression means to find its numeric value for given values of the variables.

Lesson 1-1 pp. 4–9

Got It? 1. $n + 18$ **2a.** $6n$ **b.** $\frac{18}{n}$ **c.** No; 6 less a number y means $6 - y$ and 6 less than a number y means $y - 6$. **3a.** $4x - 8$ **b.** $2(x + 8)$ **c.** $\frac{5}{12 + x}$ **4a.** the sum of a number x and 8.1 **b.** the sum of ten times a number x and 9 **c.** the quotient of a number n and 3 **d.** five times a number x less 1 **5.** subtract 2 from the number of sides in the polygon; $n - 2$
Lesson Check 1a. numerical **b.** algebraic **c.** numerical **2a.** $9t$ **b.** $x - \frac{1}{2}$ **c.** $m + 7.1$ **d.** $\frac{207}{n}$ **3.** six times a number c **4.** one less than a number x **5.** the quotient of a number t and 2 **6.** 4 less than the product of 3 and a number t **7.** Numerical expressions are mathematical phrases involving only numbers and operations. Algebraic expressions are mathematical phrases that include one or more variables. An algebraic expression includes at least one variable. A numerical expression does not include any variables. **8.** $49 + 0.75n$
Exercises 9. $p + 4$ **11.** $n - 12$ **13.** $\frac{q}{8}$ **15.** $x - 23$ **17.** $\frac{1}{3}n$ **19.** $2w + 2$ **21.** $(17 - k) + 9$ **23.** $37t - 9.85$ **25.** $15 + \frac{60}{w}$ **27.** 5 more than a number q **29.** the quotient of y and 5 **31.** 14.1 less a number w **33.** one more than the product of 9 and a number n **35.** the quotient of z and 8 less 9 **37.** the difference of 15 and the quotient of 1.5 and d **39.** 5 more than the product of 9 and a number n; $9n + 5$ **41.** $8 - 9r$ **43.** $\frac{3}{7}y - 4$ **45.** It should be "the quotient of 5 and n." **47.** $4.50t$ **49.** A **59.** $\frac{3}{4}$ **60.** $\frac{5}{14}$ **61.** $\frac{7}{10}$ **62.** $\frac{1}{6}$ **63.** 3 **64.** 3 **65.** 1 **66.** 4

Lesson 1-2 pp. 10–15

Got It? 1a. 81 **b.** $\frac{8}{27}$ **c.** 0.125 **2a.** 27 **b.** 7 **c.** 17 **d.** A fraction bar acts as a grouping symbol since you simplify numerator and denominator before you divide. **3a.** 3 **b.** 11 **c.** 20; $(xy)^2 \neq xy^2$ **4.** $c + \frac{1}{10}c$; \$47.30, \$86.90, \$104.50, \$113.30
Lesson Check 1. 25 **2.** 8 **3.** $\frac{9}{16}$ **4.** 23 **5.** 1728 **6.** 0 **7.** exponent 3; base 4 **8.** The student subtracted before multiplying; $23 - 8 \cdot 2 + 3^2 = 23 - 8 \cdot 2 + 9 = 23 - 16 + 9 = 7 + 9 = 16$
Exercises 9. 243 **11.** 16 **13.** $\frac{8}{27}$ **15.** 0.004096 **17.** 2 **19.** 4.5 **21.** 53 **23.** 16 **25.** 1728 **27.** 1024 **29.** 1024 **31.** 496 **33.** 3458 **35.** mv; 15,000, 20,000, 25,000 **37.** 256 **39.** 5 **41.** 12 **43.** $\frac{3}{8}s$; 6 oz; 9 oz; 30 oz; 37.5 oz **45.** 27 **47.** 6 **49.** 68 **51.** 3 **53.** Yes; you can simplify the expression in the first set of parentheses first, or you can simplify the expression in the second set of parentheses first. **55.** 20; $14 - 5 \cdot 3 + 3^2$ **65.** $p + 4$ **66.** $5 - 3y$ **67.** $\frac{m}{10}$ **68.** $3(7 - d)$ **69.** prime **70.** composite **71.** prime **72.** composite **73.** 0.6 **74.** 0.875 **75.** $0.\overline{6}$ **76.** $0.\overline{571428}$ **77.** $\frac{7}{10}$ **78.** $\frac{7}{100}$ **79.** $4\frac{1}{4}$ or $\frac{17}{4}$ **80.** $\frac{17}{40}$

Lesson 1-3 pp. 16–22

Got It? 1a. 8 **b.** 5 **c.** $\frac{1}{6}$ **d.** $\frac{9}{11}$ **2.** about 6 **3a.** rational numbers, natural numbers, whole numbers, integers **b.** rational numbers **c.** rational numbers **d.** irrational numbers **4a.** $\sqrt{129} < 11.52$ **b.** Yes; $4\frac{1}{3} > \sqrt{17}$ also compares the two numbers.
5. 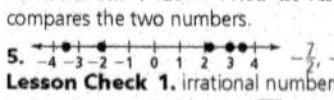 $-\frac{7}{2}, -2.1, \sqrt{5}, \sqrt{9}, 3.5$
Lesson Check 1. irrational numbers **2.** rational numbers, integers **3.** $-5, \sqrt{16}, 4.1, \frac{47}{10}$ **4.** about 4 in. **5.** rational numbers and irrational numbers **6.** Answers may vary. Sample: 0.5 **7.** Rational; its value is 10, which can be written as a ratio of two integers, $\frac{10}{1}$. **8.** Irrational; $\sqrt{0.29}$ is a nonrepeating, nonterminating number.
Exercises 9. 6 **11.** 4 **13.** $\frac{6}{7}$ **15.** $\frac{1}{3}$ **17.** 1.4 **19.** about 4 **21.** about 16 **23.** about 18 **25.** about 13 in. **27.** rational numbers **29.** rational numbers, integers **31.** irrational numbers **33.** rational numbers **35.** irrational numbers **37.** $5\frac{2}{3} > \sqrt{29}$ **39.** $\frac{4}{3} < \sqrt{2}$ **41.** $-\frac{7}{11} < -0.63$ **43.** $-\frac{22}{25} < -0.\overline{8}$ **45.** $-2, -\frac{7}{4}, \frac{1}{2}, \sqrt{5}, 2.4$ **47.** $-\frac{59}{9}, -6, 4.3, \sqrt{20}$ **49.** $-\frac{9}{4}, -\frac{13}{6}, -2.1, -\frac{26}{13}$ **51.** about 12 ft **53.** True; Answers may vary; any integer can be expressed as a rational number. **55.** False; Answers may vary; 2 is a positive number and an integer. **57.** $\frac{417}{1}$ **59.** $\frac{201}{100}$ **61.** $\frac{306}{100}$ **63.** about 12 ft **65.** $\frac{864}{275}$; its value 3.14181… is closer to the value of π than $\sqrt{10}$, which is 3.16227… **67.** no; no the real number line extends indefinitely in both the positive and negative direction. **75.** 16 **76.** 78 **77.** 512 **78.** $14 + x$ **79.** $4(y + 1)$ **80.** $\frac{3880}{2}$ **81.** $\frac{19}{3}t$ **82.** 18 **83.** 72 **84.** 442 **85.** 9

Lesson 1-4 pp. 23–28

Got It? 1a. Identity Prop. of Mult. **b.** Commutative

Prop. of Add. **2.** 720 tennis balls **3a.** $9.45x$ **b.** $9 + 4h$ **c.** $\frac{2}{3n}$ **4a.** True; Commutative Prop. of Mult. and Identity Prop. of Add. **b.** False; answers may vary. Sample: $4(2 + 1) \neq 4(2) + 1$ **c.** No; it is true when a and b are both either 0 or 2.
Lesson Check 1. Comm. Prop. of Add. **2.** Assoc. Prop. of Mult. **3.** \$4.45 **4.** $24d$ **5a.** no **b.** yes **6.** Comm. Prop. of Mult.; Assoc. Prop. of Mult.; multiply; multiply
Exercises 7. Comm. Prop. of Add. **9.** Ident. Prop. of Add. **11.** Comm. Prop. of Mult. **13.** 36 **15.** 9.7 **17.** 80 **19.** \$110 **21.** $18x$ **23.** $110p$ **25.** $11 + 3x$ **27.** $1.2 + 7d$ **29.** $1.5n$ **31.** $11y$ **33.** False; answers may vary. Sample: $8 \div 4 \neq 4 \div 8$ **35.** true; Mult. Prop. of −1 **37a.** 497 mi **b.** 497 mi **c.** The Commutative Property of Addition applies to this situation. **39.** no **41.** yes **43.** yes **45.** no **47.** Hannah can only afford to give all her friends the same gift. **49.** 390 **51.** 0 **53.** no; $(a - b) - c \neq a - (b - c)$ **55.** no; $(a \div b) \div c \neq a \div (b \div c)$ **62.** $-6, 1.6, \sqrt{6}, 6^3$ **63.** $-17, 1.4, \frac{8}{5}, 10^2$ **64.** $-4.5, 1.75, \sqrt{4}, 14^1$ **65.** 14 **66.** 1 **67.** 1.1 **68.** $\frac{1}{18}$

Lesson 1-5 pp. 30–36

Got It? 1. −4 **2a.** −24 **b.** −2 **c.** −2 **d.** −8 **3a.** 13.5 **b.** any value where $a = b$ **4.** −2473 ft, or 2473 ft below sea level
Lesson Check 1. −3 **2.** −3 **3.** −3 **4.** −7 **5.** 2 **6.** −7 **7.** 0 **8.** Subtracting is the same as adding the opposite. **9.** The opposite of a number is the number that is added to it to equal 0. If a number is positive, its opposite is negative. However, if a number is negative, its opposite is positive.
Exercises
11. 5
13. −5
15. 3
17. −12

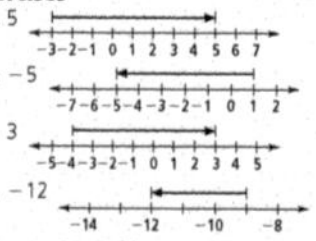

19. −11 **21.** 5 **23.** −11 **25.** 4.4 **27.** −3 **29.** $\frac{13}{36}$ **31.** −20 **33.** 48 **35.** −2 **37.** −20.3 **39.** 1.6 **41.** $\frac{15}{16}$ **43.** \$48.54 **45.** −7.1 **47.** The sum of −4 and 5 is +1, not −1; $-4 - (-5) = -4 + 5 = 1$ **49.** $-\frac{1}{12}$ **51.** 1 **53.** positive **55.** negative **57.** Find the absolute value of each number. The sign of the number with the larger absolute value will be the sign of the sum. **59.** False; if both numbers are negative, the difference is larger than the sum. If the absolute values are equal, the sum is 0. **61.** 29.62 in. **63.** −2 **75.** yes **76.** no **77.** yes **78.** rational numbers **79.** rational numbers **80.** rational numbers, whole numbers, natural numbers, and integers **81.** rational numbers **82.** irrational numbers **83.** 18.75 **84.** 17 **85.** 318

Lesson 1-6 pp. 38–44

Got It? 1a. −90 **b.** 2.4 **c.** $-\frac{21}{50}$ **d.** 16 **2a.** 8 **b.** ±4 **c.** −11 **d.** $\pm\frac{1}{6}$ **3.** −\$72 **4a.** $-\frac{3}{10}$ **b.** Yes; a positive divided by a negative is negative and the opposite of a positive divided by a positive is also negative.
Lesson Check 1. 36 **2.** $-\frac{5}{32}$ **3.** −16 **4.** $\frac{9}{8}$ **5.** −5
6. 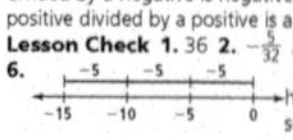 **7a.** 2; a positive number has a positive and negative square root. **b.** 1; $\sqrt{0} = 0$, so there is one square root.
Exercises 9. 96 **11.** 20.5 **13.** −25 **15.** $\frac{1}{12}$ **17.** 1 **19.** 1.44 **21.** 13 **23.** −30 **25.** $-\frac{5}{9}$ **27.** $-\frac{11}{4}$ **29.** ±0.5 **31.** −6 **33.** −3 **35.** −0.9 **37.** −250 **39.** \$115 **41.** 3 **43.** −1 **45.** $-\frac{25}{18}$ **47.** $\frac{1}{2}$ **49.** $-94\frac{1}{2}$ bushels **55.** −180 **57.** $38\frac{2}{5}$ **59.** −13°F **61.** First change $-2\frac{1}{2}$ to the improper fraction $-\frac{5}{2}$. Then multiply $-1\frac{2}{3}$ by the reciprocal of $-\frac{5}{2}$, which is $-\frac{2}{5}$. **63.** $\frac{800}{63}$, or $12\frac{44}{63}$ **65a.** If $0 \div x = y$, then $xy = 0$. Since $x \neq 0$, then $y = 0$ by the Zero Property of Multiplication. **b.** Suppose there is a value of y such that $x \div 0 = y$. Then $x = 0 \cdot y$, so $x = 0$. But this is a contradiction, since $x \neq 0$. So there is no value of y such that $x \div 0 = y$. **73.** 30 **74.** −10 **75.** −10 **76.** Ident. Prop. of Add. **77.** Comm. Prop. of Mult. **78.** Assoc. Prop. of Mult.

Lesson 1-7 pp. 46–52

Got It? 1a. $5x + 35$ **b.** $36 - 2t$ **c.** $1.2 + 3.3c$ **d.** $-2y^2 + y$ **2a.** $\frac{4}{3}x - \frac{16}{3}$ **b.** $\frac{11}{6} + \frac{1}{2}x$ **c.** $\frac{5}{4} + \frac{1}{2}x$ **d.** $\frac{1}{2} - \frac{1}{4}x$ **3a.** $-a - 5$ **b.** $x - 31$ **c.** $-4x + 12$ **d.** $-6m + 9n$ **4.** \$29 **5a.** $2y$ **b.** $-12mn^4$ **c.** $8y^3z - 6yz^3$ **d.** No; it is already simplified since there are no like terms to combine.
Lesson Check 1a. $7j + 14$ **b.** $-8x + 24$ **c.** $-4 + c$ **d.** $-11 - 2b$ **2.** $-8x^2 + 3xy + (-9x) + (-3)$ **3.** $2ab + (-5ab^2) + (-9a^2b)$ **4.** yes **5.** no **6a.** yes **b.** no; Commutative Prop. of Mult. **c.** yes **d.** no; Associative Prop. of Add. **7.** 500 − 1; answers may vary. Sample: These numbers are easily multiplied by 5, making it possible to use the Distr. Prop. to solve this using mental math. **8a.** yes; no like terms **b.** This expression can be simplified by using the Distr. Prop. **c.** No; $12xy$ and $3yx$ are like terms.
Exercises 9. $6a + 60$ **11.** $25 + 5w$ **13.** $90 - 10t$ **15.** $112b + 96$ **17.** $4.5 - 12c$ **19.** $f - 2$ **21.** $12z + 15$ **23.** $\frac{3}{11} - \frac{7d}{17}$ **25.** $\frac{2}{5}x + \frac{7}{5}$ **27.** $\frac{8}{3} - 3x$ **29.** $5 - \frac{8}{5}t$ **31.** $11 - n$ **33.** $-20 - d$ **35.** $-9 + 7c$ **37.** $-18a + 17b$ **39.** $m - n - 1$ **41.** 40.8 **43.** 897 **45.** 23.4 **47.** 24.6 **49.** \$49.50 **51.** \$4725 **53.** $20x$ **55.** $-2t$

57. $17w^2$ **59.** $5y^2$ **61.** $-3x + y + 11$ **63.** $3h^2 - 11h - 3$ **65.** the product of 3 and the difference of t and 1; $3t - 3$ **67.** one-third the difference of 6 times x and 1; $2x - \frac{1}{3}$ **69.** The sum, not the product, of the terms should be found; $4(x + 5) = 4x + 4 \cdot 5 = 4x + 20$. **71.** $33x + 22$ **73.** $35n - 63$ **75.** 0 **77.** $-5m^3n + 5mn$ **79.** $23x^2y - 8x^2y^2 - 4x^3y^2 - 9xy^2$ **81.** $\frac{1}{3}(9 + 12n) = \frac{9}{3} + \frac{12n}{3} = 3 + 4n$ **95.** −25 **96.** $\frac{9}{16}$ **97.** 1.44 **98.** 10 less than a number x **99.** 18 less than the product of 5 and x **100.** 12 more than the quotient of 7 and y

Lesson 1-8 pp. 53–58

Got It? 1a. open **b.** true **c.** false **2.** yes **3.** $49 = 14h$ **4.** 9 **5a.** −10 **b.** Answers may vary. Sample: −5 **6.** The solution is between −8 and −9.
Lesson Check 1. no **2.** 15 **3.** $p = 1.5n$ **5.** Answers may vary. Sample: $\frac{x}{3} = 15$. **6.** 9
Exercises 7. false **9.** true **11.** false **13.** open **15.** open **17.** no **19.** yes **21.** no **23.** yes **25.** $4x + (-3) = 8$ **27.** $115d = 690$ **29.** 13 **31.** 6 **33.** 12 **35.** 6 **37.** 2 **39.** 4 **41.** 6 **43.** 4 **45.** 8 **47.** between −5 and −4 **49.** 2004 **51.** An expression describes the relationship between numbers and variables. An equation shows that two expressions are equal. An expression can be simplified but has no solution. **53.** −6 **55.** between 3 and 4 **57.** between −3 and −2 **59.** 0 **63.** 120 lb **71.** $28 + 14y$ **72.** $-18b - 66$ **73.** $-16.8 - 4.2t$ **74.** $-5 + 25x$ **75.** 10 **76.** −1 **77.** −12 **78.** 7 **79.** −9 **80.** −7 **81.** 2 **82.** $-7\frac{1}{2}$ **83.** 2 **84.** −1 **85.** 3 **86.** 0

Review p. 60

1. Answers may vary. Sample: For the sum −3 for the x-coordinate, you could roll a 4 on the negative cube and a 1 on the positive cube. For the sum 4 for the y-coordinate, you could roll a 1 on the negative cube and a 5 on the positive cube. **3.** Answers may vary. The number on the negative cube must be greater than the number on the positive cube.

Lesson 1-9 pp. 61–66

Got It? 1a. yes **b.** yes **c.** no **d.** yes
2a.

Megan's and Will's Laps

Megan's laps	1	2	3	4	5
Will's laps	7	8	9	10	11

$y = x + 6$

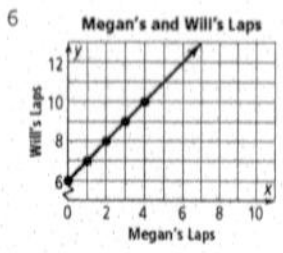

b. The graph would start at (0, 5) instead of (0, 2) and y would always be 5 greater than x.
3a.

Orange tiles	4	8	12	16
Total tiles	9	18	27	36

54 tiles

b.

Blue tiles	1	2	3	4
Yellow tiles	2	4	6	8

48 yellow tiles

Lesson Check 1. no **2.** yes
3.

Drink Cost

Drinks bought	1	2	3	4
Cost (\$)	2.50	5	7.50	10

$y = 2.50x$

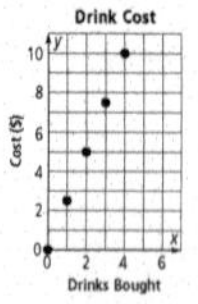

4. 110 Calories **5.** With inductive reasoning, conclusions are reached by observing patterns. With deductive reasoning, conclusions are reached by reasoning logically from given facts. **6.** Answers may vary. Sample: Both equations contain unknown values. An equation in one variable represents a situation with one unknown quantity. An equation in two variables represents a situation where two variable quantities have a relationship. **7.** All; y is 2 more than x.
Exercises 9. no **11.** no **13.** yes **15.** yes
17.

Bea's and Ty's Ages

Bea's age	4	5	6	7
Ty's age	1	2	3	4

$y = x - 3$

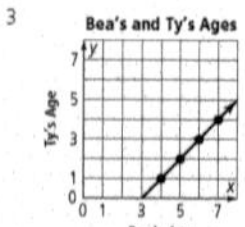

19.

Sides and Triangles

Number of sides	3	6	9	12
Number of triangles	1	2	3	4

$y = \frac{1}{3}x$

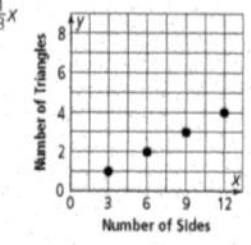

21. 56 in. **23.** $y = x - 12$; 52 in.
25.

Number of Houses	1	2	3	4	5
Number of Windows	4	8	12	16	20

36 windows

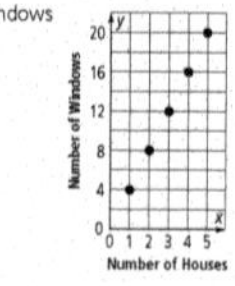

27. no **29.** no **31.** no **33.** no **35.** 13.5 h **37.** 11 h **46.** no **47.** yes **48.** yes **53.** 9 **54.** −3 **55.** −14 **56.** −27 **57.** 40 **58.** −30 **59.** −1 **60.** −81

Chapter Review pp. 68–72

1. irrational **2.** opposite **3.** like terms **4.** absolute value **5.** inductive reasoning **6.** $737w$ **7.** $q - 8$ **8.** $x + 84$ **9.** $51t + 9$ **10.** $\frac{63}{h} - 14$ **11.** $b - \frac{k}{5}$ **12.** the sum of 12 and a number a **13.** 31 less than a number r **14.** the product of 19 and a number t **15.** the quotient of b and 3 **16.** 3 less than the product of 7 and c **17.** the sum of 2 and the quotient of x and 8 **18.** 6 less than the quotient of y and 11 **19.** 13 more than the product of 21 and d **20.** 81 **21.** 125 **22.** $\frac{1}{36}$ **23.** 9.8 **24.** 100 **25.** 48 **26.** $8\frac{1}{3}$ **27.** 40 **28.** 79 **29.** 123 **30a.** 216 **b.** The surface area is reduced to a fourth of its previous value. **31.** 615 mi **32.** irrational **33.** rational **34.** irrational **35.** rational **36.** 10 **37.** 7 **38.** 5 **39.** rational numbers, integers **40.** rational numbers **41.** irrational numbers **42.** rational numbers, whole numbers, natural numbers, integers **43.** rational numbers **44.** rational numbers **45.** $-1\frac{4}{5}, -1\frac{2}{3}, 1.6$ **46.** $-0.8, \frac{7}{6}, \sqrt{3}$ **47.** $9w - 31$ **48.** −96 **49.** 0 **50.** $41 - 4t$ **51.** 1 **52.** yes **53.** no **54.** no **55.** no **56.** 5 **57.** −5 **58.** −9 **59.** 1.8 **60.** −144 **61.** 40 **62.** −3 **63.** −19 **64.** 3 **65.** −8 **66.** 60 **67.** 16 **68.** 12 **69.** −11 **70.** 19 **71.** −100 **72.** −56 **73.** 225 **74.** $-\frac{3}{10}$ **75.** $10x - 15$ **76.** $-14 + 2a$ **77.** $-\frac{1}{2}j + 4$ **78.** v^2 **79.** $6y - 6$ **80.** $\frac{3}{2}y - \frac{1}{4}$ **81.** $6 - 6y$ **82.** $y - 3$ **83.** $-\frac{1}{3}y + 6$ **84.** $-2ab^2$ **85.** \$2850 **86.** Yes; the variable parts of the terms are the same. **87.** yes **88.** no **89.** no **90.** yes **91.** 10 **92.** between 12 and 13 **93.** between 2 and 3 **94.** between 3 and 4 **95.** yes **96.** no **97.** no **98.** no **99.** y is 5 more than the product of 10 and x; $y = 10x + 5$. 55, 65, 75

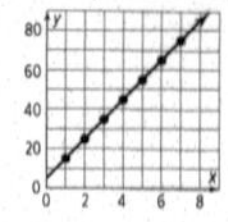

Chapter 2

Get Ready! p. 77

1. Answers may vary. Sample: For each lawn mowed, \$7.50 is earned; $y = 7.50x$. **2.** Answers may vary. Sample: 30 pages are read each hour; $y = 30x$. **3.** 3 **4.** −10 **5.** 8 **6.** −8 **7.** 7.14 **8.** 16.4 **9.** $-\frac{9}{20}$ **10.** $-\frac{7}{15}$ **11.** 17 **12.** −3 **13.** 576 **14.** −2.75 **15.** $16k^2$ **16.** $13xy$ **17.** $2t + 2$ **18.** $12x - 4$ **19.** Answers may vary. Sample: The shirts might look the same but be different sizes or different colors; the triangles will be the same shape but different sizes. **20.** Answers may vary. Sample: The model ship is the same shape but just a smaller size than the actual ship.

Lesson 2-1 pp. 81–87

Got It? 1a. −8 **b.** The Subtr. Prop. of Eq. states that subtracting the same number from each side of an equation produces another equation that is equivalent. **2a.** −6 **b.** 2 **3a.** $\frac{2}{3}$ **b.** −4.375 **4a.** 57 **b.** −72 **5a.** 16 **b.** Yes; multiplying each side of the second equation by the

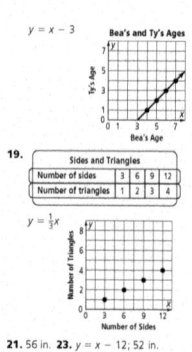

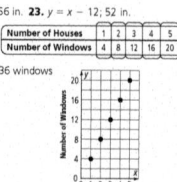

reciprocal of $\frac{2}{3}$ produces the first equation. **6.** 6 months **Lesson Check 1.** −4 **2.** 13 **3.** $4\frac{4}{5}$ **4.** $\frac{1}{3}b = 117$; 351 pages **5.** Subtr. Prop. of Eq. **6.** Div. Prop. of Eq. **7.** Add. Prop. of Eq. **8.** Mult. Prop. of Eq. **9.** Check students' work. **Exercises 11.** 19 **13.** −9 **15.** 26 **17.** 7.5 **19.** 132 **21.** 13.5 **23.** 2 **25.** −4 **27.** −4 **29.** 0.16 **31.** 5 **33.** $-\frac{1}{3}$ **35.** 175 **37.** −117 **39.** 81 **41.** −34 **43.** 12 **45.** −25 **47.** 81 **49.** 24 **51.** p = city's population at start of three-year period; $p - 7525 = 581{,}600$; 589,125 **53.** \$4500 **55.** $-\frac{1}{21}$ **57.** $7\frac{1}{3}$ **59.** $31\frac{1}{4}$ **61.** $\frac{1}{3}$ **63.** 0.8 **65.** $2\frac{1}{2}$ **67.** −25 **69.** $-\frac{1}{2}$ **71.** Each side of the equation should be multiplied by 9, not $\frac{1}{9}$; $(9)(-36) = (9)\left(\frac{x}{9}\right)$, so $x = -324$. **73.** 21 aces **75.** 2450 letters **82.** 10,000 **83.** $52x$ **84.** $6 - x$ **85.** $m + 4$ **86.** 2 **87.** $\frac{25}{36}$ **88.** 1

Lesson 2-2 pp. 88–93

Got It? 1. 16 **2.** 56 ads **3a.** 26 **b.** $6 = \frac{x}{4} - \frac{2}{4}$; 26; answers may vary. Sample: The equation in part (a) is easier because it uses fewer fractions.

4. $\frac{x}{3} - 5 + 5 = 4 + 5$ Add. Prop. of Eq.
$\frac{x}{3} = 9$ Use addition to simplify.
$\frac{x}{3} \cdot 3 = 9 \cdot 3$ Mult. Prop. of Eq.
$x = 27$ Use multiplication to simplify.

Lesson Check 1. −5 **2.** 63 **3.** −7 **4.** −13 **5.** \$.62 **6.** Subtr. Prop. of Eq. and Mult. Prop. of Eq.; subtr. **7.** Add. Prop. of Eq. and Div. Prop. of Eq.; add. **8.** Add. Prop. of Eq. and Mult. Prop. of Eq.; add. **9.** Subtr. Prop. of Eq. and Div. Prop. of Eq.; subtr. **10.** Answers may vary. Sample: No, you must either multiply both sides by 5 first or write the left side as the difference of two fractions and then add $\frac{3}{5}$ to both sides.

Exercises 11. −12 **13.** −1 **15.** −2 **17.** −27 **19.** 126 **21.** −3 **23.** 16 boxes **25.** \$1150 **27.** 29 **29.** −2 **31.** −8 **33.** 8 **35.** 6 **37.** −15 **39.** 2.7 **41.** 5 **43.** −3.8 **45.** 0.449

47. $15 - 9 = 9 - 3p - 9$ Subt. Prop. of Eq.
$6 = -3p$ Use subtraction to simplify.
$\frac{6}{-3} = \frac{-3p}{-3}$ Div. Prop of Eq.
$-2 = p$ Use division to simplify.

49. $9 + \frac{c}{-5} - 9 = -5 - 9$ Sub. Prop. of Eq.
$\frac{c}{-5} = -14$ Use subtraction to simplify.
$\frac{c}{-5} \cdot -5 = -14 \cdot -5$ Mult. Prop. of Eq.
$c = 70$ Use multiplication to simplify.

51. 4 should be added to each side; $2x - 4 + 4 = 8 + 4$ so $2x = 12$ and $x = 6$. **53a.** 4 **b.** yes **c.** Answers may vary. Sample: The method in part (a) is easier because it doesn't involve fractions. **55.** 10.5 **57.** 4 **59.** about 2 km **69.** 5 **70.** 3.8 **71.** 144 **72.** 6.5 **73.** false; sample: $|-5| - |2| \neq -5 - 2$ **74.** false; sample: $-4 + 1 = -3$, $|-4| = 4$ and $|-3| = 3$ **75.** $35 - 7t$ **76.** $4x - 10$ **77.** $-6 + 3b$ **78.** $10 - 25n$

Lesson 2-3 pp. 94–100

Got It? 1a. 6 **b.** 3 **2.** \$14 **3a.** 6 **b.** Yes; divide both sides of the equation by 3 first. **4a.** $2\frac{14}{23}$ **b.** $2\frac{1}{6}$ **5.** 12.55

Lesson Check 1. $4\frac{11}{15}$ **2.** −7 **3.** 2 **4.** 2 **5.** 16 ft **6.** Answers may vary. Sample: Subtract 1.3 from each side, and then divide each side by 0.5. **7.** Answers may vary. Sample: Apply the Distr. Prop., and then add 28 to each side and divide each side by 21. **8.** Answers may vary. Sample: Multiply each side by the common denominator 18 to clear the fractions. Add 72 to each side and then divide by −4. **9.** Answers may vary. Sample: Amelia's method: it does not involve working with fractions until the end.

Exercises 11. $2\frac{6}{7}$ **13.** 6 **15.** $5\frac{4}{7}$ **17.** −10 **19.** $3x + 6x + 20 = 92$; \$8 per h **21.** 6 **23.** 3.75 or $3\frac{3}{4}$ **25.** $7\frac{3}{7}$ **27.** $\frac{1}{6}$ **29.** 9.75 or $9\frac{3}{4}$ **31.** $\frac{7}{25}$ **33.** $2\frac{1}{3}$ **35.** $56\frac{5}{8}$ **37.** $\frac{1}{5}$ **39.** 3.5 **41.** 5 **43.** 4.27 **45.** $43\frac{3}{7}$ **47.** $3\frac{5}{16}$ **49.** 1.5 or $1\frac{1}{2}$ **51.** 2 **53.** $6\frac{2}{3}$ **55.** \$15 **57.** Answers may vary. Sample: Combine the like terms on the left side of the equation. **59.** 3 games **61.** 25 **63.** 20 **65.** 4 weeks **72.** −5 **73.** 7 **74.** 4 **75.** Inv. Prop. of Add. **76.** Assoc. Prop. of Mult. **77.** Mult. Prop. of Zero **78.** $3y$ **79.** $-3y$ **80.** 0

Lesson 2-4 pp. 102–108

Got It? 1a. −4 **b.** The answer is the same, −4. **2.** about 27 months **3a.** −5 **b.** 4 **4a.** infinitely many solutions **b.** no solution

Lesson Check 1. 7 **2.** −3 **3.** infinitely many solutions **4.** no solution **5.** 100 business cards **6.** C **7.** A **8.** B **9.** If the numeric values are the same on both sides, it is an identity. If they are different, there is no solution.

Exercises 11. −9 **13.** 6 **15.** −4 **17.** $-1\frac{3}{4}$ **19.** 22 ft **21.** 25 **23.** −37 **25.** 18 **27.** no solution **29.** no solution **31.** identity **33.** $\frac{2}{63}$ **35.** −19 **37.** no solution **39.** −9 **41a.** $\frac{d}{60}$ **b.** $\frac{d}{40}$ **c.** $\frac{d}{60} + 1 = \frac{d}{40}$; 120 mi; 48 mi/h **43.** Subtraction should be used to isolate the variable, not division by the variable. $2x = 6x$, so $0 = 4x$, and $x = 0$. **45.** 2 months **47.** about 857 bottles **49a.** always true **b.** sometimes true **c.** sometimes true **60.** 5 **61.** −6 **62.** 1 **63.** 0.9 m **64.** 22 **65.** 9 **66.** 11.2

Lesson 2-5 pp. 109–114

Got It? 1a. $\frac{4 + 5n}{2}$; −3; 2, 7 **b.** $y = 10$; $y = 4$ **2.** $x = \frac{-t - r}{p}$ **3.** 6 in. **4.** about 55 days

Lesson Check 1. $y = \frac{2x + 12}{5}$ **2.** $b = \frac{a + 10}{2}$ **3.** $x = \frac{p}{m + 2n}$ **4.** $F = \frac{9}{5}C + 32$ **5.** 40 yd **6.** literal equation **7.** literal equation **8.** both **9.** both **10.** Answers may vary. Sample: They are the same in each case since you are isolating a variable by using inverse operations. They are different because, in an equation in one variable, to isolate the variable, inverse operations are used on numbers only. In a literal equation, inverse operations are used on variables as well as numbers.

Exercises 11. $y = -2x + 5$; 7; 5; −1 **13.** $y = \frac{3x - 9}{5}$; $-\frac{12}{5}$; $-\frac{9}{5}$; $-\frac{6}{5}$ **15.** $y = -\frac{5x - 4}{4}$; $-\frac{1}{4}$; $-\frac{3}{2}$; $-\frac{11}{4}$ **17.** $y = \frac{x + 4}{4}$; $\frac{1}{2}$; 2; $\frac{5}{2}$ **19.** $x = \frac{p}{m + n}$ **21.** $x = \frac{t}{r + s}$ **23.** $x = \frac{S - C}{C}$ **25.** $x = \frac{A - C}{Bt}$ **27.** $x = 2y - 4$ **29.** 4.5 in. **31.** 7 cm **33.** 0.4 h **35.** $h = \frac{n}{7\ell}$; 8 ft **37.** $x = \frac{ay}{b} + a$ **39.** $h = \frac{3V}{\pi r^2}$ **41.** $a = 2b - x$ **43.** −108.4°F **45.** 3 was added to the left side of the equation instead of subtracted; $2m - 3 = -6n$, $\frac{2m - 3}{-6} = n$. **47.** 5 cm^3 **54.** 5 **55.** 3 **56.** −4 **57.** 3 **58.** identity **59.** no solution **60.** 147 **61.** −40 **62.** 567 **63.** 100 **64.** 3 **65.** $\frac{8}{5}$ **66.** $\frac{7}{45}$

Lesson 2-6 pp. 118–123

Got It? 1. No; Store C is still the lowest. **2.** 12.5 m **3a.** about 442 m **b.** about 205 euros **4a.** about 22 mi/h **b.** Yes; $\frac{60\text{ s}}{1\text{ min}} \cdot \frac{60\text{ min}}{1\text{ h}}$ is the same as $\frac{3600\text{ s}}{1\text{ h}}$.

Lesson Check 1. 8 bagels for \$4.15 **2.** 116 oz **3.** 12 m **4.** $80\frac{2}{3}$ ft/s **5.** not a unit rate **6.** unit rate **7.** No; a conversion factor is a ratio of two equivalent measures in different units and is always equal to 1. **8.** Greater; to convert you multiply by 16.

Exercises 9. Olga **11.** 189 ft **13.** 40 oz **15.** 240 s **17.** about 8.2 m **19.** 7900 cents **21.** about 35 in. **23.** 1.875 gal/h **25.** 87 **27.** 150 **29.** 18 **31.** 0.5 mi **33.** 5 oz **35.** recipe B **37.** Miles; kilometers; kilometers cancel out and miles are left. **39.** 1580.82 INR; 19.98 GBP **41.** Answers may vary. Sample: Estimating the size to the nearest inch is appropriate because the carpenter is leaving an estimated amount on either side of the television, not an exact amount. **48.** 5 cm **49.** 15 in. **50.** 5 **51.** 6 **52.** 0.5 **53.** 3 **54.** 27 **55.** $\frac{1}{112}$ **56.** $20m$ **57.** $\frac{2y}{7}$

Lesson 2-7 pp. 124–129

Got It? 1. 5.6 **2a.** 1.8 **3.** −5 **4.** 145.5 mg

Lesson Check 1. 4.8 **2.** 27 **3.** 3 **4.** 5 **5.** 6.75 h **6.** m and q **7.** n and p **8.** mq and np **9.** Yes; sample: One method creates an equation using the fact that the cross products are equal, and the other method creates an equivalent equation using the Mult. Prop. of Eq. to clear the denominators.

Exercises 11. −19.5 **13.** 4.2 **15.** 112.5 **17.** $16\frac{2}{3}$ **19.** 10 **21.** 14 **23.** $26\frac{2}{3}$ **25.** −15 **27.** 4.75 **29.** 11 **31.** $-6\frac{2}{3}$ **33.** −5 **35.** 8 dozen **37.** about 14 people **39.** $\frac{\$.07}{1\text{ kWh}} = \frac{\$143.32}{x\text{ kWh}}$; 2047.4 kWh **41.** at the same time as you **43.** 1.8 **45.** 2.7 **47.** 4.2 **49.** $-\frac{2}{3}$ **51.** 3 was not fully distributed when multiplying 3 and $x + 3$; $16 = 3x + 9$, $7 = 3x$, $x = \frac{7}{3}$. **63.** 1.5 **64.** 7 **65.** 90 **66.** 190 **67.** no solution **68.** $\frac{1}{5}$ **69.** identity **70.** $2\frac{4}{5}$ or 2.8 **71.** $2\frac{2}{15}$ or $2.1\overline{3}$ **72.** $6\frac{2}{3}$ or $6.\overline{6}$ **73.** $\frac{3}{5}$ or 0.6

Lesson 2-8 pp. 130–136

Got It? 1. 24 **2.** 30 ft **3a.** about 66 mi **b.** Write and solve the proportion $\frac{2}{250} = \frac{1}{x}$; 1 in. represents 125 mi. **4.** 300 ft

Lesson Check 1a. 32.5 cm **b.** 1 : 2.5 **2.** 225 km **3.** The order of the letters in each triangle tells which parts are corresponding. **4a.** yes **b.** no **c.** yes **5.** Answers may vary. Sample: No, it is greater than 100 times since 100 mi is more than 100 times greater than 1 in.

Exercises 7. $\angle F \cong \angle K$, $\angle G \cong \angle L$, $\angle H \cong \angle M$, $\angle I \cong \angle N$, $\frac{FG}{KL} = \frac{GH}{LM} = \frac{HI}{MN} = \frac{FI}{KN}$ **9.** 40 **11.** 100 **13.** 37.5 km **15.** 225 km **17.** 67.5 ft **19.** $6\frac{1}{2}$ ft × $2\frac{1}{2}$ ft **21.** no **23a.** The student used CJ instead of AJ. **b.** $\frac{BC}{AJ} = \frac{GH}{FN}$ **25.** 39,304 times **27.** Yes; all squares will have sides that are in proportion (the same length), and the measures of corresponding ∠s are equal (90°). **35.** 34 **36.** 4.5 **37.** −8 **38.** $-\frac{3}{5}$ **39.** 1.5 **40.** 8 **41.** 0.4 **42.** 0.25 **43.** 2.9

Lesson 2-9 pp. 137–143

Got It? 1. 60% **2.** 75%; the answers are the same. **3.** \$3600 **4.** $41\frac{2}{3}$ **5.** 4 yr

Lesson Check 1. 30% **2.** 120% **3.** 28 **4.** 48 **5.** \$180 **6.** 100 **7.** \$75 **8.** Answers may vary. Sample: 12 is what percent of 10?

Exercises 9. 20% **11.** 62.5% **13.** $41\frac{2}{3}$% **15.** 36 **17.** 13 **19.** 16 **21.** \$52 **23.** 400 **25.** 22.5 **27.** $22\frac{2}{3}$ **29.** \$108 **31.** part; 5.04 **33.** part; 142.5 **35.** percent; $1333\frac{1}{3}$ **37.** 66,000 mi^2 **39.** 16 **41.** 75 **43.** B **45.** 121%; it costs more to make a penny than the penny is worth. **47.** The values for a and b are reversed; $\frac{3}{1.5} = \frac{p}{100}$, $1.5p = 300$, $p = 200\%$. **49.** \$181 **51.** $29\frac{1}{6}$% **57.** 14.4 cm **58.** 18 cans **59.** $c = 1.75 + 2.4\left(m - \frac{1}{8}\right)$; $2\frac{5}{8}$ mi **60.** 1250% **61.** 0.6 **62.** 175%

Lesson 2-10 pp. 144–150

Got It? 1. about 32% **2.** about 17% **3.** about 16% **4.** 65.5 in. and 66.5 in. **5.** It would be smaller since the measurement of each dimension is closer to the actual value of each dimension.

Lesson Check 1. about 2% **2.** about 61% **3.** 7.25 ft and 7.75 ft **4a.** percent decrease **b.** percent decrease **c.** percent increase **5.** 0.05 m **6.** A percent increase involves an increase of the original amount and a percent decrease involves a decrease of the original amount.

Exercises 7. increase; 50% **9.** decrease; 7% **11.** decrease; 4% **13.** increase; 54% **15.** increase; 27% **17.** about 55% **19.** about 13% **21.** 1.05 kg; 1.15 kg **23.** about 28% **25.** 175% increase **27.** 42% decrease **29.** 39% increase **31.** 48.75 m^2; 63.75 m^2 **33.** 505.25 ft^2; 551.25 ft^2 **37.** The original amount is 12, not 18; $\frac{18 - 12}{12} = \frac{6}{12} = 0.5 = 50\%$. **39.** 12.63 **45.** $66\frac{2}{3}$% **46.** 64.75 **47.** 21 **48–51.**

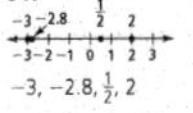

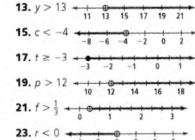

$-3, -2.8, \frac{1}{2}, 2$

Chapter Review pp. 153–156

1. inverse operations **2.** identity **3.** rate **4.** scale **5.** cross products **6.** −7 **7.** 7 **8.** 14 **9.** 65 **10.** 3.5 **11.** −4 **12.** −5 **13.** −8 **14.** \$6.50 **15.** Add. Prop. of Eq.; Simplify.; Div. Prop. of Eq.; Simplify. **16.** 11 **17.** 8 **18.** −7.5 **19.** $3\frac{18}{85}$ **20.** 28 **21.** 14.7 **22.** $4h + 8h + 50 = 164$; \$9.50 **23.** $37t + 8.50t + 14.99 = 242.49$; 5 tickets **24.** −90 **25.** 7.2 **26.** identity **27.** no solution **28.** $8h = 16 + 6h$; 8 ft **29.** $\frac{d}{65} = \frac{d}{130} + 3$; 390 mi **30.** $x = \frac{-c}{a + b}$ **31.** $x = -t - r$ **32.** $x = \frac{m - p}{5}$ **33.** $x = \frac{pqs}{p + q}$ **34.** 40 cm **35.** 15 mm **36.** 16 in. **37.** 78 in. **38.** 71 oz **39.** 2.25 min **40.** 3960 yd **41.** 240 loaves **42.** about 6 lb **43.** $\frac{5}{11}$ s or about 0.45 s **44.** 21 **45.** −4 **46.** 1.6 **47.** 21 **48.** 39 **49.** −1 **50.** 12 in. **51.** 42 in. **52.** 300% **53.** 108 **54.** 170 **55.** 60 seeds **56.** 30% **57.** 72 students **58.** increase; 11% **59.** decrease; 20% **60.** decrease; 11% **61.** increase; 32% **62.** about 47% **63.** about 39% **64.** Yes; 50% of 38° is 19° and 38° + 19° = 57°.

Chapter 3

Get Ready! p. 161

1. > **2.** = **3.** > **4.** < **5.** 7 **6.** −4 **7.** 1 **8.** 2 **9.** 3 **10.** −12 **11.** 32.4 **12.** 23 **13.** 29.5 **14.** −28 **15.** −12 **16.** 48 **17.** 5 **18.** −24 **19.** −10 **20.** 1.85 **21.** −24 **22.** −2 **23.** 3 **24.** 60 **25.** −4 **26.** 3 **27.** $\frac{1}{2}$ **28.** 2.5 **29.** 4.1 **30.** 24 **31.** Answers may vary. Sample: Two inequalities are joined together. **32.** Answers may vary. Sample: the part that the two groups of objects have in common

Lesson 3-1 pp. 164–170

Got It? 1a. $p \geq 1.5$ **b.** $t + 7 < -3$ **2a.** 1 and 3 **b.** The solution of the equation is −2. The solution of the inequality is all real numbers greater than −2.

3a. 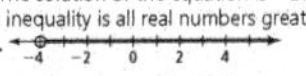

b. 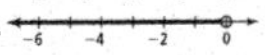

c. 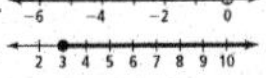

4a. $x < -3$ **b.** $x \geq 0$ **5.** No; the speed limit can only be nonnegative real numbers.

Lesson Check 1. $y \geq 12$ **2a.** no **b.** no **c.** yes **d.** yes **3.** 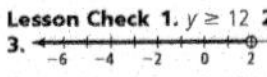 **4.** $x \leq -3$ **5.** Substitute the number for the variable and simplify. If the number makes the inequality true, then it is a solution of the inequality. **6.** Answers may vary. Sample: $x \geq 0$, whole numbers, a baseball team's score during an inning, amount in cubic centimeters of liquid in a chemistry beaker; $x > 0$, counting numbers, length of a poster, distance in blocks between your house and a park

Exercises 9. $b < 4$ **11.** $\frac{k}{9} > \frac{1}{3}$ **13a.** yes **b.** no **c.** yes **15a.** yes **b.** no **c.** no **17.** D **19.** A

21. 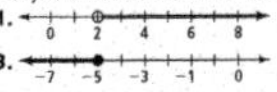

23.

25. 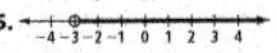

27.

29. $x > -4$ **31.** $x \geq 2$ **33.** $x \geq 5$ **35.** Let p = the number of people seated; $p \leq 172$. **37.** Let w = number of watts of the light bulb; $w \leq 75$. **39.** Let m = amount of money earned; $m > 20{,}000$. **43.** $x \leq 186{,}000$ **45.** b is greater than 0. **47.** z is greater than or equal to 25.6. **49.** 21 is greater than or equal to m. **51.** 2 less than g is less than 7. **53.** r more than 6 is greater than −2. **55.** 1.2 is greater than k. **57.** Answers may vary. Sample: *No more than* means "is less than or equal to," since the amount cannot be greater than the given number. *No less than* means "is greater than or equal to," since the amount cannot be less than the given number. **59.** 998 > 978, so Option A > Option B. **69.** increase; 20% **70.** decrease; 10% **71.** decrease; 67% **72.** 44 **73.** $-\frac{5}{24}$ **74.** −3 **75.** $-1\frac{3}{7}$ **76.** 11 **77.** −2 **78.** −11 **79.** $-\frac{1}{9}$

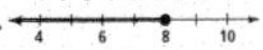

Lesson 3-2 pp. 171–177

Got It? 1. $n < 2$

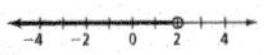

2. $m \geq 9$ 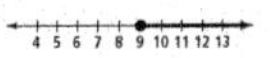

3. $y \leq -13$ 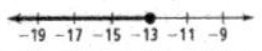

4a. $p \geq 8$ **b.** Yes. The ≥ symbol can be used to represent all 3 phrases.

Lesson Check

1. $p < 5$ 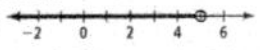

2. $d \leq 10$ 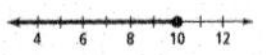

3. $y < -12$ 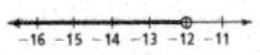

4. $c > 3$ 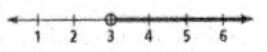

5. $w \leq 524$ **6.** Add or subtract the same number from each side of the inequality. **7a.** Subtract 4 from each side. **b.** Add 1 to each side. **c.** Subtract 3 from each side. **d.** Add 2 to each side. **8.** They are similar in that 4 is being added to or subtracted from each side of the inequalities. They are different in that one inequality adds 4 and the other subtracts 4.

Exercises 9. 6 **11.** 3.3

13. $y > 13$ 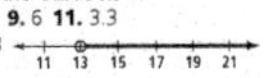

15. $c < -4$ 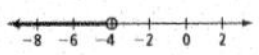

17. $t \geq -3$ 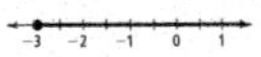

19. $p > 12$ 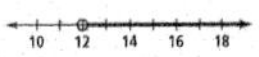

21. $f > \frac{1}{3}$ 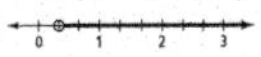

23. $r < 0$ 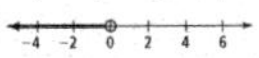

25. $s < 4.7$ 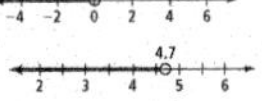

27. $c < 1\frac{3}{7}$ 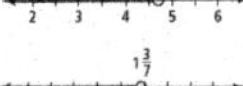

29. 3 **31.** 4.2

33. $x \leq 5$ 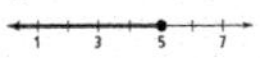

35. $c > -7$ 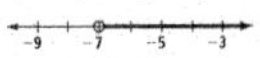

37. $a \geq -1$ 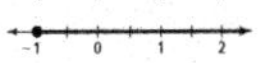

39. $n > -2\frac{2}{3}$ 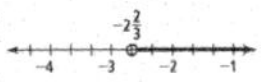

41. $d \geq -1$ 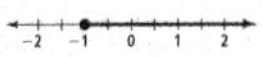

43. $3 + 4 + g \geq 10$; $g \geq 3$ **45.** Add 4 to each side. **47.** Add $\frac{1}{2}$ to each side. **49.** yes

51. 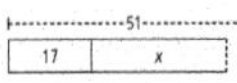

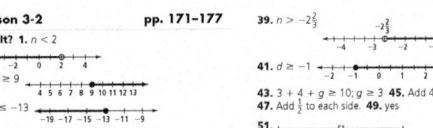

53. 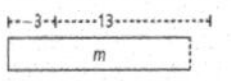

55. $d \leq 2$ **57.** $-4\frac{4}{5} > p$ **59.** $-1.2 > z$ **61.** $p > 12$ **63.** $h \geq -\frac{7}{8}$ **65.** $5\frac{7}{16} \geq m$ **67a.** yes **b.** No; in the first inequality, r is greater than or equal to the amount. In the second inequality, r is less than or equal to the amount. **c.** In part (a), these are equations with only one solution. In part (b), because the inequality relationship is different, there is no relationship between the two inequalities. **69.** Answers may vary. Sample: 94, 95, or 96. **71.** The graph should be shaded to the right, not the left.

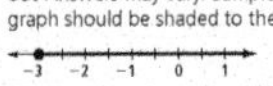

73a. No; the solution should be $a \geq 8.6 - 3.2$, or $a \geq 5.4$. **b.** Answers may vary. Sample: Other numbers that are not substituted could also be solutions to the inequality. **75.** at least \$88.74 **85.** Let h = distance in miles the hummingbird migrates; $h > 1850$. **86.** Let o = length of octopus in feet; $o \leq 18$. **87.** 72 **88.** −1 **89.** 0.56 **90.** 20 **91.** $-\frac{15}{22}$ **92.** −24

Lesson 3-3 pp. 178–183

Got It? 1. $c > 2$ 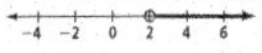

2. $n > 3$ 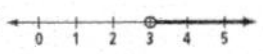

3a. 1, 2, 3, or 4 cases **b.** $\frac{75}{4.50} = 16\frac{2}{3}$, but you cannot walk $\frac{2}{3}$ of a dog. If you round down to 16, you will only make \$72. So round up to 17.

4. $x < 2$ 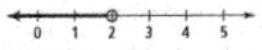

Lesson Check 1. D **2.** B **3.** A **4.** C **5a.** Multiplication by −2; it is the inverse of division by −2. **b.** Addition of 4; it is the inverse of subtraction of 4. **c.** Division by −6; it is the inverse of multiplication by −6. **6.** The inequality symbol was not reversed when multiplying by a negative. $-5\left(-\frac{n}{5}\right) < -5(2)$, $n < -10$

9. $p < 32$ **11.** $v \le -3$ **13.** $x \ge -3$ **15.** $m \le 0$ **17.** $m < 2$ **19.** $m \ge 2$ **21.** $c > 6$ **23.** $z > -3$ **25.** $b \le -\frac{1}{6}$ **27.** $h > -13$ **29.** $q \le 9$

31. no more than 66 text messages **33–35.** Answers may vary. Samples are given. **33.** $-5, -4, -3, -2$ **35.** $-6, -5, -4, -3$ **37.** Multiply each side by -4 and reverse the inequality symbol. **39.** Divide each side by 5. **41.** -2 **43.** 4 **45.** Sometimes true; sample: It is true when $x = 4$ and $y = 0.5$ but false when $x = 4$ and $y = -2$. **47.** Sometimes true; sample: It is true when $x = 4$ and $y = 2$ but false when $x = 0$ and $y = 2$. **49.** at least 0.08 mi per min

51. $3(-1) \ge 3\left(\frac{t}{3}\right)$ Mult. Prop. of Ineq.
$-3 \ge t$ Simplify.

53. $2(0.5) \le 2\left(\frac{1}{2}c\right)$ Mult. Prop. of Ineq.
$1 \le c$ Simplify.

55. $5\left(\frac{n}{5}\right) \le 5(-2)$ Mult. Prop. of Ineq.
$n \le -10$ Simplify.

57. $-\frac{7}{5}(1) > -\frac{7}{5}\left(-\frac{5}{7}s\right)$ Mult. Prop. of Ineq.
$-\frac{7}{5} > s$ Simplify.

59. If the most expensive sandwiches and drinks are ordered, the cost is $3(7) + 3(2) = 27$, leaving \$3. If the most expensive snack is bought, the least number of snacks you can afford is 1. If the least expensive sandwiches and drinks are ordered, the cost is $3(4) + 3(1) = 15$, leaving \$15. If the least expensive snack is bought, the greatest number of snacks you can afford is 15. **61.** $x < 20, x < 30, x < 40, \ldots$; any inequality following the one that a is a solution to. This is because each following inequality has the same solutions as the previous inequalities, with more values as solutions. **68.** $x \le -11$ **69.** $y \ge 13.6$ **70.** $q < 5$ **71.** $-\frac{1}{4} > c$ **72.** $-1 < b$ **73.** $y \le 75$ **74.** 2 **75.** -2 **76.** 1

Lesson 3-4 pp. 186–192

Got It? 1a. $a \ge -4$ **b.** $n < 3$ **c.** $x < 25$ **2.** any width greater than 0 ft and less than or equal to 6 ft **3.** $m \le -3$ **4a.** $b > 3$ **b.** Answers may vary. Sample: adding 1 to each side. This would gather the constant terms onto one side of the inequality. **5a.** no solution **b.** all real numbers
Lesson Check 1. $a > 2$ **2.** $t \le 5$ **3.** $z < 13$ **4.** no solution **5.** greater than 0 cm and less than or equal to 8 cm **6.** The variable terms cancel each other out and a false inequality results. **7.** Yes; each side can be divided by 2 first. **8.** No; there is no solution, since -6 is not greater than itself. If the inequality symbol were $\ge$, your friend would be correct.
Exercises 9. $f \le 3$ **11.** $y > -2$ **13.** $r \ge 3.5$ **15.** $5s \ge 250$; $s \ge 50$ mph **17.** $k \ge 1$ **19.** $j < -1$ **21.** $z < 9$ **23.** $x < 3$ **25.** $f \le 6$ **27.** $m \ge -5$ **29.** all real numbers **31.** all real numbers **33.** all real numbers **35.** $x \ge -4$ **37.** $t \ge \frac{9}{5}$ **39.** $n \ge -2$ **41.** $a \ge 0.5$ **43.** $k \le \frac{13}{6}$ **45.** 5.5 h **47.** D **49a.** $v \ge 4$ **b.** $4 \le v$ **c.** They are equivalent. **51.** at least \$3750 **53.** $3y$ was subtracted from instead of added to each side; $7y \le 2$, $y \le \frac{2}{7}$. **62.** $m \le -4$ **63.** $y \ge -8$ **64.** $y > -20$ **65.** $t \ge -3$ **66.** whole numbers **67.** natural numbers **68.** integers

Lesson 3-5 pp. 194–199

Got It? 1. $N = \{2, 4, 6, 8, 10, 12\}$; $N = \{x \mid x$ is an even natural number, $x \le 12\}$ **2.** $\{n \mid n < -3\}$ **3a.** { } or ∅, {a}, {b}, {a, b}; { } or ∅, {a}, {b}, {c}, {a, b}, {a, c}, {b, c}, {a, b, c} **b.** Yes; every element of set A is part of set B, since $-3 < 0$. **4.** A' = {February, April, June, September, November}
Lesson Check 1. $G = \{1, 3, 5, 7, 9, 11, 13, 15, 17\}$; $G = \{x \mid x$ is an odd natural number, $x < 18\}$ **2.** $\{d \mid d \le 3\}$ **3.** { } or ∅, {4}, {8}, {12}, {4, 8}, {4, 12}, {8, 12}, {4, 8, 12} **4.** W' = {spring, summer, fall} **5.** A; its complement is the set of all elements in the universal set that are not in A'. **6a.** Yes; the empty set is a subset of every set. **b.** No; the number 5 in the first set is not an element of the second set. **c.** Yes; the element in the first set is also an element of the second set. **7.** sometimes **8.** The student forgot that 0 is also a whole number.
Exercises 9. {0, 1, 2, 3}; $\{m \mid m$ is an integer, $-1 < m < 4\}$ **11.** {1, 2, 3, 4, 5, 6, 7, 8, 9, 10}; $\{p \mid p$ is a natural number, $p < 11\}$ **13.** $\{y \mid y \ge 4\}$ **15.** $\{m \mid m > -5\}$ **17.** $\{p \mid p \ge 1\}$ **19.** { } or ∅, {a}, {e}, {i}, {o}, {a, e}, {a, i}, {a, o}, {e, i}, {e, o}, {i, o}, {a, e, i}, {a, e, o}, {a, i, o}, {e, i, o}, {a, e, i, o} **21.** { } or ∅, {dog}, {cat}, {fish}, {dog, cat}, {dog, fish}, {cat, fish}, {dog, cat, fish} **23.** { } or ∅, {1}

25. {1, 4, 5} **27.** {. . . , −4, −2, 0, 2, 4, . . .} **29.** A' = {Tuesday, Thursday, Friday, Saturday} **31.** False; some elements of U are not elements of B. **33.** True; the empty set is a subset of every set. **35.** $M = \{m \mid m$ is odd integer, $1 \le m \le 19\}$ **37.** $G = \{g \mid g$ is an integer$\}$ **39.** {Mercury, Venus, Earth} **41.** { } or ∅ **43.** $\{x \mid x \le 0\}$ **45.** { } or ∅ **47.** $T' = \{x \mid x$ is an integer, $x \le 0\}$ **49.** 1 **58.** $b > 8$ **59.** $t \le 5$ **60.** $z < 13$ **61.** 6 **62.** -3 **63.** 3 **64.** **65.** **66.**

Lesson 3-6 pp. 200–206

Got It? 1a. $-4 \le x < 6$
b. $x \le 2\frac{1}{2}$ or $x > 6$
c. *x is between −5 and 7* does not include −5 or 7. *Inclusive* means that −5 and 7 are included.
2. $\frac{2}{3} < y < 6$
3. Answers may vary. Sample: No, to get a B, the average of the 4 tests must be at least 84. If x is the 4th test score, $\frac{78 + 78 + 79 + x}{4} \ge 84$, $235 + x \ge 336$, and $x \ge 101$, which is impossible.
4. $y > 3$ or $y \le -2$
5a. $-2 < x \le 7$
b. $(7, \infty)$
Lesson Check 1. $0 \le x < 8$
2. $1 \le r < 4$
3. $85 \le x \le 100$ **4.** $x \le 6$; $(-\infty, 6]$ **5.** A, C, and D **6.** Answers may vary. Sample: The bracket indicates a specific number is part of the solution. The symbol ∞ means that the numbers continue without end. So a parenthesis should follow. **7.** $x \le 7$ or $x > 7$; $(-\infty, \infty)$ **8.** The graph of a compound inequality with the word *and* contains the overlap of the graphs that form the inequality. The graph of a compound inequality with the word *or* contains both of the graphs that form the inequality.
Exercises 9. $-5 < x < 7$

11. $-7 < k < 5$ **13.** $2 < p \le 5$ **15.** $3\frac{3}{4} < x < 8\frac{1}{2}$ **17.** $b < -1$ or $b > 2$ **19.** $d \ge 2$ or $d < 2$ **21.** $y \le -2$ or $y \ge 5$ **23.** $x \le 2$ **25.** $x \le -1$ or $x > 3$ **27.** $(-2, \infty)$ **29.** $(-\infty, -2)$ or $[1, \infty)$
31. $(1, 6]$ **33.** $(-\infty, -5)$ or $[5, \infty)$ **35.** $-3 < x < 4$ **37.** $3 \le x < 6$ **39.** $2\frac{2}{3} \le v \le 6$ **41.** $-4\frac{1}{12} \le w < 12\frac{1}{4}$ **43.** $4 < x < 14$ **45.** any length greater than 6 ft and less than 36 ft **47.** any length greater than 11 m and less than 23 m **49.** any real number except 4 **56.** { } or ∅, {1}, {3}, {5}, {7}, {1, 3}, {1, 5}, {1, 7}, {3, 5}, {3, 7}, {5, 7}, {1, 3, 5}, {1, 3, 7}, {1, 5, 7}, {3, 5, 7}, {1, 3, 5, 7} **57.** $B' = \{1, 2, 3, 5, 7, 15\}$ **58.** no **59.** $\frac{1}{3} < b$ **60.** $n \le 3$ **61.** $7 \ge r$ **62.** = **63.** > **64.** >

Lesson 3-7 pp. 207–213

Got It? 1. $n = 3$ and $n = -3$
2. $x = 3$ or $x = -\frac{7}{3}$ **3.** no solution **4.** $x \ge 0.5$ or $x \le -4.5$
5a. $|w - 32| \le 0.05$; $31.95 \le w \le 32.05$ **b.** No; 213 is part of the absolute value expression. You cannot add 213 until after you write the absolute value inequality as a compound inequality.
Lesson Check 1. $x = 5$ or $x = -5$
2. $n = 7$ or $n = -7$
3. $t = 3$ or $t = -3$
4. $-2 < h < 8$

3. $t = 3$ or $t = -3$ **4.** $-2 < h < 8$ **5.** $x \le -3$ or $x \ge -1$
6. 2; there are two values on a number line that are the same distance from 0. **7.** The absolute value cannot be equal to a negative number since distance from 0 on a number line must be nonnegative. **8.** Answers may vary. Sample: The equation is set equal to 2 and -2. The first inequality is set to be ≤ 2 and ≥ -2. The second inequality is set to be ≥ 2 or ≤ -2.
Exercises 9. $b = -\frac{1}{2}$ or $b = \frac{1}{2}$
11. $n = 4$ or $n = -4$ **13.** $x = 8$ or $x = -8$ **15.** $m = 3$ or $m = -3$
17. $r = 13$ or $r = 3$ **19.** $g = -1$ or $g = -5$ **21.** no solution **23.** $v = 6$ or $v = 0$ **25.** $f = 1.5$ or $f = -2$ **27.** $y = 3$ or $y = 0$ **29.** no solution **31.** no solution
33. $-5 < x < 5$ **35.** $y \le -11$ or $y \ge -5$ **37.** $4 \le p \le 10$ **39.** $t < -3$ or $t > \frac{7}{3}$ **41.** $t \le -2.4$ or $t \ge 4$ **43.** $-4 \le v \le 5$ **45.** $-11 \le f \le 2$
47. any length between 89.95 cm and 90.05 cm, inclusive **49.** $d = 9$ or $d = -9$ **51.** no solution **53.** $y = 3.4$ or $y = -0.6$ **55.** $c = 8.2$ or $c = -0.2$ **57.** $-6\frac{1}{4} < n < 6\frac{1}{4}$ **59.** $-8 < m < 4$ **61.** 49°F ≤ T ≤ 64°F **63.** $t = 4\frac{4}{9}$ s and $17\frac{7}{9}$ s **65.** $-1 \le y + 7 \le 1$, $-8 \le y \le -6$ **67.** Answers may vary. Sample: To be more than 1 unit away from -5 on a number line means $x + 5 > 1$ or $x + 5 < -1$. **69a.** between 193.74 g and 209.26 g, inclusive **b.** Yes; answers may vary. Sample: Some nickels could weigh more and some could weigh less, and their average could be the official amount. **71.** $|x| < 4$ **73.** $|x - 6| > 2$ **75.** between 89.992 mm and 90.008 mm, inclusive **88.** $-282 \le e \le 20{,}320$ **89.** $36.9 \le T \le 37.5$ **90.** $2x + 10$ **91.** $-3y + 21$ **92.** $4\ell + 5$ **93.** $-m + 12$ **94.** $A = \{x \mid x$ is a whole number, $x < 10\}$ **95.** $B = \{x \mid x$ is an odd integer, $1 \le x \le 7\}$ **96.** $C = \{-14, -12, -10, -8, -6\}$ **97.** $D = \{8, 9, 10, 12, 14, 15, 16\}$

Lesson 3-8 pp. 214–220

Got It? 1a. $P = \{0, 1, 2, 3, 4\}$; $Q = \{2, 4\}$; $P \cup Q = \{0, 1, 2, 3, 4\}$ **b.** Answers may vary. Sample: If $B \subseteq A$, then $A \cup B$ will contain the same elements as A. **2a.** $A \cap B = \{2, 8\}$ **b.** $A \cap C = \varnothing$ **c.** $C \cap B = \{5, 7\}$ **3.** A and E **4.** 10 **5a.** $\{x \mid x \ge 3\} \cap \{x \mid x < 6\}$ **b.** $\{x \mid x < -2\} \cup \{x \mid x > 5\}$
Lesson Check 1. $X \cup Y = \{1, 2, 3, 4, 5, 6, 7, 8, 9, 10\}$ **2.** $X \cap Y = \{2, 4, 6, 8, 10\}$ **3.** $X \cap Z = \varnothing$ **4.** $Y \cup Z = \{1, 2, 3, 4, 5, 6, 7, 8, 9, 10\}$ **5.** 31 people **6.** $A \cup B$ contains more elements because it contains all the elements in both sets. **7.** The union of sets is the set that contains all elements of each set. The intersection of sets is the set of elements that are common to each set. **8.** true **9.** false
Exercises 11. $A \cup C = \{1, 2, 3, 4, 5, 7, 10\}$ **13.** $B \cup C = \{0, 2, 4, 5, 6, 7, 8, 10\}$ **15.** $C \cup D = \{1, 2, 3, 5, 7, 9, 10\}$ **17.** $A \cap C = \varnothing$ **19.** $B \cap C = \{2\}$ **21.** $C \cap D = \{5, 7\}$
23.

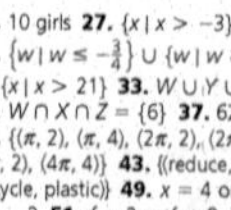

25. 10 girls **27.** $\{x \mid x > -3\} \cap \left\{x \mid x < \frac{19}{3}\right\}$ **29.** $\left\{w \mid w \le -\frac{3}{4}\right\} \cup \{w \mid w \ge 1\}$ **31.** $\{x \mid x < -7\} \cup \{x \mid x > 21\}$ **33.** $W \cup Y \cup Z = \{0, 2, 3, 4, 5, 6, 7, 8\}$ **35.** $W \cap X \cap Z = \{6\}$ **37.** 62 patients **39.** $A \cap B = A$ **41.** $\{(\pi, 2), (\pi, 4), (2\pi, 2), (2\pi, 4), (3\pi, 2), (3\pi, 4), (4\pi, 2), (4\pi, 4)\}$ **43.** {(reduce, plastic), (reuse, plastic), (recycle, plastic)} **49.** $x = 4$ or $x = -4$ **50.** $n = 2$ or $n = -2$ **51.** $f = 2$ or $f = 8$ **52.** $y = \frac{4}{3}$ or $y = -\frac{8}{3}$ **53.** $-5 \le d \le 5$ **54.** $x \le -4$ or $x \ge 10$ **55.** $w < -15$ or $w > 9$ **56.** $x = \frac{4}{3}$ or $x = -\frac{4}{3}$ **57.** yes **58.** no **59.** yes
60–63.

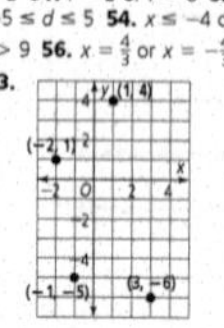

Chapter Review pp. 222–226

1. roster form **2.** union **3.** empty set **4.** solution of an inequality **5.** equivalent inequalities **6.** **7.** **8.** **9.**
10. $x > 5$ **11.** $x \le -2$ **12.** $x > -5.5$ **13.** $w > 6$
14. $v < 10$ **15.** $-12 < t$ **16.** $n \ge \frac{5}{4}$ **17.** $8.6 \le h$ **18.** $q > -2.5$ **19.** $4.25 + x \le 15.00$; $x \le 10.75$ **20.** $x < 3$ **21.** $t < -3$ **22.** $y \le 6$ **23.** $h > -24$ **24.** $g > 4$ **25.** $n \le 15$ **26.** $d \ge 16\frac{13}{27}$ **27.** $m > -1\frac{67}{171}$
28. $7.25h \ge 200$; at least 28 full hours **29.** $k \ge -0.5$ **30.** $c < -2$ **31.** $t < -6$ **32.** $y \le -56$ **33.** $x < 2\frac{2}{3}$ **34.** $x \le -13$ **35.** $a \le 5.8$ **36.** $w > 0.35$ **37.** $200 + 0.04s \ge 450$; $s \ge 6250$ **38.** { } or ∅, {s}, {t}, {s, t} **39.** { } or ∅, {5}, {10}, {15}, {5, 10}, {5, 15}, {10, 15}, {5, 10, 15} **40.** $A = \{0, 2, 4, 6, 8, 10, 12, 14, 16\}$; $A = \{x \mid x$ is an even whole number less than $18\}$ **41.** $B' = \{1, 3, 5, 7\}$ **42.** $-2\frac{1}{2} \le d < 4$ **43.** $-1.5 \le b < 0$ **44.** $t \le -2$ or $t \ge 7$ **45.** $m < -2$ or $m > 3$ **46.** $2 \le a \le 5$ **47.** $6.5 > p \ge -4.5$ **48.** $65 \le t \le 88$ **49.** $y = 3$ or $y = -3$ **50.** $n = 2$ or $n = -6$ **51.** $r = 1$ or $r = -5$ **52.** no solution **53.** $-3 \le x \le 3$ **54.** no solution **55.** $x < 3$ or $x > 4$ **56.** $k < -7$ or $k > -3$ **57.** any length between 19.6 mm and 20.4 mm, inclusive **58.** $A \cup B = A$
59.

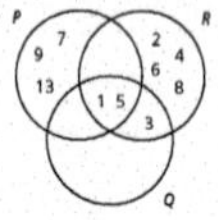

60. $N \cap P = \{x \mid x$ is a multiple of $6\}$ **61.** 5 cats

Chapter 4

Get Ready! p. 231

1. -7 **2.** -18 **3.** 2 **4.** -1

5.

Bob's and His Dog's Ages (years)

Dog's Age	0	1	2	3	4	5	6	7	8	9
Bob's Age	9	10	11	12	13	14	15	16	17	18

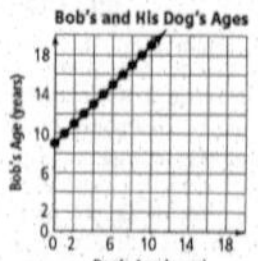

$B = 9 + d$, where B is Bob's age and d is his dog's age

6.

Sue's Number of Laps per Minute

Number of Minutes	0	1	2	3	4	5	6	7	8	9
Number of Laps	0	1.5	3	4.5	6	7.5	9	10.5	12	13.5

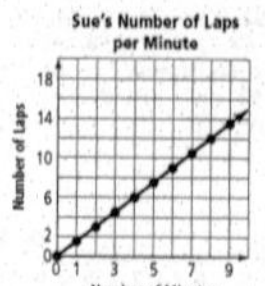

$\ell = 1.5m$, where m is the number of minutes and ℓ is the number of laps.

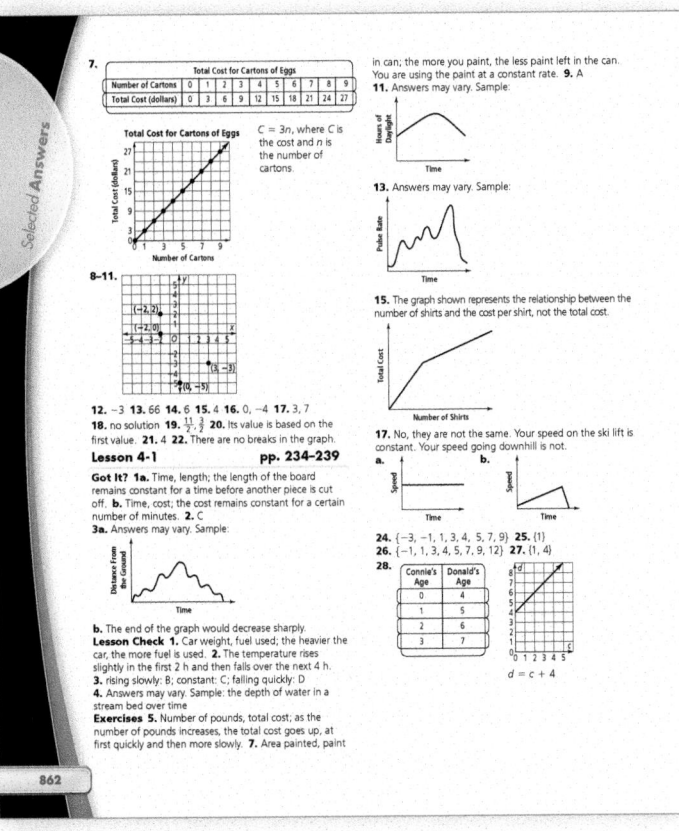

7.

Total Cost for Cartons of Eggs

Number of Cartons	0	1	2	3	4	5	6	7	8	9
Total Cost (dollars)	0	3	6	9	12	15	18	21	24	27

$C = 3n$, where C is the cost and n is the number of cartons.

8–11.

12. −3 **13.** 66 **14.** 6 **15.** 4 **16.** 0, −4 **17.** 3, 7
18. no solution **19.** $\frac{11}{2}, \frac{3}{2}$ **20.** Its value is based on the first value. **21.** 4 **22.** There are no breaks in the graph.

Lesson 4-1 pp. 234–239

Got It? 1a. Time, length; the length of the board remains constant for a time before another piece is cut off. **b.** Time, cost; the cost remains constant for a certain number of minutes. **2.** C
3a. Answers may vary. Sample:

b. The end of the graph would decrease sharply.
Lesson Check 1. Car weight, fuel used; the heavier the car, the more fuel is used. **2.** The temperature rises slightly in the first 2 h and then falls over the next 4 h.
3. rising slowly; B; constant; C; falling quickly; D
4. Answers may vary. Sample: the depth of water in a stream bed over time
Exercises 5. Number of pounds, total cost; as the number of pounds increases, the total cost goes up, at first quickly and then more slowly. **7.** Area painted, paint

in can; the more you paint, the less paint left in the can. You are using the paint at a constant rate. **9.** A
11. Answers may vary. Sample:

13. Answers may vary. Sample:

15. The graph shown represents the relationship between the number of shirts and the cost per shirt, not the total cost.

17. No, they are not the same. Your speed on the ski lift is constant. Your speed going downhill is not.

a. **b.**

24. {−3, −1, 1, 3, 4, 5, 7, 9} **25.** {1}
26. {−1, 1, 3, 4, 5, 7, 9, 12} **27.** {1, 4}
28.

Connie's Age	Donald's Age
0	4
1	5
2	6
3	7

$d = c + 4$

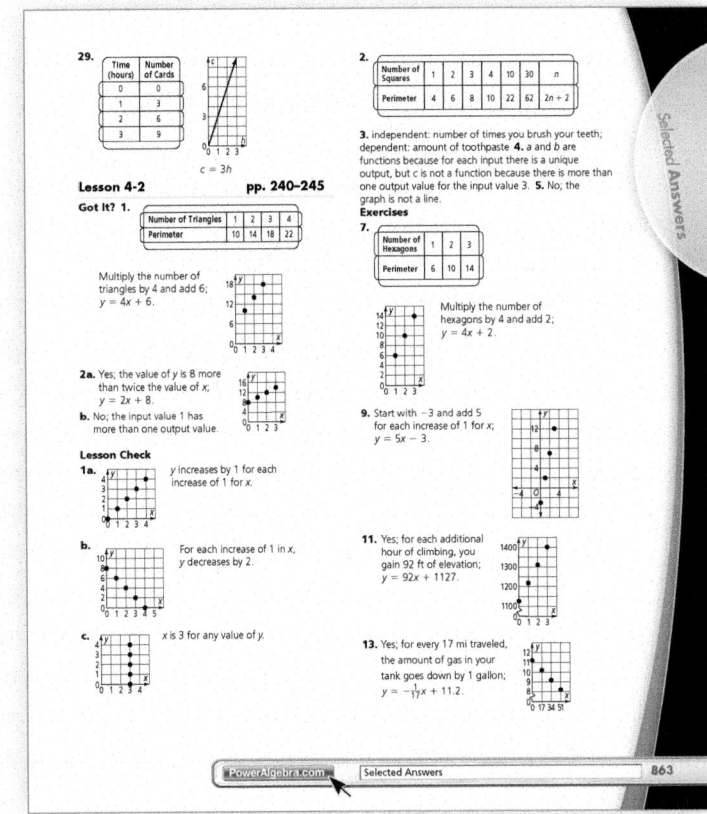

29.

Time (hours)	Number of Cards
0	0
1	3
2	6
3	9

$c = 3h$

Lesson 4-2 pp. 240–245

Got It? 1.

Number of Triangles	1	2	3	4
Perimeter	10	14	18	22

Multiply the number of triangles by 4 and add 6;
$y = 4x + 6$.

2a. Yes; the value of y is 8 more than twice the value of x;
$y = 2x + 8$.
b. No; the input value 1 has more than one output value.

Lesson Check
1a. y increases by 1 for each increase of 1 for x.

b. For each increase of 1 in x, y decreases by 2.

c. x is 3 for any value of y.

2.

Number of Squares	1	2	3	4	10	30	n
Perimeter	4	6	8	10	22	62	$2n + 2$

3. independent: number of times you brush your teeth; dependent: amount of toothpaste **4.** a and b are functions because for each input there is a unique output, but c is not a function because there is more than one output value for the input value 3. **5.** No; the graph is not a line.
Exercises
7.

Number of Hexagons	1	2	3
Perimeter	6	10	14

Multiply the number of hexagons by 4 and add 2;
$y = 4x + 2$.

9. Start with −3 and add 5 for each increase of 1 for x;
$y = 5x − 3$.

11. Yes; for each additional hour of climbing, you gain 92 ft of elevation;
$y = 92x + 1127$.

13. Yes; for every 17 mi traveled, the amount of gas in your tank goes down by 1 gallon;
$y = -\frac{1}{17}x + 11.2$.

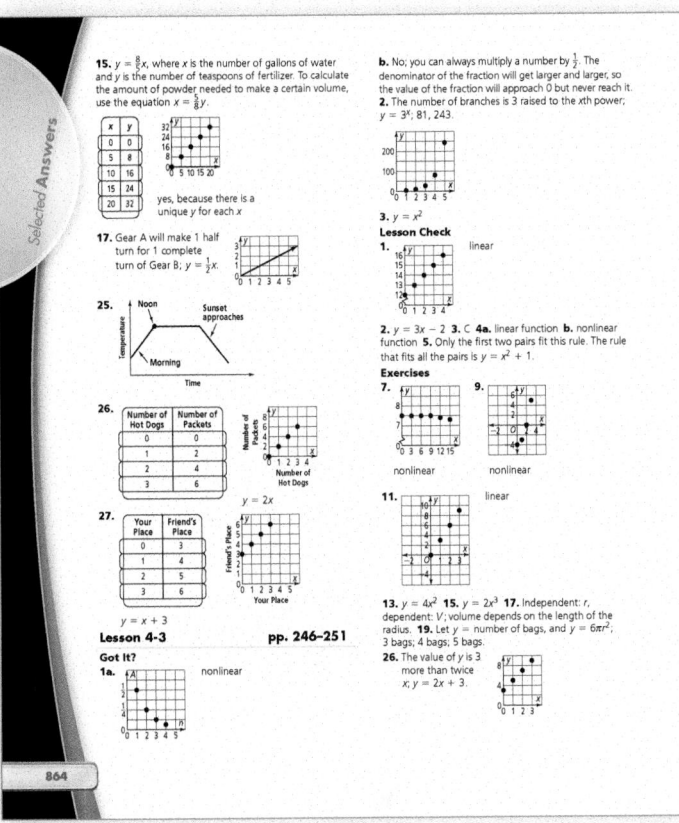

15. $y = \frac{8}{6}x$, where x is the number of gallons of water and y is the number of teaspoons of fertilizer. To calculate the amount of powder needed to make a certain volume, use the equation $x = \frac{6}{8}y$.

x	y
0	0
5	8
10	16
15	24
20	32

yes, because there is a unique y for each x

17. Gear A will make 1 half turn for 1 complete turn of Gear B; $y = \frac{1}{2}x$.

25.

26.

Number of Hot Dogs	Number of Packets
0	0
1	2
2	4
3	6

$y = 2x$

27.

Your Place	Friend's Place
0	3
1	4
2	5
3	6

$y = x + 3$

Lesson 4-3 pp. 246–251

Got It?
1a. nonlinear

b. No; you can always multiply a number by $\frac{1}{3}$. The denominator of the fraction will get larger and larger, so the value of the fraction will approach 0 but never reach it.
2. The number of branches is 3 raised to the xth power; $y = 3^x$; 81, 243.

3. $y = x^2$
Lesson Check
1. linear

2. $y = 3x − 2$ **3.** C **4a.** linear function **b.** nonlinear function **5.** Only the first two pairs fit this rule. The rule that fits all the pairs is $y = x^2 + 1$.
Exercises
7. **9.**

nonlinear nonlinear

11. linear

13. $y = 4x^2$ **15.** $y = 2x^3$ **17.** Independent: r, dependent: V; volume depends on the length of the radius. **19.** Let $y =$ number of bags, and $y = 6\pi r^2$; 3 bags; 4 bags; 5 bags.
26. The value of y is 3 more than twice x; $y = 2x + 3$.

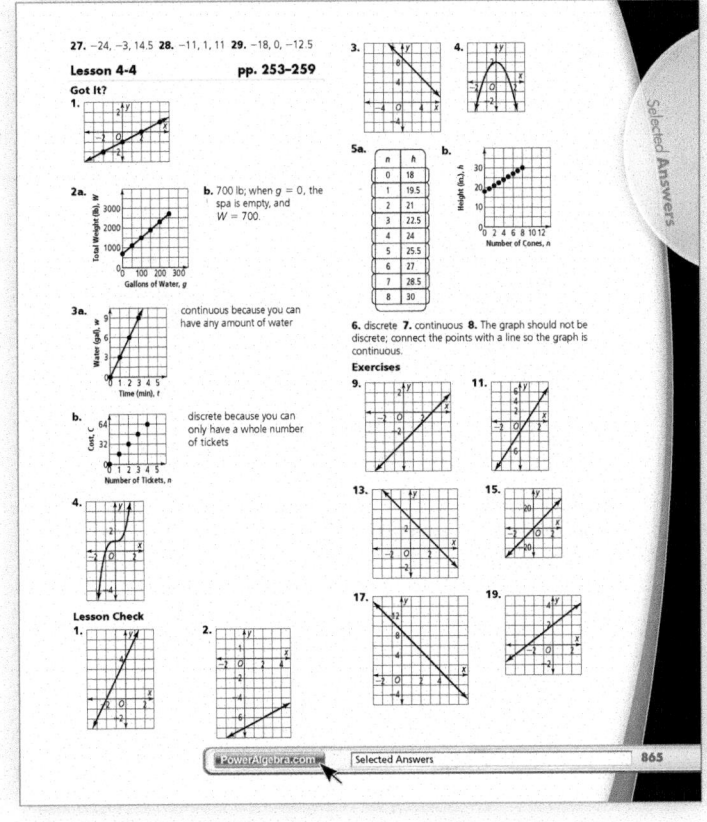

27. −24, −3, 14.5 **28.** −11, 1, 11 **29.** −18, 0, −12.5

Lesson 4-4 pp. 253–259
Got It?
1.

2a. **b.** 700 lb; when $g = 0$, the spa is empty, and $W = 700$.

3a. continuous because you can have any amount of water

b. discrete because you can only have a whole number of tickets

Lesson Check
1. **2.**

3. **4.**

5a.

n	h
0	18
1	19.5
2	21
3	22.5
4	24
5	25.5
6	27
7	28.5
8	30

b.

6. discrete **7.** continuous **8.** The graph should not be discrete; connect the points with a line so the graph is continuous.
Exercises
9. **11.**

13. **15.**

17. **19.**

Page 866

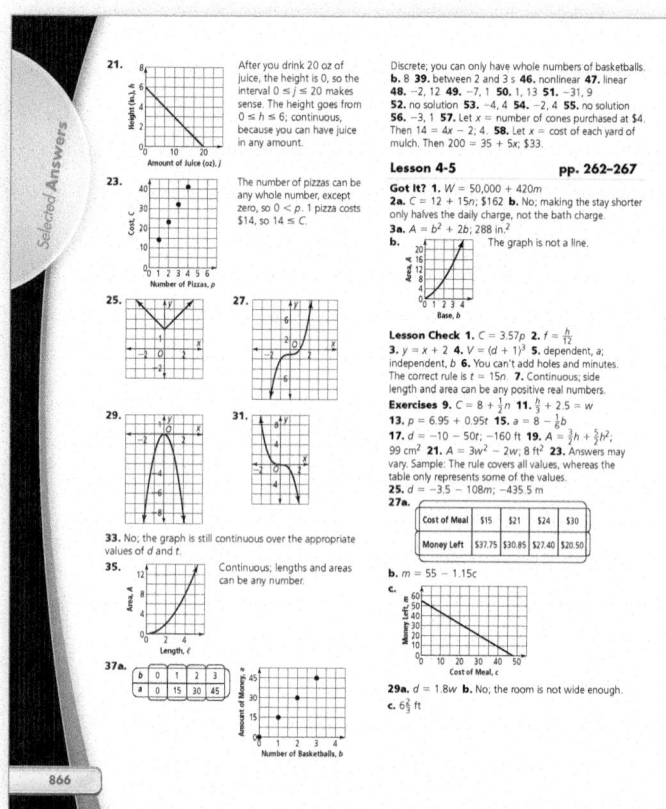

21. After you drink 20 oz of juice, the height is 0, so the interval $0 \le j \le 20$ makes sense. The height goes from $0 \le h \le 6$; continuous, because you can have juice in any amount.

23. The number of pizzas can be any whole number, except zero, so $0 < p$. 1 pizza costs $14, so $14 \le C$.

25. **27.**

29. **31.**

33. No; the graph is still continuous over the appropriate values of d and t.

35. Continuous; lengths and areas can be any number.

37a.

b	0	1	2	3
a	0	15	30	45

Discrete; you can only have whole numbers of basketballs. **b.** 8 **39.** between 2 and 3 ≤ **46.** nonlinear **47.** linear
48. −2, 12 **49.** −7, 1 **50.** 1, 13 **51.** −31, 9
52. no solution **53.** −4, 4 **54.** −2, 4 **55.** no solution
56. −3, 1 **57.** Let x = number of cones purchased at $4. Then $14 = 4x − 2$; 4. **58.** Let x = cost of each yard of mulch. Then $200 = 35 + 5x$; $33.

Lesson 4-5 pp. 262–267
Got It? 1. $W = 50{,}000 + 420m$
2a. $C = 12 + 15n$; $162 **b.** No; making the stay shorter only halves the daily charge, not the bath charge.
3a. $A = b^2 + 2b$; 288 in.²
b. The graph is not a line.

Lesson Check 1. $C = 3.57p$ **2.** $f = \frac{h}{12}$
3. $y = x + 2$ **4.** $V = (d + 1)^3$ **5.** dependent, a; independent, b **6.** You can't add holes and minutes. The correct rule is $t = 15n$. **7.** Continuous; side length and area can be any positive real numbers.
Exercises 9. $C = 8 + \frac{1}{2}n$ **11.** $\frac{3}{5} + 2.5 = w$
13. $p = 6.95 + 0.95t$ **15.** $a = 8 - \frac{1}{b}b$
17. $d = -10 - 50t$; −160 ft **19.** $A = \frac{2}{3}h + \frac{5}{2}h^2$; 99 cm² **21.** $A = 3w^2 - 2w$; 8 ft² **23.** Answers may vary. Sample: The rule covers all values, whereas the table only represents some of the values.
25. $d = -3.5 - 108m$; −435.5 m
27a.

Cost of Meal	$15	$21	$24	$30
Money Left	$37.75	$30.85	$27.40	$20.50

b. $m = 55 - 1.15c$
c.

29a. $d = 1.8w$ **b.** No; the room is not wide enough.
c. $6\frac{2}{3}$ ft

Page 867

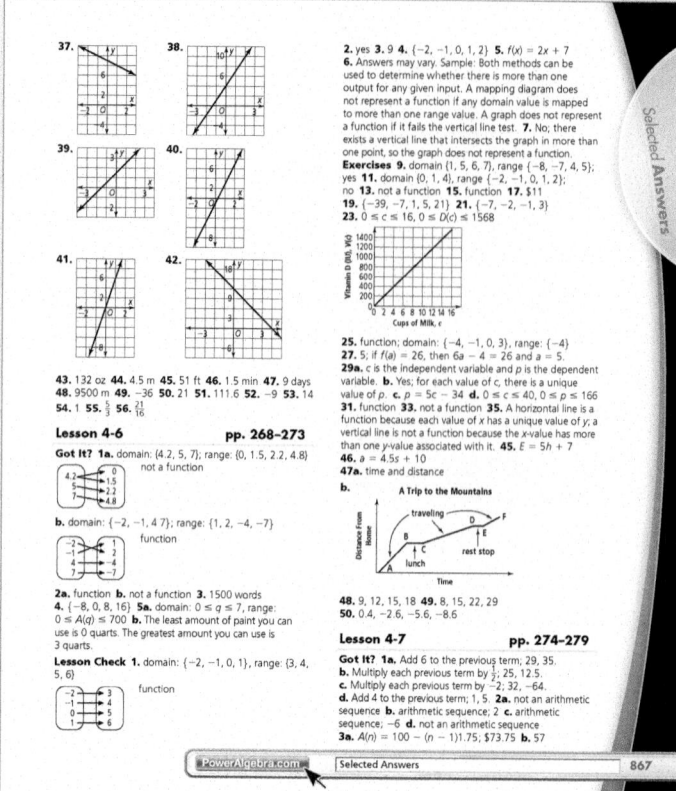

37. **38.** **39.** **40.** **41.** **42.**

43. 132 oz **44.** 4.5 m **45.** 51 ft **46.** 1.5 min **47.** 9 days
48. 9500 m **49.** −36 **50.** 21 **51.** 111.6 **52.** −9 **53.** 14
54. 1 **55.** $\frac{5}{6}$ **56.** $\frac{21}{16}$

Lesson 4-6 pp. 268–273
Got It? 1a. domain: {4.2, 5, 7}; range: {0, 1.5, 2.2, 4.8} not a function
b. domain: {−2, −1, 4 7}; range: {1, 2, −4, −7} function
2a. function **b.** not a function **3.** 1500 words
4. {−8, 0, 8, 16} **5a.** domain: $0 \le g \le 7$, range: $0 \le A(g) \le 700$ **b.** The least amount of paint you can use is 0 quarts. The greatest amount you can use is 3 quarts.
Lesson Check 1. domain: {−2, −1, 0, 1}, range: {3, 4, 5, 6} function

2. yes **3.** 9 **4.** {−2, −1, 0, 1, 2} **5.** $f(x) = 2x + 7$
6. Answers may vary. Sample: Both methods can be used to determine whether there is more than one output for any given input. A mapping diagram does not represent a function if any domain value is mapped to more than one range value. A graph does not represent a function if it fails the vertical line test. **7.** No; there exists a vertical line that intersects the graph in more than one point, so the graph does not represent a function.
Exercises 9. domain {1, 5, 6, 7}, range {−8, −7, 4, 5}; yes **11.** domain {0, 1, 4}, range {−2, −1, 0, 1, 2}; no **13.** not a function **15.** function **17.** $11
19. {−39, −7, 1, 5, 21} **21.** {−7, −2, −1, 3}
23. $0 \le c \le 16$, $0 \le D(c) \le 1568$

25. function; domain: {−4, −1, 0, 3}, range: {−4}
27. 5; if $f(a) = 26$, then $6a - 4 = 26$ and $a = 5$.
29. c is the independent variable and p is the dependent variable. **b.** Yes; for each value of c there is a unique value of p. **c.** $p = 5c - 34$ **d.** $0 \le c \le 40$, $0 \le p \le 166$
31. function **33.** not a function **35.** A horizontal line is a function because each value of x has a unique value of y; a vertical line is not a function because the x-value has more than one y-value associated with it. **45.** $E = 5h + 7$
46. $a = 4.5s + 10$
47a. time and distance
b. A Trip to the Mountains

48. 9, 12, 15, 18 **49.** 8, 15, 22, 29
50. 0.4, −2.6, −5.6, −8.6

Lesson 4-7 pp. 274–279
Got It? 1a. Add 6 to the previous term; 29, 35.
b. Multiply each previous term by $\frac{1}{2}$; 25, 12.5.
c. Multiply each previous term by −2; 32, −64.
d. Add 4 to the previous term; 1, 5. **2a.** not an arithmetic sequence **b.** arithmetic sequence; 2 **c.** arithmetic sequence; −6 **d.** not an arithmetic sequence
3a. $A(n) = 100 - (n - 1)1.75$; $73.75 **b.** 57

Page 868

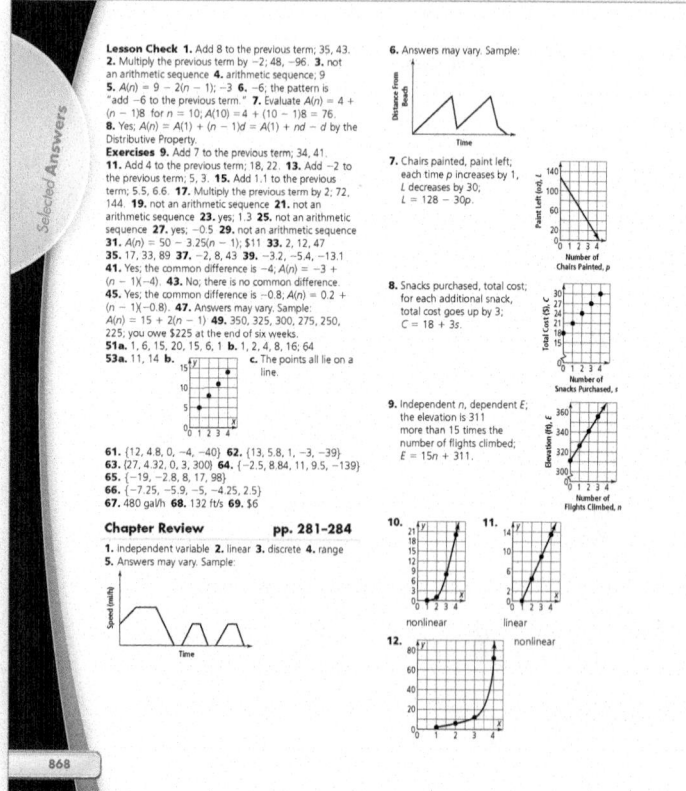

Lesson Check 1. Add 8 to the previous term; 35, 43.
2. Multiply the previous term by −2; 48, −96. **3.** not an arithmetic sequence **4.** arithmetic sequence; 9
5. $A(n) = 9 - 2(n - 1)$; −3 **6.** −6; the pattern is "add −6 to the previous term." **7.** Evaluate $A(n) = 4 + (n - 1)8$ for $n = 10$; $A(10) = 4 + (10 - 1)8 = 76$.
8. Yes; $A(n) = A(1) + (n - 1)d = A(1) + nd - d$ by the Distributive Property.
Exercises 9. Add 7 to the previous term; 34, 41.
11. Add 4 to the previous term; 18, 22. **13.** Add −2 to the previous term; 5, 3. **15.** Add 1.1 to the previous term; 5.5, 6.6. **17.** Multiply the previous term by 2; 72, 144. **19.** not an arithmetic sequence **21.** not an arithmetic sequence **23.** yes; 1.3 **25.** not an arithmetic sequence **27.** yes; −0.5 **29.** not an arithmetic sequence
31. $A(n) = 50 - 3.25(n - 1)$ **33.** 2, 12, 47
35. 17, 33, 89 **37.** −2, 8, 43 **39.** −3.2, −5.4, −13.1
41. Yes; the common difference is −4; $A(n) = -3 + (n - 1)(-4)$. **43.** No; there is no common difference.
45. Yes; the common difference is −0.8; $A(n) = 0.2 + (n - 1)(-0.8)$. **47.** Answers may vary. Sample: $A(n) = 15 + 2(n - 1)$ **49.** 350, 325, 300, 275, 250, 225; you owe $225 at the end of six weeks.
51a. 1, 6, 15, 20, 15, 6, 1 **b.** 1, 2, 4, 8, 16; 64
53a. 11, 14 **b.** **c.** The points all lie on a line.

61. {12, 4.8, 0, −4, −40} **62.** {13, 5.8, 1, −3, −39}
63. {27, 4.32, 0, 3, 300} **64.** {−2.5, 8.84, 11, 9.5, −139}
65. {−19, −2.8, 8, 17, 98}
66. {−7.25, −5.9, −5, −4.25, 2.5}
67. 480 gal/h **68.** 132 ft/s **69.** $6

Chapter Review pp. 281–284
1. independent variable **2.** linear **3.** discrete **4.** range
5. Answers may vary. Sample:

6. Answers may vary. Sample:

7. Chairs painted, paint left; each time p increases by 1, L decreases by 30; $L = 128 - 30p$.

8. Snacks purchased, total cost; for each additional snack, total cost goes up by 3; $C = 18 + 3s$.

9. Independent n, dependent E; the elevation is 311 more than 15 times the number of flights climbed; $E = 15n + 311$.

10. nonlinear **11.** linear
12. nonlinear

Page 869

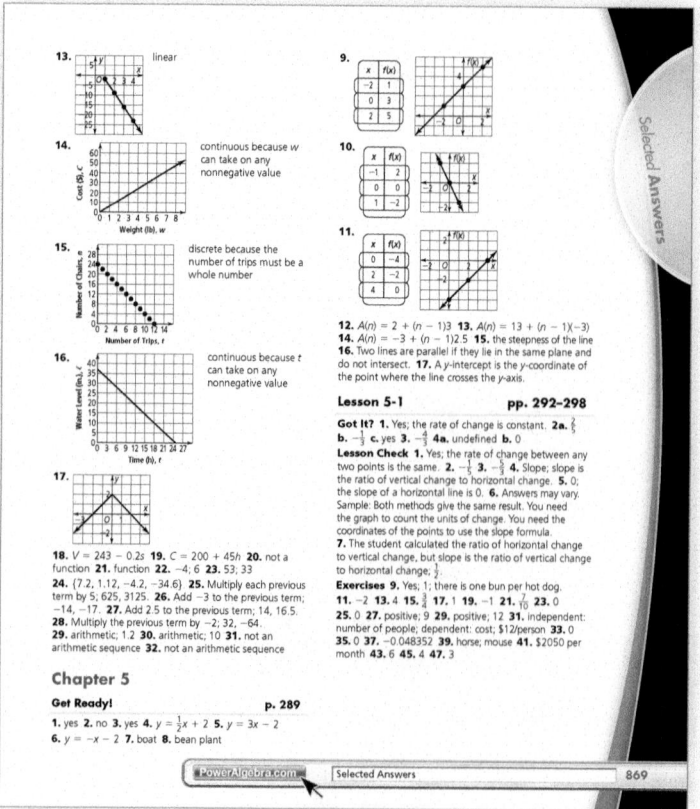

13. linear
14. continuous because w can take on any nonnegative value
15. discrete because the number of trips must be a whole number
16. continuous because t can take on any nonnegative value
17.
18. $V = 243 - 0.2s$ **19.** $C = 200 + 45n$ **20.** not a function **21.** function **22.** −4; 6 **23.** 53; 33
24. {7.2, 1.12, −4.2, −34.6} **25.** Multiply each previous term by 5; 625, 3125. **26.** Add −3 to the previous term; −14, −17. **27.** Add 2.5 to the previous term; 14, 16.5.
28. Multiply the previous term by −2; 32, −64.
29. arithmetic; 1.2 **30.** arithmetic; 10 **31.** not an arithmetic sequence **32.** not an arithmetic sequence

Chapter 5

Get Ready! p. 289
1. yes **2.** no **3.** yes **4.** $y = \frac{1}{3}x + 2$ **5.** $y = 3x - 2$
6. $y = -x - 2$ **7.** boat **8.** bean plant

9. **10.** **11.**

12. $A(n) = 2 + (n - 1)3$ **13.** $A(n) = 13 + (n - 1)(-3)$
14. $A(n) = -3 + (n - 1)2.5$ **15.** the steepness of the line **16.** Two lines are parallel if they lie in the same plane and do not intersect. **17.** A y-intercept is the y-coordinate of the point where the line crosses the y-axis.

Lesson 5-1 pp. 292–298
Got It? 1. Yes; the rate of change is constant. **2a.** $\frac{2}{5}$
b. $-\frac{1}{3}$ **c.** yes **3.** $-\frac{4}{3}$ **4a.** undefined **b.** 0
Lesson Check 1. Yes; the rate of change between any two points is the same. **2.** $-\frac{1}{3}$ **3.** $-\frac{2}{3}$ **4.** Slope; slope is the ratio of vertical change to horizontal change. **5.** 0; the slope of a horizontal line is 0. **6.** Answers may vary. Sample: Both methods give the same result. You need the graph to count the units of change. You need the coordinates of the points to use the slope formula.
7. The student calculated the ratio of horizontal change to vertical change, but slope is the ratio of vertical change to horizontal change; $\frac{1}{2}$.
Exercises 9. Yes; 1; there is one bun per hot dog.
11. −2 **13.** 4 **15.** $\frac{3}{4}$ **17.** 1 **19.** −1 **21.** $\frac{7}{10}$ **23.** 0
25. 0 **27.** positive; 9 **29.** positive; 12 **31.** independent: number of people; dependent: cost; $12/person **33.** 0
35. 0 **37.** −0.048352 **39.** horse; mouse **41.** $2050 per month **43.** 6 **45.** 4 **47.** 3

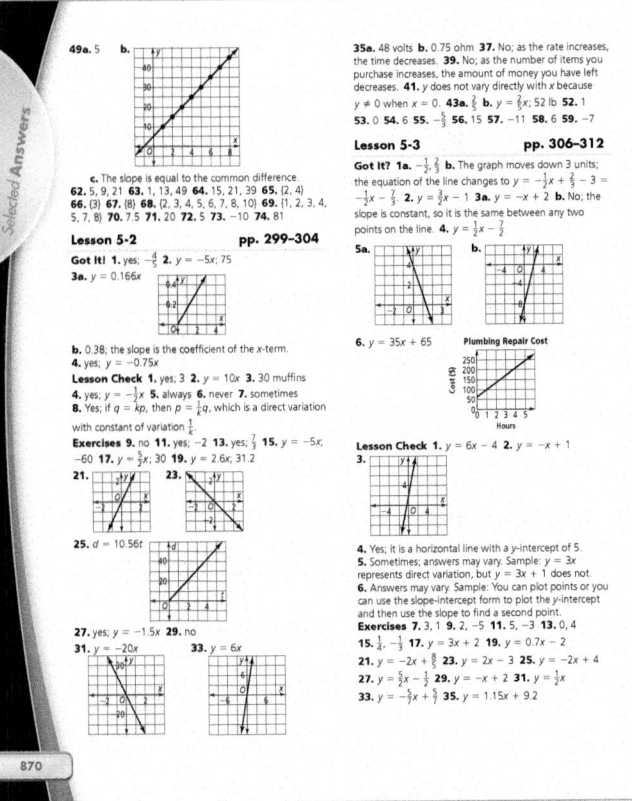

49a. 5 **b.**

c. The slope is equal to the common difference.
62. 5, 9, 21 **63.** 1, 13, 49 **64.** 15, 21, 39 **65.** (2, 4)
66. (3) **67.** {8} **68.** (2, 3, 4, 5, 6, 7, 8, 10) **69.** {1, 2, 3, 4,
5, 7, 8} **70.** 7.5 **71.** 20 **72.** 5 **73.** −10 **74.** 81

Lesson 5-2 pp. 299–304
Got It! 1. yes; $-\frac{4}{5}$ **2.** $y = -5x$; 75
3a. $y = 0.166x$

b. 0.38; the slope is the coefficient of the x-term.
4. yes; $y = -0.75x$
Lesson Check 1. yes; 3 **2.** $y = 10x$ **3.** 30 muffins
4. yes; $y = -\frac{1}{3}x$ **5.** always **6.** never **7.** sometimes
8. Yes; if $q = kp$, then $p = \frac{1}{k}q$, which is a direct variation
with constant of variation $\frac{1}{k}$.
Exercises 9. no **11.** yes; -2 **13.** yes; $\frac{7}{2}$ **15.** $y = -5x$;
-60 **17.** $y = \frac{5}{3}x$; 30 **19.** $y = 2.6x$; 31.2
21. **23.**
25. $d = 10.56t$
27. yes; $y = -1.5x$ **29.** no
31. $y = -20x$ **33.** $y = 6x$

35a. 48 volts **b.** 0.75 ohm **37.** No; as the rate increases,
the time decreases. **39.** No; as the number of items you
purchase increases, the amount of money you have left
decreases. **41.** y does not vary directly with x because
$y \neq 0$ when $x = 0$. **43a.** $\frac{5}{6}$ **b.** $y = \frac{5}{6}x$; 52 lb **52.** 1
53. 0 **54.** 6 **55.** $-\frac{5}{3}$ **56.** 15 **57.** -11 **58.** 6 **59.** -7

Lesson 5-3 pp. 306–312
Got It! 1a. $-\frac{1}{2}, \frac{2}{3}$ **b.** The graph moves down 3 units;
the equation of the line changes to $y = -\frac{1}{2}x + \frac{2}{3} - 3 =$
$-\frac{1}{2}x - \frac{7}{3}$. **2.** $y = \frac{2}{3}x - 1$ **3a.** $y = -x + 2$ **b.** No; the
slope is constant, so it is the same between any two
points on the line. **4.** $y = \frac{1}{2}x - \frac{7}{2}$

5a. **b.**
6. $y = 35x + 65$

Plumbing Repair Cost

Lesson Check 1. $y = 6x - 4$ **2.** $y = -x + 1$
3.

4. Yes; it is a horizontal line with a y-intercept of 5.
5. Sometimes; answers may vary. Sample: $y = 3x$
represents direct variation, but $y = 3x + 1$ does not.
6. Answers may vary. Sample: You can plot points or you
can use the slope-intercept form to plot the y-intercept
and then use the slope to find a second point.
Exercises 7. 3, 1 **9.** 2, -15 **11.** 5, -3 **13.** 0, 4
15. $\frac{1}{3}, -\frac{1}{2}$ **17.** $y = 3x + 2$ **19.** $y = 0.7x - 2$
21. $y = -2x + \frac{8}{3}$ **23.** $y = 2x - 3$ **25.** $y = -2x + 4$
27. $y = \frac{5}{2}x - \frac{7}{2}$ **29.** $y = -x + 2$ **31.** $y = \frac{1}{2}x$
33. $y = -\frac{2}{3}x + \frac{1}{3}$ **35.** $y = 1.15x + 9.2$

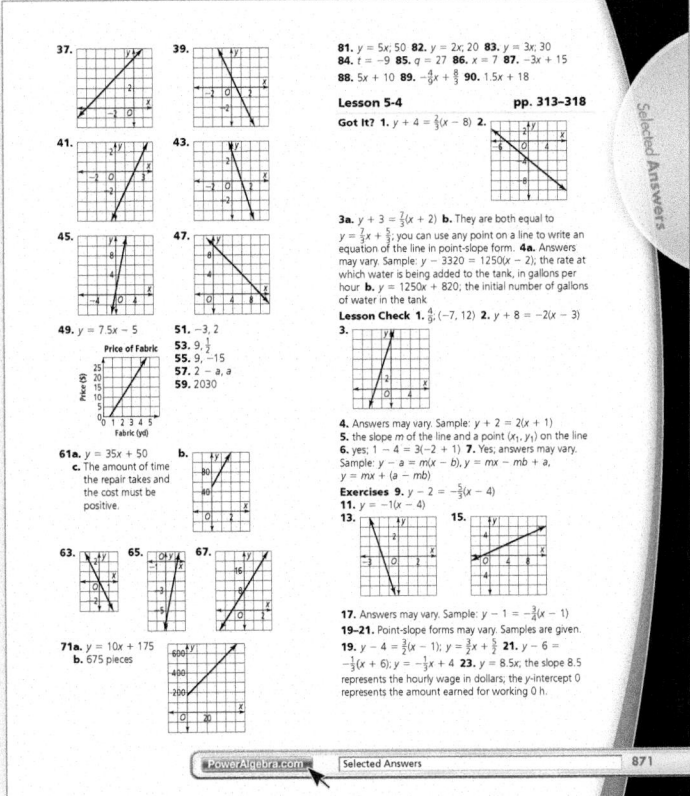

37. **39.**
41. **43.**
45. **47.**
49. $y = 7.5x - 5$
51. $-3, 2$
53. $9, \frac{1}{2}$
55. $9, -15$
57. $2 - a, a$
59. 2030

Price of Fabric

61a. $y = 35x + 50$ **b.**
c. The amount of time
the repair takes and
the cost must be
positive.

63. **65.** **67.**
71a. $y = 10x + 175$
b. 675 pieces

81. $y = 5x$; 50 **82.** $y = 2x$; 20 **83.** $y = 3x$; 30
84. $t = -9$ **85.** $q = 27$ **86.** $x = 7$ **87.** $-3x + 15$
88. $5x + 10$ **89.** $-\frac{8}{9}x + \frac{8}{9}$ **90.** $1.5x + 18$

Lesson 5-4 pp. 313–318
Got It! 1. $y + 4 = \frac{2}{3}(x - 8)$ **2.**

3a. $y + 3 = \frac{2}{3}(x + 2)$ **b.** They are both equal to
$y = \frac{2}{3}x + \frac{5}{3}$; you can use any point on a line to write an
equation of the line in point-slope form. **4a.** Answers
may vary. Sample: $y - 3320 = 1250(x - 2)$; the rate at
which water is being added to the tank, in gallons per
hour **b.** $y = 1250x + 820$; the initial number of gallons
of water in the tank
Lesson Check 1. $\frac{4}{5}, (-7, 12)$ **2.** $y + 8 = -2(x - 3)$
3.

4. Answers may vary. Sample: $y + 2 = 2(x + 1)$
5. the slope m of the line and a point (x_1, y_1) on the line
6. yes; $1 - 4 = 3(-2 + 1)$ **7.** Yes; answers may vary.
Sample: $y - a = m(x - b), y = mx - mb + a,$
$y = mx + (a - mb)$
Exercises 9. $y - 2 = -\frac{2}{3}(x - 4)$
11. $y = -1(x - 4)$
13. **15.**
17. Answers may vary. Sample: $y - 1 = -\frac{3}{4}(x - 1)$
19–21. Point-slope forms may vary. Samples are given.
19. $y - 4 = \frac{2}{3}(x - 1)$; $y = \frac{2}{3}x + \frac{10}{3}$ **21.** $y - 6 =$
$-\frac{1}{3}(x + 6)$; $y = -\frac{1}{3}x + 4$ **23.** $y = 8.5x$; the slope 8.5
represents the hourly wage in dollars; the y-intercept 0
represents the amount earned for working 0 h.

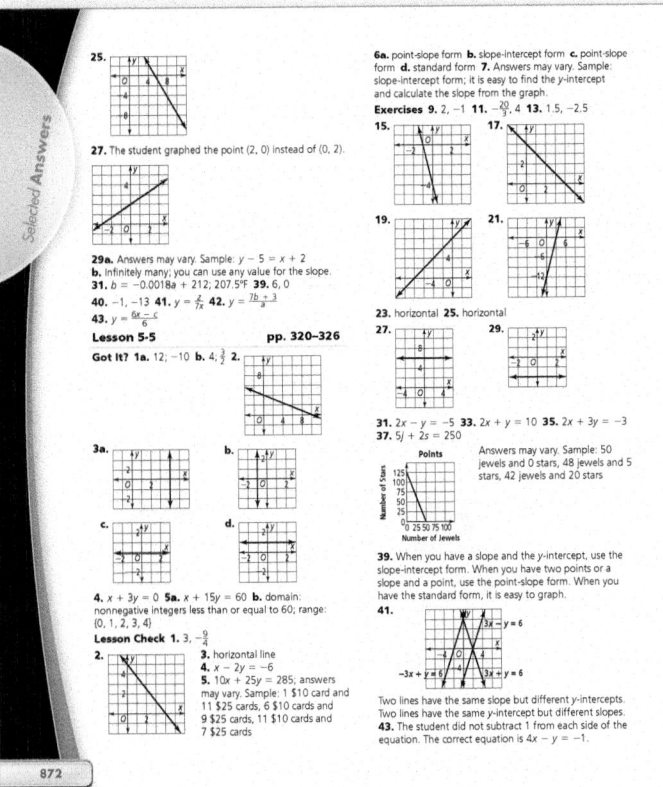

25.
27. The student graphed the point (2, 0) instead of (0, 2).
29a. Answers may vary. Sample: $y - 5 = x + 2$
b. Infinitely many; you can use any value for the slope.
31. $b = -0.0018a + 212$; 207.5°F **39.** 6, 0
40. $-1, -13$ **41.** $y = \frac{x}{7}$x **42.** $y = \frac{7b + 3}{a}$
43. $y = \frac{6x - c}{6}$

Lesson 5-5 pp. 320–326
Got It! 1a. 12; -10 **b.** 4; $\frac{2}{3}$ **2.**
3a. **b.**
c. **d.**
4. $x + 3y = 0$ **5a.** $x + 15y = 60$ **b.** domain:
nonnegative integers less than or equal to 60; range:
{0, 1, 2, 3, 4}
Lesson Check 1. 3, $-\frac{4}{3}$
2.
3. horizontal line
4. $x - 2y = -6$
5. $10x + 25y = 285$; answers
may vary. Sample: 1 \$10 card and
11 \$25 cards, 6 \$10 cards and
9 \$25 cards, 11 \$10 cards and
7 \$25 cards

6a. point-slope form **b.** slope-intercept form **c.** point-slope
form **d.** standard form **7.** Answers may vary. Sample:
slope-intercept form; it is easy to find the y-intercept
and calculate the slope from the graph.
Exercises 9. 2, -11 **11.** $-\frac{20}{7}, 4$ **13.** 1.5, -2.5
15. **17.**
19. **21.**
23. horizontal **25.** horizontal
27. **29.**
31. $2x - y = -5$ **33.** $2x + y = 10$ **35.** $2x + 3y = -3$
37. $5j + 2s = 250$
Points
Answers may vary. Sample: 50
jewels and 0 stars, 48 jewels and 5
stars, 42 jewels and 20 stars

39. When you have a slope and the y-intercept, use the
slope-intercept form. When you have two points or a
slope and a point, use the point-slope form. When you
have the standard form, it is easy to graph.
41.
Two lines have the same slope but different y-intercepts.
Two lines have the same y-intercept but different slopes.
43. The student did not subtract 1 from each side of the
equation. The correct equation is $4x - y = -1$.

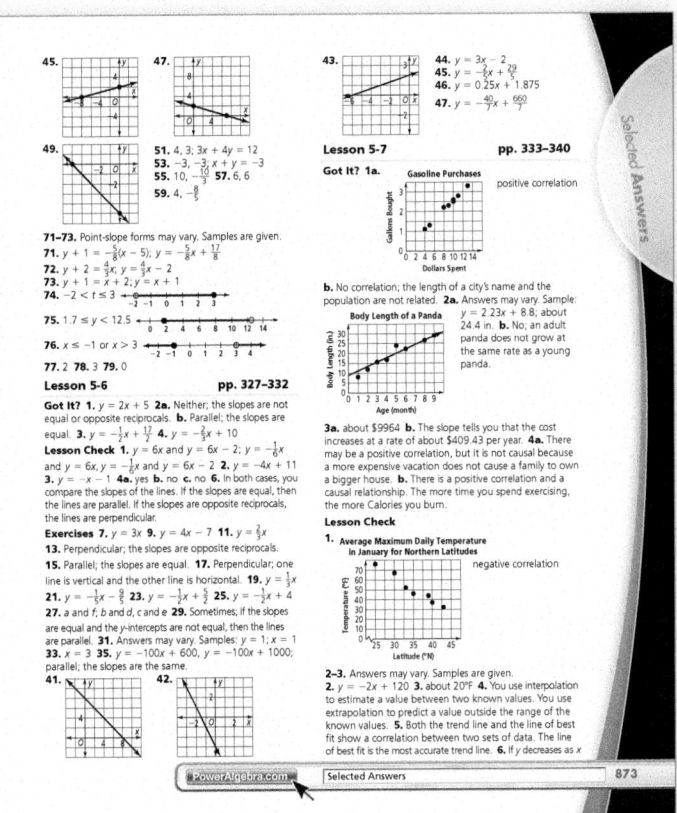

45. **47.**
49.
51. 4, 3; $3x + 4y = 12$
53. $-3, -3$; $x + y = -3$
55. 10, $-\frac{10}{3}$ **57.** 6, 6
59. 4, $-\frac{4}{5}$
71–73. Point-slope forms may vary. Samples are given.
71. $y + 1 = -\frac{5}{8}(x - 5)$; $y = -\frac{5}{8}x + \frac{17}{8}$
72. $y + 2 = \frac{4}{5}x$; $y = \frac{4}{5}x - 2$
73. $y + 1 = x + 2$; $y = x + 1$
74. $-2 < t \leq 3$
75. $1.7 \leq y < 12.5$
76. $x \leq -1$ or $x > 3$
77. 2 **78.** 3 **79.** 0

Lesson 5-6 pp. 327–332
Got It! 1. $y = 2x + 5$ **2a.** Neither; the slopes are not
equal or opposite reciprocals. **b.** Parallel; the slopes are
equal. **3.** $y = -\frac{1}{3}x + \frac{17}{3}$ **4.** $y = -\frac{2}{3}x + 10$
Lesson Check 1. $y = 6x$ and $y = 6x - 2$ **2.** $y = -4x + 11$
and $y = 6x$; $y = -\frac{1}{2}x$ and $y = 6x - 2$ **2.** $y = -4x + 11$
3. $y = -x - 1$ **4a.** yes **b.** no **c.** no **6.** In both cases, you
compare the slopes of the lines. If the slopes are equal, then
the lines are parallel. If the slopes are opposite reciprocals,
the lines are perpendicular.
Exercises 7. $y = 3x$ **9.** $y = 4x - 7$ **11.** $y = \frac{1}{5}x$
13. Perpendicular; the slopes are opposite reciprocals.
15. Parallel; the slopes are equal. **17.** Perpendicular; one
line is vertical and the other line is horizontal. **19.** $y = \frac{1}{3}x$
21. $y = -\frac{1}{5}x - \frac{2}{5}$ **23.** $y = -\frac{1}{2}x + \frac{5}{2}$ **25.** $y = -\frac{1}{3}x + 4$
27. a and f; b and d, and e **29.** Sometimes; if the slopes
are equal and the y-intercepts are not equal, then the lines
are parallel. **31.** Answers may vary. Samples: $y = 1$; $x = 1$
33. $x = 3$ **35.** $y = -100x + 600$, $y = -100x + 1000$;
parallel; the slopes are the same.
41. **42.**

43.
44. $y = 3x - 2$
45. $y = -\frac{5}{4}x + \frac{29}{4}$
46. $y = 0.25x + 1.875$
47. $y = -\frac{40}{7}x + \frac{660}{7}$

Lesson 5-7 pp. 333–340
Got It! 1a.
Gasoline Purchases
positive correlation

b. No correlation; the length of a city's name and the
population are not related. **2a.** Answers may vary. Sample:
$y = 2.23x + 8.8$; about
24.4 in. **b.** No; an adult
panda does not grow at
the same rate as a young
panda.

Body Length of a Panda

3a. about \$9964 **b.** The slope tells you that the cost
increases at a rate of about \$409.43 per year. **4a.** There
may be a positive correlation, but it is not causal because
a more expensive vacation does not cause a family to own
a bigger house. **b.** There is a positive correlation and a
causal relationship. The more time you spend exercising,
the more Calories you burn.
Lesson Check
1.
Average Maximum Daily Temperature
in January for Northern Latitudes
negative correlation

2–3. Answers may vary. Samples are given.
2. $y = -2x + 120$ **3.** about 20°F **4.** You use interpolation
to estimate a value between two known values. You use
extrapolation to predict a value outside the range of the
known values. **5.** Both the trend line and the line of best
fit show a correlation between two sets of data. The line
of best fit is the most accurate trend line. **6.** If y decreases as x

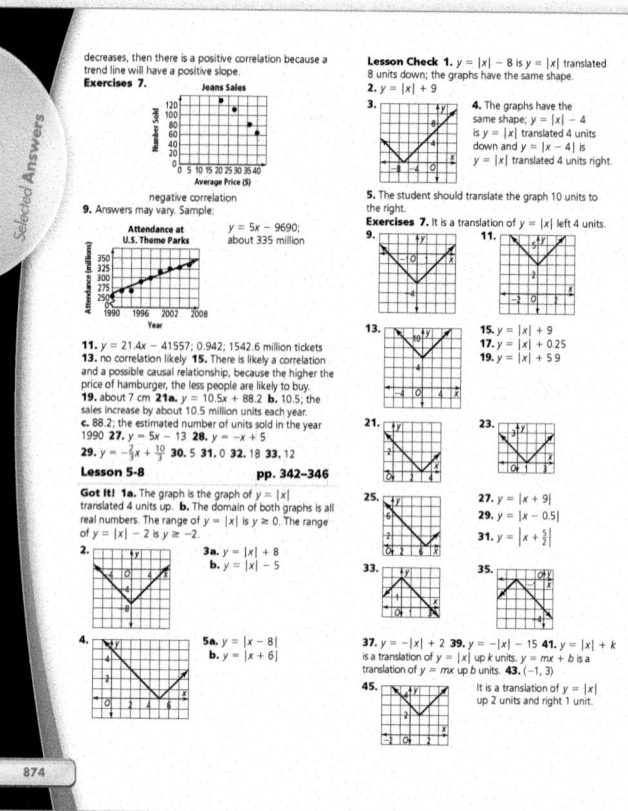

decreases, then there is a positive correlation because a trend line will have a positive slope.

Exercises 7.

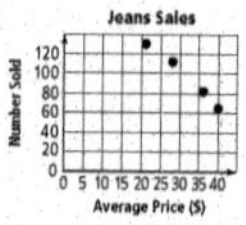

Jeans Sales
Number Sold
120
100
80
60
40
20
0
0 5 10 15 20 25 30 35 40
Average Price ($)

negative correlation

9. Answers may vary. Sample:

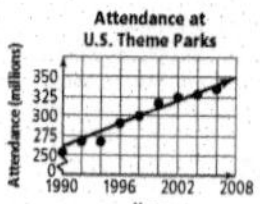

Attendance at U.S. Theme Parks
Attendance (millions)
350
325
300
275
250
0
1990
1996
2002
2008
Year

$y = 5x - 9690$; about 335 million

11. $y = 21.4x - 41557$; 0.942; 1542.6 million tickets **13.** no correlation likely **15.** There is likely a correlation and a possible causal relationship, because the higher the price of hamburger, the less people are likely to buy. **19.** about 7 cm **21a.** $y = 10.5x + 88.2$ **b.** 10.5; the sales increase by about 10.5 million units each year. **c.** 88.2; the estimated number of units sold in the year 1990 **27.** $y = 5x - 13$ **28.** $y = -x + 5$ **29.** $y = -\frac{2}{3}x + \frac{10}{3}$ **30.** 5 **31.** 0 **32.** 18 **33.** 12

Lesson 5-8 pp. 342–346

Got It! 1a. The graph is the graph of $y = |x|$ translated 4 units up. **b.** The domain of both graphs is all real numbers. The range of $y = |x|$ is $y \geq 0$. The range of $y = |x| - 2$ is $y \geq -2$.

2.

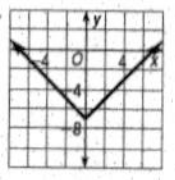

3a. $y = |x| + 8$ **b.** $y = |x| - 5$

4.

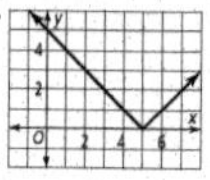

5a. $y = |x - 8|$ **b.** $y = |x + 6|$

Lesson Check 1. $y = |x| - 8$ is $y = |x|$ translated 8 units down; the graphs have the same shape. **2.** $y = |x| + 9$

3.

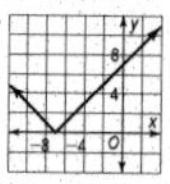

4. The graphs have the same shape; $y = |x| - 4$ is $y = |x|$ translated 4 units down and $y = |x - 4|$ is $y = |x|$ translated 4 units right.

5. The student should translate the graph 10 units to the right.

Exercises 7. It is a translation of $y = |x|$ left 4 units.

9., **11.**

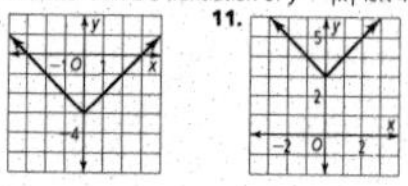

13.

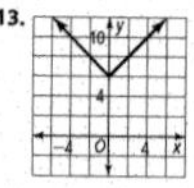

15. $y = |x| + 9$ **17.** $y = |x| + 0.25$ **19.** $y = |x| + 5.9$

21., **23.**

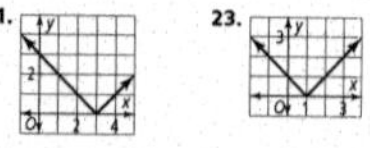

25.

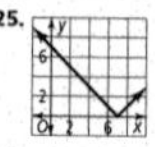

27. $y = |x + 9|$ **29.** $y = |x - 0.5|$ **31.** $y = \left|x + \frac{5}{2}\right|$

33., **35.**

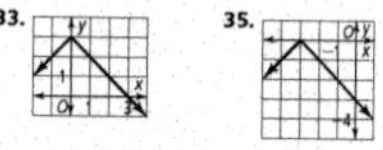

37. $y = -|x| + 2$ **39.** $y = -|x| - 15$ **41.** $y = |x| + k$ is a translation of $y = |x|$ up k units. $y = mx + b$ is a translation of $y = mx$ up b units. **43.** $(-1, 3)$

45.

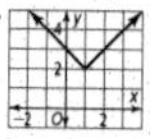

It is a translation of $y = |x|$ up 2 units and right 1 unit.

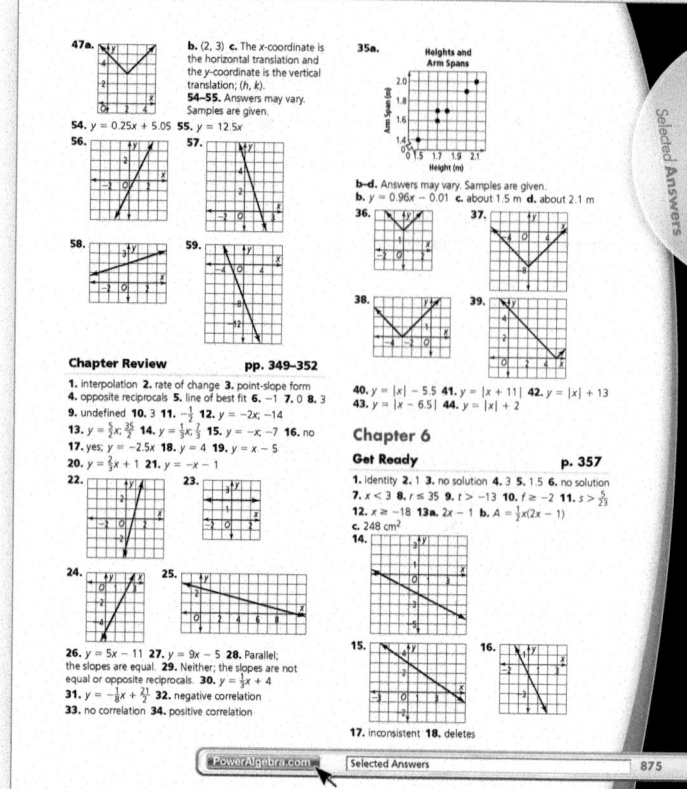

47a.

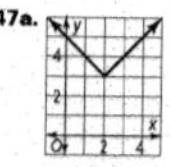

b. (2, 3) **c.** The x-coordinate is the horizontal translation and the y-coordinate is the vertical translation; (h, k).

54–55. Answers may vary. Samples are given.

54. $y = 0.25x + 5.05$ **55.** $y = 12.5x$

56., **57.**

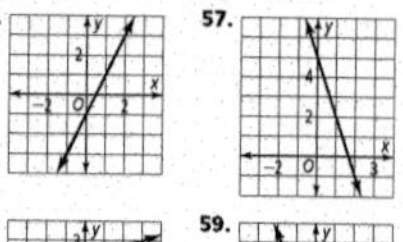

58., **59.**

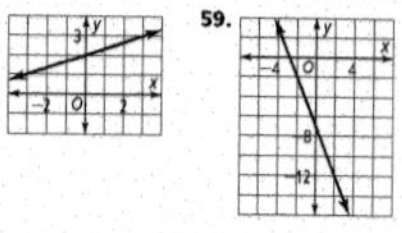

Chapter Review pp. 349–352

1. interpolation **2.** rate of change **3.** point-slope form **4.** opposite reciprocals **5.** line of best fit **6.** −1 **7.** 0 **8.** 3 **9.** undefined **10.** 3 **11.** $-\frac{1}{2}$ **12.** $y = -2x$; −14 **13.** $y = \frac{5}{2}x$; $\frac{35}{2}$ **14.** $y = \frac{1}{3}x$; $\frac{7}{3}$ **15.** $y = -x$; −7 **16.** no **17.** yes; $y = -2.5x$ **18.** $y = 4$ **19.** $y = x - 5$ **20.** $y = \frac{2}{3}x + 1$ **21.** $y = -x - 1$

22., **23.**

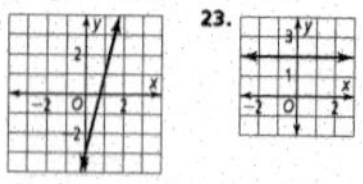

24., **25.**

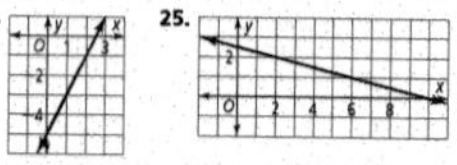

26. $y = 5x - 11$ **27.** $y = 9x - 5$ **28.** Parallel; the slopes are equal. **29.** Neither; the slopes are not equal or opposite reciprocals. **30.** $y = \frac{1}{3}x + 4$ **31.** $y = -\frac{1}{8}x + \frac{21}{2}$ **32.** negative correlation **33.** no correlation **34.** positive correlation

35a.

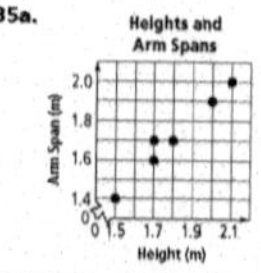

Heights and Arm Spans
Arm Span (m)
2.0
1.8
1.6
1.4
0
0 1.5 1.7 1.9 2.1
Height (m)

b–d. Answers may vary. Samples are given. **b.** $y = 0.96x - 0.01$ **c.** about 1.5 m **d.** about 2.1 m

36., **37.**

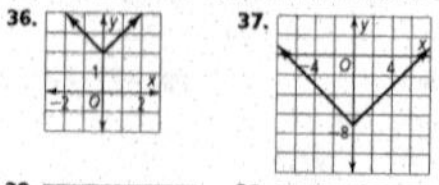

38., **39.**

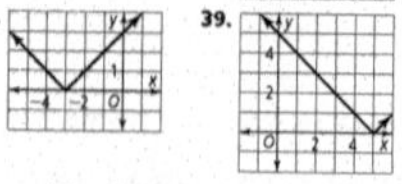

40. $y = |x| - 5.5$ **41.** $y = |x + 11|$ **42.** $y = |x| + 13$ **43.** $y = |x - 6.5|$ **44.** $y = |x| + 2$

Chapter 6

Get Ready p. 357

1. identity **2.** 1 **3.** no solution **4.** 3 **5.** 1.5 **6.** no solution **7.** $x < 3$ **8.** $r \leq 35$ **9.** $t > -13$ **10.** $f \geq -2$ **11.** $s > \frac{5}{23}$ **12.** $x \geq -18$ **13a.** $2x - 1$ **b.** $A = \frac{1}{2}x(2x - 1)$ **c.** 248 cm^2

14.

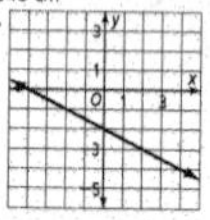

15., **16.**

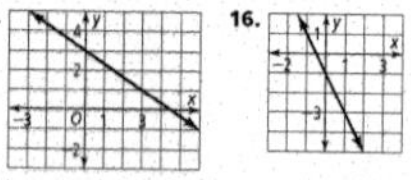

17. inconsistent **18.** deletes

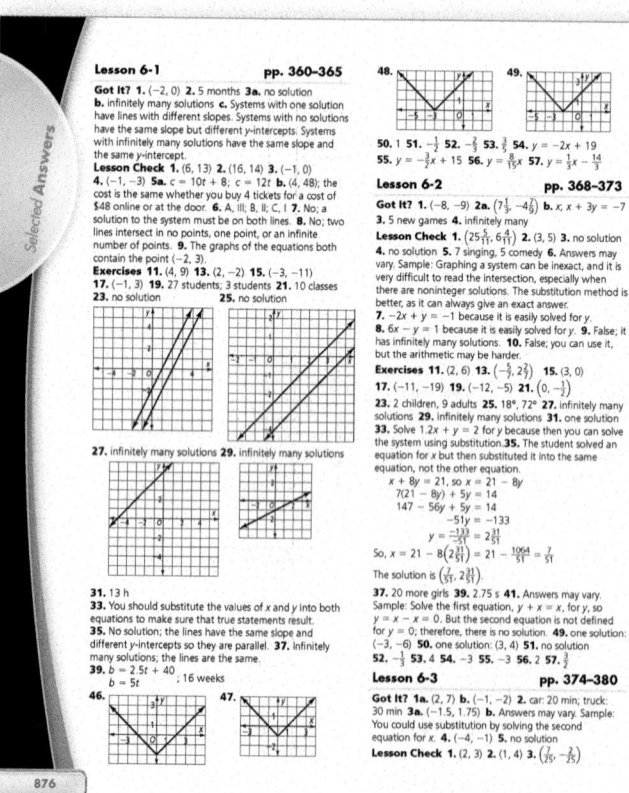

Lesson 6-1 pp. 360–365

Got It? 1. $(-2, 0)$ **2.** 5 months **3a.** no solution **b.** infinitely many solutions **c.** Systems with one solution have lines with different slopes. Systems with no solutions have the same slope but different y-intercepts. Systems with infinitely many solutions have the same slope and the same y-intercept.

Lesson Check 1. (6, 13) **2.** (16, 14) **3.** $(-1, 0)$ **4.** $(-1, -3)$ **5a.** $c = 10t + 8$; $c = 12t$ **b.** (4, 48); the cost is the same whether you buy 4 tickets for a cost of $48 online or at the door. **6.** A, III; B, II; C, I **7.** No; a solution to the system must be on both lines. **8.** No; two lines intersect in no points, one point, or an infinite number of points. **9.** The graphs of the equations both contain the point $(-2, 3)$.

Exercises 11. (4, 9) **13.** $(2, -2)$ **15.** $(-3, -11)$ **17.** $(-1, 3)$ **19.** 27 students; 3 students **21.** 10 classes **23.** no solution **25.** no solution

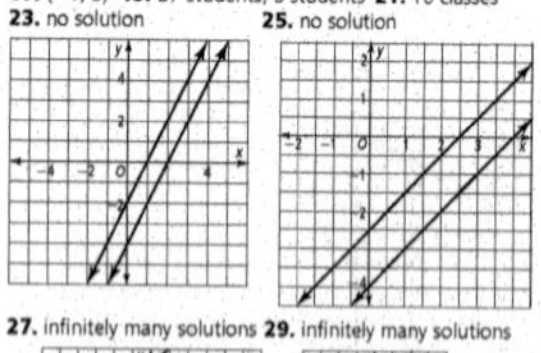

27. infinitely many solutions **29.** infinitely many solutions

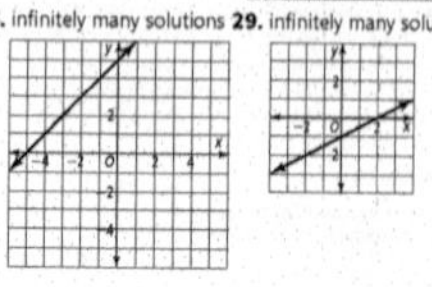

31. 13 h **33.** You should substitute the values of x and y into both equations to make sure that true statements result. **35.** No solution; the lines have the same slope and different y-intercepts so they are parallel. **37.** Infinitely many solutions; the lines are the same.

39. $b = 2.5t + 40$, $b = 5t$; 16 weeks

46., **47.**

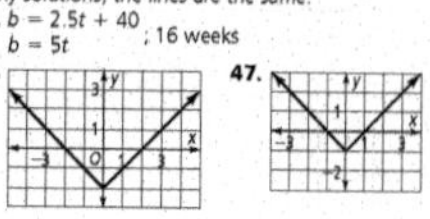

48., **49.**

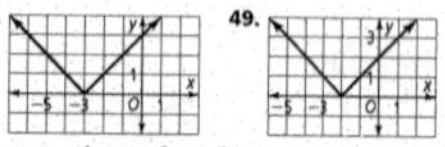

50. 1 **51.** $-\frac{1}{2}$ **52.** $-\frac{2}{3}$ **53.** $\frac{3}{5}$ **54.** $y = -2x + 19$ **55.** $y = -\frac{3}{2}x + 15$ **56.** $y = \frac{8}{15}x$ **57.** $y = \frac{1}{3}x - \frac{14}{3}$

Lesson 6-2 pp. 368–373

Got It? 1. $(-8, -9)$ **2a.** $\left(7\frac{1}{3}, -4\frac{7}{9}\right)$ **b.** x; $x + 3y = -7$ **3.** 5 new games **4.** infinitely many

Lesson Check 1. $\left(25\frac{5}{11}, 6\frac{4}{11}\right)$ **2.** (3, 5) **3.** no solution **4.** no solution **5.** 7 singing, 5 comedy **6.** Answers may vary. Sample: Graphing a system can be inexact, and it is very difficult to read the intersection, especially when there are noninteger solutions. The substitution method is better, as it can always give an exact answer. **7.** $-2x + y = -1$ because it is easily solved for y. **8.** $6x - y = 1$ because it is easily solved for y. **9.** False; it has infinitely many solutions. **10.** False; you can use it, but the arithmetic may be harder.

Exercises 11. (2, 6) **13.** $\left(-\frac{5}{7}, 2\frac{2}{7}\right)$ **15.** (3, 0) **17.** $(-11, -19)$ **19.** $(-12, -5)$ **21.** $\left(0, -\frac{1}{2}\right)$ **23.** 2 children, 9 adults **25.** 18°, 72° **27.** infinitely many solutions **29.** infinitely many solutions **31.** one solution **33.** Solve $1.2x + y = 2$ for y because then you can solve the system using substitution. **35.** The student solved an equation for x but then substituted it into the same equation, not the other equation.

$$x + 8y = 21, \text{ so } x = 21 - 8y$$
$$7(21 - 8y) + 5y = 14$$
$$147 - 56y + 5y = 14$$
$$-51y = -133$$
$$y = \frac{-133}{-51} = 2\frac{31}{51}$$

So, $x = 21 - 8\left(2\frac{31}{51}\right) = 21 - \frac{1064}{51} = \frac{7}{51}$

The solution is $\left(\frac{7}{51}, 2\frac{31}{51}\right)$.

37. 20 more girls **39.** 2.75 s **41.** Answers may vary. Sample: Solve the first equation, $y + x = x$, for y, so $y = x - x = 0$. But the second equation is not defined for $y = 0$; therefore, there is no solution. **49.** one solution: $(-3, -6)$ **50.** one solution: (3, 4) **51.** no solution **52.** $-\frac{1}{3}$ **53.** 4 **54.** −3 **55.** −3 **56.** 2 **57.** $\frac{3}{2}$

Lesson 6-3 pp. 374–380

Got It? 1a. (2, 7) **b.** $(-1, -2)$ **2.** car: 20 min; truck: 30 min **3a.** $(-1.5, 1.75)$ **b.** Answers may vary. Sample: You could use substitution by solving the second equation for x. **4.** $(-4, -1)$ **5.** no solution

Lesson Check 1. (2, 3) **2.** (1, 4) **3.** $\left(\frac{7}{25}, -\frac{2}{25}\right)$

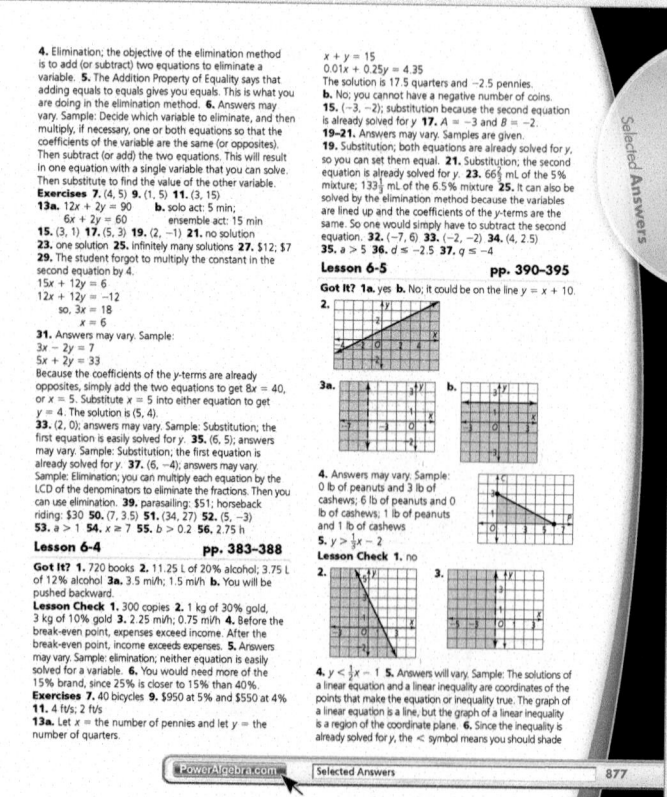

4. Elimination; the objective of the elimination method is to add (or subtract) two equations to eliminate a variable. **5.** The Addition Property of Equality says that adding equals to equals gives you equals. This is what you are doing in the elimination method. **6.** Answers may vary. Sample: Decide which variable to eliminate, and then multiply, if necessary, one or both equations so that the coefficients of the variable are the same (or opposites). Then subtract (or add) the two equations. This will result in one equation with a single variable that you can solve. Then substitute to find the value of the other variable.

Exercises 7. (4, 5) **9.** (1, 5) **11.** (3, 15)

13a. $12x + 2y = 90$, $6x + 2y = 60$ **b.** solo act: 5 min; ensemble act: 15 min

15. (3, 1) **17.** (5, 3) **19.** $(2, -1)$ **21.** no solution **23.** one solution **25.** infinitely many solutions **27.** $12; $7 **29.** The student forgot to multiply the constant in the second equation by 4.

$$15x + 12y = 6$$
$$12x + 12y = -12$$
$$\text{so, } 3x = 18$$
$$x = 6$$

31. Answers may vary. Sample:

$$3x - 2y = 7$$
$$5x + 2y = 33$$

Because the coefficients of the y-terms are already opposites, simply add the two equations to get $8x = 40$, or $x = 5$. Substitute $x = 5$ into either equation to get $y = 4$. The solution is (5, 4).

33. (2, 0); answers may vary. Sample: Substitution; the first equation is easily solved for y. **35.** (6, 5); answers may vary. Sample: Substitution; the first equation is already solved for y. **37.** $(6, -4)$; answers may vary. Sample: Elimination; you can multiply each equation by the LCD of the denominators to eliminate the fractions. Then you can use elimination. **39.** parasailing: $51; horseback riding: $30 **50.** (7, 3.5) **51.** (34, 27) **52.** $(5, -3)$ **53.** $a > 1$ **54.** $x \geq 7$ **55.** $b > 0.2$ **56.** 2.75 h

Lesson 6-4 pp. 383–388

Got It? 1. 720 books **2.** 11.25 L of 20% alcohol; 3.75 L of 12% alcohol **3a.** 3.5 mi/h; 1.5 mi/h **b.** You will be pushed backward.

Lesson Check 1. 300 copies **2.** 1 kg of 30% gold, 3 kg of 10% gold **3.** 2.25 mi/h; 0.75 mi/h **4.** Before the break-even point, expenses exceed income. After the break-even point, income exceeds expenses. **5.** Answers may vary. Sample: elimination; neither equation is easily solved for a variable. **6.** You would need more of the 15% brand, since 25% is closer to 15% than 40%.

Exercises 7. 40 bicycles **9.** $950 at 5% and $550 at 4% **11.** 4 ft/s; 2 ft/s **13a.** Let x = the number of pennies and let y = the number of quarters.

$$x + y = 15$$
$$0.01x + 0.25y = 4.35$$

The solution is 17.5 quarters and −2.5 pennies. **b.** No; you cannot have a negative number of coins. **15.** $(-3, -2)$; substitution because the second equation is already solved for y **17.** $A = -3$ and $B = -2$. **19–21.** Answers may vary. Samples are given. **19.** Substitution; both equations are already solved for y, so you can set them equal. **21.** Substitution; the second equation is already solved for y. **23.** $66\frac{2}{3}$ mL of the 5% mixture; $133\frac{1}{3}$ mL of the 6.5% mixture **25.** It can also be solved by the elimination method because the variables are lined up and the coefficients of the y-terms are the same. So one would simply have to subtract the second equation. **32.** $(-7, 6)$ **33.** $(-2, -2)$ **34.** (4, 2.5) **35.** $a > 5$ **36.** $d \leq -2.5$ **37.** $q \leq -4$

Lesson 6-5 pp. 390–395

Got It? 1a. yes **b.** No; it could be on the line $y = x + 10$.

2.

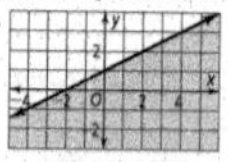

3a., **b.**

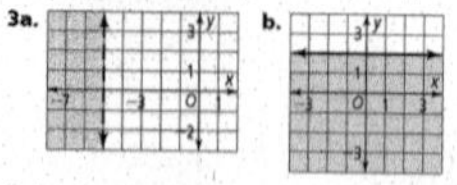

4. Answers may vary. Sample: 0 lb of peanuts and 3 lb of cashews; 6 lb of peanuts and 0 lb of cashews; 1 lb of peanuts and 1 lb of cashews

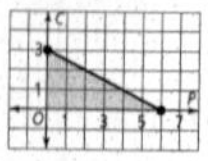

5. $y > \frac{1}{3}x - 2$

Lesson Check 1. no

2., **3.**

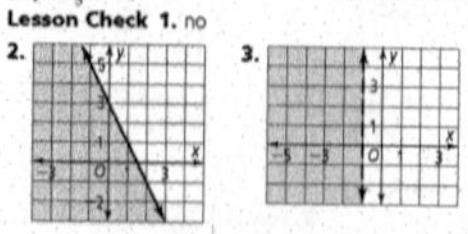

4. $y < \frac{1}{2}x - 1$ **5.** Answers will vary. Sample: The solutions of a linear equation and a linear inequality are coordinates of the points that make the equation or inequality true. The graph of a linear equation is a line, but the graph of a linear inequality is a region of the coordinate plane. **6.** Since the inequality is already solved for y, the < symbol means you should shade

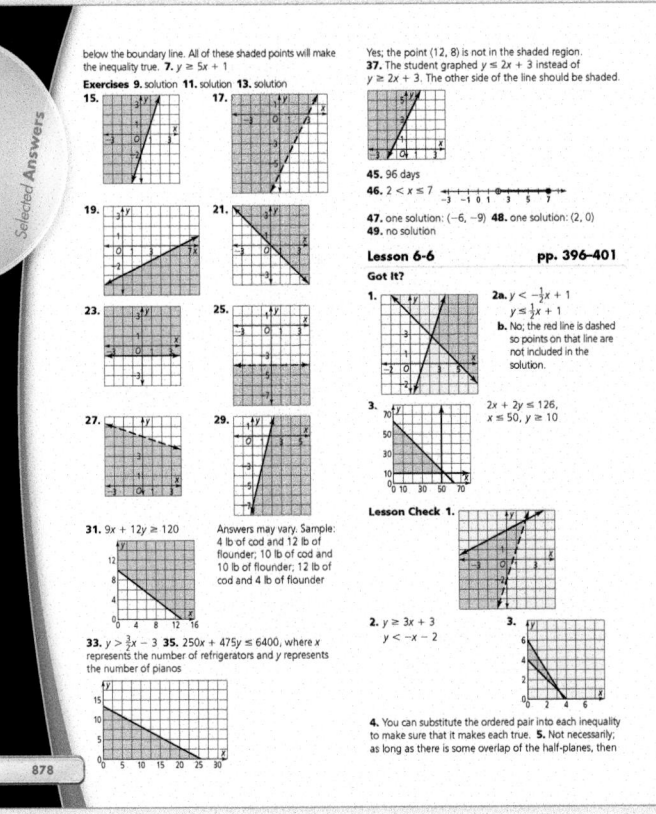

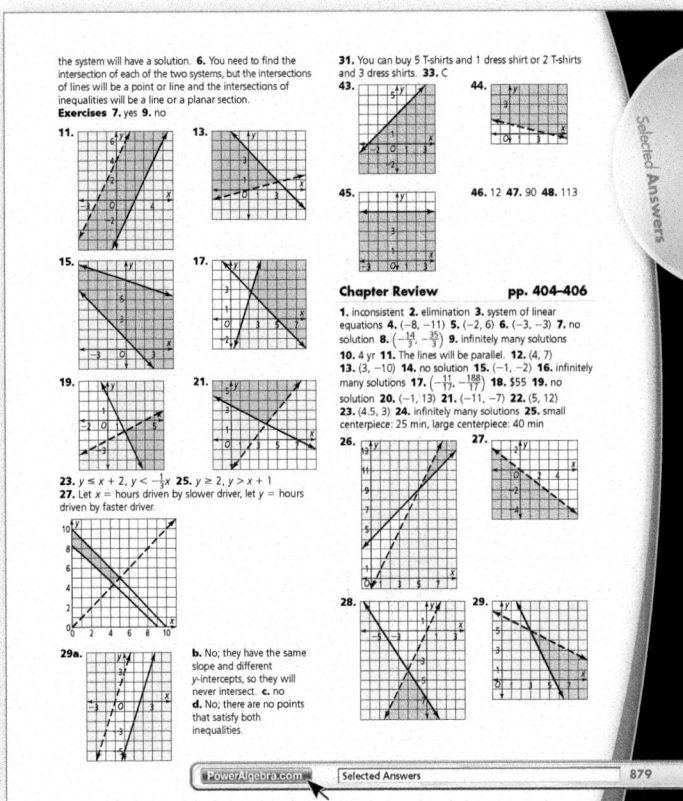

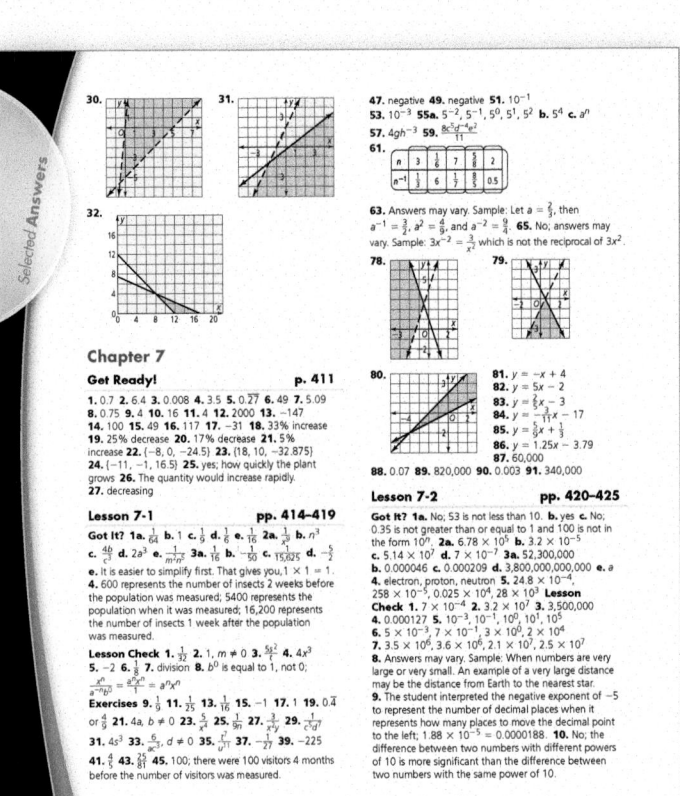

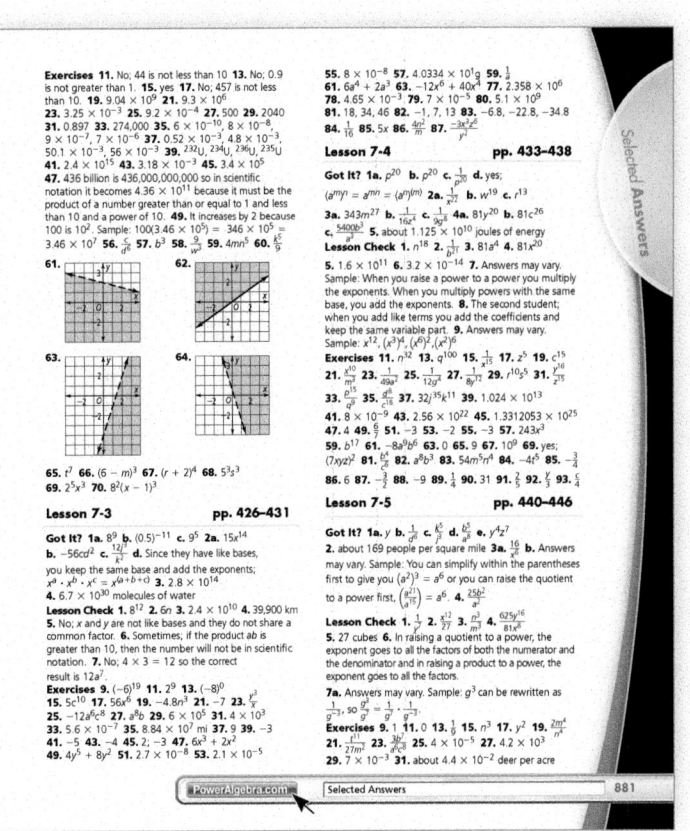

below the boundary line. All of these shaded points will make the inequality true. **7.** $y \ge 5x + 1$

Exercises **9.** solution **11.** solution **13.** solution

15. 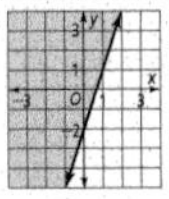 **17.** 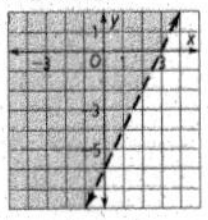

19. 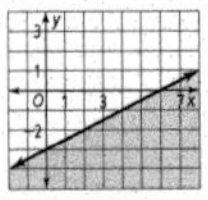 **21.** 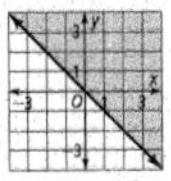

23. 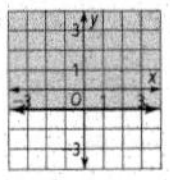 **25.** 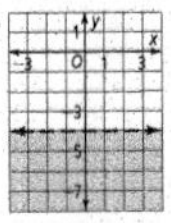

27. 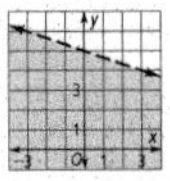 **29.** 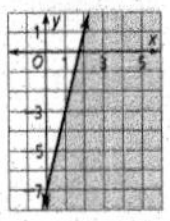

31. $9x + 12y \ge 120$

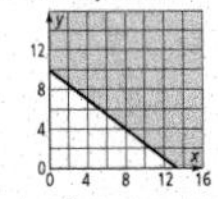

Answers may vary. Sample: 4 lb of cod and 12 lb of flounder; 10 lb of cod and 10 lb of flounder; 12 lb of cod and 4 lb of flounder

33. $y > \frac{3}{2}x - 3$ **35.** $250x + 475y \le 6400$, where x represents the number of refrigerators and y represents the number of pianos

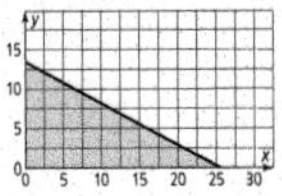

Yes; the point (12, 8) is not in the shaded region. **37.** The student graphed $y \le 2x + 3$ instead of $y \ge 2x + 3$. The other side of the line should be shaded.

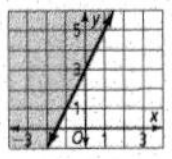

45. 96 days

46. $2 < x \le 7$ 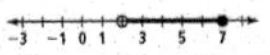

47. one solution: $(-6, -9)$ **48.** one solution: $(2, 0)$ **49.** no solution

Lesson 6-6 pp. 396–401

Got It?

1. 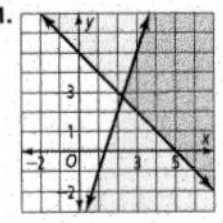

2a. $y < -\frac{1}{2}x + 1$
$y \le \frac{1}{2}x + 1$
b. No; the red line is dashed so points on that line are not included in the solution.

3. 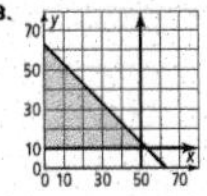

$2x + 2y \le 126$, $x \le 50$, $y \ge 10$

Lesson Check **1.** 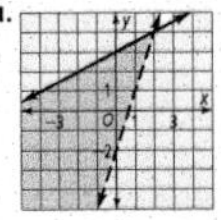

2. $y \ge 3x + 3$
$y < -x - 2$

3. 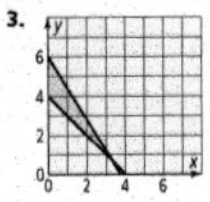

4. You can substitute the ordered pair into each inequality to make sure that it makes each true. **5.** Not necessarily; as long as there is some overlap of the half-planes, then

the system will have a solution. **6.** You need to find the intersection of each of the two systems, but the intersections of lines will be a point or line and the intersections of inequalities will be a line or a planar section.

Exercises **7.** yes **9.** no

11. 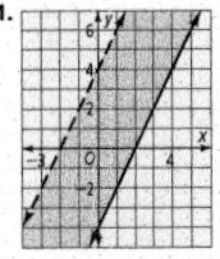 **13.** 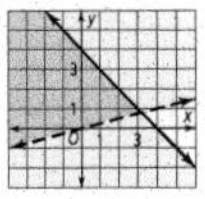

15. 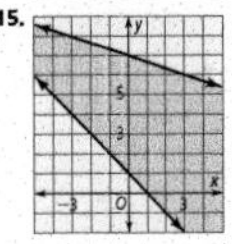 **17.** 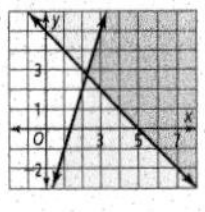

19. 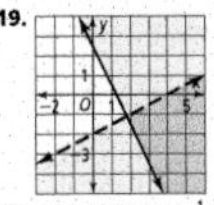 **21.** 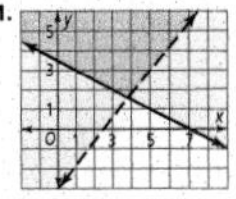

23. $y \le x + 2$, $y < -\frac{1}{3}x$ **25.** $y \ge 2$, $y > x + 1$
27. Let x = hours driven by slower driver, let y = hours driven by faster driver.

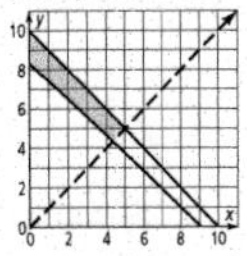

29a. 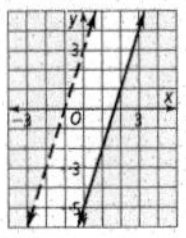

b. No; they have the same slope and different y-intercepts, so they will never intersect. **c.** no **d.** No; there are no points that satisfy both inequalities.

31. You can buy 5 T-shirts and 1 dress shirt or 2 T-shirts and 3 dress shirts. **33.** C

43. 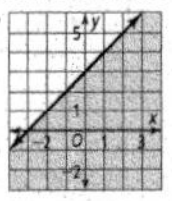 **44.** 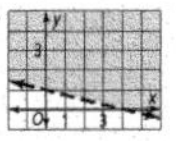

45. 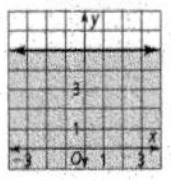

46. 12 **47.** 90 **48.** 113

Chapter Review pp. 404–406

1. inconsistent **2.** elimination **3.** system of linear equations **4.** $(-8, -11)$ **5.** $(-2, 6)$ **6.** $(-3, -3)$ **7.** no solution **8.** $\left(-\frac{14}{3}, -\frac{35}{3}\right)$ **9.** infinitely many solutions **10.** 4 yr **11.** The lines will be parallel. **12.** (4, 7) **13.** $(3, -10)$ **14.** no solution **15.** $(-1, -2)$ **16.** infinitely many solutions **17.** $\left(-\frac{11}{17}, -\frac{188}{17}\right)$ **18.** \$55 **19.** no solution **20.** $(-1, 13)$ **21.** $(-11, -7)$ **22.** (5, 12) **23.** (4.5, 3) **24.** infinitely many solutions **25.** small centerpiece: 25 min, large centerpiece: 40 min

26. 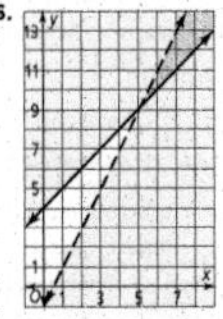 **27.** 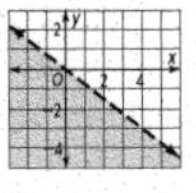

28. 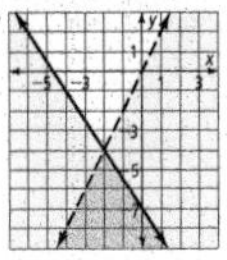 **29.** 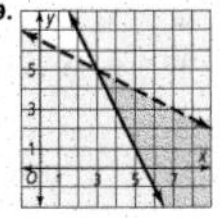

30. 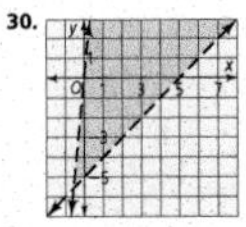 **31.** 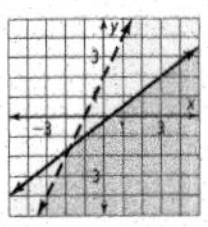

32. 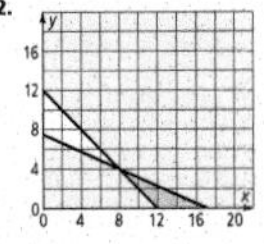

Chapter 7

Get Ready! p. 411

1. 0.7 **2.** 6.4 **3.** 0.008 **4.** 3.5 **5.** $0.\overline{27}$ **6.** 49 **7.** 5.09 **8.** 0.75 **9.** 4 **10.** 16 **11.** 4 **12.** 2000 **13.** −147 **14.** 100 **15.** 49 **16.** 117 **17.** −31 **18.** 33% increase **19.** 25% decrease **20.** 17% decrease **21.** 5% increase **22.** {−8, 0, −24.5} **23.** {18, 10, −32.875} **24.** {−11, −1, 16.5} **25.** yes; how quickly the plant grows **26.** The quantity would increase rapidly. **27.** decreasing

Lesson 7-1 pp. 414–419

Got It? **1a.** $\frac{1}{64}$ **b.** 1 **c.** $\frac{1}{9}$ **d.** $\frac{1}{6}$ **e.** $\frac{1}{16}$ **2a.** $\frac{1}{x^9}$ **b.** n^3 **c.** $\frac{4b}{c^3}$ **d.** $2a^3$ **e.** $\frac{1}{m^2n^5}$ **3a.** $\frac{1}{16}$ **b.** $-\frac{1}{50}$ **c.** $\frac{1}{15{,}625}$ **d.** $-\frac{5}{2}$ **e.** It is easier to simplify first. That gives you, $1 \times 1 = 1$. **4.** 600 represents the number of insects 2 weeks before the population was measured; 5400 represents the population when it was measured; 16,200 represents the number of insects 1 week after the population was measured.

Lesson Check **1.** $\frac{1}{32}$ **2.** 1, $m \ne 0$ **3.** $\frac{5s^2}{t}$ **4.** $4x^3$ **5.** −2 **6.** $\frac{1}{8}$ **7.** division **8.** b^0 is equal to 1, not 0; $\frac{x^n}{a^{-n}b^0} = \frac{a^n x^n}{1} = a^n x^n$

Exercises **9.** $\frac{1}{9}$ **11.** $\frac{1}{25}$ **13.** $\frac{1}{16}$ **15.** −1 **17.** 1 **19.** $0.\overline{4}$ or $\frac{4}{9}$ **21.** $4a$, $b \ne 0$ **23.** $\frac{5}{x^4}$ **25.** $\frac{1}{9n}$ **27.** $\frac{3}{x^2y}$ **29.** $\frac{1}{c^5d^7}$ **31.** $4s^3$ **33.** $\frac{6}{ac^3}$, $d \ne 0$ **35.** $\frac{t^7}{u^{11}}$ **37.** $-\frac{1}{27}$ **39.** −225 **41.** $\frac{4}{5}$ **43.** $\frac{25}{81}$ **45.** 100; there were 100 visitors 4 months before the number of visitors was measured.

47. negative **49.** negative **51.** 10^{-1} **53.** 10^{-3} **55a.** $5^{-2}, 5^{-1}, 5^0, 5^1, 5^2$ **b.** 5^4 **c.** a^n **57.** $4gh^{-3}$ **59.** $\frac{8c^5d^{-4}e^2}{11}$

61.

n	3	$\frac{1}{6}$	7	$\frac{5}{8}$	2
n^{-1}	$\frac{1}{3}$	6	$\frac{1}{7}$	$\frac{8}{5}$	0.5

63. Answers may vary. Sample: Let $a = \frac{2}{3}$, then $a^{-1} = \frac{3}{2}$, $a^2 = \frac{4}{9}$, and $a^{-2} = \frac{9}{4}$. **65.** No; answers may vary. Sample: $3x^{-2} = \frac{3}{x^2}$ which is not the reciprocal of $3x^2$.

78. 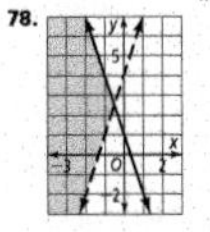 **79.** 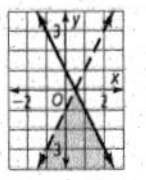

80. 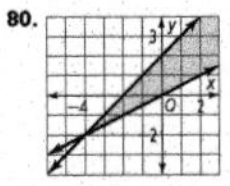

81. $y = -x + 4$
82. $y = 5x - 2$
83. $y = \frac{2}{5}x - 3$
84. $y = -\frac{3}{11}x - 17$
85. $y = \frac{5}{9}x + \frac{1}{3}$
86. $y = 1.25x - 3.79$
87. 60,000

88. 0.07 **89.** 820,000 **90.** 0.003 **91.** 340,000

Lesson 7-2 pp. 420–425

Got It? **1a.** No; 53 is not less than 10. **b.** yes **c.** No; 0.35 is not greater than or equal to 1 and 100 is not in the form 10^n. **2a.** 6.78×10^5 **b.** 3.2×10^{-5} **c.** 5.14×10^7 **d.** 7×10^{-7} **3a.** 52,300,000 **b.** 0.000046 **c.** 0.000209 **d.** 3,800,000,000,000 **e.** a **4.** electron, proton, neutron **5.** 24.8×10^{-4}, 258×10^{-5}, 0.025×10^4, 28×10^3 **Lesson Check** **1.** 7×10^{-4} **2.** 3.2×10^7 **3.** 3,500,000 **4.** 0.000127 **5.** $10^{-3}, 10^{-1}, 10^0, 10^1, 10^5$ **6.** $5 \times 10^{-3}, 7 \times 10^{-1}, 3 \times 10^0, 2 \times 10^4$ **7.** $3.5 \times 10^6, 3.6 \times 10^6, 2.1 \times 10^7, 2.5 \times 10^7$ **8.** Answers may vary. Sample: When numbers are very large or very small. An example of a very large distance may be the distance from Earth to the nearest star. **9.** The student interpreted the negative exponent of −5 to represent the number of decimal places when it represents how many places to move the decimal point to the left; $1.88 \times 10^{-5} = 0.0000188$. **10.** No; the difference between two numbers with different powers of 10 is more significant than the difference between two numbers with the same power of 10.

Exercises **11.** No; 44 is not less than 10 **13.** No; 0.9 is not greater than 1. **15.** yes **17.** No; 457 is not less than 10. **19.** 9.04×10^9 **21.** 9.3×10^6 **23.** 3.25×10^{-3} **25.** 9.2×10^{-4} **27.** 500 **29.** 2040 **31.** 0.897 **33.** 274,000 **35.** $6 \times 10^{-10}, 8 \times 10^{-8}, 9 \times 10^{-7}, 7 \times 10^{-6}$ **37.** $0.52 \times 10^{-3}, 4.8 \times 10^{-3}, 50.1 \times 10^{-3}, 56 \times 10^{-3}$ **39.** $^{232}U, ^{234}U, ^{236}U, ^{235}U$ **41.** 2.4×10^{15} **43.** 3.18×10^{-3} **45.** 3.4×10^5 **47.** 436 billion is 436,000,000,000 so in scientific notation it becomes 4.36×10^{11} because it must be the product of a number greater than or equal to 1 and less than 10 and a power of 10. **49.** It increases by 2 because 100 is 10^2. Sample: $100(3.46 \times 10^5) = 346 \times 10^5 = 3.46 \times 10^7$ **56.** $\frac{c}{d^6}$ **57.** b^3 **58.** $\frac{9}{w^3}$ **59.** $4mn^5$ **60.** $\frac{k^5}{9}$

61. **62.** 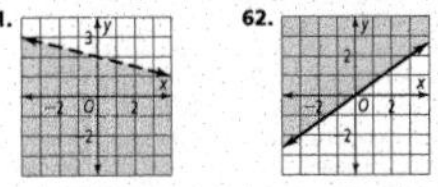

63. **64.** 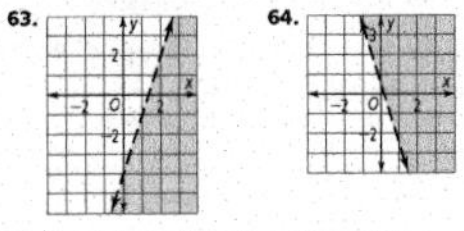

65. t^7 **66.** $(6 - m)^3$ **67.** $(r + 2)^4$ **68.** 5^3s^3 **69.** 2^5x^3 **70.** $8^2(x - 1)^3$

Lesson 7-3 pp. 426–431

Got It? **1a.** 8^9 **b.** $(0.5)^{-11}$ **c.** 9^5 **2a.** $15x^{14}$ **b.** $-56cd^2$ **c.** $\frac{12j^3}{k^2}$ **d.** Since they have like bases, you keep the same base and add the exponents; $x^a \cdot x^b \cdot x^c = x^{(a+b+c)}$ **3.** 2.8×10^{14} **4.** 6.7×10^{30} molecules of water

Lesson Check **1.** 8^{12} **2.** $6n$ **3.** 2.4×10^{10} **4.** 39,900 km **5.** No; x and y are not like bases and they do not share a common factor. **6.** Sometimes; if the product ab is greater than 10, then the number will not be in scientific notation. **7.** No; $4 \times 3 = 12$ so the correct result is $12a^7$.

Exercises **9.** $(-6)^{19}$ **11.** 2^9 **13.** $(-8)^0$ **15.** $5c^{10}$ **17.** $56x^6$ **19.** $-4.8n^3$ **21.** −7 **23.** $\frac{y^3}{x}$ **25.** $-12a^6c^8$ **27.** a^8b **29.** 6×10^5 **31.** 4×10^3 **33.** 5.6×10^{-7} **35.** 8.84×10^7 mi **37.** 9 **39.** −3 **41.** −5 **43.** −4 **45.** 2; −3 **47.** $6x^3 + 2x^2$ **49.** $4y^5 + 8y^2$ **51.** 2.7×10^{-8} **53.** 2.1×10^{-5}

55. 8×10^{-8} **57.** 4.0334×10^1 g **59.** $\frac{1}{a}$ **61.** $6a^4 + 2a^3$ **63.** $-12x^6 + 40x^4$ **77.** 2.358×10^6 **78.** 4.65×10^{-3} **79.** 7×10^{-5} **80.** 5.1×10^9 **81.** 18, 34, 46 **82.** −1, 7, 13 **83.** −6.8, −22.8, −34.8 **84.** $\frac{1}{16}$ **85.** $5x$ **86.** $\frac{4n^2}{m}$ **87.** $\frac{-3x^3z^6}{y^2}$

Lesson 7-4 pp. 433–438

Got It? **1a.** p^{20} **b.** p^{20} **c.** $\frac{1}{p^{20}}$ **d.** yes; $(a^m)^n = a^{mn} = (a^n)^{(m)}$ **2a.** $\frac{1}{x^{22}}$ **b.** w^{19} **c.** r^{13} **3a.** $343m^{27}$ **b.** $\frac{1}{16z^4}$ **c.** $\frac{1}{9g^8}$ **4a.** $81y^{20}$ **b.** $81c^{26}$ **c.** $\frac{5400b^3}{a^3}$ **5.** about 1.125×10^{10} joules of energy

Lesson Check **1.** n^{18} **2.** $\frac{1}{b^{21}}$ **3.** $81a^4$ **4.** $81x^{20}$ **5.** 1.6×10^{11} **6.** 3.2×10^{-14} **7.** Answers may vary. Sample: When you raise a power to a power you multiply the exponents. When you multiply powers with the same base, you add the exponents. **8.** The second student; when you add like terms you add the coefficients and keep the same variable part. **9.** Answers may vary. Sample: $x^{12}, (x^3)^4, (x^6)^2, (x^2)^6$

Exercises **11.** n^{32} **13.** q^{100} **15.** $\frac{1}{x^{15}}$ **17.** z^5 **19.** c^{15} **21.** $\frac{x^{10}}{m^3}$ **23.** $\frac{1}{49a^2}$ **25.** $\frac{1}{12g^4}$ **27.** $\frac{1}{8y^{12}}$ **29.** $r^{10}s^5$ **31.** $\frac{y^{16}}{z^{15}}$ **33.** $\frac{p^{15}}{q^9}$ **35.** $\frac{d^8}{c^{18}}$ **37.** $32j^{35}k^{11}$ **39.** 1.024×10^{13} **41.** 8×10^{-9} **43.** 2.56×10^{22} **45.** 1.3312053×10^{25} **47.** 4 **49.** $\frac{6}{7}$ **51.** −3 **53.** −2 **55.** −3 **57.** $243x^3$ **59.** b^{17} **61.** $-8a^9b^6$ **63.** 0 **65.** 9 **67.** 10^9 **69.** yes; $(7xyz)^2$ **81.** $\frac{b^4}{c^6}$ **82.** a^8b^3 **83.** $54m^5n^4$ **84.** $-4t^5$ **85.** $-\frac{3}{4}$ **86.** 6 **87.** $-\frac{3}{2}$ **88.** −9 **89.** $\frac{1}{4}$ **90.** 31 **91.** $\frac{2}{5}$ **92.** $\frac{y}{3}$ **93.** $\frac{c}{4}$

Lesson 7-5 pp. 440–446

Got It? **1a.** y **b.** $\frac{1}{d^6}$ **c.** $\frac{k^5}{j^3}$ **d.** $\frac{b^5}{a^8}$ **e.** y^4z^7 **2.** about 169 people per square mile **3a.** $\frac{16}{x^6}$ **b.** Answers may vary. Sample: You can simplify within the parentheses first to give you $(a^2)^3 = a^6$ or you can raise the quotient to a power first, $\left(\frac{a^{21}}{a^{15}}\right) = a^6$. **4.** $\frac{25b^2}{a^2}$

Lesson Check **1.** $\frac{1}{y^7}$ **2.** $\frac{x^{12}}{27}$ **3.** $\frac{n^3}{m^3}$ **4.** $\frac{625y^{16}}{81x^8}$ **5.** 27 cubes **6.** In raising a quotient to a power, the exponent goes to all the factors of both the numerator and the denominator and in raising a product to a power, the exponent goes to all the factors.

7a. Answers may vary. Sample: g^3 can be rewritten as $\frac{1}{g^{-3}}$, so $\frac{g^3}{g^7} = \frac{1}{g^7} \cdot \frac{1}{g^{-3}}$.

Exercises **9.** 1 **11.** 0 **13.** $\frac{1}{9}$ **15.** n^3 **17.** y^2 **19.** $\frac{2m^4}{n^4}$ **21.** $\frac{t^{11}}{27m^2}$ **23.** $\frac{3b^7}{a^6c^8}$ **25.** 4×10^{-5} **27.** 4.2×10^3 **29.** 7×10^{-3} **31.** about 4.4×10^{-2} deer per acre

33. $\frac{9}{64}$ **35.** $\frac{81x^4}{y^4}$ **37.** $\frac{216}{15,625}$ **39.** $\frac{262,144}{n^{30}}$ **41.** $\frac{5}{2}$ **43.** $\frac{25y^8}{49x^{10}}$ **45.** $\frac{x^6}{25}$ **47.** b^{15} **49.** 5^3 should be 125. **51.** Each factor should be raised to the fourth power and simplified. **53.** The base d should only appear once. **55a.** about 1636 h **b.** about 31 h **57.** dividing powers with the same base, definition of negative exponent **59.** raising a power to a power, dividing powers with the same base, definition of negative exponent **61.** $\frac{1}{16m^8}$ **63.** a^4 **65.** $\frac{1}{a^9}$ **67.** $\frac{y^{10}}{2x^5}$ **69.** Answers may vary. Samples are given.

I. $\left(\frac{3}{x^2}\right)^{-3} = \left(\frac{x^2}{3}\right)^3$ Rewrite using the reciprocal.
$= \frac{(x^2)^3}{3^3}$ Raise the numerator and denominator to the third power.
$= \frac{x^6}{27}$ Simplify.

II. $\left(\frac{3}{x^2}\right)^{-3} = \frac{3^{-3}}{(x^2)^{-3}}$ Raise a quotient to a power rule
$= \frac{3^{-3}}{x^{-6}}$ Power to a power rule
$= \frac{x^6}{3^3}$ Definition of negative exponent
$= \frac{x^6}{27}$ Simplify.

III. $\left(\frac{3}{x^2}\right)^{-3} = \left(\frac{x^2}{3}\right)^3$ Rewrite using the reciprocal.
$= \frac{x^2}{3} \cdot \frac{x^2}{3} \cdot \frac{x^2}{3}$ Definition of an exponent
$= \frac{x^6}{27}$ Simplify.

71. $\frac{x^6}{9y^8}$ **73.** $\frac{2}{27}$ **75.** $\frac{c^6}{a^{18}b^6}$ **77.** $\frac{y^6}{256x^2}$ **79.** about $3\frac{1}{3}$ m **81.** $x = 7$ and $y = 4$; use the two given expressions to find the system of equations, $x - y = 3$ and $x - 3y = -5$. Solve the system to find the values of x and y. **83.** $\left(\frac{m}{n}\right)^7$ **85.** $\left(\frac{3x}{2y}\right)^3$ **87a.** a^{-n} **b.** $\frac{1}{a^n}$ **c.** Since $\frac{a^0}{a^n}$ equals both a^{-n} and $\frac{1}{a^n}$, a^{-n} must equal $\frac{1}{a^n}$, which is the definition of a negative exponent.

98. $\frac{8}{m^{21}}$ **99.** $\frac{2s^6}{27}$ **100.** $\frac{1}{64c^2}$ **101.** $9r^{10}$ **102.** n^{15}

103. (0, 0)

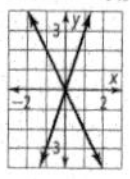

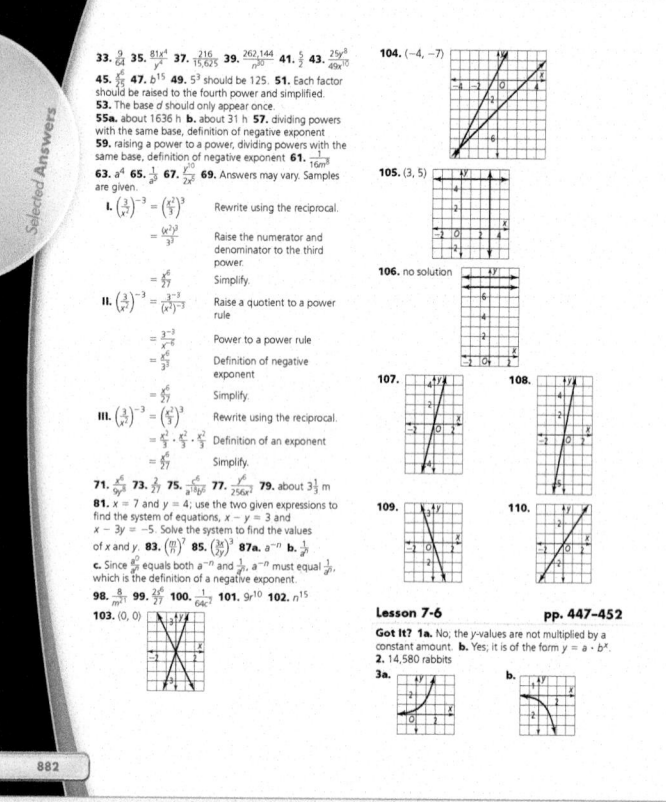

104. (−4, −7)

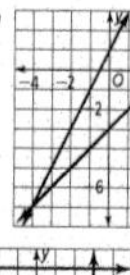

105. (3, 5)

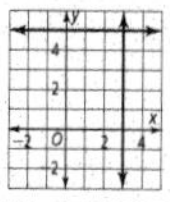

106. no solution

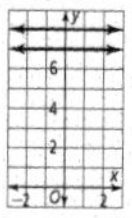

107.

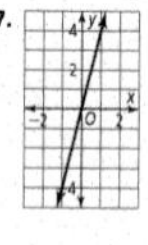

108.

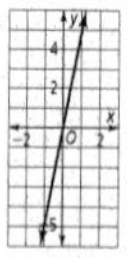

109.

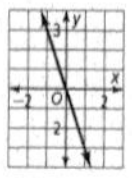

110.

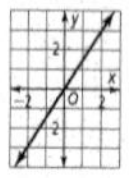

Lesson 7-6 pp. 447–452

Got It? 1a. No; the y-values are not multiplied by a constant amount. **b.** Yes; it is of the form $y = a \cdot b^x$. **2.** 14,580 rabbits

3a.

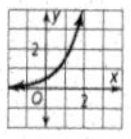

b.

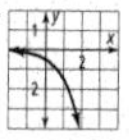

4a.

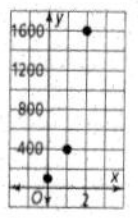

b. 300%

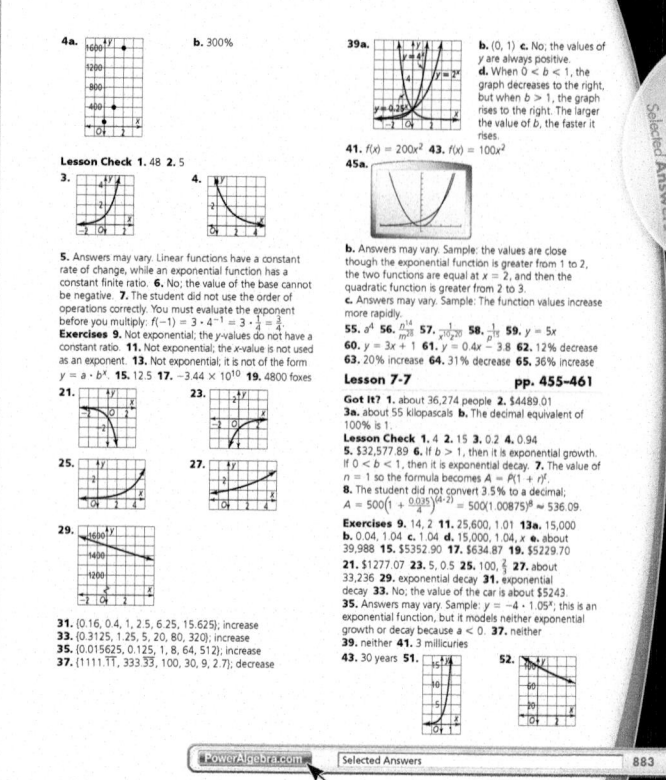

Lesson Check 1. 48 **2.** 5

3.

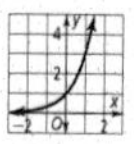

4.

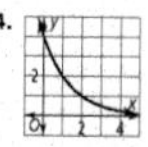

5. Answers may vary. Linear functions have a constant rate of change, while an exponential function has a constant finite ratio. **6.** No; the value of the base cannot be negative. **7.** The student did not use the order of operations correctly. You must evaluate the exponent before you multiply: $f(-1) = 3 \cdot 4^{-1} = 3 \cdot \frac{1}{4} = \frac{3}{4}$.

Exercises 9. Not exponential; the y-values do not have a constant ratio. **11.** Not exponential; the x-value is not used as an exponent. **13.** Not exponential; it is not of the form $y = a \cdot b^x$. **15.** 12.5 **17.** -3.44×10^{10} **19.** 4800 foxes

21.

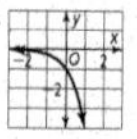

23.

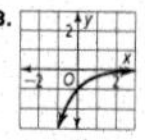

25.

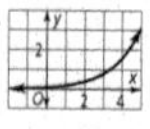

27.

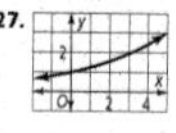

29.

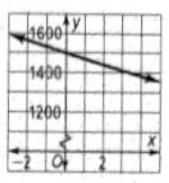

31. {0.16, 0.4, 1, 2.5, 6.25, 15.625}; increase
33. {0.3125, 1.25, 5, 20, 80, 320}; increase
35. {0.015625, 0.125, 1, 8, 64, 512}; increase
37. {$1111.\overline{11}$, $333.\overline{33}$, 100, 30, 9, 2.7}; decrease

39a.

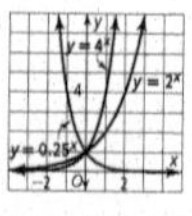

b. (0, 1) **c.** No; the values of y are always positive. **d.** When $0 < b < 1$, the graph decreases to the right, but when $b > 1$, the graph rises to the right. The larger the value of b, the faster it rises.

41. $f(x) = 200x^2$ **43.** $f(x) = 100x^2$

45a.

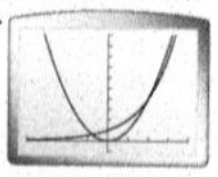

b. Answers may vary. Sample: the values are close though the exponential function is greater from 1 to 2, the two functions are equal at $x = 2$, and then the quadratic function is greater from 2 to 3. **c.** Answers may vary. Sample: The function values increase more rapidly.

55. a^4 **56.** $\frac{n^{14}}{m^{28}}$ **57.** $\frac{1}{x^{10}z^{20}}$ **58.** $\frac{1}{p^{15}}$ **59.** $y = 5x$ **60.** $y = 3x + 1$ **61.** $y = 0.4x - 3.8$ **62.** 12% decrease **63.** 20% increase **64.** 31% decrease **65.** 36% increase

Lesson 7-7 pp. 455–461

Got It? 1. about 36,274 people **2.** \$4489.01 **3a.** about 55 kilopascals **b.** The decimal equivalent of 100% is 1.

Lesson Check 1. 4 **2.** 15 **3.** 0.2 **4.** 0.94 **5.** \$32,577.89 **6.** If $b > 1$, then it is exponential growth. If $0 < b < 1$, then it is exponential decay. **7.** The value of $n = 1$ so the formula becomes $A = P(1 + r)^t$. **8.** The student did not convert 3.5% to a decimal; $A = 500\left(1 + \frac{0.035}{4}\right)^{(4 \cdot 2)} = 500(1.00875)^8 \approx 536.09$.

Exercises 9. 14, 2 **11.** 25,600, 1.01 **13a.** 15,000 **b.** 0.04, 1.04 **c.** 1.04 **d.** 15,000, 1.04, x **e.** about 39,988 **15.** \$5352.90 **17.** \$634.87 **19.** \$5229.70 **21.** \$1277.07 **23.** 5, 0.5 **25.** 100, $\frac{2}{3}$ **27.** about 33,236 **29.** exponential decay **31.** exponential decay **33.** No; the value of the car is about \$5243. **35.** Answers may vary. Sample: $y = -4 \cdot 1.05^x$; this is an exponential function, but it models neither exponential growth or decay because $a < 0$. **37.** neither **39.** neither **41.** 3 millicuries **43.** 30 years **51.**

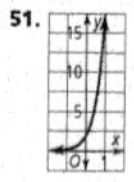

52.

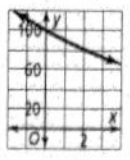

53.

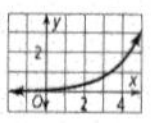

54. $x < 2$ **55.** $t \geq 12$ **56.** $k < 0.2$ **57.** $19t$ **58.** $-8k$ **59.** $11b - 6$ **60.** $-3n^2$ **61.** $9x^2$

Chapter Review pp. 463–466

1. scientific notation **2.** growth factor **3.** decay factor **4.** exponential growth **5.** exponential decay **6.** 1 **7.** $\frac{1}{49}$ **8.** $\frac{4y^8}{x^2}$ **9.** $\frac{q^4}{p^2}$ **10.** 9 **11.** $\frac{9}{16}$ **12.** 1 **13.** 45 **14.** $\frac{25}{9}$ **15.** $-\frac{20}{9}$ **16.** No; −3 should be raised to the fourth power instead of multiplying it by 4. **17.** No; 950 is not between 1 and 10. **18.** No; 100 is not written as a power of 10. **19.** yes **20.** No; 0.84 is not between 1 and 10. **21.** 2.793×10^6 **22.** 1.89×10^8 **23.** 4.3×10^{-5} **24.** 2.7×10^{-9} **25.** 3.86×10^{12} **26.** 4.78×10^{-6} **27.** 8 **28.** 2 **29.** 3; 6 **30.** 3 **31.** −5 **32.** 2 **33.** $2d^5$ **34.** $q^{12}r^4$ **35.** $-20c^4m^2$ **36.** 1.7956 **37.** $\frac{243x^3y^{11}}{16}$ **38.** $-\frac{4}{3r^{10}z^8}$ **39.** 7.8×10^3 pores **40.** $\frac{1}{w^3}$ **41.** $7x^4$ **42.** $\frac{n^{35}}{v^{21}}$ **43.** $\frac{e^{20}}{81c^{12}}$ **44.** 2×10^{-3} **45.** 2.5×10^2 **46.** 5×10^{-5} **47.** 3×10^3

48. Answers may vary. Sample:
1) Simplify the expression within the parentheses.
2) Take the reciprocal of the rational expression raised to the third power.
3) Use the quotient raised to a power rule by applying the exponent to both the numerator and denominator.
4) Simplify the numerator.
5) Simplify the denominator using the power rule.

49. 4, 16, 64 **50.** 0.01, 0.0001, 0.000001 **51.** 20, 10, 5 **52.** 6, 12, 24

53.

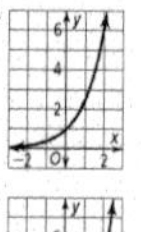

54.

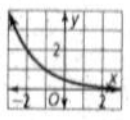

55.

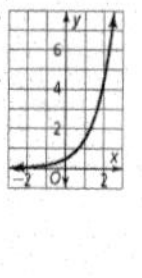

56.

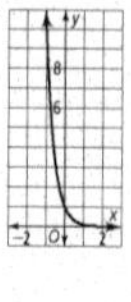

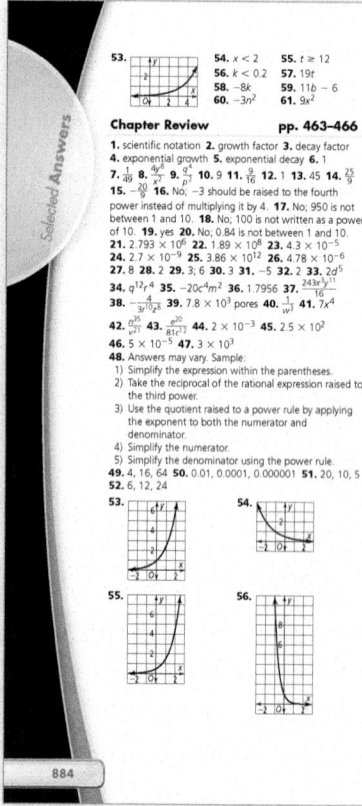

57a. 800 bacteria **b.** about 1.4×10^{16} bacteria **58.** exponential growth; 3 **59.** exponential decay; 0.32 **60.** exponential growth; $\frac{3}{2}$ **61.** exponential decay; $\frac{1}{4}$ **62.** \$2697.20 **63.** 463 people

Chapter 8

Get Ready! p. 471

1. 1, 2, 3, 4, 6, 12 **2.** 1, 2, 3, 6, 9, 18 **3.** 1, 2, 4, 5, 10, 20, 25, 50, 100 **4.** 1, 3, 9, 27, 81 **5.** 1, 2, 3, 4, 6, 8, 9, 12, 18, 24, 36, 72 **6.** 1, 2, 3, 4, 5, 6, 10, 12, 15, 20, 25, 30, 50, 60, 75, 100, 150, 300 **7.** 1, 2, 5, 10, 25, 50, 125, 250 **8.** 1, 3, 9, 23, 69, 207 **9.** $x^2 - 9x$ **10.** $3d + 15$ **11.** $24r^2 - 15r$ **12.** $34m - 29$ **13.** $-36a^2 - 6a$ **14.** $-s^2 - 7s - 2$ **15.** $25x^2$ **16.** $9v^3$ **17.** $64c^6$ **18.** $56m^7$ **19.** $81b^6$ **20.** $36p^2q^2$ **21.** $7n^4$ **22.** $-125t^{12}$ **23.** p^2q^3 **24.** $5x$ **25.** $-\frac{1}{8n^5}$ **26.** $3y^2$ **27.** 3 **28.** A binomial is an expression with two terms. **29.** b; $(x + 4)(x + 4) = (x + 4)^2$, which is a square, and $(x + 4)(x + 4) = x^2 + 8x + 16$, which is a trinomial.

Lesson 8-1 pp. 474–479

Got It? 1a. 2 **b.** 5 **c.** 0 **2.** $5x^4$, $-5x^2y^4$ **3a.** $8x^2 + 2x - 3$, quadratic trinomial **b.** Answers may vary. Sample: Writing a polynomial in standard form allows you to see which monomial term has the greatest degree and how many terms the polynomial has. **4.** $-12x^3 + 120x^2 - 255x + 6022$ **5.** $-4m^3 - 4m^2 - 2m + 21$

Lesson Check 1. 4 **2.** 5 **3.** $11r^3 + 11$ **4.** $x^2 - 3x - 7$ **5.** quadratic trinomial **6.** linear binomial **7.** The coefficient of the sum of like monomials is the sum of the coefficients. To add polynomials, you group like terms and add their coefficients. A monomial has only one term and a polynomial can have more than one term.

Exercises 9. 3 **11.** 10 **13.** 0 **15.** no degree **17.** $11m^3n^3$ **19.** $14t^4$ **21.** $18v^4w^3$ **23.** $-8bc^4$ **25.** $-2q + 7$; linear binomial **27.** $-7x^2 - 4x + 4$; quadratic trinomial **29.** $3z^4 - 2z^2 - 5z$; fourth degree trinomial **31.** $9x^2 + 8$ **33.** $20x^2 + 5$ **35.** $-18x^2 + 228x + 2300$ **37.** $2x^3 + 8$ **39.** $5h^4 + h^3$ **41.** $9x - 1$ **43.** The student forgot to distribute the negative sign to all the terms in the second set of parentheses.
$(4x^2 - x + 3) - (3x^2 - 5x - 6) =$
$4x^2 - x + 3 - 3x^2 - (-5x) - (-6) =$
$4x^2 - 3x^2 - x + 5x + 3 + 6 =$
$x^2 + 4x + 9$ **45.** $-5y^3 + 2y^2 - 6$ **47.** $3z^3 + 15z^2 - 10z - 5$ **49.** No. Answers may vary. Sample: $(x^2 - x + 3) + (x - x^2 + 1) = 4$,

which is a monomial. **56.** 3 **57.** 2.1 **58.** 4 **59.** 5 **60.** $-\frac{2}{5}$ **61.** 8 **62.** $-\frac{8}{3}$ **63.** $-\frac{2}{3}$ **64.** a^5 **65.** $18r^3$ **66.** $28x^8$ **67.** $-10t^6$

Lesson 8-2 pp. 480–484

Got It? 1. $15n^4 - 5n^3 + 40n$ **2.** $3x$ **3a.** $3x^2(3x^4 + 5x^2 + 4)$ **b.** $-6x^2(x^2 + 3x + 2)$ **4.** $9x^2(4 - \pi)$

Lesson Check 1. $12x^4 + 42x^2$ **2.** $2a^2$ **3.** $3m(2m - 5)$ **4.** $4x(x^2 + 2x + 3)$ **5.** B **6.** C **7.** A **8.** Answers may vary. Sample: $18x^3 + 27x^2$

Exercises 9. $7x^2 + 28x$ **11.** $30m^2 + 3m^3$ **13.** $8x^4 - 28x^3 + 4x^2$ **15.** 4 **17.** 9 **19.** 4 **21.** $3(3x - 2)$ **23.** $7(2n^3 - 5n^2 + 4)$ **25.** $2x(7x^2 - x + 4)$ **27.** $25x^2(9 - \pi)$ **29.** $-10x^3 + 8x^2 - 26x$ **31.** $-60a^3 + 20a^2 - 70a$ **33.** $-t^3 + t^2 + t$ **35.** $20x^2 + 5x$; $5x(4x + 1)$ **37.** $17xy^3(y + 3x)$ **39.** $a^5(31ab^3 + 63)$ **41.** 49; $p = 7a$ and $q = 7b$, where a and b have no common factors other than 1, so $p^2 = 49a^2$ and $q^2 = 49b^2$. Since a^2 and b^2 have no common factors other than 1, the GCF of p^2 and q^2 is 49. **49.** $8x^2 + 4x + 5$ **50.** $7x^4 + 3x^2 - 1$ **51.** $-5x^3 - 6x$ **52.** $7x^4 + 2x^3 - 8x^2 + 4$

53. $y \leq \frac{4}{5}x - 2$

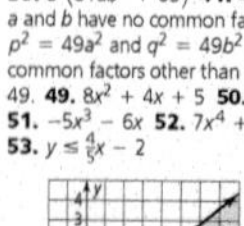

54. $y \geq \frac{7}{2}x - 4$

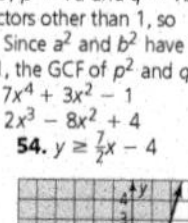

55. $y < -\frac{1}{3}x - 3$

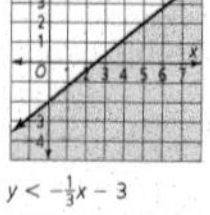

56. $8x - 40$ **57.** $-3w - 12$ **58.** $1.5c + 4$

Lesson 8-3 pp. 486–491

Got It? 1. $4x^2 - 21x - 18$ **2.** $3x^2 + 13x + 4$ **3a.** $3x^2 + 2x - 8$ **b.** $4n^2 - 31n + 42$ **c.** $4p^3 - 10p^2 + 6p - 15$ **4.** $4\pi x^2 + 20\pi x + 24\pi$

5a. $2x^3 - 9x^2 + 10x - 3$ **b.** Answers may vary. Sample: Distribute the trinomial to each term of the binomial. Then continue distributing and combining like terms as needed.

Lesson Check 1. $x^2 + 9x + 18$ **2.** $2x^2 + x - 15$ **3.** $x^3 + 5x^2 + 2x - 8$ **4.** $x^2 + 2x - 15$ **5.** Find the sum of the products of the FIRST terms, OUTER terms, INNER terms, and LAST terms. **6.** $3x^2 + 11x + 8$ **7.** The degree of the product is the sum of the degrees of the two polynomials.

Exercises 9. $y^2 + 5y - 24$ **11.** $c^2 - 15c + 50$ **13.** $6x^2 + 13x - 28$ **15.** $a^2 - 12a + 11$ **17.** $2h^2 + 11h - 63$ **19.** $6p^2 + 23p + 20$ **21.** $4x^2 + 11x - 20$ **23.** $b^2 - 12b + 27$ **25.** $45z^2 - 7z - 12$ **27.** $4w^2 + 21w + 26$ **29.** $4\pi x^2 + 22\pi x + 28\pi$ **31.** $x^3 + 2x^2 - 14x + 5$ **33.** $10a^3 + 12a^2 + 9a - 20$ **35.** $x^2 + 200x + 9375$ **37.** $-n^3 - 3n^2 - n - 3$ **39.** $2m^3 + 10m^2 + m + 5$ **41.** $12z^4 + 4z^3 + 3z^2 + z$ **45a. i.** $x^2 + 2x + 1$, 121 **ii.** $x^2 + 3x + 2$, 132 **iii.** $x^2 + 4x + 3$, 143 **b.** The digits in the product of the two integers are the coefficients of the terms in the product of the two binomials. **55.** $2(3x - 2)$ **56.** $b(b + 8)$ **57.** $5t(2t^2 - 5t + 4)$ **58.** $36x^2$ **59.** $4y^2$ **60.** $9m^2$ **61.** $25n^2$

Lesson 8-4 pp. 492–497

Got It? 1a. $n^2 - 14n + 49$ **b.** $4x^2 + 36x + 81$ **2.** $(16x + 64)$ ft^2 **3a.** 7225 **b.** Answers may vary. Sample: You could write 85 as (80 + 5) or as (100 − 15). **4a.** $x^2 - 81$ **b.** $36 - m^4$ **c.** $9c^2 - 16$ **5.** 2496

Lesson Check 1. $c^2 + 6c + 9$ **2.** $g^2 - 8g + 16$ **3.** $4r^2 - 9$ **4.** $4x^2 + 12x + 9$ in.^{2} **5.** The Square of a Binomial **6.** The Product of a Sum and Difference **7.** The Square of a Binomial **8.** Answers may vary. Sample: You can use the rule for the product of a sum and difference to multiply two numbers when one number can be written as $a + b$ and the other number can be written as $a - b$.

Exercises 9. $w^2 + 10w + 25$ **11.** $9s^2 + 54s + 81$ **13.** $a^2 - 16a + 64$ **15.** $25m^2 - 20m + 4$ **17.** $(10x + 15)$ units^2 **19.** $36 - x^2$ in.^{2} **21.** 6241 **23.** 162,409 **25.** $v^2 - 36$ **27.** $z^2 - 25$ **29.** $100 - y^2$ **31.** 1596 **33.** 3591 **35.** 89,991 **37.** $4a^2 + 4ab + b^2$ **39.** $g^2 - 14gh + 49h^2$ **41.** $64r^2 - 80rs + 25s^2$ **43.** $p^8 - 18p^4q^2 + 81q^4$ **45.** $a^2 - 36b^2$ **47.** $r^4 - 9s^2$ **49.** $9w^6 - z^4$ **51.** $8x^2 + 32x + 32$

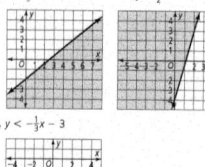

53. Answers may vary. Sample:
$a^2 = b(a - b) + b^2 + (a - b)^2 + b(a - b)$ Area of big square = sum of areas of the 4 interior rectangles
$= 2b(a - b) + b^2 + (a - b)^2$ Combine like terms.
$= 2ab - 2b^2 + b^2 + (a - b)^2$ Distributive Property
$= 2ab - b^2 + (a - b)^2$ Combine like terms.
So, $(a - b)^2 = a^2 - 2ab + b^2$ by the Add. and Subtr. Prop. of =.
55. No; $\left(3\frac{1}{2}\right)^2 = \left(3 + \frac{1}{2}\right)^2 = \left(3 + \frac{1}{2}\right)\left(3 + \frac{1}{2}\right) = 3^2 + 2(3)\left(\frac{1}{2}\right) + \left(\frac{1}{2}\right)^2 = 9 + 3 + \frac{1}{4} = 12\frac{1}{4} \neq 9\frac{1}{4}$
62. $6x^2 - 11x - 10$ **63.** $24m^2 - 34m + 7$ **64.** $5x^2 + 53x + 72$ **65.** decrease of 25% **66.** increase of 25% **67.** increase of 25% **68.** decrease of 12.5% **69.** $6x(2x^3 + 5x^2 + 7)$ **70.** $9(8x^3 + 6x^2 + 3)$ **71.** $7x(5x^2 + x + 9)$

Lesson 8-5 pp. 500–505

Got It? 1. $(r + 8)(r + 3)$ **2a.** $(y - 4)(y - 2)$ **b.** No. There are no factors of 2 with sum −1. **3a.** $(n + 12)(n - 3)$ **b.** $(c - 7)(c + 3)$ **4.** $x + 8$ and $x - 9$ **5.** $(m + 9n)(m - 3n)$
Lesson Check 1. $(x + 4)(x + 3)$ **2.** $(r - 7)(r - 6)$ **3.** $(p + 8)(p - 5)$ **4.** $(a + 4b)(a + 8b)$ **5.** $n - 7$ and $n + 4$ **6.** positive **7.** positive **8.** negative **9.** when the constant term is positive and the coefficient of the second term is negative
Exercises 11. 2 **13.** 2 **15.** $(t + 2)(t + 8)$ **17.** $(n - 7)(n - 8)$ **19.** $(q - 6)(q - 2)$ **21.** 6 **23.** 1 **25.** $(w + 1)(w - 8)$ **27.** $(x + 6)(x - 1)$ **29.** $(n + 2)(n - 5)$ **31.** $r - 4$ and $r + 1$ **33.** A **35.** $(r + 9s)(r + 10s)$ **37.** $(m - 7n)(m + 4n)$ **39.** $(w - 10z)(w - 4z)$ **41a.** p and q must have the same sign. **b.** p and q must have opposite signs. **43.** $x - 12$ **45.** $4x^2 + 12x + 5$; $(2x + 5)(2x + 1)$ **47a.** They are opposites. **b.** Since the coefficient of the middle term is negative, the number with the greater absolute value must be negative. So, p must be a negative integer. **49.** $(x + 25)(x + 2)$ **51.** $(k - 21)(k + 3)$ **53.** $(s + 5t)(s - 15t)$ **65.** $c^2 + 8c + 16$ **66.** $4v^2 - 36v + 81$ **67.** $9w^2 - 49$ **68.** $\frac{ad}{b}$ **69.** $\frac{8d}{7}$ **70.** $mn - c$ **71.** $7x$ **72.** 6 **73.** 3

Lesson 8-6 pp. 506–510

Got It? 1a. $(3x + 5)(2x + 1)$ **b.** The factors are both negative. **2.** $(2x + 7)(5x - 2)$ **3.** $2x + 3$ and $4x + 5$ **4.** $4(2x + 1)(x - 5)$
Lesson Check 1. $(3x + 1)(x + 5)$ **2.** $(5q + 2)(2q + 1)$ **3.** $(2w - 1)(2w + 3)$ **4.** $3x + 8$ and $2x - 9$ **5.** There are no factors of 20 with sum 7. **6.** 24 **7.** Answers may vary. Sample: If $a = 1$, you look for factors of c whose sum is b. If $a \neq 1$, you look for factors of ac whose sum is b.
Exercises 9. $(3d + 2)(d + 7)$ **11.** $(4p + 3)(p + 1)$ **13.** $(2g - 3)(4g - 1)$ **15.** $(2k + 3)(k - 8)$ **17.** $(3x - 4)(x + 9)$ **19.** $(2d + 5)(2d - 7)$ **21.** $5x + 2$ and $3x - 4$ **23.** $2(4v - 3)(v + 5)$ **25.** $5(w - 2)(4w - 1)$ **27.** $3(3r - 5)(r + 2)$ **29–33.** Answers may vary. Samples are given. **29.** −31, $(5v + 3)(3v - 8)$; 31, $(5v - 3)(3v + 8)$ **31.** 20, $(3g + 2)(3g + 2)$; 15, $(3g + 1)(3g + 4)$ **33.** 41, $(8r - 7)(r + 6)$; −5, $(8r - 21)(r + 2)$ **35.** $6x + 4$ **37a.** $(2x + 2)(x + 2)$; $(x + 1)(2x + 4)$ **b.** yes **c.** Answers may vary. Sample: Neither factoring is complete. Each one has a common factor, 2. **39.** $3(11k + 4)(2k + 1)$ **41.** $28(h - 1)(h + 2)$ **43.** $(11n - 6)(5n - 2)$ **45.** $(9g - 5)(7g - 6)$ **47.** 2; explanations may vary. Sample: $ax^2 + bx + c$ factors to $(ax + 1)(x + c)$ or $(ax + c)(x + 1)$ so $b = ac + 1$ or $b = a + c$. **57.** $(w + 4)(w + 11)$ **58.** $(t - 7)(t + 4)$ **59.** $(x - 5)(x - 12)$ **60.** 12.5 **61.** 12 **62.** 37.5 **63.** 21 **64.** $a^2 + 18a + 81$ **65.** $q^2 - 30q + 225$ **66.** $h^2 - 100$ **67.** $4x^2 - 49$

Lesson 8-7 pp. 511–516

Got It? 1a. $(x + 3)^2$ **b.** $(x - 7)^2$ **2.** $4m - 9$ **3a.** $(v - 10)(v + 10)$ **b.** $(s - 4)(s + 4)$ **4a.** $(5d + 8)(5d - 8)$ **b.** No; $25d^2 + 64$ is not a difference of two squares. **5a.** $12(t + 2)(t - 2)$ **b.** $3(2x + 1)^2$
Lesson Check 1. $(y - 8)^2$ **2.** $(3q + 2)^2$ **3.** $(p + 6)(p - 6)$ **4.** $6w + 5$ **5.** perfect-square trinomial **6.** perfect-square trinomial **7.** difference of two squares **8.** In a difference of two squares, both terms are perfect squares separated by a subtraction symbol.
Exercises 9. $(h + 4)^2$ **11.** $(d - 10)^2$ **13.** $(q + 1)^2$ **15.** $(8x + 7)^2$ **17.** $(3n - 7)^2$ **19.** $(5z + 4)^2$ **21.** $10r - 11$ **23.** $5r + 3$ **25.** $(a + 7)(a - 7)$ **27.** $(t + 5)(t - 5)$ **29.** $(m + 15)(m - 15)$ **31.** $(9r + 1)(9r - 1)$ **33.** $(8q + 9)(8q - 9)$ **35.** $(3n + 20)(3n - 20)$ **37.** $3(3w + 2)(3w - 2)$ **39.** $3(3x + 5)^2$ **41.** $8(s - 4)^2$ **43.** Answers may vary. Sample: Rewrite the absolute value of both terms as squares. The factorization is the product of two binomials. The first is the sum of square roots of the squares. The second is the difference of the square roots of the squares. Example 1: $x^2 - 4 = (x + 2)(x - 2)$; Example 2: $4y^2 - 25 = (2y + 5)(2y - 5)$
45. [1] Subtract by combining like terms.
$(49x^2 - 56x + 16) - (16x^2 + 24x + 9) =$
$(49x^2 - 16x^2) + (-56x - 24x) + (16 - 9) =$
$33x^2 - 80x + 7$
[2] Factor each expression, then use the rule for factoring the difference of two squares. $(49x^2 - 56x + 16) - (16x^2 + 24x + 9) = (7x - 4)^2 - (4x + 3)^2 =$
$[(7x - 4) - (4x + 3)] - [(7x - 4) + (4x + 3)] =$
$(3x - 7)(11x - 1) = 33x^2 - 80x + 7$

47. 11, 9 **49.** 14, 6 **51a.** Answers may vary. Sample: $x^2 + 6x + 9$ **b.** because the first term x^2 is a square, the last term 3^2 is a square, and the middle term is $2(x)(3)$ **64.** $(6x + 7)(3x - 2)$ **65.** $(2x + 3)(4x + 3)$ **66.** $(4x - 7)(3x - 5)$ **67.** 2 **68.** $3m$ **69.** $4h^2$

Lesson 8-8 pp. 517–521

Got It? 1a. $(2t^2 + 5)(4t + 7)$ **b.** Answers may vary. Sample: In Lesson 8-6, you rewrote the middle term as the sum of two terms and then factored by grouping. In this problem, there were already two middle terms. **2.** $3h(h^2 + 2)(2h + 3)$ **3.** Answers may vary. Sample: $2x$, $5x + 2$, and $6x + 1$
Lesson Check 1. $(4r^2 + 3)(5r + 2)$ **2.** $(3d^2 - 5)(2d + 1)$ **3.** $6(2x^2 + 3)(2x + 5)$ **4.** Answers may vary. Sample: $4x$, $3x + 1$, and $3x + 2$ **5.** No; the polynomial is a perfect square. **6.** Yes; when you write $23w$ as $20w + 3w$ the resulting two groups of terms have the same factor, $w + 5$. **7.** Yes; two groups of terms have the same factor, $4t - 7$. **8.** No; when you factor out the GCF from each pair of terms, there is no common factor.
Exercises 9. $2z^2$, 3 **11.** $2r^2$, −5 **13.** $(5q^2 + 1)(3q + 8)$ **15.** $(7z^2 + 8)(2z - 5)$ **17.** $(2m + 1)(2m - 1)(2m + 3)$ **19.** $(4v^2 - 5)(5v + 6)$ **21.** $(4y^2 - 3)(3y + 1)$ **23.** $w(w^2 + 6)(3w - 2)$ **25.** $3q(q + 2)(q - 2)(2q + 1)$ **27.** $2(d^2 + 4)(2d - 3)$ **29.** Answers may vary. Sample: $4c$, $c + 8$, and $c + 5$ **31.** $9t(t - 8)(t - 2)$ **33.** $8(m^2 + 5)(m + 4)$ **35.** The factorization is correct, but it is not complete. The GCF of all the terms is $4x$, not 4. $4x^4 + 12x^3 + 8x^2 + 24x = 4x(x^3 + 3x^2 + 2x + 6) = 4x[x^2(x + 3) + 2(x + 3)] = 4x(x^2 + 2)(x + 3)$ **37.** Answers may vary. Sample: Split the expression into three binomials. Find the GCF of each binomial, then factor again. **39.** Answers may vary. Sample: $30x^3 + 36x^2 + 40x + 48 = 2(3x^2 + 4)(5x + 6)$ **52.** $(m + 6)^2$ **53.** $(8x - 9)^2$ **54.** $(7p + 2)(7p - 2)$ **55.** not a function **56.** function **57.** function

58.
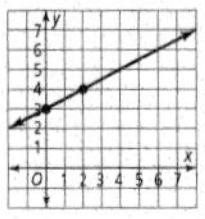

59.
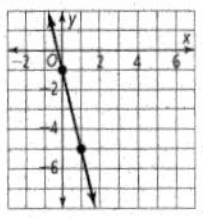

60.
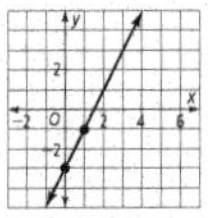

61.
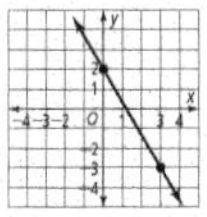

Chapter Review pp. 523–526

1. binomial **2.** polynomial **3.** monomial **4.** perfect-square trinomial **5.** degree of the monomial **6.** $-9r^2 + 11r + 3$; quadratic trinomial **7.** $b^3 + b^2 + 3$; cubic trinomial **8.** $8t^2 + 3$; quadratic binomial **9.** $4n^5 + n$; fifth degree binomial **10.** $6x + 8$; linear binomial **11.** p^3q^3; sixth degree monomial **12.** $v^3 + 5$ **13.** $14s^4 - 4s^2 + 9s + 7$ **14.** $9h^3 - 3h + 3$ **15.** $7z^3 - 2z^2 - 16$ **16.** $-20k^2 + 15k$ **17.** $36m^3 + 8m^2 - 24m$ **18.** $6g^3 - 48g^2$ **19.** $3d^3 + 18d^2$ **20.** $-8n^4 - 10n^3 + 18n^2$ **21.** $-2q^3 + 8q^2 + 11q$ **22.** $4p(3p^3 + 4p^2 + 2)$ **23.** $3b(b^3 - 3b + 2)$ **24.** $9c(5c^4 - 7c^2 + 3)$ **25.** $4g(g + 2)$ **26.** $3(t^4 - 2t^3 - 3t + 4)$ **27.** $3h^3(10h^2 - 2h - 5)$ **28.** 30; if the GCF of p and q is 5, then the GCF of $6p$ and $6q$ is $6(5) = 30$. **29.** $w^2 + 13w + 12$ **30.** $10s^2 - 7s - 12$ **31.** $9r^2 - 12r + 4$ **32.** $6g^2 - 41g - 56$ **33.** $21q^2 + 62q + 16$ **34.** $12n^4 + 20n^3 + 15n + 25$ **35.** $t^2 + 6t - 27$ **36.** $36c^2 + 60c + 25$ **37.** $49h^2 - 9$ **38.** $3y^2 - 11y - 42$ **39.** $32a^2 - 44a - 21$ **40.** $16b^2 - 9$ **41.** $(3x + 5)(x + 7)$; $3x^2 + 26x + 35$ **42.** $(g - 7)(g + 2)$ **43.** $(2n - 1)(n + 2)$ **44.** $2(3k - 2\ell)(k - \ell)$ **45.** $(p + 6)(p + 2)$ **46.** $(r + 10)(r - 4)$ **47.** $(2m + n)(3m + 11n)$ **48.** $(t + 2)(t - 15)$ **49.** $(2g - 1)(g - 17)$ **50.** $3(x + 2)(x - 1)$ **51.** $(d - 3)(d - 15)$ **52.** $(w + 3)(w - 18)$ **53.** $7(3z - 7)(z - 1)$ **54.** $-2(h - 7)(h + 5)$ **55.** $(x + 2)(x + 19)$ **56.** $(5v + 8)(2v - 1)$ **57.** $5(g + 2)(g + 1)$ **58.** Answers may vary. Sample: If the expression is factorable then there must be factors of 18 whose sum is $b = 15$. The factors of 18 are 1 and 18, 2 and 9, 3 and 6. None of these have a sum equal to 15, so the expression is not factorable. **59.** $(s - 10)^2$ **60.** $(4q + 7)^2$ **61.** $(r + 8)(r - 8)$ **62.** $(3z + 4)(3z - 4)$ **63.** $(5m + 8)^2$ **64.** $(7n + 2)(7n - 2)$ **65.** $(g + 15)(g - 15)$ **66.** $(3p - 7)^2$ **67.** $(6h - 1)^2$ **68.** $(w + 12)^2$ **69.** $8(2v + 1)(2v - 1)$

70. $(5x - 6)(5x + 6)$ **71.** $3n + 9$ **72.** It is a perfect-square trinomial. **73.** $3y^2$; 1 **74.** $8m^2$; 3 **75.** $2d(d + 1)(d - 1)(3d + 2)$ **76.** $(b^2 + 1)(11b - 6)$ **77.** $(5z^2 + 1)(9z + 4)$ **78.** $3(a^2 + 2)(3a - 4)$

Chapter 9

Get Ready! p. 531

1. −13 **2.** −3.5 **3.** −9 **4.** −0.5 **5.** −23 **6.** −3

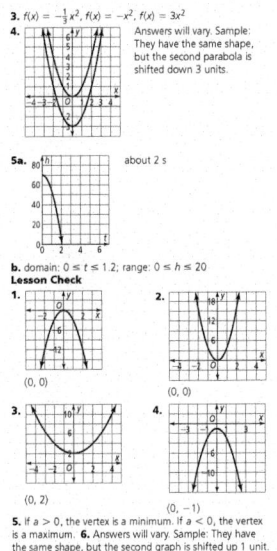

7.
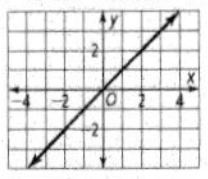

8.
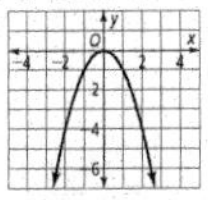

9.
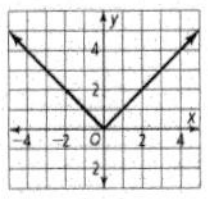

10.
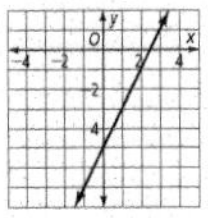

11.
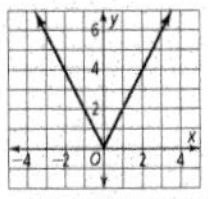

12.
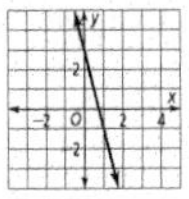

13. −108 **14.** 0 **15.** 49 **16.** 25 **17.** 24 **18.** 144 **19.** $(2x + 1)^2$ **20.** $(5x - 3)(x + 7)$ **21.** $(4x - 3)(2x - 1)$ **22.** $(x - 9)^2$ **23.** $(6y - 5)(2y + 3)$ **24.** $(m - 9)(m + 2)$ **25.** A quadratic function is of the form $f(x) = ax^2 + bx + c$, where $a \neq 0$. **26.** Answers will vary. Sample: You can fold the graph along the axis of symmetry and the two halves of the graph will match. **27.** Answers will vary. Sample: the product of two factors can only be zero if at least one of the factors is zero.

Lesson 9-1 pp. 534–540

Got It? 1. $(-2, -3)$; minimum

2.
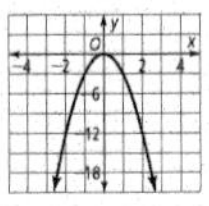

domain: all real numbers, range: $y \leq 0$

3. $f(x) = -\frac{1}{3}x^2$, $f(x) = -x^2$, $f(x) = 3x^2$

4.
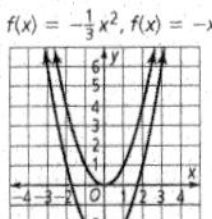

Answers will vary. Sample: They have the same shape, but the second parabola is shifted down 3 units.

5a.
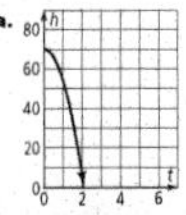

about 2 s

b. domain: $0 \leq t \leq 1.2$; range: $0 \leq h \leq 20$

Lesson Check

1.
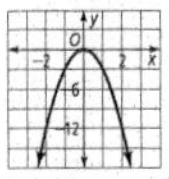

(0, 0)

2.
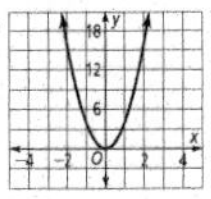

(0, 0)

3.
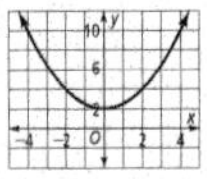

(0, 2)

4.
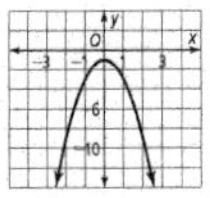

(0, −1)

5. If $a > 0$, the vertex is a minimum. If $a < 0$, the vertex is a maximum. **6.** Answers will vary. Sample: They have the same shape, but the second graph is shifted up 1 unit.
Exercises 7. (2, 3); maximum **9.** (2, 1); minimum

11.
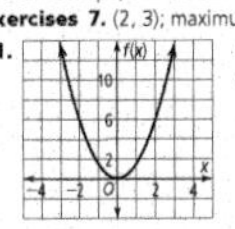

domain: all real numbers; range: $f(x) \geq 0$

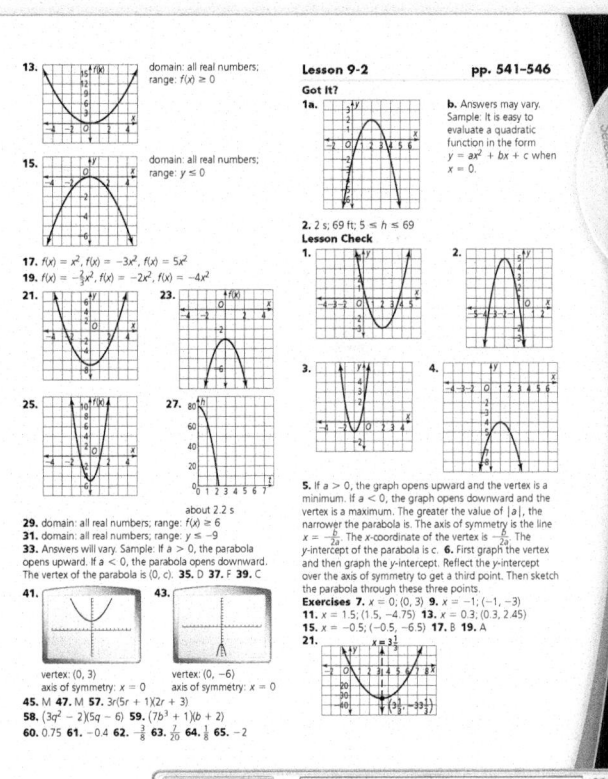

13.
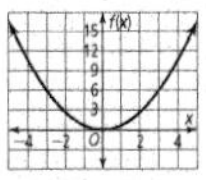

domain: all real numbers; range: $f(x) \geq 0$

15.
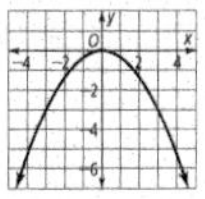

domain: all real numbers; range: $y \leq 0$

17. $f(x) = x^2$, $f(x) = -3x^2$, $f(x) = 5x^2$
19. $f(x) = -\frac{2}{3}x^2$, $f(x) = -2x^2$, $f(x) = -4x^2$

21.
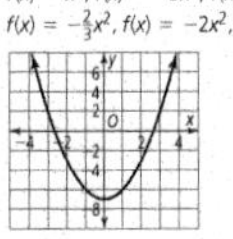

23.
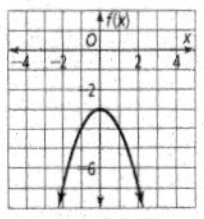

25.
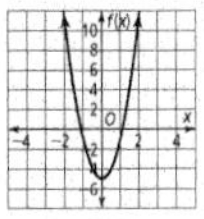

27.
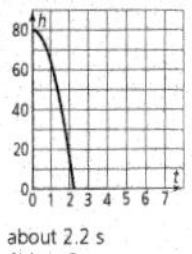

about 2.2 s

29. domain: all real numbers; range: $f(x) \geq 6$
31. domain: all real numbers; range: $y \leq -9$
33. Answers will vary. Sample: If $a > 0$, the parabola opens upward. If $a < 0$, the parabola opens downward. The vertex of the parabola is $(0, c)$. **35.** D **37.** F **39.** C

41.
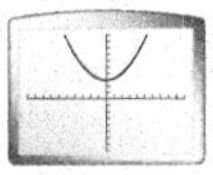

vertex: (0, 3)
axis of symmetry: $x = 0$

43.
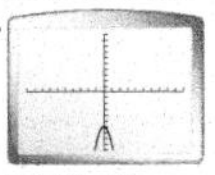

vertex: (0, −6)
axis of symmetry: $x = 0$

45. M **47.** M **57.** $3r(5r + 1)(2r + 3)$ **58.** $(3q^2 - 2)(5q - 6)$ **59.** $(7b^3 + 1)(b + 2)$ **60.** 0.75 **61.** −0.4 **62.** $-\frac{3}{8}$ **63.** $\frac{7}{20}$ **64.** $\frac{1}{8}$ **65.** −2

Lesson 9-2 pp. 541–546

Got It?

1a.
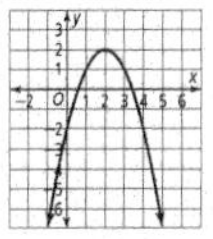

b. Answers may vary. Sample: It is easy to evaluate a quadratic function in the form $y = ax^2 + bx + c$ when $x = 0$.

2. 2 s; 69 ft; $5 \leq h \leq 69$

Lesson Check

1.
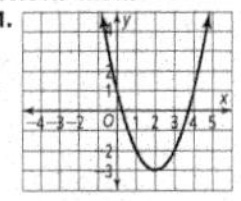

2.
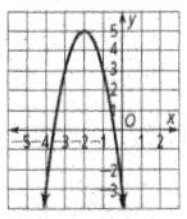

3.
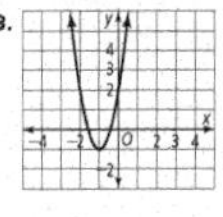

4.
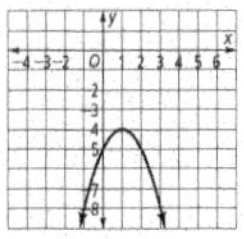

5. If $a > 0$, the graph opens upward and the vertex is a minimum. If $a < 0$, the graph opens downward and the vertex is a maximum. The greater the value of $|a|$, the narrower the parabola is. The axis of symmetry is the line $x = -\frac{b}{2a}$. The x-coordinate of the vertex is $-\frac{b}{2a}$. The y-intercept of the parabola is c. **6.** First graph the vertex and then graph the y-intercept. Reflect the y-intercept over the axis of symmetry to get a third point. Then sketch the parabola through these three points.
Exercises 7. $x = 0$; (0, 3) **9.** $x = -1$; (−1, −3) **11.** $x = 1.5$; (1.5, −4.75) **13.** $x = 0.3$; (0.3, 2.45) **15.** $x = -0.5$; (−0.5, −6.5) **17.** B **19.** A

21.
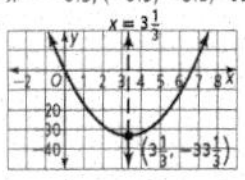

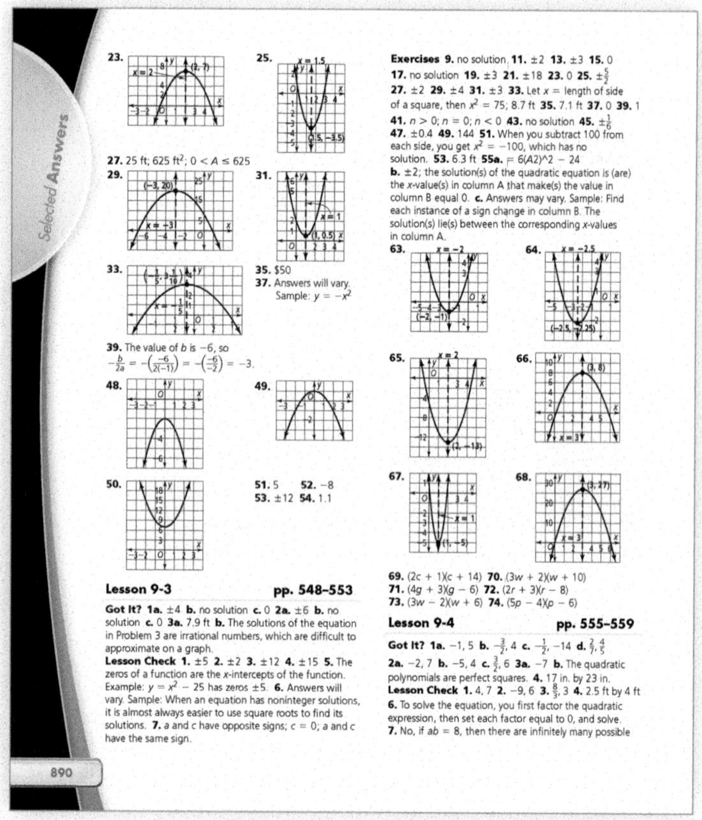

23.

25.

27. 25 ft; 625 ft^2; $0 < A \le 625$

29.

31.

33.

35. \$50
37. Answers will vary. Sample: $y = -x^2$

39. The value of b is -6, so $-\frac{b}{2a} = -\left(\frac{-6}{2(-1)}\right) = -\left(\frac{-6}{-2}\right) = -3$.

48.

49.

50.

51. 5 **52.** −8
53. ±12 **54.** 1.1

Lesson 9-3 **pp. 548–553**

Got It? 1a. ±4 **b.** no solution **c.** 0 **2a.** ±6 **b.** no solution **c.** 0 **3a.** 7.9 ft **b.** The solutions of the equation in Problem 3 are irrational numbers, which are difficult to approximate on a graph.
Lesson Check 1. ±5 **2.** ±2 **3.** ±12 **4.** ±15 **5.** The zeros of a function are the x-intercepts of the function. Example: $y = x^2 - 25$ has zeros ±5. **6.** Answers will vary. Sample: When an equation has noninteger solutions, it is almost always easier to use square roots to find its solutions. **7.** a and c have opposite signs; $c = 0$; a and c have the same sign.

Exercises 9. no solution **11.** ±2 **13.** ±3 **15.** 0 **17.** no solution **19.** ±3 **21.** ±18 **23.** 0 **25.** $\pm\frac{5}{2}$ **27.** ±2 **29.** ±4 **31.** ±3 **33.** Let x = length of side of a square, then $x^2 = 75$; 8.7 ft **35.** 7.1 ft **37.** 0 **39.** 1 **41.** $n > 0$; $n = 0$; $n < 0$ **43.** no solution **45.** $\pm\frac{1}{6}$ **47.** ±0.4 **49.** 144 **51.** When you subtract 100 from each side, you get $x^2 = -100$, which has no solution. **53.** 6.3 ft **55a.** = 6(A2)^2 − 24
b. ±2; the solution(s) of the quadratic equation is (are) the x-value(s) in column A that make(s) the value in column B equal 0. **c.** Answers may vary. Sample: Find each instance of a sign change in column B. The solution(s) lie(s) between the corresponding x-values in column A.

63.

64.

65.

66.

67.

68.

69. $(2c + 1)(c + 14)$ **70.** $(3w + 2)(w + 10)$
71. $(4g + 3)(g - 6)$ **72.** $(2r + 3)(r - 8)$
73. $(3w - 2)(w + 6)$ **74.** $(5p - 4)(p - 6)$

Lesson 9-4 **pp. 555–559**

Got It? 1a. −1, 5 **b.** $-\frac{3}{2}$, 4 **c.** $-\frac{1}{2}$, −14 **d.** $\frac{2}{7}, \frac{4}{5}$ **2a.** −2, 7 **b.** −5, 4 **c.** $\frac{3}{2}$, 6 **3a.** −7 **b.** The quadratic polynomials are perfect squares. **4.** 17 in. by 23 in.
Lesson Check 1. 4, 7 **2.** −9, 6 **3.** $\frac{8}{3}$, 3 **4.** 2.5 ft by 4 ft
6. To solve the equation, you first factor the quadratic expression, then set each factor equal to 0, and solve.
7. No, if $ab = 8$, then there are infinitely many possible

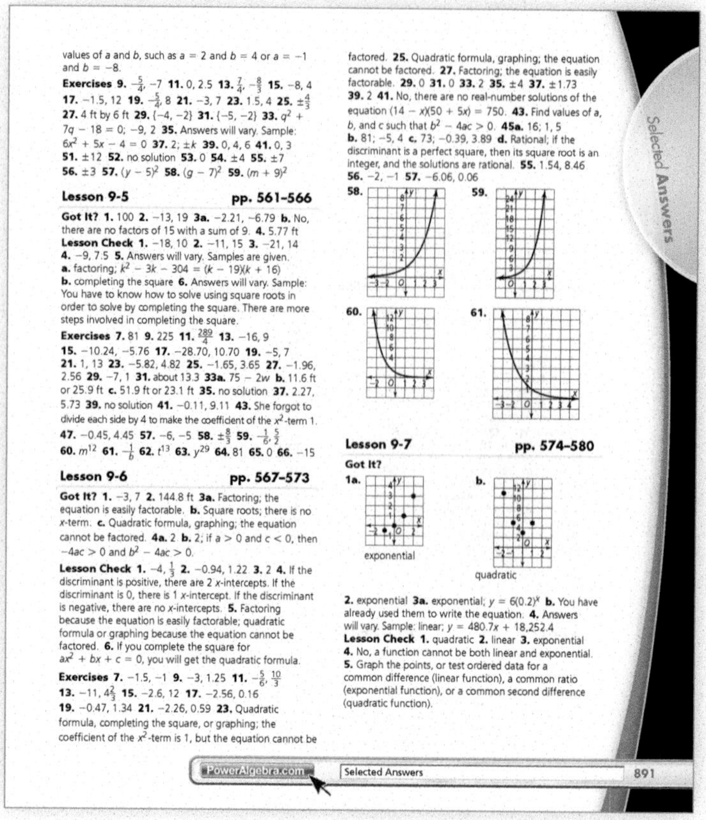

values of a and b, such as $a = 2$ and $b = 4$ or $a = -1$ and $b = -8$.
Exercises 9. $-\frac{5}{4}$, −7 **11.** 0, 2.5 **13.** $\frac{7}{4}, -\frac{8}{3}$ **15.** −8, 4 **17.** −1.5, 12 **19.** $-\frac{5}{4}$, 8 **21.** −3, 7 **23.** 1.5, 4 **25.** $\pm\frac{4}{3}$ **27.** 4 ft by 6 ft **29.** {−4, −2} **31.** {−5, −2} **33.** $q^2 + 7q - 18 = 0$; −9, 2 **35.** Answers will vary. Sample: $6x^2 + 5x - 4 = 0$ **37.** 2; $\pm k$ **39.** 0, 4, 6 **41.** 0, 3 **51.** ±12 **52.** no solution **53.** 0 **54.** ±4 **55.** ±7 **56.** ±3 **57.** $(y - 5)^2$ **58.** $(g - 7)^2$ **59.** $(m + 9)^2$

Lesson 9-5 **pp. 561–566**

Got It? 1. 100 **2.** −13, 19 **3a.** −2.21, −6.79 **b.** No, there are no factors of 15 with a sum of 9. **4.** 5.77 ft
Lesson Check 1. −18, 10 **2.** −11, 15 **3.** −21, 14 **4.** −9, 7.5 **5.** Answers will vary. Samples are given.
a. factoring; $k^2 - 3k - 304 = (k - 19)(k + 16)$
b. completing the square **6.** Answers will vary. Sample: You have to know how to solve using square roots in order to solve by completing the square. There are more steps involved in completing the square.
Exercises 7. 81 **9.** 225 **11.** $\frac{289}{4}$ **13.** −16, 9 **15.** −10.24, −5.76 **17.** −28.70, 10.70 **19.** −5, 7 **21.** 1, 13 **23.** −5.82, 4.82 **25.** −1.65, 3.65 **27.** −1.96, 2.56 **29.** −7, 1 **31.** about 13.3 **33a.** $75 - 2w$ **b.** 11.6 ft or 25.9 ft **c.** 51.9 ft or 23.1 ft **35.** no solution **37.** 2.27, 5.73 **39.** no solution **41.** −0.11, 9.11 **43.** She forgot to divide each side by 4 to make the coefficient of the x^2-term 1. **47.** −0.45, 4.45 **57.** −6, −5 **58.** $\pm\frac{8}{3}$ **59.** $-\frac{1}{6}, \frac{5}{2}$ **60.** m^{12} **61.** $-\frac{1}{b}$ **62.** t^{13} **63.** y^{29} **64.** 81 **65.** 0 **66.** −15

Lesson 9-6 **pp. 567–573**

Got It? 1. −3, 7 **2.** 144.8 ft **3a.** Factoring; the equation is easily factorable. **b.** Square roots; there is no x-term. **c.** Quadratic formula, graphing; the equation cannot be factored. **4a.** 2 **b.** 2; if $a > 0$ and $c < 0$, then $-4ac > 0$ and $b^2 - 4ac > 0$.
Lesson Check 1. −4, $\frac{1}{3}$ **2.** −0.94, 1.22 **3.** 2 **4.** If the discriminant is positive, there are 2 x-intercepts. If the discriminant is 0, there is 1 x-intercept. If the discriminant is negative, there are no x-intercepts. **5.** Factoring because the equation is easily factorable; quadratic formula or graphing because the equation cannot be factored. **6.** If you complete the square for $ax^2 + bx + c = 0$, you will get the quadratic formula.
Exercises 7. −1.5, −1 **9.** −3, 1.25 **11.** $-\frac{5}{6}, \frac{10}{3}$ **13.** −11, $4\frac{2}{3}$ **15.** −2.6, 12 **17.** −2.56, 0.16 **19.** −0.47, 1.34 **21.** −2.26, 0.59 **23.** Quadratic formula, completing the square, or graphing; the coefficient of the x^2-term is 1, but the equation cannot be factored. **25.** Quadratic formula, graphing; the equation cannot be factored. **27.** Factoring; the equation is easily factorable. **29.** 0 **31.** 0 **33.** 2 **35.** ±4 **37.** ±1.73 **39.** 2 **41.** No, there are no real-number solutions of the equation $(14 - x)(50 + 5x) = 750$. **43.** Find values of a, b, and c such that $b^2 - 4ac > 0$. **45a.** 16; 1, 5 **b.** 81; −5, 4 **c.** 73; −0.39, 3.89 **d.** Rational; if the discriminant is a perfect square, then its square root is an integer, and the solutions are rational. **55.** 1.54, 8.46 **56.** −2, −1 **57.** −6.06, 0.06

58.

59.

60.

61.

Lesson 9-7 **pp. 574–580**

Got It?
1a.
exponential

b.
quadratic

2. exponential **3a.** exponential; $y = 6(0.2)^x$ **b.** You have already used them to write the equation. **4.** Answers will vary. Sample: linear; $y = 480.7x + 18{,}252.4$
Lesson Check 1. quadratic **2.** linear **3.** exponential **4.** No, a function cannot be both linear and exponential. **5.** Graph the points, or test ordered data for a common difference (linear function), a common ratio (exponential function), or a common second difference (quadratic function).

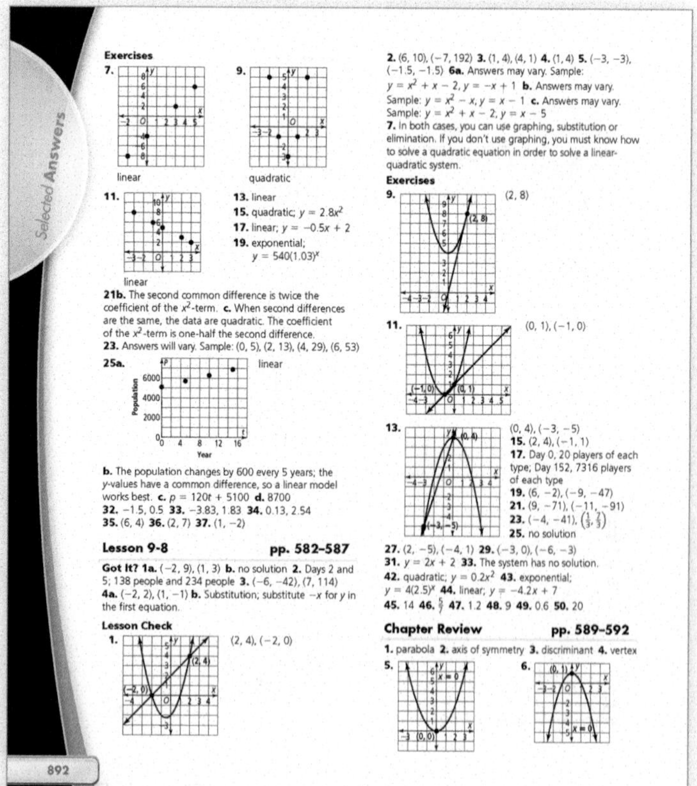

Exercises
7.
linear

9.
quadratic

11.
linear

13. linear
15. quadratic; $y = 2.8x^2$
17. linear; $y = -0.5x + 2$
19. exponential; $y = 540(1.03)^x$

21b. The second common difference is twice the coefficient of the x^2-term. **c.** When second differences are the same, the data are quadratic. The coefficient of the x^2-term is one-half the second difference.
23. Answers will vary. Sample: (0, 5), (2, 13), (4, 29), (6, 53)
25a. linear

b. The population changes by 600 every 5 years; the y-values have a common difference, so a linear model works best. **c.** $p = 120t + 5100$ **d.** 8700
32. −1.5, 0.5 **33.** −3.83, 1.83 **34.** 0.13, 2.54 **35.** (6, 4) **36.** (2, 7) **37.** (1, −2)

Lesson 9-8 **pp. 582–587**

Got It? 1a. (−2, 9), (1, 3) **b.** no solution **2.** Days 2 and 5; 138 people and 234 people **3.** (−6, −42), (7, 114) **4a.** (−2, 2), (1, −1) **b.** Substitution; substitute $-x$ for y in the first equation.
Lesson Check
1. (2, 4), (−2, 0)

2. (6, 10), (−7, 192) **3.** (1, 4), (4, 1) **4.** (1, 4) **5.** (−3, −3), (−1.5, −1.5) **6a.** Answers may vary. Sample: $y = x^2 + x - 2$, $y = -x + 1$ **b.** Answers may vary. Sample: $y = x^2 - x$, $y = x - 1$ **c.** Answers may vary. Sample: $y = x^2 + x - 2$, $y = x - 5$
7. In both cases, you can use graphing, substitution or elimination. If you don't use graphing, you must know how to solve a quadratic equation in order to solve a linear-quadratic system.
Exercises
9. (2, 8)

11. (0, 1), (−1, 0)

13. (0, 4), (−3, −5)
15. (2, 4), (−1, 1)
17. Day 0, 20 players of each type; Day 152, 7316 players of each type
19. (6, −2), (−9, −47)
21. (9, −71), (−11, −91)
23. (−4, −41), $\left(\frac{1}{3}, \frac{7}{3}\right)$
25. no solution
27. (2, −5), (−4, 1) **29.** (−3, 0), (−6, −3) **31.** $y = 2x + 2$ **33.** The system has no solution. **42.** quadratic; $y = 0.2x^2$ **43.** exponential; $y = 4(2.5)^x$ **44.** linear; $y = -4.2x + 7$ **45.** 14 **46.** $\frac{5}{7}$ **47.** 1.2 **48.** 9 **49.** 0.6 **50.** 20

Chapter Review **pp. 589–592**

1. parabola **2.** axis of symmetry **3.** discriminant **4.** vertex
5.

6.

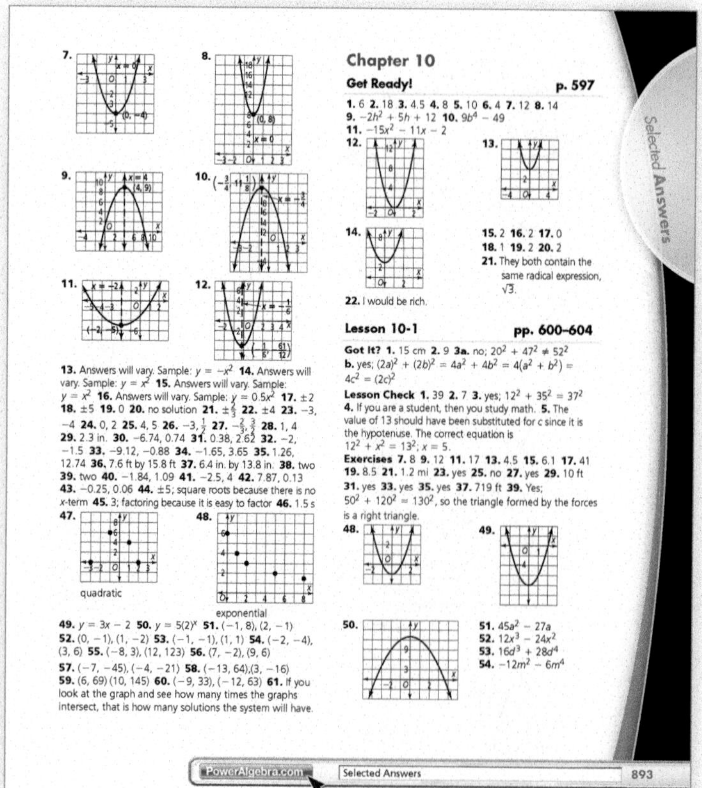

7.

8.

9.

10.

11.

12.

13. Answers will vary. Sample: $y = -x^2$ **14.** Answers will vary. Sample: $y = x^2$ **15.** Answers will vary. Sample: $y = x^2$ **16.** Answers will vary. Sample: $y = 0.5x^2$ **17.** ±2 **18.** ±5 **19.** 0 **20.** no solution **21.** $\pm\frac{2}{3}$ **22.** ±4 **23.** −3, −4 **24.** 0, 2 **25.** 4, 5 **26.** −3, $\frac{1}{2}$ **27.** $-\frac{2}{3}, \frac{3}{2}$ **28.** 1, 4 **29.** 2.3 in. **30.** −6.74, 0.74 **31.** 0.38, 2.62 **32.** −2, −1.5 **33.** −9.12, −0.88 **34.** −1.65, 3.65 **35.** 1.26, 12.74 **36.** 7.6 ft by 15.8 ft **37.** 6.4 in. by 13.8 in. **38.** two **39.** two **40.** −1.84, 1.09 **41.** −2.5, 4 **42.** 7.87, 0.13 **43.** −0.25, 0.06 **44.** ±5; square roots because there is no x-term **45.** 3; factoring because it is easy to factor **46.** 1.5 s

47.
quadratic

48.
exponential

49. $y = 3x - 2$ **50.** $y = 5(2)^x$ **51.** (−1, 8), (2, −1) **52.** (0, −1), (1, −2) **53.** (−1, −1), (1, 1) **54.** (−2, −4), (3, 6) **55.** (−8, 3), (12, 123) **56.** (7, −2), (9, 6)
57. (−7, −45), (−4, −21) **58.** (−13, 64),(3, −16) **59.** (6, 69) (10, 145) **60.** (−9, 33), (−12, 63) **61.** If you look at the graph and see how many times the graphs intersect, that is how many solutions the system will have.

Chapter 10

Get Ready! **p. 597**

1. 6 **2.** 18 **3.** 4.5 **4.** 8 **5.** 10 **6.** 4 **7.** 12 **8.** 14 **9.** $-2h^2 + 5h + 12$ **10.** $9b^4 - 49$ **11.** $-15x^2 - 11x - 2$
12.

13.

14.

15. 2 **16.** 2 **17.** 0
18. 1 **19.** 2 **20.** 2
21. They both contain the same radical expression, $\sqrt{3}$.
22. I would be rich.

Lesson 10-1 **pp. 600–604**

Got It? 1. 15 cm **2.** 9 **3a.** no; $20^2 + 47^2 \ne 52^2$ **b.** yes; $(2a)^2 + (2b)^2 = 4a^2 + 4b^2 = 4(a^2 + b^2) = 4c^2 = (2c)^2$
Lesson Check 1. 39 **2.** 7 **3.** yes; $12^2 + 35^2 = 37^2$ **4.** If you are a student, then you study math. **5.** The value of 13 should have been substituted for c since it is the hypotenuse. The correct equation is $12^2 + x^2 = 13^2$; $x = 5$.
Exercises 7. 8 **9.** 12 **11.** 17 **13.** 4.5 **15.** 6.1 **17.** 41 **19.** 8.5 **21.** 1.2 mi **23.** yes **25.** no **27.** yes **29.** 10 ft **31.** yes **33.** yes **35.** yes **37.** 719 ft **39.** Yes; $50^2 + 120^2 = 130^2$, so the triangle formed by the forces is a right triangle.
48.

49.

50.

51. $45a^2 - 27a$
52. $12x^3 - 24x^2$
53. $16d^3 + 28d^4$
54. $-12m^2 - 6m^4$

Lesson 10-2 pp. 606–612

Got It? 1. $6\sqrt{2}$ **2.** $-4m^5\sqrt{5m}$ **3a.** $18\sqrt{3}$ **b.** $3a^2\sqrt{2}$ **c.** $210x^3$ **d.** yes; $\sqrt{14t^2} = t\sqrt{14}$ **4.** $w\sqrt{17}$ **5a.** 4 **b.** $\frac{3}{a}$ **c.** $\frac{5y\sqrt{y}}{2}$ **6a.** $\frac{\sqrt{6}}{3}$ **b.** $\frac{\sqrt{10m}}{6m}$ **c.** $\frac{\sqrt{21s}}{3}$
Lesson Check 1. $7\sqrt{2}$ **2.** $4b^2\sqrt{b}$ **3.** $12m^2$ **4.** $\frac{\sqrt{15}}{x}$ **5.** $\frac{\sqrt{15}}{3}$ **6.** $\frac{\sqrt{3n}}{n}$ **7a.** Yes; there are no perfect-square factors in 31, there are no fractions in the radicand, and there are no radicals in the denominator. **b.** No; there is a fraction in the radicand. **c.** No; 25 is a perfect-square factor of 175. **8.** Answers may vary. Sample:
$\frac{3}{\sqrt{12}} = \frac{3}{2\sqrt{3}} \cdot \frac{\sqrt{3}}{\sqrt{3}} = \frac{3\sqrt{3}}{6} = \frac{\sqrt{3}}{2}$;
$\frac{3}{\sqrt{12}} = \frac{3}{\sqrt{12}} \cdot \frac{\sqrt{12}}{\sqrt{12}} = \frac{3\sqrt{12}}{12} = \frac{\sqrt{12}}{4} = \frac{2\sqrt{3}}{4} = \frac{\sqrt{3}}{2}$
9. A radical expression is in simplified form if the radicand has no perfect-square factors other than 1, the radicand contains no fractions, and no radicals appear in the denominator of a fraction.
Exercises 11. $3\sqrt{11}$ **13.** $-2\sqrt{15}$ **15.** $50\sqrt{7}$ **17.** $5t^2\sqrt{2t}$ **19.** $-63x^4\sqrt{3x}$ **21.** $-18y\sqrt{3y}$ **23.** 4 **25.** 30 **27.** $42n^2$ **29.** $16y^3$ **31.** $-126a\sqrt{a}$ **33.** $24c^7$ **35.** $w\sqrt{26}$ **37.** $\frac{7\sqrt{3}}{4}$ **39.** $\frac{\sqrt{3x}}{8}$ **41.** $\frac{77a}{2}$ **43.** $\frac{\sqrt{10x}}{4x}$ **45.** $2\sqrt{11}$ **47.** $\frac{4}{3}$ **49.** $2\sqrt{6}$ in. **51.** not simplest form; radical in the denominator of a fraction **53.** Simplest form; radicand has no perfect-square factors other than 1. **55a.** $f\sqrt{3f}$ **b.** $\frac{1}{x^2}$ **c.** $\frac{\sqrt{2a}}{2a}$ **d.** $\frac{\sqrt{2m}}{4m}$ **57a.** $\sqrt{18 \cdot 10} = \sqrt{180} = \sqrt{36} \cdot \sqrt{5} = 6\sqrt{5}$ **b.** Answers may vary. Sample: 4 and 45 **59.** $2\sqrt{13}$ **61.** $\frac{-2\sqrt{a}}{a^2}$ **63.** $\frac{x\sqrt{y}}{y^2}$ **65.** $4\sqrt{5}$ **67.** $ab^2c\sqrt{abc}$ **69.** $\frac{8\sqrt{6a}}{3a}$ **71.** $1 \pm \sqrt{5}$ **73.** Answers may vary. Sample: 12, 27, 48 **83.** yes **84.** yes **85.** no **86.** $(8y + 3)(8y - 3)$ **87.** $(a + 9)(a - 9)$ **88.** $(5 + 4b)(5 - 4b)$ **89.** $6a^2 - 5a - 4$ **90.** $-4m^2 + 14mn - 12n^2$ **91.** $4x^2 + 16x + 15$

Lesson 10-3 pp. 613–618

Got It? 1a. $-\sqrt{2}$ **b.** $7\sqrt{5}$ **2a.** $8\sqrt{7}$ **b.** $8\sqrt{2}$ **c.** No; if they are unlike and have no common factors other than 1, even if they can be simplified, they still will not be like. **3a.** $2\sqrt{3} + 5\sqrt{2}$ **b.** $15 - 4\sqrt{11}$ **c.** $-6\sqrt{2} - 6$ **4.** $\frac{-3\sqrt{10} + 3\sqrt{5}}{5}$ **5.** $(6\sqrt{5} - 6)$ in., or about 7.4 in.
Lesson Check 1. $5\sqrt{3}$ **2.** $\sqrt{6}$ **3.** $\sqrt{21} - 2\sqrt{7}$ **4.** $41 - 12\sqrt{5}$ **5.** $3\sqrt{5} - \sqrt{10}$ **6.** $2\sqrt{7} - 4$ **7a.** $\sqrt{13} + 2$ **b.** $\sqrt{6} - \sqrt{3}$ **c.** $\sqrt{5} + \sqrt{10}$ **8.** $\sqrt{3} \cdot \sqrt{3} \neq 9$; $\frac{\sqrt{3} + 1}{3 - 1} = \frac{\sqrt{3} + 1}{2}$
Exercises 9. $7\sqrt{5}$ **11.** $8\sqrt{3}$ **13.** 0 **15.** $-7\sqrt{5}$ **17.** $9\sqrt{10}$ **19.** $\frac{19\sqrt{5}}{2}$ **21.** $2\sqrt{3} + 3\sqrt{2}$ **23.** $3\sqrt{7} - 21$ **25.** $5\sqrt{33} - 15\sqrt{22}$ **27.** -6 **29.** $62 - 20\sqrt{6}$ **31.** $\frac{3\sqrt{7} + 3\sqrt{3}}{4}$ **33.** $-2\sqrt{5} - 5$ **35.** $\frac{7\sqrt{13} - 7\sqrt{5}}{8}$ **37.** $\frac{23\sqrt{5} - 23}{2}$ ft, or about 14.2 ft **39.** $-\frac{4}{3}$; -1.3 **41.** $\frac{-1 + \sqrt{7}}{4}$; -0.4 **43.** $9 + 6\sqrt{2} + 4\sqrt{5} + 3\sqrt{10}$; 35.9 **45.** No; yes; you can simplify $\sqrt{12}$ to $2\sqrt{3}$ and then combine the like radicals. **47.** $5\sqrt{10}$ **49.** $22\sqrt{3} - 6$ **51.** $\frac{13 + \sqrt{65} + \sqrt{130} + 5\sqrt{2}}{8}$ **53.** -24 **55.** $4\sqrt{3} + 4\sqrt{2} + 3\sqrt{6} + 6$ **57.** $s\sqrt{3}$ **59a.** $x^{\frac{n}{2}}$ **b.** $x^{\frac{n-1}{2}}\sqrt{x}$ **68.** $6\sqrt{3}$ **69.** $15\sqrt{6}$ **70.** $\frac{2\sqrt{2}}{3c}$ **71.** 15 **72.** 8^{16} **73.** 2^{11} **74.** 5^{27} **75.** 3^3 **76.** -1 **77.** $-4, 3$ **78.** $-5, 3$ **79.** $-3, \frac{2}{3}$ **80.** $-2, \frac{1}{2}$ **81.** -7

Lesson 10-4 pp. 620–625

Got It? 1. 9 **2.** 0.825 ft **3.** 7 **4.** -2 **5a.** no solution **b.** The principal root of a number is never negative.
Lesson Check 1. 12 **2.** 3 **3.** 1 **4.** no solution **5.** C **6.** If $x^2 = y^2$, then $x = y$; no, if $x = -1$ and $y = 1$, then $x^2 = y^2$, but $x \neq y$.
Exercises 7. 4 **9.** 36 **11.** 8 **13.** 16 **15.** -2 **17.** about 5.2 ft **19.** 4.5 **21.** 7 **23.** 4 **25.** 2 **27.** none **29.** -7 **31.** 3 **33.** no solution **35.** no solution **37.** The student did not check the solutions in the original equations. Both of those solutions are extraneous, so the equation has no solution. **39a.** 25 **b.** 11.25 **41.** Add $\sqrt{y + 2}$ to each side of the equation. Square each side of the equation. Solve for y. Check each apparent solution in the original equation. **43.** 3 **45.** no solution **47.** 1.5 **49.** 1600 ft **57.** $5\sqrt{2}$ **58.** -24 **59.** $-\frac{2\sqrt{3} - 4\sqrt{2}}{5}$ **60.** no solution **61.** $-2, 2$ **62.** $-\frac{3}{2}, -\frac{2}{3}$

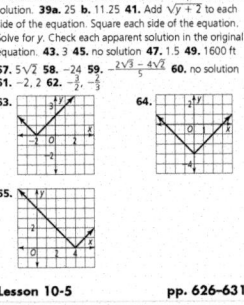

63.
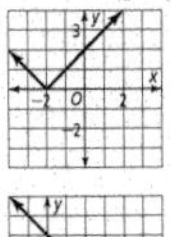

64.
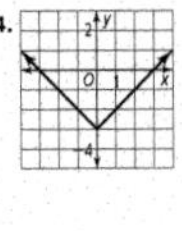

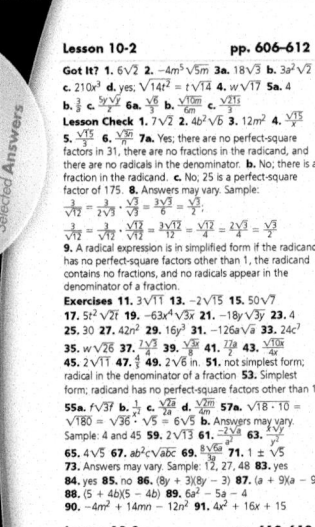

65.
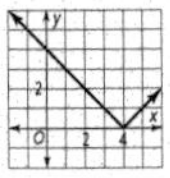

Lesson 10-5 pp. 626–631

Got It? 1. $x \leq 2.5$ **2a.** when the power is more than 56.25 watts **b.** 4

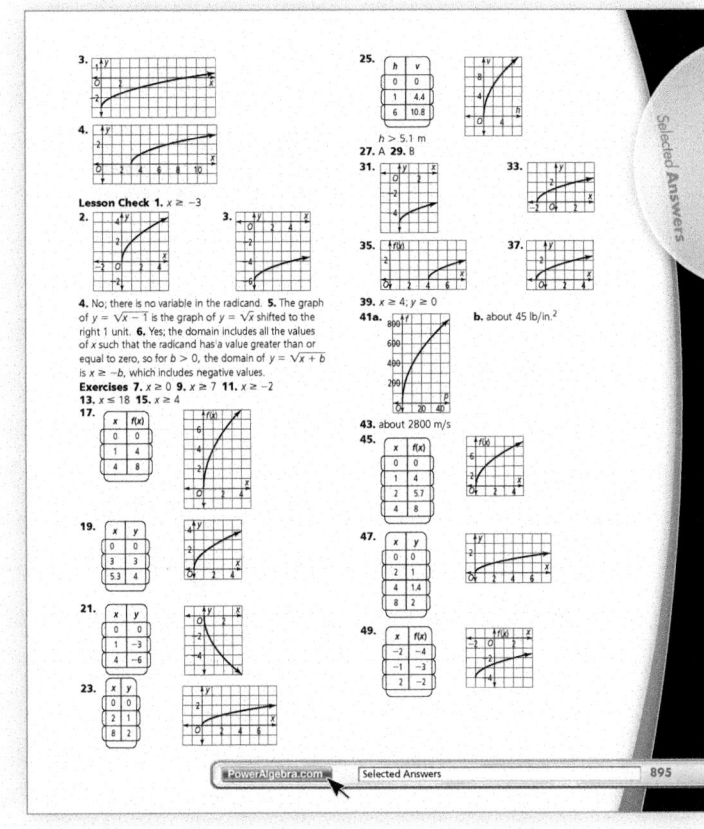

3.
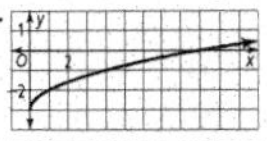

4.
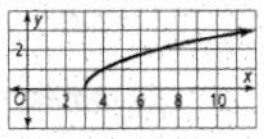

Lesson Check 1. $x \geq -3$

2.
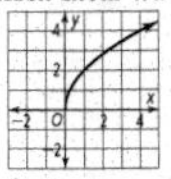

3.
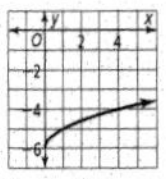

4. No; there is no variable in the radicand. **5.** The graph of $y = \sqrt{x - 1}$ is the graph of $y = \sqrt{x}$ shifted to the right 1 unit. **6.** Yes; the domain includes all the values of x such that the radicand has a value greater than or equal to zero, so for $b > 0$, the domain of $y = \sqrt{x + b}$ is $x \geq -b$, which includes negative values.
Exercises 7. $x \geq 0$ **9.** $x \geq 7$ **11.** $x \geq -2$ **13.** $x \leq 18$ **15.** $x \geq 4$

17.

x	$f(x)$
0	0
1	4
4	8

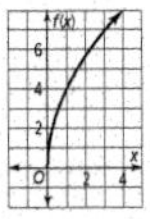

19.

x	y
0	0
3	3
5.3	4

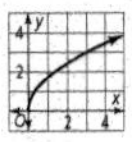

21.

x	y
0	0
1	-3
4	-6

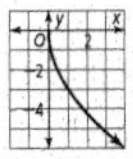

23.

x	y
0	0
2	1
8	2

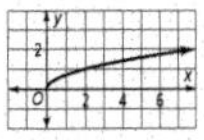

25.

h	v
0	0
1	4.4
6	10.8

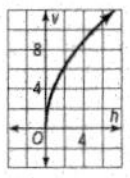

$h > 5.1$ m
27. A **29.** B

31.
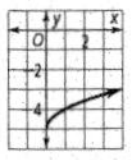

33.
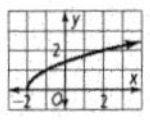

35.
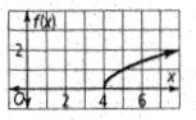

37.
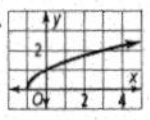

39. $x \geq 4$; $y \geq 0$

41a.
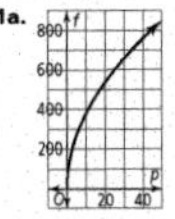

b. about 45 lb/in.^{2}

43. about 2800 m/s

45.

x	$f(x)$
0	0
1	4
2	5.7
4	8

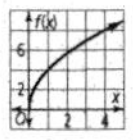

47.

x	y
0	0
2	1
4	1.4
8	2

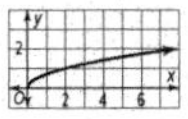

49.

x	$f(x)$
-2	-4
-1	-3
2	-2

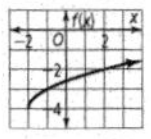

51.

x	y
-3	1
-2	2.4
-1	3
0	3.4

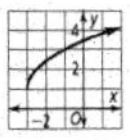

53a. No; the graph does not pass the vertical-line test. **b.** The graph of $y = \sqrt{x}$ is the first-quadrant portion of the graph of $x = y^2$. **c.** $y = -\sqrt{x}$

55.
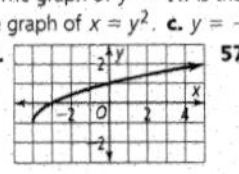

57.
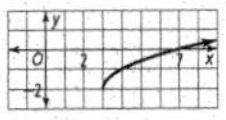

59.
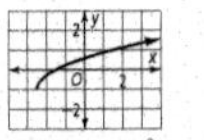

69. 4 **70.** no solution **71.** no solution **72.** $-\frac{4}{3}$ **73.** no solution **74.** 4 **75.** $5m + 12$ **76.** $12h^3 + 8h$ **77.** $-3b - 6$ **78.** $a^2 + 9a + 1$ **79.** $9p^2 + 24p + 1$ **80.** $6c^5 + 8c^3 - 1$ **81.** 9 ft **82.** 13.5 ft **83.** $\frac{4}{3}$ ft

Lesson 10-6 pp. 633–639

Got It? 1. $\frac{3}{5}$; $\frac{4}{5}$; $\frac{3}{4}$ **2a.** 0.9848 **b.** 1 **c.** 0.9659 **d.** 0.1564 **e.** $\sin 45° = \cos 45°$; a 45°-45°-90° triangle is an isosceles right triangle, so the legs have the same length, and the sine and cosine are the same ratio. **3.** 1.9 **4.** 41.8° **5.** about 130 ft
Lesson Check 1. $\frac{4}{5}$ **2.** $\frac{3}{5}$ **3.** $\frac{4}{3}$ **4.** about 6.4 cm **5.** 73.7° **6.** To find the sine of an angle, you find the ratio of the length of the opposite leg to the length of the hypotenuse. To find the cosine of an angle, you find the ratio of the length of the adjacent leg to the length of the hypotenuse. **7.** The student should use the $\sin^{-1}$ key; $\sin^{-1}(0.9) = 64.15806724$.
Exercises 9. $\frac{5}{13}$ **11.** $\frac{8}{17}$ **13.** $\frac{8}{17}$ **15.** $\frac{5}{13}$ **17.** 0.1736 **19.** 0.0872 **21.** 0.9397 **23.** 0.9455 **25.** 5.5 **27.** 19.2 **29.** 66.0 **31.** 60° **33.** 37° **35.** about 47.7 ft **37.** Divide the length of the adjacent side by the cosine of the acute angle. **39.** 514.3 **41.** 78.4 **43a.** about 1,720,000 ft **b.** about 326 mi

52.
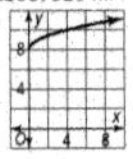

53.
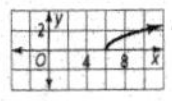

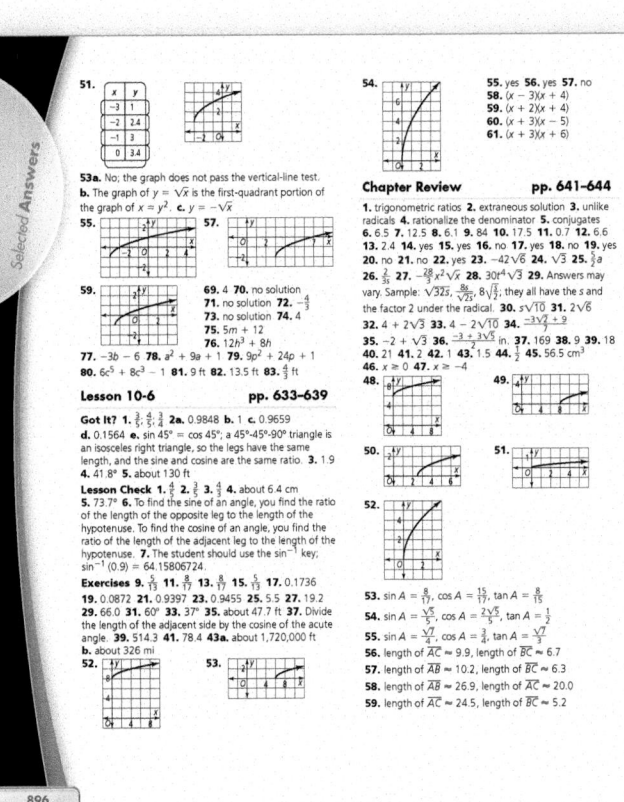

54.
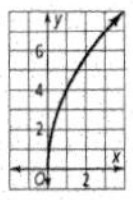

55. yes **56.** yes **57.** no **58.** $(x - 3)(x + 4)$ **59.** $(x + 2)(x + 4)$ **60.** $(x + 3)(x - 5)$ **61.** $(x + 3)(x + 6)$

Chapter Review pp. 641–644

1. trigonometric ratios **2.** extraneous solution **3.** unlike radicals **4.** rationalize the denominator **5.** conjugates **6.** 6.5 **7.** 12.5 **8.** 6.1 **9.** 84 **10.** 17.5 **11.** 0.7 **12.** 6.6 **13.** 2.4 **14.** yes **15.** yes **16.** no **17.** yes **18.** no **19.** yes **20.** no **21.** no **22.** yes **23.** $-42\sqrt{6}$ **24.** $\sqrt{3}$ **25.** $\frac{5}{2}a$ **26.** $\frac{2}{3s}$ **27.** $-\frac{28}{3}x^2\sqrt{x}$ **28.** $30t^4\sqrt{3}$ **29.** Answers may vary. Sample: $\sqrt{32s}$, $\frac{8s}{\sqrt{2s}}$, $8\sqrt{\frac{s}{2}}$; they all have the s and the factor 2 under the radical. **30.** $s\sqrt{10}$ **31.** $2\sqrt{6}$ **32.** $4 + 2\sqrt{3}$ **33.** $4 - 2\sqrt{10}$ **34.** $\frac{-3\sqrt{2} + 9}{7}$ **35.** $-2 + \sqrt{3}$ **36.** $\frac{-3 + 3\sqrt{5}}{2}$ in. **37.** 169 **38.** 9 **39.** 18 **40.** 21 **41.** 2 **42.** 1 **43.** 1.5 **44.** $\frac{1}{2}$ **45.** 56.5 cm^3 **46.** $x \geq 0$ **47.** $x \geq -4$

48.
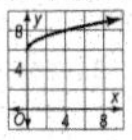

49.
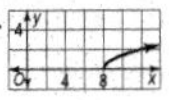

50.
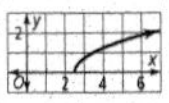

51.
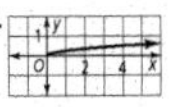

52.
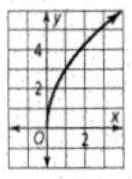

53. $\sin A = \frac{8}{17}$, $\cos A = \frac{15}{17}$, $\tan A = \frac{8}{15}$
54. $\sin A = \frac{\sqrt{5}}{5}$, $\cos A = \frac{2\sqrt{5}}{5}$, $\tan A = \frac{1}{2}$
55. $\sin A = \frac{\sqrt{7}}{4}$, $\cos A = \frac{3}{4}$, $\tan A = \frac{\sqrt{7}}{3}$
56. length of $\overline{AC} \approx 9.9$, length of $\overline{BC} \approx 6.7$
57. length of $\overline{AB} \approx 10.2$, length of $\overline{BC} \approx 6.3$
58. length of $\overline{AB} \approx 26.9$, length of $\overline{AC} \approx 20.0$
59. length of $\overline{AC} \approx 24.5$, length of $\overline{BC} \approx 5.2$

Chapter 11

Get Ready! p. 649

1. $2\frac{1}{30}$ **2.** $3\frac{1}{4}$ **3.** $-\frac{73}{120}$ **4.** $\frac{11}{35}$ **5.** $\frac{q^6}{p^5}$ **6.** $6\frac{30}{49}$ **7.** $\frac{64}{729}$ **8.** $\frac{8yz^6}{5x^6}$ **9.** $-7, 9$ **10.** $-\frac{5}{3}, \frac{7}{4}$ **11.** -13 **12.** 0, 3 **13.** $-\frac{4}{3}, 5$ **14.** $-5, -\frac{2}{3}$ **15.** $-10, -1$ **16.** $-3, 7$ **17.** $-\frac{1}{2}, \frac{5}{3}$ **18.** no solution **19.** 1 **20.** 4 **21.** The excluded values are not allowed. **22.** A rational expression involves a ratio. **23.** One is decreasing as the other increases.

Lesson 11-1 pp. 652–657

Got It? 1a. $\frac{3}{a}$, $a \neq 0$ **b.** $\frac{9d^2}{2d + 4}$, $d \neq -2$ **c.** $\frac{1}{3}$, $n \neq \frac{3}{2}$ **d.** $13c$, none **2a.** $\frac{2}{x + 2}$; $x \neq -2, x \neq 4$ **b.** $\frac{a - 2}{3}$; $a \neq 1$ **c.** $\frac{6}{2z + 3}$; $z \neq -2, z \neq -\frac{3}{2}$ **d.** $\frac{c - 3}{c + 3}$; $c \neq -3, c \neq -2$ **3a.** -1; $x \neq 2.5$ **b.** $-y - 4$; $y \neq 4$ **c.** $-\frac{3}{2d + 1}$; $d \neq -\frac{1}{2}$, $d \neq \frac{1}{3}$ **d.** $-\frac{3}{2z + 2}$; $z \neq \pm 1$ **4a.** $12x + 4$ **b.** No, h must be greater than 2π in order for the value of a to be greater than 0. If h is less than or equal to 2π, then a will be negative, and length cannot be negative.
Lesson Check 1. 3; $x \neq -3$ **2.** $-\frac{1}{x + 3}$; $x \neq -3, x \neq 5$ **3.** $4x$ **4a.** No, the expression is not the ratio of two polynomials. **b.** Yes, the expression is the ratio of two polynomials. **5.** If the denominator contains a polynomial, there may be values of the variable that make the denominator equal to zero, and division by zero is undefined. **6.** The only way the rational expression is not in simplest form is if the numerator and the denominator are equal. **7a.** yes, $3 - x = -(x - 3)$ **b.** no, $2 - y = -(y - 2)$
Exercises 9. $\frac{1}{7x}$, $x \neq 0$ **11.** $\frac{1}{2}$, $p \neq 12$ **13.** $\frac{x + 2}{x^2}$, $x \neq 0$ **15.** $\frac{2}{b + 4}$, $b \neq \pm 4$ **17.** $\frac{w}{w - 7}$, $w \neq \pm 7$ **19.** $\frac{m + 3}{m + 2}$, $m \neq -4, m \neq -2$ **21.** $b + 3$, $b \neq -5$ **23.** -1, $n \neq \frac{5}{4}$ **25.** -2, $m \neq 2$ **27.** $\frac{-1}{v + 5}$, $v \neq \pm 5$ **29.** $w + 1$ **31.** $\frac{2r - 1}{r + 5}$, $r \neq -5$ **33.** $\frac{5t - 4}{3t - 1}$, $t \neq -2, t \neq \frac{1}{3}$ **35.** $\frac{3(z + 4)}{z^3}$, $z \neq 0$ **37.** $-\frac{2a + 1}{a + 3}$, $a \neq -3, a \neq \frac{5}{2}$ **39.** $-\frac{c(3c + 5)}{5c + 4}$, $c \neq -\frac{4}{5}, c \neq 2$ **41.** No, $y = \frac{x^2 - 9}{x + 3}$ is not defined for $x = -3$ but $x - 3$ is. **43.** The student canceled terms instead of factors; $\frac{x^2 + 2x}{2x} = \frac{x(x + 2)}{2x} = \frac{x + 2}{2}$. **45.** Answers may vary. Sample: $\frac{1}{(x - 4)(x + 3)}$ **47.** $\frac{5w}{5w + 6}$ **58.** $\frac{15}{17}$ **59.** $\frac{15}{17}$ **60.** $\frac{8}{15}$ **61.** $10\sqrt{2}$ **62.** $a^2b^3c^4\sqrt{b}$ **63.** $3x\sqrt{11}$ **64.** $\frac{\sqrt{2}}{5m^2}$ **65.** $2\sqrt{2}$ **66.** $2y\sqrt{y}$ **67.** $(2c + 1)(c + 7)$ **68.** $(15t - 11)(t - 1)$ **69.** $(3q + 2)^2$ **70.** $(2c - 1)(2c - 5)$ **71.** $(6t + 1)(4t - 3)$ **72.** $(3q - 7)(q + 2)$

Lesson 11-2 pp. 658–664

Got It? 1a. $\frac{15}{y^4}$, $y \neq 0$ **b.** $\frac{x(x + 1)}{(x - 2)(x - 3)}$, $x \neq 3, x \neq 2$ **2a.** $3x(x + 1)$ **b.** Yes, but you will have to simplify the resulting expression. **3a.** $(x - 7)(3x - 2)$ **b.** $(x + 1)(x + 3)$ **4a.** $\frac{1}{y}$ **b.** $\frac{6}{k + 4}$ **5.** $\frac{z - 1}{z^2 + 2}$ **6.** $\frac{1}{q^2}$
Lesson Check 1. $\frac{6}{5t^6}$ **2.** $\frac{(2x + 5)(x - 5)}{4}$ **3.** $3k^2(k + 1)$ **4.** $\frac{4x}{(x + 7)(2x + 3)}$ **5.** $\frac{(a - 2)^2}{3a}$ **6.** x^2 **7.** no; $\frac{\frac{a}{b}}{c} = \frac{a}{b} \div c = \frac{a}{b} \cdot \frac{1}{c} = \frac{a}{bc}$, where $\frac{a}{\frac{b}{c}} = a \div \frac{b}{c} = a \cdot \frac{c}{b} = \frac{ac}{b}$ **8.** The procedures are the same, but when you multiply rational expressions, there may be values of the variables for which the rational expressions are not defined. **9.** The variables b, c, and d appear in the denominators, and division by 0 is not defined. **10a.** Write the product of the rational expression and the polynomial, factor, divide out common factors, and write the product in factored form. **b.** Rewrite the quotient of the rational expression and the polynomial as the product of the rational expression and the reciprocal of the polynomial. Factor the numerators and denominators, divide out common factors, and write the answer in factored form.
Exercises 11. $\frac{35x}{36}$ **13.** $\frac{40}{3a^5}$ **15.** $\frac{2x(x - 1)}{3(x + 1)}$ **17.** $\frac{2c(c + 2)}{c - 1}$ **19.** $\frac{(r + 2)(r - 2)}{2r}$ **21.** $t - 4$ **23.** $4(t + 1)(t + 2)$ **25.** $\frac{(x - 1)(x - 2)}{3}$ **27.** $\frac{(h - 1)(h + 4)}{3}$ **29.** $\frac{x + 1}{2}$ **31.** $\frac{1}{c^2 - 1}$ **33.** 6 **35.** $-\frac{1}{2}$ **37.** $\frac{n - 3}{4n + 5}$ **39.** $\frac{11}{7k - 15}$ **41.** $\frac{b - 1}{3(b + 1)}$ **43.** 18 **45.** $\frac{1}{2(x + 1)}$ **47.** $\frac{2(3g + 1)}{g(3g - 1)}$ **49.** $\frac{1}{3z(z + 10)}$ **51.** $t + 3$ **53.** $\frac{3t - 5}{7t^2}$ **55.** $\frac{x - 2}{x - 3}$ **57.** \$88.71 **59.** \$518,011.65 **61.** The student forgot to rewrite the divisor as its reciprocal before canceling. $\frac{3a}{a + 2} \div \frac{(a + 2)^2}{a - 4} = \frac{3a}{a + 2} \cdot \frac{a - 4}{(a + 2)^2} = \frac{3a(a - 4)}{(a + 2)^3}$ **63.** 0, 4, and -4 make the denominators equal 0. **65.** $\frac{2m^2(m + 2)}{(m - 1)(m + 4)}$ **74.** $\frac{7}{3}$, $m \neq 2$ **75.** $\frac{1}{2a^2 - 3}$, $a \neq 0, a \neq \pm\frac{\sqrt{6}}{2}$ **76.** $\frac{2c - 9}{2c + 8}$, $c \neq -4, c \neq 4.5$ **77.** $2x^2 + 10x + 12$ **78.** $-3n^2 + 11n + 20$ **79.** $6a^3 - 21a^2 + 2a - 7$

Lesson 11-3 pp. 666–671

Got It? 1a. $2a + 5 + \frac{3}{2a}$ **b.** $b - \frac{3}{b} + \frac{1}{5b^3}$ **c.** $2c^3 + 3c + \frac{3}{2}$ **2.** $2m - 3$ **3a.** $q^3 + q^2 + 2q + 3$ **b.** $h^2 - 3h + 5 - \frac{3}{h + 3}$ **4a.** $2y - \frac{19}{3} + \frac{55}{3(3y + 4)}$ **b.** $3a + 1 - \frac{3}{6a + 5}$ **c.** Check whether $(2x - 3)(2x + 2) - 7$ equals $4x^2 - 10x - 1$.

Lesson Check 1. $4m + 2 - \frac{1}{m} - \frac{3}{5m^2}$
2. $20c + 43 + \frac{36}{c} - \frac{1}{5m}$ **3.** $5n^2 - 4n + 1$ **4.** $3a - 5$
5. Both processes involve dividing, multiplying, and subtracting, then "bringing down," and repeating as needed. When dividing polynomials you may need to insert a term with a coefficient of 0 as a placeholder.
6. Divide, multiply, subtract, bring down, and repeat as necessary. **7.** $-x^4 + 0x^3 + 0x^2 + 0x + 1$
Exercises 9. $3x^4 - \frac{5}{x}$ **11.** $n^2 - 18n + 3$
13. $t^3 + 2t^2 - 4t + 5$ **15.** $3t^2 + \frac{3t}{2} - \frac{11}{2}$
17. $y - 3 + \frac{8}{x+2}$ **19.** $-2q - 10 + \frac{22}{q+1}$
21. $2w^2 + 2w + 5 - \frac{10}{w-1}$ **23.** $c^2 - \frac{1}{2c+1}$
25. $4c^2 - 8c + 16$ **27.** $a - 1 + \frac{7}{4a+3}$
29. $t + 5 + \frac{21}{t-6}$ **31.** $4q^2 + 2q + \frac{3}{2} + \frac{9}{2q-2}$
33. $4c^2 + 9c + 7 + \frac{36}{4c-4}$
35. $3y^2 + 5y + \frac{22}{x3y} + \frac{124}{x3y}$ **37.** $2x + 2$
39. $5t^3 - 25t^2 + 115t - 575 + \frac{2881}{t+5}$
41. $3s - 8 + \frac{29}{2s+3}$ **43.** $2r^4 + r^2 - 7$
45. $z^3 - 3z^2 + 10z - 30 + \frac{88}{z+3}$
47. $6m^2 - 24m + 99 - \frac{326}{m+4}$ **49.** $m^2 + 5m + 4$
51. $s^2 - \frac{301}{2009} + \frac{1203}{400}$ **53a.** $t = \frac{d}{r}$
b. $(t^2 - 7t + 12)$ h **64.** $n + 2$
65. $\frac{(t-5)(3t+1)(2t+11)}{3t(2t-55)(t+1)}$ **66.** $\frac{3c+8}{2c+1}$ **67.** $\frac{(x+5)(x+4)^2}{(x+7)(x+8)^2}$
68. $\frac{2}{3}$ **69.** $-\frac{1}{12}$ **70.** x **71.** $\frac{1}{2y}$

Lesson 11-4 pp. 672–677

Got It? 1. $\frac{5a}{3a-4}$ **2a.** $\frac{-5}{4}$ **b.** $\frac{3n-4}{5n}$ **c.** $\frac{1}{q-2}$
3. $\frac{9+14q^2}{21q^4}$ **4.** $\frac{c^2-14c-4}{(3c-1)(c-2)}$ **5a.** $\frac{45}{5}$ **b.** $\frac{4m}{5}$; if n is the miles per gallon when the truck is full, then $m = 1.25n$ and therefore $n = \frac{m}{1.25}$ or $\frac{4m}{5}$.
Lesson Check 1. $\frac{11}{x-7}$ **2.** $\frac{1}{x} - \frac{2}{3}$ **3.** $\frac{16b+15}{24b^2}$ **4.** $\frac{10}{3x}$
5. If the expressions have like denominators, add or subtract numerators as indicated and place over the denominator. If they have unlike denominators, factor if needed, find the LCD, rewrite the expressions with the common denominator, add or subtract as indicated, and simplify. **6.** The procedure is the same. The LCD is the LCM of the denominators. **7a.** yes **b.** No, it will give you a common denominator, but not necessarily the least common denominator.
Exercises 9. $\frac{14}{c-5}$ **11.** $\frac{6c-28}{2c+7}$ **13.** $\frac{1}{n-12}$ **15.** 2
17. $2x^2$ **19.** $7z$ **21.** $5(x+2)$ **23.** $(m+n)(m-n)$
25. $\frac{35+6a}{15a}$ **27.** $\frac{18y-9n}{7n^3}$ **29.** $\frac{(y+4)(y-3)}{6(y+3)(a+5)}$
31. $\frac{a^2+12a+15}{4(a+3)}$ **33a.** $\frac{1}{r} + \frac{1}{0.7r}$ **b.** $\frac{17}{7r}$

c. about 0.81 h or 48.6 min **35.** Not always; the numerator may contain a factor of the LCD.
37. $\frac{x^2+2y+2}{3y+1}$ **39.** $\frac{r-2x-6}{9+p^3}$ **41.** $\frac{10x+15}{x+2}$
43. $\frac{5000r+250,000}{r(r+100)}$ **45.** $\frac{8x^2-1}{4}$ **47.** $\frac{-3a-5}{x(x-5)}$
59. $\frac{1}{2}x^2 + 2x - 1$ **60.** 5b **61.** $\frac{y^2(y-1)}{y-3}$ **62.** 6 **63.** 3
64. no solution **65.** $\frac{5}{3}$ **66.** $\frac{6}{5}$ **67.** 1

Lesson 11-5 pp. 679–685

Got It? 1a. -3 **b.** $\frac{3y}{7}$ **2a.** $-\frac{3}{2}$, $\frac{2}{3}$ **b.** -7, -1 **c.** The expression $\frac{x}{x^2}$ cannot be negative. **3.** 4.8 h **4a.** -8
b. -3, 7 **5.** 0
Lesson Check 1. -1 **2.** 1, 5 **3.** 0 **4.** about 28 min
5. An extraneous solution of a rational equation is an excluded value of the associated rational function.
6. Answers may vary. Sample: $\frac{x^2}{x-1} = \frac{1}{x-1}$
7. The student forgot to first multiply both sides of the equation by the LCD, 5m.
Exercises 9. 3 **11.** -1, 6 **13.** -2 **15.** 5 **17.** -2, 4
19. $\frac{16}{5}$ **21.** -1 **23.** $1\frac{1}{2}$ h **25.** 3 **27.** $-\frac{3}{2}$, 4 **29.** no solution
31. You could rewrite the right side of the equation as $\frac{3x}{x-6}$ and then cross multiply. **33.** -14 **35.** -5, 2
37. $-\frac{5}{6}$, -1 **39.** 12 h
41a.

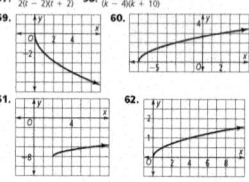

b. $(-9.53, 1.07)$, $(-4.16, 1.35)$, $(-1.12, 5.76)$, $(0.81, 10.16)$

c. Yes; the x-values are solutions to the original equation since both sides are equal. **43.** 20 Ω **56.** $\frac{1}{x^2y^2}$
57. $\frac{3h^2+2hk+4h}{2t^2-2Xt+2}$ **58.** $\frac{-4k-61}{4t-40k+10}$
59.
60.
61.
62.
63. yes **64.** no **65.** yes; $-\frac{1}{3}$ **66.** yes; $\frac{6}{3}$

Lesson 11-6 pp. 686–692

Got It? 1. $xy = 54$ **2.** 7.5 ft
3a.

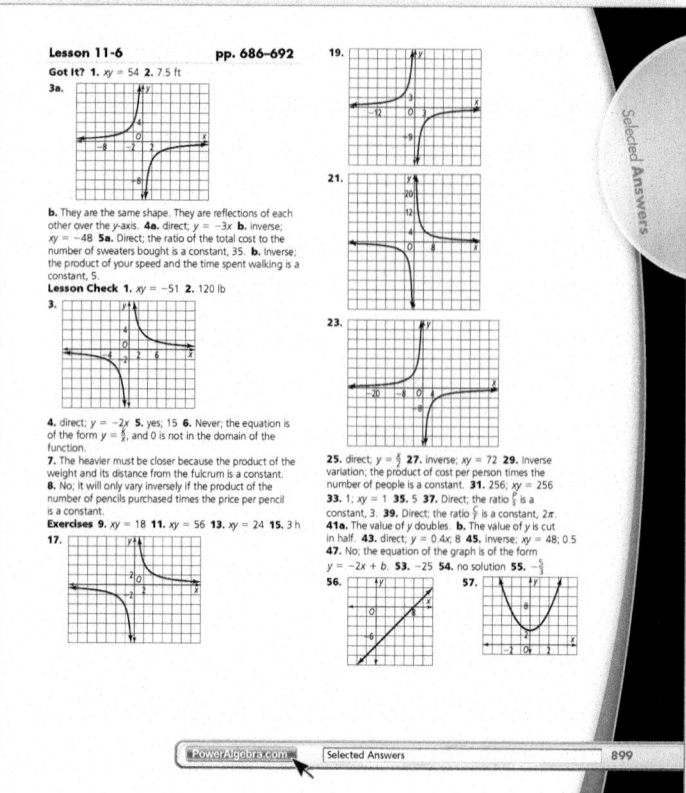

b. They are the same shape. They are reflections of each other over the y-axis. **4a.** direct; $y = -3x$ **b.** inverse; $xy = -48$ **5a.** Inverse; the ratio of the total cost to the number of sweaters bought is a constant, 35. **b.** Inverse; the product of your speed and the time spent walking is a constant, 5.
Lesson Check 1. $xy = -51$ **2.** 120 lb
3.
4. direct; $y = -2x$ **5.** yes; 15 **6.** Never; the equation is of the form $y = \frac{k}{x}$, and 0 is not in the domain of the function.
7. The heavier must be closer because the product of the weight and its distance from the fulcrum is a constant.
8. No; it will only vary inversely if the product of the number of pencils purchased times the price per pencil is a constant.
Exercises 9. $xy = 18$ **11.** $xy = 56$ **13.** $xy = 24$ **15.** 3 h
17.
19.
21.
23.
25. direct; $y = \frac{x}{2}$ **27.** inverse; $xy = 72$ **29.** Inverse variation; the product of cost per person times the number of people is a constant. **31.** 256; $xy = 256$
33. 1; $xy = 1$ **35.** 5 **37.** Direct; the ratio $\frac{y}{x}$ is a constant, 3. **39.** Direct; the ratio $\frac{y}{x}$ is a constant, 2π.
41a. The value of y doubles. **b.** The value of y is cut in half. **43.** direct; $y = 0.4x$; 8 **45.** inverse; $xy = 48$; 0.5
47. No; the equation of the graph is of the form $y = -2x + b$. **53.** -25 **54.** no solution **55.** $-\frac{5}{3}$
56.
57.

58.
59.
4. 5; $x = 5$, $y = 1$ **5.** Answers will vary. Sample: $y = \frac{1}{x+2} + 4$ **6.** The vertical asymptote is $x + 5 = 0$, or $x = -5$. **7.** If the excluded value is a, then the vertical asymptote is $x = a$.
Exercises 9. 2 **11.** 3 **13.** $x = 1$, $y = -1$
15. $x = 0$, $y = 0$
17. $x = 5$, $y = 0$
19. $x = 0$, $y = -5$
21. $x = -1$, $y = 4$
23a. $C = \frac{1920}{n} + 100$

Lesson 11-7 pp. 693–700

Got It? 1. -7
2. $x = 6$
3a. $x = -3$, $y = -4$

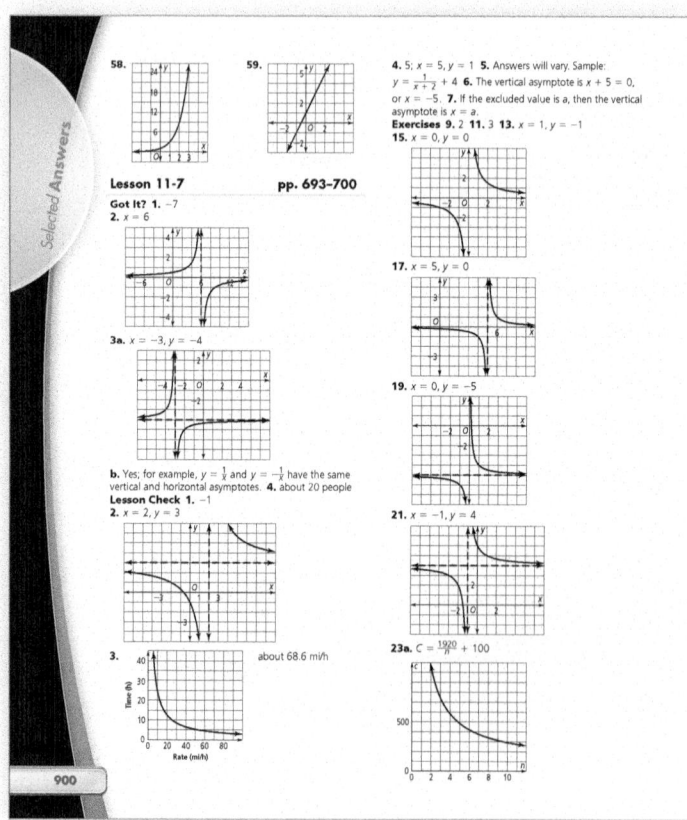

b. Yes; for example, $y = \frac{1}{x}$ and $y = -\frac{1}{x}$ have the same vertical and horizontal asymptotes. **4.** about 20 people
Lesson Check 1. -1
2. $x = 2$, $y = 3$
3. about 68.6 mi/h

b. 5 people **25.** translates the graph 1 unit to the left
27. translates the graph 1 unit up **29.** translates the graph 3 units to the right **31.** about 4.2 ft
33a.

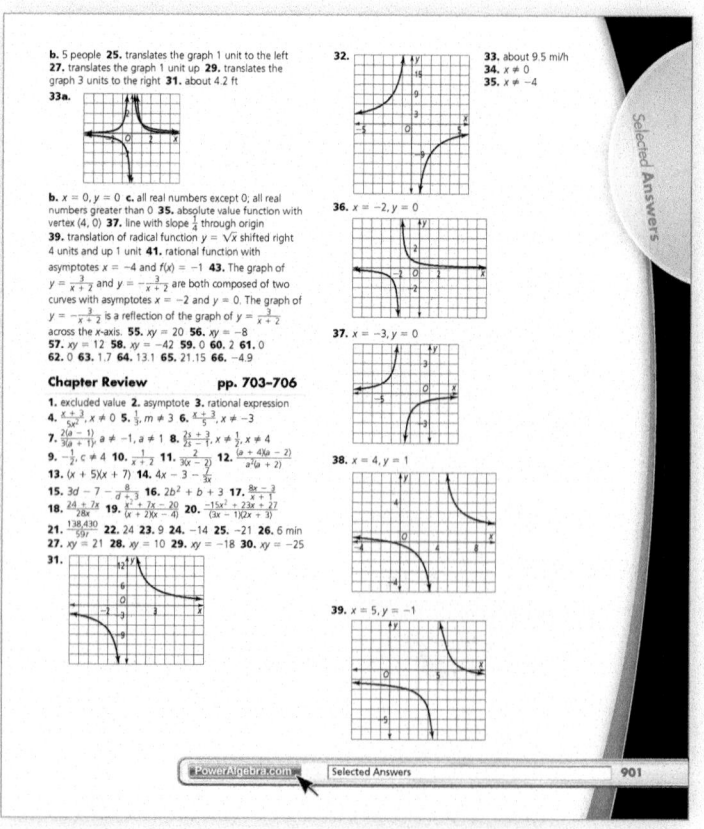

b. $x = 0$, $y = 0$ **c.** all real numbers except 0; all real numbers greater than 0 **35.** absolute value function with vertex (4, 0) **37.** line with slope $\frac{1}{4}$ through origin
39. translation of radical function $y = \sqrt{x}$ shifted right 4 units and up 1 unit **41.** rational function with asymptotes $x = -4$ and $f(x) = -1$ **43.** The graph of $y = \frac{3}{x+2}$ and $y = -\frac{3}{x+2}$ are both composed of two curves with asymptotes $x = -2$ and $y = 0$. The graph of $y = -\frac{3}{x+2}$ is a reflection of the graph of $y = \frac{3}{x+2}$ across the x-axis. **55.** $xy = 20$ **56.** -8
57. $xy = 12$ **58.** $xy = -42$ **59.** 0 **60.** 2 **61.** 0
62. 0 **63.** 1.7 **64.** 13.1 **65.** 21.15 **66.** -4.9

Chapter Review pp. 703–706

1. excluded value **2.** asymptote **3.** rational expression
4. $\frac{x+3}{5n^2}$, $x \ne 0$ **5.** $\frac{1}{3}$, $m \ne 3$ **6.** $\frac{x+3}{x+7}$, $x \ne -3$
7. $\frac{2(a-1)}{3(a+1)}$, $a \ne -1$, $a \ne 1$ **8.** $\frac{2x-3}{x^2-1}$, $x \ne \frac{1}{2}$, $x \ne 4$
9. $-\frac{1}{2}$, $c \ne 4$ **10.** $\frac{1}{x+2}$ **11.** $\frac{2}{3(x-2)}$ **12.** $\frac{(a+4)(a-2)}{a^2(a+2)}$
13. $(x+5)(x+7)$ **14.** $4x - 3 - \frac{1}{4x}$
15. $3d - 7 - \frac{9}{d+8}$ **16.** $2b^2 + b + 3$ **17.** $\frac{8x-3}{x+2}$
18. $\frac{24+7x}{28x}$ **19.** $\frac{x^2+7x-20}{x^2+2Xx-4}$ **20.** $\frac{-15x^2+23X+27}{(3x-1)(2x+3)}$
21. $\frac{138,430}{59x}$ **22.** 24 **23.** 9 **24.** -14 **25.** -21 **26.** 6 min
27. $xy = 21$ **28.** $xy = 10$ **29.** $xy = -18$ **30.** $xy = -25$
31.

32.
33. about 9.5 mi/h
34. $x \ne 0$
35. $x \ne -4$
36. $x = -2$, $y = 0$
37. $x = -3$, $y = 0$
38. $x = 4$, $y = 1$
39. $x = 5$, $y = -1$

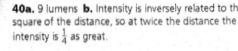

40a. 9 lumens **b.** Intensity is inversely related to the square of the distance, so at twice the distance the intensity is $\frac{1}{4}$ as great.

Chapter 12
Get Ready   p. 711

1. $\frac{7}{6}$ **2.** $-\frac{7}{24}$ **3.** $\frac{47}{50}$ **4.** $\frac{5}{13}$ **5.** $\frac{1}{7}$ **6.** 3 **7.** 11 **8.** $6x - 42$
9. $2x + 3$ **10.** $-10 + 2x$ **11.** $25 + 2x$ **12.** {1, 2, 3, 5, 6, 7, 9, 10, 11, 13, 15, 16} **13.** {9} **14.** {2, 6, 10, 16}
15. {0, 1, 2, 3, 4, 5, 6, 7, 8, 9, 10, 11, 12, 13, 14, 15, 16, 18}
16.

Messenger Bag Sales

negative

17.

Driving Distances and Times

positive
18. heads or tails **19.** into two parts with an equal number of data values **20.** no

Lesson 12-1   pp. 714–719
Got It?
1a. $\begin{bmatrix} -4 \\ 1.5 \\ -16 \end{bmatrix}$ **b.** $\begin{bmatrix} 1 & 1 \\ 2.5 & 10 \end{bmatrix}$
c. You add or subtract matrices by adding or subtracting the corresponding elements. If matrices are not the same size they will not have corresponding elements in each case.
2a. $[6 \quad -14.2 \quad -10]$ **b.** $\begin{bmatrix} -16.5 & 4.5 \\ 0 & -2.25 \end{bmatrix}$
3. Portland
Lesson Check
1. $\begin{bmatrix} -3 & 9 \\ 0 & 4 \end{bmatrix}$ **2.** $\begin{bmatrix} 2 & 3 \\ 2 & -3 \end{bmatrix}$
3. $\begin{bmatrix} 8 & 0 & 10 \\ -4 & 2 & 4 \end{bmatrix}$ **4.** $\begin{bmatrix} -30 & 0 \\ -12 & 18 \end{bmatrix}$

5. 9 **6.** The student added entries across the rows, but the matrices are not the same size so they cannot be added.
Exercises
9. $\begin{bmatrix} -1 & -1 \\ 0 & 0 \end{bmatrix}$ **11.** $\begin{bmatrix} 2 & -1 \\ 5 & -1 \\ 0 & 10 \end{bmatrix}$ **13.** $\begin{bmatrix} 2.4 & -7.6 \\ 8 & 0.3 \\ -7.7 & 1.3 \end{bmatrix}$
15. $\begin{bmatrix} -6 & 2 \\ -14 & 4 \end{bmatrix}$ **17.** $\begin{bmatrix} -19 & -10.5 & -35 \\ -47 & 30 & 0 \end{bmatrix}$
19. $\begin{bmatrix} -12.4 & -23.25 \\ -27.9 & 15.5 \\ -3.1 & -14.26 \end{bmatrix}$ **21.** $\begin{bmatrix} -1.66 & 0.6 & 0 \\ -0.9 & -1.2 & -0.2 \\ 0.2 & -0.58 & -1.4 \end{bmatrix}$
23. Factory B **25.** $\begin{bmatrix} 9 & 1 & 2 \\ -10 & 2 & 0 \end{bmatrix}$
27. $\begin{bmatrix} -28.2 & 30.1 & -20.9 \\ 7.9 & 27.9 & -37 \\ -8 & -36.4 & 7.8 \end{bmatrix}$
29. chicken **37.** 5 **38.** 0 **39.** 4
40. not likely

41. Causal; the amount of sales is related to earnings.

Lesson 12-2   pp. 720–725
Got It?
1. Answers may vary. Sample:

Home Runs	Frequency
2–6	4
7–11	5
12–16	4
17–21	1

2. Answers may vary. Sample:

Finishing Times

3a.

Dollars Spent on Lunch — uniform

b. Answers may vary. Sample: $70 for the week; the data is fairly uniform, so on average he spends about $10 per day.

4.

Interval	Frequency	Cumulative Frequency
0–4	6	6
5–9	4	10
10–14	4	14
15–19	2	16

Lesson Check
1. **Battery Life**

Hours	Frequency
9–12	7
13–16	3
17–20	1
21–24	2

2. **Battery Life**

3. **Battery Life**

Hours	Frequency	Cumulative Frequency
9–12	7	7
13–16	2	9
17–20	1	10
21–24	2	12

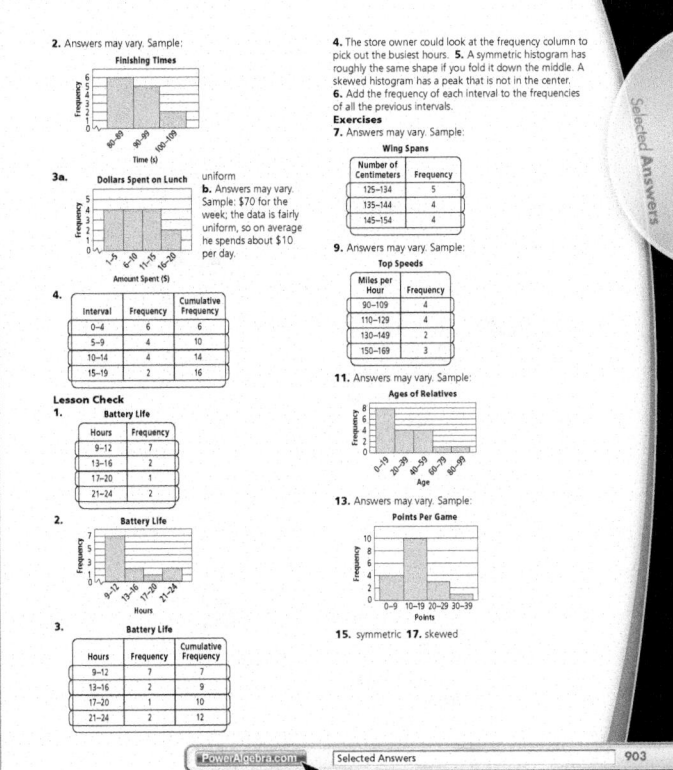

4. The store owner could look at the frequency column to pick out the busiest hours. **5.** A symmetric histogram has roughly the same shape if you fold it down the middle. A skewed histogram has a peak that is not in the center.
6. Add the frequency of each interval to the frequencies of all the previous intervals.
Exercises
7. Answers may vary. Sample:

Wing Spans

Number of Centimeters	Frequency
125–134	5
135–144	4
145–154	4

9. Answers may vary. Sample:

Top Speeds

Miles per Hour	Frequency
90–109	4
110–129	4
130–149	2
150–169	3

11. Answers may vary. Sample:

Ages of Relatives

13. Answers may vary. Sample:

Points Per Game

15. symmetric **17.** skewed

---

19. Answers may vary. Sample:

Heights of Buildings

Feet	Frequency	Cumulative Frequency
100–149	2	2
150–199	3	5
200–249	3	8
250–299	2	10
300–349	2	12

21a.

The Perpendicular Bisectors

Time/Song (min)	Frequency	Cumulative Frequency
0–1:19	0	0
1:20–2:39	2	2
2:40–3:59	5	7
4:00–5:19	3	10

b. 70%; 7 out of 10 songs are shorter than 4 min.
23. Answers may vary. Sample:

Test Scores

25. Answers may vary. Sample:

Test Scores

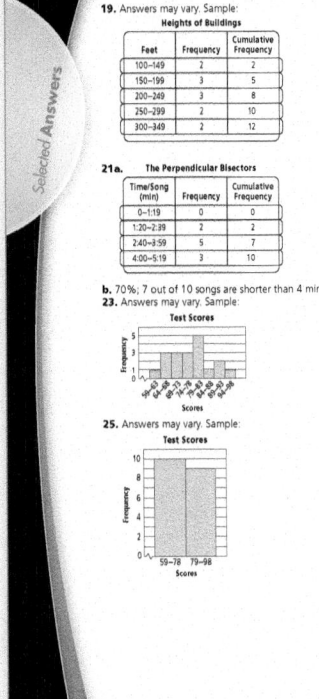

27. $99 **29.** 9 customers **31.** There were no numbers in the range of 30 to 39 so the student just left out this interval. The intervals in a frequency table should not have any gaps, so the student should have included the interval 30–39.

Interval	Frequency
20–29	6
30–39	0
40–49	9
50–59	4

38. $\begin{bmatrix} 12 & 16 \\ 14 & 18 \end{bmatrix}$ **39.** $\begin{bmatrix} -2.1 & -5.3 \\ -0.7 & -0.5 \end{bmatrix}$ **40.** $-16, -4, 0, \frac{1}{2}, \frac{5}{4}$, 2, 13, 16 **41.** $-1, -0.2, 0, 0.1, 0.9, 1.2, 2, 5$

Lesson 12-3   pp. 726–732
Got It? 1. 112.4, 109, 104; mean **2a.** 88% **b.** No; you would need a grade of 104. **3.** Stock C: 6, 4.2; Stock D: 22, 11.2; Stock C had a range of 6 and a mean of 4.2, while Stock D had a range of 22 and a mean of 10.8 for this 5-day period. **4.** 48, 45, 35, 30 **5.** $345, $284.25, $359.25, $866.25
Lesson Check 1. 26.2, 30.5, 33; the median, since there is an outlier in this set **2.** 8.76, 8.8, no mode; the mean, since there is no outlier **3.** 14.1, 15, 15, 24
4. All are describing the data set by finding a representative measure of central tendency. The mean can be influenced by outliers, which can overstate or understate the measure. The median is the middle value of the ranked data, and the mode is the most commonly occurring piece of data.
5. The correct range is 8 because the range is defined as the difference between the highest and lowest values.
6. Since an outlier is either much larger or much smaller than most of the data, it causes the range to get larger.
Exercises 7. 12, 11, 10; mean **9.** 63, 52, no mode; median **11.** 5.9 **13.** 125 **15.** 15 **17.** Set C: 3.8, 6.7; Set D: 28.3, 9.0; the range of Set C is 3.8 with a mean of 6.7, while Set D has a range of 28.3 and a mean of 9.
19. First player: .062, .300; Second player: .029, .302; the second player had a slightly higher mean over the six seasons and was more consistent as shown by the smaller range. **21.** 23.4, 24.9, 25.6, 10.6 **23.** 104, 84, 84, 168 **25.** 20.4, 20.7, 16.7, 8 **27.** 3.3, 4, 4.3, 4.1 **29.** 229.7, 144, 96 and 300, 528 **31a.** Plant A: 5.8, 5.8, 5.4, 1.2; Plant B: 5.6, 5.5, no mode; 2.9 **b.** Plant A: mean as there is no outlier; Plant B: either mean or median, if you consider 7.2 to be an outlier **c.** Plant A; it has a smaller range. **33.** The mean, median and mode will each decrease by that amount, while the range will stay the same. If you subtract the same number d from each set then the sum will decrease by nd where n is the number

of data values. Therefore when you divide the total by n, the mean will decrease by d $\left(\frac{\sum - nd}{n} \text{ or } \frac{\sum}{n} - d\right)$. For the median, the middle number will decrease by d. The mode will decrease by d. The range, on the other hand, will remain the same since (highest value $- d$) $-$ (lowest value $- d$) = highest $-$ lowest. **35.** 88.5
37. Yes; because one salesperson earned $150,000, the mean was $47,500, but a better indicator might be the median, which was only $39,500.
44. Answers may vary. Sample:

Heights of Basketball Players

45. Answers may vary. Sample:

Number of Cars by Day

46. exponential

47. linear

48. 21, 0 **49.** 50, 22.5 **50.** 8.9, 2.1

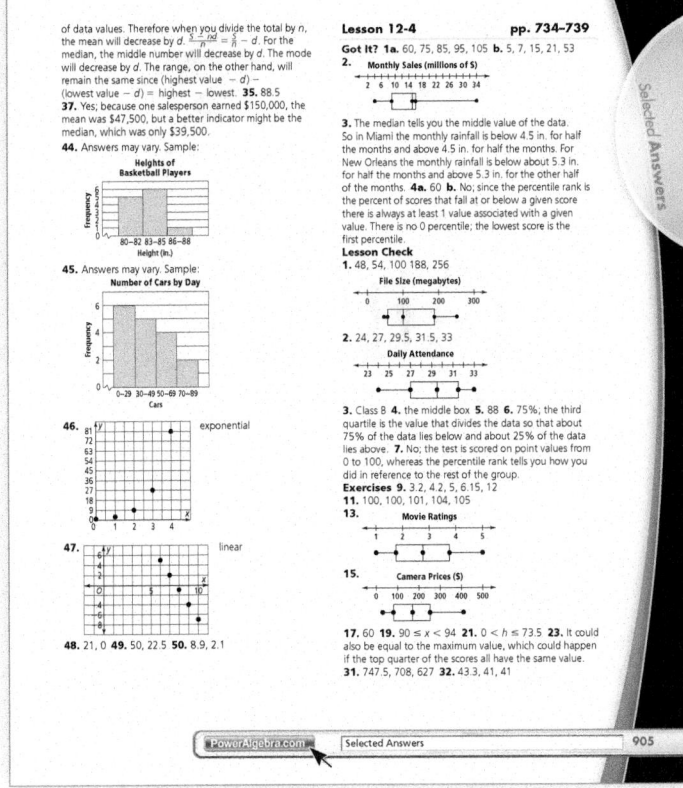

Lesson 12-4   pp. 734–739
Got It? 1a. 60, 75, 85, 95, 105 **b.** 5, 7, 15, 21, 53
2.

Monthly Sales (millions of $)

3. The median tells you the middle value of the data. So in Miami the monthly rainfall is below 4.5 in. for half the months and above 4.5 in. for half the months. For New Orleans the monthly rainfall is below 5.3 in. for half the months and above 5.3 in. for the other half of the months. **4a.** 60 **b.** No; since the percentile rank is the percent of scores that fall at or below a given score there is always at least 1 value associated with a given value. There is no 0 percentile; the lowest score is the first percentile.
Lesson Check
1. 48, 54, 100 188, 256

File Size (megabytes)

2. 24, 27, 29.5, 31.5, 33

Daily Attendance

3. Class 8 **4.** the middle box **5.** 88 **6.** 75%; the third quartile is the value that divides the data so that about 75% of the data lies below and about 25% of the data lies above. **7.** No; the test is scored on point values from 0 to 100, whereas the percentile rank tells you how you did in reference to the rest of the group.
Exercises 9. 3.2, 4.2, 5, 6.15, 12
11. 100, 100, 101, 104, 105
13.

Movie Ratings

15.

Camera Prices ($)

17. 60 **19.** $90 \le x < 94$ **21.** $0 < h \le 73.5$ **23.** It could also be equal to the maximum value, which could happen if the top quarter of the scores all have the same value.
31. 747.5, 708, 627 **32.** 43.3, 41, 41

33.

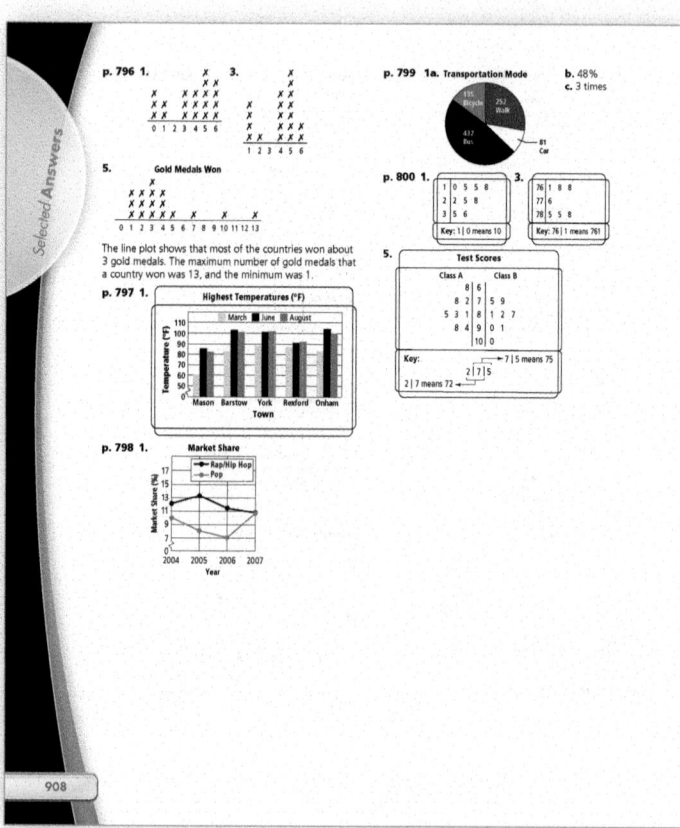

Answers may vary. Sample: $y = -81x + 167,509$; about 4300 bowling establishments

Lesson 12-5 pp. 741–747

Got It? 1a. quantitative; numerical quantities
b. qualitative; not numerical **2a.** Bivariate; there are two variables. **b.** Univariate; there is only one variable.
3. No; if you are using a stratified sampling method, you should sample at random from each group. **4.** Answers may vary. Sample: Do you prefer action movies or documentaries? **5.** Students who have e-mail may be more likely to have a cell phone.
Lesson Check 1. systematic **2.** random **3.** stratified
4. quantitative **5.** The words *delicious* and *plain* are biased and might influence a respondent's answer.
6. Univariate data involves one variable and bivariate data involves two variables.
Exercises 7. qualitative **9.** quantitative **11.** univariate
13. univariate **15.** stratified; not a good sample as it assumes each town has a similar number of voters
17. random; good sample **19.** not biased; respondent is not influenced by question **21.** During the day many people are at work so your sample is not representative of the population. **23.** Because each sample is random, it would not be expected to be exactly the same.
25a. People at an airport are more likely to be travelers.
b. Your question is influencing the result. Respondents might prefer "neither." **c.** The sample is biased as it includes mostly people who might prefer France.
27. people who are customers at the store; every fifteenth customer; systematic **29.** attendees at the game; random attendees; random **31.** quantitative; univariate
33. qualitative; bivariate **35a.** Responses are voluntary and there are sports that are not listed. **b.** no for the reasons listed in part (a) **37.** Response is voluntary and only those who like the scent are probably going to return the card. **45.** 40 **46.** 60 **47.** $a > 1$ **48.** $x \geq -3$
49. $b > 0.2$ **50.** 20 **51.** 42 **52.** 6

Lesson 12-6 pp. 750–756

Got It? 1a. 48 **b.** No; the tree diagram would be very large, so using the Multiplication Counting Principle

would be easier. **2.** 40,320 ways **3.** 20,160 **4.** 455 ways
Lesson Check 1. 5040 **2.** 6,227,020,800 **3.** 120
4. 5040 **5.** 10 **6.** 35 **7.** 24 outfits **8.** permutations
9. Permutations are used to count in situations where order is important. Combinations are used to count in situations where selection, not order, is important.
10. There is only one way to take n things, n at a time. Also, $_nC_n = \frac{n!}{n!0!} = \frac{n!}{n!} = \frac{1}{1} = 1$.
Exercises 11a. 8, 10 **b.** 8×10^6 or 8,000,000
13. 3,628,800 **15.** 1680 **17.** 5040 **19.** 42 **21.** 6
23. 90 **25.** 5040 ways **27.** 1 **29.** 9 **31.** 56 **33.** 28
35. 10 **37.** 220 ways **39.** 142,506 groups **41.** $_9P_7$
43. $_9P_6$ **45.** $_8C_5$ **47a.** 24 ways **b.** No; there is a limited number of ways that you can arrange the letters so someone can figure it out. **49.** 60 **51.** 210
53. Combination; the order of the books does not matter. **55a.** 35,152 call signs **b.** 913,952 call signs
57. 2 **59.** 4 **61.** 1 **70.** qualitative **71.** quantitative
73. quantitative **73.** qualitative **74.** 0.81, −6.81
75. 6.70, 0.30 **76.** 1.46, −5.46 **77.** −1, −1.67
78. 32% **79.** 9% **80.** 22.5% **81.** 18%

Lesson 12-7 pp. 757–762

Got It? 1. $\frac{5}{8}$ **2.** It will be $1 - \frac{20}{100 + x}$, where x is the number of other samples added. The probability will increase. **3.** 3 : 1 **4.** 98% **5.** about 34,995 light bulbs
Lesson Check 1. $\frac{1}{4}$ **2.** $\frac{1}{3}$ **3.** $\frac{3}{8}$ **4.** $\frac{1}{5}$ **5.** 1 : 5 **6.** 16%
7. Theoretical probability is based on the number of favorable outcomes when all of the outcomes are equally likely. Experimental probability is based on the results of an experiment. **8.** There are only two outcomes that are favorable, getting a 1 or a 2, therefore the probability is $\frac{2}{10}$ or $\frac{1}{5}$.
Exercises 11. 0 **13.** $\frac{1}{6}$ **15.** $\frac{1}{3}$ **17.** $\frac{1}{6}$ **19.** $\frac{1}{3}$ **21.** $\frac{1}{3}$
23. 5 : 1 **25.** 5 : 1 **27.** 1 : 5 **29.** 43% **31.** 85%
33. about 201 trees **35.** 98.4% **39.** 40% **41.** 25%
50. 840 **51.** 6 **52.** 30 **53.** 9 **54.** 5 **55.** {1, 4, 5, 6, 7, 10}
56. {4, 6} **57.** {0, 2, 4, 5, 6, 7, 8, 10} **58.** {4, 10}
59. {0, 1, 2, 4, 6, 7, 8, 10}

Lesson 12-8 pp. 764–770

Got It? 1a. $\frac{5}{6}$ **b.** $\frac{1}{2}$ **2.** $\frac{5}{225}$ **3.** $\frac{1}{4}$ **4.** $\frac{1}{55}$ **5a.** $\frac{5}{13}$ **b.** No; the numerators and the denominators are the same, so the product is the same.
Lesson Check 1a. $\frac{2}{5}$ **b.** $\frac{1}{5}$ **c.** 1 **d.** $\frac{4}{5}$ **2.** $\frac{1}{9}$ **3.** $\frac{2}{7}$
4. Answers may vary. Sample: find the probability of spinning a number less than 5 that is even. **5.** Mutually exclusive; answers may vary. Sample: The complement of being even on a number die is being odd, and even and odd are mutually exclusive. **7.** Because a tile can be both yellow and a letter, the formula should be
$P(\text{yellow or letter}) = P(\text{yellow}) + P(\text{letter}) - P(\text{yellow and letter}) = \frac{2}{5} + \frac{4}{5} - \frac{1}{5} = \frac{4}{5}$.

Exercises 9. $\frac{4}{5}$ **11.** $\frac{1}{2}$ **13.** $\frac{2}{5}$ **15.** $\frac{7}{10}$ **17.** $\frac{1}{4}$ **19.** $\frac{1}{6}$
21. $\frac{2}{81}$ **23.** $\frac{1}{9}$ **25.** $\frac{5}{27}$ **27.** $\frac{7}{36}$ **29.** $\frac{1}{30}$ **31.** $\frac{1}{12}$ **33.** 0
35. $\frac{2}{23}$ **37.** Dependent; the outcome of the first event affects the outcome of the second. **39.** For independent events, the outcome of the first event does not affect the outcome of the second event, while for dependent events, the outcome is affected. An example of two independent events is the rolling of two number cubes. An example of two dependent events is picking two cards from a deck without replacing the first one. **41.** about 4.7% **49.** $\frac{11}{51}$ **50.** $\frac{4}{17}$ **51.** $\frac{4}{7}$ **52.** $\frac{8}{21}$ **53.** −22
54. $\frac{a+5}{5(a-5)}$ **55.** $\frac{7y+1)}{7y+1}$

Chapter Review pp. 774–778

1. element **2.** frequency **3.** outlier **4.** quartile
5. $\begin{bmatrix} -12 & 7 \\ 4 & 6 \end{bmatrix}$ **6.** $\begin{bmatrix} 4.4 & 4.5 \\ 9.5 & -10.2 \\ 3.4 & -2.6 \end{bmatrix}$
7. $\begin{bmatrix} -12.6 & -4.62 \\ -12.6 & 8.4 \\ 4.2 & -12.18 \end{bmatrix}$

8. Customers

9. Workout Times

10. skewed
11. symmetric
12. 26.3, 26, 23 and 25 and 29, 9
13. 12.1, 12, 12, 2
14. 11.1, 11.3, 13.4; mean or median
15. 27

16. Movie Lengths (min)
100 110 120 130 140 150 160 170 180 190

17. Dog Weights (lb)
10 20 30 40 50 60 70 80 90

18. Book Lengths (Number of Pages)
140 180 220 260 300 340 380 420

19. B; the box in A is from about 90 to 110, where the box in B is from about 75 to 125. **20.** Systematic; good sample; do you plan on seeing more or fewer movies in the coming year? **21.** Stratified; good sample; who do you support for student council president? **22.** 15,120
23. 6 **24.** 336 **25.** 20 **26.** 360 **27.** 42 **28.** 28 **29.** 126
30. 10 **31.** 20 **32.** 35 **33.** 5 **34.** 10 **35.** 40,320 ways
36. 126 outfits **37.** $\frac{1}{5}$ **38.** $\frac{1}{2}$ **39.** $\frac{9}{10}$ **40.** $\frac{2}{5}$ **41.** 0 **42.** $\frac{1}{6}$
43. about 93.3% **44.** $\frac{1}{3}$ **45.** $\frac{1}{4}$ **46.** $\frac{5}{36}$ **47.** $\frac{1}{4}$
48. Dependent; the outcome of the first event affects the outcome of the second event. **49.** Independent; the outcome of the spinner does not affect the outcome of the pick.

Skills Handbook

p. 786 1. composite **3.** composite **5.** prime
7. composite **9.** prime **11.** composite **13.** 1, 2, 23, 46
15. 1, 11 **17.** 1, 3, 9, 27 **19.** $2 \cdot 3 \cdot 3$ **21.** $3 \cdot 3 \cdot 3$
23. $2 \cdot 2 \cdot 2 \cdot 2 \cdot 2$
p. 787 1. 2 **3.** 24 **5.** 80 **7.** 33
p. 788 1–11. Answers may vary. Samples are given.
1. \$350 **3.** \$300 **5.** \$17 **7.** 6.90 **9.** 7 **11.** \$30.80
p. 789 1. $\frac{1}{2}$ **3.** $\frac{5}{10}$ **5.** $\frac{4}{6}$ **7.** $\frac{9}{12}$ **9.** $\frac{6}{12}$ **11.** $\frac{15}{18}$
5. $\frac{10}{12}, \frac{15}{18}, \frac{20}{24}, \frac{25}{30}, \frac{30}{36}$ **7.** 9 **9.** 48 **11.** 2 **13.** yes **15.** no; $\frac{1}{2}$
17. yes **19.** $\frac{1}{2}$ **21.** $\frac{4}{5}$ **23.** $\frac{1}{10}$
p. 790 1. 0.3 **3.** 0.2 **5.** $0.7\overline{14285}$ **7.** $\frac{7}{100}$ **9.** $\frac{7}{8}$ **11.** $6\frac{1}{2}$
p. 791 1. $\frac{5}{9}$ **3.** $\frac{2}{5}$ **5.** $10\frac{5}{12}$ **7.** $6\frac{5}{8}$ **9.** $6\frac{7}{13}$ **11.** $9\frac{5}{8}$
13. $13\frac{7}{16}$ **15.** $\frac{1}{2}$ **17.** $1\frac{5}{9}$ **19.** $2\frac{7}{8}$ **21.** $3\frac{1}{3}$ **23.** $9\frac{4}{63}$
25. $2\frac{1}{8}$
p. 792 1. $\frac{9}{10}$ **3.** $8\frac{4}{5}$ **5.** $3\frac{1}{2}$ **7.** $25\frac{5}{6}$ **9.** $2\frac{4}{5}$ **11.** $\frac{1}{2}$
13. $\frac{1}{2}$ **15.** $1\frac{17}{24}$ **17.** $\frac{8}{9}$ **19.** $\frac{7}{24}$
p. 793 1. 56% **3.** 602% **5.** 820% **7.** 14.3% **9.** 11.1%
11. 75% **13.** 0.07 **15.** 0.009 **17.** 0.83 **19.** 0.15
21. 0.0003 **23.** 3.65 **25.** $\frac{19}{100}$ **27.** $4\frac{1}{2}$ **29.** $\frac{16}{25}$ **31.** $\frac{7}{25}$
33. $\frac{7}{800}$ **35.** $\frac{4}{5}$
p. 794 1. 6^4 **3.** $5 \cdot 2^4$ **5.** $4^2 \cdot 3^2 \cdot 2$ **7.** 64 **9.** 141
11. 3267 **13.** $(1 \cdot 10^3) + (2 \cdot 10^2) + (5 \cdot 10^1) \cdot (4 \cdot 10^0)$ **15.** $(8 \cdot 10^4) + (3 \cdot 10^3) + (4 \cdot 10^2) + (0 \cdot 10^1) + (1 \cdot 10^0)$
p. 795 1. 22 cm **3.** 24 cm² **5.** 216 cm³ **7.** 352 cm³

---

p. 796 1. **3.**

5. Gold Medals Won
0 1 2 3 4 5 6 7 8 9 10 11 12 13

The line plot shows that most of the countries won about 3 gold medals. The maximum number of gold medals that a country won was 13, and the minimum was 1.

p. 797 1. Highest Temperatures (°F)
March   June   August
Mason Barstow York Rexford Onham
Town

p. 798 1. Market Share
— Rap/Hip Hop
— Pop
2004 2005 2006 2007
Year

p. 799 1a. Transportation Mode
195 Bicycle   252 Walk   437 Bus   81 Car
b. 48%
c. 3 times

p. 800 1.
1	0 5 5 8
2	2 5 8
3	5 6
Key: 1 | 0 means 10

3.
76	1 8 8
77	1 6
78	5 5 8
Key: 76 | 1 means 761

5. Test Scores
Class A   Class B
8 6
8 2 | 7 | 5 9
5 3 1 | 8 | 1 2 7
8 4 | 9 | 0 1
| 10 | 0
Key: → 7 | 5 means 75
2 | 7 | 5 means 72

Additional Answers

Chapter 3

Lesson 3-2

Practice and Problem-Solving Exercises   page 174

13. $y > 13$

14. $v < 1$

15. $c < -4$

16. $f \geq 12$

17. $t \geq -3$

18. $s \leq 11$

19. $p > 12$

20. $x \leq -2$

21. $f > \frac{1}{3}$
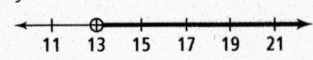

22. $z \leq 8$

23. $r < 0$

24. $y \geq 2.5$

25. $s < 4.7$
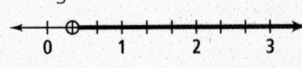

26. $n < -1.6$

27. $c < 1\frac{3}{7}$
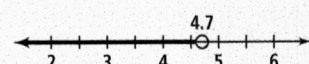

28. $p > 3$
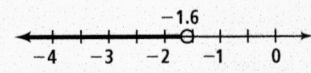

Lesson 3-3

Practice and Problem-Solving Exercises   page 181

7. $x \geq -10$

8. $w < 6$

9. $p < 32$

10. $y \leq -\frac{4}{5}$
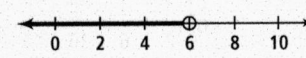

11. $v \leq -3$

12. $x > -9$

13. $x \geq -3$

14. $k < 12$

15. $m \leq 0$
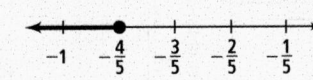

16. $b > -4$

17. $m < 2$

18. $y \geq 9$

19. $m \geq 2$

20. $t < -3$

21. $c > 6$

22. $w \geq -5$

23. $z > -3$

24. $d < -8$

25. $b \leq -\frac{1}{6}$
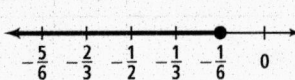

26. $y \leq -2\frac{3}{7}$
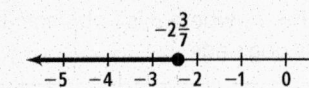

27. $h > -13$

28. $t \leq 8$

29. $q \leq 9$

30. $x < -11$

Lesson 3-5

Practice and Problem-Solving Exercises   page 197

19. { } or ∅, {a}, {e}, {i}, {o}, {a, e}, {a, i}, {a, o}, {e, i}, {e, o}, {i, o}, {a, e, i}, {a, e, o}, {a, i, o}, {e, i, o}, {a, e, i, o}

20. { } or ∅, {0}, {1}, {2}, {0, 1}, {0, 2}, {1, 2}, {0, 1, 2}

21. { } or ∅, {dog}, {cat}, {fish}, {dog, cat}, {dog, fish}, {cat, fish}, {dog, cat, fish}

22. { } or ∅, {−2}, {2}, {−2, 2}

Chapter 4

Get Ready! page 231

5.

Bob's and His Dog's Ages (years)										
Dog's Age	0	1	2	3	4	5	6	7	8	9
Bob's Age	9	10	11	12	13	14	15	16	17	18

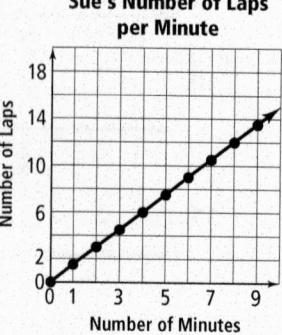

Bob's and His Dog's Ages

$B = 9 + d$, where B is Bob's age and d is his dog's age

6.

Sue's Number of Laps per Minute										
Number of Minutes	0	1	2	3	4	5	6	7	8	9
Number of Laps	0	1.5	3	4.5	6	7.5	9	10.5	12	13.5

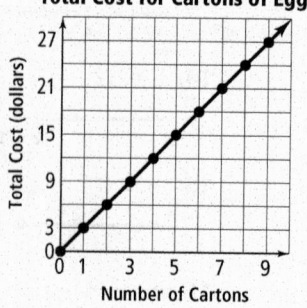

Sue's Number of Laps per Minute

$\ell = 1.5m$, where m is the number of minutes and ℓ is the number of laps.

7.

Total Cost for Cartons of Eggs										
Number of Cartons	0	1	2	3	4	5	6	7	8	9
Total Cost (dollars)	0	3	6	9	12	15	18	21	24	27

Total Cost for Cartons of Eggs

$C = 3n$, where C is the cost and n is the number of cartons.

8-11.

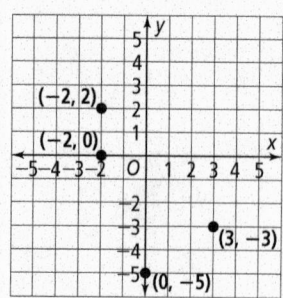

(−2, 2), (−2, 0), (3, −3), (0, −5)

Lesson 4-2

Practice and Problem-Solving Exercises page 243

6.

Number of Pentagons	1	2	3
Perimeter	5	8	11

Multiply the number of pentagons by 3 and add 2; $y = 3x + 2$.

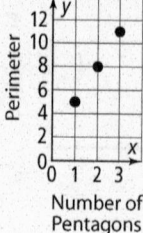

Number of Pentagons

7.

Number of Hexagons	1	2	3
Perimeter	6	10	14

Multiply the number of hexagons by 4 and add 2; $y = 4x + 2$.

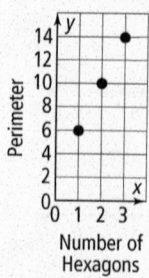

Number of Hexagons

8. Start with 5 and add 3 for each increase of 1 for x; $y = 3x + 5$.

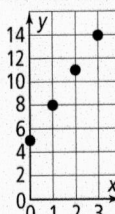

9. Start with -3 and add 5 for each increase of 1 for x; $y = 5x - 3$.

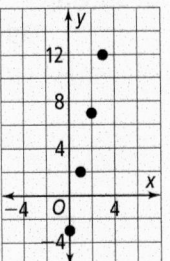

10. Start with 43 and subtract 11 for each increase of 1 for x; $y = -11x + 43$.

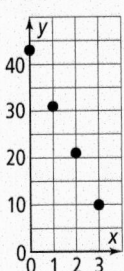

Lesson 4-4

Lesson Check   page 257

5. a.

n	h
0	18
1	19.5
2	21
3	22.5
4	24
5	25.5
6	27
7	28.5
8	30

b.

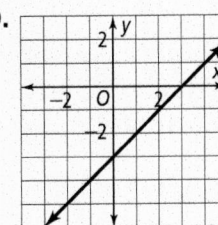

6. discrete

7. continuous

8. The graph should not be discrete; connect the points with a line so the graph is continuous.

Practice and Problem-Solving Exercises   page 257

9.

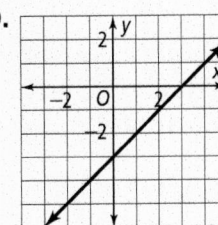

10.

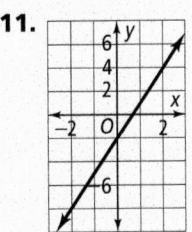

11.

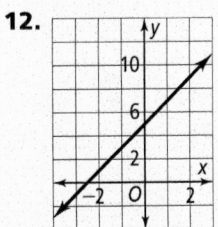

12.

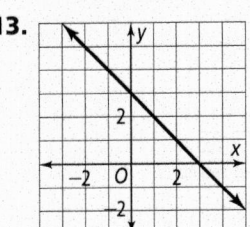

13.

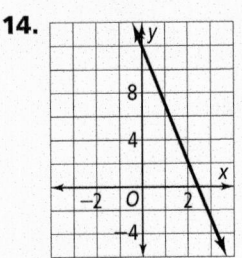

14.

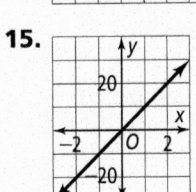

15.

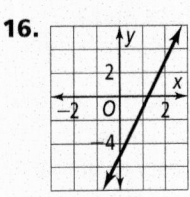

16.

17.

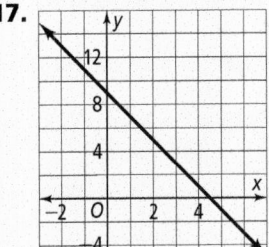

18.

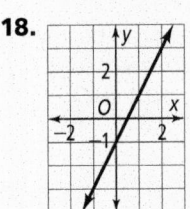

19.

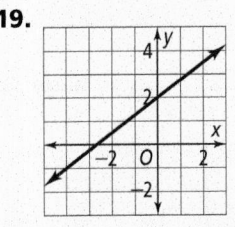

20.

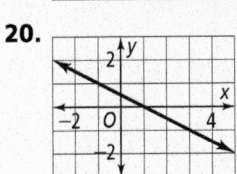

21.

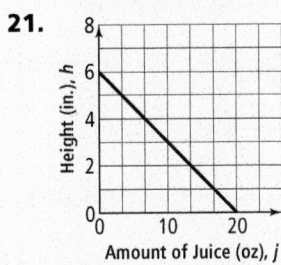

After you drink 20 oz of juice, the height is 0, so the interval $0 \leq j \leq 20$ makes sense. The height goes from $0 \leq h \leq 6$; continuous, because you can have juice in any amount.

22.

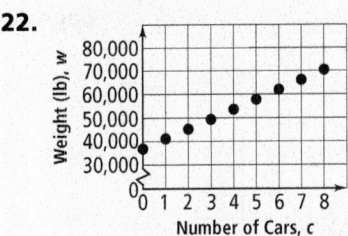

The truck can carry 8 cars, so the interval $0 \leq t \leq 8$ makes sense. The maximum weight is 70,600 lb, so an interval of $0 \leq w \leq 70,600$ makes sense. Discrete; the number of cars must be a whole number.

23.

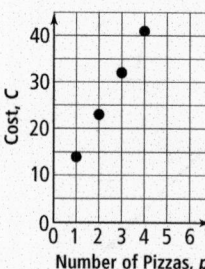

The number of pizzas can be any whole number except zero, so $0 < p$. 1 pizza costs $14, so $14 \leq C$.

Chapter 5

Lesson 5-5

Got It?   page 321

3. a.

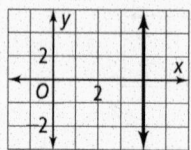

b.

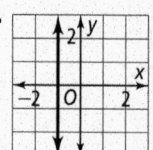

c.

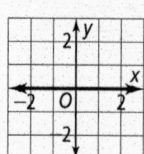

d.

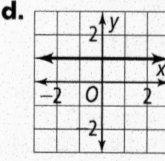

Practice and Problem-Solving Exercises   page 324

20.

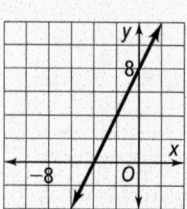

21.

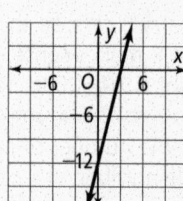

22.

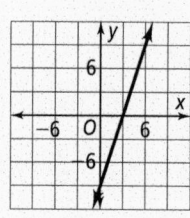

23. horizontal   **24.** vertical
25. horizontal   **26.** vertical

27.

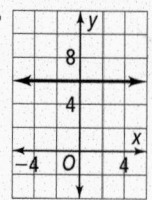

28.

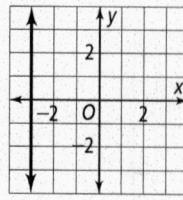

29.

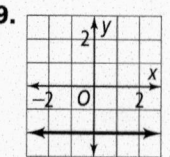

30.

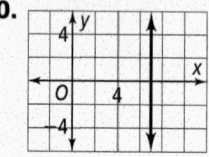

31. $2x - y = -5$ **32.** $4x - y = 7$
33. $2x + y = 10$ **34.** $x - 4y = 8$
35. $2x + 3y = -3$ **36.** $2x - 3y = -2$
37. $5j + 2s = 250$

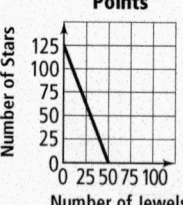

Points

Answers may vary. Sample: 50 jewels and 0 stars, 48 jewels and 5 stars, 42 jewels and 20 stars

38. $12t + 15s = 120$

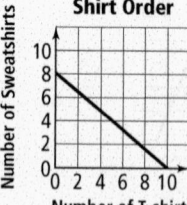

Shirt Order

Answers may vary. Sample: 10 T-shirts and 0 sweatshirts, 0 T-shirts and 8 sweatshirts, 5 T-shirts and 4 sweatshirts

39. When you have a slope and the y-intercept, use the slope-intercept form. When you have two points or a slope and a point, use the point-slope form. When you have the standard form, it is easy to graph.

40.

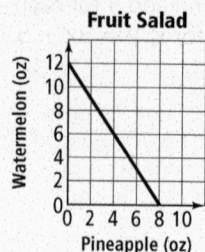

Fruit Salad

Lesson 5-8

Practice and Problem-Solving Exercises   page 345

6. It is a translation of $y = |x|$ up 3 units.

7. It is a translation of $y = |x|$ left 4 units.

8. It is a translation of $y = |x|$ down 4 units.

9.

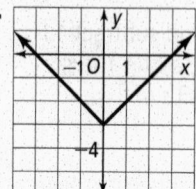

10.

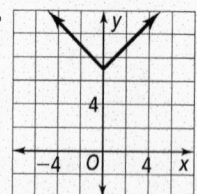

11.

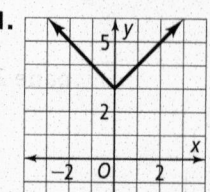

12.

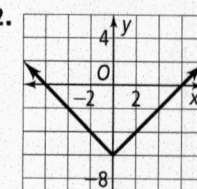

13.

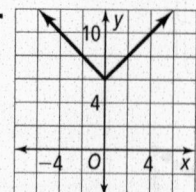

14.

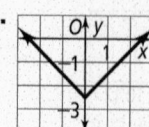

15. $y = |x| + 9$ **16.** $y = |x| - 7$
17. $y = |x| + 0.25$
18. $y = |x| - 3.25$
19. $y = |x| + 5.9$ **20.** $y = |x| - 1$

21. 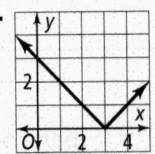　**22.**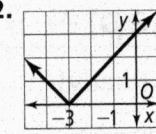

23.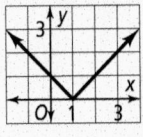

24.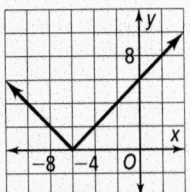

25. 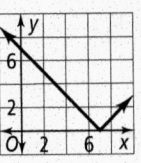　**26.**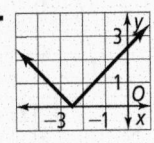

27. $y = |x + 9|$　**28.** $y = |x - 9|$
29. $y = |x - 0.5|$　**30.** $y = \left|x + \frac{3}{2}\right|$
31. $y = \left|x + \frac{5}{2}\right|$　**32.** $y = |x - 8.2|$

33. 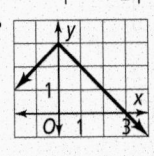　**34.**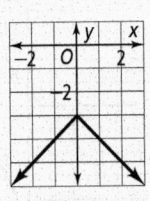

35. 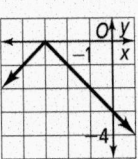　**36.**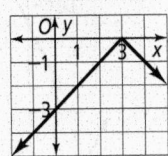

37. $y = -|x| + 2$
38. $y = -|x + 2.25|$
39. $y = -|x| - 15$
40. $y = -|x - 4|$
41. $y = |x| + k$ is a translation of $y = |x|$ up k units. $y = mx + b$ is a translation of $y = mx$ up b units.

42.

x	$y = |x|$	$y = |x| + 5$
−3	3	8
−2	2	7
−1	1	6
0	0	5
1	1	6
2	2	7
3	3	8

Each y-value of $y = |x| + 5$ is 5 more than the corresponding y-value of $y = |x|$.

Concept Byte Exercises　**page 347**

1a.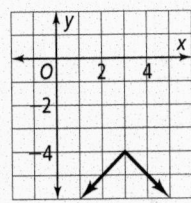

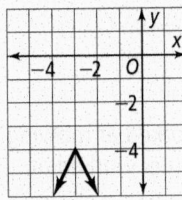

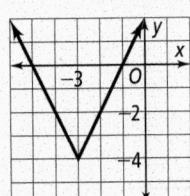

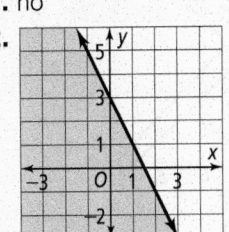

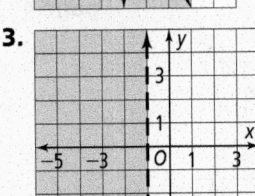

Chapter 6

Lesson 6-5

Lesson Check　**page 393**

1. no

2.

3.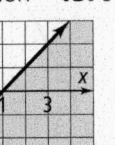

4. $y < \frac{1}{2}x - 1$

5. Answers will vary. Sample: The solutions of a linear equation and a linear inequality are coordinates of the points that make the equation or inequality true. The graph of a linear equation is a line, but the graph of a linear inequality is a region of the coordinate plane.

6. Since the inequality is already solved for y, the < symbol means you should shade below the boundary line. All of these shaded points will make the inequality true.

7. $y \geq 5x + 1$

Practice and Problem-Solving Exercises　**page 393**

8. not a solution　**9.** solution
10. solution　**11.** solution
12. not a solution　**13.** solution

14.

15.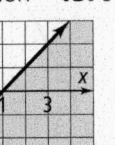

16.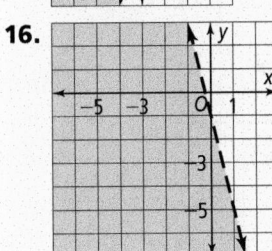

17.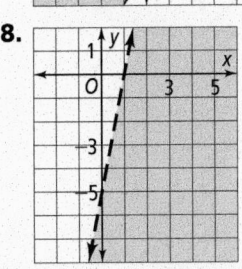

18.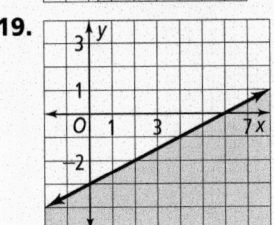

19.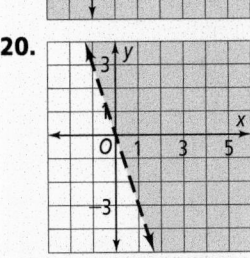

20.

21.

Lesson 6-6

Practice and Problem-Solving Exercises page 399

12.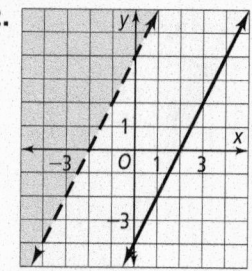

13.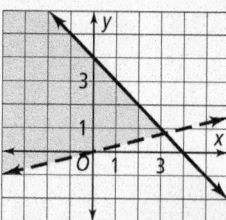

14.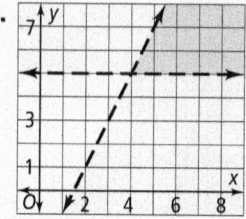

15.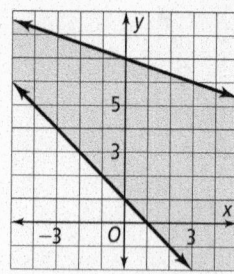

16.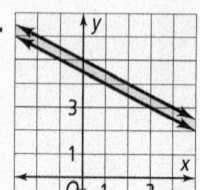

17.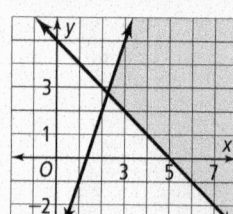

18.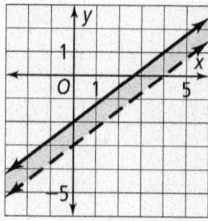

19.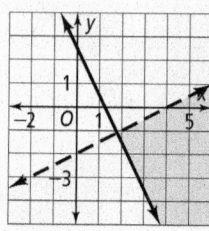

20.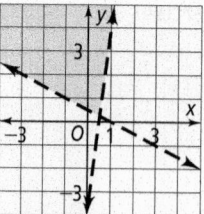

21.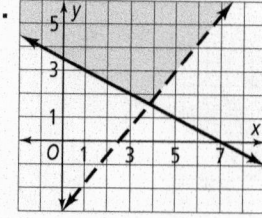

22. $y > 3x - 2$, $y \geq -2x + 2$

23. $y \leq x + 2$, $y < -\frac{1}{3}x$

24. $x < 1$, $y < -\frac{3}{2}x + 3$

25. $y \geq 2$, $y > x + 1$

26. Let x = hours worked at mowing lawns, let y = hours worked at clothing store.

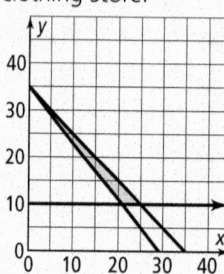

27. Let x = hours driven by slower driver, let y = hours driven by faster driver.

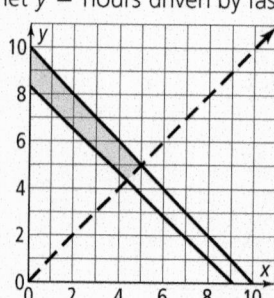

Exercises page 402

12.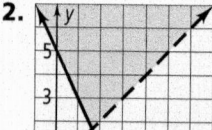

13.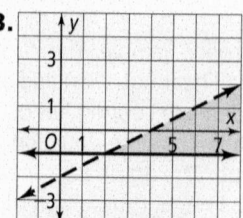

14.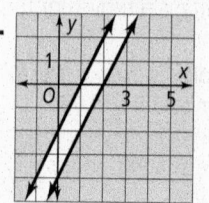

Chapter 9

Get Ready!

Get Ready! page 531

7.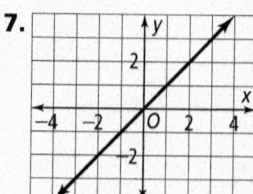

8.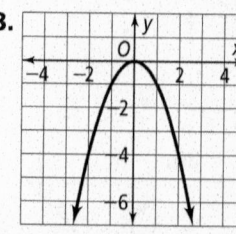

9.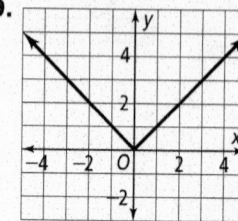

10.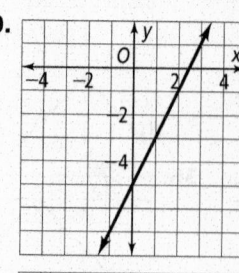

11.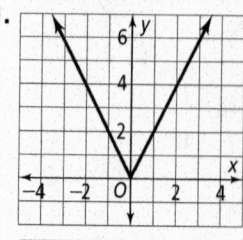

12.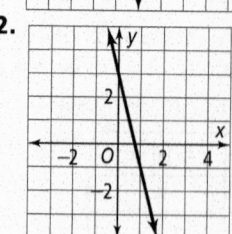

Chapter 10

Lesson 10-5

Lesson Check page 622

2.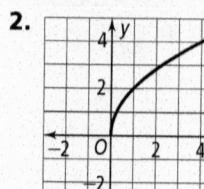

3.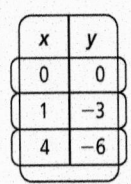

4. No; there is no variable in the radicand.

5. The graph of $y = \sqrt{x - 1}$ is the graph of $y = \sqrt{x}$ shifted to the right 1 unit.

6. Yes; the domain includes all the values of x such that the radicand has a value greater than or equal to zero, so for $b > 0$, the domain of $y = \sqrt{x + b}$ is $x \geq -b$, which includes negative values.

Practice and Problem-Solving Exercises   page 623

21.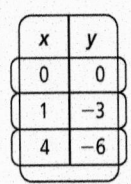

22.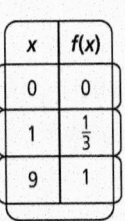

23.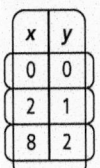

24.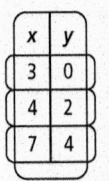

25.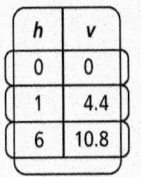
$h > 5.1$ m

26. D   **27.** A   **28.** C   **29.** B

30. 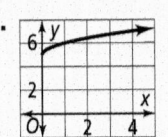   **31.**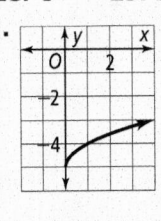

32. 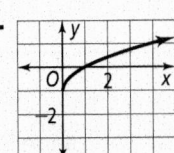   **33.**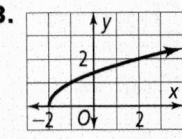

34.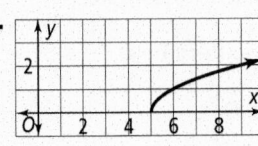

35.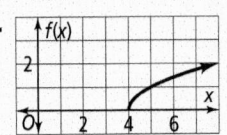

36. 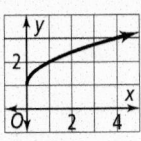   **37.**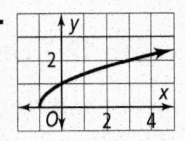

38.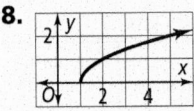

39. $x \geq 4$; $y \geq 0$ **40.** $x \leq 4$; $y \geq 0$

Chapter 11

Lesson 11-7

Practice and Problem-Solving Exercises   page 692

14. $x = 0$, $y = 2$ **15.** $x = 0$, $y = 0$

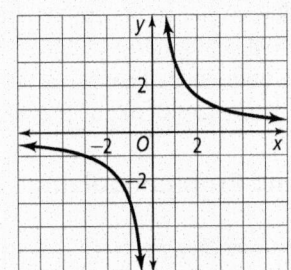

16. $x = 0$, $y = 0$

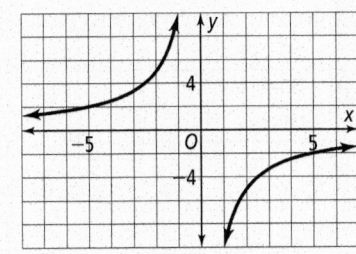

17. $x = 5$, $y = 0$

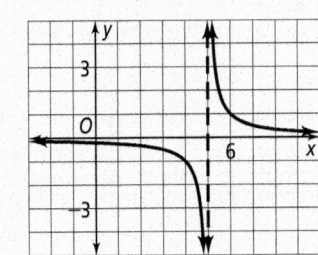

18. $x = -4$, $y = 0$

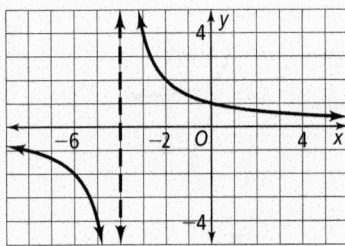

19. $x = 0$, $y = -5$

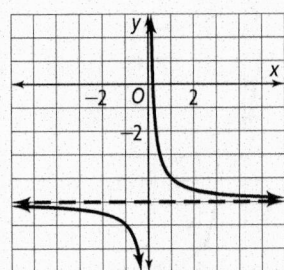

20. $x = 0$, $y = 6$

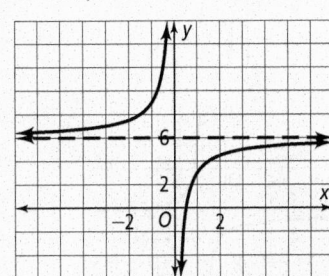

21. $x = -1$, $y = 4$

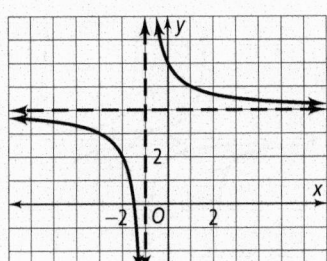

22. $x = 3$, $y = -5$

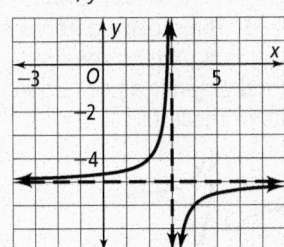

23. a. $C = \frac{1920}{n} + 100$

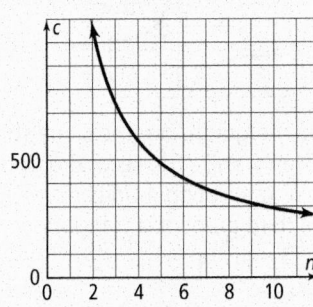

b. 5 people

Exercises   page 695

5.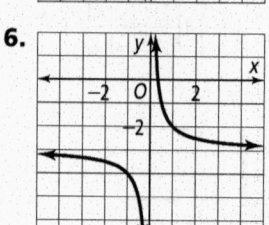

6.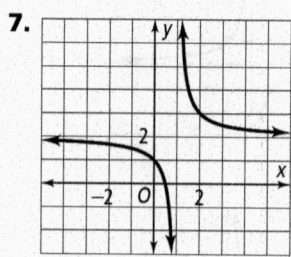

7.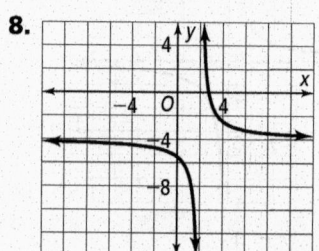

8.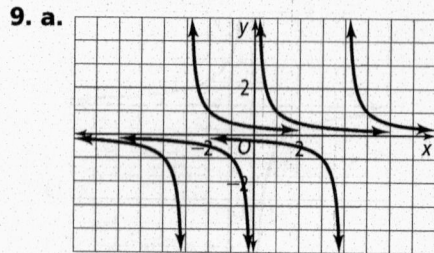

9. a.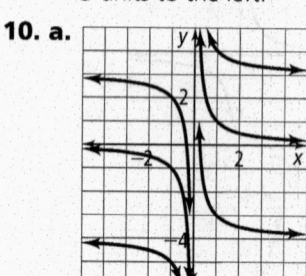

b. The graphs are the same shape as $y = \frac{1}{x}$. The second graph is a translation 4 units to the right. The third graph is a translation 3 units to the left.

10. a.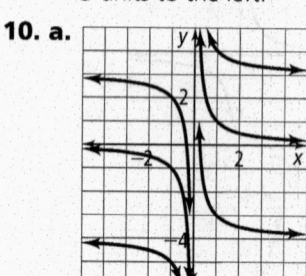

b. The graphs are the same shape as $y = \frac{1}{x}$. The second graph is a translation 4 units down. The third graph is a translation 3 units up.

Chapter 12

Lesson 12-2

Got It   page 721

2. Answers may vary. Sample:

Finishing Times

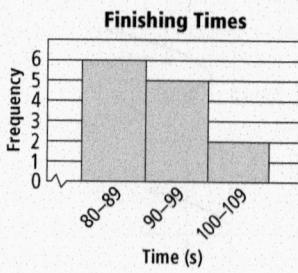

Lesson 12-2 Lesson Chack

Practice and Problem-Solving Exercises   page 692

3.

Battery Life

Hours	Frequency	Cumulative Frequency
9–12	7	7
13–16	2	9
17–20	1	10
21–24	2	12

4. The store owner could look at the frequency column to pick out the busiest hours.

5. A symmetric histogram has roughly the same shape if you fold it down the middle. A skewed histogram has a peak that is not in the center.

6. Add the frequency of each interval to the frequencies of all the previous intervals.

Practice and Problem-Solving Exercises

7. Answers may vary. Sample:

Wing Spans

Number of Centimeters	Frequency
125–134	5
135–144	4
145–154	4

8. Answers may vary. Sample:

Marathon Times

Minutes	Frequency
130–149	1
150–169	2
170–189	2
190–209	3
210–229	2
230–249	2

9. Answers may vary. Sample:

Top Speeds

Miles per Hour	Frequency
90–109	4
110–129	4
130–149	2
150–169	3

10. Answers may vary. Sample:

Costs of Items

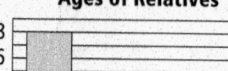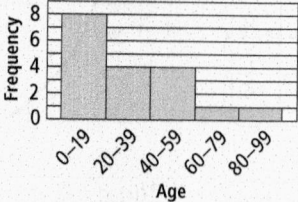

11. Answers may vary. Sample:

Ages of Relatives

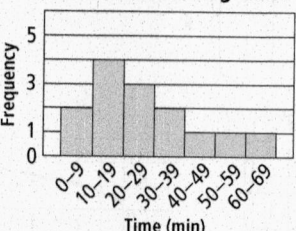

12. Answers may vary. Sample:

Restaurant Waiting Times

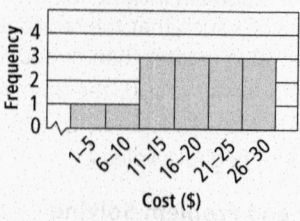

13. Answers may vary. Sample:

Points Per Game

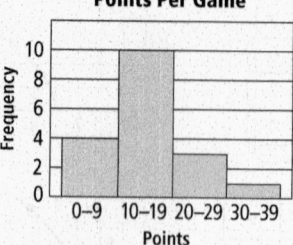

14. skewed

15. symmetric

16. uniform

17. skewed

Index

A

absolute value, 31, 71

absolute value equations
graphing, 207–208
with no solution, 208–209
solving, 207–208

absolute value functions
defined, 342, 352
graphing, 342
parent, 342
vertex of, 346

absolute value inequalities
graphing, 209–210
solving, 209–210

absolute value parent function, 342

absolute value symbol, 31

Activities, Games, and Puzzles
worksheets, 9B, 15B, 22B, 28B,
36B, 44B, 52B, 58B, 66B, 87B,
93B, 100B, 108B, 114B, 123B,
129B, 136B, 143B, 150B, 170B,
177B, 183B, 192B, 199B, 206B,
214B, 220B, 239B, 245B, 251B,
259B, 267B, 273B, 279B, 298B,
304B, 312B, 318B, 326B, 332B,
340B, 346B, 365B, 373B, 380B,
388B, 395B, 401B, 419B, 425B,
431B, 438B, 446B, 452B, 461B,
479B, 484B, 491B, 497B, 505B,
510B, 516B, 521B, 540B, 546B,
553B, 559B, 566B, 573B, 580B,
587B, 598B, 606B, 612B, 619B,
625B, 633B, 604B, 610B, 618B,
625B, 631B, 639B, 657B, 664B,
671B, 677B, 685B, 692B, 700B

Activity. *See also* Extension; Technology
Always, Sometimes, Never, 37
Characteristics of Absolute Value
Graphs, 347
Closure, 45
Collecting Linear Data, 341
Collecting Quadratic Data, 547
Conditional Probability, 771
Conducting Simulations, 763
Designing Your Own Survey, 740
Distance and Midpoint Formulas, 605
Dividing Polynomials Using Algebra
Tiles, 665
Dynamic. *See* Dynamic Activity
Finding Perimeter, Area, and Volume,
115–116
Finding Roots, 554
Geometric Sequences, 453–454
Graphing Functions and Solving
Equations, 260–261
Graphing Linear Equations, 402

Graphing Rational Functions, 701
Investigating $y = mx + b$, 305
Matrices and Solving Systems,
381–382
Misleading Graphs and Statistics, 748
Modeling Equations With Variables on
Both Sides, 101
Modeling Multi-Step Inequalities, 185
Modeling One-Step Equations, 80
More Algebraic Properties, 184
Performing Regressions, 581
Powers of Powers and Powers of
Products, 432
Right Triangle Ratios, 632
Solving Systems Using Algebra Tiles,
367
Solving Systems Using Tables and
Graphs, 366
Standard Deviation, 733
Using Models to Factor, 499
Using Models to Multiply, 485
Using Tables to Solve Equations, 59

ACT test prep. *See* Cumulative Test Prep;
End-of-Course Assessment; Gridded
Response; Multiple Choice;
Standardized Test Prep

addend, 23

Adding and Subtracting Fractions, 791

addition
of decimals, 24
of fractions, 31, 791
involving measures of central tendency,
729
of matrices, 715
of numbers with different signs, 31
of numbers with same sign, 31
of polynomials, 475, 476
properties of. *See* property(ies)
of rational expressions, 672, 673
of real numbers, 30–31, 33
solving equations using, 80, 82
solving inequalities using, 171, 172
solving systems of linear equations
using, 374

Additional Problems, 6, 12, 18, 25, 32,
40, 48, 55, 63, 84, 90, 96, 104,
111, 120, 126, 132, 139, 146, 166,
173, 180, 188, 196, 202, 209, 216,
236, 242, 248, 255, 264, 270, 276,
294, 301, 308, 315, 322, 329, 335,
344, 362, 370, 376, 385, 392, 398,
416, 422, 428, 435, 442, 449, 457,
472, 482, 488, 494, 502, 508, 513,
519, 536, 543, 550, 557, 563, 569,
576, 584, 596, 602, 609, 616, 622,
629, 602, 608, 615, 622, 628, 635,
654, 660, 668, 674, 681, 688, 695

Addition Property
of Equality, 81, 153
of Inequality, 171

additive inverse, 32

algebraic expressions
defined, 4, 69
dividing, 441
evaluating, 12
multiplying powers in, 427
simplifying, 48–49
writing, 4–5

algebra tiles
modeling equations, 80, 101
modeling factoring, 499
modeling multiplication, 485
modeling multi-step inequalities, 185
modeling quadratic equations, 561
solving systems, 367

alpha key, of graphing calculator, 402

Always, Sometimes, Never, 37

analysis
of data, 713, 773, 774
of errors. *See* Error Analysis exercises
of graphs, 234

and, **compound inequalities**
containing, 200, 201, 217–218

angle of depression, 636

angle of elevation, 636

applications
admissions, 451
ages, 62
agriculture, 332, 373, 736
aircraft, 436
airports, 387
air travel, 65, 169, 705
allowance, 223
antennas, 22
apples, 778
aquarium, 550
aquarium fish, 182
architecture, 106, 119, 135, 154, 330,
616, 638
arithmetic sequences, 298
athletics, 245, 729
auto loans, 663
automobiles, 467
aviation, 265, 638
bakery, 128
baking, 265, 285
banking, 12, 177, 212, 364, 467, 579,
656
baseball, 113, 720, 752
basketball, 57, 183, 211, 738, 749, 776
beverages, 257
bicycle sales, 57
bicycling, 157, 319, 690

667, 668, 672, 673, 674, 675, 680, 681, 682, 687, 688, 689, 690, 693, 694, 696, 715, 716, 720, 721, 722, 727, 728, 729, 735, 736, 737, 742, 743, 744, 751, 752, 753, 758, 759, 760, 765, 766, 767, 768
Mid-Chapter Quiz, 29, 117, 193, 252, 319, 389, 439, 498, 560, 619, 678, 749
Mixed Review, 9, 15, 22, 28, 36, 44, 52, 58, 66, 87, 93, 100, 108, 114, 123, 129, 136, 143, 150, 170, 177, 183, 192, 199, 206, 213, 220, 239, 245, 251, 259, 267, 273, 279, 298, 304, 312, 318, 326, 332, 340, 346, 365, 373, 380, 388, 395, 401, 419, 425, 431, 438, 446, 452, 461, 479, 484, 491, 497, 505, 510, 516, 521, 540, 546, 553, 559, 566, 573, 580, 587, 604, 612, 618, 625, 631, 639, 657, 664, 671, 677, 685, 692, 700, 719, 725, 732, 739, 747, 756, 762, 770
Open-Ended exercises, 9, 14, 21, 43, 52, 56, 57, 66, 86, 100, 108, 114, 128, 141, 142, 149, 157, 167, 169, 176, 183, 191, 198, 212, 227, 238, 250, 252, 261, 265, 272, 278, 279, 295, 297, 311, 317, 326, 330, 331, 338, 353, 364, 379, 387, 389, 400, 407, 419, 430, 436, 443, 445, 461, 467, 490, 496, 498, 509, 515, 516, 520, 527, 545, 552, 553, 558, 560, 565, 579, 585, 590, 593, 611, 619, 624, 642, 645, 656, 663, 670, 676, 683, 699, 707, 717, 738, 749, 760, 761, 768, 769, 779
Quick Review, 69–72, 153–156, 223–226, 282–284, 350–352, 405–406, 464–466, 524–526, 590–592, 642–644, 704–706, 775–778
Standardized Test Prep, 9, 15, 22, 28, 36, 44, 52, 58, 66, 87, 93, 100, 108, 114, 123, 129, 136, 143, 150, 87, 93, 100, 108, 114, 123, 129, 136, 143, 150, 170, 177, 183, 192, 199, 206, 213, 220, 228–230, 239, 245, 251, 259, 267, 273, 279, 286–288, 298, 304, 312, 318, 326, 332, 340, 346, 354–356, 365, 373, 380, 388, 395, 401, 408–410, 419, 425, 431, 438, 446, 452, 461, 419, 425, 431, 438, 446, 452, 461, 468–470, 479, 484, 491, 497, 505, 510, 516, 521, 528–530, 540, 546, 553, 559, 566, 573, 580, 587, 604, 612, 618, 625, 631, 639, 657, 664, 671, 677, 685, 692, 700, 719, 725, 732, 739, 747, 756, 762, 770

***Assignment Guides*, 8, 14, 21, 27, 34, 43, 50, 57, 65, 86, 92, 98, 106, 113, 122, 128, 134, 142, 149, 168, 175, 182, 190, 198, 205, 211, 219, 238, 244, 250, 258, 265, 272, 278, 296, 303, 310, 317, 324, 331, 338, 345, 364, 372, 378, 387, 394, 399, 418, 424, 430, 437, 444, 451, 459, 476, 483, 490, 496, 504, 509, 515, 520, 538, 545, 551, 558, 565, 572, 586, 597, 605, 611, 618, 623, 632, 603, 611, 617, 624, 629, 638, 656, 662, 670, 676, 684, 691, 699**

Associative Property
of Addition, 23
of Multiplication, 23

astronomy, 156, 429, 439, 444, 446, 758

asymptote
defined, 694, 706
horizontal, 695
identifying, 695
vertical, 694–695

***Auditory Learners*, 47**

average, 726. *See also* mean

axes, 60, 234

axis of symmetry, 534, 590

B

Bar Graphs, 797

base
defined, 10
of exponent, 427
finding, 139
multiplying powers with same, 426

best fit, line of. *See* line of best fit

bias
defined, 743, 777
in samples, 744
in survey questions, 743

Big Ideas
Data Collection and Analysis, 713, 773, 774
Data Representation, 713, 773, 774
Equivalence, 79, 151, 152, 163, 221, 222, 413, 462, 463, 473, 522, 523, 599, 640, 641, 651, 702, 703
Functions, 233, 280, 281, 291, 348, 349, 413, 462, 533, 588, 589, 599, 640, 641, 651, 702, 703
Modeling, 233, 280, 281, 291, 348, 349, 359, 403, 404, 533, 588, 589
Probability, 713, 773, 774
Properties, 3, 67, 68, 413, 462, 463, 522, 523
Proportionality, 79, 151, 152, 291, 348, 349
Solving Equations and Inequalities, 79, 151, 152, 163, 221, 359, 403, 404, 533, 588, 589, 599, 640, 641, 651, 702, 703
Variable, 3, 67, 68, 163, 221, 222

***Big Ideas*, 3A, 79A, 163A, 233A, 291A, 359A, 413A, 473A, 533A, 593A, 599A, 651A**

binomials
dividing polynomials by, 667
modeling multiplication of, 485
multiplying, 486, 487
squaring, 492–493

biology, 17, 84, 111, 128, 191, 212, 335, 361, 421, 429, 466, 615, 616

bivariate, 742

***Block Scheduling, See* Pacing Assignment**

box-and-whisker plot
defined, 735, 776
interpreting, 736
making, 736

braces, 17, 194

brackets, 11, 203

break-even point, 384

C

calc key, of graphing calculator, 261, 336, 366, 543, 554, 581, 584

calculator, 663. *See also* graphing calculator
degree mode, 634
equations in slope-intercept form, 305
exercises that use, 451, 460, 539, 544, 637
histograms, 721
linear inequalities, 402
line of best fit, 336
permutations, 752
rational functions, 695, 696, 701
regressions, 581
roots, 554
scientific notation, 420
systems of quadratic equations, 584
trigonometric ratios, 634
vertical motion model, 543

cards, 45

causation, 337

Challenge exercises, 9, 15, 22, 28, 36, 44, 52, 58, 66, 87, 93, 100, 108, 114, 123, 129, 136, 143, 150, 170, 177, 183, 192, 199, 206, 213, 220, 239, 245, 251, 259, 267, 273, 279, 298, 304, 311, 317, 325, 332, 340, 365, 373, 379, 388, 394, 400, 419, 431, 438, 452, 479, 484, 491, 497, 505, 510, 516, 521, 540, 546, 553, 559, 566, 573, 580, 586, 604, 612, 618, 625, 630, 639, 656, 664, 671, 677, 684, 700, 719, 725, 732, 739, 747, 756, 762, 770

H

half-plane, 391

Here's Why It Works

deriving the quadratic formula by completing the square for $ax^2 + bx + c = 0$, 568

equivalency of dividing by a fraction and multiplying by the fraction's reciprocal, 41

reversing the inequality symbol when multiplying or dividing an inequality by a negative number, 179

using repeated multiplication to rewrite a product of powers, 427

using the definition of slope to derive point-slope form, given a point on a line and the line's slope, 314

using the Multiplication Property of Equality to prove the Cross Products Property, 125

histograms

defined, 721, 775

describing, 721

interpreting, 722

making, 721

skewed, 721

symmetric, 721

uniform, 721

history, 43, 603, 617

of math, 266

Homework Quick Check, 8, 14, 21, 27, 34, 43, 50, 57, 65, 86, 92, 98, 106, 113, 122, 128, 134, 142, 149, 168, 175, 182, 190, 198, 205, 211, 219, 238, 244, 250, 258, 265, 272, 278, 296, 303, 310, 317, 324, 331, 338, 345, 364, 372, 378, 387, 394, 399, 418, 424, 430, 437, 444, 451, 459, 478, 483, 490, 496, 504, 509, 515, 520, 538, 545, 551, 558, 565, 572, 597, 605, 611, 618, 623, 632, 603, 611, 617, 624, 629, 638, 656, 662, 670, 676, 684, 691, 699

horizontal asymptote, 695

horizontal lines, 294, 321, 328, 391

horizontal translations, 344

hypotenuse

defined, 600

finding length of, 601

hypothesis, 601

I

identity, 104, 154

Identity Property

of Addition, 24

of Multiplication, 24, 25

if-then **statement,** 601

inclusive, 200

inconsistent systems of linear equations, 361–362

increase, percent, 145

independent events, 765–766, 778

independent systems of linear equations, 361–362

independent variables, 240, 241, 249, 255, 292, 448

indirect measurement, 131

INDPNT feature, of graphing calculator, 554

inductive reasoning, 63

INEQUAL feature, of graphing calculator, 402

inequality(ies). *See also* solving inequalities

absolute value, 209–210

comparing real numbers using, 19

compound, 200–204, 217–218

defined, 19, 164

equivalent, 171

graphing, 167

graphs of, 165, 166, 172–173, 179, 181, 200–204, 209–210, 396

linear. *See* linear inequalities

multiple ways of representing, 167

multi-step, 185, 186–189

solution as union or intersection of sets, 218

solving using Addition Property of Inequality, 171, 172

solving using Division Property of Inequality, 180–181

solving using Multiplication Property of Inequality, 178–179

solving using Subtraction Property of Inequality, 173

with special solutions, 189

symbols for, 19, 166, 173

Triangle Inequality Theorem, 205

with variables on both sides, 188

writing, 164, 187, 201–203, 218

writing from a graph, 166

inequality, properties of. *See* property(ies)

input, 240

input value, 282

integers

square of, 17

in standard form, 322

as subset of rational numbers, 18

Interactive Learning, 4, 10, 16, 23, 30, 38, 46, 53, 61, 81, 88, 94, 102, 109, 118, 124, 130, 137, 144, 164, 171, 178, 186, 194, 200, 207, 214, 234, 240, 246, 253, 262, 268, 274, 292, 299, 306, 313, 320, 327, 333, 342, 360, 368, 374, 383, 390, 396, 414, 420, 426, 433, 440, 447, 455, 474, 480, 486, 492, 500, 506, 511, 517, 534, 541, 548, 555, 561, 567, 574, 582, 594, 600, 607, 614, 620, 627, 600, 606, 613, 620, 626, 633, 652, 658, 668, 672, 679, 686, 693

intercepts. *See x*-intercept; *y*-intercept

interdisciplinary

art, 143, 372, 483, 520, 527, 564, 608

astronomy, 156, 429, 439, 444, 446, 758

biology, 17, 84, 111, 128, 191, 212, 335, 361, 421, 429, 466, 615, 616

chemistry, 35, 205, 206, 387, 407, 428, 430, 617, 684

earth science, 93

economics, 142, 425, 456

geography, 142, 422, 438

geometry, 14, 15, 21, 51, 92, 99, 107, 113, 117, 143, 149, 150, 176, 187, 190, 192, 258, 264, 279, 302, 317, 325, 332, 371, 372, 379, 389, 400, 430, 437, 439, 445, 478, 484, 490, 495, 498, 502, 507, 519, 521, 525, 526, 527, 552, 553, 558, 566, 586, 590, 593, 604, 612, 618, 623, 624, 642, 643, 645, 655, 664, 667, 670, 678, 704, 707, 762

government, 175

history, 43, 603, 617

language, 86

music, 71, 85, 126, 127, 466, 724, 749, 752

physical science, 421

physics, 169, 205, 271, 304, 309, 424, 425, 445, 458, 539, 552, 604, 629, 687, 692, 699, 706

reading, 56, 269, 754

science, 113, 133

statistics, 128

U.S. history, 86

interest

compound, 139, 456, 457

simple, 139, 140

interpolation, 334, 352

interquartile range, 734

INTERSECT feature, of graphing calculator, 261, 366, 584

intersection

defined, 215, 226

point, of system of linear equations, 360

symbol for, 215

interval notation, 203

inverse

additive, 32

multiplicative, 40

of a relation, 273

Index

Performing Regressions, 581
Solving Systems Using Tables and Graphs, 366
Using Tables to Solve Equations, 59

temperature
finding, 211, 212
formula for converting, 110, 191

terms
of arithmetic sequences, 274, 275–276
constant. *See* constant
defined, 48
in geometric sequences, 453
like, 48, 49, 71, 94
reordering in polynomial division, 668

test-taking strategies, 73, 158, 228, 286, 354, 408, 468, 528, 594, 646, 708

Texas Instrument^{TM} activities, 3D, 79D, 163D, 233D, 291D, 359D, 413D, 473D, 533D, 593D, 599D, 651D

theorems
Pythagorean, 600
Triangle Inequality, 205

theoretical probability
defined, 757, 778
finding, 758

Think About a Plan exercises, 8, 14, 21, 27, 35, 43, 51, 57, 65, 86, 92, 99, 107, 113, 128, 135, 142, 149, 169, 176, 182, 190, 198, 205, 211, 219, 238, 244, 251, 258, 266, 272, 278, 297, 303, 311, 317, 324, 332, 339, 346, 364, 372, 378, 387, 394, 400, 418, 424, 430, 437, 444, 451, 460, 478, 483, 490, 496, 504, 509, 515, 520, 539, 545, 551, 558, 565, 572, 579, 586, 603, 611, 617, 624, 630, 638, 656, 663, 670, 676, 684, 691, 699, 718, 724, 731, 738, 745, 755, 761, 769

Think About a Plan worksheets, 9B, 15B, 22B, 28B, 36B, 44B, 52B, 58B, 66B, 87B, 93B, 100B, 108B, 114B, 123B, 129B, 136B, 143B, 150B, 170B, 177B, 183B, 192B, 199B, 206B, 214B, 220B, 239B, 245B, 251B, 259B, 267B, 273B, 279B, 298B, 304B, 312B, 318B, 326B, 332B, 340B, 346B, 365B, 373B, 380B, 388B, 395B, 401B, 419B, 425B, 431B, 438B, 446B, 452B, 461B, 479B, 484B, 491B, 497B, 505B, 510B, 516B, 521B, 540B, 546B, 553B, 559B, 566B, 573B, 580B, 587B, 598B, 606B, 612B, 619B, 625B, 633B, 604B, 610B, 618B, 625B, 631B, 639B, 657B, 664B, 671B, 677B, 685B, 692B, 700B

Think-Write problems, 41, 82, 140, 166, 172, 179, 209, 294, 315, 415, 421, 422, 423, 434, 435, 437, 441, 442, 448, 449, 456, 457, 458, 481, 494, 508, 513, 549, 571, 627, 653, 660, 694

time. *See* distance-rate-time problems

Tips for Success, 73, 158, 228, 286, 354, 408, 468, 528, 594, 646, 708

trace key, of graphing calculator, 696, 701

Transitive Property
of Equality. *See* property(ies)
of Inequality. *See* property(ies)

translations
defined, 342, 352
graphing, 343, 344, 628
horizontal, 344, 628
vertical, 343, 628

tree diagrams, 772

trend. *See* correlation

trend line, 334, 335

triangle(s)
area of, 110, 192, 258
inequality in, 205
isosceles right, 258
length of side of, 190

Triangle Inequality Theorem, 205

trigonometric ratios
cosine, 633
defined, 633
finding, 634–635
in right triangles, 633
sine, 633
tangent, 633

trinomials
factoring, 500–502, 506–508, 511–514
of the form $ax^2 + bx + c$, 506–508
of the form $x^2 + bx + c$, 500–502
multiplying a binomial by, 489
multiplying a monomial by, 480
perfect-square, 511
in rational expressions, 653, 659
with two variables, 502

try, check, revise, 442

two-step equations, 88–90

U

Understanding by Design, 2, 78, 162, 232, 290, 358, 412, 472, 523, 592, 598, 650

uniform histogram, 721

union, of two sets, 214–215, 216–218

unit analysis, 119

unit rates, 118, 119

units, 119, 120

univariate, 742

universal set, 196

unlike radicals, 613

U.S. history, 86

using diagrams, 483

Using Estimation, 788

Using Models to Factor, 499

Using Models to Multiply, 485

Using Tables to Solve Equations, 59

V

Variable, as Big Idea, 3, 67, 68, 163, 221, 222

variable(s)
on both sides of an equation, 102–104
in data sets, 742
defined, 4, 69
dependent, 240
in direct variation equations, 299–300, 301
eliminating, 377
in equations, 53–55, 61–62, 101, 102–104
independent, 240, 241, 249, 255, 292
in like terms, 48
in linear equations, 306
in linear inequalities, 390–393
substituting numbers for, 12

Venn diagram
of disjoint sets, 215
drawing, 216, 217
of intersection of sets, 216–217
of sets, 196, 215–217
of union of two sets, 214, 215

vertex of a parabola, 535, 590

vertical asymptote, 694–695

vertical lines, 294, 321, 327, 328, 391

vertical line test, 269

vertical motion model, 543–544
applying, 591, 593

vertical translations, 343

Visual Learners, See also Math Background, Performance Task, Summative Questions, 18, 19, 31, 33, 39, 101, 130, 165, 180, 187, 195, 208, 215, 216, 218, 236, 241, 242, 253, 308, 328, 337, 344, 393, 397, 422, 427, 481, 487, 493, 495,

Index

Acknowledgments

Staff Credits

The people who made up the High School Mathematics team—representing composition services, core design digital and multimedia production services, digital product development, editorial, editorial services, manufacturing, marketing, and production management—are listed below.

Dan Anderson, Scott Andrews, Christopher Anton, Carolyn Artin, Michael Avidon, Margaret Banker, Charlie Bink, Niki Birbilis, Suzanne Biron, Beth Blumberg, Kyla Brown, Rebekah Brown, Judith Buice, Sylvia Bullock, Stacie Cartwright, Carolyn Chappo, Christia Clarke, Tom Columbus, Andrew Coppola, AnnMarie Coyne, Bob Craton, Nicholas Cronin, Patrick Culleton, Damaris Curran, Steven Cushing, Sheila DeFazio, Cathie Dillender, Emily Dumas, Patty Fagan, Frederick Fellows, Jorgensen Fernandez, Mandy Figueroa, Suzanne Finn, Sara Freund, Matt Frueh, Jon Fuhrer, Andy Gaus, Mark Geyer, Mircea Goia, Andrew Gorlin, Shelby Gragg, Ellen Granter, Jay Grasso, Lisa Gustafson, Toni Haluga, Greg Ham, Marc Hamilton, Chris Handorf, Angie Hanks, Scott Harris, Cynthia Harvey, Phil Hazur, Thane Heninger, Aun Holland, Amanda House, Chuck Jann, Linda Johnson, Blair Jones, Marian Jones, Tim Jones, Gillian Kahn, Brian Keegan, Jonathan Kier, Jennifer King, Tamara King, Elizabeth Krieble, Meytal Kotik, Brian Kubota, Roshni Kutty, Mary Landry, Christopher Langley, Christine Lee, Sara Levendusky, Lisa Lin, Wendy Marberry, Dominique Mariano, Clay Martin, Rich McMahon, Eve Melnechuk, Cynthia Metallides, Hope Morley, Christine Nevola, Michael O'Donnell, Michael Oster, Ameer Padshah, Jeffrey Paulhus, Jonathan Penyack, Valerie Perkins, Brian Reardon, Wendy Rock, Marcy Rose, Carol Roy, Irene Rubin, Hugh Rutledge, Vicky Shen, Jewel Simmons, Ted Smykal, Emily Soltanoff, William Speiser, Jayne Stevenson, Richard Sullivan, Dan Tanguay, Dennis Tarwood, Susan Tauer, Tiffany Taylor-Sullivan, Catherine Terwilliger, Maria Torti, Mark Tricca, Leonid Tunik, Ilana Van Veen, Lauren Van Wart, John Vaughan, Laura Vivenzio, Samuel Voigt, Kathy Warfel, Don Weide, Laura Wheel, Eric Whitfield, Sequoia Wild, Joseph Will, Kristin Winters, Allison Wyss, Dina Zolotusky

Additional Credits: Michele Cardin, Robert Carlson, Kate Dalton-Hoffman, Dana Guterman, Narae Maybeth, Carolyn McGuire, Manjula Nair, Rachel Terino, Steve Thomas

Illustration
Kevin Banks: 330; **Jeff Grunewald:** 238, 265, 266, 534, 555, 566, 606, 608, 626, 633, 681; **Christopher Wilson:** 253, 268, 276, 325, 368, 390, 474, 492, 550, 663, 674, 714, 718, 720, 724, 726, 750, 751, 755, 757, 764, 766; **XNR Productions:** 4, 132, 142, 151, 169, 171, 385, 422, 449

Technical Illustration
GGS Book Services

Photography

Every effort has been made to secure permission and provide appropriate credit for photographic material. The publisher deeply regrets any omission and pledges to correct errors called to its attention in subsequent editions.

Unless otherwise acknowledged, all photographs are the property of Pearson Education, Inc.

Photo locators denoted as follows: Top (T), Center (C), Bottom (B), Left (L), Right (R), Background (Bkgd)

Cover
Gary Bell/Corbis

Front Matter
ix, x, xviii Stan Liu/Getty Images

3 (T) Joel Kiesel/Getty Images; **43 (BR)** The Art Gallery Collection/Alamy Images; **54 (CR)** Satellite Imaging Corp./GeoEye Inc.; **79 (T)** Reuters/Tobias Schwarz/Landov LLC; **84 (CR)** Livio Soares/BrazilPhotos, (BR) Island Effects/iStockphoto, (CC) Wildlife Bildagentur GmbH/Kimball Stock; **113 (CR)** Reuters/Corbis; **133 (TR)** Courtesy of the Historical and Interpretive Collections of the Franklin Institute, (CC) Ingram Publishing/SuperStock, (TC) Medi-Mation Ltd/Photo Researchers, Inc.; **163 (T)** Michael Newman/PhotoEdit, Inc.; **164 (CR)** Google, Inc.; **167 (TR)** ©Shubroto Chattopadhyay/Corbis, (TL) Macduff Everton/Getty Images; **196 (C)** acilo/iStockphoto; **221 (BR)** ©DK Images, (TR) ©Ned Frisk Photography/Corbis; **233 (T)** Ed Ou/©AP Images; **255 (CC)** Ian O'Leary/©DK Images, (CL) iStockphoto, (CR) Taylor S. Kennedy/National Geographic Image Collection; **291 (T)** Sacramento Bee/MCT/Landov LLC; **300 (TCR)** Friedrich Saurer/Photo Researchers, Inc., (CR) GSFC/NASA, (BR) NASA/©AP Images; **309 (T)** David Joyner/iStockphoto, (TR) Tobias Bernhard/Corbis; **359 (T)** WILDLIFE GmbH/Alamy Images; **361 (TL)** Ilian Animal/Alamy Images, (TR) James Carmichael Jr./Photoshot; **413 (T)** Jeff Vanuga/Corbis; **418 (TR)** Kevin Schafer/Photoshot; **420 (CR)** Andrew Syred/Photo Researchers, Inc.; Robert Markus; **451 (CR)** Biophoto Associates/Photo Researchers, Inc.; **473 (T)** Stan Liu/Getty Images; **482 (TR)** brt PHOTO/Alamy Images, (TCR) Paulo Fridman/Corbis; **500 (TCR)** iStockphoto; **506 (TCR)** iStockphoto, (CR) wingmar/iStockphoto; **512 (CR)** Brandon Alms/Shutterstock; **533 (T)** Bernd Opitz/Getty Images; **557 (TR)** Jxpfeer/Dreamstime LLC; **564 (BR)** ©DK Images; **599 (T)** Roine Magnusson/The Image Bank/Getty Images; **601 (TR)** Rob Belknap/iStockphoto; **603 (BR)** Geoffrey Morgan/Alamy Images; **611 (TR)** Laure Neish/iStockphoto; **615 (BR)** Art Wolfe/Getty Images; **617 (TC)** Thomas Sakoulas/Greeklandscapes; **651 (T)** Peter Essick/Aurora; **663 (CR)** Scott Krycia/iStockphoto; **674 (C)** Theo Allofs/PhotoLibrary Group/Getty Images; **713 (T)** Jamie Wilson/iStockphoto.

Acknowledgments